Roger Anderson

BIOCHEMISTRY

BIOCHEMISTRY

THE MOLECULAR BASIS

OF CELL STRUCTURE AND FUNCTION

ALBERT L. LEHNINGER

THE JOHNS HOPKINS UNIVERSITY

SCHOOL OF MEDICINE

WORTH PUBLISHERS, INC.

BIOCHEMISTRY

by Albert L. Lehninger

Printed in the United States of America

Library of Congress Catalog Card No. 73-110738

Designed by Malcolm Grear Designers, Inc.

Fifth printing, November 1971

Worth Publishers, Inc.

70 Fifth Avenue

New York, N.Y. 10011

For Jan

PREFACE

This book is written for students who are taking their first and perhaps their only course in biochemistry, whether as undergraduates or as graduate or medical students. I undertook this task because I want to convey to students my picture of what this science has recently become. Biochemistry is no longer a mere catalog of the biological occurrence and enzymatic reactions of a large number of organic compounds. In the last few years it has acquired, along with many new facts, a set of organizing principles which have made it a much simpler field to comprehend, and, at the same time, a more powerful way of analyzing many important problems in biology.

How has this come about? Each field of scientific study at some time in its evolution undergoes a profound transition in which a collection of widely scattered facts and hypotheses crystallizes into a logical pattern, unified by a few basic concepts. Biochemistry has been undergoing such a transition, stimulated by new experimental findings and new insights. Among these are the recognition of the principles of energy transfer in cells, the mechanisms by which the major metabolic pathways are regulated, the importance of membranes, ribosomes, and other ultrastructural elements of cells in their molecular activities, and the far-reaching conclusion that the amino acid sequence determines the three-dimensional conformation of protein molecules and thus their biological functions. The new knowledge of the molecular basis of genetics, which has transformed all of biology, has had the most profound influence. Because of these developments biochemistry now has a central story, a *leitmotiv*, which I have tried to express in simple terms in the *Introduction*.

This book is concerned primarily with biochemistry at the cell level, where its organizing principles are most clearly evident. Central concepts are emphasized rather than an encyclopedic treatment of biochemical details. There are four major parts in the book:

1. Biomolecules
2. Energy-yielding processes
3. Energy-requiring processes
4. Transfer of genetic information

These are subdivided into what I believe is a logical progression of chapters, each of which is a manageable "package" for both students and teachers, equivalent to the content of one lecture or discussion period. I agree with many teachers that the structure and properties of some biomolecules may best be taught together with their metabolism. This approach is quite feasible using this book, although for student convenience I have chosen to collect most of the material on the structure, chemistry, and occurrence of the various types of biomolecules into one section. I believe this makes for easy reference, while still allowing for flexibility of approach.

Biochemistry has many new frontiers today. I have tried to sketch out some of the most promising in chapters on the regulation of protein synthesis and its role in cell differentiation, the molecular basis of self-assembly and morphogenesis, and the origin of life. These chapters may well be out-of-date soon, but I hope they will serve to acquaint students with some of the biochemistry of the future.

Acknowledgments

Many may think it foolhardy for a single author to attempt to write a comprehensive textbook of biochemistry. However, my publishers have made it possible to enlist the criticism and advice of a number of chemists, biochemists, and biologists expert in research and/or teaching in the areas covered by the book. Each chapter has been read and criticized by at least one and often several authorities. To them I owe a great deal, not only for kind encouragement and sometimes deservedly blunt criticism, but also for the insight and perspective that only the real expert can convey. It is perhaps inevitable that some errors of fact, interpretation, or emphasis will be found, but I trust no one will attribute these to anyone but me. I will greatly appreciate receiving from students and teachers alike their comments, criticisms, notice of errors, and advice about improvements that can be made in later printings or editions.

To the following reviewers I give my most sincere thanks: Jay Martin Anderson, Christian B. Anfinsen, Robert E. Beyer, R. G. S. Bidwell, Rodney L. Biltonen, Konrad E. Bloch, Benjamin Bouck, Daniel Branton, Robert H. Burris, Melvin Calvin, Roderick K. Clayton, Helena Curtis, Robert E. Davies, Bernard D. Davis, John T. Edsall, Paul T. Englund, Allan H. Fenselau, J. Lawrence Fox, Richard Goldsby, Ursula Johnson Goodenough, Guido Guidotti, Gordon G. Hammes, William F. Harrington, Edward C. Heath, Harold G. Hempling, Donald P. Hollis, Lloyd L. Ingraham, Andre T. Jagendorf, William P. Jencks, Daniel E. Koshland, Jr., Sir Hans A. Krebs, Myron Ledbetter, William J. Lennarz, Richard C. Lewontin, Julius Marmur, Daniel Nathans, Leslie Orgel, Peter L. Pedersen, Keith R. Porter, David Prescott, John Sinclair, Gunther Stent, Jack L. Strominger, Maurice Sussman, Serge N. Timasheff, and William B. Wood. My thanks go to many others, acknowledged at the end of the book, who generously gave me permission to use drawings, electron micrographs, and other illustrative material.

I am also grateful to the officers and staff of Worth Publishers for their genuine interest in the needs of both students and teachers, their appreciation of the struggles of a university author, and above all, their desire to produce an educationally useful book.

My colleagues in the Department of Physiological Chemistry of The Johns Hopkins School of Medicine furnished much advice and also took on many responsibilities which the gestation of this book had forced me to neglect. I also owe a great deal to Johns Hopkins medical students, who taught me whatever I have learned about teaching. Two of them, Bill Scott and Penny Pate, gave me much help in the early stages of preparation of the manuscript; one happy outcome is that they are now Mr. and Mrs. William Wallace Scott, Jr. To Linda Hansford I am particularly indebted for invaluable help with proofreading, indexing, checking of problems, and collection of data and references. Thanks also to Ronald Garrett, who photographed the molecular models and to my secretary Peggy Ford, who not only effectively marshalled my time and attention among teaching, research, departmental administration, and book-writing, but also typed many chapters of the manuscript.

Finally, I want to express my deep appreciation to my family, who patiently endured the many weekends and evenings that were devoted to writing and who gave encouragement when it was most needed.

ALBERT L. LEHNINGER

Sparks, Maryland
March, 1970

CONTENTS

INTRODUCTION **THE MOLECULAR LOGIC OF LIVING ORGANISMS**

INTRODUCTION

THE MOLECULAR LOGIC OF LIVING ORGANISMS

Living things are composed of lifeless molecules. These molecules, when isolated and examined individually, conform to all the physical and chemical laws that describe the behavior of inanimate matter. Yet living organisms possess extraordinary attributes not shown by collections of inanimate matter. If we examine some of these special properties, we can approach the study of biochemistry with a better understanding of the fundamental questions it seeks to answer.

The Identifying Characteristics of Living Matter

Perhaps the most conspicuous attribute of living organisms is that they are complicated and highly organized. They possess intricate internal structures, containing many kinds of complex molecules. Furthermore, they occur in an astonishing variety of different species. In contrast, the inanimate matter in their environment, as represented by soil, water, and rocks, usually consists of random mixtures of simple chemical compounds, with comparatively little structural organization.

Secondly, each component part of a living organism appears to have a specific purpose or function. This is true not only of intracellular structures, such as the nucleus and the cell membrane, but also of individual chemical compounds in the cell, such as lipids and proteins and nucleic acids. In living organisms it is quite legitimate to ask what the function of a given molecule is. However, to ask such questions about molecules in collections of inanimate matter is irrelevant and meaningless.

Third, living organisms have the capacity to extract and transform energy from their environment, which they use to build and maintain their own intricate structures from simple raw materials. They can also carry out other forms of purposeful work, such as the mechanical work of locomotion. Inanimate matter does not have this capacity to utilize external energy to maintain its own structural organization. In fact, inanimate matter usually decays to a more random state when it absorbs external energy such as heat or light.

But the most extraordinary attribute of living organisms is their capacity for precise self-replication, a property which can be regarded as the very quintessence of the living state. Collections of inanimate matter with which we are familiar show no apparent capacity to reproduce themselves in forms identical in mass, shape, and internal structure, through "generation" after "generation."

Biochemistry and the Living State

We may now ask: If living organisms are composed of molecules that are intrinsically inanimate, why is it that living matter differs so radically from nonliving matter, which also consists of intrinsically inanimate molecules? Why does the living organism appear to be more than the sum of its inanimate parts? The medieval philosopher would have answered that living organisms are endowed with a mysterious and divine life-force. But this doctrine, called vitalism, is nothing more than superstition and it has been rejected by modern science. Today it is the basic goal of biochemistry to determine how the collections of inanimate molecules that constitute living organisms interact with each other to maintain and perpetuate the living state. A corollary goal is to determine how the living state first arose in the early history of the earth.

Biology and chemistry have traditionally been regarded as separate and distinct bodies of knowledge, each with its own set of laws and principles. However, since living organisms are composed of specifically interacting molecules, we must be prepared to consider the concept that biology *is* chemistry. This is not to say that biology is merely another field of chemistry, comparable to organic chemistry, physical chemistry, or inorganic chemistry. Actually, biology is a kind of superchemistry, which includes, but at the same time transcends, the traditional areas of chemistry. This is because the molecules comprising living organisms not only conform to all the familiar physical and chemical principles governing the behavior of inanimate matter but, in addition, interact with each other in accordance with another set of principles, which we shall refer to collectively as the *molecular logic of the living state*. These principles do not necessarily involve any new or as yet undiscovered physical laws or forces. Rather they should be regarded as a unique set of "ground rules" that govern the nature, function, and interactions of the specific types of molecules found in living organisms, and endow them with the capacity for self-organization and self-replication. Not all the principles comprising the molecular logic of the living state have yet been identified, and some are only dimly perceived. In fact, it is perhaps more appropriate to speak of these principles as axioms or hypotheses, since some of them are intuitive and not yet provable.

Now let us see if we can identify some of the important axioms in the molecular logic of the living state. We shall begin with a brief survey of the structure and function of the molecules found in living matter, which we shall call *biomolecules*.

Biomolecules

The chemical composition of living organisms is qualitatively quite different from that of the physical environment in which they live. Most of the chemical components of living organisms are organic compounds of carbon, in which the carbon is relatively reduced, or hydrogenated. Many organic biomolecules also contain nitrogen. In contrast, the elements carbon and nitrogen are not abundant in nonliving matter and occur in the atmosphere and the earth's crust only in simple inorganic forms, such as carbon dioxide, molecular nitrogen, carbonates, and nitrates.

The organic compounds present in living matter occur in extraordinary variety, and most of them are extremely complex. For example, even the simplest and smallest cells, the bacteria, contain a very large number of different organic molecules. It is estimated that the bacterium *Escherichia coli* contains about 5,000 different organic compounds, including some 3,000 different kinds of proteins and 1,000 different kinds of nucleic acids. Moreover, proteins and nucleic acids are complex molecules, and the structures of only a few of them are known.

If we turn to larger and more complex organisms, the higher animals and plants, we find that they, too, contain proteins and nucleic acids, and in much greater variety. In the human organism, for example, there may be as many as 5 million different kinds of proteins, compared with about 3,000 in *E. coli*. None of the protein molecules of *E. coli* is identical with any of the proteins found in man, although some function in quite similar ways. In fact, each species of organism has its own chemically distinct set of protein molecules and nucleic acid molecules. Since there are probably over 1,200,000 species of living organisms, ranging in complexity from *E. coli* to the human organism, it may be calculated that all living species together must contain somewhere between 10^{10} and 10^{12} different kinds of protein molecules and about 10^{10} different kinds of nucleic acids. If we compare these figures with the total number of *all* organic compounds that have been synthesized to date, which is only about 1 million, or 10^6, it is clear that we know the precise structure of only a trivially small fraction of all the organic molecules that are believed to exist in living matter. Therefore, for biochemists to attempt to isolate, identify, and synthesize all the different organic molecules present in living matter would appear to be a hopeless undertaking.

Paradoxically, however, the immense diversity of organic molecules in living organisms is ultimately reducible to an almost absurd simplicity. We now know that the macromolecules in the cell are composed of many simple, small, building-block molecules, strung together in long chains. Proteins, for example, consist of covalently linked chains of 100 or more residues of amino acids, which are small compounds of known structure. Only 20 different kinds of amino acids are found in proteins, but they are arranged in many different sequences to form many different kinds of proteins. Thus, all the 3,000 or more proteins in the *E. coli* cell are built from only 20 different small molecules. Similarly, all the 1,000 or more nucleic acids of the

E. coli cell, which also are long, polymeric molecules, are constructed from only eight different building blocks, called mononucleotides. Moreover, the 20 different amino acids from which proteins are built and the eight different nucleotides from which nucleic acids are built are identical in all living species. Although we have precise knowledge of the covalent structure of only some 50 proteins today, the techniques of protein chemistry are sufficiently well developed that—in principle, at least—it is within the capability of biochemistry to elucidate the structure of any protein from any species of organism.

The few simple building-block molecules from which all macromolecules are constructed have another striking characteristic. Each of them serves more than one function in living cells. Indeed, some are extremely versatile and play a number of roles. The amino acids serve not only as building blocks of protein molecules but also as precursors of hormones, alkaloids, porphyrins, pigments, and many other biomolecules. The mononucleotides serve not only as building blocks of nucleic acids but also as coenzymes and as energy-carrying molecules. It therefore appears probable that the building-block biomolecules were selected during the course of biological evolution for their capacity to serve several functions. So far as we know, living organisms normally contain no functionless compounds, although there are some biomolecules whose functions are not yet understood.

Now we can see emerging some of the axioms in the molecular logic of the living state. We can see that *there is an underlying simplicity in the molecular organization of the cell;* its thousands of different macromolecules are constructed from only a few simple building-block molecules. Since the building-block biomolecules are identical in all known species, we can infer that *all living organisms have a common ancestor.* We can see that *the identity of each species of organism is preserved by its possession of a distinctive set of nucleic acids and proteins.* Furthermore, in the functional versatility of the building-block biomolecules, we can see that *there is an underlying principle of molecular economy.* Perhaps living cells contain only the simplest possible molecules in the least number of different types, just enough to endow them with the attribute of life and with species identity under the environmental conditions in which they exist.

Energy Transformations in Living Cells

The molecular complexity and the orderliness of structure of living organisms, in contrast to the randomness of inanimate matter, have profound implications to the physical scientist. The second law of thermodynamics, the branch of physics dealing with energy and its transformations, states that physical and chemical processes tend to increase the disorder, or randomness, in the world, that is, its entropy. Natural processes never occur in such a way that the total disorder or entropy in the world decreases. How is it, then, that living organisms can create and maintain their intricate orderliness in an environment that is relatively disordered and becoming more so with time?

Living organisms do not constitute exceptions to the laws of thermodynamics. Their high degree of molecular orderliness must be paid for in some way, since it cannot arise spontaneously from disorder. The first law of thermodynamics states that energy can be neither created nor destroyed. Living organisms thus cannot consume or use up energy; they can only transform one form of energy into another. They absorb from their environment a form of energy that is useful to them under the special conditions of temperature and pressure in which they live and then return to the environment an equivalent amount of energy in some other, less useful form. The useful form of energy that cells take in is called *free energy*, which may be simply defined as that type of energy that can do work at constant temperature and pressure. The less useful type of energy that cells return to their environment consists of heat and other forms, which quickly become randomized in the environment and thus increase its disorder, or entropy. We may now state an extremely important axiom in the molecular logic of the living state: *Living organisms create and maintain their essential orderliness at the expense of their environment, which they cause to become more disordered and random.*

The environment of living organisms is absolutely essential to them, not only as a source of free energy but also as a source of raw materials. In the language of thermodynamics, living organisms are "open" systems because they exchange both energy and matter with their environment and, in so doing, transform both. It is characteristic of open systems that they are not in equilibrium with their environment. Although living organisms may *appear* to be in equilibrium, because they may not change visibly as we observe them over a period of time, actually they exist in what is called a *steady state*, which is that condition of an open system in which the rate of transfer of matter and energy from the environment into the system is exactly balanced by the rate of transfer of matter and energy out of the system. It is therefore part of the molecular logic of the living state that *the cell is a nonequilibrium open system*, a machine for extracting free energy from the environment, which it causes to increase in entropy. Moreover, and this is another reflection of the principle of maximum economy, *living cells are highly efficient in handling energy and matter*. They greatly exceed most man-made machines in the efficiency with which they convert input energy into work performed.

The energy-transforming machinery of living cells is built entirely of relatively fragile and unstable organic molecules that are unable to withstand high temperatures, strong electrical currents, or extremely acid or basic conditions. The living cell is also essentially isothermal; at any given time, all parts of the cell have essentially the same temperature. Furthermore, there are no significant differences in pressure from one part of the cell to another. For these reasons, cells are unable to use heat as a source of energy, since heat can do work at constant pressure only if it passes from a zone of higher temperature to a zone of lower temperature. Living cells therefore do not resemble heat engines or electrical engines, the types of engines with which we are most familiar. Instead, and this is another important axiom in the molecular logic of the living state, *the living cell is an isothermal chemical engine*. The energy that cells absorb from their environment is recovered in the form of chemical energy, which is then transformed to carry out the chemical work involved in the biosynthesis of cell components, the osmotic work required to transport materials into the cell, or the mechanical work of contraction and locomotion.

Among man-made machines, chemical energy is rarely used to do other than pressure-volume work, such as occurs during combustion of fuel in a gasoline engine. A possible exception is the fuel cell, which utilizes a combustion reaction to produce electrical energy; however, fuel cells have not been perfected for economical everyday use. Actually, engineering technology has yet to produce a useful engine that can convert chemical energy isothermally into mechanical energy, yet this type of energy conversion is familiar to all of us in the contraction of muscles.

Chemical Reactions in Living Cells

Cells can function as chemical engines because they possess *enzymes*, catalysts capable of greatly enhancing the rate of specific chemical reactions. The enzymes are highly specialized protein molecules, made by cells from simple amino acids. Each type of enzyme can catalyze only one specific type of chemical reaction; well over a thousand different enzymes are known. Enzymes far exceed man-made catalysts in their reaction specificity, their catalytic efficiency, and their capacity to operate under mild conditions of temperature and hydrogen-ion concentration. They can catalyze in milliseconds complex sequences of reactions that would require days, weeks, or months of work in the chemical laboratory.

But there is one especially remarkable property of chemical reactions in living cells which ultimately makes possible their efficient function as chemical engines; enzyme-catalyzed reactions proceed with a 100 percent yield; there are no by-products. In contrast, the reactions of organic chemistry carried out in the laboratory with man-made catalysts are nearly always accompanied by the formation of one or more by-products, so that yields are usually much less than 100 percent and intensive purification of the product is required at each step. Because enzymes can enhance a single reaction pathway of a given molecule without enhancing its other possible reactions, living organisms can carry out, simultaneously, many different individual reactions without bogging down in a morass of useless by-products. This high degree of specificity of enzymes results from the operation of still another fundamental axiom in the molecular logic of the living state, namely, *the principle of structural complementarity*. Enzyme molecules must combine with their substrates during the catalytic cycle, and the active site of the enzyme molecule will accept only those molecules as substrates that fit it with a near-perfect complementarity. We shall see that the principle of structural complementarity underlies the specificity of many different types of molecular interactions in cells.

The hundreds of enzyme-catalyzed chemical reactions in the cell do not take place independently of each other. Rather they are linked into many different sequences of consecutive reactions having common intermediates, so that the product of the first reaction becomes the substrate or reactant of the second, and so on. Such sequences, which may have anywhere from 2 to 20 or more reaction steps, are in turn linked to form networks of converging or diverging patterns. This arrangement has several important biological implications. One is that such systems of consecutive reactions provide for the channeling of chemical reactions along specific routes. Another is that sequential reactions make possible transfer of chemical energy under isothermal conditions. Energy transfer cannot take place between two reactions under conditions of constant temperature and pressure unless the two reactions have a common intermediate. If two independent reactions, such as

$$A \longrightarrow B$$

$$C \longrightarrow D$$

occur in the same container under constant temperature and pressure, each will proceed with the same decrease in free energy regardless of the presence of the other. However, in two consecutive reactions, such as

$$A \longrightarrow B$$

$$B \longrightarrow C$$

some chemical energy may be carried from the first reaction to the second by the common intermediate B. Now let us examine energy transfers in the cell more closely.

Living cells can be divided into two great classes, depending on the type of energy they obtain from their environment. *Photosynthetic cells* utilize sunlight as their main source of energy; the radiant energy is absorbed by the pigment chlorophyll and transformed into chemical energy. *Heterotrophic cells* utilize the energy of highly reduced, energy-rich organic molecules, such as glucose, which they obtain from the environment. Most cells of the animal world are heterotrophic. In heterotrophic cells, glucose is oxidized to carbon dioxide and water; in this process some of the free energy of the glucose molecule is conserved in a chemical form and is then employed to carry out various types of cellular work.

Although these two classes of living organisms obtain energy from their environment in different forms, both recover and use it largely in the form of one specific molecule—*adenosine triphosphate*, or *ATP*. ATP functions as the major carrier of chemical energy in the cells of all living species. As it transfers its energy to other molecules, it loses its terminal phosphate group and becomes *adenosine diphosphate*, or *ADP*, which is the discharged, or energy-poor, counterpart of ATP. ADP can, in turn, accept chemical energy again by regaining a phosphate group to become ATP, at the expense of either solar energy (in photosynthetic cells) or chemical energy (in heterotrophic cells).

Consecutive chemical reactions make possible the specific biological function of the ATP-ADP system as the connecting link between two large networks of enzyme-catalyzed reactions in the cell. One of these networks conserves chemical energy derived from the environment by causing the phosphorylation of the energy-poor ADP to the energy-rich ATP. The other network utilizes the energy of ATP to carry out the biosynthesis of cell components from simple precursors, with simultaneous breakdown of the ATP to ADP. Like the building-block biomolecules, these consecutively linked networks of enzyme-catalyzed reactions are essentially identical in all living species.

Self-Regulation of Cell Reactions

There is another important result of the fact that all chemical reactions in the cell are enzyme-catalyzed and are linked by common intermediates. A simple bacterial cell such as the *E. coli* cell synthesizes simultaneously all its thousands of different complex molecular components from just three simple precursors—glucose, ammonia, and water. Here the living cell employs a kind of chemical logic which is still beyond the current state of the art of synthetic chemistry. If a chemist were confronted with the problem of synthesizing two products, let us say an amino acid and a lipid, he would never dream of synthesizing them from the same precursors simultaneously, in the same reaction vessel. He would start each synthesis with different precursors and would use different sequences of reactions. He would carry out the two syntheses independently, in separate vessels, and probably at different times. Yet, in living cells, the synthesis of hundreds and thousands of widely different molecules is carried out simultaneously, literally in the same vessel, starting from only a few common precursors. The linking of enzyme-catalyzed reactions into sequences of consecutive reactions makes possible the orderly channelling of the thousands of chemical reactions taking place in cells, so that all the specific biomolecules required in cell structure and function are produced in appropriate amounts and rates to maintain the normal steady state.

A bacterial cell synthesizes simultaneously perhaps 3,000 or more different kinds of protein molecules in specific molar ratios to each other. Each of these protein molecules contains a minimum of 100 amino acid units in a chain; most contain many more than 100. Yet at 37°C the bacterial cell requires only a few seconds to complete the synthesis of any single protein molecule. In contrast, the synthesis of a protein by man in the laboratory, a feat which only recently was accomplished for the first time, required the work of highly skilled chemists, many expensive reagents, hundreds of separate operations, complex automated equipment, and months of time in preparation and execution. Not only can the bacterial cell make individual protein molecules very rapidly, but it can make 3,000 or more different kinds of proteins simultaneously, in the precise molar ratio required to constitute a living, functioning cell.

In the linkage of enzyme-catalyzed reactions into consecutive sequences, we find still another axiom in the molecular logic of living organisms: *The rate of a specific reaction in one portion of the complex network of enzymatic reactions in the cell can be controlled or modulated by the rates of reactions in another part of the network.* In the simplest case, the accumulation of an intermediate or metabolite beyond a certain critical concentration acts as a signal that can slow down the rate of the reactions by which it was formed, a type of control known as *feed-back inhibition*. Certain enzymes in the cell, particularly those at the beginning of a reaction sequence or at a branch point, function as "regulatory" enzymes; they are inhibited by the end product of that reaction sequence.

Moreover, living cells possess the power to regulate the synthesis of their own catalysts. Thus the cell can "turn off" the synthesis of the enzymes required to make a given product from its precursors whenever that product is available, ready-made, from the environment. Such self-adjusting and self-regulating properties are fundamental in the maintenance of the steady state of the living cell and are essential to its energy-transforming efficiency.

The Self-Replication of Living Organisms

The most remarkable of all the properties of living cells is their capacity to reproduce themselves with nearly perfect fidelity, not just once or twice, which would be remarkable enough, but for hundreds and thousands of generations. Three features immediately stand out. First, some living organisms are so immensely complex that the amount of genetic information that is transmitted seems out of all proportion to the minute size of the cells that must carry it, namely, the single sperm cell and the single egg. We know today that all this information is compressed into the nucleus of these cells, contained in the nucleotide sequence of a very small amount of deoxyribonucleic acid (DNA), weighing altogether no more than 6×10^{-12} gram. We therefore come to another axiom in the molecular logic of the living state: *The symbols in which the genetic information is coded have the dimensions of parts of single DNA molecules.*

A second remarkable characteristic of the self-replicating property of living organisms is the extraordinary stability of the genetic information stored in DNA. Very few early historical records prepared by man have survived for long, even though they have been etched in copper or stone and preserved against the elements. The Dead Sea scrolls and the Rosetta stone, for example, are only a few thousand years old. But there is good reason to believe that present-day bacteria have nearly the same size, shape, internal structure, and contain the same kinds of building block molecules, and the same kinds of enzymes, as those that lived millions of years ago, despite the fact that bacteria, like all organisms, have been undergoing constant evolutionary change. Genetic information is preserved, not on a copper scroll or etched in stone, but in the form of deoxyribonucleic acid (DNA), an organic molecule so fragile that when isolated in solution, it will break into many pieces if the solution is merely stirred or pipetted. The remarkable capacity of living cells to preserve their genetic information is the result of *structural complementarity*. One DNA strand serves as the template for the enzymatic replication of a structurally complementary DNA strand. In fact, the DNA-synthesizing enzymes of the cell cannot make DNA without a template. It now appears certain that, even in the intact cell, the DNA molecule may break frequently, but it is quickly and automatically repaired. Errors or mutations occur only infrequently, but even these are not always deleterious and may possess advantages in preserving the identity of the species.

There is a third remarkable characteristic of genetic information transfer in living organisms. Since the genetic information is encoded in the form of a specific sequence of four basic mononucleotide building blocks in the linear, polymeric DNA molecule, it is one-dimensional. But living cells are three-dimensional in structure and they have three-dimensional parts or components. Quite simply, *the one-dimensional information of DNA is translated into the three-dimensional information inherent in the macromolecular and supramolecular components of living organisms by translation of DNA structure into protein structure.* The specific linear base sequence of DNA is translated into a corresponding linear amino acid sequence of a polypeptide chain in the process of protein synthesis. However, unlike a DNA molecule, a polypeptide chain is not stable in extended linear form. It spontaneously curls up and folds into a specific stable three-dimensional structure, the precise geometry of which is determined by the amino acid sequence. Since each type of polypeptide chain has its own specific amino acid sequence, it assumes its own specific three-dimensional configuration. Moreover, the many different kinds of highly folded protein molecules that serve as the components of such biostructures as membranes, ribosomes, and organelles then group themselves automatically into precisely reproducible three-dimensional assemblies because they fit each other in only one specific way—again, according to the principle of structural complementarity.

We have now described a number of the characteristic interactions and interrelationships of biomolecules that together constitute the molecular logic of the living state. We may summarize these principles by the following statement: *A living cell is a self-assembling, self-adjusting, self-perpetuating isothermal open system. This system consists of many consecutive, linked organic reactions that are promoted by organic catalysts produced by the cell; it operates on the principle of maximum economy of parts and processes.* At no point in our examination of the molecular logic of living cells have we encountered any violation of known physical laws, nor have we needed to define new ones. The machinery of living cells functions within the same set of laws that governs the operation of man-made machines, but the chemical reactions and processes of cells have been refined far beyond the present-day capabilities of chemical engineering. Perhaps we shall one day be able to trace the origin and evolutionary history of biomolecules and of the enzymatic reactions that link them. Then we may see exactly how the molecular logic of living organisms arose.

In this orienting survey, we have seen that biochemistry has an underlying system, a set of organizing principles. It is not merely a collection of unrelated chemical facts about living matter. As we begin more detailed study of biochemistry, these organizing principles should serve as our framework of reference. We shall start with a description of the various classes of biomolecules (Part I). We shall then proceed to analyze the isothermal, self-adjusting, consecutively linked, enzyme-catalyzed reactions that constitute the open system through which both energy and matter flow, i.e., the process of metabolism. Metabolism, as we have seen, consists of two networks of reactions. That network which yields chemical energy as ATP will be the subject of Part II. In Part III, we shall examine the other great network, which utilizes ATP for cell synthesis and performance of work. Finally, in Part IV we shall consider the molecular basis of the self-replication of cells and the assembly of cell components. The book will end by returning to the origin of life and its molecular logic.

PART 1 THE MOLECULAR COMPONENTS OF CELLS

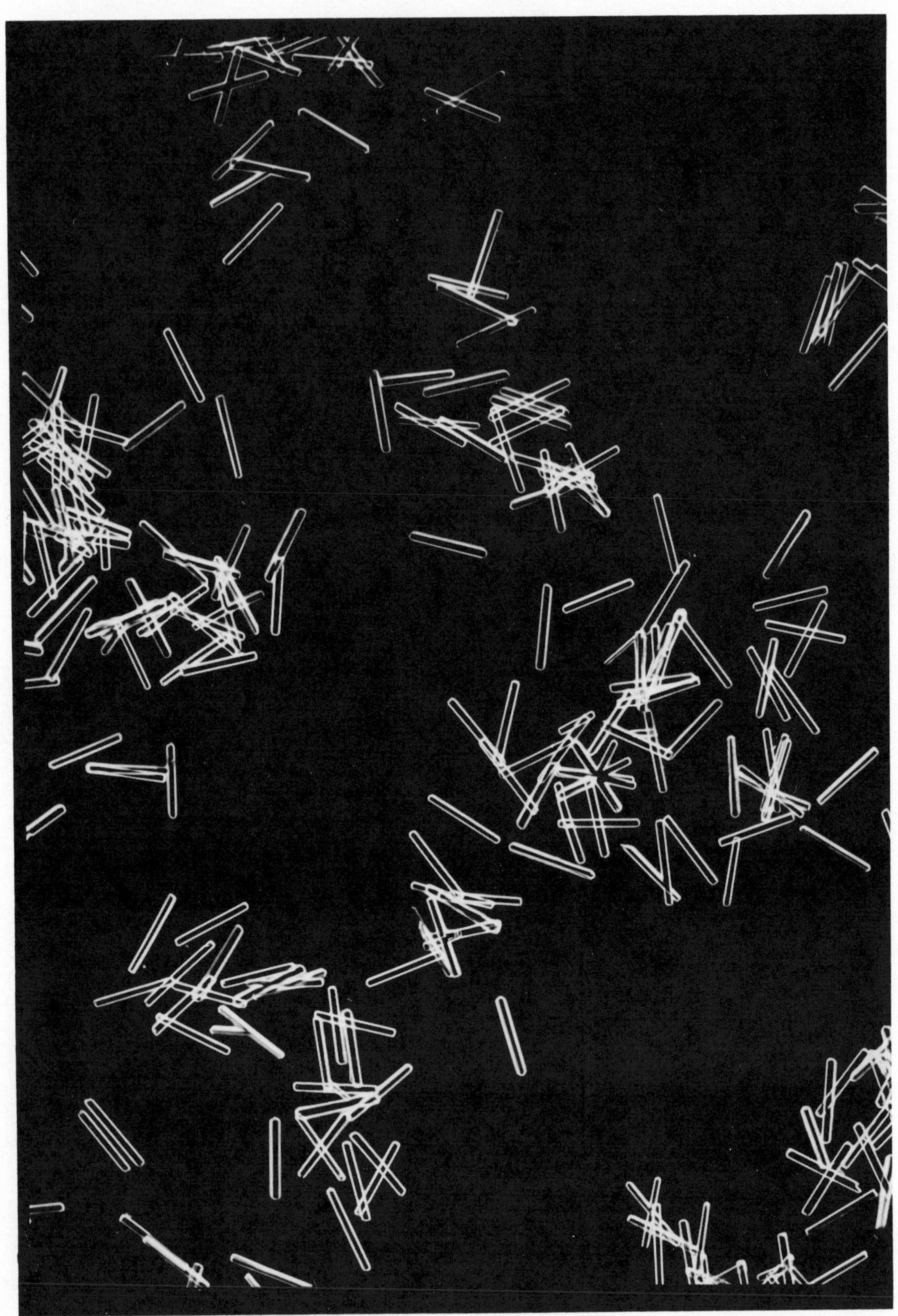

Crystals of bovine trypsin.

CHAPTER 1 BIOMOLECULES AND CELLS

In this chapter, the first in a series of 12 devoted to the structures and properties of the major classes of biomolecules, we shall develop the idea that biomolecules should be studied from two points of view. We must of course examine their structure and properties as we would those of nonbiological molecules, by the principles and approaches used in classical chemistry. But we must also examine them in the light of the hypothesis that biomolecules are the products of evolutionary selection, that they may be the fittest possible molecules for their biological function, and that they interact with each other in the set of very specific relationships which we have called the molecular logic of the living state. In particular, we must examine closely the size and shape of biomolecules, since they determine not only biological specificity but also the dimensions and ultrastructures of living cells and their component organelles.

Table 1-1 The bioelements

Those in color are found in all organisms. The remainder are essential for only certain species.

The elements of organic matter
O
C
N
H
P
S
The monoatomic ions
Na^+
K^+
Mg^{2+}
Ca^{2+}
Cl^-
The trace elements
Mn
Fe
Co
Cu
Zn
B
Al
V
Mo
I
Si

The Biological Fitness of Organic Compounds

The fact that the elementary composition of living matter is very different from that of the lithosphere and atmosphere suggests that some chemical elements are more "fit" than others to make up the molecules of living organisms. Only 22 of the 100 chemical elements found in the earth's crust are essential components in living organisms (Table 1-1), and of these, only 16 are found in all classes of organisms. Moreover, the distribution of these chemical elements in living organisms is not in proportion to their occurrence in the earth's crust. The four most abundant elements in living organisms are hydrogen, oxygen, carbon, and nitrogen; they make up about 99 percent of the mass of most cells, whereas the four most abundant elements in the earth's crust are oxygen, silicon, aluminum, and sodium (Table 1-2). Actually, carbon, hydrogen, and nitrogen are far more abundant in living matter than in the earth's crust. We may therefore presume that compounds of these elements possess unique molecular fitness for the processes that collectively constitute the living state.

Let us now inquire into the chemical basis for the biological fitness of carbon, hydrogen, nitrogen, and oxygen. These four elements possess a common property: they readily form covalent bonds by electron-pair sharing. Hydrogen needs one electron, oxygen two, nitrogen three, and carbon four to complete their outer electron shells and thus form stable covalent bonds. All four elements can readily react with each other to fill their outer shells. Furthermore, three of these elements (C, N, and O) can share either one or two electron pairs to yield either single or double bonds, a capacity which endows them with considerable versatility of chemical bonding. Carbon is also capable of forming triple bonds with other carbon or nitrogen atoms. This type of bonding occurs only rarely in nature.

Carbon, nitrogen, hydrogen, and oxygen are uniquely fit in another way: they are the lightest elements capable of forming covalent bonds. Since the strength of a covalent bond is inversely related to the atomic weights of the bonded atoms, it appears that living organisms have selected those elements capable of forming the strongest covalent bonds.

Particularly significant is the capacity of carbon atoms to interact with each other to form stable, covalent carbon-carbon bonds. Since carbon atoms may either accept or donate four electrons to complete an outer octet, each carbon atom can form covalent bonds with four carbon atoms. In this way, covalently-linked carbon atoms may constitute the backbones for an immense variety of different organic molecules. Moreover, since carbon atoms readily form covalent bonds with oxygen, hydrogen, and nitrogen, as well as with sulfur, a large number of different kinds of functional groups can be introduced into the structure of organic molecules. Organic compounds of carbon have yet another distinctive feature. Because of the tetrahedral configuration of the shared electron pairs around each carbon atom, different types of organic molecules possess different three-dimensional structures. No other chemical element can form stable molecules of such widely different sizes and shapes, nor with such a variety of functional groups. Silicon is the only other element that possesses this capacity to combine with itself by electron-pair sharing. Although it is far more abundant in the lithosphere, silicon is evidently inferior to carbon for the purposes of living organisms. Perhaps the major reason is that silicon-silicon bonds are unstable in the presence of oxygen, leading to the formation of silicates and insoluble silicon dioxide polymers, such as quartz.

One other point: The organic compounds of carbon found in living organisms are highly reduced, or hydrogenated, whereas the carbon of the earth's crust is largely present in oxidized form as bicarbonates or carbonates. Because oxygen is very abundant in the atmosphere, carbon and hydrogen normally tend to become oxidized to carbon dioxide and water, compounds which are stable and energy-poor. The reduced organic molecules found in living matter are energy-rich since, to make them from CO_2 and water, living organisms must expend free energy. We may therefore conclude that organic carbon com-

Table 1-2

The relative abundance of some chemical elements in the earth's crust

Element	*Atoms percent*
O	62.5
Si	21.2
Al	6.47
Na	2.64
Ca	1.94
Fe	1.92
Mg	1.84
P	1.42
C	0.08
N	0.0001

Table 1-2 (Continued)

The relative abundance of some chemical elements in the human body

Element	*Atoms percent*
H	60.3
O	25.5
C	10.5
N	2.42
Na	0.73
Ca	0.226
P	0.134
S	0.132
K	0.036
Cl	0.032

pounds must be especially well suited for the purposes of living organisms, since they were selected despite the relative sparseness of carbon in the lithosphere and despite the fact that energy must be expended to reduce inorganic carbon.

The Hierarchy of Molecular Organization of Cells

The biomolecules of living organisms are ordered into a hierarchy of increasing molecular complexity, as shown in Figure 1-1. All organic biomolecules are ultimately derived from very simple, low-molecular-weight *precursors* obtained from the environment, namely, carbon dioxide, water, and atmospheric nitrogen. These precursors are converted by living matter, via sequences of metabolic *intermediates* of increasing molecular size, into the *building-block biomolecules*, organic compounds of intermediate molecular weight. These building blocks are then linked to each other covalently to form the *macromolecules* of the cell, which have relatively high molecular weights. Thus the amino acids are the building blocks of

Figure 1-1
The hierarchy of molecular organization in cells.

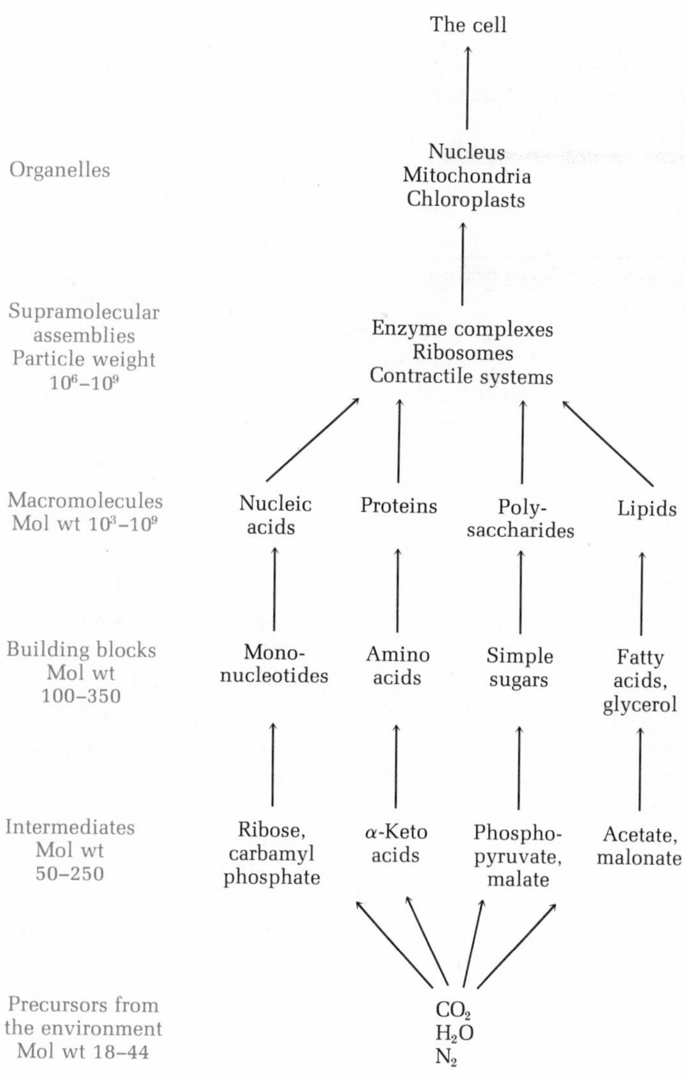

the proteins, the mononucleotides are the building blocks of the nucleic acids, the monosaccharides are the building blocks of the polysaccharides, and fatty acids are building blocks of most lipids. [Although the molecular weights of individual lipids are low (mol wt 750–2,500) compared with those of proteins, nucleic acids, and polysaccharides, lipids spontaneously associate into high molecular weight structures and usually function as macromolecular systems. We therefore include them, if somewhat arbitrarily, in the class of macromolecules.]

At the next higher level of organization, macromolecules of different classes associate with each other to form *supramolecular complexes,* such as lipoproteins, which are complexes of lipids and proteins, and ribosomes, which, in turn, are complexes of nucleic acid and proteins. However, there is now a distinctive difference in the manner in which the components are assembled. In supramolecular complexes, the component macromolecules are not covalently bonded to each other. For example, the nucleic acid and protein components of ribosomes are not attached to each other covalently; rather, they are "stuck together" by weak noncovalent forces, such as ionic interactions, hydrogen bonding, hydrophobic interactions, and van der Waals interactions. Nevertheless, the noncovalent association of macromolecules into supramolecular complexes is very specific and, usually, very stable, the result of the precise geometrical "fit" or complementarity between and among the component parts. As we shall see, there are good reasons for cells to employ noncovalent rather than covalent interactions to form supramolecular complexes from macromolecular components.

At the highest level of organization in the hierarchy of cell structure, various supramolecular complexes are further assembled into *organelles,* such as nuclei, mitochondria, and chloroplasts, and into other bodies and inclusions, such as lysosomes, microbodies, and vacuoles. Here again, so far as is known, the various components are associated by noncovalent interactions.

The distribution of the four major classes of biomacromolecules in the "living" portion of the *Escherichia coli* cell is shown in Table 1-3. As you can see, the proteins (Greek *proteios,* "first") are the most abundant macromolecules, and this is the case in all types of cells. Actually, all four major classes of biomacromolecules are found in about these proportions in all cells, if we exclude from consideration such non-living parts of living organisms as the exoskeleton, the mineral portion of bone, extracellular materials such as hair, feathers, and inert storage materials such as starch and fat, which may vary widely from one organism to another.

The four major types of biomacromolecules also have identical functions in all species of cells. The nucleic acids universally function to store and transmit genetic information. The proteins are the direct products and effectors of gene action, and into them the genetic information is incorporated. Most proteins have specific catalytic activity and function as enzymes; others serve as structural elements. Many other biological functions are served

Table 1-3 Molecular components of an *E. coli* cell

	Percent total weight	*Number of each kind*
Water	70	
Proteins	15	~3,000
Nucleic acids		
DNA	1	1
RNA	6	~1,000
Carbohydrates	3	~50
Lipids	2	~40
Building-block molecules and intermediates	2	~500
Inorganic ions	1	12

Figure 1-2
Informational and noninformational macromolecules of the cell. The letters A, T, G, *and* C *symbolize the four bases of the mononucleotide building-blocks of* DNA. *The amino acid building-blocks of proteins are symbolized by their 3-letter abbreviations,* Arg, Ala, Trp, *etc. Glucose is symbolized by* Glc.

Informational		Noninformational
A	Arg	Glc
T	Ala	Glc
G	Trp	Glc
A	Met	Glc
C	Asn	Glc
G	Glu	Glc
A	Tyr	Glc
C	Phe	Glc
G	Ile	Glc
G	Ile	Glc
A	Tyr	Glc
T	Ala	Glc
T	Lys	Glc
G	Lys	Glc
C	Arg	
A	Phe	
Nucleotide sequence in a DNA molecule	Amino acid sequence in a protein molecule	Repeating glucose units in a polysaccharide

by proteins, which are the most versatile of all biomolecules. (This is why we have made the proteins the subject of 7 of these 12 chapters devoted to the biomolecules.) The polysaccharides have two major functions: some, such as starch, serve as storage forms of energy-yielding fuels for cell activity; and some, such as cellulose, serve as extracellular structural elements. The lipids serve two chief roles: as major structural components of membranes, and as a storage form of energy-rich fuel.

There is an important and fundamental difference between the nucleic acids and proteins on the one hand and the polysaccharides and lipids on the other (Figure 1-2). Nucleic acids and proteins are *informational macromolecules* by virtue of their structure. Each nucleic acid molecule contains four or more types of mononucleotides arranged in a specific information-rich sequence. Similarly, each protein molecule contains a specific information-rich sequence of some 20 different amino acids. On the other hand, the various polysaccharides do not bear information; their recurring building blocks either are all identical, as is the case in starch, a polymer of D-glucose, or consist of only two types of sugar building blocks, which merely alternate. Similarly, lipids are noninformational, since their fatty acid components are also constructed from repeating, identical units that have two carbon atoms.

The Primordial Biomolecules

We have seen that the immensely large number of different proteins and nucleic acids in living matter are made from a small number of different building-block molecules, which are identical in all species of living organisms. Recent studies of the chemical composition of the simplest cells, among them the *Mycoplasma,* suggest that the first cells to have arisen on earth may have been built from only some 30 different organic molecules. This set of 30 primordial biomolecules includes 20 amino acids, five nitrogenous aromatic bases, a fatty acid, two sugars, the alcohol glycerol, and the amine choline (Figure 1-3). In fact, this list may be shortened to 25, since recent research on the genetic code suggests that the first living cells required only 16 amino acids rather than the 20 known to be present in proteins today. Whatever their precise number, the primordial biomolecules may be regarded as the ancestors of all other biomolecules; they are the first alphabet of living matter. We should look upon this group of substances with some awe and wonder, since an extraordinary and unique relationship exists among them.

Although many of the primordial biomolecules appear at first glance to be chemically unrelated to each other, they are, in fact, related through the enzymatic reactions of metabolism, which we have seen proceed through consecutive reactions having common intermediates. For example, although the sugar glucose and the fatty acid palmitic acid and the amino acid alanine appear to be wholly different molecules, it has been found as a result of isotope-tracer and metabolic studies that all the carbon

THE PRIMORDIAL BIOMOLECULES

The amino acids

Glycine

NH_2 | CH_2COOH

Alanine

$CH_3CH(NH_2)COOH$

Valine

$CH_3CH(CH_3)CH(NH_2)COOH$

Leucine

$CH_3CH(CH_3)CH_2CH(NH_2)COOH$

Isoleucine

$CH_3CH_2CH(CH_3)CH(NH_2)COOH$

Serine

$HOCH_2CH(NH_2)COOH$

Methionine

$CH_3—S—CH_2CH_2CH(NH_2)COOH$

Threonine

$CH_3CH(OH)CH(NH_2)COOH$

Phenylalanine

$C_6H_5CH_2CH(NH_2)COOH$

Tyrosine

$HO—C_6H_4—CH_2CH(NH_2)COOH$

Tryptophan

$CCH_2CH(NH_2)COOH$, =CH, N, H (indole ring)

Cysteine

$CH_2(SH)CH(NH_2)COOH$

Proline

$CH_2—CH_2$, CH_2, $CH—COOH$, N, H

Aspartic acid

$HOOCCH_2CH(NH_2)COOH$

Asparagine

$H_2NC(=O)CH_2CH(NH_2)COOH$

Glutamic acid

$HOOCCH_2CH_2CH(NH_2)COOH$

Glutamine

$H_2NC(=O)CH_2CH_2CH(NH_2)COOH$

Histidine

$HC{=}CCH_2CH(NH_2)COOH$, N, NH, CH

Arginine

$H_2NC(=NH)NHCH_2CH_2CH_2CH(NH_2)COOH$

Lysine

$H_2NCH_2CH_2CH_2CH_2CH(NH_2)COOH$

The pyrimidines

Uracil

O, C, HN, CH, O=C, CH, N, H

Thymine

O, C, HN, $C—CH_3$, O=C, CH, N, H

Cytosine

NH_2, N, CH, O=C, CH, N, H

The purines

Adenine

NH_2, C, N, N, C, CH, HC, N, C, N, H

Guanine

O, C, HN, C, N, CH, $H_2N—C$, N, C, N, H

The sugars

α-D-Glucose

CH_2OH, O, H, H, H, OH, H, HO, OH, H, OH

α-D-Ribose

$HOCH_2$, O, H, H, H, H, OH, OH, OH

A sugar alcohol

Glycerol

CH_2OH | CHOH | CH_2OH

A nitrogenous alcohol

Choline

$(CH_3)_3N^+—CH_2CH_2OH$

A fatty acid

Palmitic acid

$CH_3—(CH_2)_{14}—COOH$

atoms of glucose can be used by living cells to form the carbon skeleton of alanine and that four of the six carbon atoms of glucose can be converted into the carbon skeleton of palmitic acid via the intermediate acetic acid (Figure 1-4). Many other metabolic interconversions of the primordial biomolecules are known to take place. It therefore appears likely that the primordial biomolecules were particularly suited to be the components of living matter not only because of their intrinsic structures and properties but also because feasible chemical pathways existed for their enzymatic interconversion.

Figure 1-3
The Primordial Biomolecules (left). Although they are somewhat arbitrarily chosen, the compounds shown may be regarded as the simplest ancestors from which all other organic biomolecules have been derived during the course of biochemical evolution. They are grouped according to their chemical structure and are shown in un-ionized form. Below is shown a classification of the primordial biomolecules according to their building-block functions.

Cell component	*Building-blocks*
Proteins	Amino acids
Nucleic acids	Pyrimidines Purines D-Ribose
Polysaccharides	D-Glucose
Lipids	Glycerol Choline Palmitic acid

The Specialization and Differentiation of Biomolecules

As living organisms evolved into more highly differentiated and complex forms, new biomolecules of greater complexity and variety also evolved. These more specialized and differentiated biomolecules are structural and metabolic derivatives of the 30 primordial biomolecules. For example, over 150 different biologically occurring amino acids are known today. Nearly all of these are derived from the basic 20 amino acids used for the construction of proteins. Similarly, dozens of different nucleotides and nucleotide derivatives are known, all descendants of

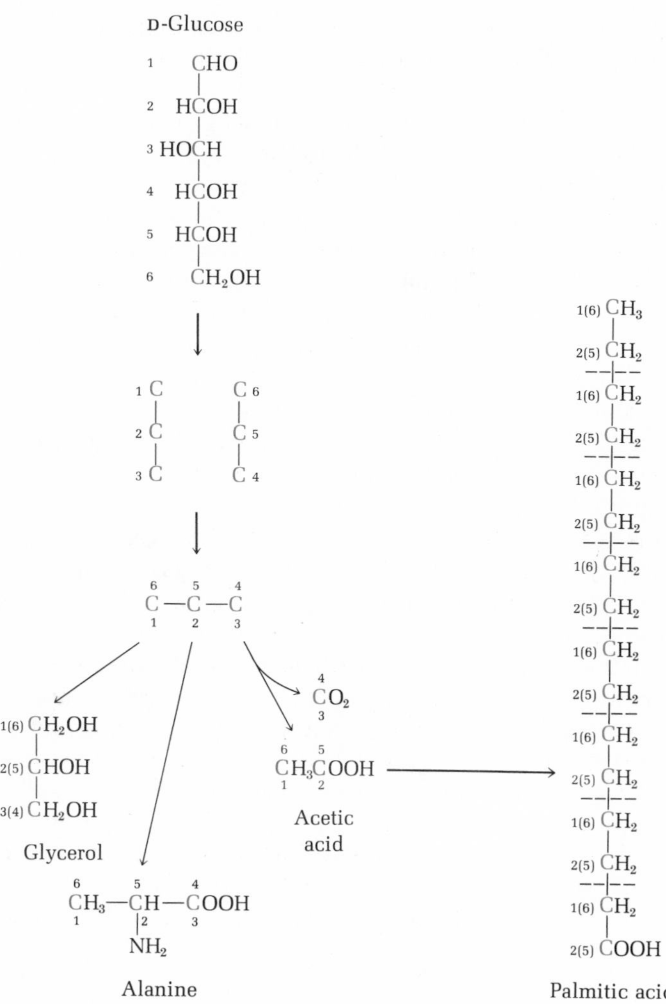

Figure 1-4
Metabolic conversion of D-glucose to an amino acid (alanine), a fatty acid (palmitic acid) and a sugar alcohol (glycerol). The glucose molecule is first cleaved into two identical 3-carbon fragments. The carbon atoms in the products are numbered to show their origin from the carbon atoms of D-glucose.

the five major nitrogenous bases found in nucleic acids. Over 70 simple sugars derive from glucose, and from these a large variety of polysaccharides are formed in different organisms. There are many different fatty acids, which are all descended from palmitic acid. Some examples are given in Table 1-4.

Many specialized biomolecules known today are extremely complex and appear to bear little resemblance to the 30 primordial biomolecules. Among these are pigments, odor-bearing essential oils, waxes, hormones, molecules such as antibiotics and alkaloids that are toxic to some organisms, and various structural molecules, such as lignin of wood. Nevertheless, recent research on the biogenesis of many of these substances shows that they can be classed into a few different types, all of which are ultimately derived from the primordial biomolecules or their breakdown products. Among these are the *acetogenins*, so named because they are formed by head-to-tail condensations of acetic acid, a degradation product of both glucose and fatty acids, and the *terpenes*, which are built of 5-carbon isoprene units, which also derive from acetic acid. Most of the alkaloids are in turn derived from the primordial amino acids.

Table 1-4 Some specialized derivatives of the primordial biomolecules

Primordial biomolecule	Derivatives
Arginine	Ornithine Citrulline
Proline	3-Hydroxyproline 4-Hydroxyproline 4-Hydroxymethylproline 4-Methyleneproline 4-Ketoproline
Leucine	β-Hydroxyleucine δ-Hydroxyleucine γ,δ-Dihydroxyleucine γ-Hydroxyleucine N-Methylleucine
Guanine	1-Methylguanine 2-Methylguanine 2-Dimethylguanine 2-O-Methylguanine 7-Methylguanine
D-Glucose	D-Mannose D-Fructose D-Galactose N-Acetylglucosamine D-Glucuronic acid D-Glucose 6-phosphate Ascorbic acid Inositol Sucrose Maltose Lactose
Palmitic acid	Oleic acid Stearic acid Lauric acid Palmitoleic acid Palmitaldehyde Stearaldehyde

The Origin of Biomolecules

We have seen (Table 1-2) that organic compounds occur only in traces in the earth's crust. How is it, then, that the first living organisms, which were presumably formed from chemical components in the primitive sea, acquired the primordial biomolecules?

Recent research suggests that early in the history of the earth, conditions favored the existence of many different organic compounds in relatively high concentration in the surface waters of the ocean and that the first living cells arose in this warm "soup" of organic compounds. It is now generally believed that the earth is approximately 4.6 billion (4.6×10^9) years old. It first arose from condensation of interstellar gases and dust, which culminated in the formation of a firm, solid mantle, consisting largely of iron and magnesium silicate and surrounding a central core of partially molten iron and nickel. Geological evidence indicates that the outer crust of the earth stabilized about 4.0 to 4.5 billion years ago. Living organisms probably first arose earlier than 3.5 billion years ago; in fact, there is fossil evidence that bacteria similar to those known today already existed about 3.1 billion years ago.

In the late 1920s, A. I. Oparin, a biochemist in the Soviet Union, suggested that chemical and physical processes occurring in the primitive atmosphere could have led to the spontaneous formation of simple organic compounds, such as amino acids and sugars, from methane, ammonia, and water vapor which he postulated to be present in the primitive atmosphere. According to his theory, these gases were activated by the radiant energy of sunlight or by lightning discharges to react with each other. The

Figure 1-5
Spark-discharge apparatus for demonstrating abiotic formation of organic compounds under primitive-atmosphere conditions.

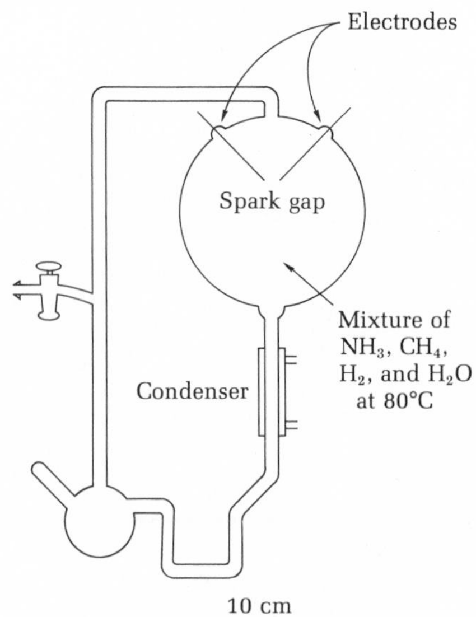

Table 1-5 Some organic compounds generated by spark discharges under primitive-atmosphere conditions

Glycine
Alanine
Sarcosine
β-Alanine
α-Aminobutyric acid
N-Methylalanine
Aspartic acid
Glutamic acid
Iminodiacetic acid
Iminoacetopropionic acid
Formic acid
Acetic acid
Glycolic acid
Lactic acid
α-Hydroxybutyric acid
Succinic acid
Urea
Methylurea

Table 1-6 Chemical reactions in spark discharges

$CH_4 + NH_3 \longrightarrow HCN + 3H_2$	(1)
$C_2H_4 + HCN \longrightarrow CH_3CH_2CN$ (A nitrile)	(2)
$CH_3CH_2CN \xrightarrow{H_2O} CH_3CH_2COOH$ (Propionic acid)	(3)
$CH_3CHOHCN \longrightarrow CH_3CHNH_2CN$ (An aminonitrile)	(4)
$CH_3CHNH_2CN \xrightarrow{H_2O} CH_3CHNH_2COOH$ (Alanine)	(5)

simple organic products so formed condensed and dissolved in the primitive ocean, which gradually became enriched in a large variety of organic compounds. Oparin postulated that the first living cell arose spontaneously from this warm, concentrated solution of organic compounds.

Oparin's hypothesis was not immediately accepted, for lack of evidence. There has been continuing disagreement about the constitution of the atmosphere during the period when life is believed to have begun, particularly whether it contained the relatively reduced gases methane and ammonia. The most recent research indicates that the atmosphere 3.0 to 3.5 billion years ago was rich in nitrogen, hydrogen, carbon monoxide and carbon dioxide, but that its content of the reduced compounds methane and ammonia was probably not very high; free oxygen was not present. The temperature of the earth's crust and atmosphere during this period is now believed to have been higher than at present, but well below 100°C. Most of the surface of the earth was covered with water.

That the gaseous components thought to be present in the primitive atmosphere can be the precursors of organic compounds is now well supported by laboratory studies. Among the early experiments on the abiotic origin of organic molecules were those carried out in 1953 by Miller. He subjected gas mixtures of methane, ammonia, water, and hydrogen, then believed to be predominant in the primitive atmosphere, in a closed flask at 80°C to electrical sparking across a pair of electrodes, to simulate lightning, for periods of a week or more (Figure 1-5). Then he collected and analyzed the contents of the system. The gas phase was found to contain carbon monoxide, carbon dioxide, and nitrogen, which were evidently formed from the gases initially introduced. In the chilled condensate, he found significantly large amounts of water-soluble organic substances, which he separated by chromatographic methods. Among the compounds Miller identified were a number of α-amino acids, including some present in proteins, such as glycine, alanine, aspartic acid, and glutamic acid. He also found several simple organic acids known to occur in living organisms, such as formic, acetic, propionic, lactic, and succinic acids (Table 1-5).

Miller postulated that the various organic compounds formed in these experiments arose by the sequence of reactions shown in Table 1-6. In the first reaction, hydrogen cyanide was formed from methane and ammonia. Methane also was converted by the electrical discharge into ethylene and other hydrocarbons. The hydrogen cyanide reacted with the ethylene to form a nitrile (reaction 2), which then underwent hydrolysis to propionic acid (reaction 3). Similarly, α-hydroxynitriles reacted with ammonia to form α-aminonitriles (reaction 4), which then underwent hydrolysis to form α-amino acids, such as alanine (reaction 5). Miller's experiments were carried out in a system rich in the reduced compounds methane and ammonia. In more recent experiments in which mixtures containing nitrogen, hydrogen, carbon monoxide, and carbon dioxide, but no methane or ammonia, were exposed to radiant energy, amino acids and other organic molecules were again formed, also via hydrogen cyanide, showing that preformed ammonia and methane are not essential for the abiotic formation of organic molecules.

Many different forms of irradiation have yielded organic compounds from such gas mixtures, including visible light, ultraviolet light, x-rays, gamma radiation, sparking and silent electrical discharges, ultrasonic irradiation, and high-energy α- and β-particles. Several hundred different organic compounds have been formed in such experiments, including representatives of all the important types of molecules found in cells, as well as many not found in cells. All the common amino acids present in proteins, the nitrogenous bases adenine, guanine, cytosine, uracil, and thymine, which serve as the building blocks of nucleic acids, and many biologically occurring organic acids and sugars have been detected. In view of these results, it now appears quite plausible that the primordial ocean was rich in dissolved organic compounds and that these may have included many or all of the basic building-block molecules we recognize in living cells today.

We may now ask: Why do abiotically formed organic molecules no longer exist in the surface waters of the earth, and why must present-day organisms synthesize their own biomolecules? The atmosphere and surface of the earth apparently underwent substantial changes during and after the period when life began, with the result that the rate of formation of new organic molecules declined. For one thing, the surface of the earth gradually cooled. Hydrogen and carbon monoxide were gradually lost from the atmosphere and were replaced by oxygen and carbon dioxide. In all probability, the concentration of abiotic organic compounds in the oceans was also reduced as a result of the metabolic activity of primitive organisms, which used them as fuel and as building blocks for forming new cells. As the abiotic organic compounds in the sea became increasingly scarce, those organisms that were capable of internally synthesizing their own biomolecules from simpler precursors such as CO_2, H_2O, ammonia, and nitrogen had a selective advantage. Presumably it was under these conditions that the first photosynthetic cells arose, capable of utilizing light energy to convert atmospheric CO_2 to glucose and other cell components.

The Fitness of Biomolecules

Why should living organisms have selected the specific types of organic molecules which they now possess? Why should 20 α-amino acids be the building blocks of proteins? Why not only 10? Why not 40? Why are they all α-amino acids? Could we not equally well construct large "protein" molecules from amino acids having their amino groups in the β-positions? Why should the purines adenine and guanine and the pyrimidines cytosine and thymine have been selected, out of the dozens of purine and pyrimidine derivatives known, to be the essential building blocks of DNA in all species? Current evidence supports the concept that the biomolecules we know today were selected from a much larger number of available compounds because of their special fitness, which gave cells containing them superior survival value. Since several hundred organic compounds have been isolated during experiments on the abiotic origin of organic molecules, such as those described above, and only some 30 different compounds may have been required to form the first cells, it appears very likely that a process of selection took place.

Evidence for the fitness concept is inherent in other facts already mentioned. Over 150 different amino acids have been found to occur biologically, yet all proteins in all species are built from the same set of 20 primordial amino acids. If any of the other amino acids had proved to be more "fit" as protein building blocks than the primordial amino acids, there was ample evolutionary time available for organisms to have acquired the ability to use them. This would particularly be the case with bacteria, which, because of their short generation time, could have selected the fittest amino acids for protein structure faster than other kinds of organisms. Yet the proteins of bacteria today are made of the same building-block amino acids as those in all other species. Since the newer, more highly specialized amino acids are more complex than the primordial amino acids from which they were derived, we may also conclude that a given biomolecule is no more complex than it needs to be to fulfill its function.

It may sometimes appear that a given biomolecule is less suited for a given function than some other substance could be. However, we must remember that a biomolecule usually has more than one biologically important function or property, and its biological fitness must be assessed on the basis of all its functions. For example, although chlorophylls are the universal light-trapping pigments of photosynthetic cells, they are not particularly effective light absorbers at those wavelengths of sunlight that are transmitted to algal cells through the turbid water of a pond. However, as we shall see in Chapter 21, the chlorophyll molecule possesses other important properties whose advantages greatly outweigh this particular disadvantage. We conclude that each biomolecule possesses properties that are optimal for *all* its biological functions considered together.

Units of mass and length

Mass

1 dalton = mass of one hydrogen atom
= 1.67×10^{-24} gram

Length

1 meter (m) = 1000 millimeters (mm)
1 micron (μ) = 1 micrometer (μm)
= 1000 millimicrons (mμ)
= 1000 nanometers (nm)
1 nm = 10 angstroms (Å)

† The term nanometer (10^{-9} m) is now preferred to millimicron. Accordingly, throughout this book wavelengths will be given in nm rather than mμ.

The Dimensions and Shapes of Biomolecules

In the next chapters we shall examine the structures and properties of the major classes of biomolecules. In particular, we shall take special notice of the sizes and shapes of biomolecules, since these attributes are of great significance in biochemistry and molecular biology. We have already seen that the precision of the complementary fit of the substrate to the active site of an enzyme is so great that it makes possible the selectivity of enzymatic catalysis and the absence of by-products. For example, the enzyme trypsin hydrolyzes only those peptide bonds of proteins in which the amino acids lysine or arginine contribute the carbonyl group. We now know that a change of but a fraction of an angstrom unit in some critical dimension of a substrate molecule can cause it to become inactive as a substrate. It is therefore essential to become familiar not only with the dimensions of biomolecules, but also the dimensions of cells and their components. In the margin are shown the basic units of mass and length.

The flat, two-dimensional projections in which the structures of organic molecules are necessarily shown on the printed page are quite insufficient to describe the true, three-dimensional configuration of biomolecules. The configuration of a molecule in space can be represented by the use of atomic models, of which there are two general types (Figure 1-6). *Crystallographic models* show the covalent skeleton and the bond angles and lengths, but they do not indicate the actual space occupied by the molecule. *Space-filling models*, on the other hand, show little detail with regard to bond angles and distances in the backbone, but they do show the van der Waals contour or surface of the molecule. While both types of model are useful in studying the structure of biomolecules, it is the space-filling model that represents the molecule as it is "seen" by the cell or by one of its specific components, such as an enzyme.

Actually, an enzyme "sees" much more than the three-dimensional shape of its substrate. It sees the location and sign of its electrical charges and the precise distance between them. It sees the positions of uncharged polar groups, such as hydroxyl, carbonyl, and amide groups, which can potentially enter into hydrogen-bond formation. It sees the sizes and shapes of the nonpolar hydrocarbon areas on the surface of the biomolecule, which may provide important contact areas in hydrophobic interactions.

Three-dimensional shape and surface topography are especially important in the case of macromolecules, particularly the proteins. A protein has only one specific three-dimensional conformation under normal intracellular conditions, called the *native conformation*, which is indispensable for its biological activity. Only the native conformation of an enzyme molecule has catalytic activity. The three-dimensional conformation of a large biomolecule cannot be extrapolated from a two-dimensional structure on the printed page, nor can it be arrived at easily with ordinary space-filling models. A very complex physical method, namely, *x-ray diffraction analysis*, is required to establish the precise conformation of a biological macromolecule. To date, the native conformations of only a few proteins are known exactly, but the charting of biomolecular structure by x-ray and computer methods has become a major objective of molecular biology.

There is another way in which the sizes and shapes of biomolecules are of crucial importance. We have seen that in living cells there is a hierarchy of molecular organization (Figure 1-1); simple biomolecules are the building

Figure 1-6
Different representations of the structure of alanine, shown in un-ionized form.

Empirical formula

$C_3H_7O_2N$

Structural formula

$$CH_3-\underset{\displaystyle NH_2}{\overset{\displaystyle H}{\overset{|}{\underset{|}{C}}}}-COOH$$

Crystallographic models

Ball-and-stick

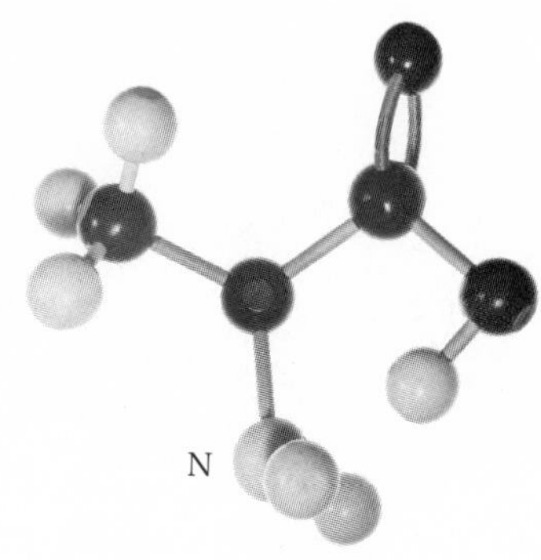

Dreiding

O
C
O
C
C
N

Space-filling model

blocks of macromolecules, macromolecules, in turn, are the building blocks of supramolecular complexes, and supramolecular complexes are the building blocks of organelles. The dimensions of biomolecules must therefore be related to the dimensions of cells and their components (Table 1-7). Just as the sizes and shapes of the component building blocks determine the sizes and shapes of cell macromolecules, such as proteins, so may the sizes and shapes of the component macromolecules determine the sizes and shapes of supramolecular complexes and thus, ultimately, of the cell organelles.

Space-filling models of atoms (in scale)

1Å

Carbon

Hydrogen

Nitrogen

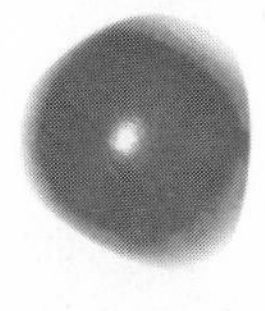

Sulfur

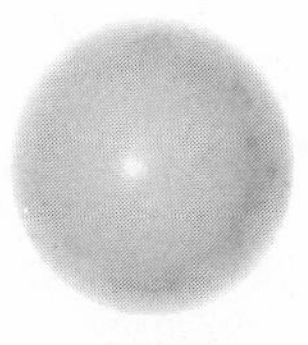

Phosphorus

Table 1-7 Approximate dimensions and weights of some biomolecules and cell components

	Long dimension (Å)	*Weight* (*daltons*)
Alanine	5	89
Glucose	7	180
Phospholipid	35	750
Myoglobin (a small protein)	36	16,900
Hemoglobin (a medium-size protein)	68	65,000
Myosin (a large rod-shaped protein)	1,600	470,000
Glutamate dehydrogenase (a very large globular protein)	130	1,000,000
Ribosome of *E. coli*	180	2,800,000
Bacteriophage ϕX174 of *E. coli*	250	6,200,000
Tobacco mosaic virus (a rod)	3,000	40,000,000
Mitochondrion (liver cell)	15,000	1×10^{-12} gram
E. coli cell	20,000	2×10^{-12} gram
Chloroplast (spinach leaf)	80,000	1.3×10^{-10} gram
Liver cell	200,000	2×10^{-9} gram

Biomolecules in Relation to Cell Structure

Throughout this book we shall relate the structures and dynamic functions of each type of biomolecule to the structures and functions of cell components, such as mitochondria, contractile systems, ribosomes, endoplasmic reticulum, chloroplasts, membranes, and cell walls. Before we begin the detailed study of biomolecules, therefore, it may be useful to review the major structural elements of cells, with special reference to their dimensions and molecular composition. This review is presented schematically in Figures 1-7, 1-8 and 1-9, which represent three types of cells. The first cell is the bacterium *E. coli*, which is the best-known member, biochemically and genetically speaking, of the great class of procaryotic cells (Figure 1-7). The second is the *hepatocyte*, or liver parenchymal cell, perhaps the most thoroughly studied eucaryotic cell (Figure 1-8). Both the *E. coli* cell and the hepatocyte are heterotrophic cells, which require carbon from the environment in a complex, reduced form. Figure 1-9 shows the structure of a third type of cell, a eucaryotic photosynthetic cell, in this case a green leaf cell.

Figure 1-7 **The structural organization of procaryotic cells.**
Procaryotes are very small, simple cells having only a single membrane, the cell membrane. They contain no membrane-surrounded nucleus and no membranous organelles such as mitochondria or endoplasmic reticulum. The procaryotes include the eubacteria, the blue-green algae, the spirochetes, the rickettsiae, and the mycoplasma or pleuropneumonialike organisms. They contain only one chromosome, which consists of a single molecule of double-helical DNA, densely coiled in the nuclear zone. Procaryotes are probably the first cells that arose in biological evolution.

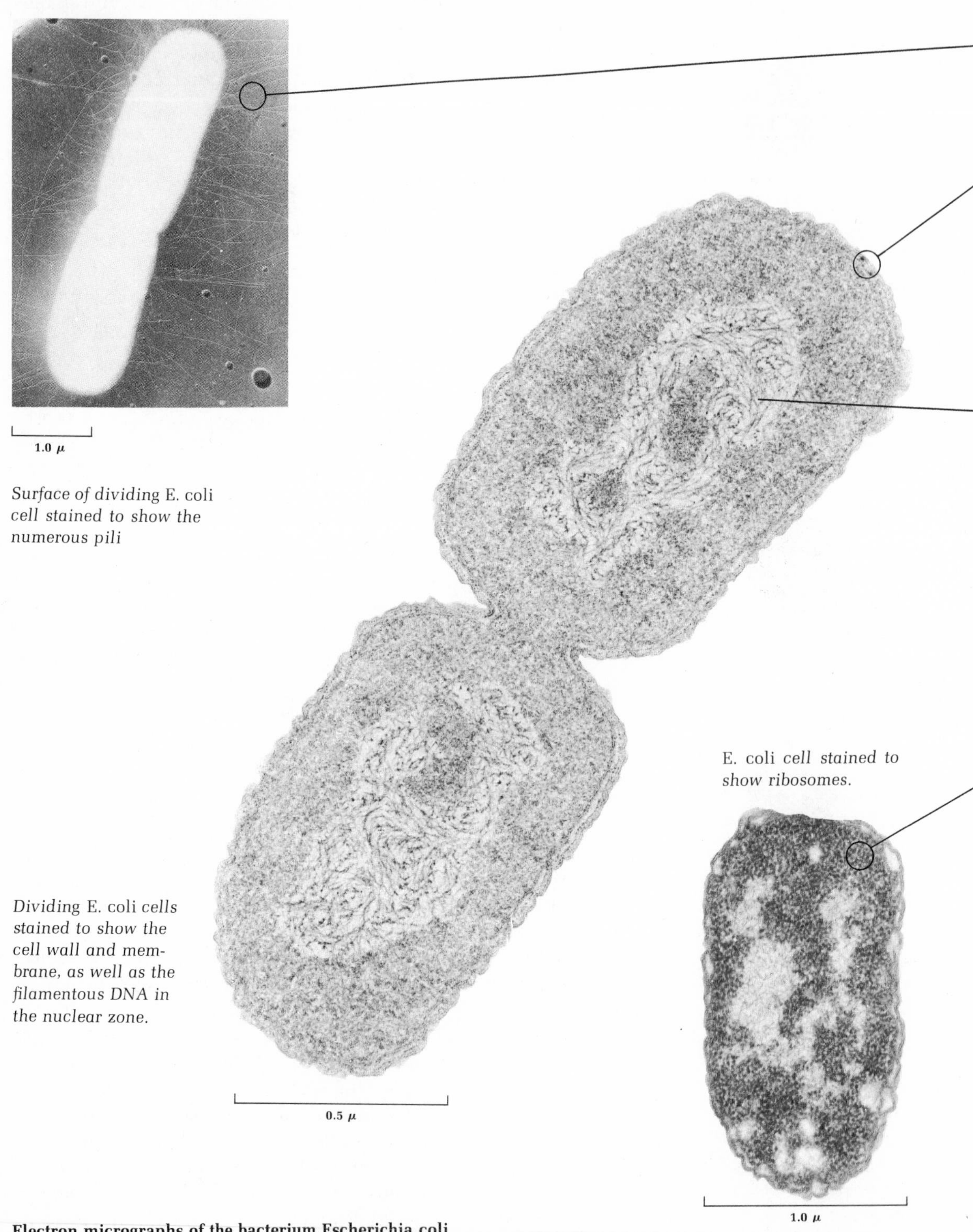

Surface of dividing E. coli cell stained to show the numerous pili

Dividing E. coli cells stained to show the cell wall and membrane, as well as the filamentous DNA in the nuclear zone.

E. coli cell stained to show ribosomes.

Electron micrographs of the bacterium Escherichia coli
This aerobic organism is a member of the coliform group of bacteria, typically found in the intestinal tract of man. The mature cell is a cylindrical rod about 2 μ long and 1 μ in diameter; it weighs about 2×10^{-12} gram. E. coli cells grow rapidly on a simple medium containing only glucose as carbon source and ammonium ions as nitrogen source; the division time may be as short as 20 min at 37°C. Most of the important recent developments in biochemical genetics have arisen from the study of various strains and mutants of E. coli and E. coli bacteriophages. More is known about the biochemistry and genetics of E. coli than for any other cell.

Schematic drawing	Molecular composition	Properties, function
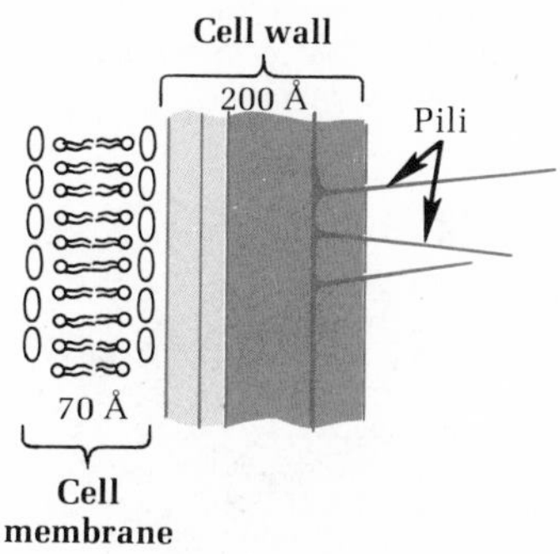 Cell wall 200 Å Pili 70 Å Cell membrane	The cell wall contains a rigid framework consisting of polysaccharide chains cross-linked with short peptide chains. The interstices are filled with rubbery lipopolysaccharides. Pili are not found in all bacteria. They are apparently extensions of the cell wall. Membranes consist of about 45% lipids and 55% protein, possibly arranged in layers. Bacterial lipids are few and relatively simple. Infoldings of the membrane are called *mesosomes*.	The wall prevents bacteria from swelling when placed in hypotonic medium. It is porous and allows most small molecules to pass. Some of the pili are hollow and may serve to transfer DNA during sexual conjugation. Semipermeable boundary which allows water to pass freely but not most simple electrolytes. Enzymes of respiration and phosphorylation and for wall synthesis are located in the membrane.
Nuclear zone 	Single, tightly coiled molecule of double-helical DNA (20 Å in diameter, about 1.2 mm long). No proteins appear to be bound to the DNA.	DNA is the carrier of genetic information. During division, each strand is replicated to yield two daughter double-helical molecules.
Ribosomes 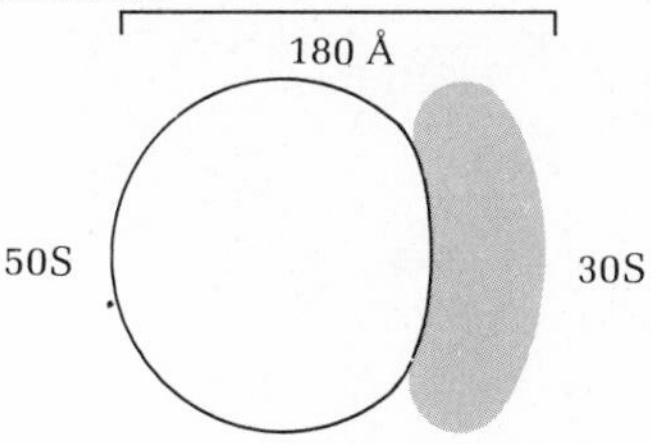 180 Å 50S 30S	*E. coli* contains about 15,000 ribosomes. Each has a major and a minor subunit. Each subunit contains about 65% RNA and 35% protein.	Sites of protein synthesis. Messenger RNA binds to groove between the subunits. The peptide chain is made alongside messenger RNA which serves as the template.
Storage granules 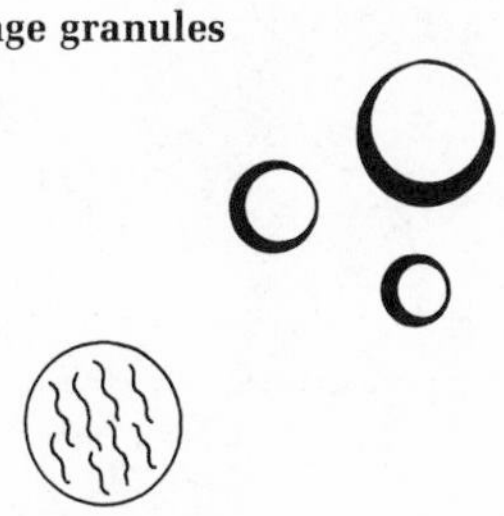	In *E. coli*, storage granules contain granulose, a polymer of glucose. Other bacteria contain granules of poly-β-hydroxybutyric acid.	When needed as fuel, these polymers are enzymatically degraded to yield free glucose or free β-hydroxybutyric acid.
Cytosol 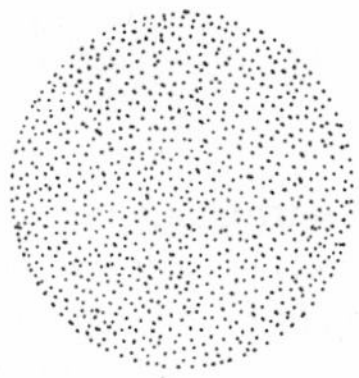	The cytosol is relatively uniform, structureless, and highly viscous; the protein concentration is very high, exceeding 20%.	The cytosol contains most of the enzymes of *E. coli*, as well as metabolic intermediates and inorganic salts.

Figure 1-8 **The structural organization of eucaryotic cells.**
Eucaryotic cells are much larger and much more complex than procaryotic cells. The cell volume of most eucaryotes is from 1,000 to 10,000 times larger than that of procaryotes. Nearly all the cells of higher organisms in both animal and plant worlds are eucaryotic, as are the fungi, protozoa and most algae. Eucaryotes contain a membrane-surrounded nucleus. The nuclear material is divided into several or many chromosomes, which undergo mitosis during cell division. Eucaryotes also contain membranous organelles such as mitochondria and Golgi bodies, as well as an endoplasmic reticulum. Many of their metabolic reactions are segregated into structural compartments. Eucaryotes are more recent in evolutionary origin than procaryotes; presumably they were derived from the latter.

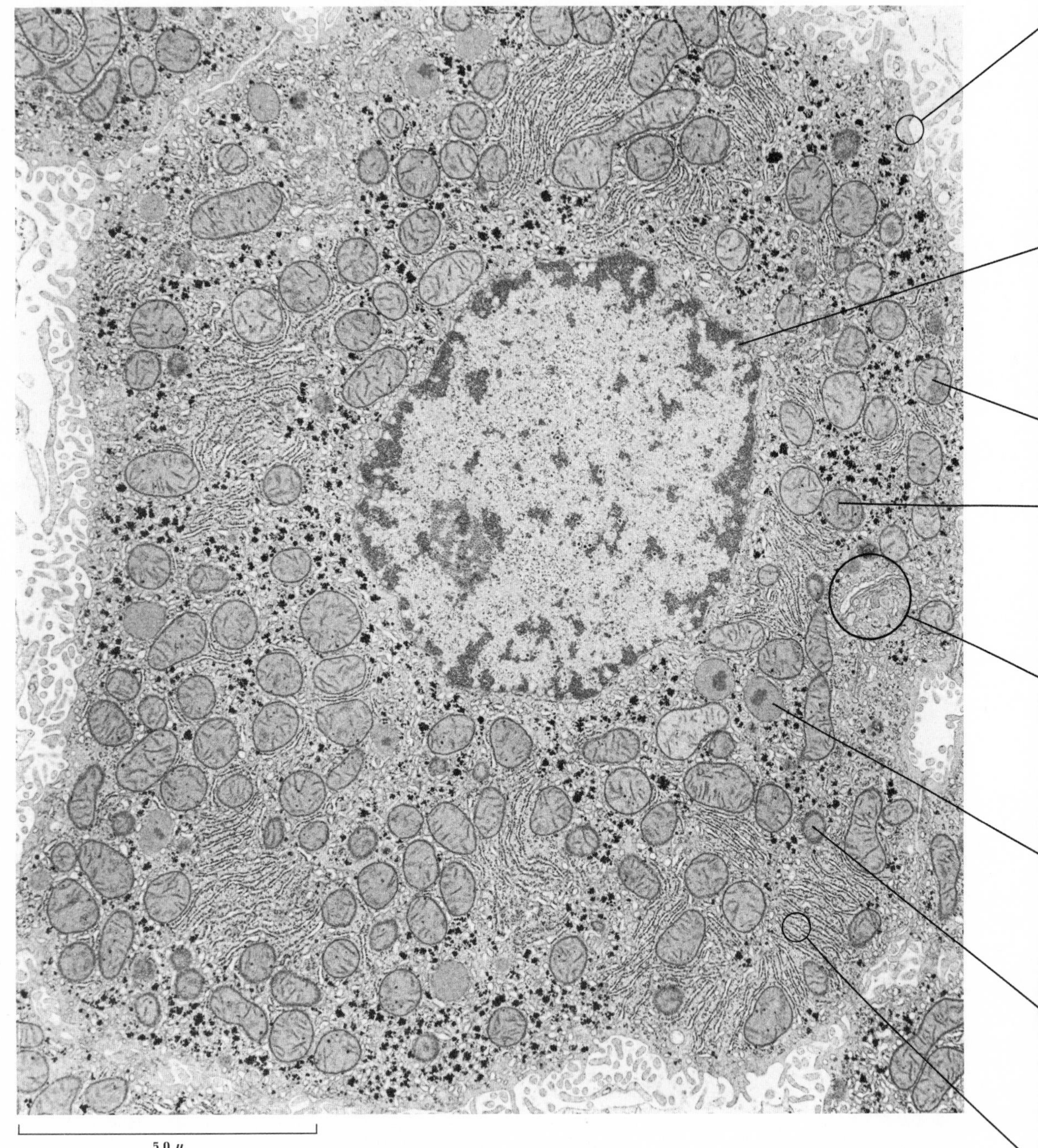

Electron micrograph of a thin section of a single rat-liver cell (hepatocyte) fixed in osmium tetroxide.
Rat-liver hepatocytes are polyhedral and about 20 μ in diameter. They are metabolically versatile cells whose most important function is the biochemical processing and distribution of foodstuff molecules brought to the liver from the intestinal tract. They store glucose as glycogen, prepare nitrogenous wastes for excretion, and synthesize blood plasma proteins and lipids. They are capable of carrying out all the major "mainstream" metabolic activities of cells. They are perhaps the most thoroughly studied animal cells because of their ready availability and the ease with which nuclei, mitochondria, endoplasmic reticulum (the "microsome" fraction), and other subcellular fractions can be recovered by differential centrifugation of sucrose homogenates of liver.

Schematic drawing	Molecular composition	Properties, functions
Cell membrane 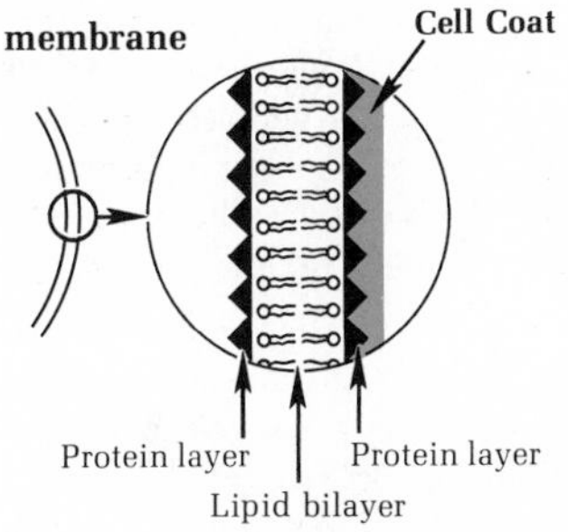 Cell Coat Protein layer Protein layer Lipid bilayer	The cell wall is flexible and very thin in hepatocytes. It is composed of acid mucopolysaccharides, glycolipids, and glycoproteins. The membrane is about 90 Å thick. It contains a greater variety of lipids than do bacterial membranes. Desmosomes, or tight junctions, are zones of continuity with membranes of adjacent cells.	The adhesive properties of cell coats are specific and play an important role in cell-cell recognition and thus tissue organization. The plasma membrane is the true permeability barrier. It contains important enzymes and active transport systems for Na^+ and K^+.
Nucleus 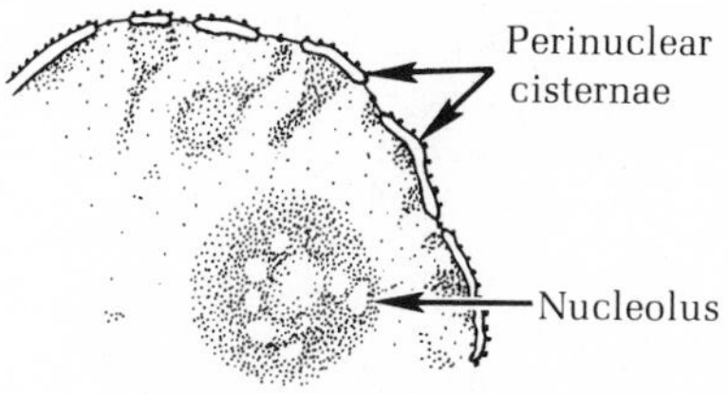 Perinuclear cisternae Nucleolus	Diameter, 4-6 μ. The nucleus is surrounded by a perinuclear envelope with large pores. The DNA is combined with histones and organized into chromosomes, which are located in the chromatin. The nucleolus is rich in RNA.	During mitosis, chromosomes undergo segregation, alignment, crossing-over, replication of DNA, and separation into daughter chromosomes. The nucleolus is active in forming RNA.
Mitochondria  Cristae Granules Matrix	There are about 800 mitochondria in the hepatocyte. They are globular in shape and a little over 1.0μ in diameter. They occupy about 20% of the cytoplasmic volume. The outer and inner membranes differ in lipid composition and in enzymatic activity. The matrix is rich in enzymes and contains DNA.	Site of oxidation of carbohydrates, lipids, amino acids to CO_2 and H_2O by molecular oxygen. The enzymes of electron transport and energy conversion are located in the inner membrane. Mitochondria may have arisen from parasitizing, symbiotic aerobic bacteria in the cytoplasm during the evolution of eucaryotic cells.
Golgi complex 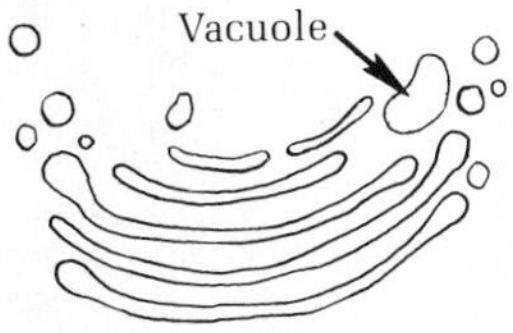 Vacuole	Consists of flattened membrane-surrounded vesicles, which are often stacked. Small vesicles arise peripherally by pinching off from the large vesicles. Some become vacuoles in which secretory products are concentrated.	The Golgi apparatus functions in the secretion of cell products such as proteins to the exterior, and are especially active in the formation of the plasma membrane and lysosomal membrane.
Microbodies (Peroxisomes) 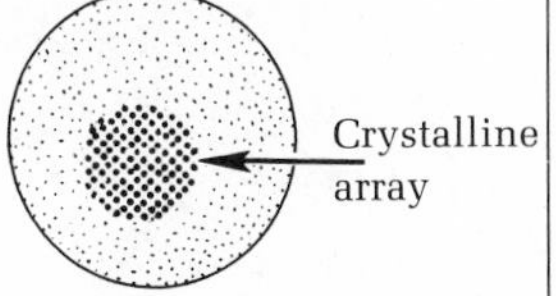 Crystalline array	Single-membrane vesicles about 0.5 μ in diameter containing catalase, D-amino acid oxidase, urate oxidase, and other oxidative enzymes. Crystalline arrays often visible; presumably they are enzyme crystals.	Primitive oxidative organelles.
Lysosomes 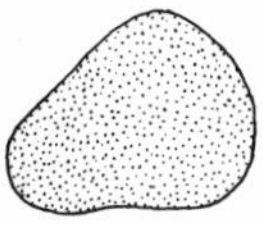	Single-membrane vesicles (0.25–0.5 μ in diameter) containing hydrolytic enzymes (ribonuclease, phosphatase, and cathepsin).	Function in the digestion of materials brought into the cell by phagocytosis or pinocytosis.
Endoplasmic reticulum and Ribosomes 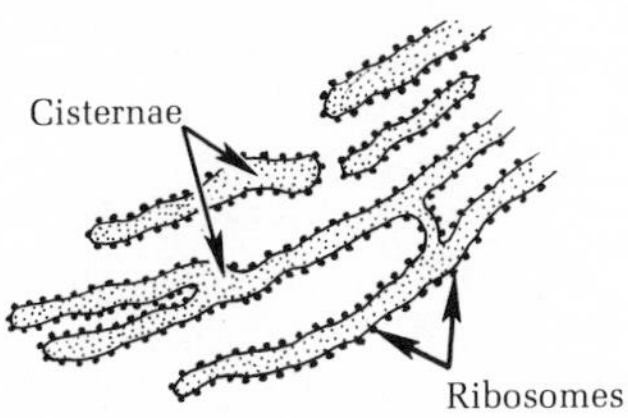 Cisternae Ribosomes	The endoplasmic reticulum consists of flattened vesicles, whose inner compartments, called cisternae, interconnect to form channels through the cytoplasm. The rough-surfaced endoplasmic reticulum is studded with ribosomes. The ribosomes are larger than in procaryotes.	Proteins synthesized by the adhering ribosomes cross the membrane and appear in the intracisternal space, which forms a highly ramified channel for intracellular transport to the periphery of the cell.

Figure 1-9 **Structural organization of a photosynthetic leaf cell of a higher plant.**

The parenchymal cells of the mesophyll of leaves of higher plants are active in photosynthesis. They contain most of the distinctive organelles and structures observed in eucaryotic cells of animals, such as nucleus, mitochondria, Golgi apparatus (often called a dictyosome in plants), endoplasmic reticulum, and ribosomes. In addition, leaf cells contain three other major structures which are usually absent or much less conspicuous in animal cells: plastids (*including chloroplasts*), large vacuoles, *and* thick, rigid, cell walls. *Green cells are rich in the pigment chlorophyll, which is localized in the chloroplasts. The major biochemical activities of the parenchymal cell are photosynthetic formation of glucose from CO_2 and H_2O and the storage of glucose as starch. In the dark, photosynthetic cells respire at the expense of atmospheric oxygen and oxidize glucose.*

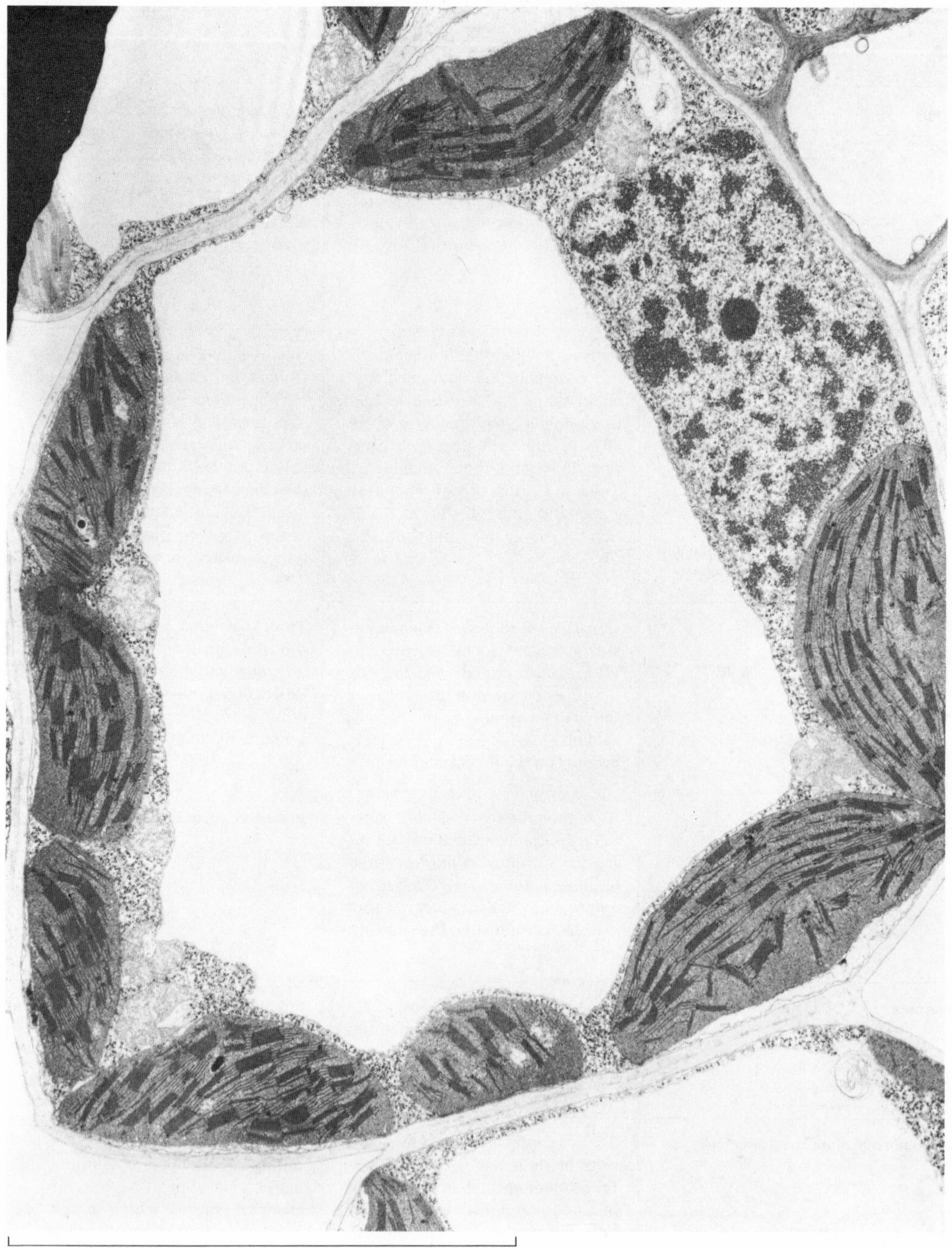

10.0 μ

Electron micrograph of a section through a parenchymal leaf cell of *Phleum pretense* **(timothy).**

Cell wall: Plant cell walls are thick, rigid, and box-like. The primary wall consists of cellulose fibrils which are encased in a cement of polysaccharides and proteins. The cell wall protects the cell membrane from mechanical or osmotic rupture. It also firmly fixes the position of the cell.

Cell membrane: Similar in thickness, structure, and properties to animal cell membranes. The lipid components are somewhat different, as are the active transport systems.

Nucleus: The nucleus, perinuclear membrane, and nucleolus are grossly similar to those in animal cells; the chromosome numbers may of course be different.

Schematic drawing

Chloroplasts: Cells of higher plants characteristically contain plastids, membrane-surrounded organelles, some of which possess DNA different from that of the nucleus. Some plastids contain pigments (chromoplasts); others are unpigmented (leucoplasts). Plastids containing chlorophyll are called chloroplasts and are active in photosynthesis. Other chromoplasts store carotenoid pigments. Among the leucoplasts are the amyloplasts, which store starch granules.

Chloroplasts are relatively large ($> 8\ \mu$) compared to mitochondria. There are several or many chloroplasts per cell, and they may assume different forms. The inner membranes form regular stacks of disk-like flattened vesicles called thylakoids, in which chlorophyll and the photosynthetic electron carriers are located. Chloroplasts are the site of photosynthetic formation of ATP, reducing power, and oxygen. The reduction of CO_2 to form glucose and starch also takes place in chloroplasts.

Mitochondria: Fewer in number than in hepatocytes. The cristae are relatively sparse. In the light, leaf cells obtain most of their energy requirement from photosynthetic phosphorylation in chloroplasts. However, in the dark, mitochondrial respiration is the main energy supply. The enzymatic and structural organization of plant mitochondria is similar to that of animal cells.

Vacuoles: Vacuoles are surrounded by a semipermeable membrane. They are small in young cells and increase in size with age, causing the cytoplasm to become flattened against the cell wall in a thin layer. Vacuoles contain dissolved sugars, organic acids, proteins, salts, oxygen, CO_2, and pigments. Vacuoles function in the segregation of wastes and solutes, which gradually accumulate during the life of the cell and become more concentrated. Solutes sometimes crystallize within vacuoles.

Endoplasmic reticulum: The ribosomes attached to the endoplasmic reticulum are slightly different in size and composition from those in animal cells. The endoplasmic reticulum functions as the site of protein synthesis and in the channeling of protein products through the cytoplasm.

Biochemistry today is increasingly concerned with the structure of cells and their organelles. Some of the most illuminating recent progress has come from correlated biochemical and electron-microscopic studies of cellular processes. Indeed, the dividing lines between biochemistry and cell biology, and between biochemistry and molecular biophysics, are becoming difficult to identify, since these areas form a logical continuum. The application of exact physical methods to the analysis of cell components is yielding significant data on the precision with which biomolecules are constructed and with which they interact in their cellular functions.

Summary

Living matter requires only 22 of the 100 chemical elements found in the crust of the earth; the four elements carbon, hydrogen, nitrogen, and oxygen make up 99 percent of the total mass of most living organisms. Nearly all the nonaqueous portion of living cells consists of organic compounds of carbon, which are very sparse in the earth's crust. Carbon appears to be uniquely "fit" for the backbone structure of biomolecules because of its capacity to form stable covalent bonds with hydrogen, oxygen, and nitrogen and, above all, with other carbon atoms.

The molecular organization of cells begins with simple precursor molecules obtained from the environment. These are transformed by enzymatic reactions into building-block molecules, which are covalently bonded to form the cell macromolecules. These, in turn, are noncovalently associated into supramolecular assemblies and these ultimately into cell organelles.

The first cells may have been formed from about 30 primordial biomolecules, which include 20 amino acids, five purine and pyrimidine bases, two sugars, a fatty acid, glycerol, and choline. From these biomolecules are descended hundreds of other biomolecules, serving more specialized and differentiated functions in various organisms. The primordial biomolecules may have had an abiotic origin, arising by interaction of the components of the primitive atmosphere under the influence of radiant energy or lightning discharges. The primitive sea, it is believed, contained a large number of simple organic compounds, from which were selected those molecules most suited for the survival of the first living organisms. Presumably the biomolecules are the simplest, most versatile, and most fit molecules for their multiple functions in cells. The sizes, shapes, and surface characteristics of biomolecules are exceedingly important in the specificity of their biological interactions and also in their role as building blocks in the structural elements of cells.

References

Books

ALLEN, J. M. (ed.): *Molecular Organization and Biological Function*, Harper & Row, Publishers, Inc., New York, 1967. Short readable papers on the molecular organization of cells.

FAWCETT, D. W.: *The Cell. An Atlas of Fine Structure*, W. B. Saunders Company, Philadelphia, 1966. Excellent electron micrographs of cells and their organelles and inclusions.

HENDERSON, L. J.: *The Fitness of the Environment,* The Macmillan Company, New York, 1927 (reprinted 1958). A classic statement.

HENDRICKSON, J. B.: *The Molecules of Nature,* W. A. Benjamin, Inc., New York, 1965. A paperback review of the structural interrelationships among alkaloids, terpenes, acetogenins, and other natural products.

KEOSIAN, J.: *The Origin of Life,* 2d ed., Reinhold Publishing Corp., New York, 1968. Excellent paperback review of the problem, including abiotic synthesis of organic molecules.

OPARIN, A. I.: *Life: Its Nature, Origin, and Development,* Academic Press Inc., New York, 1962.

SPEAKMAN, J. C.: *Molecules,* McGraw-Hill Book Company, New York, 1966. Excellent paperback on the structure and properties of molecules in relation to biology.

Articles

PALADE, G. E.: "The Organization of Living Matter," in *The Scientific Endeavor,* Rockefeller Institute Press, New York, 1964, pp. 179–203.

WALD, G.: "The Origins of Life," in *The Scientific Endeavor,* Rockefeller Institute Press, New York, 1964, pp. 113–134.

Problems

1. Calculate the number of lipid molecules in an *E. coli* cell. Assume that the average molecular weight of lipids is 700 and that lipid molecules make up 2 percent of the total wet weight of the *E. coli* cell, which is 2×10^{-12} gram.

2. A single *E. coli* cell is assumed to contain 3,000 different types of proteins (mol wt 30,000) in equimolar numbers. Assume that 15 percent of the total weight of the cell is protein and that 90 percent of the protein is in the cytoplasm.
   (*a*) Calculate the molar concentration of each type of protein in the cytoplasm.
   (*b*) Calculate the total protein concentration in the cytoplasm in moles per liter.
   (*c*) Calculate the concentration of total protein in the cytoplasm in grams per liter.

3. The single DNA molecule in an *E. coli* chromosome (mol wt 2,800,000,000) contains about 4.5 million mononucleotide units, which are spaced about 3.4 Å apart. Calculate the total length of this DNA molecule and compare it with the length of the *E. coli* cell.

4. An *E. coli* culture will grow to a limiting concentration of about 10^9 cells per cm^3. At this concentration, what percentage of the total volume of the culture medium is occupied by the cells? (Use the data of Figure 1-7.)

5. What percentage of the volume of an *E. coli* cell is occupied by the 15,000 ribosomes which it contains? *E. coli* ribosomes are about 180 Å in diameter and may be assumed to be spheres.

6. (*a*) Calculate the ratio of the volume of an hepatocyte (a eucaryote) to that of an *E. coli* cell (a procaryote). Assume the hepatocyte to be a cube 20 μ on an edge.
   (*b*) Calculate the ratio of their surface areas.
   (*c*) Also calculate the surface/volume ratios for each.

7. Calculate the percentage of the total wet weight of an hepatocyte (of the dimensions given in Problem 6) that is contributed by the cell membrane. Assume that the membrane is 90 Å thick and that its specific gravity, as well as that of the entire cell, is 1.0.

8. Calculate the total surface area of the outer and inner membranes of all the mitochondria of a liver cell, assuming it contains 1,000 mitochondria, each a right circular cylinder of 2.0 μ height and 1.0 μ diameter. Assume also that each mitochondrion contains 10 disklike cristae, each side of which is equal in area to the base of the mitochondrion. Compare the total surface of the mitochondrion with that of the cell membrane (see Problem 6 for dimensions).

CHAPTER 2 WATER

Because it is ubiquitous, water is often regarded as a bland, inert liquid, a mere space filler in living organisms. Actually, water is a highly reactive substance with unusual properties, and it is very different, both chemically and physically, from most other common liquids. The first cells to arise in the primordial sea had to learn to cope with the singular properties of water, and ultimately, as we shall see, living organisms evolved means of exploiting these properties. We now recognize that water and its ionization products, hydrogen and hydroxyl ions, are important factors in determining the structure and biological properties of proteins, nucleic acids, lipids, membranes, and many other cell components.

Physical Properties and Structure of Water

When compared with other common liquids, water has a high melting point, boiling point, heat of vaporization, specific heat, heat of fusion, and surface tension. These properties indicate that the forces of attraction between molecules in liquid water, and thus its internal cohesion, are relatively high. For example, in Table 2-1 we see that the heat of vaporization of water is considerably higher than that of any of the other common liquids listed. The heat of vaporization is a direct measure of the amount of energy required to overcome the attractive forces between adjacent molecules in a liquid so that individual molecules can escape from each other and enter the gaseous state.

Table 2-1 Heat of vaporization of some common liquids at their boiling point (1.0 atm)

	ΔH_{vap} *cal gm*$^{-1}$
Water	540
Methanol	263
Ethanol	204
n-Propanol	164
Acetone	125
Benzene	94
Chloroform	59

The strong intermolecular forces in liquid water are caused by the electrical polarity of the water molecule, which in turn is the consequence of the specific arrangement of electrons in its oxygen and hydrogen atoms (Figure 2-1). The oxygen atom shares a pair of electrons with each of the two hydrogen atoms, through overlap of the 1s orbitals of the hydrogen atoms with two hybridized sp^3 orbitals of the oxygen atom. Each of these electron pairs has about one-third ionic and two-thirds covalent character. From spectroscopic and x-ray analyses, the precise bond angles and lengths have been determined. The average H—O—H bond angle in water is 104.5°, which represents a slight deviation from a perfectly tetrahedral arrangement of the four possible sp^3 orbitals of the oxygen atom, which would have an angle of 109.5°. One explanation for this deviation is that the unpaired electrons of oxygen tend to repel the paired electrons. The average H—O interatomic distance is 0.965 Å.

This arrangement of electrons in the water molecule gives it electrical asymmetry. The more electronegative oxygen atom tends to attract the single electrons of the hydrogen atoms, leaving the hydrogen nuclei bare. As a result, each of the two hydrogen atoms has a local partial positive charge (designated σ^+). The oxygen atom, in turn, has a local partial negative charge (designated σ^-), located in the zone of the unshared orbitals. Thus, although the water molecule has no net charge, it is an electrical dipole. The degree of separation of positive and negative charges in dipolar molecules is given by the dipole moment, a measure of the tendency of a molecule to orient itself in an electrical field. From the dipole moment of water, it has been calculated that each hydrogen atom has a partial positive charge of about $+0.33 \times 10^{-10}$ electrostatic unit (esu) and the oxygen atom a partial negative charge of about -0.66×10^{-10} esu.

Figure 2-1
The water molecule. The outline of the space-filling model represents the border at which van der Waals attractions are counterbalanced by repulsive forces. Below is shown a ball-and-stick or crystallographic model of the water molecule, giving the bond angle and length.

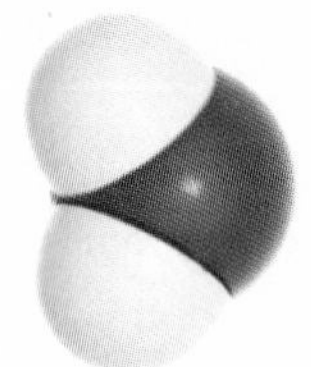

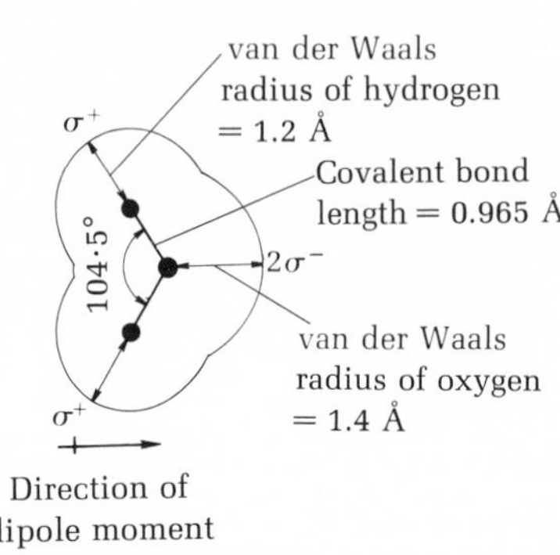

Hydrogen Bonding

The dipolar nature of the water molecule is largely responsible for the attractive forces between water molecules, since a strong electrostatic attraction occurs between the partial negative charge on the oxygen atom of one water molecule and the partial positive charge on the hydrogen atom of an adjacent water molecule. This type of electrostatic interaction, which has a small covalent component, is called hydrogen bonding. Because of the

Figure 2-2
(Below) Tetrahedral hydrogen bonding around a water molecule in ice. Molecules 1 and 2 and the central molecule are in the plane of the paper; molecule 3 is above it, and molecule 4 is behind it. (Right) Schematic diagram of the lattice of water molecules in ice.

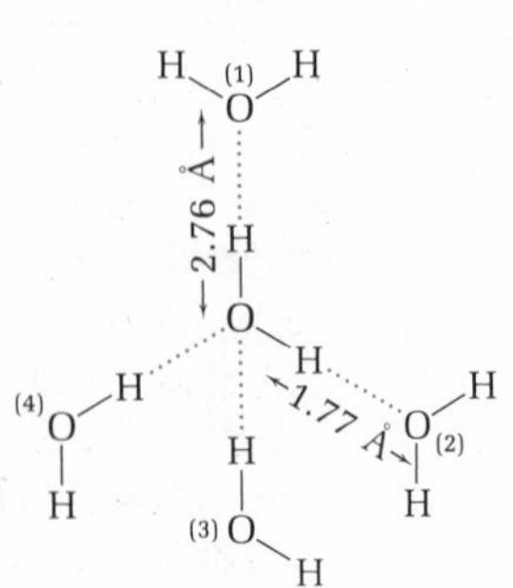

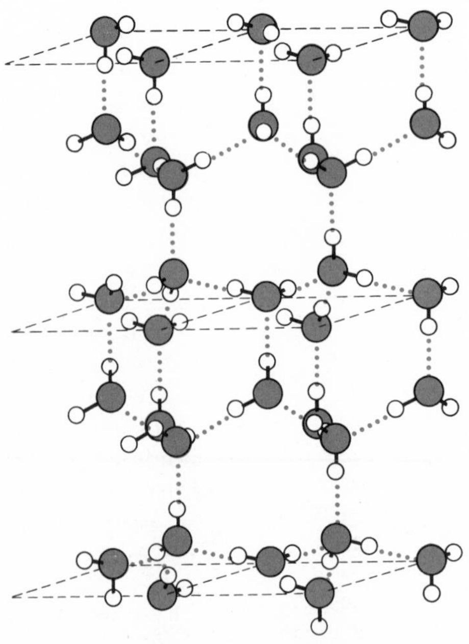

Figure 2-3
Directionality of the hydrogen bond. (Above) When the O—H bond is linear with the acceptor atom, the hydrogen bond formed will have maximum stability. (Below) When the acceptor oxygen is not on the electrical vector of the O—H bond, a weaker hydrogen bond is formed.

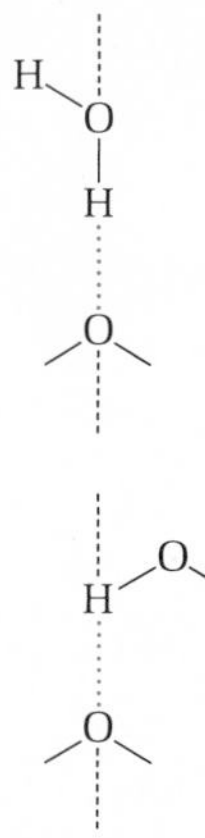

Figure 2-4
Some hydrogen bonds of biological importance.

Between a hydroxyl group and H_2O

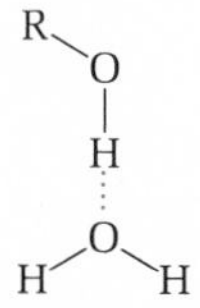

Between a carbonyl group and H_2O

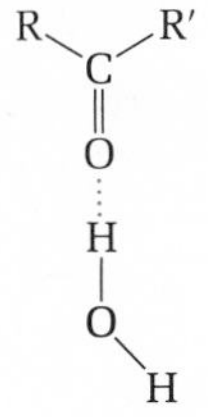

Between two peptide chains

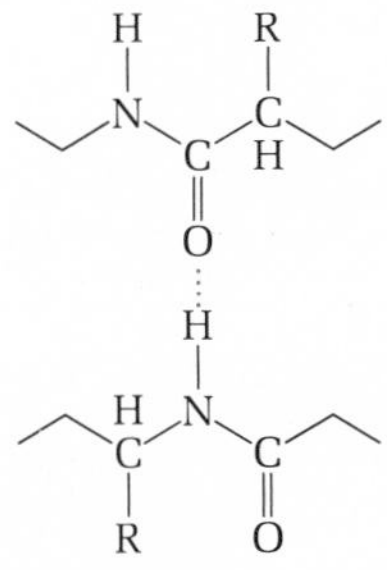

Between complementary base pairs in DNA

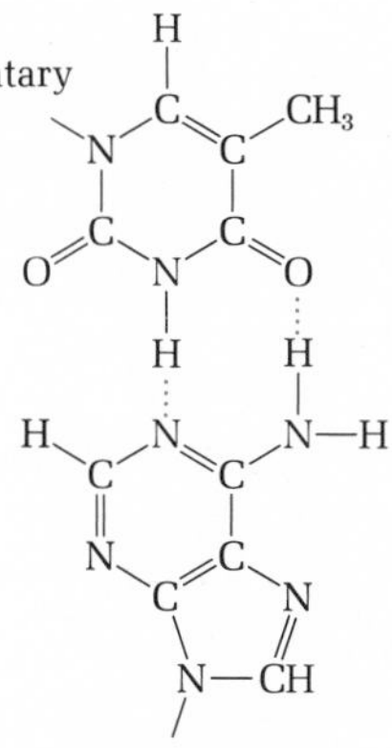

Thymine

Adenine

nearly tetrahedral arrangement of the electrons about the oxygen atom, each water molecule tends to hydrogen-bond with four neighboring water molecules (Figure 2-2).

An important property of hydrogen bonds is that they are much weaker than covalent bonds. The H bonds in liquid water are estimated to have a bond energy of only about 4.5 kcal $mole^{-1}$, compared with 110 kcal $mole^{-1}$ for the H—O electron-pair bonds in water. (*Note:* Bond energy is the energy required to break a bond.) Another important property of hydrogen bonds is that they have a high degree of directionality, which is conferred by the characteristic arrangement of the bonding orbitals of the hydrogen and oxygen atoms (Figure 2-3). Hydrogen bonds also possess a specific bond length, which differs from one type of H bond to another, depending on the structural geometry and the electron distribution in the molecules involved. In ice, each water molecule is hydrogen-bonded; the length of the hydrogen bond is 1.77 Å (Figure 2-2). Hydrogen bonds therefore form and remain stable only under specific geometrical conditions.

Hydrogen bonding between water molecules occurs not only in liquid water but also in ice and in water vapor. In the most common crystalline form of ice, called ice I, each water molecule is hydrogen-bonded with exactly four nearest neighbors and the average oxygen-oxygen distance is 2.76 Å. In liquid water, each water molecule at 0° is hydrogen-bonded at any given time with an average of about 3.4 other water molecules; the average oxygen-oxygen distance is only slightly greater than in ice, about 2.90 Å at 15°C and 3.05 Å at 83°C. It has been estimated from the heat of fusion of ice that only about 15 percent of the hydrogen bonds in ice are broken when ice is melted to water at 0°C. Thus liquid water can be regarded as slightly broken-down ice, with considerable short-range molecular order but no long-range order. Strong attractions between water molecules still exist in water at 100°C, as is indicated by its high heat of vaporization. In fact, hydrogen bonding between water molecules is completely overcome only when water vapor is heated to nearly 600°C.

Hydrogen bonds are not unique to water. They tend to form between any electronegative atom, such as oxygen, nitrogen, or fluorine, and a hydrogen atom covalently bonded to another electronegative atom. Hydrogen bonds may form between two molecules or between two parts of the same molecule. Some examples of biologically important hydrogen bonds are shown in Figure 2-4. Single hydrogen bonds between two solute molecules in aqueous systems are very weak because the surrounding water molecules compete to form hydrogen bonds with the solutes. However, when a number of hydrogen bonds exist between two structures, the energy required to separate them is much greater than the sum of the bond energies of the individual hydrogen bonds. This phenomenon is called *cooperative hydrogen bonding*, and it is characteristically seen in proteins and some nucleic acid molecules, which may contain dozens or even hundreds of cooperating hydrogen bonds. Such bonding yields structures that are surprisingly stable in water.

The Kinetics of Hydrogen Bonding

We have seen that between ice and liquid water there is only a small difference in the amount of hydrogen bonding. This may appear surprising in view of the rigidity of ice and the fluidity of liquid water. The explanation lies in the rate at which hydrogen bonds are made and broken. Although at any given time most of the molecules in liquid water are hydrogen-bonded, the half-life of each hydrogen bond is only about 10^{-10} to 10^{-11} seconds. The structure of liquid water is therefore only statistical, since it is the result of an average over both space and time. Consequently, liquid water is at once fluid and stable. The apt term "flickering clusters" has been applied to the short-lived icelike groups of water molecules in liquid water. The precise structure of such clusters and the number of hydrogen bonds per cluster are still unknown and are the subjects of much current research.

The rate at which hydrogen bonds form and break in aqueous systems greatly exceeds the rate of making and breaking of most covalent bonds. This fact endows hydrogen bonds with a great biological advantage over covalent bonds in certain types of biomolecular phenomena.

Solvent Properties of Water

Water dissolves or disperses many substances because of its dipolar nature. It is a much better solvent than most common liquids.

Many crystalline salts and other ionic compounds readily dissolve in water but are nearly insoluble in nonpolar liquids such as chloroform or benzene. Since the crystal lattice of salts, such as sodium chloride, is held together by very strong electrostatic attractions between alternating positive and negative ions, considerable energy is required to pull these ions away from each other. However, water dissolves crystalline sodium chloride because the strong electrostatic attraction between water dipoles and the Na^+ and Cl^- ions, to form the very stable hydrated Na^+ and Cl^- ions, greatly exceeds the tendency of Na^+ and Cl^- to attract each other.

Ion solvation is also aided by the tendency of the solvent to oppose the electrostatic attraction between positive and negative ions. This is given by the *dielectric constant D,* which is defined by the relationship

$$F = \frac{e_1 e_2}{Dr^2}$$

where F is the attractive force between two ions of opposite charge, e_1 and e_2 are the charges on the ions, and r is the distance between them. As you can see in Table 2-2, water has an extremely high dielectric constant and benzene a very low one. The attractive force between Na^+ and Cl^- ions at a given distance in water is only one-fortieth that in benzene, a factor which greatly favors hydration of the ions and dissolution of the crystal lattice.

Table 2-2 Dielectric constants of some liquids (20°C)

	D
Water	80
Methanol	33
Ethanol	24
Acetone	21.4
Benzene	2.3
Hexane	1.9

Figure 2-5
Formation of a soap micelle in water. The non-polar tails of the sodium oleate are hidden from the water, whereas the negatively charged carboxyl groups are exposed.

Sodium oleate

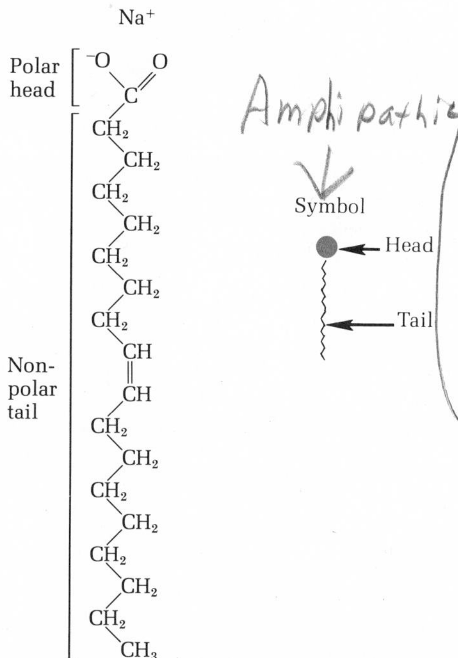

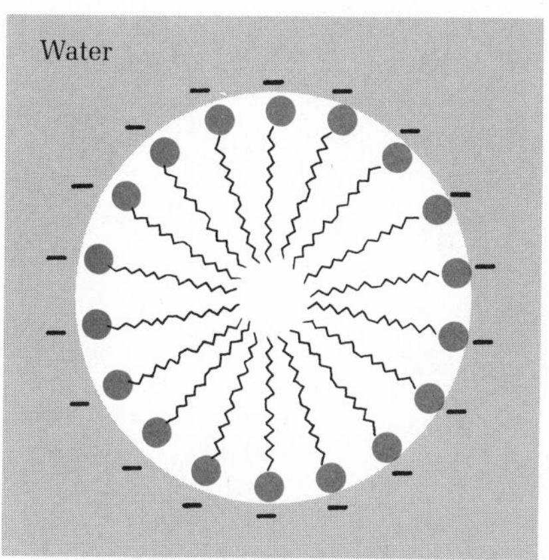

Sodium oleate micelle

A second large class of substances readily dissolved by water includes nonionic but polar compounds such as sugars, simple alcohols, aldehydes, and ketones. Their solubility is due to the propensity of water molecules to hydrogen-bond with polar functional groups, such as the hydroxyl groups of sugars and alcohols and the carbonyl oxygen atom of aldehydes and ketones (Figure 2-4).

Hydrophobic Interactions

Water also disperses many compounds containing nonpolar or hydrophobic groups in the form of *micelles* providing such compounds also contain strongly polar groups. This type of "solubilization" is made possible by hydrogen bonding, not between solute and solvent molecules but among the solvent molecules. Compounds containing both highly hydrophobic and highly polar groups are called *amphipathic.*

The most common amphipathic biomolecules that tend to form micelles are fatty acids and polar lipids. A simple example is the sodium salt of the long-chain fatty acid oleic acid. Because its long hydrocarbon chain is intrinsically insoluble in water, there is very little tendency for sodium oleate (a soap) to dissolve in water in the form of a truly molecular solution. However, it readily disperses in water to form micelles in which the negatively charged carboxyl groups are exposed to the water phase and the nonpolar, insoluble hydrocarbon chains are hidden within the micellar structure (Figure 2-5). Such micelles have a net negative charge, and they remain suspended because of mutual repulsion.

Micelles may contain hundreds or even thousands of molecules of amphipathic substance. The characteristic internal location of the nonpolar groups in micelles is the result of the tendency of water molecules to assume the state of maximum randomness, or entropy. In this state, water has enormous internal cohesion because of hydrogen bonding. To insert a nonpolar structure such as a hydrocarbon chain into water would require energy since the surrounding water molecules would be forced into a more regular arrangement, one with less entropy or randomness than in pure water. Put in another way, micelles form because water likes water more than it likes nonpolar structures.

Within micelles, there are additional attractive forces between adjacent hydrocarbon structures through van der Waals interactions. It must be emphasized that there is no true stoichiometric bonding between hydrocarbon groups in a micelle. For this reason, the term *hydrophobic interaction* is more properly used than *hydrophobic bond* to refer to the association of the hydrophobic portions of amphipathic molecules. Compared with hydrogen bonds, hydrophobic interactions have relatively little directionality, but they do tend to produce systems of high stability.

As we shall see later, many other cell components are amphipathic and tend to form structures in which the nonpolar, hydrophobic parts are hidden from water—in particular, the proteins and the nucleic acids.

Effect of Solutes on Water Structure

The presence of an ionic solute such as NaCl causes a distinct change in the structure of liquid water since each Na^+ and Cl^- ion is surrounded by a shell of water dipoles. These hydrated ions have a geometry somewhat different from the clusters of hydrogen-bonded water molecules; they are more highly ordered and regular in structure. Table 2-3 gives the average interionic distance in aqueous NaCl solutions as a function of the concentration of NaCl. We see that at 0.15 *M* NaCl, the approximate concentration of NaCl in blood plasma (and of K^+ salts in the cytoplasm of cells), Na^+ and Cl^- ions are separated by only about 19 Å, on the average. Since each hydrated Na^+ and Cl^- ion is 5 to 7 Å in diameter and a tetrahedral cluster of five water molecules is about 5 Å in diameter, it is clear that a considerable change must occur in the three-dimensional structure and properties of liquid water when NaCl is dissolved in it in a concentration approximating that occurring in biological fluids. Salts therefore "break" the structure of water.

Table 2-3 Average interionic distance in solutions of NaCl

Concentration (M)	*Distance* (Å)
0.001	94
0.010	44
0.10	20
0.150	19
1.00	9.4

The effect of a solute on the solvent is manifest in another set of properties, namely, the *colligative properties* of solutions, which are dependent on the number of solute particles per unit volume of solvent. Solutes produce such characteristic effects in the solvent as depression of the freezing point, elevation of the boiling point, and depression of the vapor pressure. They also endow a solution with the property of osmotic pressure. One gram molecular weight of an ideal nondissociating nonassociating solute dissolved in 1,000 grams of water at a pressure of 760 mm of mercury depresses the freezing point by 1.86°C and elevates the boiling point by 0.543°C. Such a solution also yields an osmotic pressure of 22.4 atmospheres in an appropriate apparatus. Since aqueous solutions usually deviate considerably from ideal behavior, these relationships are quantitative only at infinite dilution, i.e., on extrapolation to zero concentration of solute.

Ionization of Water

Because of the small mass of the hydrogen atom and the fact that its single electron is tightly held by the oxygen atom, there is a finite tendency for the hydrogen atom to dissociate from the oxygen atom to which it is covalently bound in one water molecule and "jump" to the oxygen atom of the adjacent water molecule to which it is hydrogen-bonded, provided that the internal energy of each molecule is favorable (see below). In this reaction, two ions are produced, the hydronium (H_3O^+) ion and the hydroxyl (OH^-) ion. In a liter of pure water at 25°C, there are at any given time only 1.0×10^{-7} mole of H_3O^+ ions and an equal amount of OH^- ions, as shown by electrical-conductivity measurements.

Figure 2-6
Hydrated form of hydronium ion ($H_9O_4^+$). *The hydration shell is stable to 100°.*

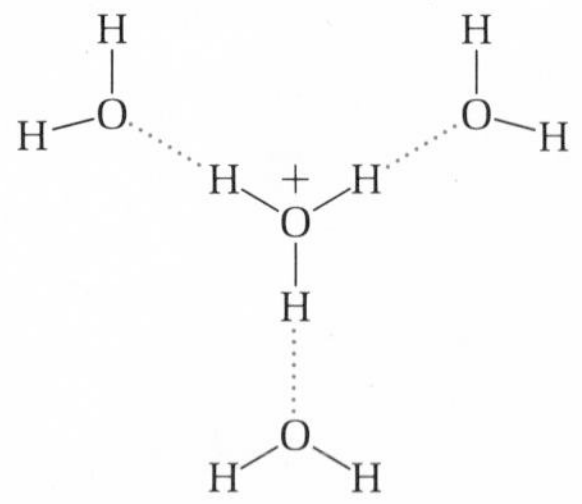

Although the ionization of water is by convention written simply as

$$H_2O \rightleftharpoons H^+ + OH^-$$

Table 2-4 Electrical mobility of some cations at infinite dilution (25°C)

Ion	Mobility $cm^2\ volt^{-1}\ sec^{-1}$ ($\times 10^4$)
H^+	36.3
Na^+	5.2
K^+	7.62
NH_4^+	7.60
Mg^{2+}	5.4
Li^+	4.0

"bare" protons do not exist in water. Actually, the H_3O^+ ion is itself hydrated through further hydrogen bonding to form the ion $H_9O_4^+$ (Figure 2-6).

In Table 2-4, we see that the rate of migration of H^+ ions in an electrical field is many times greater than that of Na^+ or K^+ ions. The high electrical mobility of the H_3O^+ ion is due to the fact that a proton may "jump" from a hydronium ion to a neighboring water molecule, a reaction that occurs with an extremely high frequency. A series of proton jumps has the effect of translocating protons at a rate that is much higher than the rate of diffusive or bulk movement of H_3O^+ ions per se (Figure 2-7). Such proton jumps also are responsible for the exceptionally high electrical conductivity of ice. Conduction of protons through hydrogen-bonded water molecules may be an important phenomenon in biological systems.

Figure 2-7
Proton jumps.

This H_2O molecule becomes a hydronium ion at the end of the series of proton jumps.

The Ion Product of Water; the pH Scale

The dissociation of water is an equilibrium process:

$$H_2O \rightleftharpoons H^+ + OH^-$$

for which we can write the equilibrium constant

$$K_{eq} = \frac{[H^+][OH^-]}{[H_2O]}$$

where the brackets indicate concentrations in moles per liter. The magnitude of this equilibrium constant at any given temperature can be calculated from conductivity measurements on pure distilled water. Since the concentration of water in pure water is very high (it is equal to the number of grams of H_2O in a liter divided by the gram mol wt, or $1000/18 = 55.5\ M$) and the concentration of H^+ and OH^- ions very low ($1 \times 10^{-7}\ M$ at 25°C), the molar concentration of water is not significantly changed by its very slight ionization. The equilibrium-constant expression may thus be simplified to

$$55.5 \times K_{eq} = [H^+][OH^-]$$

and the term $55.5 \times K_{eq}$ can then be replaced by a "lumped" constant K_w, called the *ion product* of water,

$$K_w = [H^+][OH^-]$$

The value of K_w at 25°C is 1.0×10^{-14}. In an acid solution, the H^+ concentration is relatively high and the OH^- concentration correspondingly low; in a basic solution, the situation is reversed.

K_w, the ion product of water, is the basis for the *pH scale* (Table 2-5), a means of designating the actual concentration of H^+ (and thus of OH^-) ions in any aqueous solution in the acidity range between 1.0 M H^+ and 1.0 M OH^-. The term pH is defined as

$$pH = \log_{10} \frac{1}{[H^+]} = -\log_{10} [H^+]$$

Table 2-5 The pH scale

$[H^+]$ (M)	pH	$[OH^-]$ (M)
1.0	0	10^{-14}
0.1	1	10^{-13}
0.01	2	10^{-12}
0.001	3	10^{-11}
0.0001	4	10^{-10}
0.00001	5	10^{-9}
10^{-6}	6	10^{-8}
10^{-7}	7	10^{-7}
10^{-8}	8	10^{-6}
10^{-9}	9	10^{-5}
10^{-10}	10	10^{-4}
10^{-11}	11	0.001
10^{-12}	12	0.01
10^{-13}	13	0.1
10^{-14}	14	1.0

In a precisely neutral solution at 25°C,

$$[H^+] = [OH^-] = 1.0 \times 10^{-7}\ M$$

The pH of such a solution is

$$pH = \log_{10} \frac{1}{1 \times 10^{-7}} = 7.0$$

The value of 7.0 for the pH of a precisely neutral solution is thus not an arbitrarily chosen figure; it is derived from the absolute value of the ion product of water at 25°C. It is especially important to note that the pH scale is logarithmic, not arithmetic. To say that two solutions differ in pH by 1 pH unit means that one solution has ten times the hydrogen-ion concentration of the other. Table 2-6 lists the pH of some fluids.

Table 2-6 pH of some fluids

	pH
Seawater	7.0–7.5
Blood plasma	7.4
Interstitial fluid	7.4
Intracellular fluids	
Muscle	6.1
Liver	6.9
Gastric juice	1.2–3.0
Pancreatic juice	7.8–8.0
Saliva	6.35–6.85
Cow's milk	6.6
Urine	5–8
Tomato juice	4.3
Grapefruit juice	3.2
Soft drink (cola)	2.8
Lemon juice	2.3

Measurement of pH

Measurement of pH is one of the most important and frequently used analytical procedures in biochemistry since the pH determines many important features of the structure and activity of biological macromolecules, and thus of the behavior of cells and organisms. The primary standard for measurement of H^+-ion concentration (and thus of pH) is the *hydrogen electrode*. This is a specially treated platinum electrode that is immersed in the solution whose pH is to be measured. The solution is in equilibrium with gaseous hydrogen at a known pressure and temperature. The electromotive force at the electrode responds to the equilibrium.

$$H_2 \rightleftharpoons 2H^+ + 2e^-$$

The potential difference between the hydrogen electrode and a reference electrode of known emf (for example, a calomel electrode) is measured and used to calculate the H^+-ion concentration.

The hydrogen electrode is too cumbersome for general use and has been replaced by the *glass electrode*, which is directly sensitive to H^+-ion concentration in the absence of hydrogen gas. The response of the glass electrode must be calibrated against buffers of precisely known pH. Another way of measuring pH is by the use of acid-base indicators (see below).

Acids and Bases

The most general and comprehensive definitions of acids and bases, applicable to nonaqueous as well as aqueous systems, are those of G. N. Lewis. A Lewis acid is a potential *electron-pair acceptor*, and a Lewis base a potential *electron-pair donor*. The Lewis definitions are very useful in the analysis of reaction mechanisms, as we shall see later (Chapter 9). However, the formalism introduced by J. N. Brönsted and T. M. Lowry is more useful than that of Lewis in describing acid-base reactions in dilute aqueous systems. According to the Brönsted-Lowry concepts, an

Conjugate acid-base pairs of acetic acid, ammonium ion, and water.

Proton donor		Proton acceptor
$CH_3COOH \rightleftharpoons$	$H^+ +$	CH_3COO^-
$NH_4^+ \rightleftharpoons$	$H^+ +$	NH_3
$HOH \rightleftharpoons$	$H^+ +$	OH^-

acid is a proton donor and a base is a proton acceptor (margin). An acid-base reaction always involves a *conjugate acid-base pair*, made up of a proton donor and the corresponding proton acceptor. For example, acetic acid (CH_3COOH) and the acetate anion (CH_3COO^-) form a conjugate acid-base pair. Each acid has a characteristic affinity for its proton. Those with high affinity for protons are weak acids and dissociate only slightly; those with low affinity are strong acids and lose H^+ ions readily. The tendency of any given acid to dissociate is given by its dissociation constant. For the acid HA, the dissociation constant at a given temperature is

$$K' = \frac{[H^+][A^-]}{[HA]}$$

where the brackets indicate concentrations in moles per liter. It is the convention in biochemistry to employ dissociation constants based on the analytically measured concentrations of reactants and products under a given set of experimental conditions, i.e., at a given total concentration and ionic strength and with other solutes specified. Such a constant is called an *apparent* dissociation constant and is designated K' to distinguish it from the true, or *thermodynamic*, dissociation constant K employed by the physical chemist, which is corrected for deviation of the system from ideal behavior caused by such factors as concentration and ionic strength.

The apparent dissociation constants of some acids and bases are given in Table 2-7. Note that in the Brönsted-Lowry formalism, acids and bases are treated alike, i.e., solely in terms of the tendency of protons to dissociate from the proton-donor species. (So-called "basic dissociation constants," such as K_b for the dissociation $NH_4OH \rightleftharpoons NH_4^+ + OH^-$, are not employed. In fact, in the Brönsted-Lowry formalism, NH_4OH is *neither* an acid

Table 2-7 Apparent dissociation constant and pK' of some acids (25°C)

Acid (*proton donor*)	K' (M)	pK'
HCOOH	1.78×10^{-4}	3.75
CH_3COOH	1.74×10^{-5}	4.76
CH_3CH_2COOH (propionic acid)	1.35×10^{-5}	4.87
$CH_3CHOHCOOH$ (lactic acid)	1.38×10^{-4}	3.86
$COOHCH_2CH_2COOH$ (succinic acid)	6.16×10^{-5}	4.21
$COOHCH_2CH_2COO^-$	2.34×10^{-6}	5.63
H_3PO_4	7.25×10^{-3}	2.14
$H_2PO_4^-$	6.31×10^{-8}	7.20
HPO_4^{2-}	3.98×10^{-13}	12.4
H_2CO_3	1.70×10^{-4}	3.77
HCO_3^-	6.31×10^{-11}	10.2
NH_4^+	5.62×10^{-10}	9.25
$CH_3NH_3^+$	2.46×10^{-11}	10.61
HOH	1.0×10^{-14}	14.00

nor a base.) Table 2-7 also gives values for the expression pK', which is a logarithmic transformation of K', just as the term pH is a logarithmic transformation of $[H^+]$:

$$pK' = \log_{10}\frac{1}{K'} = -\log_{10} K'$$

Strong acids have low pK' values, and strong bases have high pK' values.

Figure 2-8 shows the titration curves of some conjugate acid-base pairs. The pH after each increment of NaOH is added during the titration of an acid is plotted vs. the equivalents of OH^- added. The shapes of such titration curves are very similar from one acid to another; the important difference is that the curves are displaced vertically along the pH scale. The pH intercept at the midpoint of the titration is numerically equal to the pK' of the acid titrated. At the midpoint, equimolar concentrations of proton-donor (HA) and proton-acceptor species (A^-) of the acid are present. In fact, the pK' of an acid can be calculated from the pH at any point on the titration curve of an acid if the concentrations of the proton-donor and proton-acceptor species at this point are known. The shape of the titration curve can be expressed by the *Henderson-Hasselbalch equation*, which is a logarithmic transformation of the expression for the dissociation constant. It is derived as follows:

$$K' = \frac{[H^+][A^-]}{[HA]}$$

Solve for $[H^+]$:

$$H^+ = K'\frac{[HA]}{[A^-]}$$

Take the negative logarithm of both sides:

$$-\log [H^+] = -\log K' - \log\frac{[HA]}{[A^-]}$$

Substitute pH for $-\log [H^+]$ and pK' for $-\log K'$:

$$pH = pK' - \log\frac{[HA]}{[A^-]}$$

If we now change signs, we obtain the Henderson-Hasselbalch equation:

$$pH = pK' + \log\frac{[A^-]}{[HA]}$$

which, in more general form, is

$$pH = pK' + \log\frac{[\text{proton acceptor}]}{[\text{proton donor}]}$$

This equation makes it possible to calculate the pK' of any acid from the molar ratio of proton-donor and proton-

Figure 2-8
(Right) *Acid-base titration curves of some acids, showing the major ionic species at beginning, midpoint, and end of titration.* (Below) *The relative buffering power plotted against* pH. *Maximum buffering power is given at* pH = p*K*′.

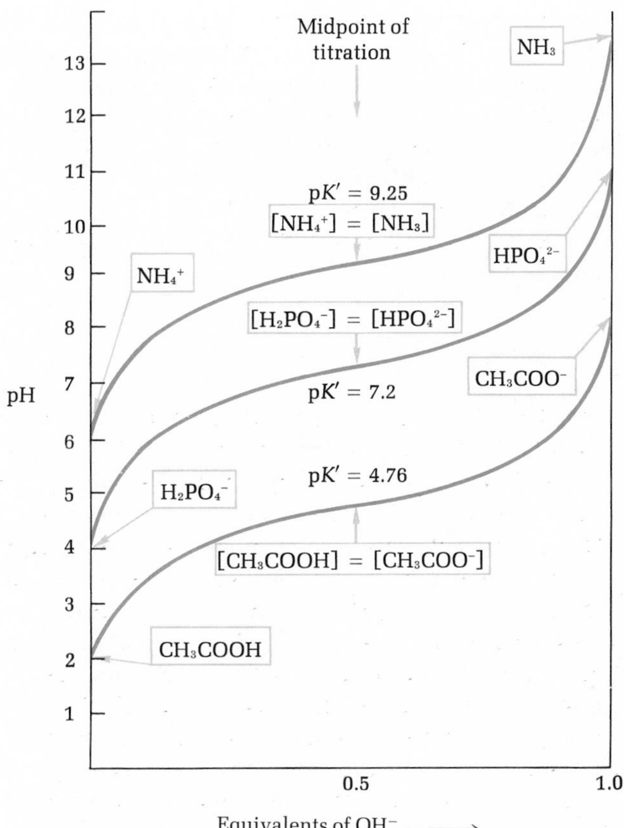

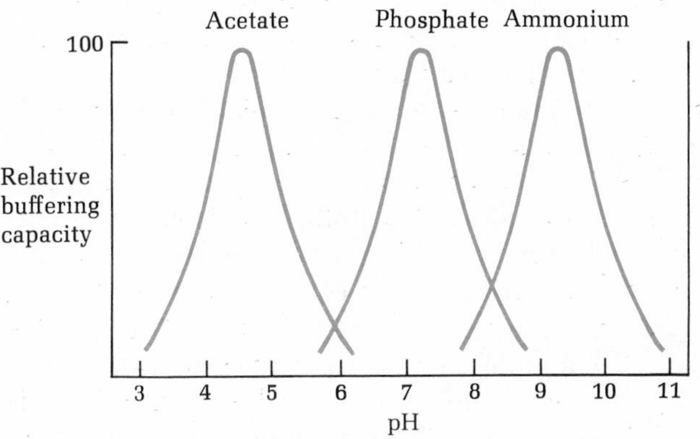

acceptor species at a given pH, to calculate the pH of a conjugate acid-base pair of a given p*K*′ and a given molar ratio, and to calculate the molar ratio of proton donor and proton acceptor given the pH and p*K*′. The Henderson-Hasselbalch equation is fundamental for quantitative treatment of all acid-base equilibria in biological systems.

Acid-Base Indicators

The pH of a solution can be determined by using indicators, most of which are weak acids (designated HInd). The anionic or proton-acceptor species of indicator (Ind^-) has a different absorption spectrum than the proton-donor species:

$$\underset{\text{Proton donor}}{\text{HInd}} \rightleftharpoons H^+ + \underset{\text{Proton acceptor}}{\text{Ind}^-}$$

The equilibrium position of this dissociation, and thus the amount of light absorbed by the species Ind^- at its characteristic wavelength, is determined by the ambient H^+-ion concentration. In a strongly acid solution, the species HInd is favored by mass action and little light will be absorbed at the wavelength of maximum absorption of Ind^-. In a basic solution, the species Ind^- is favored since excess OH^- ions will "trap" H^+ ions as H_2O; in this case, much light will be absorbed.

Buffers

You may have noticed in Figure 2-8 that the titration curve of each acid has a flat zone extending about 1.0 pH unit on either side of its midpoint. In this zone, the pH of the system changes relatively little when small increments of H^+ or OH^- are added. This is the zone in which the conjugate acid-base pair acts as a *buffer*, i.e., a system which tends to resist change in pH when H^+ or OH^- is added. At pH values outside this zone, there is less capacity to resist changes in pH. The buffering power is maximum at the exact midpoint of the titration curve, i.e., when the ratio [proton acceptor]/[proton donor] = 1.0, at which pH = pK' (Figure 2-8). Each conjugate acid-base pair has a characteristic pH at which its buffering capacity is greatest, namely, the point at which pH = pK'.

Intracellular and extracellular fluids of living organisms contain conjugate acid-base pairs which act as buffers at the normal pH of these fluids. The major intracellular buffer is the conjugate acid-base pair $H_2PO_4^-$-HPO_4^{2-} ($pK' = 7.2$). Organic phosphates such as glucose 6-phosphate and ATP also contribute buffering power in the cell. The major extracellular buffer in the blood and interstitial fluid of vertebrates is the bicarbonate buffer system. The extraordinary buffering power of blood plasma may be shown by the following comparison. If 1 ml of 10 *N* HCl is added to 1.0 liter of neutral physiological saline (i.e., about 0.15 *M* NaCl), the pH of the saline will fall to pH 2.0, since NaCl solutions have no buffering power. However, if 1 ml of 10 *N* HCl is added to 1 liter of blood plasma, the pH will decline only slightly, from pH 7.4 to about pH 7.2.

The bicarbonate buffer system (H_2CO_3–HCO_3^-) has some distinctive features. While it functions as a buffer in the same way as other conjugate acid-base pairs, the pK' of H_2CO_3, a relatively strong acid, is about 3.8 (Table 2-7), which is far lower than the normal range of blood pH. In a bicarbonate buffer system, the proton-donor species carbonic acid is in reversible equilibrium with dissolved CO_2:

$$H_2CO_3 \rightleftharpoons CO_2(\text{diss.}) + H_2O$$

If such an aqueous system is in contact with a gas phase, then the dissolved CO_2 will, in turn, equilibrate between the gaseous and aqueous phases:

$$CO_2(\text{diss.}) \rightleftharpoons CO_2(\text{gas})$$

Since by Henry's law the solubility of a gas in water is proportional to its partial pressure, the pH of the bicarbonate buffer system is a function of the partial pressure of CO_2 in the gas phase over the buffer solution. If the CO_2 pressure is increased, all other variables remaining constant, the pH of the bicarbonate buffer declines, and vice versa. The bicarbonate system can buffer effectively near pH 7.0, at which the proton acceptor/proton donor ratio is very high, because a small amount of proton donor H_2CO_3 is in labile equilibrium with a relatively large reserve capacity of gaseous CO_2 in the lungs. Under any conditions in which the blood must absorb excess OH^-, the H_2CO_3 which is used up and converted to HCO_3^- is quickly replaced from the large pool of gaseous CO_2 in the lungs.

There is another distinctive feature of the bicarbonate buffer system. CO_2 is the end product of the aerobic combustion of fuel molecules in the vertebrate and is ultimately expired from the lungs. The steady-state ratio of $[HCO_3^-]/[H_2CO_3]$ in the blood is a reflection of the rate of CO_2 production during tissue oxidation and of the rate of loss of CO_2 by expiration.

Figure 2-9
The effect of pH on the activity of some enzymes. Each enzyme has a characteristic pH-activity profile. The pH may influence the degree of ionization not only of enzymes but also of coenzyme and substrate molecules.

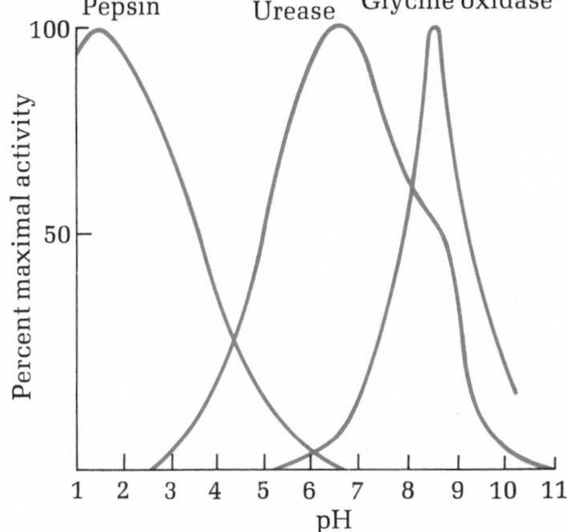

The pH of blood plasma in vertebrates is held at remarkably constant values. The blood plasma of man normally has a pH of 7.40. Should the pH-regulating mechanisms fail, as may happen in disease, and the pH of the blood fall below 7.0 or rise above 7.8, irreparable damage may occur. We may ask: What molecular mechanisms in cells are so extraordinarily sensitive that a change in H^+ concentration of as little as 3×10^{-8} M (approximately the difference between blood at pH 7.4 and blood at pH 7.0) can be lethal? Although many aspects of cell structure and function are influenced by pH, it is the catalytic activity of enzymes that is especially sensitive. The typical curves in Figure 2-9 show that enzymes have maximal activity at a characteristic pH, called the *optimum pH*, and that their activity declines sharply on either side of the optimum. Thus biological control of the pH of cells and body fluids is of central importance in all aspects of intermediary metabolism and cellular function.

The Fitness of the Aqueous Environment for Living Organisms

Living organisms have effectively adapted to their aqueous environment and have even evolved means of exploiting the unusual properties of water. The high specific heat of water is useful to the cell because cell water acts as a "heat buffer," allowing the temperature of the cell to remain relatively constant as the temperature of the environment fluctuates. Furthermore, the high heat of evaporation of water is exploited as an effective means for vertebrates to lose heat by evaporation of sweat. The high degree of internal cohesion of liquid water, due to hydrogen bonding, is exploited by higher plants to transport dissolved nutrients from the roots up to the leaves during the process of transpiration. Even the fact that ice has a lower density than liquid water and therefore floats has important biological consequences in the ecology of aquatic organisms. But most fundamental to all living organisms is the fact that many important biological properties of cell macromolecules, particularly the proteins and nucleic acids, derive from their interactions with water molecules of the surrounding medium, as we shall see.

Summary

Water is the most abundant compound in living organisms. Its relatively high freezing point, boiling point, heat of vaporization, and surface tension are the result of strong intermolecular attractions in the form of hydrogen bonding between water molecules. Liquid water has considerable short-range order and consists of "flickering clusters" of very short half-life.

The polarity and hydrogen-bonding properties of the water molecule make it a potent solvent for many ionic compounds and neutral molecules. Water also disperses amphipathic molecules, such as soaps and polar lipids, to form micelles, clusters of molecules in which the hydrophobic groups are hidden from exposure to water and the polar groups are located on the external surface. The formation of micelles is the result of the tendency of surrounding water molecules to engage in maximum hydrogen bonding to each other.

Water ionizes very slightly to form hydronium (H_3O^+) and hydroxyl (OH^-) ions. The hydronium ion is itself hydrated ($H_9O_4^+$). Protons may "jump" from H_3O^+ to H_2O molecules with extremely high frequency. These proton jumps account for the high electrical mobility of protons in water and ice. In dilute aqueous solutions, the concentrations of H^+ and OH^- ions are inversely related by the expression $K_w = [H^+][OH^-] = 1 \times 10^{-14}$ (25°C). The hydrogen-ion concentration of biological systems is expressed in terms of pH, defined as $\text{pH} = -\log [H^+]$. The pH of aqueous solutions is measured by means of the glass electrode or with indicators.

Acids are defined as proton donors, and bases as proton acceptors. A conjugate acid-base pair consists of a proton donor (HA) and its corresponding proton acceptor (A^-). The tendency of an acid HA to donate protons is expressed by its dissociation constant K' or by the function pK', defined as $-\log K'$. The pH of a solution of a weak acid is quantitatively related to its pK' and to the ratio of the concentrations of its proton-donor and proton-acceptor species by the Henderson-Hasselbalch equation. A conjugate acid-base pair can act as a buffer and resist changes in pH; its capacity to do so is greatest at the pH numerically equal to its pK'. The most important biological buffer pairs are H_2CO_3–HCO_3^- and $H_2PO_4^-$-HPO_4^{2-}. The catalytic activity of enzymes is strongly influenced by pH.

References

General reference works in biochemistry and physical chemistry are given in the Appendix.

Books

DAWES, E. A.: *Quantitative Problems in Biochemistry*, 2d ed., The Williams & Wilkins Company, Baltimore, 1968. Succinct treatment of quantitative aspects of biochemistry; problem solving.

DICK, D. A. T.: *Cell Water*, Butterworth, Inc., Washington, D.C., 1966. Structure, properties, movement, and control of cellular water.

EDSALL, J. T., and J. WYMAN: *Biophysical Chemistry*, vol. 1, Academic Press Inc., New York, 1958. Detailed treatment of water and solutions of electrolytes, including amino acids.

EISENBERG, D., and W. KAUZMANN: *The Structure and Properties of Water*, Oxford University Press, Fair Lawn, N.J., 1969. Most recent and authoritative monograph.

HENDERSON, L. J.: *The Fitness of the Environment*, The Macmillan Company, New York, 1927 (reprinted 1958). A classic statement which is still absorbing reading.

MONTGOMERY, R., and C. A. SWENSON: *Quantitative Problems in Biochemical Sciences*, W. H. Freeman Co., San Francisco, 1969. Problems in acid-base chemistry and buffer action, as well as in many other aspects of biochemistry.

SEGEL, I. H.: *Biochemical Calculations*, John Wiley and Sons, New York, 1968. Another useful book on quantitative aspects of biochemistry.

WHIPPLE, H. E. (ed.): "Forms of Water in Biological Systems," *Ann. N.Y. Acad. Sci.*, **125**:249–772 (1965). A collection of articles given at a symposium.

Articles

KAVANAU, J. L.: "Water," in *Structure and Function in Biological Membranes*, Holden-Day, Inc., San Francisco, 1965, pp. 170–248. Properties of water in relation to membrane structure.

KLOTZ, I. M.: "Water," in M. Kasha and B. Pullman (eds.), *Horizons in Biochemistry*, Academic Press Inc., New York, 1962, pp. 523–550. Water and protein structure.

WICKE, E.: "Structure, Formation, and Molecular Mobility in Water and Aqueous Solutions," *Angew. Chem. Intern. Ed.* (English), **5**:106–112 (1966). An alternative to the flickering-cluster hypothesis.

Problems

1. Calculate the pH of solutions containing the following concentrations of H^+ or OH^- ions: (*a*) 0.001 *M* H^+, (*b*) 10^{-9} *M* H^+, (*c*) 0.135 N OH^-, (*d*) 1.4×10^{-11} *M* H^+, (*e*) 7.8×10^{-4} *M* OH^-.

2. Calculate the H^+-ion concentrations of the following fluids: (*a*) blood plasma, (*b*) intracellular fluid of muscle, (*c*) gastric juice (pH 1.4), (*d*) tomato juice, (*e*) grapefruit juice, (*f*) seawater. (See Table 2-6.)

3. An *E. coli* cell is 1.0 μ in diameter and 2.0 μ long and may be assumed to be cylindrical. It contains 80 percent water. If the intracellular pH is 6.4, calculate the number of H^+ ions in a single cell.

4. If the average life time of the hydrogen bonds between water molecules is 10^{-10} sec, how many hydrogen bonds would be made and broken in the water phase of a single *E. coli* cell in 1.0 sec? Use the data of Problem 3.

5. Calculate the number of K^+ ions in the cytoplasm of an *E. coli* cell. Assume that K^+ is present at a concentration of 150 m*M*.

6. The hydrated K^+ and Cl^- ions are approximately spherical in shape, with a diameter of 6.0 Å. What fraction of the total volume of the water phase of an *E. coli* cell is occupied by these ions?

7. Conductivity measurements show that a 0.1 *M* solution of propionic acid (CH_3CH_2COOH) is ionized 1.16 percent at 25°C. Calculate the dissociation constant and pK′ of propionic acid.

8. The internal pH of a liver cell is 6.4. Calculate the ratio of the concentrations of $H_2PO_4^-$ and HPO_4^{2-} in the cell. K' for the second dissociation of phosphoric acid is 6.31×10^{-8} *M*.

9. You have available 0.1 *N* NaOH and 0.1 *N* solutions of H_2SO_4, acetic acid (pK′ = 4.76), lactic acid (pK′ = 3.86), phosphoric acid (pK′ = 7.2), and ammonium chloride (pK′ = 9.25). How would you prepare a buffer to keep the pH essentially constant at 5.4 in an enzyme experiment in which acid will be produced?

10. What volume of 0.10 *N* HCl must be added to 20.0 ml of 0.04 *M* phosphate buffer pH 6.50 containing urease in order to diminish its enzymatic activity by exactly 50 percent, when assayed under conditions in which pH is the rate-limiting factor? What will be the hydrogen-ion concentration in such a solution? (Use data in Figure 2-9; neglect buffering capacity of urease.)

CHAPTER 3 PROTEINS AND THEIR BIOLOGICAL FUNCTIONS: A SURVEY

Proteins are the most abundant organic molecules within cells, constituting 50 percent or more of their dry weight. They are fundamental to all aspects of cell structure and function since they are the molecular instruments by which the genetic information is expressed. In this chapter we shall take a bird's-eye view of the chemistry and biology of proteins. Our purpose will be to provide orientation and to define essential terms in preparation for the much more detailed treatment of different aspects of protein structure and function that will follow in Chapters 4 to 9.

The Composition of Proteins

Crystals of horse cytochrome *c*, a protein functioning in electron transport.

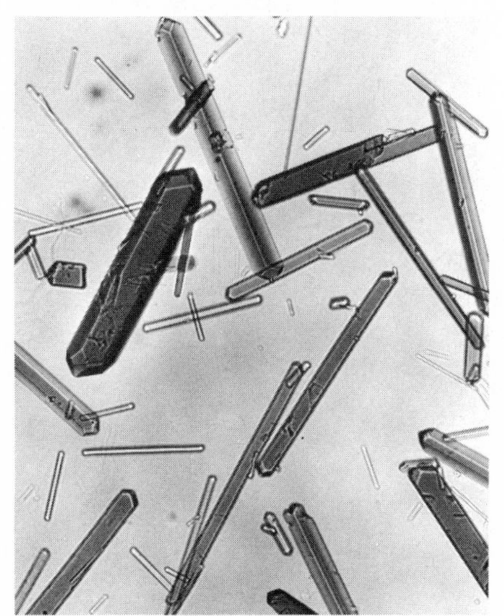

Many proteins have been isolated in pure crystalline form. All contain carbon, hydrogen, nitrogen, and oxygen, and nearly all contain sulfur. Some proteins contain additional elements, particularly phosphorus, iron, zinc, and copper. The molecular weights of proteins are extremely high, but on acid hydrolysis, protein molecules yield a series of simple organic compounds of low molecular weight. These are the α-amino acids (Figures 1-3 and 3-1), which differ from each other in the structure of their R groups, or side-chains. Only 20 different α-amino acids are commonly found as the building blocks of proteins.

In protein molecules, the successive amino acid residues are covalently bonded together to form long unbranched polymers. They are united in a head-to-tail arrangement through substituted amide linkages, called *peptide bonds*, which arise by elimination of the elements of water from the carboxyl group of one amino acid and the α-amino group of the next. Such polymers, which are called *polypeptide chains*, may contain hundreds of amino acid units, and there may be more than one polypeptide chain in a protein molecule. However, proteins are not merely random polymers of varying length; each type of protein molecule has a specific chemical composition, molecular weight, and sequential order of its amino acid building blocks.

Proteins are divided into two major classes on the basis of their composition: simple and conjugated. *Simple pro-*

teins are those which on hydrolysis yield only amino acids and no other major organic or inorganic hydrolysis products. They usually contain about 50 percent carbon, 7 percent hydrogen, 23 percent oxygen, 16 percent nitrogen, and from 0 to 3 percent sulfur. *Conjugated proteins* are those yielding not only amino acids but also other organic or inorganic components. The non-amino acid portion of a conjugated protein is called its *prosthetic group*. Conjugated proteins may be classified on the basis of the chemical nature of their prosthetic groups (Table 3-1). Thus we have nucleoproteins and lipoproteins, which contain nucleic acids and lipids, respectively, as well as phosphoproteins, metalloproteins, and glycoproteins.

The Size of Protein Molecules

By physical methods to be described later, the molecular weights of highly purified proteins can be determined. Some characteristic values are given in Table 3-2. They range from about 6,000, which is arbitrarily the lower limit, to 1,000,000 or more. Even among proteins having the same type of function we cannot make generalizations about size. Enzymes, for example, have molecular weights that vary over a wide range, from about 12,000 to over 1 million. The upper limit of the molecular weight of proteins can be set only arbitrarily, since it depends on definition of the terms protein and molecule, as we shall see.

Some proteins exist in the form of complexes of very high molecular weight and stability which can often be isolated in homogeneous or even crystalline form from cells and tissues. An example is the fatty acid synthetase complex, a group of seven functional enzymes, which can be isolated in homogeneous form as a stable cluster from yeast cells (Table 3-2). The largest supramolecular protein complexes are the viruses, complexes of proteins and nucleic acids. Tobacco mosaic virus, which can be crystallized, is one of the smaller viruses. It has a particle weight of nearly 40 million, of which about 5 percent, or 2 million, consists of ribonucleic acid. The remaining 38 million, corresponding to about 345,000 amino acid residues, is contributed by the protein portion, which consists of a large number of individual polypeptide chains. Although tobacco mosaic and other viruses are often called nucleoproteins and behave as single homogeneous particles, they actually consist of thousands of separate molecules with no covalent bonds between them.

We can calculate the approximate number of amino acid building-block molecules in a simple protein containing no prosthetic group by dividing its molecular weight by 120. The average molecular weight of the 20 different amino acids in proteins is about 138, but since a molecule of water (mol wt 18.0) is removed to create each peptide bond, the average amino acid "residue" weight is about 120. Table 3-2 gives the approximate number of amino acid residues for some proteins of different sizes and functions. Ribonuclease, cytochrome *c*, and myoglobin, which are among the best-known small proteins, contain between 100 and 155 amino acid residues.

Figure 3-1
The structure of α-amino acids (top) *and a typical peptide* (bottom). *The R groups of amino acid residues are the side-chains of peptides.*

Common to all amino acids

NH_2
R—C—COOH
H

General structure of α-amino acids

R group	Name of amino acid
H—	Glycine
CH_3—	Alanine
$HOCH_2$—	Serine
(phenyl)CH_2—	Phenylalanine

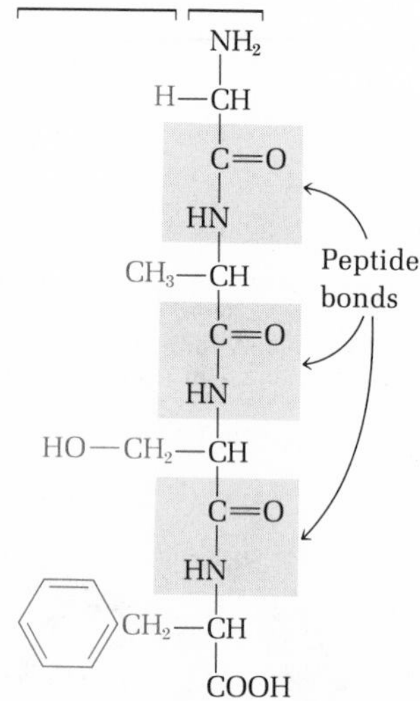

Glycylalanylserylphenylalanine
A tetrapeptide

Table 3-1 Some conjugated proteins

Class	Prosthetic group	Approx. percentage of weight
Nucleoprotein systems		
Ribosomes	RNA	50–60
Tobacco mosaic virus	RNA	5
Lipoproteins		
Plasma β_1-lipoproteins	Phospholipid, cholesterol, neutral lipid	79
Glycoproteins		
γ-Globulin	Hexosamine, galactose, mannose, sialic acid	2
Plasma orosomucoid	Galactose, mannose, N-acetylgalactosamine, N-acetylneuraminic acid	40
Phosphoproteins		
Casein (milk)	Phosphate esterified to serine residues	4
Hemoproteins		
Hemoglobin	Iron protoporphyrin	4
Cytochrome *c*	Iron protoporphyrin	4
Flavoproteins		
Succinate dehydrogenase	Flavin nucleotide	2
D-Amino acid oxidase	Flavin nucleotide	2
Metalloproteins		
Ferritin	$Fe(OH)_3$	23
Tyrosine oxidase	Cu	0.2
Alcohol dehydrogenase	Zn	0.3

Table 3-2 Molecular weights of some proteins

	Molecular weight	No. of residues	No. of chains
Insulin (bovine)	5,733	51	2
Ribonuclease (bovine pancreas)	12,640	124	1
Lysozyme (egg white)	13,930	129	1
Myoglobin (horse heart)	16,890	153	1
Chymotrypsin (bovine pancreas)	22,600	241	3
Hemoglobin (human)	64,500	574	4
Serum albumin (human)	68,500	~550	1
Hexokinase (yeast)	96,000	~800	4
Tryptophan synthetase (*E. coli*)	117,000	~975	4
γ-Globulin (horse)	149,900	~1,250	4
Glycogen phosphorylase (rabbit muscle)	495,000	~4,100	4
Glutamate dehydrogenase (bovine liver)	1,000,000	~8,300	~40
Fatty acid synthetase (yeast)	2,300,000	~20,000	~21
Tobacco mosaic virus	~40,000,000	~336,500	2,130

The Conformation of Proteins

Each type of protein molecule has, in its native state, a characteristic three-dimensional shape, which is referred to as its *conformation*. Proteins can be placed into two major classes, depending on their conformation (Figure 3-2). The *fibrous proteins* are physically tough materials insoluble in water or dilute salt solutions. They consist of polypeptide chains arranged in a parallel fashion along a single axis, to yield long fibers or sheets. Fibrous proteins are the basic structural elements in the connective tissue of higher animals, such as the collagen of tendons and bone matrix, the α-keratin of hair, horn, leather, nails, and feathers, and the elastin of elastic connective tissue. The *globular proteins*, on the other hand, consist of polypeptide chains that are tightly folded into compact spherical, or globular, shapes (Figure 3-2). Most globular proteins are soluble in aqueous systems and diffuse readily. They usually have a mobile or dynamic function in the cell. Of the thousand or more different enzymes known to date, nearly all are globular proteins, as are the antibodies, some hormones, and many proteins having a transport function, such as serum albumin and hemoglobin.

Some proteins fall between the fibrous and globular types. Like the fibrous proteins, they consist of long, rodlike structures, and like the globular proteins, they are soluble in aqueous salt solutions. Among these are myosin, an important structural element of muscle, and fibrinogen, the precursor of fibrin, the structural element of blood clots.

Specific terms are commonly used to refer to different aspects or levels of protein structure. The term *primary structure* refers to the covalent backbone of the polypeptide chain and specifically denotes the sequence of its amino acid residues. *Secondary structure* refers to the extended or helically coiled conformation of polypeptide chains, particularly as they occur in fibrous proteins. The term *tertiary structure* refers to the manner in which the polypeptide chain is bent or folded to form the compact, tightly folded structure of globular proteins (Figure 3-2). The more general term *conformation* is used to refer to the combined secondary and tertiary structure of the peptide chain in proteins. The term *quaternary structure* denotes the manner in which the individual polypeptide chains of a protein having more than one chain are arranged or clustered in space. Most larger proteins, whether fibrous or globular, contain two or more polypeptide chains, between which there may be no covalent linkages (Figure 3-2). In general, the polypeptide chains of proteins usually have between 100 to 300 amino acid units (mol wt 12,000 to 36,000). A few proteins have longer chains, such as serum albumin (~550 residues) and myosin (~1,800 residues). However, any protein having a molecular weight exceeding 50,000 can be suspected to have two or more chains.

Proteins possessing more than one chain are known as *oligomeric proteins;* their component chains are called *protomers*. A well-known example of an oligomeric protein is hemoglobin, which consists of four polypeptide

Figure 3-2
Conformations of protein molecules.

Fibrous proteins

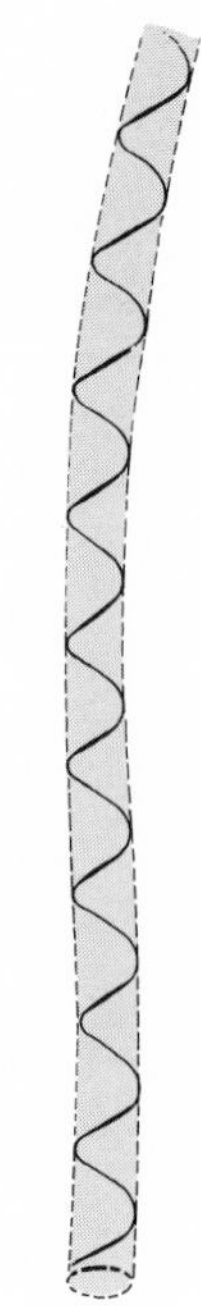

α-helical coil

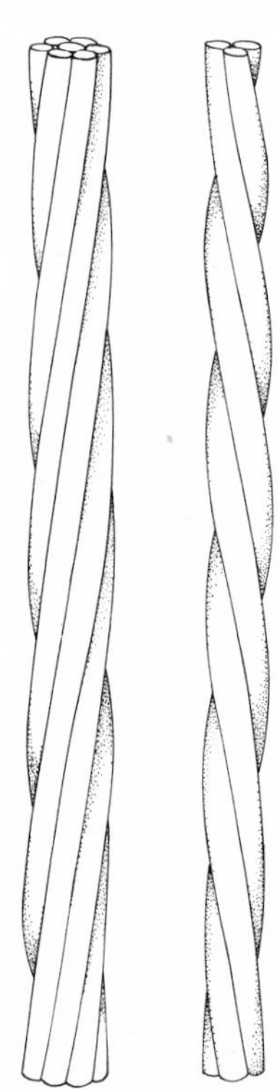

Supercoiling of α-helical coils to form ropes

chains, two identical α-chains and two identical β-chains. Each chain has about 140 amino acids. The four chains fit together tightly to form a globular assembly of great stability, despite the fact that there are no covalent linkages. Oligomeric proteins usually contain an even number of peptide chains. There may be anywhere from two to twelve subunit chains among the smaller oligomeric proteins to dozens or even hundreds among the larger proteins. Tobacco mosaic virus particles have over 2,000 peptide chains.

Globular proteins

Single chain

Oligomeric

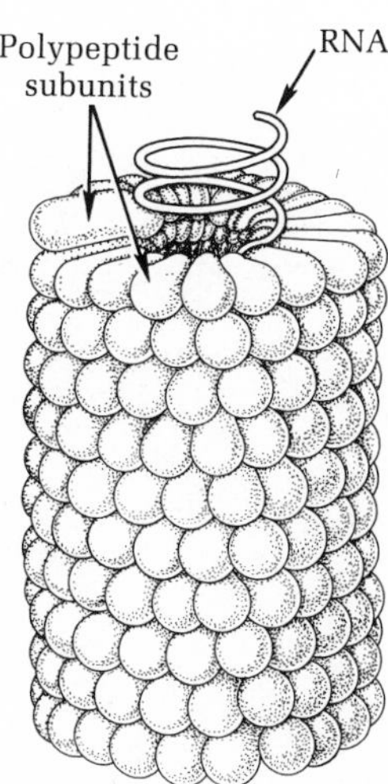

Portion of tobacco mosaic virus particle, a supramolecular assembly with $\sim$2200 polypeptide chains

Since oligomeric proteins contain two or more polypeptide chains, which are usually not covalently attached to each other, it may appear improper or at least ambiguous to refer to oligomeric proteins as "molecules" and to speak of their "molecular weight." However, in most oligomeric proteins, the separate chains are so tightly associated that the complete particle usually behaves in solution like a single molecule. Moreover, all the component chains or subunits of oligomeric proteins are usually necessary for their function.

Denaturation

Most protein molecules retain their biological activity or capacity to function only within a very limited range of temperature and pH. Exposure of protein molecules to extremes of pH or temperature causes them to undergo a change known as *denaturation*, in which the most visible effect in globular proteins is a decrease in solubility. Most proteins undergo denaturation when heated over 50 to 60°C; some also denature when cooled below 10 to 15°C. The formation of an insoluble white coagulum during the heating of egg white is a good example of heat denaturation.

Denaturation also causes proteins to lose their characteristic biological activity. For example, when enzymes are heated their ability to catalyze a specific chemical reaction is usually lost. Since the covalent chemical bonds in the peptide backbone of proteins are not broken during denaturation, it has been concluded that denaturation is due to the unfolding of the characteristic folded structure of the polypeptide chain in the native protein molecule (Figure 3-3). In the denatured state, the polypeptide chains are randomly and irregularly looped or coiled and the conformation of any given polypeptide chain may change with time.

Renaturation

Each type of protein has a fixed amino acid composition and sequence, coded into it during its biosynthesis. Although the amino acid sequence is not by itself the essential feature of the protein molecule required for its biological function, the amino acid sequence ultimately determines the native conformation, or folded state, of a protein through interactions of the amino acid side-chains with each other and with the solvent. This conclusion follows from the relatively recent discovery that denaturation, or unfolding, of native proteins into randomly coiled, biologically inactive forms is not irreversible, as was once thought. Many cases have now been observed in which an unfolded molecule will return to its native form in the test tube, in a process called *renaturation*, *refolding*, or *annealing* (Figure 3-3). Moreover, if the denatured protein was an enzyme, its catalytic activity may also return on renaturation, without change in the specificity of the reaction catalyzed. Renaturation of a denatured protein thus may restore the original biological activity; however, it does not evoke any biological activity that was not present in the original protein.

The refolding of a denatured protein does not require the input of chemical work from the outside; it proceeds spontaneously, provided that the conditions of pH and temperature are adjusted to be compatible with the stability of the native form. For this reason, the denaturation of many proteins gives the appearance of being irreversible, because refolding to the native state often is a very slow process. Since each type of protein molecule has its own characteristic amino acid sequence, it appears likely that the native conformation of a protein is determined by its amino acid sequence. As we shall see, it is probable that the native conformation of a protein molecule is its most stable form under biological conditions, i.e., the state in which it has the least free energy.

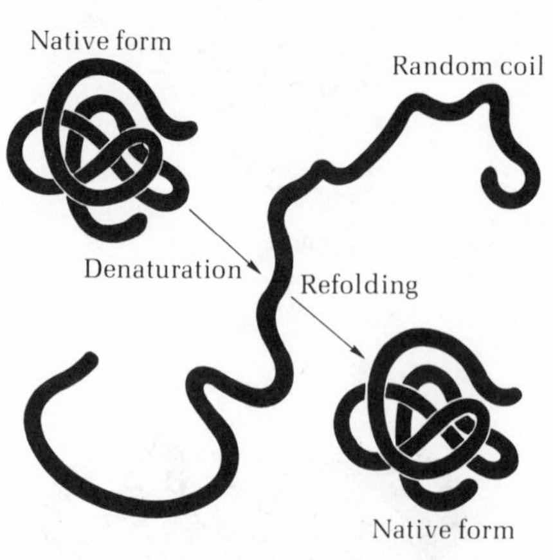

Figure 3-3
Denaturation and renaturation of a globular protein. After the peptide chain has been unfolded—by heating, by exposure to low pH, *or by treatment with urea—it will often spontaneously refold to the native form.*

The Functional Diversity of Proteins

As a class, proteins have great functional versatility. Table 3-3 gives some representative examples of different types of proteins, classified according to biological function. The largest and most important class of proteins, in terms of biological function, are the enzymes. Over a thousand different enzymes are known, each catalyzing a different kind of chemical reaction. Homologous enzymes from different species are different chemical entities, even though they may catalyze the same reaction and may superficially appear to be identical. Thus, trypsin of the pig and trypsin of the cow are different molecules. Enzyme molecules are usually globular in conformation. Some contain a single polypeptide chain, and some contain several or many chains. Every enzyme contains an *active site*, or *catalytic site*, which binds the substrate during the catalytic cycle. Some enzymes are further specialized to serve a regulatory function; these are called *regulatory* or *allosteric* enzymes.

The second major class of proteins includes those serving as structural elements. In higher animals, the fibrous protein collagen, which is synthesized by fibroblasts, is the major extracellular structural protein in connective tissue and in bone. Collagen fibrils also aid in forming a structural continuum binding a group of cells together to form a tissue. Other cells secrete the elastin of yellow elastic tissue and the α-keratin of skin, hair, nails, horn, and feathers. Cartilage is made up of a combination of a specific protein with a complex acidic polysaccharide, chrondroitin sulfate. The mucoproteins endow mucous secretions and synovial fluid in the joints of vertebrates with a slippery lubricating quality. The various mem-

Table 3-3 Classification of proteins by biological function

Type and examples	*Occurrence or function*
Enzymes	
Ribonuclease	Hydrolyzes RNA.
Cytochrome *c*	Transfers electrons.
Trypsin	Hydrolyzes some peptides.
Storage proteins	
Ovalbumin	Egg-white protein
Casein	Milk protein
Ferritin	Iron storage in spleen
Gliadin	Seed protein of wheat
Zein	Seed protein of corn
Transport proteins	
Hemoglobin	Transports O_2 in blood of vertebrates.
Hemocyanin	Transports O_2 in blood of some invertebrates.
Myoglobin	Transports O_2 in muscle.
Serum albumin	Transports fatty acids in blood.
β_1-Lipoprotein	Transports lipids in blood.
Iron-binding globulin	Transports iron in blood.
Ceruloplasmin	Transports copper in blood.
Contractile proteins	
Myosin	Stationary filaments in myofibril
Actin	Moving filaments in myofibril
Dynein	Cilia and flagella
Protective proteins in vertebrate blood	
Antibodies	Form complexes with foreign proteins.
Complement	Complexes with some antigen-antibody systems.
Fibrinogen	Precursor of fibrin in blood clotting
Thrombin	Component of clotting mechanism
Toxins	
Clostridium botulinum toxin	Causes bacterial food poisoning.
Diphtheria toxin	Bacterial toxin
Snake venoms	Enzymes which hydrolyze phosphoglycerides.
Ricin	Toxic protein of castor bean
Hormones	
Insulin	Regulates glucose metabolism.
Adrenocorticotrophic hormone	Regulates corticosteroid synthesis.
Growth hormone	Stimulates growth of bones.
Structure proteins	
Viral-coat proteins	Sheath around chromosome
Glycoproteins	Cell coats and walls
Membrane-structure proteins	Component of membranes
α-Keratin	Skin, feathers, nails, hoofs
Sclerotin	Exoskeletons of insects
Fibroin	Silk of cocoons, spider webs
Collagen	Fibrous connective tissue (tendons, bone, cartilage)
Elastin	Elastic connective tissue (ligaments)
Mucoproteins	Mucous secretions, synovial fluid

branes of the cell contain proteins of an insoluble nature, which, together with polar lipids, constitute the core of membrane structure. Since membranes may make up a large fraction of the total mass of eucaryotic cells, membrane proteins are among the most abundant cell proteins.

Other types of proteins function as essential elements in contractile and motile systems. Actin and myosin are the two major elements of the contractile system of muscle; actin is a long filament composed of single subunits of a small globular protein arranged like a string of beads, and myosin is a long rod-like molecule consisting of two helically-intertwined polypeptide chains.

Some proteins have a transport function; they are capable of binding and transporting specific types of molecules via the blood. Serum albumin binds free fatty acids tightly and thus serves to transport these molecules between adipose tissue and other organs in vertebrates. Serum β-lipoprotein, which consists of about 21 percent protein and 79 percent lipid, transports complex lipids via the bloodstream. Hemoglobin of vertebrate erythrocytes transports oxygen from the lungs to the tissues; the oxygen is bound to the iron atoms of the four heme groups in the molecule. Invertebrates possess other types of oxygen-carrying protein molecules, among them hemocyanins.

Other proteins besides the enzymes have intense biological activity. Among these are certain hormones, such as somatotrophin, the growth hormone of the anterior pituitary gland. Insulin, secreted by the pancreas, is a hormone regulating glucose metabolism; its deficiency in humans causes diabetes mellitus. Proteins which are extremely toxic to higher animals include ricin, diphtheria toxin, and the toxin of the anaerobic bacterium *Clostridium botulinum*, which is responsible for some types of food poisoning.

It is extraordinary that all proteins, including those having intense biological or toxic effects, contain the same set of 20 amino acids, which by themselves have no intrinsic biological activity or toxicity. It is the three-dimensional conformation that gives a protein its specific biological activity, and this conformation is determined by the specific sequence of the amino acids in the polypeptide chain.

Antibodies and the Immune Response; Species Specificity of Proteins

Among the great variety of different proteins in living organisms, there is one type, included in Table 3-3, that has been of the utmost importance in demonstrating that proteins are specific for each species of organism. These are the *antibodies*, or *immune globulins*. Antibody molecules appear in the blood serum and the tissues of a given vertebrate in response to injection of an *antigen*, a protein or other macromolecule foreign to that species. This reaction is called the *immune response*, and it is the basis of the whole field of immunology. Antibody molecules can combine with the antigen which elicited their formation to form an *antigen-antibody complex.* Immunity to infectious diseases can often be conferred by injecting very

Figure 3-4
The antigen-antibody reaction.

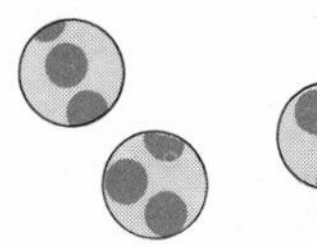

Antigen molecules

Colored sites are determinants of antigenic specificity

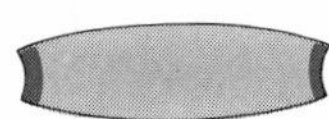

Antibody molecule

Colored sites are structurally complementary to determinant sites of antigen molecules

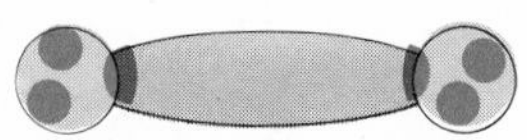

Antigen-antibody complex

The antibody is divalent but the antigen may be multivalent

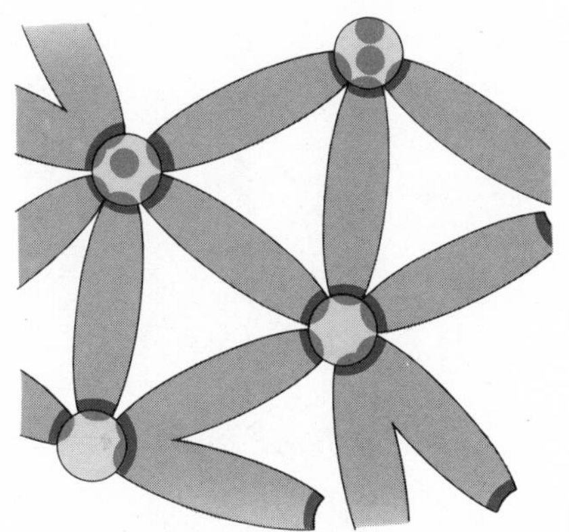

Insoluble antigen-antibody lattice (precipitin)

small amounts of certain macromolecular components (i.e, antigens) of the causative microorganism or virus. Antibodies are formed, and if the microorganism should happen to gain access to the blood or lymph at a later time, these antibodies can neutralize or inactivate this microorganism by combining with its antigenic components. The immune response is given only by vertebrates and sharks and is thus a rather recent product of biological evolution.

The formation of antibodies can be quantitatively studied by means of the *precipitin reaction*. A recipient vertebrate, often a rabbit, is immunized against a specific foreign protein, such as ovalbumin from a hen's egg. The blood serum of the immunized rabbit (the *antiserum*), which contains the antibody or precipitin, is then mixed with a small amount of the antigen, i.e., hen's-egg albumin. The mixture becomes turbid, and a precipitate is formed, which contains the antigen-antibody complex. A more refined and sensitive test is provided if the antigen and antibody are allowed to diffuse toward each other in a gel matrix. A thin, opaque line is formed at the site of deposition of the antigen-antibody complex.

Antibodies (mol wt 150,000) are rod-shaped molecules containing four polypeptide chains. They possess binding sites which are believed to be complementary to specific structural features of the antigen (Figure 3-4). Usually the antibody molecule has two binding sites, making possible the formation of a three-dimensional lattice of alternating antigen and antibody molecules. After a certain amount of growth, the lattice precipitates from the serum. The structure and origin of immune globulins are given in more detail in Chapter 32.

Antibodies are highly specific for the foreign proteins that evoke their formation. A rabbit antibody formed to hen's-egg albumin, for example, will combine with the latter but not with unrelated proteins such as human hemoglobin. Such an antibody is specific for the three-dimensional structure of hen's-egg albumin, so that if the latter is heated or denatured to unfold its polypeptide chains, or if it is chemically modified, the antibody will no longer combine with it.

Application of the highly specific antigen-antibody reaction to the study of various proteins from different species of organisms has yielded a number of important conclusions. The first is that functionally different proteins from any single species lead to the formation of different antibodies. Thus, when a rabbit is immunized against horse hemoglobin, the antibodies formed will precipitate horse hemoglobin but not other horse proteins, such as horse serum albumin or horse muscle proteins.

The second major conclusion, one with far-reaching biological implications, is that *homologous* proteins of different species are not immunologically identical. Homologous proteins are those with evidently similar functions, such as the hemoglobins of different vertebrate species. Although the hemoglobins of different mammals have the same function and about the same molecular weight and although all contain four iron atoms, four porphyrin rings, and four peptide chains, they are nevertheless immunologically distinct molecules. The antibodies produced by the rabbit after immunization with horse hemoglobin, for example, react maximally with horse hemoglobin in the precipitin reaction; hemoglobins from other vertebrates are much less active in forming a precipitate with an antibody specific for horse hemoglobin.

A third conclusion is that antibody specificity reflects phylogenetic relationships. Homologous proteins of closely related species are more nearly identical than are those of widely separated species (Table 3-4). Thus, while antibodies generated by the rabbit to horse hemoglobin will react best with horse hemoglobin, they will also react with the hemoglobins of those species most closely related to the horse, i.e., zebra, cow, pig, and other ungulates, whereas hemoglobins from rodents, birds, and amphibians will be far less reactive.

Table 3-4 Reactivity of serum albumins from different species with rabbit antibody to bovine serum albumin

	Reactivity in precipitin test
Cow	(100)
Sheep	76
Pig	32
Cat	25
Horse	16
Human	15
Hamster	15
Rat	14
Dog	14
Mouse	9

The structural differences among homologous proteins of different species, which were first revealed by the antigen-antibody reaction, have more recently been found to be the result of differences in their amino acid sequences. The more closely related are two species of organism, the more nearly identical are the amino acid sequences of homologous proteins.

Sequence Isomerism in Polypeptide Chains

Earlier (Chapter 1), we estimated that the total number of different kinds of proteins in all species of living organisms is of the order of 10^{10} to 10^{12}. Can this enormous number of different proteins, each having its own specific amino acid sequence, be made from only 20 different amino acids? It is possible to answer this question from mathematical considerations alone. In a dipeptide containing two different amino acids A and B, two sequence isomers are possible, that is, A–B and B–A. In a tripeptide having three different amino acids, six sequential arrangements of the three amino acids are possible. In permutation theory, the general expression for the number of possible sequential arrangements of different objects is given by the expression $n!$ (factorial n), where n is the number of different objects. For a tetrapeptide having four different amino acids, $4! = 4 \times 3 \times 2 \times 1 = 24$ different sequences are possible. For a polypeptide of 20 different amino acids, in which each of the acids occurs only once, the number of possible sequential arrangements is given by 20!, or $20 \times 19 \times 18 \times 17 \times 16 \times \ldots$, which comes out to the startlingly large figure of 2×10^{18}. But this is only a small polypeptide chain (mol wt about 2,400), and each of the amino acids occurs only once. If we now consider a protein of mol wt 34,000, containing 12 different amino acids in equal numbers, it has been calculated that some 10^{300} sequence isomers are possible. Just as the alphabet of 26 letters can be used to make an enormously large number of written words, so the 20 different amino acids can be used to make an almost limitless number of different proteins. Unraveling the amino acid sequences of different proteins and relating each sequence to the properties and functions of the protein and to the phylogenetics of the organism are major objectives of contemporary biochemistry.

Figure 3-5
Colinearity of DNA and amino acid sequence. The triplets of bases in DNA determine the sequence of amino acids in proteins through the intermediate formation of messenger RNA, which has triplets complementary to those of DNA.

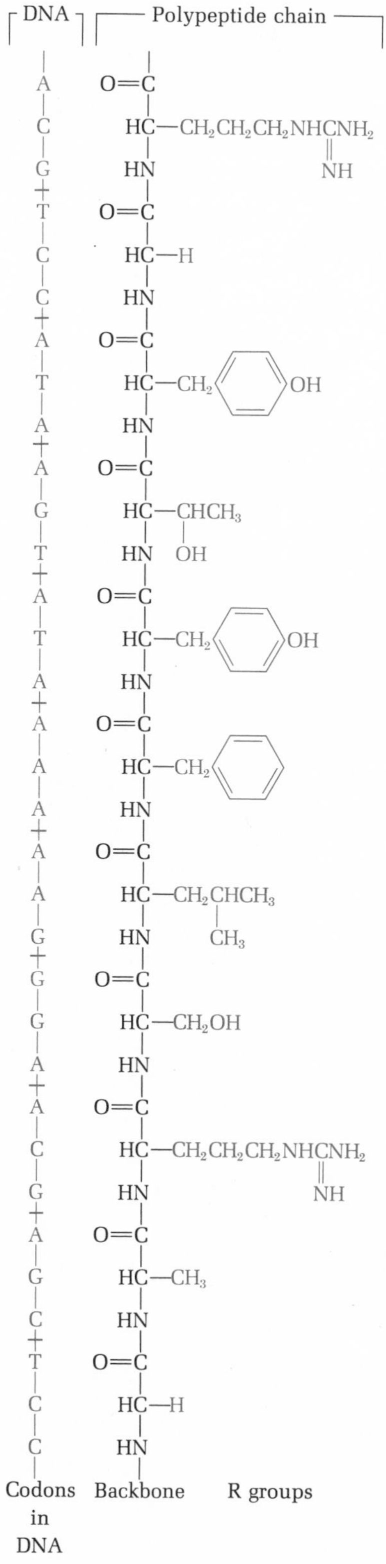

DNA — Polypeptide chain

Codons in DNA — Backbone — R groups

The Genetic Coding of Amino Acid Sequences in Proteins

From recent advances in molecular genetics, which will be discussed in detail in Part IV, it is now known that the sequence of amino acids in each protein is specified by the sequence of mononucleotide building blocks in a segment of the linear deoxyribonucleic acid (DNA) molecule. The relationship between the sequence of mononucleotides in DNA and the sequence of amino acids in the polypeptide chain it codes is illustrated schematically in Figure 3-5. Specific triplets of mononucleotides in the DNA chain, called *codons*, correspond to specific amino acids. The sequence of codons in DNA is colinear with the amino acid sequence of the polypeptide chain it codes. The segment of a DNA molecule which specifies one complete polypeptide chain is called a *cistron* or *gene*. Because the structure and function of proteins are ultimately a reflection of their amino acid sequence, we can hardly discuss proteins and their biological activities without at least rudimentary knowledge of the molecular relationships between genes and proteins. Moreover, these relationships have yielded penetrating insight into the comparative biochemistry of proteins in different species and the evolution of protein molecules.

Occasionally, the normal amino acid sequence in a protein is altered during synthesis to yield an abnormal protein, which may be defective in its biological function. Such an abnormal protein is usually the result of a genetic *mutation*. A mutation occurs when a mononucleotide unit of the DNA specifying a given polypeptide chain is chemically changed or deleted or when an extra mononucleotide is inserted. As a result, the normal, commaless sequence of coding triplets of the gene is altered and produces a corresponding alteration in the amino acid sequence of the polypeptide chain it codes. Often such alterations involve the replacement of a single amino acid by another. Study of mutationally altered proteins is of great importance since it can reveal which amino acid residues in a polypeptide chain are essential for the structure and function of a protein.

Summary

Proteins are made up of one or more polypeptide chains, each having 100 or more α-amino acid residues covalently linked together by peptide bonds; their molecular weights vary from about 6,000 to 1,000,000 or more. All proteins, regardless of function or species of origin, are constructed from a basic set of 20 amino acids, arranged in various specific sequences. Simple proteins yield only α-amino acids on hydrolysis, whereas conjugated proteins contain additional organic or inorganic prosthetic groups. Proteins are classified according to their conformation. Fibrous proteins exist as rods or sheets; they possess parallel and relatively extended peptide chains. They are insoluble and serve as structural elements. Globular proteins have tightly folded polypeptide chains and are spherical or football-shaped; they have dynamic functions.

The primary structure of a protein is its specific amino acid sequence. The secondary structure is the hydrogen-bonded helical or zig-zag arrangement of polypeptide chains along the long axis in fibrous proteins. Tertiary structure refers to the way in which the polypeptide chains are folded to form globular proteins. In oligomeric proteins, the quaternary structure is the manner in which the individual polypeptide chains are clustered together. Ultimately, it is the amino acid sequence that determines the three-dimensional conformation of protein molecules. Proteins are denatured, or unfolded, without cleavage of the peptide chain backbone, by extremes of pH and temperature and by other agencies. Denaturation causes proteins to lose their biological activity; in some instances, denaturation is fully reversible.

Proteins serve many diverse functions: as catalysts, structural elements, and contractile systems; for nutrient storage; as vehicles of transport; as hormones; and as protective agents. In this last category are the immune globulins, or antibodies, formed by vertebrates in response to antigens, i.e., substances foreign to the species. Antigen-antibody specificity studies have led to the conclusion that homologous proteins of different species are species-specific. The amino acid sequence of a protein is specified during its biosynthesis by a colinear sequence of codons, which are consecutive triplets of mononucleotides in the DNA molecule. Each segment of DNA that codes one polypeptide chain is called a gene.

References

References to more specific aspects of protein biochemistry are given at the ends of Chapters 4 to 9.

Books

DAVIS, B. D., R. DULBECCO, H. N. EISEN, H. C. GINSBERG, and W. B. WOOD, JR.: *Principles of Microbiology and Immunology*, Harper & Row, Publishers, Inc., New York, 1968. Elementary textbook giving an excellent account of the immune response and the biology of the antigen-antibody reaction.

NEURATH, H.: *The Proteins*, 3d ed., vols. I–IV, Academic Press Inc., New York, 1963–1966. Authoritative and comprehensive monograph on proteins.

PRESSMAN, D., and A. L. GROSSBERG: *The Structural Basis of Antibody Specificity*, W. A. Benjamin, Inc., New York, 1968. Review of recent research on the specificity of the antigen-antibody reaction.

WATSON, J. D.: *The Molecular Biology of the Gene*, W. A. Benjamin, Inc., New York, 1965. Elementary account of the genetic background of protein synthesis.

CHAPTER 4 PROTEINS: THE AMINO ACID BUILDING BLOCKS

We shall now consider the physical and chemical properties of the amino acids in some detail since they are the alphabet of protein structure and determine many of the important properties of proteins. The first amino acid isolated from a protein hydrolyzate was glycine, obtained in 1820 from gelatin by Braconnot. The most recently discovered of the 20 amino acids commonly found in proteins is threonine, first isolated from hydrolyzates of fibrin by Rose in 1935. Since then, a few other amino acids have been found in certain proteins, but they are rare in occurrence. Although much important information on the structure, synthesis, optical properties, and chemical reactions of amino acids arose from early investigations many years ago, a full appreciation of the role of amino acids in determining protein conformation has come only relatively recently.

The Common Amino Acids of Proteins

The structural formulas and space-filling models of the 20 α-amino acids commonly found in proteins are given in Figures 4-1 to 4-3. All the amino acids found in proteins (except proline) have as a common denominator a free carboxyl group and a free unsubstituted amino group on the α-carbon atom. Since the α-amino group of proline is substituted, it is really an α-imino acid (Figure 4-1). In addition, each amino acid has a characteristic R group. The R groups are the "letters" in the molecular alphabet of protein structure.

Various ways of classifying the amino acids on the basis of their R groups have been proposed. The most meaningful is based on the polarity of the R groups. There are four main classes: (1) nonpolar or hydrophobic, (2) polar but uncharged, (3) positively charged, and (4) negatively charged (at pH 6.0–7.0, the zone of intracellular pH). Within any single class, there are considerable variations in the size, shape, and polarity of the R groups. Later we shall see that this way of classifying amino acids may bear a relationship to the genetic code words for the different amino acids found in proteins.

Amino acids are ordinarily designated by three-letter symbols. Recently a set of one-letter symbols has also been adopted, to facilitate comparative display of amino acid sequences of homologous proteins (Table 4-1).

Table 4-1 Amino acid symbols

Amino acid	*Three-letter symbol*	*One-letter symbol*
Alanine	Ala	A
Arginine	Arg	R
Asparagine	Asn	N
Aspartic acid	Asp	D
Asn + Asp	Asx	B
Cysteine	Cys	C
Glutamine	Gln	Q
Glutamic acid	Glu	E
Gln + Glu	Glx	Z
Glycine	Gly	G
Histidine	His	H
Isoleucine	Ile	I
Leucine	Leu	L
Lysine	Lys	K
Methionine	Met	M
Phenylalanine	Phe	F
Proline	Pro	P
Serine	Ser	S
Threonine	Thr	T
Tryptophan	Trp	W
Tyrosine	Tyr	Y
Valine	Val	V

Amino Acids with Nonpolar, or Hydrophobic, R Groups

Figure 4-1 shows the structural formulas and space-filling models of the nonpolar amino acids, together with their symbols. This family contains five amino acids with aliphatic hydrocarbon R groups (alanine, leucine, isoleucine, valine, and proline), two with aromatic rings (phenylalanine and tryptophan), and one containing sulfur (methionine). As a group, these amino acids are less soluble in water than the polar amino acids. The least hydrophobic member of this class is alanine.

Figure 4-1
Amino acids with nonpolar R groups.
In this Figure, as well as in Figures 4-2 to 4-5, the amino acids are shown with their α-amino groups and α-carboxyl groups ionized, as they would occur at pH 6–7.

Amino Acids with Uncharged Polar R Groups

These amino acids (Figure 4-2) are more soluble in water than the hydrophobic amino acids because their polar R groups can hydrogen-bond with water. The polarity of serine, threonine, and tyrosine is contributed by their hydroxyl groups; that of asparagine and glutamine by their amide groups; and that of cysteine by its —SH group. Glycine is difficult to classify; however, its R group, a hydrogen atom, is too small to influence the high degree of polarity of the α-amino and α-carboxyl groups.

Asparagine and glutamine are the amides of aspartic acid and glutamic acid (below), to which they are easily hydrolyzed by acid or base. The three-letter symbols Asx and Glx and the one-letter symbols B and Z are used to designate the sum of aspartic acid and asparagine and the sum of glutamic acid and glutamine, respectively, when the amide content is not known or is unspecified.

Cysteine and tyrosine have the most polar functions of this class of amino acids, namely the thiol and phenolic hydroxyl groups, respectively. These groups tend to lose protons by ionization far more readily than the R groups of other amino acids of this class, although they are only slightly ionized at pH 7.0.

Amino Acids with Negatively Charged (Acidic) R Groups

The members of this class, which possess a net negative charge at pH 6.0–7.0, are aspartic acid and glutamic acid, each with a second carboxyl group (Figure 4-3).

Amino Acids with Positively Charged (Basic) R Groups

The basic amino acids (Figure 4-3), in which the R groups have a net positive charge at pH 7.0, consist of lysine, which bears a second amino group at the ϵ position on its aliphatic chain, and arginine, which bears a positively charged guanidinium group. Histidine, which contains the weakly basic imidazolium function, is borderline in its properties. At pH 6.0 more than 50 percent of histidine molecules possess a protonated or positively charged R-group, but at pH 7.0, less than 10 percent have a positive charge.

R groups		R groups
Alanine	$CH_3-\overset{H}{\underset{\overset{+}{N}H_3}{C}}-COO^-$	+ −
Valine	$\overset{CH_3}{\underset{CH_3}{}}\!\!>CH-\overset{H}{\underset{\overset{+}{N}H_3}{C}}-COO^-$	
Leucine	$\overset{CH_3}{\underset{CH_3}{}}\!\!>CH-CH_2-\overset{H}{\underset{\overset{+}{N}H_3}{C}}-COO^-$	
Isoleucine	$CH_3-CH_2-\underset{CH_3}{CH}-\overset{H}{\underset{\overset{+}{N}H_3}{C}}-COO^-$	
Proline	H_2C, $\overset{H_2}{C}$, H_2C, $\underset{H}{N}$ ring; $\underset{H}{C}-COO^-$	N
Phenylalanine	$C_6H_5-CH_2-\overset{H}{\underset{\overset{+}{N}H_3}{C}}-COO^-$	
Tryptophan	indole: $\underset{H}{N}$, CH, $C-CH_2-\overset{H}{\underset{\overset{+}{N}H_3}{C}}-COO^-$	N
Methionine	$CH_3-S-CH_2-CH_2-\overset{H}{\underset{\overset{+}{N}H_3}{C}}-COO^-$	S

5 Å

Figure 4-2
Amino acids with uncharged polar R groups.

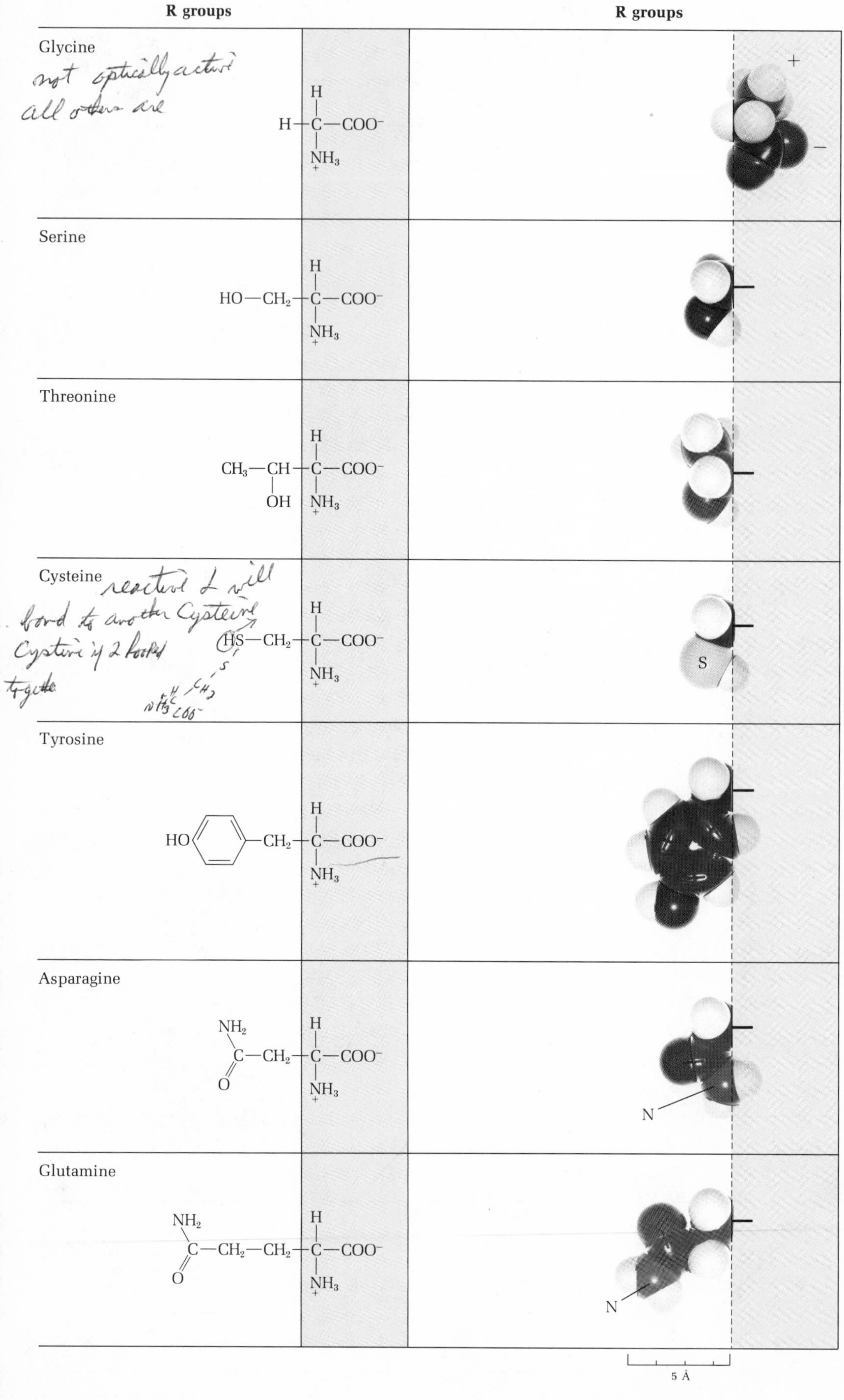

	R groups		R groups
Glycine	$H-$	$H-\overset{\displaystyle H}{\underset{\displaystyle \overset{+}{N}H_3}{C}}-COO^-$	+ / −
Serine	$HO-CH_2-$	$\overset{\displaystyle H}{\underset{\displaystyle \overset{+}{N}H_3}{C}}-COO^-$	
Threonine	$CH_3-\underset{\displaystyle OH}{CH}-$	$\overset{\displaystyle H}{\underset{\displaystyle \overset{+}{N}H_3}{C}}-COO^-$	
Cysteine	$HS-CH_2-$	$\overset{\displaystyle H}{\underset{\displaystyle \overset{+}{N}H_3}{C}}-COO^-$	S
Tyrosine	$HO-C_6H_4-CH_2-$	$\overset{\displaystyle H}{\underset{\displaystyle \overset{+}{N}H_3}{C}}-COO^-$	
Asparagine	$\overset{\displaystyle NH_2}{\underset{\displaystyle O}{C}}-CH_2-$	$\overset{\displaystyle H}{\underset{\displaystyle \overset{+}{N}H_3}{C}}-COO^-$	N
Glutamine	$\overset{\displaystyle NH_2}{\underset{\displaystyle O}{C}}-CH_2-CH_2-$	$\overset{\displaystyle H}{\underset{\displaystyle \overset{+}{N}H_3}{C}}-COO^-$	N

5 Å

Figure 4-3
Amino acids with charged polar groups at pH 6.0–7.0.

Acidic amino acids (negatively charged) **R groups**

Aspartic acid

$^{-}O(O=)C-CH_2-C(H)(NH_3^+)-COO^-$

− + − −

Glutamic acid

$^{-}O(O=)C-CH_2-CH_2-C(H)(NH_3^+)-COO^-$

−

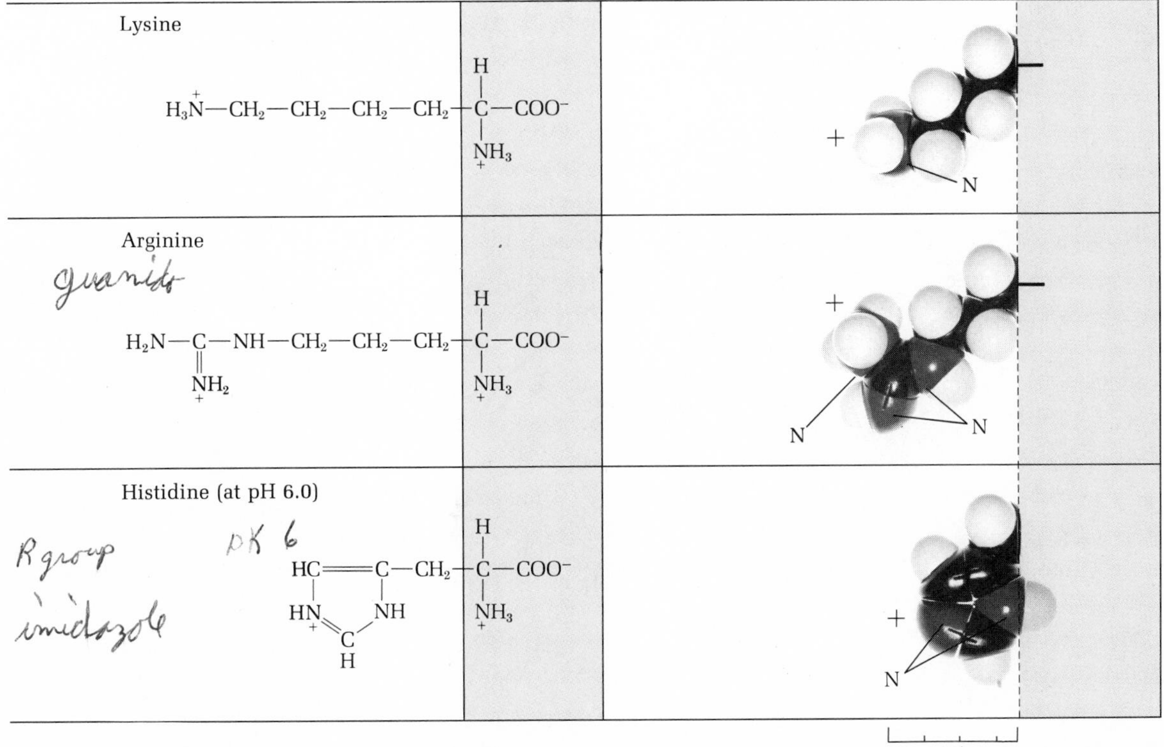

The Rare Amino Acids of Proteins

In addition to the 20 common amino acids, there are a number of others that have been isolated from hydrolyzates of a few specialized types of proteins. All are derivatives of the normal amino acids. Among these is 4-hydroxyproline, a derivative of proline which is found in some abundance in the fibrous protein collagen and in some plant proteins (Figure 4-4). Hydroxylysine, the 5-hydroxy derivative of lysine, has also been found in hydrolyzates of collagen. Desmosine and isodesmosine have been isolated from hydrolyzates of the fibrous protein elastin; presumably they are found only in this protein. Their rather extraordinary structures can be visualized as consisting of four lysine molecules which have their R groups joined to form a substituted pyridine ring. Possibly this structure permits desmosine and isodesmosine to connect four peptide chains in a radial array; elastin differs from other fibrous proteins in that it is capable of undergoing a "two-way stretch."

It is likely that other rare amino acids of proteins will be discovered. However, on genetic grounds we can assume that these will be very few in number, that they will be derivatives of presently known common amino acids, and that they will be limited in occurrence to single proteins or to a class of proteins. The rare amino acids in proteins are genetically distinctive since there are no triplet code words for them. In all known cases, they arise by modification of their parent or precursor amino acids *after* these have already been inserted into the polypeptide chain.

Figure 4-4
Some "rare" amino acids found in fibrous proteins.

4-hydroxyproline

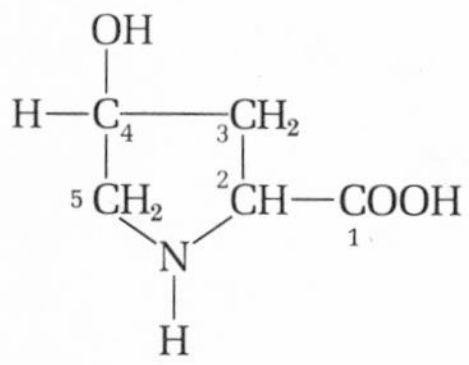

Desmosine

5-hydroxylysine

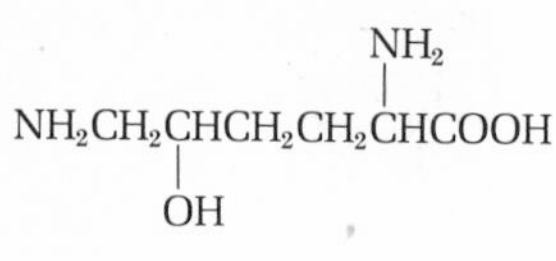

$NH_2CH_2CH(OH)CH_2CH_2CH(NH_2)COOH$

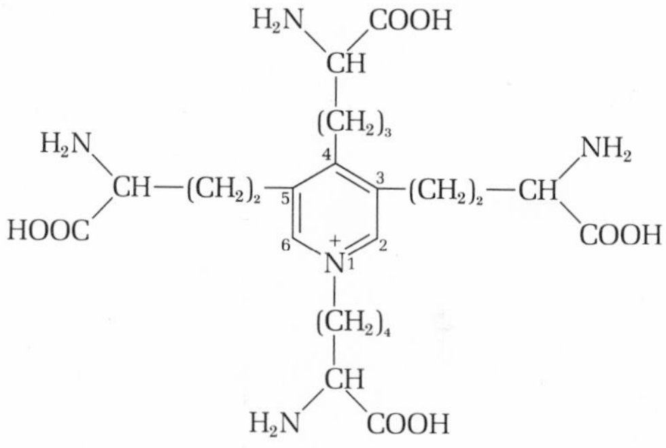

Isodesmosine

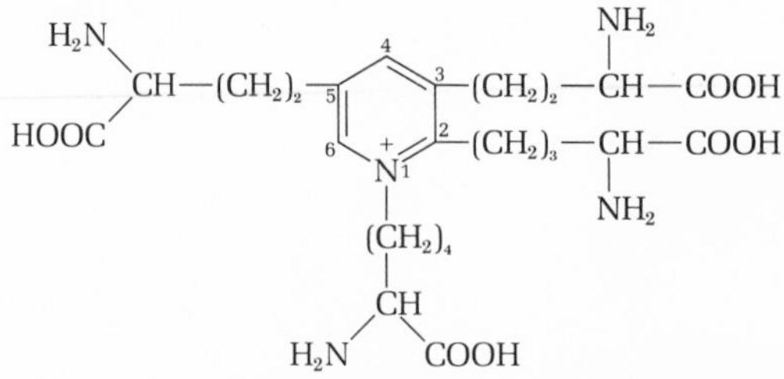

Nonprotein Amino Acids

In addition to the 20 common and several rare amino acids of proteins, over 150 other amino acids are known to occur in different cells and tissues in either free or combined form, but never in proteins. Most of these are derivatives of the α-amino acids found in proteins, but β-, γ-, and δ-amino acids are also known (Figure 4-5). Some nonprotein amino acids occur in the D configuration, such as D-glutamic acid, found in the cell walls of bacteria.

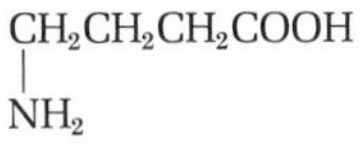

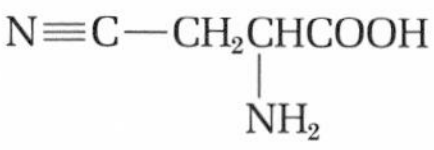

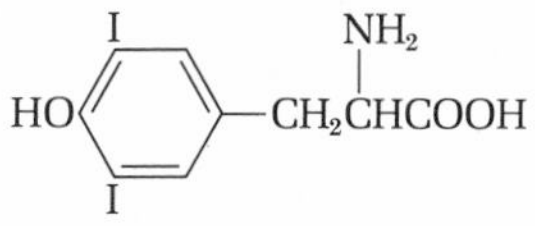

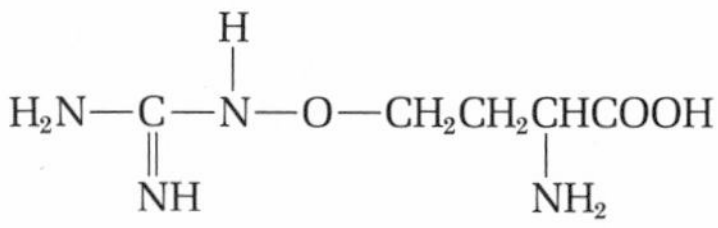

Some nonprotein amino acids function as important precursors or intermediates in metabolism. Thus, β-alanine is the precursor of the vitamin pantothenic acid. Citrulline and ornithine are intermediates in the synthesis of arginine. Other nonprotein amino acids function as chemical agents for the transmission of nerve impulses, such as γ-aminobutyric acid.

Fungi and higher plants contain an extraordinary variety of amino acids, some having very curious structures. The metabolic functions of most of these specialized plant amino acids are not yet understood. It is interesting that some plant amino acids, such as canavanine, djenkolic acid and β-cyanoalanine, are toxic to other forms of life.

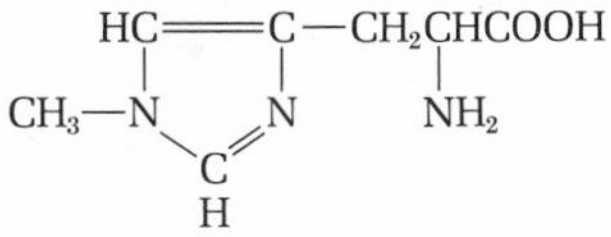

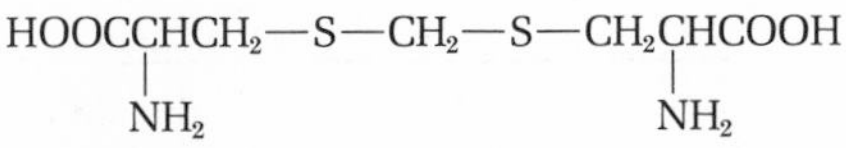

Figure 4-5
Some naturally occurring amino acids not found in proteins.

β-Alanine

CH_2CH_2COOH (with NH_2 on the first carbon)

γ-Aminobutyric acid

$CH_2CH_2CH_2COOH$ (with NH_2 on the first carbon)

β-Cyanoalanine

$N{\equiv}C{-}CH_2CHCOOH$ (with NH_2 on CH)

3,5-Diiodotyrosine

HO–(benzene ring with I at 3 and 5)–$CH_2CHCOOH$ (with NH_2 on CH)

3-Methylhistidine

$HC{=}C{-}CH_2CHCOOH$; $CH_3{-}N$, N, C–H ring (with NH_2 on CH)

Canavanine

$H_2N{-}C({=}NH){-}N(H){-}O{-}CH_2CH_2CHCOOH$ (with NH_2 on CH)

Djenkolic acid

$HOOCCHCH_2{-}S{-}CH_2{-}S{-}CH_2CHCOOH$ (with NH_2 on each CH)

L-Azaserine

$N_2{>}CHC({=}O){-}O{-}CH_2CHCOOH$ (with NH_2 on CH)

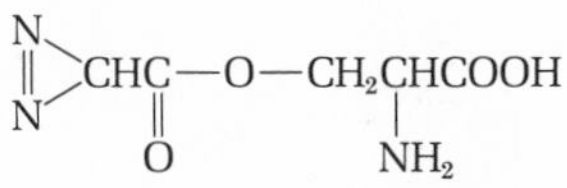

γ-Methyleneglutamic acid

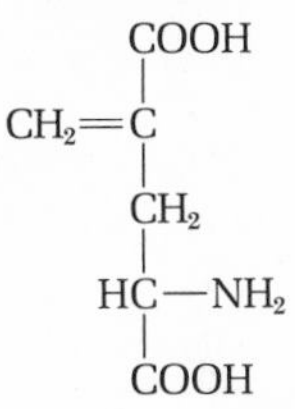

$CH_2{=}C(COOH){-}CH_2{-}CH(NH_2){-}COOH$

The Acid-Base Properties of Amino Acids

A knowledge of the acid-base properties of amino acids is extremely important in understanding and analyzing the properties of proteins. Furthermore, the entire art of separating, identifying, and quantitating the different amino acids, which are necessary steps in determining the amino acid composition and sequence in proteins, is based on these properties.

Crystalline amino acids have relatively high melting or decomposition points, usually above 200°C. They are much more soluble in water than in less polar solvents. These properties are precisely those to be expected if the lattice of amino acid molecules in the crystalline state is stabilized by electrostatic forces of attraction between oppositely charged groups, as is the case for the high-melting NaCl lattice. If amino acids crystallized in a nonionic form, they would be stabilized by the much weaker van der Waals forces and would have low melting points. This and many other points of evidence have led to the conclusion that amino acids crystallize from neutral aqueous solutions as dipolar ions, also called zwitterions, rather

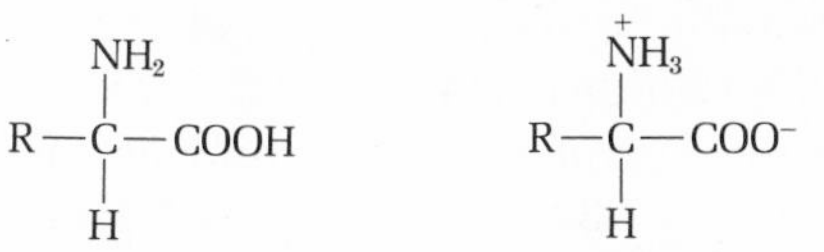

$$R{-}\underset{H}{\overset{NH_2}{C}}{-}COOH \qquad\qquad R{-}\underset{H}{\overset{\overset{+}{N}H_3}{C}}{-}COO^-$$

Undissociated form — Dipolar, or zwitterion, form

than as undissociated molecules. That amino acids exist as dipolar ions in neutral aqueous solution is also indicated by their high dielectric constants and their large dipole moments, which are reflections of the discrete separation of positive and negative charges in their dipolar ionic form.

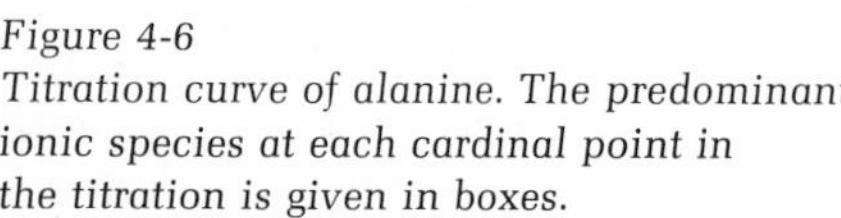

Figure 4-6
Titration curve of alanine. The predominant ionic species at each cardinal point in the titration is given in boxes.

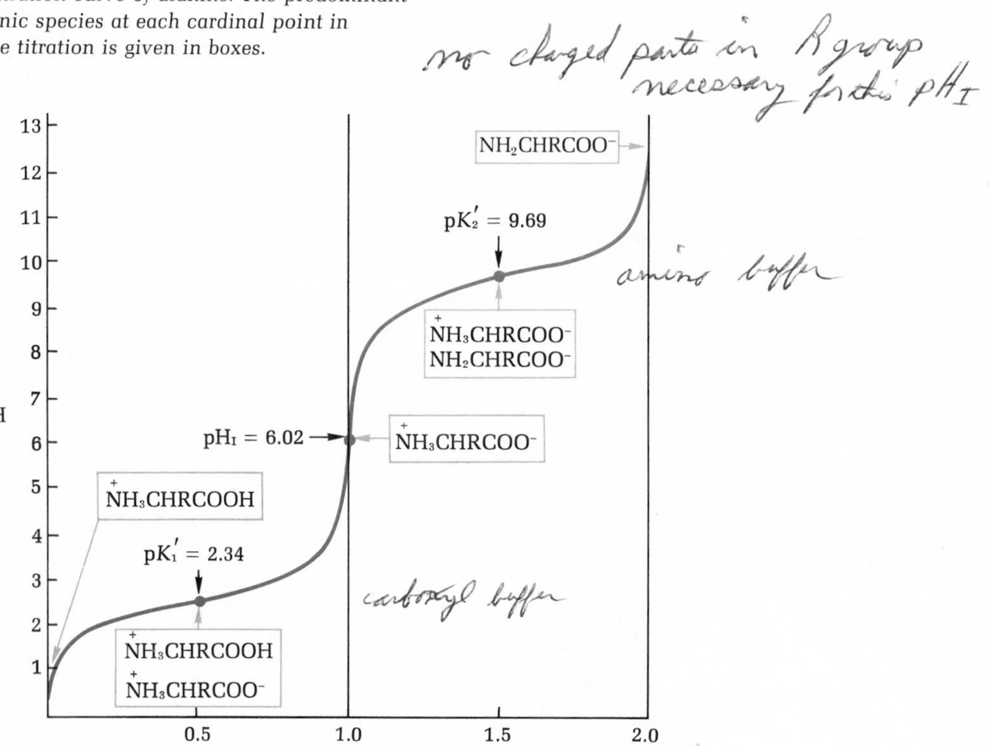

The acid-base behavior of the common amino acids is most simply formalized in terms of the Bronsted-Lowry theory of acids and bases (Chapter 2). A simple monoamino monocarboxylic α-amino acid such as alanine is a dibasic acid in its fully protonated form; it can donate two protons during its complete titration with a base. The course of such a two-stage titration with NaOH can be represented in the following equations, which indicate the nature of each ionic species involved:

$$^{+}NH_3CHRCOOH \longrightarrow {}^{+}NH_3CHRCOO^- + H^+$$

$$^{+}NH_3CHRCOO^- \longrightarrow NH_2CHRCOO^- + H^+$$

Figure 4-6 shows the biphasic titration curve of alanine. The pK′ values of the two stages of dissociation are sufficiently wide apart to yield two clearly separate legs. Each leg has a midpoint where there is minimal change in pH as increments of OH^- are added. The apparent pK′ values for the two dissociation steps may be extrapolated from the midpoints of each step; they are $pK_1' = 2.34$ and $pK_2' = 9.69$. At pH 2.34, the midpoint of the first step, equimolar concentrations of proton donor ($^+NH_3CHRCOOH$) and proton acceptor ($^+NH_3CHRCOO^-$) species are present. At pH 9.69, equimolar concentrations of $^+NH_3CHRCOO^-$ and $NH_2CHRCOO^-$ are present. Each of the two legs of the biphasic curve can be expressed mathematically to a very close approximation by the Henderson-Hasselbalch equation (Chapter 2); this means that we can calculate the ratios of ionic species at any pH, given the values for pK_1' and pK_2'.

Table 4-2 The pK′ values for the ionizing groups of some amino acids (25°C)

	pK_1' α-COOH	pK_2' α-NH_3^+	pK_R' *R group*
Glycine	2.34	9.6	
Alanine	2.34	9.69	
Leucine	2.36	9.60	
Serine	2.21	9.15	
Threonine	2.63	10.43	
Glutamine	2.17	9.13	
Aspartic acid	2.09	9.82	3.86
Glutamic acid	2.19	9.67	4.25
Histidine	1.82	9.17	6.0
Cysteine	1.71	10.78	8.33
Tyrosine	2.20	9.11	10.07
Lysine	2.18	8.95	10.53
Arginine	2.17	9.04	12.48

Figure 4-7
Titration curves of glutamic acid, lysine, and histidine. In each case, the pK′ of the R group is designated pK'_R.

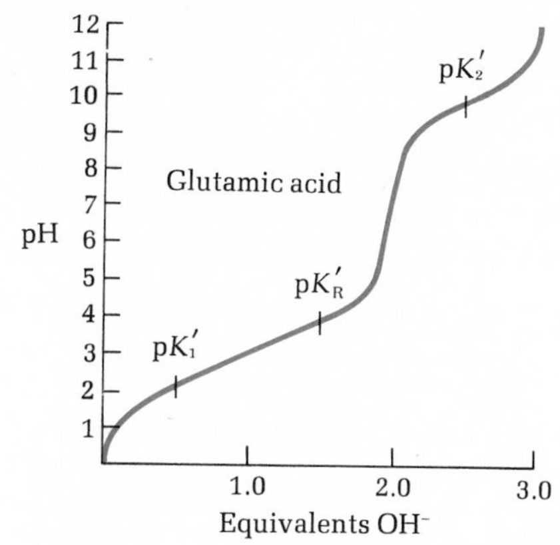

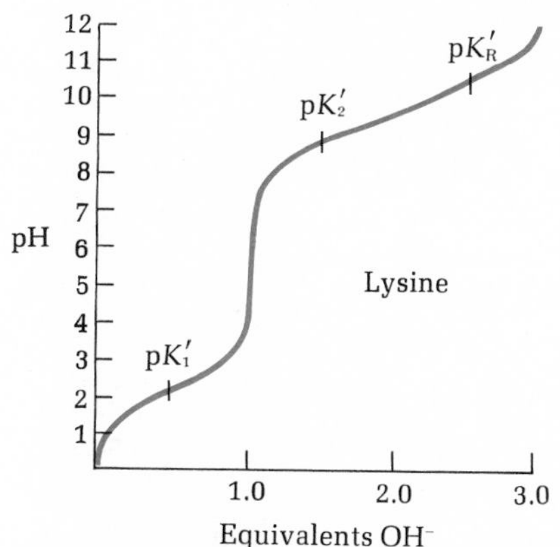

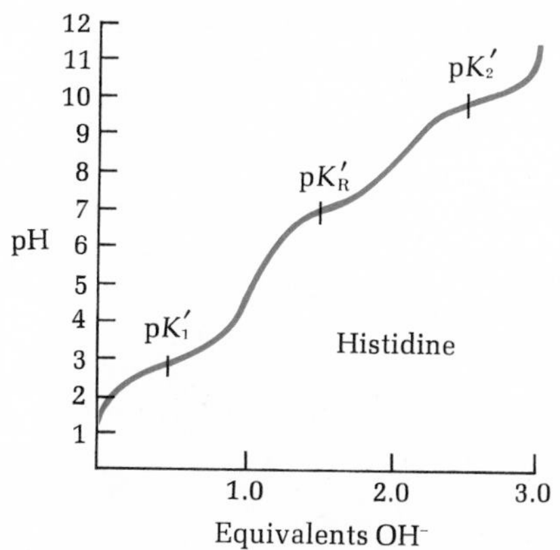

At pH 6.02, there is a point of inflection between the two separate legs of the titration curve of alanine. There is no *net* electrical charge on the molecule at this pH, and the molecule will not move in an electrical field. This is the *isoelectric* pH (symbolized pH_I), which is the arithmetic mean of pK'_1 and pK'_2, that is, $pH_I = 1/2(pK'_1 + pK'_2)$. These relationships are sufficiently exact for most purposes. However, a small but finite amount of the uncharged form ($NH_2CHRCOOH$) is also present in equilibrium with the charged forms. All monoamino monocarboxylic acids show essentially the same behavior.

Table 4-2 gives the pK′ values for the ionizing groups of some amino acids. A number of important generalizations follow from these data:

1 The carboxyl group of monoamino monocarboxylic acids is a stronger acid than the carboxyl group of comparable aliphatic acids such as acetic acid (pK′ = 4.76) and lactic acid (pK′ = 3.86). Presumably, the nearby positively charged amino group tends to repel the positively charged H^+ of the carboxyl group and thus increase its tendency to dissociate.
2 The α-amino group of monoamino monocarboxylic acids is a stronger acid (or weaker base) than the amino group of comparable aliphatic amines.
3 All the monoamino monocarboxylic amino acids having uncharged R groups have nearly identical pK'_1 values and nearly identical pK'_2 values.
4 None of the monoamino monocarboxylic amino acids has significant buffering capacity at the physiological pH zone, that is, pH 6.0 to 8.0. They do show buffering capacity in the zones near their pK′ values, i.e., the zones pH 1.3 to 3.3 and pH 8.6 to 10.6. There is only one amino acid with significant buffering capacity at pH 6 to 8, namely, histidine.
5 The β-carboxyl group of aspartic acid and the γ-carboxyl group of glutamic acid, although fully ionized at pH 7.0, have pK′ values that are considerably higher than the pK′ values of α-carboxyl groups and more nearly equal to that of simple carboxylic acids such as acetic acid.
6 The thiol or sulfhydryl group (—SH) of cysteine and the *p*-hydroxy group of tyrosine are only very weakly acidic. At pH 7.0, the former is about 8 percent ionized and the latter about 0.01 percent ionized.
7 The ε-amino group of lysine and the guanidine group of arginine are strongly basic; they lose their protons only at a very high pH. At pH 7.0, these amino acids have a net positive charge.

The titration curves of amino acids with R groups that ionize (such as histidine, lysine, and glutamic acid) are complex since the curve corresponding to the R group dissociation is superimposed on the curves for the α-amino and α-carboxyl groups (Figure 4-7).

Formol Titration

Formaldehyde in excess readily combines with the free (i.e., unprotonated) amino groups of amino acids to give methylol derivatives. This reaction causes an isoelectric amino acid to lose a proton from the $^{+}NH_3$— group of the zwitterion form:

$$^{+}NH_3CHRCOO^- \rightleftharpoons NH_2CHRCOO^- + H^+$$

$$NH_2CHRCOO^- + 2HCHO \longrightarrow (HOCH_2)_2NCHRCOO^-$$

The proton so liberated may be titrated directly with NaOH to the end point of phenolphthalein (pH 8.0). Titration of amino acids or amino acid mixtures in the presence of excess formaldehyde in this manner (the *formol titration*) is used as an analytical method, particularly in following the formation of free amino acids during hydrolysis of proteins by proteolytic enzymes.

The Stereochemistry of Amino Acids

With the single exception of glycine, all amino acids obtained from hydrolysis of proteins under sufficiently mild conditions show optical activity, i.e., they can rotate the plane of plane-polarized light when examined in a polarimeter. Optical activity is given by all compounds capable of existing in two forms whose structures are nonsuperimposable mirror images of each other. This condition is met by compounds having an asymmetric carbon atom, i.e., one with four different substituents. Because of the tetrahedral nature of the sp^3 orbitals of the carbon atom, the four different substituent groups can occupy two different arrangements in space around the carbon atom. The number of possible stereoisomers is 2^n, where n is the number of asymmetric carbon atoms. Glycine has no asymmetric carbon atom. All the rest of the amino acids commonly found in proteins have one asymmetric carbon, except threonine and isoleucine, which possess two.

Optical activity is expressed quantitatively as the *specific rotation* $[\alpha]_D^{20°}$:

$$[\alpha]_D^{20°} = \frac{\text{observed rotation}° \times 100}{\text{optical path length (dm)} \times \text{concentration (grams/100 ml)}}$$

Table 4-3 Specific rotation of some L- and D-amino acids in water

	$[\alpha]_D^{25°}$
L-Alanine	+ 1.8
L-Leucine	−11.0
L-Isoleucine	+12.4
L-Phenylalanine	−34.5
L-Glutamic acid	+12.0
L-Aspartic acid	+ 5.0
L-Lysine	+13.5
L-Serine	− 7.5
L-Proline	−86.2
L-Tryptophan	−33.7
D-Alanine	− 1.8
D-Glutamic acid	−12.0
D-Lysine	−13.5

The temperature and the wavelength of the light employed (usually the D line of sodium, 5,461 Å) must be specified From the representative values of their specific rotations given in Table 4-3, it is clear that some α-amino acids isolated from proteins are *dextrorotatory* (Ala, Ile, Glu, etc.) whereas others are *levorotatory* (Trp, Leu, Phe) when measured at pH 7.0. Dextrorotatory compounds are designated with the symbol (+), and levorotatory compounds with (−). Figure 4-8 shows that the specific rotation of an amino acid varies with the pH at which it is measured; in general, the rotation of a monoamino monocarboxylic amino acid is at its most levorotatory when it is in its isoelectric form. From the data in Table 4-3, we can also conclude that the specific rotation of an amino acid depends on the nature of its R group.

The stereochemistry of the amino acids normally found in proteins is best discussed not in terms of specific rotation measurements, such as those described above, but rather in terms of the absolute configuration of the four different substituents in the tetrahedron around the asym-

Figure 4-8
Effect of pH *on* $[\alpha]_D^{20°}$ *of two* L-*amino acids.*

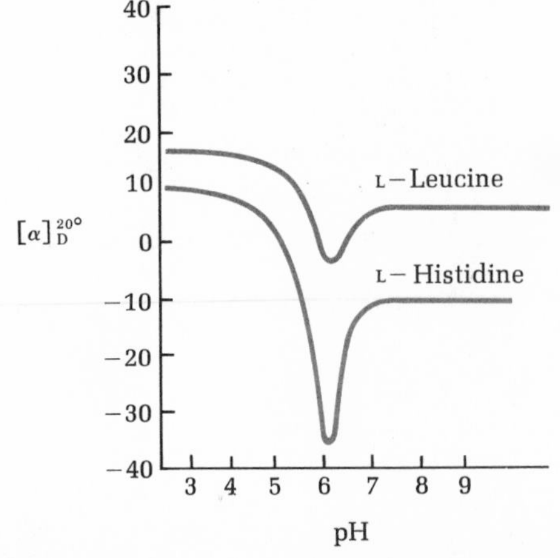

metric carbon atom. All optically active compounds may be related stereochemically—by means of appropriate reaction sequences carried out in such a way that optical activity is not lost by racemization—to a single parent compound that has been arbitrarily chosen to serve as a standard of reference for stereoisomers. This is the 3-carbon sugar glyceraldehyde, the smallest sugar to have an asymmetric carbon atom.

By convention, the two possible stereoisomers of glyceraldehyde are designated L and D (note the use of small capital letters), as shown in Figure 4-9. Directly underneath the stereoisomers of glyceraldehyde are shown the two possible stereoisomers of alanine. We see that the substituent amino group on the asymmetric carbon atom of alanine (or of any other α-amino acid) can be sterically related to the substituent hydroxyl group on the asymmetric carbon atom of glyceraldehyde, that the carboxyl group of the amino acid can be related to the aldehyde group of glyceraldehyde, and that the R group of the amino acid can be related to the —CH_2OH group of glyceraldehyde. Thus the stereoisomers of all the naturally occurring amino acids can be structurally related to the two stereoisomers of glyceraldehyde. All stereoisomers that are stereochemically related to L-glyceraldehyde are designated L, and those that are related to D-glyceraldehyde are designated D, regardless of the direction of rotation of plane-polarized light given by the isomers. The symbols D and L thus refer

Figure 4-9
Relationship of stereoisomers of alanine to stereoisomers of glyceraldehyde. In both cases, the D- and L-isomers are mirror images of each other.

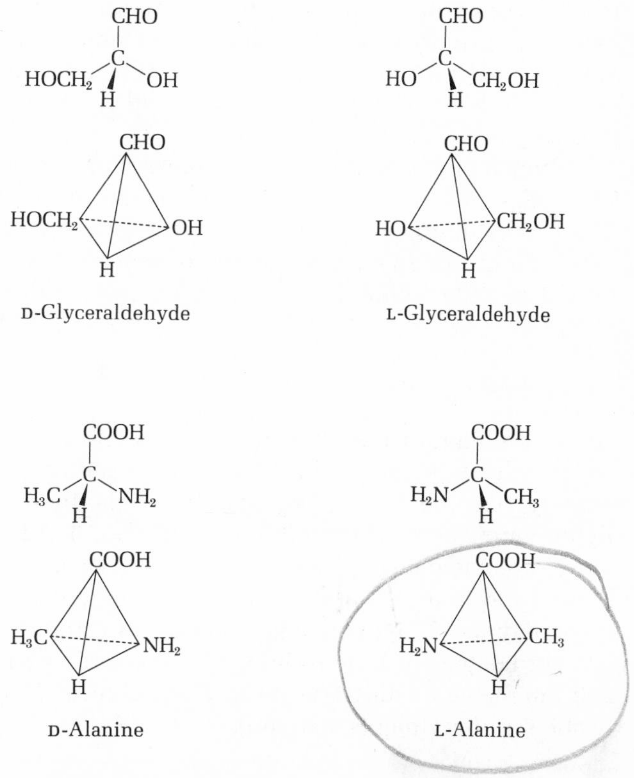

D-Glyceraldehyde

L-Glyceraldehyde

D-Alanine

L-Alanine

to *absolute configuration*, not direction of rotation. It has been recommended that the prefixes *d*- and *l*-, which indicate direction of rotation, be replaced by the signs (+) and (−) to eliminate confusion and ambiguity. Whenever the absolute configuration of a compound having an asymmetric carbon atom is known, it is the convention to designate it by D or L; specification of the direction of rotation is then unnecessary. If the absolute configuration of an optically active compound has not been established, then by convention such compounds may be designated (+) or (−) to indicate direction of rotation, but the conditions of measurement must then be specified.

All naturally occurring amino acids found in proteins belong to the L stereochemical series; their optical activity can be preserved without racemization if the hydrolysis of the protein is carried out under appropriate conditions. However, when an amino acid is synthesized by simple organic chemical reactions in the laboratory, then an optically inactive form is usually obtained. This is designated a *racemate*, and it consists of an equimolar mixture of the D- and L-stereoisomers, symbolized by the prefix DL.

Optically active amino acids are racemized, i.e., converted to DL mixtures, during any chemical reaction in which the asymmetric carbon atom passes through a symmetrical intermediate state—by boiling in strong base, for example. Acid hydrolysis yields very little racemization.

Those amino acids with two asymmetric carbon atoms have four stereoisomers. In the case of threonine, all four are known. That form of threonine which is isolated from protein hydrolyzates is by convention designated L; its mirror image is the D form. The other two stereoisomers are *diastereoisomers*, or *allo* forms; they, too, are mirror images of each other. Whenever an amino acid has more than one asymmetric carbon atom, it is the configuration about the α-carbon atom that is the basis for configurational assignment. Cystine, which contains two asymmetric carbon atoms in each half of the molecule, can assume a form in which the pairs of asymmetric carbon atoms are mirror images of each other. When this occurs, the isomer is *internally compensated* and is a *meso* form (margin).

Stereoisomers of threonine

```
      COOH                  COOH
       |                     |
  NH2—C—H              NH2—C—H
       |                     |
   H—C—OH               HO—C—H
       |                     |
      CH3                   CH3

  L-Threonine          L-allo-Threonine

      COOH                  COOH
       |                     |
   H—C—NH2               H—C—NH2
       |                     |
  HO—C—H                 H—C—OH
       |                     |
      CH3                   CH3

  D-Threonine          D-allo-Threonine
```

Isomers of cystine

```
      COOH                   COOH
       |                      |
  NH2—C—H               NH2—C—H
       |                      |
      CH2————S—S————CH2

             L-Cystine

      COOH                   COOH
       |                      |
  NH2—C—H                 H—C—NH2
       |                      |
      CH2————S—S————CH2

            meso-Cystine

      COOH                   COOH
       |                      |
   H—C—NH2                H—C—NH2
       |                      |
      CH2————S—S————CH2

             D-Cystine
```

Although only L-amino acids are present in true protein molecules, many different D-amino acids are found in living cells in other chemical forms—for example, in the cell walls of certain microorganisms or as part of the structure of peptide antibiotics such as gramicidin and actinomycin D.

Absorption Spectra

Although none of the 20 amino acids found in proteins absorbs light in the visible range, three amino acids—namely, tyrosine, tryptophan, and phenylalanine—absorb light significantly in the ultraviolet (Figure 4-10). Since most proteins contain tyrosine residues, measurement of light absorption at 280 nm in a spectrophotometer is an extremely rapid and convenient means of estimating the protein content of a solution. Cystine absorbs weakly at 240 nm due to its disulfide group. All amino acids absorb in the far ultraviolet (<220 nm).

Figure 4-10
The ultraviolet absorption spectra of tryptophan, tyrosine, and phenylalanine.

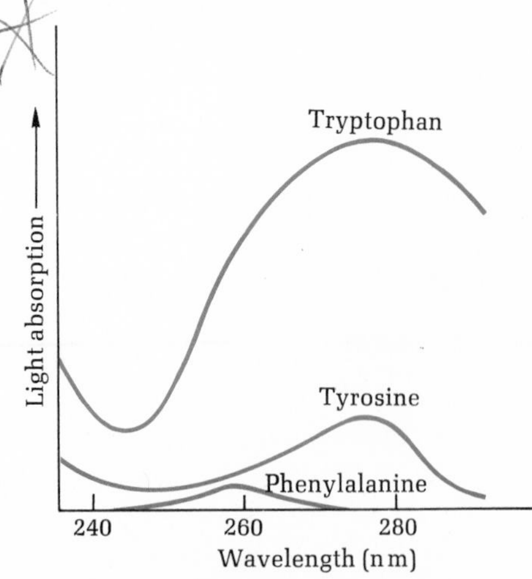

The Chemical Reactions of Amino Acids

Reactions of the α-Carboxyl Group

The characteristic reactions of amino acids are those of their functional groups, namely, the α-carboxyl and α-amino groups, as well as the functional groups present in the side-chains. The α-carboxyl groups of all α-amino acids undergo well-known organic reactions leading to the formation of amides, esters, and acyl halides. These reactions need not be detailed here, but since they are of some importance in the laboratory synthesis of polypeptides, they will be discussed in Chapter 5.

A reaction that is often used in the analysis of amino acids and polypeptides is the reduction of the carboxyl group to yield the corresponding α-amino alcohol, with the potent reducing agent sodium borohydride (margin).

Reduction of carboxyl group

$NH_2—C(R)(H)—COOH$

↓ Reduction $NaBH_4$

$NH_2—C(R)(H)—CH_2—OH$

An α-amino-alcohol

Reactions of the α-Amino Group

The α-amino group of amino acids may be acylated by treatment with acid halides or anhydrides; this procedure is commonly used to protect the α-amino group. When acylations are carried out under mild conditions, the stereochemical integrity of the α-carbon atom is retained. However, under drastic conditions, i.e., if heat is applied, racemization may occur.

One of the most characteristic and widely used reactions of the α-amino group is the ninhydrin reaction, which can be used to estimate amino acids quantitatively in very small amounts. Heating an α-amino acid with two equivalents of ninhydrin yields an intensely colored product. A blue color is given in the ninhydrin reaction by all amino acids and peptides having a free α-amino group, whereas proline and hydroxyproline, in which the α-amino group is substituted, yield somewhat different derivatives having a characteristic yellow color.

(Structure: two indanedione rings joined by C=N—C; labels O, O, C, C=N—C, C, C, O, O⁻)

Structure of blue pigment formed in ninhydrin reaction.

Another important reaction of the α-amino group is with the reagent 1-fluoro-2,4-dinitrobenzene (abbreviated FDNB), introduced by Frederick Sanger for the quantitative labeling of amino groups in amino acids and peptides. In mildly alkaline solution, FDNB converts α-amino acids into yellow 2,4-dinitrophenyl derivatives, called DNP-amino acids, in which the α-amino group is substituted with a 2,4-dinitrophenyl group. This reaction is extremely valuable in the identification of the amino-terminal amino acid of a polypeptide chain (Chapter 5). FDNB also reacts with the ε-amino group of lysine, but this derivative can be differentiated easily from DNP derivatives of the α-amino group by chromatographic methods.

The Sanger reaction

(2,4-dinitrofluorobenzene: NO_2, NO_2, F) FDNB

\+

$H—N(H)—C(H)(R)—COOH$

↓ → HF

(2,4-dinitrophenyl: NO_2, NO_2) $—N(H)—C(H)(R)—COOH$

2,4-dinitrophenylamino acid

More recently a very similar reaction between amino groups and the labeling reagent 1-dimethylaminonaphthalene-5-sulfonyl chloride (abbreviated *dansyl chloride*) has been employed with great success. Since the dansyl group is highly fluorescent, dansyl derivatives of amino acids can be detected and measured in minute amounts by fluorimetric methods.

Dansyl chloride

HCl

A dansyl amino acid

Another extremely useful reaction of the α-amino group is the *Edman reaction*. Phenylisothiocyanate reacts quantitatively with α-amino acids to yield corresponding phenylthiocarbamylamino acid derivatives. On treatment with acid in nitromethane solvent, the latter cyclize to form the corresponding phenylthiohydantoins. These derivatives, which are colorless, are easily separated and identified by chromatographic means. The Edman reaction is widely used to identify the NH_2-terminal amino acid of a polypeptide chain. As we shall see in Chapter 5, the Edman reaction has some major advantages in the determination of amino acid sequence in polypeptides.

The α-amino groups of amino acids react reversibly with aldehydes to form compounds called *Schiff's bases*, which are very labile. Schiff's bases appear to be intermediates in some enzymatic reactions involving α-amino acid substrates.

A Schiff's base

The Edman reaction

Phenylisothiocyanate

A phenylthiohydantoin

Reactions of the R Groups

Amino acids also show reactions typical of the functions present in their R groups, such as the —SH group of cysteine, the phenolic hydroxyl group of tyrosine, and the guanidinium group of arginine. Although these reactions are sometimes useful for qualitative identification, amino acids are more accurately identified and measured in very low concentrations by means of paper chromatography or ion-exchange chromatography (see below).

The R group of cysteine, the thiol or sulfhydryl group, is worthy of special note. This group, which is weakly acid,

Oxidation of cysteine

$$\mathrm{NH_2{-}CH(COOH){-}CH_2{-}SH}\ \text{(Cysteine)} + \mathrm{HS{-}CH_2{-}CH(NH_2){-}COOH}\ \text{(Cysteine)} \xrightarrow[-2H]{\text{Oxidant}} \mathrm{NH_2{-}CH(COOH){-}CH_2{-}S{-}S{-}CH_2{-}CH(NH_2){-}COOH}\ \text{(Cystine)}$$

is extremely reactive. In alkaline solutions, sulfur is lost from cysteine in a series of complex reactions. When cysteine is exposed to trace concentrations of some heavy metal ions, it forms mercaptides. The thiol group of cysteine also readily undergoes oxidation, particularly in the presence of iron salts, to the disulfide; in this process, cysteine is oxidized to cystine (margin).

The thiol group of specific cysteine residues is an important component of the active or catalytic site of many enzymes. Treatment of these SH enzymes with heavy metals, such as Ag^+ or Hg^{2+}, which form mercaptides, causes their inactivation.

$$\mathrm{HS{-}CH_2{-}CH(NH_2){-}COOH} + Ag^+ \xrightarrow{} H^+ + \mathrm{Ag{-}S{-}CH_2{-}CH(NH_2){-}COOH}$$

Silver mercaptide of cysteine

Cystine plays a special role as a cross-linking agent in protein structure since the two cysteine half-residues are joined by the covalent disulfide linkage. This linkage undergoes cleavage by the action of alkali in a series of complex reactions, and also by the action of reducing agents, which yield two molecules of cysteine. It can also be oxidized by such agents as performic acid, to yield two molecules of cysteic acid, an important reaction to be discussed in Chapter 5.

Analysis of Amino Acid Mixtures

The quantitative separation and estimation of each amino acid in a complex mixture such as the hydrolyzate of a protein is a formidable problem when attacked by classical separation methods. Actually, it was not until partition and ion-exchange chromatography were applied to the analysis of amino acid mixtures that any significant progress was achieved in the detailed study of protein structure. Analytical methods based on these principles have since been vastly refined and are capable of great precision and sensitivity; they have also been successfully automated. These methods are applicable not only to amino acid analysis but also to the separation of peptide mixtures, the separation of proteins from each other, the separation and analysis of nucleic acids and nucleotides, and the separation of lipid and carbohydrate mixtures. For this reason, we shall briefly review the physical principles underlying these methods. It will become evident that the entire science of amino acid analysis by chromatographic and electrophoretic methods is based on a knowledge of the relative solubility and acid-base behavior of the different amino acids.

Partition Methods

Liquid extraction

When a solute is distributed between equal volumes of two immiscible liquids, the ratio of the concentrations of solute in the two phases at equilibrium at a given temperature is called the *partition coefficient*. Amino acids can be partitioned in this manner between two liquid phases, such as the pairs phenol–water or *n*-butanol–water; each amino acid has a distinctive partition coefficient for any given pair of immiscible solvents. A mixture of substances having different partition coefficients can be quantitatively separated by a process known as *countercurrent distribution*, in which many repetitive partition steps take place. The principle of the method is outlined in Figure 4-11, which shows with an easily understood example how two substances of different partition coefficients are separated by a series of partitions between two immiscible solvents. We see that solute Z, having a low partition co-

Figure 4-11
Countercurrent distribution principle.

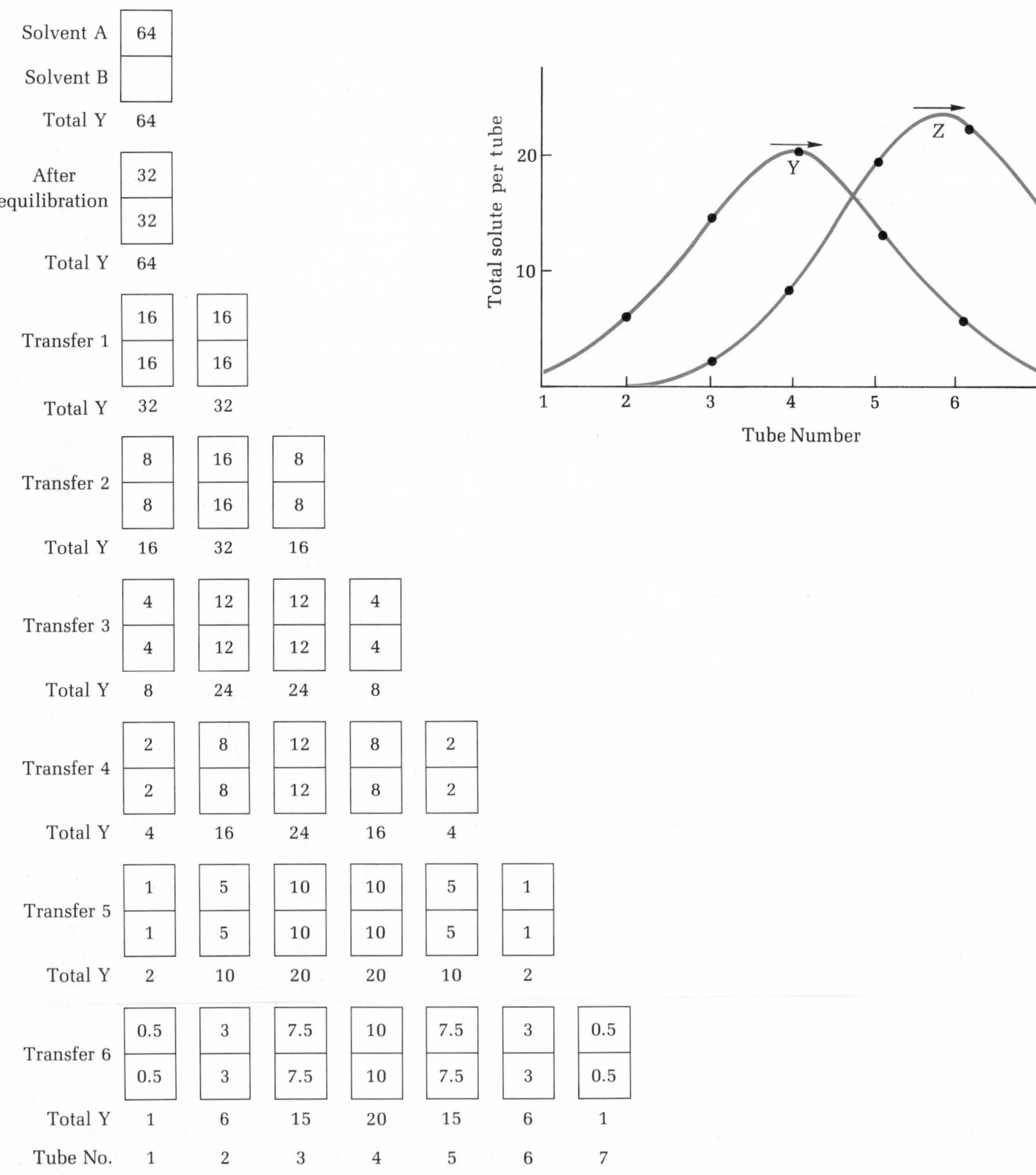

efficient, "moves" along a series of partition tubes faster than solute Y, which has a higher partition coefficient. Furthermore, each substance tends to localize in a series of tubes in a peaked distribution. If the countercurrent process is continued along a much longer series of tubes, both peaks ultimately separate completely from each other. This is done in automated equipment; some instruments are capable of hundreds of partition steps.

Partition chromatography is the separation of similar substances by the partition principle described above, in which the separation is achieved in an enormously large number of separate partition steps, each of microscopic dimensions, in a column (from 10 to 100 cm long) packed with granules of a hydrated insoluble inert substance such

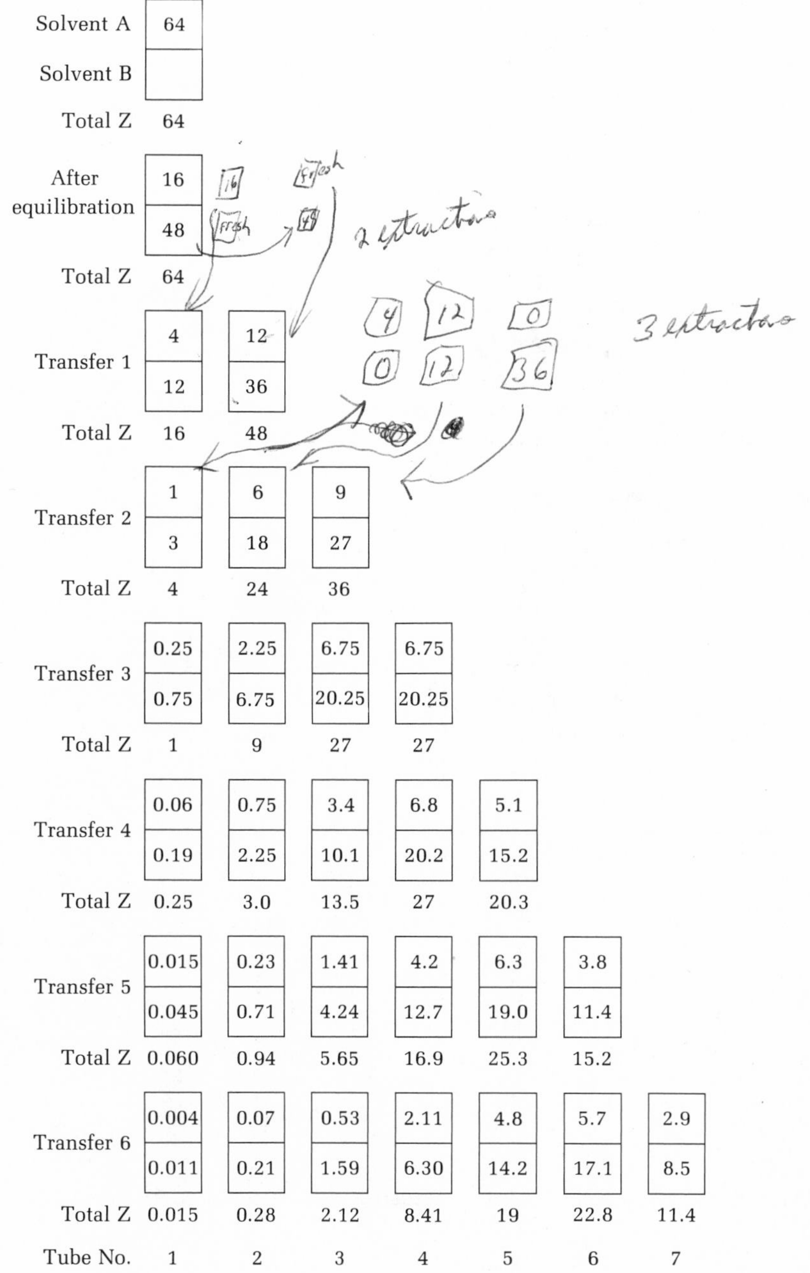

as starch. Starch granules contain a layer of tightly bound water, which serves as a stationary aqueous phase past which an immiscible solvent flows as it passes down the column by gravity. Each starch granule thus acts as a microscopic separatory funnel. The individual partition process occurring in such microscopic zones in a starch column is not specifically defined as to dimensions, nor is each microscopic step complete to the point of equilibrium. Nevertheless, the total number of steps in the column is so very great that the different amino acids in a mixture will move down the column at different rates as water-saturated butanol flows down the column. The liquid appearing at the bottom of the column, called the *eluate*, is caught in small fractions with an automatic fraction collector and is analyzed by means of the quantitative ninhydrin reaction. A plot of the amount of amino acid in each tube will show a series of peaks, each corresponding to a different amino acid.

Precisely the same principle is involved in *filter-paper chromatography* of amino acids. The cellulose of the filter-paper fibers is hydrated. As a solvent containing an amino acid mixture ascends in the vertically held paper by capillary action (or descends, in descending chromatography), many microscopic distributions of the amino acids occur between the flowing phase and the stationary water phase bound to the paper fibers. At the end of the process, the different amino acids have moved different distances from the origin. The paper is dried, sprayed with ninhydrin solution, and heated in order to locate the amino acids. Paper chromatography of a mixture of amino acids may be carried out in two directions successively on a square of filter paper, using two different solvent systems. A two-dimensional map of the different amino acids then results. Mapping of amino acids and peptides by two-dimensional paper chromatography or paper electrophoresis (see below) is widely used in establishing the amino acid sequence in polypeptide chains (Chapter 5).

Ion-Exchange Chromatography

The partition principle has been further refined in ion-exchange chromatography, in which the different amino acids are sorted out by the differences in their acid-base

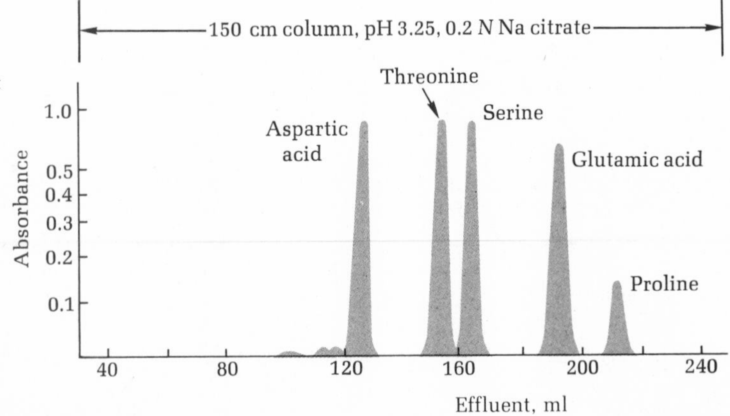

Figure 4-12
Automatically recorded chromatographic analysis of amino acids on an ion-exchange resin. The elution is carried out with different buffers of successively higher pH. The effluent is caught in small volumes, and the amino acid content of each tube is automatically analyzed. The area under each peak is proportional to the amount of each amino acid in the mixture.

behavior. In this process, the column is filled with a synthetic resin containing fixed charged groups. There are two major classes of ion-exchange resins: cation exchangers and anion exchangers.

Amino acids are usually separated on cation-exchange columns filled with solid particles of a sulfonated polystyrene resin previously equilibrated with an NaOH solution so that its sulfonic acid groups are fully "charged" with Na^+. This form of the resin is the "sodium form"; the resin may also be prepared in the protonated form, or "hydrogen form," by washing it with acid. To the Na^+ form of the resin is added an acid solution (pH = 3.0) of the amino acid mixture; at pH 3.0, amino acids are largely cations with net positive charge. The cationic amino acids tend to displace some of the bound Na^+ ions from the resin particles; the amount of displacement will vary slightly among different amino acids because of small differences in degree of ionization. At pH 3.0, the most basic amino acids (lysine, arginine, and histidine) will be bound to the resin most tightly, by electrostatic forces, and the most acid (glutamic acid, aspartic acid) will be bound the least. As the pH and the NaCl concentration of the eluting aqueous medium are gradually increased, the amino acids move down the column at different rates and can be collected in many small fractions. These may be analyzed quantitatively by means of the ninhydrin reaction. An elution curve can then be constructed, as in Figure 4-12. The entire analytical procedure has been automated, so that elution, collection of fractions, analysis of each fraction, and the recording of data are performed automatically by servomechanisms in an apparatus called an amino acid analyzer.

Another method of separating amino acids is *paper electrophoresis*. In this process, a drop of a solution of the amino acid mixture is placed on a filter-paper sheet, which is then moistened with a buffer of a given pH. The ends of the sheet dip into electrode vessels, and a high-voltage electrical field is applied with cooling. Because of their different pK' values, the amino acids migrate in different directions and at different rates, depending on the pH of the system and the emf applied. For example, at pH 1, histidine, arginine, and lysine have a charge of +2 whereas all other amino acids have a charge of +1. At pH 11, as-

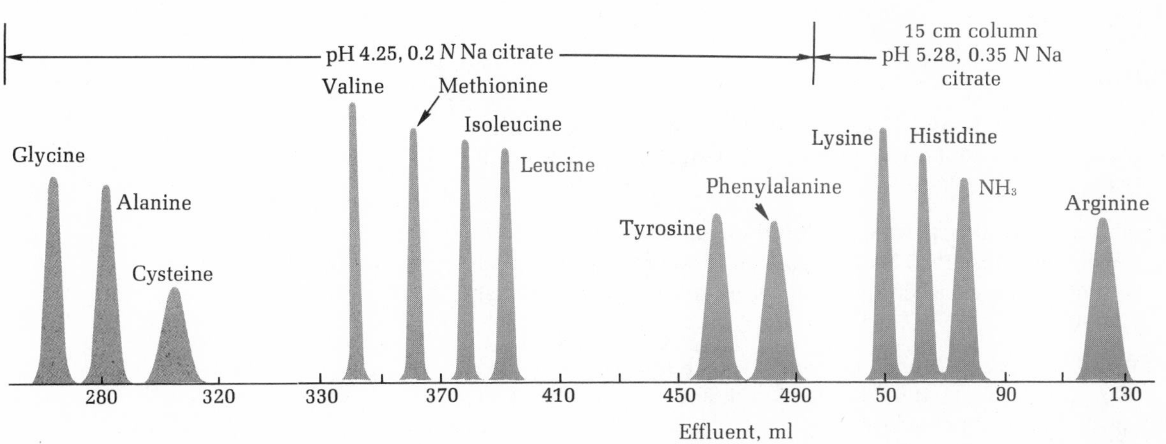

partate and glutamate have a charge of −2 and all others a charge of −1. Knowledge of the acid-base properties of amino acids permits conditions to be selected to achieve separation of any given mixture of amino acids. Amino acids may also be separated by *thin-layer chromatography*, a refinement of partition chromatography which will be described in Chapter 10.

Summary

The 20 amino acids commonly found as hydrolysis products of proteins are alike in containing an α-carboxyl group and an α-amino group but differ in the chemical nature of the R groups substituted on the α-carbon atom. They are classified on the basis of the polarity of their R groups. The nonpolar, or hydrophobic, class includes alanine, leucine, isoleucine, valine, proline, phenylalanine, tryptophan, and methionine. The polar neutral class includes glycine, serine, threonine, cysteine, tyrosine, asparagine, and glutamine. The negatively charged (acidic) class contains aspartic acid and glutamic acid, and the positively charged (basic) class contains arginine, lysine, and histidine. In a few specialized proteins, other amino acids may occur, such as hydroxyproline, hydroxylysine, and desmosine.

Monoamino monocarboxylic amino acids are dibasic acids ($H_3N^+CHRCOOH$) at low pH. As the pH is raised to about 6, the proton is lost from the carboxyl group to form the dipolar, or zwitterion, species $H_3N^+CHRCOO^-$, which is electrically neutral. Further increase in pH causes loss of the second proton, to yield the ionic species $NH_2CHRCOO^-$. The pK' of the first ionization, i.e., of the α-carboxyl group, is about 2.0 to 2.5; the pK' of the second step is about 9 to 10. Amino acids possessing ionizable R groups may exist in additional ionic species, depending on the pK' values of their R groups. The α-carbon atom of the amino acids (except glycine) is asymmetric and thus can exist in at least two stereoisomeric forms; only the L-stereoisomers, which are related to L-glyceraldehyde, are found in proteins.

All α-amino acids form analytically useful colored derivatives with ninhydrin. The α-amino group can also be substituted with the yellow 2,4-dinitrophenyl group by reaction with 2,4-dinitrofluorobenzene (Sanger's reagent). Reaction of the α-amino group with phenyl isothiocyanate (the Edman reaction) yields characteristic phenylthiohydantoin derivatives. These two reactions are extremely useful for identification and analysis.

Complex mixtures of amino acids can be separated, identified, and estimated by means of chromatography on paper or on ion-exchange columns or by means of countercurrent distribution. These methods exploit differences in the acid-base behavior and solubility of the amino acids.

References

Books

BLACKBURN, S.: *Amino Acid Determination*, Marcel Dekker, Inc., New York, 1968. Comprehensive treatise on analytical methods.

EDSALL, J. T., AND J. WYMAN: *Biophysical Chemistry*, vol. 1, Academic Press Inc., New York, 1958. Excellent treatment of amino acids as electrolytes in terms of physical-chemical theory.

HEFTMAN, E. (ed.): *Chromatography*, 2d ed., Reinhold Publishing Corp., New York, 1967. Compendium and reference book of principles and procedures.

MEISTER, A.: *Biochemistry of the Amino Acids*, 2d ed., 2 vols., Academic Press Inc., 1965. Authoritative and comprehensive treatment of structure, occurrence, and metabolism of both protein and nonprotein amino acids.

RANDERATH, K.: *Thin-layer Chromatography*, 2d ed., Academic Press Inc., New York, 1966.

Articles and Reviews

FOWDEN, L., D. LEWIS, and H. TRISTRAM: "Toxic Amino Acids: Their Actions as Antimetabolites," *Advan. Enzymol.* **29:**89–163 (1968).

KEKWICK, R. A. (ed.): "The Separation of Biological Materials," *Brit. Med. Bull.*, **22:**103–193 (1966). Various separation methods applicable to biological materials.

SPACKMAN, D. H., W. H. STEIN, and S. MOORE: "Automatic Recording Apparatus for Use in the Chromatography of Amino Acids," *Anal. Chem.*, **30:**1190–1206 (1958). The automatic amino acid analyzer.

Problems

1. Calculate the pH_I values of glycine, alanine, serine, threonine, and glutamic acid from their pK' values (Table 4-2).

2. Referring to Table 4-2 for the necessary pK' values, indicate the net charge (−, 0, or +) of glycine, aspartic acid, lysine, and histidine at (*a*) pH 1.0, (*b*) pH 2.10, (*c*) pH 4.0, (*d*) pH 10.

3. Paper electrophoresis at pH 6.0 was carried out on a mixture of glycine, alanine, glutamic acid, lysine, arginine, and serine.
   (*a*) Which compound moved toward the anode?
   (*b*) Which moved toward the cathode?
   (*c*) Which remained at the origin?

4. How many grams of NaOH would you have to add to 500 ml of 0.01 *M* histidine in its fully protonated form to yield a buffer of pH 7.0?

5. To 1.0 liter of a 1.0 *M* solution of glycine at the isoelectric pH is added 0.3 mole of HCl. What will be the pH of the resultant solution? What would be the pH if 0.3 mole of NaOH were added instead?

6. Using data in Table 4-3, calculate the optical rotation of a 1.10 *M* solution of alanine in water at 25°C in a 25-cm polarimeter tube with the sodium D line as light source.

7. Glycine is four times as soluble in solvent A as in solvent B. Phenylalanine is only two times as soluble in A as in B. Countercurrent distribution between solvents A and B was used to separate glycine and phenylalanine. If we started with 100 mg of glycine and 81 mg of phenylalanine:
   (*a*) Which tube of a four-tube countercurrent system (see Figure 4-11) contains the most glycine and which the most phenylalanine?
   (*b*) How many mg of each amino acid is there in each of these tubes?

8. A solution of L-alanine (400 ml) was brought to pH 8.0. It was then treated with an excess of formaldehyde. The resultant solution required a total of 250 ml of 0.2 *M* NaOH solution to titrate it back to pH 8.0. How many grams of L-alanine did the original solution contain?

CHAPTER 5 PROTEINS: COVALENT BACKBONE AND AMINO ACID SEQUENCE

In this chapter, we shall start by considering the properties of simple peptides. Then we shall examine three major problems in the chemistry of proteins: (1) the determination of amino acid sequence, (2) the analysis of variations in the amino acid sequences of different proteins in different species, and (3) the laboratory synthesis of polypeptide chains.

The Structure of Peptides

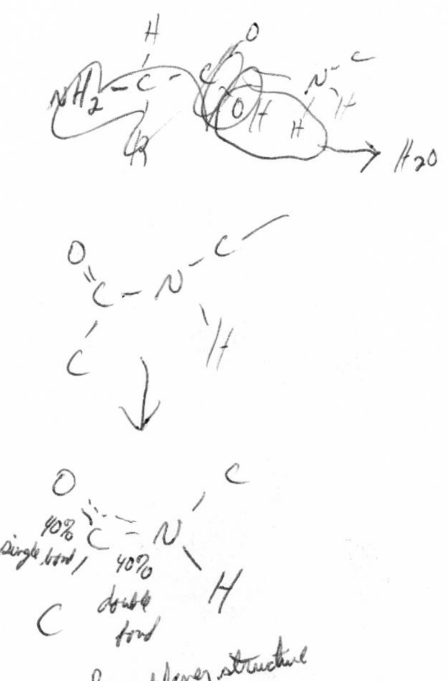

Simple peptides containing two, three, four, or more amino acid residues (i.e., dipeptides, tripeptides, tetrapeptides, etc.) are formed on partial hydrolysis of the very long polypeptide chains of proteins. As shown in Figure 5-1, peptides are named from their component amino acid residues, in the sequence beginning with the NH_2-terminal residue. The peptide bond linking successive residues may be regarded as a substituted amide linkage. As in the simple amide group, the peptide linkage shows a high degree of resonance stabilization; the C—N "single" bond in the peptide linkage has about 40 percent double-bond character, and the C═O "double" bond about 40 percent single-bond character. This fact has two important consequences: (1) The imino (—NH—) group of the peptide linkage has no significant tendency to ionize or to be protonated in the pH range 0 to 14. (2) The C—N bond of the peptide linkage cannot rotate freely, a property of supreme importance with respect to the three-dimensional conformation of polypeptide chains (Chapter 7).

The fact that the peptide bond is the sole covalent linkage between amino acids in the backbone structure of proteins is confirmed not only by the enzymatic and chemical degradation studies described below but also by physical measurements. Proteins have absorption bands in the far ultraviolet (180 to 220 nm) and in the infrared that are similar to those given by authentic peptides. Furthermore, x-ray diffraction analysis (Chapter 6) directly shows the presence of peptide bonds in native proteins. There is only one other important type of covalent linkage between amino acids in proteins, namely, the disulfide bridge or cross-linkage between two cystine half-residues in two separate peptide chains (interchain —S—S— linkage) or in different positions within a single chain (intrachain —S—S— linkage). These will be discussed later.

In addition to the large number of different peptides that have been identified as partial hydrolysis products of proteins, many other peptides that do not derive from protein structure occur biologically. Among these are the simple peptides glutathione and carnosine (see opposite margin), whose biological functions are still not understood, as well as larger peptides having pronounced biological activity, such as the posterior pituitary hormones oxytocin and vasopressin and the nonapeptide bradykinin of blood plasma, which assists in regulating blood pressure. (See page 104.)

Figure 5-1
Structure of a pentapeptide. Peptides are named beginning with the NH_2-terminal residue.

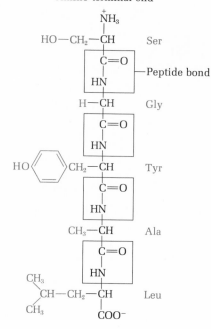

Amino-terminal end

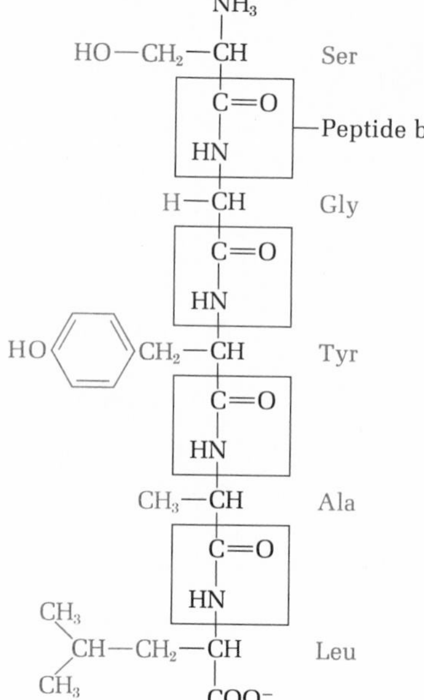

Carboxyl-Terminal End

Space-filling model

Serylglycyltyrosylalanylleucine
(Ser-Gly-Tyr-Ala-Leu)

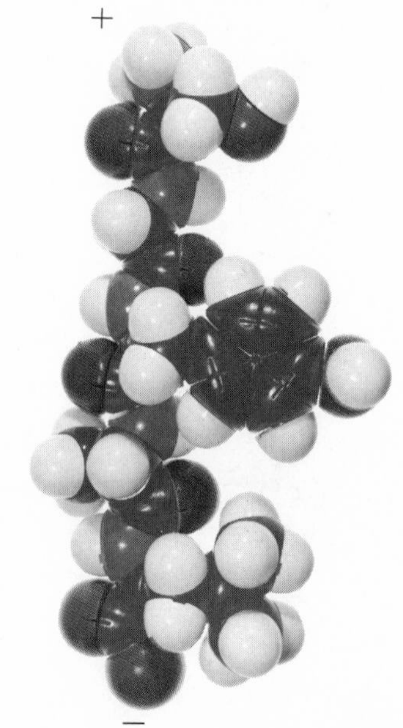

Acid-base Properties of Peptides

Many small peptides have been obtained in pure crystalline form. They usually have high melting points, indicating that they crystallize from neutral solutions in an ionic lattice as dipolar ions. Since none of the α-carboxyl groups and none of the α-amino groups that are combined in the form of peptide linkages can ionize in the zone pH 0 to 14, the acid-base behavior of peptides is contributed by the free α-amino group of the NH_2-terminal residue, the free α-carboxyl group of the COOH-terminal residue, and those R groups that are capable of ionization. In long peptide chains, the ionizing R groups usually greatly outnumber the single ionizing groups at the two terminal residues. Since the free α-amino and α-carboxyl groups are farther away from each other in peptides than in simple amino acids, electrostatic interactions between them are diminished; the pK' values for the terminal α-carboxyl groups are somewhat higher and those for the α-amino groups are somewhat lower than in free α-amino acids (Table 5-1). The pK' values for the R groups in short peptides are close to those of the corresponding free amino acids.

Table 5-1 pK' values for some peptides (25°C)

	pK'_1 α-COOH	pK'_2 α-NH_3^+	pK'_R *R group*	pH_I
Gly-Gly	3.06	8.13	—	5.59
Gly-Gly-Gly	3.26	7.91	—	5.58
Gly-Ala	3.17	8.23	—	5.70
Ala-Gly	3.16	8.24	—	5.70
Ala-Ala-Ala-Ala	3.42	7.94	—	5.68
Ala-Ala-Lys-Ala	3.58	8.01	10.58	~9.3
Gly-Asp	2.81	8.60	4.45	~3.6

The titration curves of simple peptides are very similar to those of free α-amino acids. The predominant ionic species at different stages in the titration curves can be deduced using the same methods as those developed for free amino acids (see Figure 5-2). Peptides also have an isoelectric pH, which can be calculated from the pK' values (Table 5-1).

Optical Properties of Peptides

If partial hydrolysis of a protein is carried out under sufficiently mild conditions, so that no racemization of the

Two peptides not derived from proteins

Carnosine
(β-alanylhistidine)

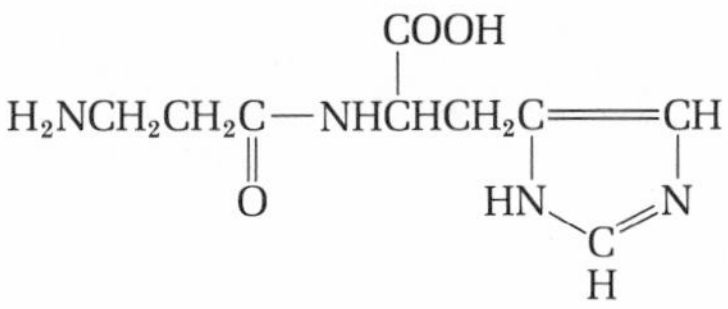

$H_2NCH_2CH_2C(=O)-NHCH(COOH)CH_2C=CH$ (imidazole ring: HN–CH=N)

Glutathione
(γ-glutamylcysteinylglycine)

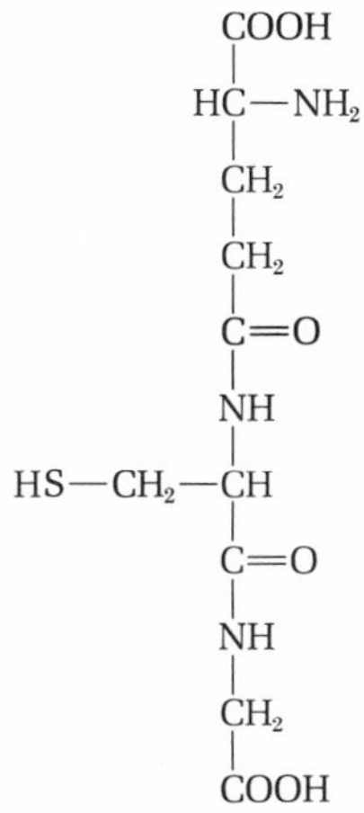

COOH–HC(NH$_2$)–CH$_2$–CH$_2$–C(=O)–NH–CH(CH$_2$–SH)–C(=O)–NH–CH$_2$–COOH

Figure 5-2
The major ionic species of alanylglycine.

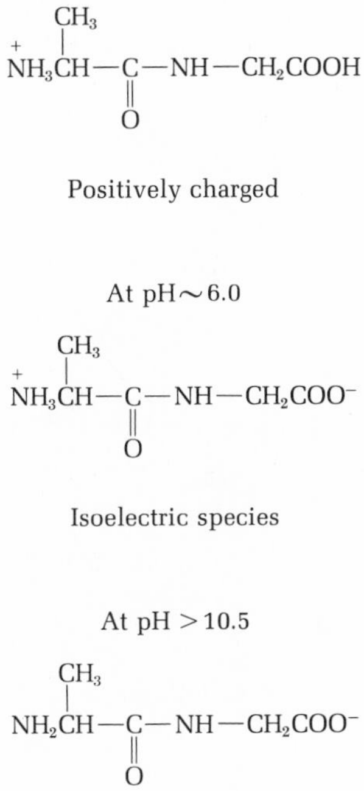

At pH < 1.0

$\overset{+}{N}H_3CH(CH_3)-C(=O)-NH-CH_2COOH$

Positively charged

At pH ~ 6.0

$\overset{+}{N}H_3CH(CH_3)-C(=O)-NH-CH_2COO^-$

Isoelectric species

At pH > 10.5

$NH_2CH(CH_3)-C(=O)-NH-CH_2COO^-$

Negatively charged

asymmetric α-carbon atom occurs, the peptides formed are optically active, since they contain only L-amino acid residues. In relatively short peptides, the total observed optical activity is approximately an additive function of the optical activities of the component amino acid residues. However, in long peptide chains, the total rotation is no longer a simple additive function. The importance of this observation will be discussed in Chapter 6.

Chemical Reactions of Peptides

The free NH_2-terminal amino groups of peptides undergo the same kinds of chemical reactions as those given by the α-amino groups of free amino acids, such as acylation and reactions with 2,4-dinitrophenylfluorobenzene or phenylisothiocyanate (Chapter 4). Similarly, the COOH-terminal carboxyl group of a peptide may be esterified or reduced. The various R groups of the different amino acid residues found in peptides usually yield the same characteristic reactions and color tests as those described for free amino acids. The NH_2-terminal amino acid residue of peptides also reacts quantitatively with ninhydrin to form colored derivatives; this reaction is widely used for detection and quantitative estimation of peptides in electrophoretic and chromatographic procedures.

One widely employed color reaction of peptides and proteins that is not given by free amino acids is the biuret reaction. Treatment of a peptide or protein with $CuSO_4$ and alkali yields a purple complex of Cu^{2+} and the peptide, which can be measured quantitatively in a spectrophotometer.

Separation and Analysis of Peptides

Complex mixtures of peptides resulting from partial hydrolysis of proteins are best separated and analyzed by ion-exchange chromatography or by paper electrophoresis, which exploit differences in the acid-base behavior of different peptides. Peptide analysis is more complex and laborious than amino acid analysis because the number of possible peptides that may be encountered is much greater. Often peptide mixtures are first grossly separated into acidic, basic, and neutral peptides by electrophoresis at pH 6.0. At this pH, acidic peptides (i.e., those containing excess aspartic or glutamic acid residues) will be negatively charged and will move to the anode, whereas the basic peptides (those containing excess arginine and lysine residues) will be positively charged and will migrate to the cathode. The neutral peptides (those containing no acidic or basic residues, or equal numbers of them) will not move significantly in an electrical field at this pH. Each class may then be separated into its individual components by a second stage of electrophoresis at an appropriate pH or by ion-exchange chromatography. Peptide mixtures are also very effectively separated by countercurrent distribution. After the individual peptides of a mixture have been separated and recovered, each peptide is completely hydrolyzed by heating with 6 N HCl and the amino acid residues present are identified, again by electrophoresis or chromatography.

Two-dimensional paper chromatography or electrophoresis is another valuable tool in peptide analysis; its special usefulness in the comparison of mutant and normal proteins will be shown later.

Cleavage of Cross-linkages and Separation of Chains

Before analyzing the amino acid sequence of a protein, the investigator must first determine whether the protein contains more than one peptide chain and, if so, whether the chains are covalently cross-linked. The number of chains can usually be deduced from the number of NH_2-terminal residues per molecule of protein (see below; also Chapter 6). If there are no covalent cross-linkages between the chains, they may be dissociated by treating the protein with acid or base or with high concentrations of salt or urea (Chapter 6). The dissociated chains may then be separated and purified by electrophoresis or chromatography.

If the chains are covalently cross-linked by the —S—S— bridge of a cystine molecule or if a single chain has an intrachain —S—S— linkage, these linkages must first be cleaved. Insulin is a classic case in point (Figure 5-3). It contains two peptide chains cross-linked by two —S—S— bridges. In addition, the A chain has an intrachain —S—S— cross-linkage between positions 6 and 11. Such —S—S— cross-linkages may be cleaved by oxidation with performic acid, which converts the two cystine half-residues into cysteic acid residues (Figure 5-4). The chains may then be separated, and each hydrolyzed. The positions of the cysteic acid residues in the chains can ultimately be determined from the positions of the peptide fragments containing the cysteic acid residues.

Figure 5-3
The amino acid sequence of bovine insulin and the positions of the —S—S— cross-linkages.

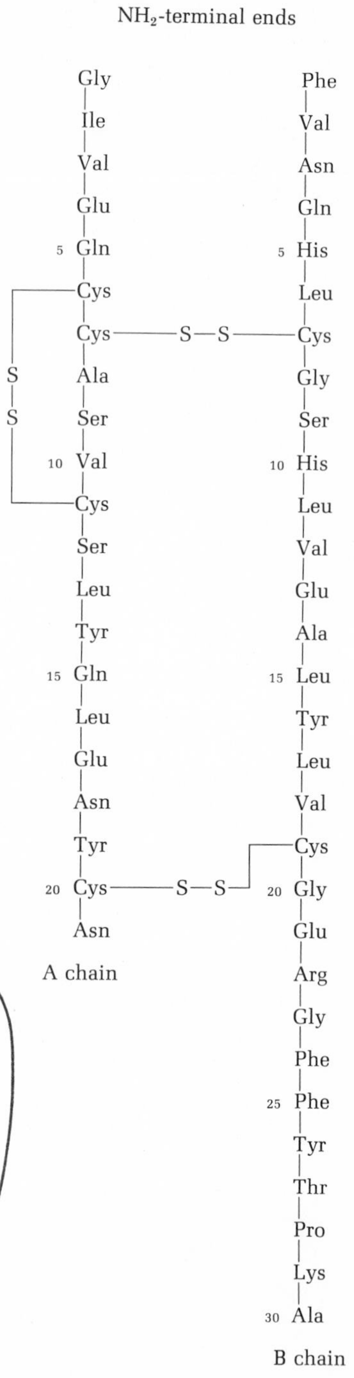

NH_2-terminal ends

A chain: Gly—Ile—Val—Glu—5 Gln—Cys—Cys—Ala—Ser—10 Val—Cys—Ser—Leu—Tyr—15 Gln—Leu—Glu—Asn—Tyr—20 Cys—Asn

B chain: Phe—Val—Asn—Gln—5 His—Leu—Cys—Gly—Ser—10 His—Leu—Val—Glu—Ala—15 Leu—Tyr—Leu—Val—Cys—20 Gly—Glu—Arg—Gly—Phe—25 Phe—Tyr—Thr—Pro—Lys—30 Ala

S—S (A6–A11); Cys—S—S—Cys (A7–B7); Cys—S—S—Cys (A20–B19)

Quantitative Analysis of the Amino Acid Composition of Proteins

An essential step in determining the amino acid sequence of a protein is complete hydrolysis and quantitative analysis of the types and numbers of amino acids in the hydrolyzate. The standard procedure for total hydrolysis of a peptide or protein is heating with excess 6 *N* HCl at 100 to 120°C for 10 to 24 hours in an evacuated sealed pyrex tube. Following complete hydrolysis, the excess HCl is removed under reduced pressure. The resulting hydrolyzate contains the amino acids as their hydrochlorides. Little or no racemization of the amino acids takes place during acid hydrolysis. Not all the amino acids of a given peptide or protein will be quantitatively recovered, however; usually tryptophan is destroyed by the strong acid treatment. Furthermore, the amide groups of glutamine and asparagine will cleave to yield glutamic acid and aspartic acid, plus ammonium ions. From the amount of ammonia in the hydrolyzate, the total amide content of the protein can be estimated.

Proteins may also be hydrolyzed by boiling with alkali. However, alkaline hydrolysis causes destruction of cysteine, cystine, serine, and threonine; furthermore, it causes racemization of all the amino acids. This method is therefore normally used only for the separate estimation of tryptophan, which is stable to heating with a base.

Figure 5-4
Cleavage of disulfide cross-linkages by oxidation with performic acid.

```
              H         O
Chain 1       |         ‖
         —C—N—CH—C—N—
          ‖      |       |
          O     CH₂      H
                 |
   Cystine       S
   cross-        |
   linkage       S
                 |
              H CH₂      H
Chain 2       |  |       |
         —C—N—CH—C—N—
          ‖          ‖
          O          O

   Performic  |  Oxidation
   acid       ↓

              H         O
Chain 1       |         ‖
         —C—N—CH—C—N—
          ‖      |       |
          O     CH₂      H
                 |
                SO₃H
                 +
                SO₃H
                 |
              H CH₂      H
Chain 2       |  |       |
         —C—N—CH—C—N—
          ‖          ‖
          O          O

         Cysteic acid
           residues
```

Table 5-2 Relative frequency of use of amino acids in *E. coli* proteins

	Relative frequency (Ala = 100)
Ala	100
Glx	83
Asx	76
Leu	60
Gly	60
Lys	54
Ser	46
Val	46
Arg	41
Thr	35
Pro	35
Ile	34
Met	29
Phe	25
Tyr	17
Cys	14
Trp	8
His	5

The first pure protein for which the complete amino acid composition was deduced was β-lactoglobulin, a milk protein. This analysis, which required some years of work, was completed in 1947. Within ten years, chromatographic methods became sufficiently refined so that the complete amino acid composition of proteins could be determined accurately and rapidly by ion-exchange chromatography. Table 5-2 shows the composition of the total proteins of *E. coli* cells, illustrating the widely varying frequency of occurrence of different amino acids. Table 5-3 shows the amino acid composition of some representative pure proteins. Some generalizations may be made from these and other available data:

1 Not all proteins contain all the 20 amino acids normally found in proteins. For example, ribonuclease lacks tryptophan. Fibrous proteins such as silk fibroin and collagen lack several amino acids.
2 Amino acids do not occur in equimolar frequency in any known protein. They do occur in fixed molar ratios to each other, but there are no simple numerical relationships among these ratios.
3 Some amino acids occur much less frequently than others. For example, most proteins have relatively few histidine and tryptophan residues, as is also evident in Table 5-2.
4 The fibrous proteins α-keratin, silk, collagen, and elastin, which are insoluble in water, contain a rather large percentage of nonpolar, or hydrophobic, amino acids (Ala, Val, Leu, Ile, Pro), up to 93 percent in the case of elastin. Even globular proteins that are freely soluble contain a surprisingly large number of hydrophobic amino acid residues, up to 50 percent. The significance of these data will be considered in Chapter 7.
5 In some proteins, such as the histones, salmine, and cytochrome *c*, the positively charged R groups predominate; such proteins are basic. In others, the negatively charged groups of glutamic or aspartic acid predominate, as in pepsin, which is highly acidic.

Identification of NH_2-Terminal Residues of Peptides

Two methods are available. One method uses the Sanger reaction (see Chapter 4). The free unprotonated α-amino group of amino acids and peptides reacts with 2,4-dinitrofluorobenzene to form yellow 2,4-dinitrophenyl (DNP) derivatives. When the DNP derivative of a peptide, regardless of its length, is subjected to hydrolysis with 6 N HCl, all the peptide bonds are hydrolyzed. However, the bond between the 2,4-dinitrophenyl group and the α-amino group of the NH_2-terminal amino acid is relatively stable to acid hydrolysis. Consequently, the hydrolyzate will contain all the residues of the peptide chain as free amino acids except the NH_2-terminal amino acid, which will be present as a 2,4-dinitrophenyl derivative (Figure 5-5). This can be easily separated from the unsubstituted amino acids and identified by chromatographic comparison with authentic DNP derivatives of the dif-

Table 5-3 Amino acid composition of some proteins (number of residues per molecule). The species of origin are as follows: lysozyme (chicken), serum albumin (human), cytochrome c (horse), myosin (rabbit), β-lactoglobulin, pepsin, chymotrypsinogen, collagen, and elastin (cow).

	Lysozyme	*β-Lactoglobulin*	*Serum albumin*	*Pepsin*	*Chymotrypsinogen*	*TMV protein*	*Cytochrome c*	*Myosin*	*Silk fibroin*	*Collagen*	*Elastin*	*Wool keratin*
Ala	12	30	3	18	22	14	6	78	334	107	58	46
Val	6	18	45	21	23	14	3	42	31	29	118	40
Leu	8	44	58	28	19	12	6	79	7	28	56	86
Ile	6	17	9	27	10	9	6	42	8	15	26	
Pro	2	17	31	15	9	8	4	22	6	131	136	83
Phe	3	9	33	14	6	8	4	27	20	15	29	22
Trp	6	3	1	6	8	3	1	4	0	0		9
Met	2	8	6	5	2	0	2	22		5	0	5
Gly	12	7	15	38	23	6	12	39	581	363	376	87
Asx	21	32	46	44	23	18	8	85	21	47	4	54
Glx	5	48	80	27	15	16	12	155	15	77	22	96
Lys	6	29	58	1	14	2	19	85	5	31	3	19
Arg	11	6	25	2	4	11	2	41	6	49	6	60
Ser	10	14	22	44	28	16	0	41	154	32	9	95
Thr	7	16	27	28	23	16	10	41	13	19	10	54
Cys	8	6	20	4	10	1	2	4		0		
Tyr	3	8	18	18	4	4	4	18	71	5	8	36
His	1	4	16	1	2	0	3	15	2	5	0	7
Percent nonpolar	46	50	55	50	49	46	44	29	78	72	93	48
No. positively charged	17	39	99	4	20	13	24	141	13	85	9	86
No. negatively charged	26	80	126	71	33	34	20	240	36	124	26	150

ferent amino acids. The NH_2-terminal residues may also be identified by the dansylation reaction (Chapter 4).

A second and more useful method for identifying the NH_2-terminal amino acid is by the Edman degradation (Figure 5-6). The peptide is allowed to react with phenylisothiocyanate to form a phenylthiocarbamyl derivative (Chapter 4). When this is treated with acid, usually in an organic solvent, cyclization to a phenylthiohydantoin derivative of the NH_2-terminal amino acid occurs. During this cyclization, the NH_2-terminal amino acid is cleaved from the next residue. The conditions of the cyclization

Figure 5-5
Identification of the NH_2-terminal amino acid residue by means of the Sanger reaction.

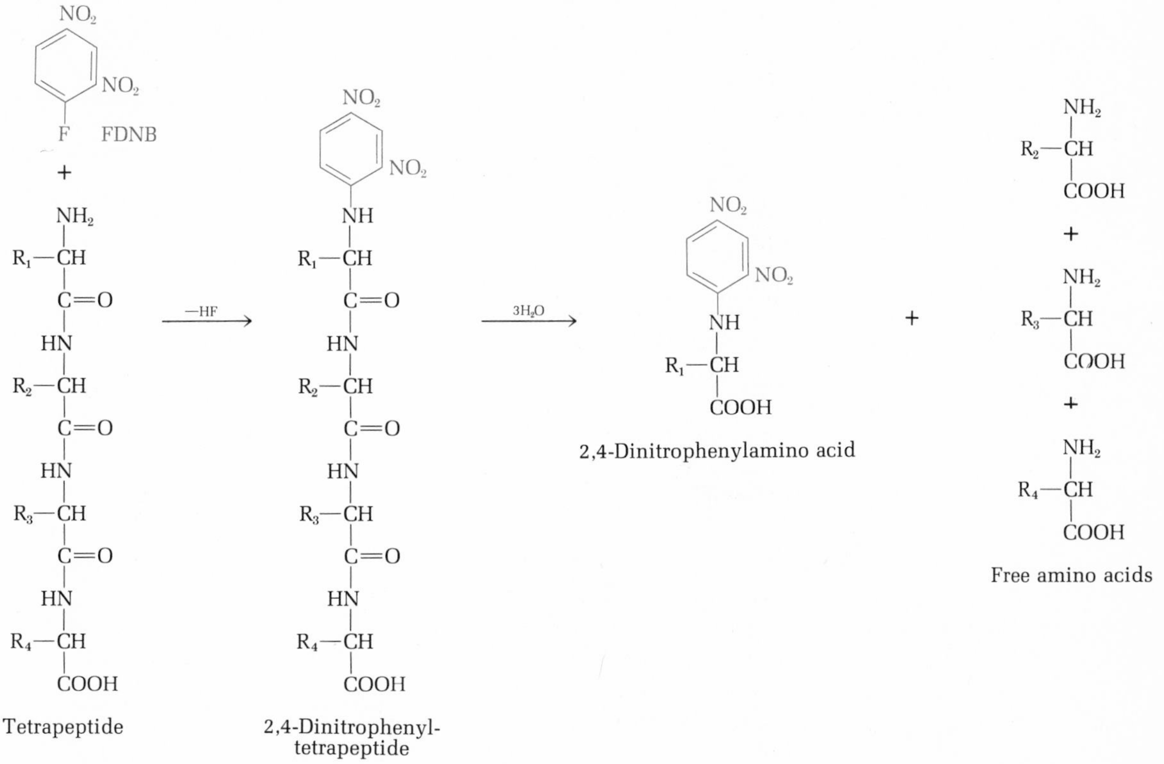

NO_2 NO_2 F FDNB

\+

NH_2—R_1—CH—C=O—HN—R_2—CH—C=O—HN—R_3—CH—C=O—HN—R_4—CH—COOH

Tetrapeptide

—HF →

NO_2 NO_2 NH—R_1—CH—C=O—HN—R_2—CH—C=O—HN—R_3—CH—C=O—HN—R_4—CH—COOH

2,4-Dinitrophenyl-tetrapeptide

$3H_2O$ →

NO_2 NO_2 NH—R_1—CH—COOH

2,4-Dinitrophenylamino acid

\+

NH_2—R_2—CH—COOH + NH_2—R_3—CH—COOH + NH_2—R_4—CH—COOH

Free amino acids

Figure 5-6
Identification of the NH_2-terminal residue by the Edman degradation. Note that the peptide chain remains intact after removal of the NH_2-terminal residue.

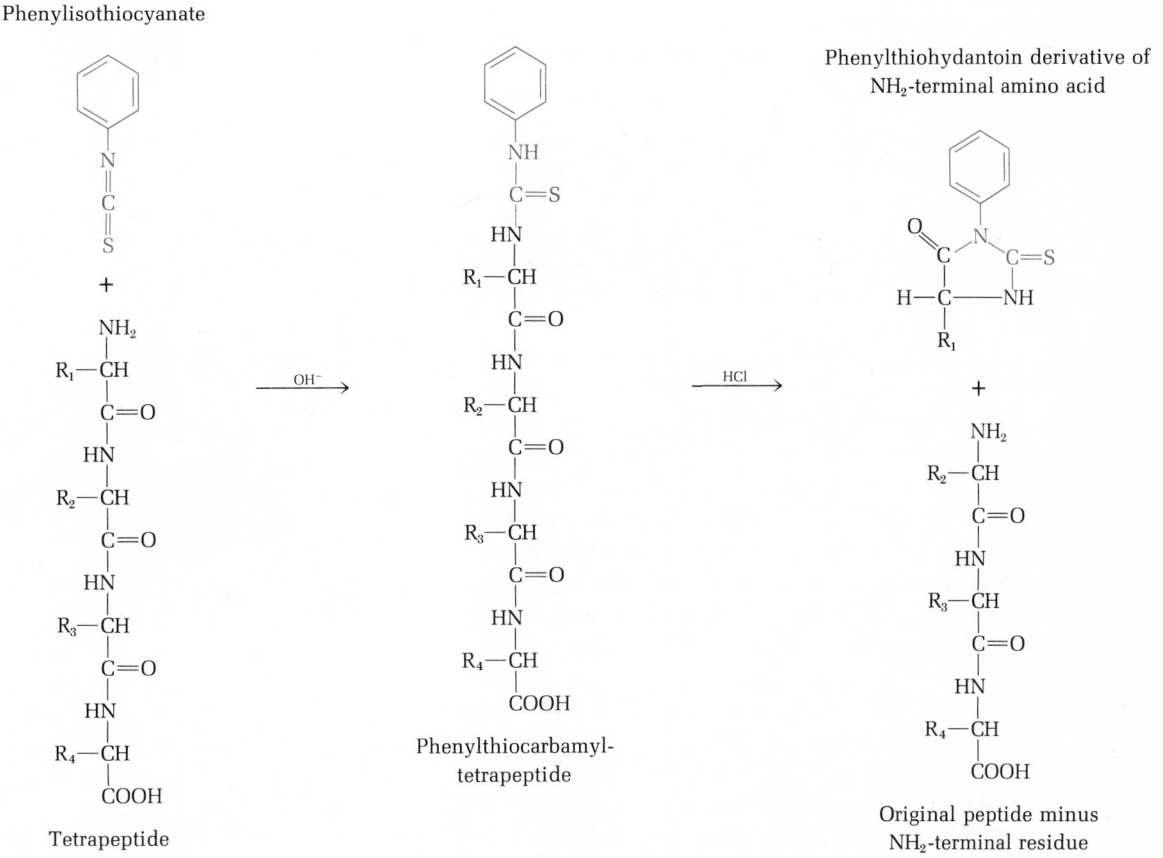

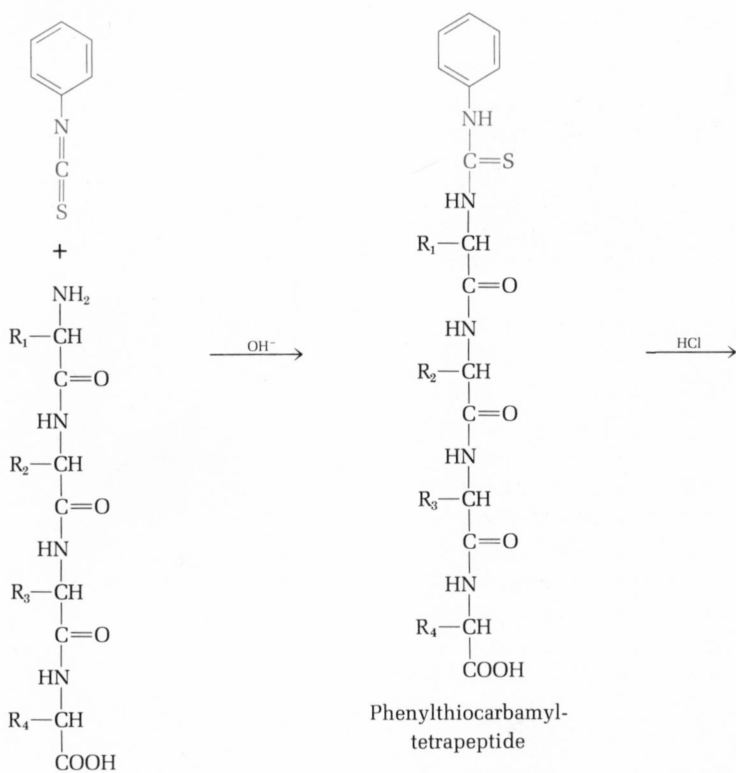

and cleavage are so mild that the other peptide bonds of the polypeptide are not attacked. As a result, the products of the cyclization are (1) a phenylthiohydantoin derivative, formed from the NH_2-terminal amino acid residue, and (2) the intact peptide chain minus its original NH_2-terminal residue. The derivative of the NH_2-terminal amino acid can be identified chromatographically. The great advantage of the Edman method is that the remaining peptide chain can be recovered intact and subjected to another cycle of treatment with phenylisothiocyanate to yield ultimately the phenylthiohydantoin corresponding to the second amino acid residue of the peptide (starting from the NH_2-terminal end). The Edman degradation is thus subtractive in nature and can be applied repetitively to determine the complete amino acid sequence of peptides. Edman has designed automatic equipment for analyzing the sequence of amino acids in long peptides by this method; with it he has identified the sequence of the first 60 residues of whale myoglobin, beginning with the NH_2-terminal end.

In some native proteins, the NH_2-terminal residue is buried deep within the tightly folded molecule and is not accessible to the labeling reagent; in such cases, denaturation of the protein can render the residue accessible. In other proteins (for example, the tobacco mosaic virus coat protein), the α-amino group of the NH_2-terminal amino acid is acetylated and hence not reactive with NH_2-terminal reagents. Some peptides show no NH_2-terminal amino acid because they are cyclic; an example is the antibiotic valinomycin, which has 12 residues in a circular arrangement. However, there is no evidence that circular peptide chains occur in proteins.

Identification of COOH-Terminal Residues of Peptides

The free carboxyl group of amino acids and peptides can be reduced to the corresponding α-amino alcohol (Chapter 4). If the peptide chain is then completely hydrolyzed, the hydrolyzate will contain one molecule of an α-amino alcohol corresponding to the original COOH-terminal amino acid. This can be easily identified by chromatographic methods; all the other residues will be found as free amino acids.

The COOH-terminal amino acid of a peptide can also be selectively removed by action of the enzyme carboxypeptidase, which specifically attacks the COOH-terminal peptide bond of peptides. A drawback is that the enzyme, after removal of the terminal residue, proceeds to attack the new COOH-terminal peptide bond. It is therefore necessary to measure the rate of liberation of the amino acids from the peptide in order to identify the COOH-terminal residue unequivocally. In some peptides and proteins, the COOH-terminal carboxyl group may occur as the amide.

Fragmentation of Peptide Chains by Partial Hydrolysis

The long polypeptide chain must be fragmented into smaller peptides in such a manner that the cleavage at

Cleavage of peptide bonds

```
H      H  R2
|      |  |
—C—C—┆—N—C—
 |  ‖      |
 R1 O      H
```

Trypsin	R_1 = Lys, Arg
Chymotrypsin	R_1 = Phe, Trp, Tyr
Pepsin	R_2 = Phe, Trp, Tyr, Leu, Asp, Glu.
Cyanogen bromide	R_1 = Met

The cyanogen bromide reaction

```
  |
  NH
  |
  HC—R1
  |
  C=O
  |
  NH
  |
  HC—CH2—CH2—S—CH3
  |
  C=O
  |
  NH
  |
  HC—R3
  |
  C=O
  |
  ↓ BrCN
  |
  NH
  |
  HC—R1
  |
  C=O
  |
  NH
  |   H2
  HC—C
  |     \CH2
O=C—O/
  +
  NH2
  |
  HC—R3
  |
  C=O
  |
  +
  CH3SCN
```

The COOH-terminal homoserinelactone residue is in color.

each point is essentially quantitative. Partial hydrolysis of polypeptides by acid or base is inadequate since the peptide bonds between various pairs of amino acids do not differ sufficiently in their susceptibility to acid or base hydrolysis. The method of choice is enzymatic hydrolysis using the proteolytic enzyme trypsin, which is secreted into the small intestine from the pancreas in the form of its precursor trypsinogen. This enzyme, which is readily isolated and crystallized, catalyzes the hydrolysis of only those peptide bonds in which the carbonyl function is donated by either a lysine or an arginine residue, regardless of the length or amino acid sequence of the chain. The number of peptide fragments (and free amino acids) can thus be predicted from the total number of lysine or arginine residues in the chain.

In amino acid sequence analysis, the original peptide chain must be fragmented in at least two different ways, so that the small peptide fragments resulting from one procedure "overlap" those resulting from the other (see below). If trypsin is used for the first cleavage, the second cleavage must be carried out with some other proteolytic enzyme, such as chymotrypsin (secreted by the pancreas as its precursor chymotrypsinogen) or pepsin (found in gastric juice). The former hydrolyzes peptide bonds in which the carbonyl function is contributed by phenylalanine, tyrosine, or tryptophan, and the latter hydrolyzes peptide bonds in which the amino function is contributed by these amino acids, as well as leucine and the acidic amino acids. Neither enzyme is as specific as trypsin; they often attack other types of peptide bonds (margin).

New chemical methods are being developed for cleaving peptide chains at specific amino acid residues. The most successful to date involves reaction with cyanogen bromide, which cleaves those peptide bonds whose carbonyl function is contributed by methionine residues. The methionine residue is converted into a COOH-terminal homoserine lactone residue. This method is often used for the second fragmentation step (margin).

Steps in the Determination of Amino Acid Sequence

The general approach used today is in principle that devised by Sanger in his pioneering work on the amino acid sequence of insulin, which he completed in 1953 and for which he was awarded the Nobel Prize. However, many refinements have since been added. Each protein offers special problems, but the following steps are generally used. It is axiomatic, of course, that each peptide to be analyzed must be free of contaminating peptides or amino acids.

1 The NH_2-terminal and COOH-terminal residues of the polypeptide chain are first identified.
2 The intact chain is then cleaved into a series of smaller peptides by the action of trypsin.
3 The peptide fragments resulting from step 2 are separated by electrophoresis or chromatography. Samples of each fragment are completely hydrolyzed, and their amino acid content is determined.

4 The NH_2-terminal and COOH-terminal residues of each fragment obtained in step 2 are determined. From the data to this point, the amino acid sequence in the dipeptide and tripeptide fragments will be known. For the rest of the peptides, the NH_2- and COOH-terminals will be known but the sequence of the amino acids between them will not be known.
5 The longer peptide fragments from step 2 are then subjected to sequential Edman degradation, which can yield their complete sequence.
6 Another intact sample of the original polypeptide chain is partially hydrolyzed by a second method, one that fragments the chain at points other than those cleaved by the first partial hydrolysis. Generally, chymotrypsin, pepsin, or cyanogen bromide is used for this second partial hydrolysis. The peptide fragments are then separated and analyzed as in steps 3 and 4.
7 By comparing the amino acid compositions and the identities of the NH_2-terminal and COOH-terminal residues of the two sets of peptide fragments, particularly where the second set of fragments overlaps the cleavage points in the first fragmentation, the peptide fragments can be ordered into the correct sequence.

Although this approach is simple in principle, the frustrating situation often arises in which much of the amino acid sequence of a given protein is determined fairly easily but, because of analytical problems or the failure to find a means of fragmentation to provide the appropriate overlaps, the sequence of a few remaining amino acid residues presents considerable experimental difficulties.

With the newly developed automated equipment for carrying out subtractive Edman degradation, the amino acid sequence of many polypeptide chains may be determined directly without the necessity of cleaving the chain.

The Amino Acid Sequence of Some Peptides and Proteins

Figure 5-3 shows the complete amino acid sequence of bovine insulin, which consists of two peptide chains: the A chain, which has 21 amino acid residues, and the B chain, which has 30. The two chains are cross-linked by two —S—S— bridges; in addition, there is one intrachain —S—S— bridge in the A chain. For analysis, the two chains were separated by oxidative cleavage using performic acid, and the sequence of each was determined.

Recently it has been discovered that insulin is first synthesized in the pancreas as a single-chain precursor (proinsulin) having from 81 to 84 residues. Proinsulin is then converted by the enzymatic cleavage of two peptide bonds into the A and B chains of insulin and an inactive connecting chain of 30 to 33 residues, depending on the species.

Following the successful determination of insulin structure in 1953, two separate research groups soon reported the sequence of amino acids in adrenocorticotrophin, the hormone of the anterior pituitary gland that stimulates the adrenal cortex. This hormone consists of a single chain of 39 residues with a molecular weight of about

The activation of bovine proinsulin. Proinsulins in some other species differ in the length of the connecting chain.

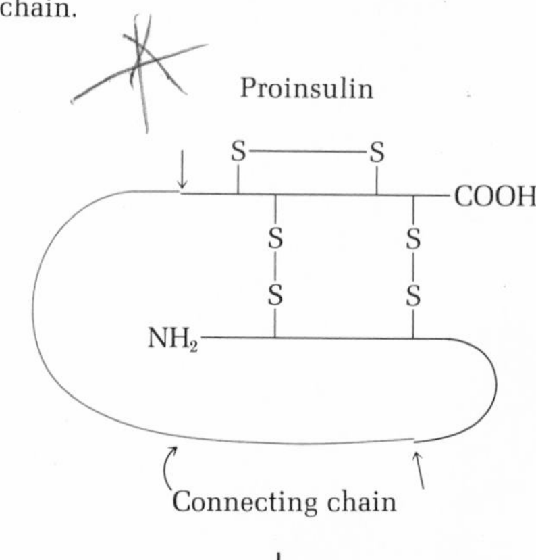

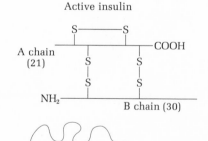

Figure 5-7
Amino acid sequences of human adrenocorticotrophin and bovine ribonuclease (below). The position of S—S cross linkages in bovine ribonuclease is also shown.

Human adrenocorticotrophin. The residues from 24 to 39 are not required for hormonal activity

Ser-Tyr-Ser-Met-Glu-His-Phe-Arg-Trp-Gly-$_{10}$
Lys-Pro-Val-Gly-Lys-Lys-Arg-Arg-Pro-Val-$_{20}$
Lys-Val-Tyr-Pro-Asp-Ala-Gly-Glu-Asp-Gln-$_{30}$
Ser-Ala-Glu-Ala-Phe-Pro-Leu-Glu-Phe$_{39}$

Bovine ribonuclease

Lys·Glu·Thr·Ala·Ala·Ala·Lys·Phe·Glu·Arg·$_{10}$
Gln·His·Met·Asp·Ser·Ser·Thr·Ser·Ala·Ala·$_{20}$
Ser·Ser·Ser·Asn·Tyr·Cys·Asn·Gln·Met·Met·$_{30}$
Lys·Ser·Arg·Asn·Leu·Thr·Lys·Asp·Arg·Cys·$_{40}$
Lys·Pro·Val·Asn·Thr·Phe·Val·His·Glu·Ser·$_{50}$
Leu·Ala·Asp·Val·Gln·Ala·Val·Cys·Ser·Gln·$_{60}$
Lys·Asn·Val·Ala·Cys·Lys·Asn·Gly·Gln·Thr·$_{70}$
Asn·Cys·Tyr·Gln·Ser·Tyr·Ser·Thr·Met·Ser·$_{80}$
Ile·Thr·Asp·Cys·Arg·Glu·Thr·Gly·Ser·Ser·$_{90}$
Lys·Tyr·Pro·Asn·Cys·Ala·Tyr·Lys·Thr·Thr·$_{100}$
Gln·Ala·Asn·Lys·His·Ile·Ile·Val·Ala·Cys·$_{110}$
Glu·Gly·Asn·Pro·Tyr·Val·Pro·Val·His·Phe·$_{120}$
Asp·Ala·Ser·Val$_{124}$

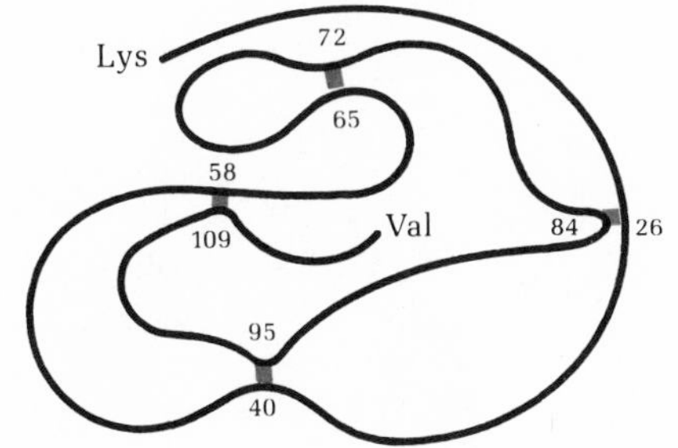

4,600. Somewhat later, the first successful sequence analysis of an enzyme protein was achieved, namely, that of ribonuclease, which has 124 amino acid residues in a single chain (Figure 5-7). Ribonuclease contains four intrachain —S—S— cross-linkages.

The next important landmark was the identification of the amino acid sequences of the two types of peptide chains in hemoglobin (Figure 5-8). This was the first sequence analysis of an oligomeric, or multichain, protein. Hemoglobin contains four peptide chains, two identical α-chains (141 residues) and two identical β-chains (146 residues). This feat was carried out by two groups in the United States and another in Germany. As you can see in Figure 5-8, the α- and β-chains have identical amino acid residues in many positions. This indicates that the two chains possess some *sequence homology*. The single polypeptide chain of myoglobin, which resembles hemoglobin in its ability to bind oxygen, also possesses some sequence homology with the hemoglobin chains. The significance of sequence homologies in functionally similar proteins or in homologous proteins of different species will be discussed further in Chapter 6.

The longest polypeptide chains for which complete amino acid sequences have been deduced to date are those of bovine trypsinogen (229 residues), bovine chymotrypsinogen (245 residues), and most recently, the polypeptide chains of glyceraldehyde 3-phosphate dehydrogenase of lobster muscle (333 residues).

From analysis of the amino acid sequences of many globular proteins, a few cautious generalizations can be made. To date, no periodic, frequently recurring sequences such as ABABABABAB · · · or ABCDABCDABCD · · · have been found in globular proteins. Only rarely does a single amino acid occur more than three times in succession. There is, therefore, little obvious regularity in the amino acid sequence. Statistical analysis of the known sequences of globular proteins shows that all or nearly all the possible short sequences of two and three amino acids do occur but with no apparent periodic pattern. Nor is there any apparent regularity in the presence or the position of intrachain —S—S— cross-linkages; some proteins have none, others may have several.

On the other hand, some fibrous proteins show evidence of periodicity of occurrence of certain amino acids, although their complete sequences are not yet known. Collagen has a preponderance of alanine, glycine, proline, and hydroxyproline residues, which appear to occur in periodic sequences. Nearly 80 percent of the amino acid residues of silk fibroin are contributed by alanine, glycine, and serine, and there is a definite periodicity in the spacing of the alanine and glycine residues (Chapter 6).

Species and Mutational Variations in Amino Acid Sequence

Species Differences

Important information is now available on the amino acid sequences of homologous proteins from different species.

Figure 5-8
Amino acid sequence of α- and β-chains of human hemoglobin. Residues identical in both chains are in color. Residues identical in both chains and in myoglobin are in boxes.

NH_2-terminal ends

	α	β
	Val	Val
		His
	Leu	Leu
	Ser	Thr
	Pro	Pro
	Ala	Glu
	Asp	Glu
	Lys	Lys
	Thr	Ser
	Asn	Ala
10	Val	Val
	Lys	Thr
	Ala	Ala
	Ala	Leu
	Trp	Trp
	Gly	Gly
	Lys	Lys
	Val	Val
	Gly	Asn
	Ala	
20	His	
	Ala	Val
	Gly	Asp
	Glu	Glu
	Tyr	Val
	Gly	Gly
	Ala	Gly
	Glu	Glu
	Ala	Ala
	Leu	Leu
30	Glu	Gly
	Arg	Arg
	Met	Leu
	Phe	Leu
	Leu	Val
	Ser	Val
	Phe	Tyr
	Pro	Pro
	Thr	Trp
	Thr	Thr
40	Lys	Gln

	α	β
	Thr	Arg
	Tyr	Phe
	Phe	Phe
	Pro	Glu
	His	Ser
	Phe	Phe
		Gly
	Asp	Asp
	Leu	Leu
	Ser	Ser
50	His	Thr
	Gly	Pro
	Ser	Asp
	Ala	Ala
		Val
		Met
		Gly
		Asn
		Pro
	Gln	Lys
	Val	Val
	Lys	Lys
	Gly	Ala
	His	His
	Gly	Gly
60	Lys	Lys
	Lys	Lys
	Val	Val
	Ala	Leu
	Asp	Gly
	Ala	Ala
	Leu	Phe
	Thr	Ser
	Asn	Asp
	Ala	Gly
70	Val	Leu
	Ala	Ala
	His	His
	Val	Leu
	Asp	Asp
75	Asp	Asn

	α	β
	Met	Leu
	Pro	Lys
	Asn	Gly
	Ala	Thr
80	Leu	Phe
	Ser	Ala
	Ala	Thr
	Leu	Leu
	Ser	Ser
	Asp	Glu
	Leu	Leu
	His	His
	Ala	Cys
	His	Asp
90	Lys	Lys
	Leu	Leu
	Arg	His
	Val	Val
	Asp	Asp
	Pro	Pro
	Val	Glu
	Asn	Asn
	Phe	Phe
	Lys	Arg
100	Leu	Leu
	Leu	Leu
	Ser	Gly
	His	Asn
	Cys	Val
	Leu	Leu
	Leu	Val
	Val	Cys
	Thr	Val
	Leu	Leu
110	Ala	Ala
	Ala	His
	His	His
	Leu	Phe
	Pro	Gly
	Ala	Lys
116	Glu	Glu

	α	β
	Phe	Phe
	Thr	Thr
	Pro	Pro
120	Ala	Pro
	Val	Val
	His	Gln
	Ala	Ala
	Ser	Ala
	Leu	Tyr
	Asp	Gln
	Lys	Lys
	Phe	Val
	Leu	Val
130	Ala	Ala
	Ser	Gly
	Val	Val
	Ser	Ala
	Thr	Asp
	Val	Ala
	Leu	Leu
	Thr	Ala
	Ser	His
	Lys	Lys
140	Tyr	Tyr
	Arg	His

COOH-terminal ends

The complete amino acid sequences of insulins isolated from many different vertebrate species are now known. These insulins have virtually the same specific hormonal activity and molecular weight. All possess an A chain of 21 residues and a B chain of 30. The A chains of the insulins of man, pig, dog, rabbit, and sperm whale are identical. The B chains of cow, pig, dog, sei, sperm whale, sheep, goat, and horse insulins are identical. The B chains

Figure 5-9
The 35 invariant amino acid residues in cytochrome c. The following species were used to compile these data: horse, man, hog, chicken, yeast, cow, sheep, tuna, Macacus mulatta monkey, Samia cynthia moth, dog, kangaroo, rattlesnake, snapping turtle, turkey, duck, pigeon, king penguin, screw-worm fly, Neurospora crassa mold, Candida krusei yeast, donkey, and chimpanzee. The cytochrome c's of invertebrates, plants and fungi have four to eight additional amino acids at the NH_2-terminal end.

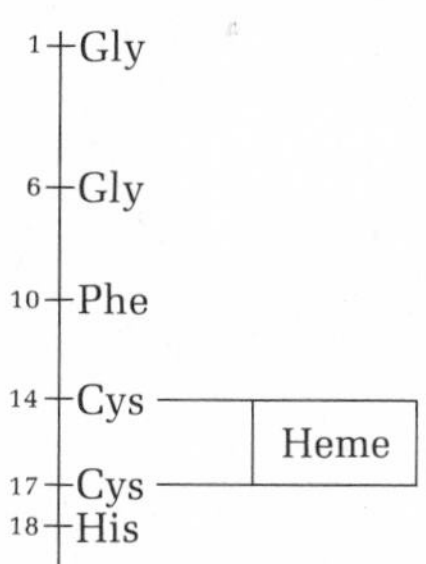

of human and elephant insulins are also identical. In the A chain, the amino acid replacements from one species to another usually occur at positions 8, 9, and 10, i.e., the positions between the two half-cystine residues that form the intrachain cross-link (Table 5-4). However, replacements have also been observed at positions 4, 13, 14, 15, and 18, especially in fish insulins. The B chain was for some time thought to vary only in the COOH-terminal residue; however, more recent work shows that the only invariant residue is phenylalanine at position 26. Further study of insulin sequences shows that replacements from one species to another involve only certain types of amino acids (Table 5-4). At position A8, alanine and threonine replace each other; at A9, serine and glycine; and at A10, valine, isoleucine, and threonine. Specific genetic relationships are implicit in the types of amino acid replacements that occur from one species to another among the variable amino acids (Chapter 31).

Table 5-4 Amino acid replacements in A chains of insulins from different species

	Position		
	8	*9*	*10*
Beef	Ala	Ser	Val
Pig	Thr	Ser	Ile
Sheep	Ala	Gly	Val
Horse	Thr	Gly	Ile
Sperm whale	Thr	Ser	Ile
Sei whale	Ala	Ser	Thr
Man	Thr	Ser	Ile
Dog	Thr	Ser	Ile
Rabbit	Thr	Ser	Ile

Table 5-5 Amino acid differences and times of divergence of species (cytochrome c)

	Number of amino acid differences	*Time of divergence (millions of years ago)*
Man–monkey	1	50–60
Man–horse	12	70–75
Man–dog	10	70–75
Pig–cow–sheep	0	
Horse–cow	3	60–65
Mammals–chick	10–15	280
Mammals–tuna	17–21	400
Vertebrates–yeast	43–48	1,100

Sequence data have also been compiled on the electron-carrying protein cytochrome *c*, which occurs in all animals, plants, and aerobic microorganisms. Cytochrome *c* has a single chain of 104 residues in most of the 25 or more species that have been studied to date. In these species, 35 amino acid residues are absolutely invariant (Figure 5-9). The invariant residues are irregularly spaced along the entire chain, although there is a solid block of 11 invariant residues at positions 70 to 80. The number of residue differences between species is in proportion to their phylogenetic differences (Table 5-5). Forty-eight residues differ in the cytochrome *c* molecules from the horse and from yeast, whereas only two residues differ in the cytochrome *c*'s of the duck and the chicken. The cytochrome *c* molecule is identical in the chicken and the turkey; it is also identical in the pig, cow, and sheep.

The information available on the amino acid sequences of cytochrome *c* from many species has been used to verify taxonomic relationships between different species and to construct a phylogenetic tree that not only shows the course of biological evolution from unicellular organisms but also allows estimates of the probable times of divergence of the major genera and species of living organisms. However, the number of amino acid differences in homologous proteins of two species varies considerably depending on the protein. In general, if a given protein plays a central role in nearly all forms of life, as is true of enzymes catalyzing glycolysis and respiration, it tends to show considerable sequence homology in widely different species.

Photomicrograph of normal (disk-like) and sickle (crescent-shaped) red blood cells.

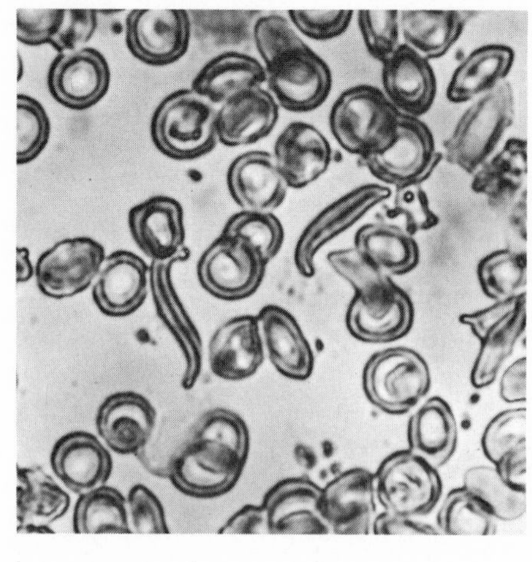

20.0 μ

Mutational Changes in Amino Acid Sequence within a Species

Linus Pauling and H. Itano have shown that the hemoglobin isolated from erythrocytes of patients suffering from sickle-cell anemia is different from normal, or A (for adult), hemoglobin. In sickle-cell anemia, the erythrocytes tend to "sickle" at low oxygen tensions, i.e., assume a crescentlike shape instead of the flat, disklike conformation of normal erythrocytes. The electrophoretic mobility of the sickle-cell hemoglobin was found to be slightly different from that of hemoglobin A.

Later, Ingram discovered that sickle-cell hemoglobin differs from normal hemoglobin in only a single amino acid residue. He found that the α-chains of the two forms are identical but that the glutamic acid residue at position 6 in the β-chain of normal hemoglobin is replaced by a valine residue in sickle-cell hemoglobin. Since glutamic acid has an acidic R group and valine an uncharged R group, sickle-cell hemoglobin has a slightly different electrical charge at neutral pH. Sickle-cell anemia is thus a "molecular disease" of genetic origin; the amino acid replacement is the result of a mutation in the DNA molecule that codes the synthesis of the hemoglobin β-chain.

Altogether, about 150 different kinds of mutant hemoglobins have been found in humans. An abnormal hemoglobin is found in 1 out of every 10,000 individuals and is usually detected by electrophoretic methods. The specific amino acid replaced in a mutant protein can be determined very simply by application of the "fingerprint," or peptide-map, technique (Figure 5-10). Nearly all the genetic changes observed in mutant hemoglobins are due to only a single amino acid replacement, which may be in either the α-chain or the β-chain. Table 5-6 lists some of the many mutations that have been detected; the names of these abnormal forms are derived from the location of their discovery.

Some hemoglobin mutations are lethal; i.e., the patient may never live to maturity because the amino acid replacement results in a functionally defective molecule. On the other hand, some limit the physiological function of the hemoglobin less seriously, and some are apparently harmless. Such mutations are not limited to hemoglobin; it is very likely that all types of proteins in a given species are susceptible to mutation.

Figure 5-10
Peptide maps of trypsin peptides of hemoglobin A and sickle-cell hemoglobin. Only a single peptide (color) is displaced; it contains the genetically replaced amino acid.

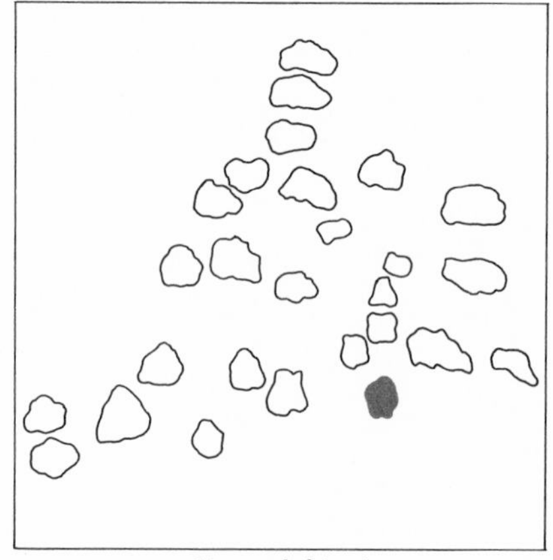

Hemoglobin A

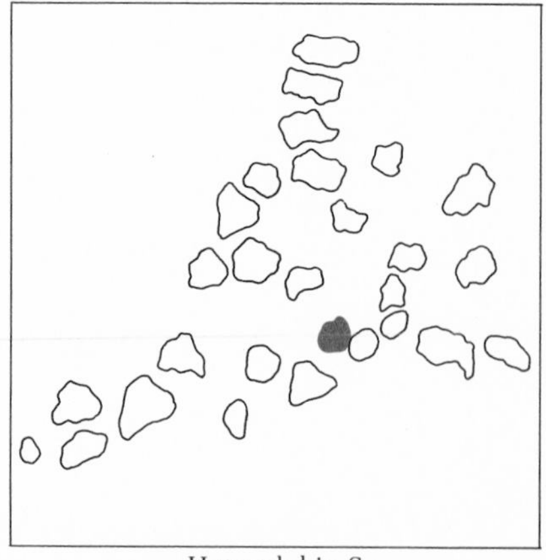

Hemoglobin S

Table 5-6 Amino acid replacements in human hemoglobins

Abnormal Hb	*Normal residue and position*	*Replacement*
	α-chain	
I	16 Lys	→ Glu
$G_{Honolulu}$	30 Glu	→ Gln
Norfolk	57 Gly	→ Asp
M_{Boston}	58 His	→ Tyr
$G_{Philadelphia}$	68 Asn	→ Lys
$O_{Indonesia}$	116 Glu	→ Lys
	β-chain	
C	6 Glu	→ Lys
S	6 Glu	→ Val
$G_{San\ Jose}$	7 Glu	→ Gly
E	26 Glu	→ Lys
$M_{Saskatoon}$	63 His	→ Tyr
Zürich	63 His	→ Arg
$M_{Milwaukee}$	67 Val	→ Glu
D_{Punjab}	121 Glu	→ Gln

Laboratory Synthesis of Polypeptide Chains

A detailed discussion of the laboratory synthesis of biologically occurring molecules is beyond the scope of this book, but we shall look briefly at the synthesis of long polypeptide chains, which is of special interest not only because of the formidable technical difficulties involved but also because of the ingenious methods that are being applied to the problem. The synthesis of the peptide bond between two amino acids poses no special problems by itself. The difficulty lies in the fact that the reagents required to form peptide bonds can also react with other functional groups not involved in the peptide linkage, such as the free amino group of the NH_2-terminal residue, the free carboxyl group of the COOH-terminal residue, or certain R groups, e.g., the thiol group of cysteine. These sensitive groups must therefore first be "blocked," or covered by appropriate reactions, to protect them from the reagent. After the peptide bond has been formed, the protective blocking groups must be removed. For this reason, the addition of each amino acid residue during the synthesis of a polypeptide chain requires several individual reaction steps. Obviously, the yield of each step must be rather high if a peptide chain of any length is to be prepared (see bottom of page).

Despite the practical difficulties involved, a number of successes have been achieved, particularly in the synthesis of the peptide hormones, whose readily measured biological activity serves as a criterion for successful synthesis. The first breakthrough came in 1953 with the work of DuVigneaud and his colleagues, who succeeded in the synthesis of oxytocin and vasopressin, which contain nine amino acid residues (Figure 5-11). Since then, a number of active peptides such as bradykinin (9 residues), α-melanocyte stimulating hormone (24 residues), and adrenocorticotrophin (39 residues) (Figure 5-7) have been synthesized by standard laboratory procedures. Moreover, the two chains of insulin were synthesized, by groups in Germany, the United States, and China.

The most significant recent advance in the laboratory synthesis of polypeptides is the development by R. B. Merrifield and his colleagues of an automatically programmed machine that performs, with high yields, the

Condensation of an amino-protected and a carboxyl-protected amino acid to yield a protected dipeptide. The protecting groups are then removed to yield the free dipeptide.

Protecting group
NH
R—CH
COOH
+
NH_2
R′—CH
C=O
Protecting group

Condensing agent →

Protecting group
NH
R—CH
C=O
HN
R′—CH
C=O
Protecting group

Removal of protecting groups →

Dipeptide
NH_2
R—CH
C=O
HN
R′—CH
C=O
OH

many repetitive chemical steps for adding each amino acid to the growing polypeptide chain. A programmed sequence of reactions takes place in a single reaction chamber, with reagents from reservoirs automatically added by means of measuring pumps. The apparatus employs exactly timed reaction periods at each step and uses an ingenious method, called the solid-phase technique, for separating the desired reaction product from by-products in high yield. The synthesis of a peptide chain (Figure 5-12) is begun by attaching the carboxyl group of the COOH-terminal amino acid residue of the chain to be built to an insoluble resin particle large enough to be easily separated from a liquid phase by filtration. The next amino acid to be introduced, following the blocking of its amino group, is allowed to react with the free amino group of the COOH-terminal residue in the presence of the condensing agent dicyclohexylcarbodiimide. This forms an amino-blocked dipeptide that is covalently attached to the insoluble resin particle via the COOH-terminal carboxyl group. The amino-blocking group is then removed by acidification; it decomposes into the gaseous products carbon dioxide and isobutylene. These steps are repeated many times. The entire polypeptide chain is built with the COOH-terminal residue anchored to the solid resin particle. Excess reagents and by-products at each step are removed by filtration of the particles and thorough washing with appropriate solvents—simple operations that can be carried out by means of a programmed machine. When the chain is complete, it is cleaved from its "anchor" by a reaction that does not attack the newly formed peptide linkages.

Because of the simple filtration and washing operations between reaction steps and the elimination of the necessity to obtain each intermediate product in pure crystalline form, this procedure has very high yields at each step and requires relatively little time. Merrifield and his colleagues reported the complete synthesis of the nonapeptide bradykinin by this automated procedure, in an overall yield of 85 percent. The entire chain was synthesized in 27 hours; the average rate of synthesis was thus about 3 hours per peptide bond. More recently, they also synthesized the two chains of insulin by the same procedure; the A chain (21 residues) required only 8 days, and the B chain (30 residues) only 11 days. As this book went to press, they reported a most spectacular achievement, the complete automated synthesis of the polypeptide chain of bovine pancreatic ribonuclease (124 residues), the first protein to be synthesized in the laboratory from its amino acid components. The overall yield was 18 percent. A second group of investigators simultaneously succeeded in synthesizing ribonuclease using a somewhat different approach. They synthesized several segments of the ribonuclease chain and then spliced them together.

Amino Acid Homopolymers

Extremely long peptide chains may be quite easily synthesized if they contain only one type of amino acid residue. Such chains are called homopolypeptides, and examples are polyglycine, polyalanine, and polyglutamic

Figure 5-11
Three peptide hormones.

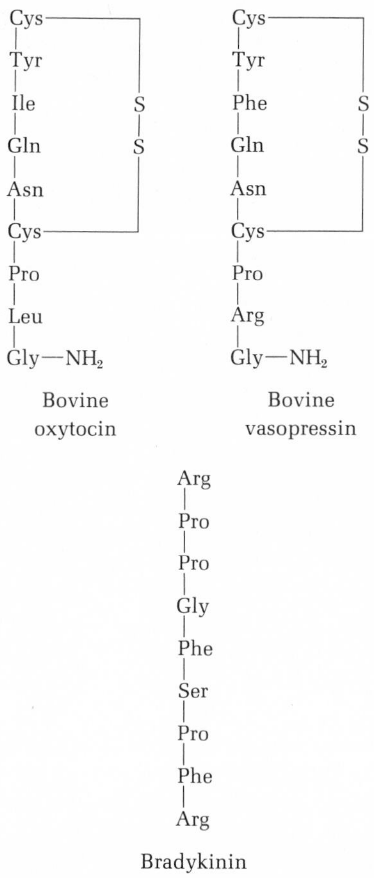

Cys—Tyr—Ile—Gln—Asn—Cys—Pro—Leu—Gly—NH_2 (S—S bridge between the two Cys)
Bovine oxytocin

Cys—Tyr—Phe—Gln—Asn—Cys—Pro—Arg—Gly—NH_2 (S—S bridge between the two Cys)
Bovine vasopressin

Arg—Pro—Pro—Gly—Phe—Ser—Pro—Phe—Arg
Bradykinin

Dicyclohexylcarbodiimide is a powerful condensing agent. It becomes hydrated to dicyclohexylurea when it removes the elements of water from two amino acid residues.

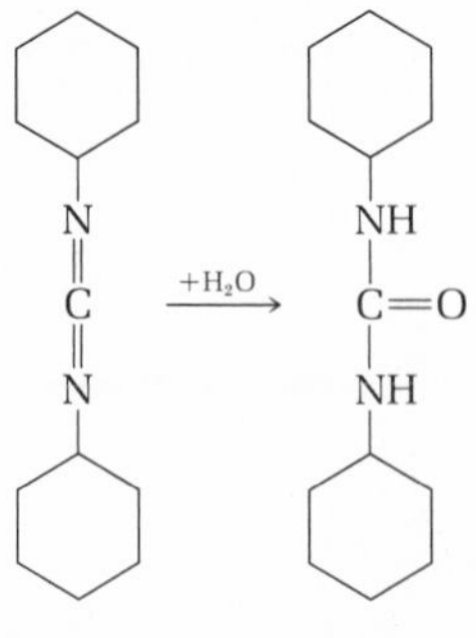

$$C_6H_{11}—N{=}C{=}N—C_6H_{11} \xrightarrow{+H_2O} C_6H_{11}—NH—C({=}O)—NH—C_6H_{11}$$

Dicyclohexylcarbodiimide   Dicyclohexylurea

Figure 5-12
Essential steps in the solid-phase synthesis of a tripeptide. By repetition of these steps, very long polypeptides can be prepared. The finished chain can then be cleaved from the resin particle.

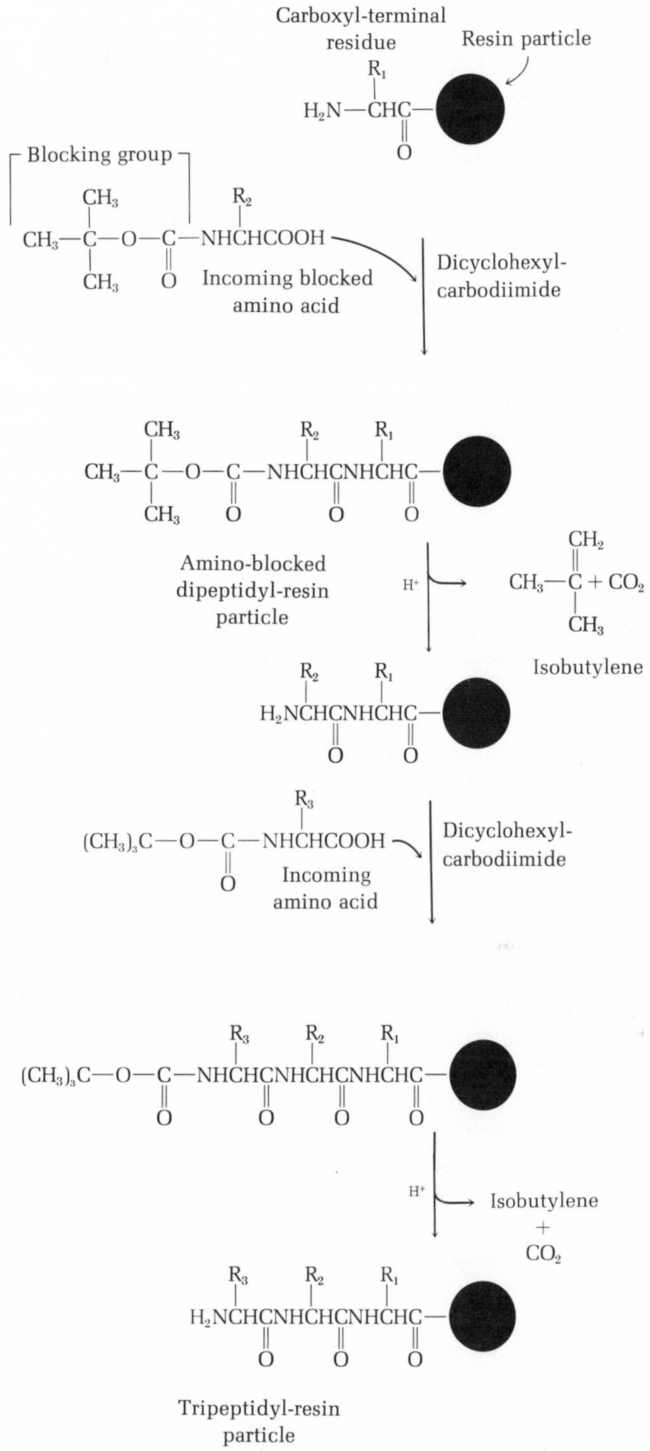

Carboxyl-terminal residue
Resin particle
Blocking group
Incoming blocked amino acid
Dicyclohexyl-carbodiimide
Amino-blocked dipeptidyl-resin particle
H^+
Isobutylene
Dicyclohexyl-carbodiimide
Incoming amino acid
H^+
Isobutylene + CO_2
Tripeptidyl-resin particle

acid. The procedure involves the use of relatively simple polymerization reactions. Once started, the polymerization reactions become self-sustaining. The length of the homopolymer can be controlled by the nature of the reaction initiator, the temperature, and the solvent. Although homopolymers of amino acids are not found in nature, they have proved to be exceedingly valuable model compounds for the study of the various parameters influencing the structure and behavior of peptide chains. They have, for example, led to important insights into the relationship between the optical rotation of peptides and their secondary structure (Chapter 6).

Summary

The peptide bond is the only covalent linkage between successive amino acids in the backbone of polypeptide chains. The acid-base behavior of a polypeptide is a function of its NH_2-terminal amino group, its COOH-terminal carboxyl group, and those R groups that ionize. Partial hydrolysis of polypeptide chains by boiling with acid or by the action of enzymes yields mixtures of smaller peptides, which can be separated by chromatography or electrophoresis. Complete hydrolysis of a protein yields all its amino acids in free form. Not all proteins contain all the amino acids, nor do the amino acids occur in equal frequency.

To determine the sequence of amino acids in a protein, its peptide chains are first separated. Their NH_2-terminal and COOH-terminal residues and their amino acid content are then determined. One sample of the chain is partially cleaved by using trypsin, which hydrolyzes those peptide bonds in which lysine or arginine contributes the carbonyl carbon. The tryptic peptides are separated, their amino acid content determined, and their sequence established by the Edman degradation. Another, intact sample of the polypeptide chain is then cleaved by a second method, using chymotrypsin, pepsin, or cyanogen bromide, to yield a different set of fragments, which are separated and analyzed as in the first cleavage. From the "overlaps" between the two sets of fragments, the sequence of the fragments can be deduced.

Each protein has a characteristic amino acid sequence, and all molecules of a given type are identical in sequence. Functionally homologous proteins of different species, such as hemoglobins and cytochromes, possess the same amino acid residues at certain invariant positions in the chain; the other residues may vary from one species to another. The more distant are two species, the greater the number of amino acid differences in the variant positions, a fact which permits construction of phylogenetic "trees." A given type of protein, such as hemoglobin, may show replacement of a single amino acid residue as a result of mutation of the gene coding that protein. Long polypeptide chains of specific amino acid sequence may be synthesized by automated laboratory processes.

References

Books

BAILEY, J. L.: *Techniques of Protein Chemistry*, 2d ed., American Elsevier Publishing Company, New York, 1967. Valuable compendium of laboratory methods.

DAYHOFF, M. O., and R. V. ECK: *Atlas of Protein Sequence and Structure*, National Biomedical Research Foundation, Silver Spring, Md., 1968. Annual compilation of amino acid sequences of proteins and nucleotide sequence of nucleic acids; protein mutation and its evolutionary significance.

HIRS, C. H. W. (ed.): *Enzyme Structure*, vol. XI of *Methods in Enzymology*, Academic Press Inc., New York, 1967. Laboratory methods.

SCHRÖDER, E., and L. LÜBKE (trans. by E. Gross): *The Peptides*, 2 vols., Academic Press Inc., New York, 1966. Synthesis, occurrence, and function of peptides.

Articles and Reviews

EDMAN, P.: "A Protein Sequenator," *Europ. J. Biochem.*, **1**:80–91 (1967). Automated equipment for sequence determination.

FITCH, W. M., and E. MARGOLIASH: "Construction of Phylogenetic Trees," *Science*, **155**:279–284 (1967). Evolution of cytochrome *c*.

GUTTE, B., and R. B. MERRIFIELD: "The total synthesis of an enzyme with ribonuclease A activity," *J. Am. Chem. Soc.*, **91**:501–502 (1969).

HIRSCHMANN, R., R. F. NUTT, D. F. VEBER, R. A. VITALI, S. L. VARGA, T. A. JACOB, F. W. HOLLY, and R. G. DENKEWALTER, "Studies on the total synthesis of an enzyme. The preparation of enzymatically active material," *J. Am. Chem. Soc.*, **91**:507–508 (1969).

MERRIFIELD, R. B.: "Automated Synthesis of Peptides," *Science*, **150**:178–185 (1965). Details of the solid-phase method.

NEURATH, H., K. A. WALSH, and W. P. WINTER: "Evolution of Structure and Function of Proteases," *Science*, **158**:1638–1644 (1967). Evolutionary relationships among proteolytic enzymes secreted into digestive tract.

SANGER, F., and H. TUPPY: "The Amino Acid Sequence in the Phenylalanyl Chain of Insulin," *Biochem. J.*, **49**:463–490 (1951); and F. SANGER and E. O. P. THOMPSON: "The Amino Acid Sequence in the Glycyl Chain of Insulin," *Biochem. J.*, **53**:353–374 (1963). These two papers describe the classical work in protein sequencing.

SMITH, E. L.: "The Evolution of Proteins," *Harvey Lectures*, **62**:231–256 (1966/1967).

WITKOP, B.: "Chemical Cleavage of Proteins," *Science*, **162**:318–326 (1968). New methods for selective fragmentation of polypeptides.

Problems

1. Predict the action of trypsin on the following peptides. Each of the resulting fragments is then treated with 2,4-dinitrofluorobenzene, followed by hydrolysis of the peptide linkages. List the resulting 2,4-dinitrophenyl amino acids.
   (*a*) Lys-Asp-Gly-Ala-Ala-Glu-Ser-Gly
   (*b*) Ala-Ala-His-Arg-Glu-Lys-Phe-Ile
   (*c*) Tyr-Cys-Lys-Ala-Arg-Arg-Gly
   (*d*) Phe-Ala-Glu-Ser-Ala-Gly

2. List the peptides formed when the following polypeptide is treated with chymotrypsin. Suppose these peptides are then reacted with cyanogen bromide; list the products. Val-Ala-Lys-Glu-Glu-Phe-Val-Met-Tyr-Cys-Glu-Trp-Met-Gly-Gly-Phe

3. List the peptides formed when the polypeptide in Problem 2 is treated first with trypsin and the resulting fragments treated with cyanogen bromide.

4. What treatments would you apply to the following hemoglobin fragment to obtain two sets of peptides with overlaps so that the complete amino acid sequence can be established? Val-Leu-Ser-Pro-Ala-Lys-Thr-Asn-Val-Lys-Ala-Ala-Trp-Gly-Lys-Val-Gly-Ala-His-Ala-Gly-Glu-Tyr-Gly-Ala-Glu-Ala-Thr-Glu

5. Reaction of a tetrapeptide with FDNB, followed by a 6 *N* HCl hydrolysis, yielded the DNP derivative of valine and three other amino acids. Hydrolysis of another sample of

the tetrapeptide with trypsin gave two fragments. One of these fragments was reduced with $LiBH_4$ and then hydrolyzed. In the hydrolyzate, the amino alcohol corresponding to glycine was detected, together with an amino acid forming a yellow reaction product with ninhydrin. What amino acids were probably present in the original tetrapeptide and what was their sequence?

6. Predict the direction of migration [i.e., stationary (0), toward cathode (C), or toward anode (A)] of the following peptides during paper electrophoresis at pH 1.9, pH 3.0, pH 6.5, and pH 10.0: (*a*) Lys-Gly-Ala-Gly, (*b*) Lys-Gly-Ala-Glu, (*c*) His-Gly-Ala-Glu, (*d*) Glu-Gly-Ala-Glu, (*e*) Glu(NH_2)-Gly-Ala-Lys.

7. If the five peptides of Problem 6 were present in a mixture, predict the relative order of elution of each peptide from an ion-exchange resin column containing Dowex-1 (an anion exchanger) when the column is eluted with a buffer system whose pH is continuously changing from an initial value of 10 to a final value of 1.0.

8. The following data were collected by Sanger on the structure of the A chain of beef insulin. Total hydrolysis of the A chain gave Gly, Ala, Val_2, Leu_2, Ile, Cys_4, Asp_2, Glu_4, Ser_2, Tyr_2. Treatment of the A chain with FDNB gave DNP-glycine; COOH-terminal analysis gave aspartate. Partial acid hydrolysis gave the following oligopeptides, among others: Cys-Cys-Ala, Glu-Asp-Tyr, Glu-Glu-Cys, Glu-Leu-Glu, Cys-Asp, Tyr-Cys, Ser-Val-Cys, Glu-Cys-Cys, Ser-Leu-Tyr, Leu-Tyr-Glu, Gly-Ile-Val-Glu-Glu. Cleavage of the A chain with pepsin yielded a peptide, which on hydrolysis gave Ser-Val-Cys and Ser-Leu. Give the complete structure of the A chain.

9. A peptide A of the composition Lys, His, Asp, Glu_2, Ala, Pro, Val, Tyr, and $ammonia_2$ gave DNP aspartate on reaction with FDNB and free valine on reaction with carboxypeptidase. Digestion of A with trypsin yielded two peptides. One (Lys, Asp, Glu, Ala, Tyr) was neutral at pH 6.4. The other (His, Glu, Pro, Val) gave DNP-histidine and was positively charged at pH 6.4. Two chymotryptic peptides were also formed from A. One (Asp, Ala, Tyr) was neutral, and the other (Lys, His, Glu_2, Pro, Val) was basic at pH 6.4. Deduce a structure for peptide A.

10. Indicate how the following abnormal hemoglobins will differ in electrophoretic behavior from normal human hemoglobin at pH 7.0: HbS, HbI, HbE, $HbM_{Milwaukee}$, and $Hb_{Zürich}$.

CHAPTER 6 PROTEINS: CONFORMATION

In this chapter we shall be concerned with the three-dimensional conformation of the polypeptide chains in different classes of proteins. The application of x-ray diffraction analysis and other physical methods to this problem represents one of the great triumphs of modern research in molecular biology. These methods have also provided illuminating insight into the functions and comparative biology of some proteins.

Native Conformation of Protein Molecules

In organic molecules, single bonds have potentially complete freedom of rotation while double and triple bonds are rigid. In the simple aliphatic hydrocarbon ethane, for example, there is complete freedom of rotation around the C—C single bond, and an infinite number of configurations of the molecule are thus possible. However, one configuration of the molecule is more stable than all others, and one is least stable. Figure 6-1 shows the *staggered* and *eclipsed* forms of the ethane molecule, which, respectively, represent these two extremes. The two forms cannot be separated from each other since they are interconverted very rapidly, but there is physical-chemical evidence that the staggered form has the least energy (and thus predominates) while the eclipsed form possesses the greatest energy.

Figure 6-1
Ball-and-stick models showing end views of eclipsed and staggered configurations of ethane. (CH_3—CH_3).

The covalent backbone of a polypeptide chain is, formally at least, single-bonded. We would therefore expect that polypeptide chains would have an infinite number of possible conformations and, furthermore, that the conformation of any given molecule would undergo constant change because of thermal motion. However, it is now certain that the polypeptide chain(s) of a protein have only one conformation under normal conditions of temperature and pH, called its native conformation. This conformation is usually so much more stable than all other possible forms that the molecule can be readily isolated and retained in its native state. Physical studies on the fibrous proteins, which have the simplest conformations among the proteins, gave the first important clues to the nature of the constraints on the freedom of rotation of the bonds in the peptide-chain backbone.

The Secondary Structure of Fibrous Proteins

The ultimate experimental method for determining the position of the atoms of a molecule or crystal in space is x-ray diffraction analysis. The spacing of regularly repeating atomic or molecular units in crystals can be determined by studying the angles and intensities at which x-rays of a given wavelength are scattered or diffracted by the electrons that surround each atom. Those atoms having the highest electron density, such as heavy metal atoms, diffract x-rays most, and those having lowest electron density (hydrogen atoms) diffract x-rays least. X-ray analysis of crystals of salts like NaCl is relatively simple because only two different atoms are involved and they are regularly spaced. In principle, crystals of complex organic molecules, even very large ones such as proteins, can also be analyzed by x-ray diffraction methods, but the mathematical analysis of the diffraction patterns is very complex because of the large number of atoms in the molecule, which may yield thousands of diffraction spots.

In the early 1930s, William Astbury in England recorded the x-ray diffraction patterns of various fibrous proteins, which he chose because of the probability that their peptide chains were oriented in one specific direction. Hair and wool and certain other fibrous proteins gave rather similar patterns, which indicated that they all possess a major periodicity or *repeat unit* of about 5.0 to 5.5 Å along their axes. These observations suggested that the peptide chains in this family of fibrous proteins (the α-keratins) are twisted or folded in some regular way, since a fully extended peptide chain could not give spacings of these dimensions. On the other hand, fibroin, the protein comprising silk fibers, had a distinctly different x-ray diffraction pattern, suggesting a repeat unit of 7.0 Å. Significantly, when the α-keratins (hair and wool) were stretched after steaming, they assumed an x-ray pattern resembling that of silk, with a periodicity of about 6.6 Å; the stretched form of keratin was designated β-keratin. Astbury concluded that the peptide chains in α- and β-keratins are folded in different ways. The fibrous protein collagen was found to show a third type of periodicity on x-ray analysis.

Beginning in 1939, Linus Pauling and R. B. Corey in the United States began a long series of studies on the conformation of the peptide chains in proteins. First they recorded the x-ray diffraction patterns of crystals of amino acids and of simple dipeptides and tripeptides. From these, they deduced the precise three-dimensional structure of each molecule and, in particular, the structure of the peptide bond itself. The most important conclusion was that the C—N bond of the peptide linkage, which is shorter than most C—N single bonds, has some double-bond character and thus cannot rotate freely. The four atoms comprising the peptide bond and the two α-carbon atoms lie in a single plane; the oxygen of the carbonyl group and the hydrogen of the —NH— group are *trans* to each other (Figure 6-2). This configuration is the result of resonance stabilization of the atoms comprising the peptide group (Chapter 5). From these findings, the backbone of a peptide chain may be pictured as consisting of a

fibrousproteins α keratins

Figure 6-2
Dimensions of the peptide linkage from x-ray data. The six atoms in the shaded zone lie in a plane. Because the central C—N bond has some double-bond character, this plane tends to be rigid.

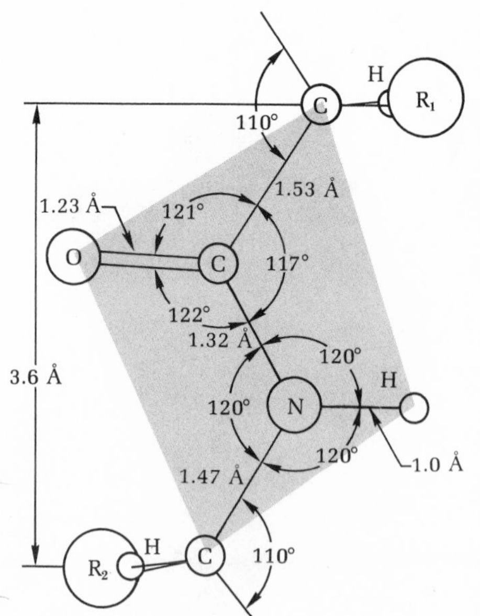

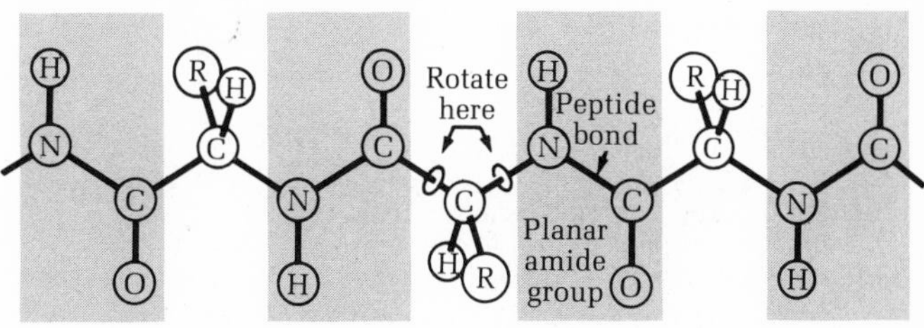

Figure 6-3
Limited rotation in the peptide-chain backbone. Every third bond is rigid, fixed in the plane of the peptide linkage (shaded). The other backbone bonds are free to rotate, as shown.

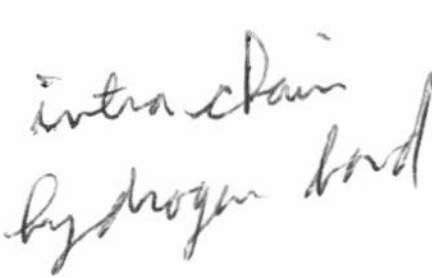

series of relatively rigid planes separated by substituted methylene groups (—CHR—) (Figure 6-3). In a peptide chain of 100 residues, regardless of the nature of the R groups, there are 300 formal single bonds in the backbone. However, in such a chain there are only 200 single bonds with potentially complete freedom of rotation.

The α-Helix

Pauling and Corey then studied, with the help of precisely constructed models, the possible ways in which a peptide chain can twist or fold in view of the constraint imposed by the peptide bonds and their specific dimensions. Particularly they sought conformations that could account for the repeat units of 5.0 to 5.5 Å in α-keratin. They found that the simplest arrangement is the helical structure shown in Figure 6-4. In this structure, called the *α-helix*, there are about 3.6 amino acid residues per turn. The R groups of the amino acids would extend outward from the rather tight helix formed by the backbone. In such a structure the repeat unit, a single turn of the helix, would extend about 5.4 Å along the axis, corresponding closely to the major periodicity of 5.0 to 5.5 Å observed on x-ray analysis of α-keratins. In this coil, the spacing per residue is about 1.5 Å, corresponding to the minor periodicity of 1.5 Å also observed in the diffraction patterns. The α-helical arrangement of the peptide chain is favored over other possible coiled or helical arrangements because it permits the formation of intrachain hydrogen bonds between successive winds of the helix. In the α-helix, each hydrogen bond is formed between the H atom attached to the electronegative N atom of one peptide linkage and the oxygen of the carbonyl group of the fourth amino acid behind it (Figure 6-4). Significantly, the electrical vectors of the H bonds are so oriented that they give nearly maximal bond strength. Most important is the fact that *each* peptide bond of the chain participates in hydrogen bonding; the system is maximally hydrogen-bonded. Other ways of coiling peptide chains are possible, but they would not account for the characteristic spacing of repeat units in the α-keratin family of proteins, nor would they be as stable. Peptide chains can be expected to assume the α-helix configuration spontaneously because this form is the stablest possible and has the least free energy, providing there are no opposing interactions of the R groups or of the solvent.

An α-helix may form with either L- or D-amino acids; however, the amino acids must be one or the other since a helix cannot form from a peptide chain containing a mixture of L- and D-residues. Furthermore, starting from

Figure 6-4
The α-helix.

Formation of a right-handed α-helix. The planes of the rigid peptide bonds are parallel to the long axis of the helix.

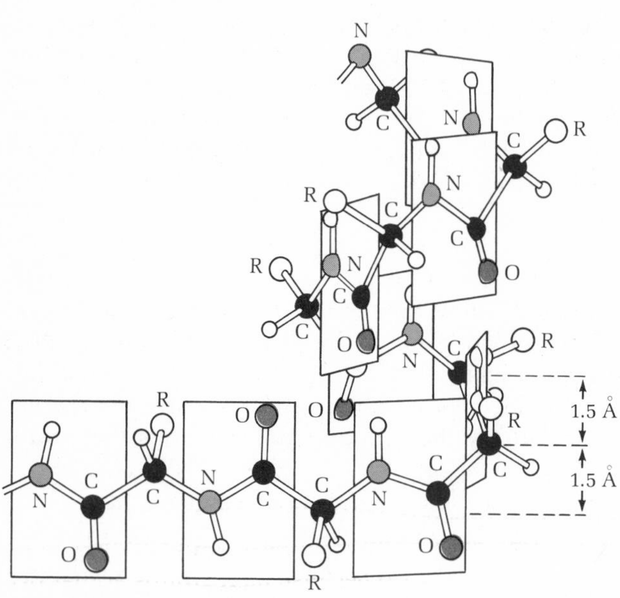

Ball-and-stick model of α-helix, showing intrachain hydrogen bonds.

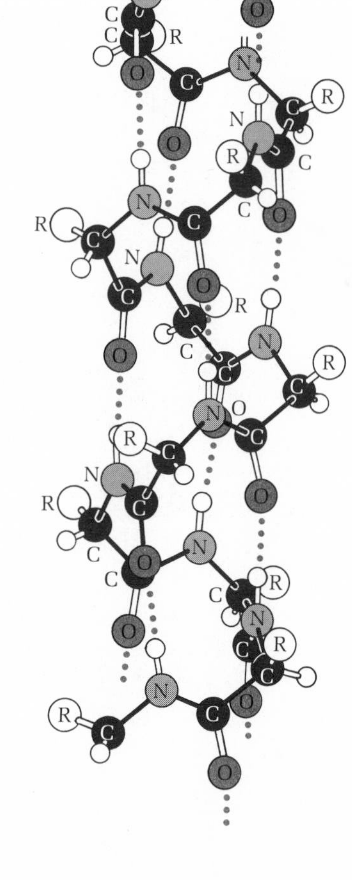

The average dimensions of the α-helix. The pitch and the rise per residue correspond to the major and minor periodicities of 5.4 and 1.5 Å, respectively. This drawing shows a left-handed α-helix; all the others on this page are right-handed.

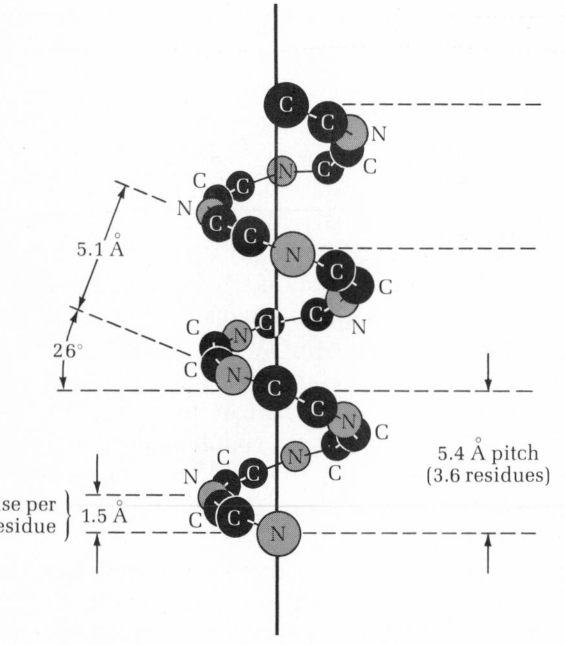

Space-filling model of α-helix.

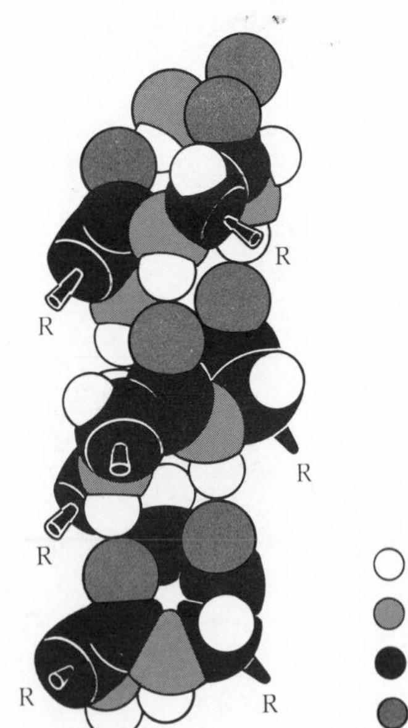

Supercoiling of α-helical coils in hair and wool keratins.

the naturally occurring L-amino acids, either right-handed or left-handed helical coils can be built; however, the right-handed helix is significantly more stable. In all native proteins examined to date, the α-helix of L-amino acids is right-handed. It is now generally accepted that the fibrous α-keratins (hair, wool, horn, nails, skin, feathers, etc.) consist of parallel peptide chains in right-handed α-helical arrangements. In hair and wool, three or seven α-helices may be coiled around each other to form three-strand or seven-strand ropes (margin).

Not all peptide chains can exist in α-helical form since the tendency of a given peptide chain to form a stable α-helical coil is determined by the nature and sequence of the R groups in the chain. This extremely important conclusion has come in part from study of the polyamino acids (Chapter 5). Polyalanine, whose R groups are small and uncharged, spontaneously forms α-helical coils in aqueous solution at pH 7.0. However, polylysine does not form an α-helix at pH 7.0, but exists as a *random coil*, the term used to denote a flexible, changing, statistically random structure. At pH 7.0, the R groups of polylysine all have a positive charge. These closely spaced, positively charged R groups repel each other so strongly that they overcome the tendency for intrachain hydrogen bonds to form. However, at pH 12, the lysyl groups bear no charge and do not repel each other; at this pH, polylysine spontaneously forms an α-helix. Similarly, polyglutamic acid is a random coil at pH 7.0 because its R groups at that pH are all negatively charged. However, at pH 2.0, its R groups have no charge, and it readily forms an α-helix (Figure 6-5). Polyisoleucine also fails to form an α-helix since its R groups have bulky substituents next to the α-carbon atom; these groups offer steric hindrance to formation of the helix. Polyserine forms helical arrangements other than the α-helix because of the capacity of the serine hydroxyl group to hydrogen-bond. However, the most striking case is that of polyproline. In proline, the nitrogen atom is part of a rigid ring and no rotation of the N—C bond is possible. Furthermore, since there are no substituent hydrogens on the nitrogen atoms of proline residues in peptide linkage, no intrachain hydrogen bonds can form in polyproline. Although polyproline cannot form an α-helix, it does spontaneously form two other types of helix, one of which closely resembles in periodicity that found in the fibrous protein collagen. Whenever proline (or hydroxyproline) occurs in a peptide chain, it interrupts the α-helix and creates a kink or bend. Although polyglycine can form an α-helix, it tends to assume another type of conformation, the *β-conformation*, in which the chains are relatively extended. Table 6-1 classifies the various amino acids with regard to their potentiality for forming α-helical coils.

Figure 6-5
The effect of pH on the transition between random-coil and α-helix forms of poly-L-lysine and poly-L-glutamic acid. The unfolding of the α-helix is accompanied by a large change in optical rotation to a more negative value.

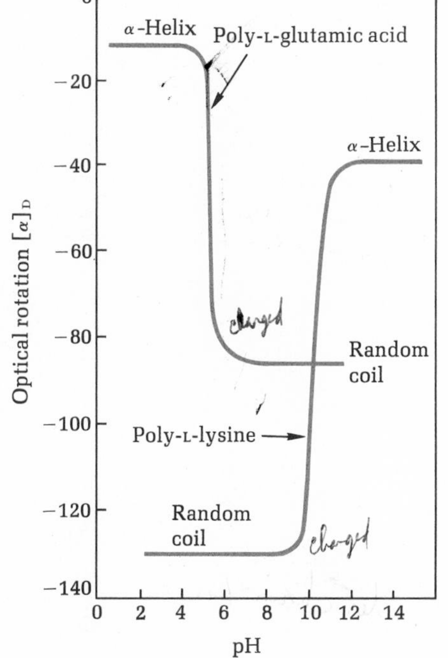

Optical Properties of Helical Coils

When peptide chains are longer than about five to seven amino acid residues, their optical rotation is not simply an additive function of the rotations of the separate residues. In long polypeptides and proteins, the optical rotation is significantly more dextrorotatory than the sum of the individual rotations contributed by each asymmetric α-carbon atom. Such "extra" dextrorotatory power is maximal in the α-helix form; randomly coiled peptide chains tend to show only simple additivity of rotatory power. The specific rotation of poly-L-glutamic acid at pH 2 (at which it is an α-helix) is about $-15°$, whereas its specific rotation at pH 7 (at which it is a random coil) is about $-85°$ (Figure 6-5). Nearly all globular proteins become more levorotatory when they are denatured.

The capacity to rotate the plane of plane-polarized light is given by asymmetric molecules; the most common type of asymmetry is that produced by asymmetric carbon atoms (Chapter 4). However, in an α-helix of L-amino acids, the total asymmetry of the molecule is the sum of that contributed by the asymmetric carbon atoms and that contributed by the α-helical coil, which is asymmetric since it can exist in right-handed or left-handed forms. The optical rotatory power can therefore be used to determine the approximate amount of α-helical coiling in any given polypeptide. It can also be used to study the factors influencing the transition between the α-helix and the random coil. Measurements of optical rotation of proteins and peptides have become an important tool in the study of their secondary structure, particularly when the wavelength of the incident light is varied.

Table 6-1 Helix-forming and destabilizing amino acids

Allow stable α-helix
- Alanine
- Leucine
- Phenylalanine
- Tyrosine
- Tryptophan
- Cysteine
- Methionine
- Histidine
- Asparagine
- Glutamine
- Valine

Destabilize α-helix
- Serine
- Isoleucine
- Threonine
- Glutamic acid
- Aspartic acid
- Lysine
- Arginine
- Glycine

Break α-helix
- Proline
- Hydroxyproline

β-Keratins: The Pleated Sheet

When fibers of α-keratin are subjected to moist heat and stretched to almost double their original length, they yield x-ray diffraction patterns resembling that of silk fibroin. Pauling and Corey have provided evidence that the transition from α-keratin to β-keratin structure during steaming is caused by the thermal breakage of the intrachain hydrogen bonds that normally stabilize the α-helix and the consequent stretching of the relatively tight α-helix into a more extended, zig-zag conformation of the polypeptide chain, which they designated the β-conformation. Parallel chains in the β-conformation form structures called *pleated sheets*, which are cross-linked by interchain hydrogen bonds (Figure 6-6). All the peptide linkages participate in this cross-linking and thus lend the structure great stability. The R groups lie above or below the zigzagging planes of the pleated sheet. In one type of silk fibroin, every other amino acid is glycine; thus all the R groups on one side of the sheet are H atoms. Since alanine makes up most of the rest of the amino acids of fibroin, most of the R groups on the other side of the sheet are methyl groups. If the R groups are bulky or have like charges, the pleated sheet cannot exist because of R group interactions. This is why the stretched form of hair or wool is unstable and reverts spontaneously to the α-helical form. Statistically, the R groups of α-keratins are bulkier and more highly charged than those of silk fibroin (see Table 5-3).

There are two other differences between α-keratins and fibroin. In the former, all the peptide chains are *parallel*, i.e., run in the same direction, whereas in fibroin, adjacent

Figure 6-6
The β-conformation of the polypeptide chain.

Schematic representation of three parallel chains in β-structure, showing the pleated-sheet arrangement. All the R-groups project above or below the plane of the page.

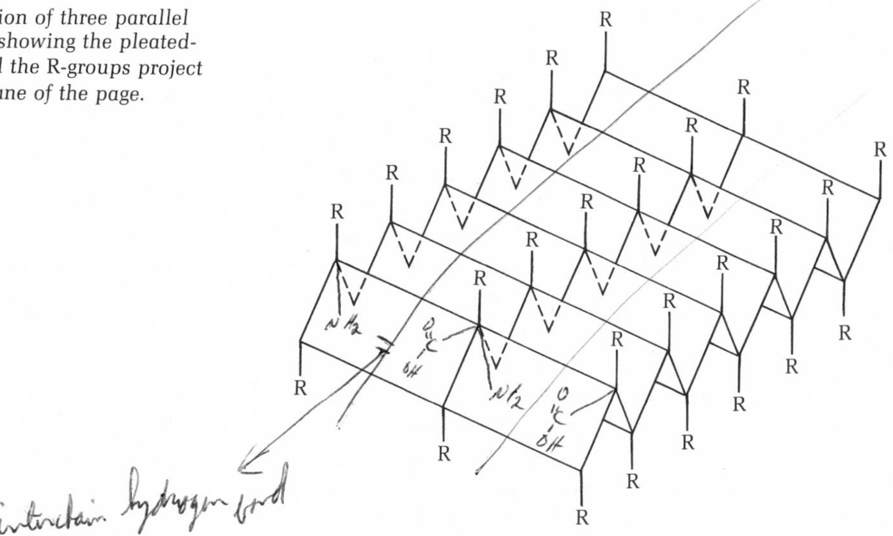

Ball-and-stick models. Note the maximal hydrogen bonding between the chains to form a sheet.

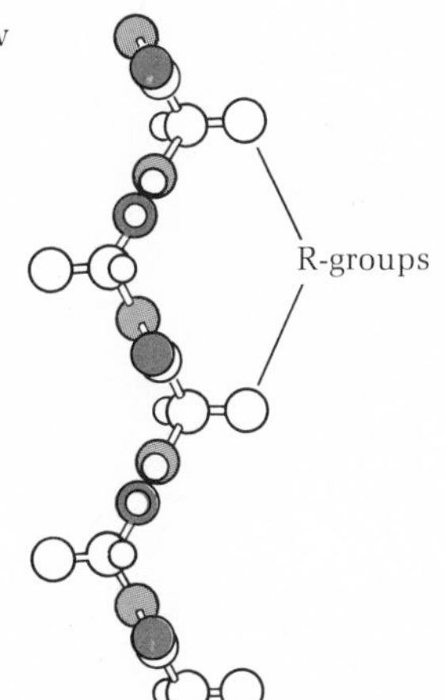

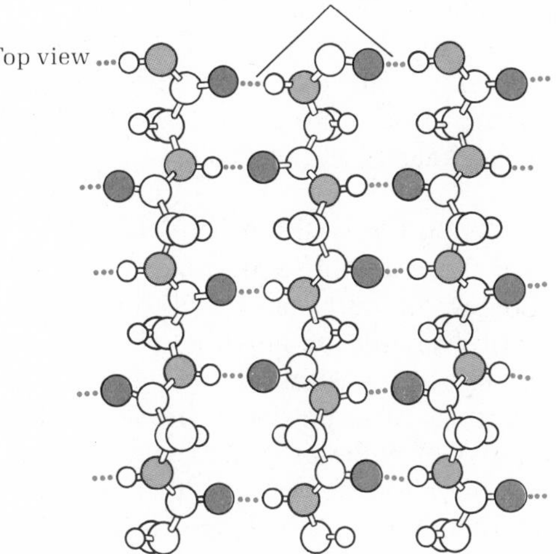

peptide chains are *antiparallel* and run in opposite directions. Also, α-keratin contains many cystine residues, which are so arranged as to provide interchain —S—S— cross-linkages between adjacent peptide chains. These give the α-keratins considerable stability and strength. However, when their —S—S— cross-links are broken by reduction to the —SH form, α-keratins dissociate into separate peptide chains of about 100 residues. Fibroin has no —S—S— cross-linkages.

The Collagen Helix

The third major type of fibrous protein in higher animals is collagen. Collagen is the most abundant of all proteins in higher vertebrates, making up one-third or more of total body protein. Tendons contain parallel bundles of collagen molecules. Unlike the α-keratins, collagen does not stretch readily. It is also distinctive in that one-third of all its amino acids are glycine and a quarter or more are proline or hydroxyproline.

The extremely high content of amino acids that tend to break α-helix structure suggests that collagen does not form an α-helix. X-ray diffraction studies show that in collagen three polypeptide chains are twisted together to form a triple helix (Figure 6-7). The regularly spaced proline and hydroxyproline residues force the chain to assume a peculiar, kinked type of helix because of the rigidity of the proline R groups and the fact that the peptide linkages involving proline and hydroxyproline cannot form hydrogen bonds. The N—H groups of the peptide bonds involving glycine residues form interchain H bonds, which also help keep the ropelike packing arrangement of collagen stable and resistant to stretching. Each peptide chain of collagen has a molecular weight of 95,000 and contains about 1,000 amino acid residues. The complete triple-helix unit is called *tropocollagen*. Such tropocollagen units are arranged in a staggered fashion in the collagen fibrils of tendon, thus accounting for the characteristic spacing of the repeat units observed in collagen fibrils, which varies from 600 to 700 Å, depending on their source and degree of hydration.

Figure 6-7
The structure of collagen. (Below) Electron micrograph of collagen fibrils of connective tissue. Note periodicity of cross-striations, which have a repeat distance of 700 Å.

The secondary structure of the polypeptide chains in other fibrous proteins is not yet known. Studies are under way on elastin and on sclerotins, the light, rigid proteins present in the exoskeleton of insects.

The Tertiary Structure of Globular Proteins

Interpretation of the x-ray diffraction patterns of globular proteins is far more difficult than for fibrous proteins because the peptide chains of globular proteins are not oriented along one dimension. By the introduction of intensely diffracting, electron-dense heavy metal atoms into the molecules of globular proteins, in order to provide reference points for the mathematical interpretation of the diffraction patterns, the three-dimensional structures of several globular proteins to a resolution of 6 Å, and in some cases 2 Å, have been obtained. The proteins for which the tertiary structures are reasonably well known are myoglobin, hemoglobin, lysozyme, ribonuclease, papain, chymotrypsinogen, carboxypeptidase *A*, and subtilisin, a proteolytic enzyme from a bacterium. Much information is also available on the structure of cytochrome *c*. Although only a few proteins are known in detail, the results have already yielded some important generalizations that are probably applicable to many globular proteins.

The first important breakthrough came from the x-ray studies of J. C. Kendrew and his colleagues on sperm-whale myoglobin. Myoglobin is a relatively small globular protein (mol wt 16,700) that contains a single polypeptide chain of 153 amino acid residues. The complete amino acid sequence of this chain is now known. Myoglobin contains an iron-porphyrin heme group identical with that of hemoglobin, and like hemoglobin, it is capable of reversible oxygenation and deoxygenation. It is, in fact, a functional and structural relative of hemoglobin, which con-

Conformation of polypeptide chains in triple-stranded tropocollagen molecule. Each chain is a coil with many repeating sequences of Gly-Pro-Hypro.

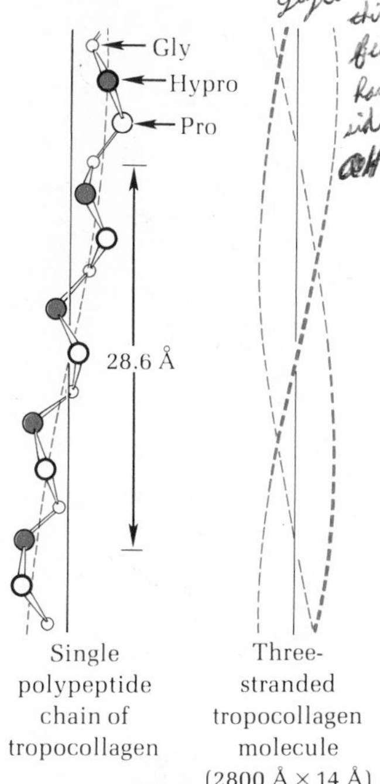

The staggered alignment of tropocollagen molecules, which possess "heads," is responsible for the 700-Å repeat units in hydrated collagen fibres.

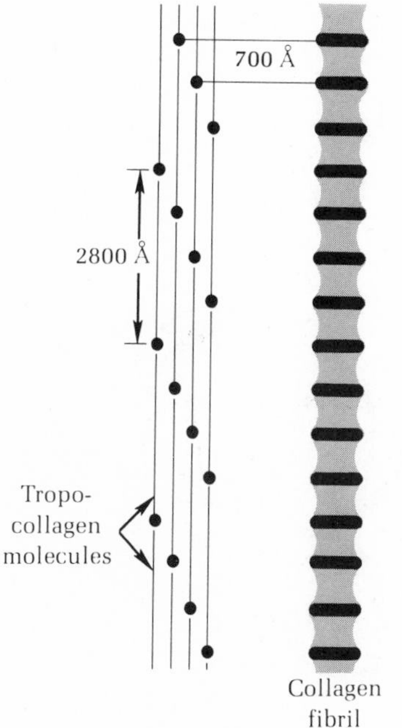

tains four peptide chains and four hemes and has four times the molecular weight of myoglobin. Myoglobin is found in skeletal muscle cells and is particularly abundant in diving mammals such as the whale, seal, and walrus, whose muscles are so rich in myoglobin that they are deep brown in color. Myoglobin serves not only to store oxygen but also to enhance the rate of diffusion of oxygen through the cell. The x-ray diffraction pattern of crystalline myoglobin, which contains about 2,500 atoms, consists of nearly 25,000 reflections.

The x-ray analysis of the structure of myoglobin took place in two stages. In the first, completed in 1957, the results were calculated to 6-Å resolution, a feat which required precise analysis of 400 diffraction spots (Figure 6-8). This degree of resolution is insufficient to reveal the exact positions of individual atoms or functional groups in the molecule, but it does indicate the manner in which the peptide chain is folded in the myoglobin molecule. The outline of the peptide chain resembles a long sausage, folded in an irregular manner. This specific folded arrangement of the polypeptide chain of myoglobin is its tertiary structure. From measurements of the length of the "sausage" in this model, which is much shorter than calculated for a fully extended peptide chain of 151 residues, it was deduced that the peptide chain of myoglobin must be coiled along a large part of its length, particularly in the longer segments.

In the second stage, the x-ray analysis of myoglobin was carried out to 2-Å resolution. This required the analysis of some 10,000 reflections, and high-speed electronic computing methods were used. This level of resolution was sufficiently high to reveal the contours of the backbone, and most of the R groups. The model so obtained, shown in a projection drawing in Fig. 6-8, gave the exact location of the carbon skeleton of the peptide chain, as well as the carbon skeletons of all the R groups. Nearly all the amino acids in the chain could be identified; these were found to agree with the amino acid sequence that had been determined by chemical methods. The backbone of the myoglobin molecule, it was found, consists of eight relatively straight segments separated by bends. Each segment is a length of α-helix, the longest consisting of 23 amino acids and the shortest of 7 amino acids, and all are right-handed. Some 70 percent of the amino acids present in the molecule are in these straight α-helical regions; this figure confirmed the results of optical-rotation measurements on myoglobin solutions.

Some other important features of the myoglobin structure were found: (1) The molecule is very compact, and in its interior there is room for only four molecules of water. (2) All the polar R groups of the amino acid residues are located on the outer surface of the molecule and are hydrated. (3) Nearly all the nonpolar or hydrophobic R groups are in the interior of the molecule and are thus hidden from exposure to water. (4) Proline residues are present only at the bends, which also contain some amino acids known not to form α-helical coils readily, such as isoleucine and serine, as well as amino acids having side-chains of like charge at pH 7.0. (5) The gross conformation

Figure 6-8
The structure of myoglobin.

X-ray diffraction pattern of myoglobin (sperm whale). From J. C. Kendrew, Scientific American, December 1961.

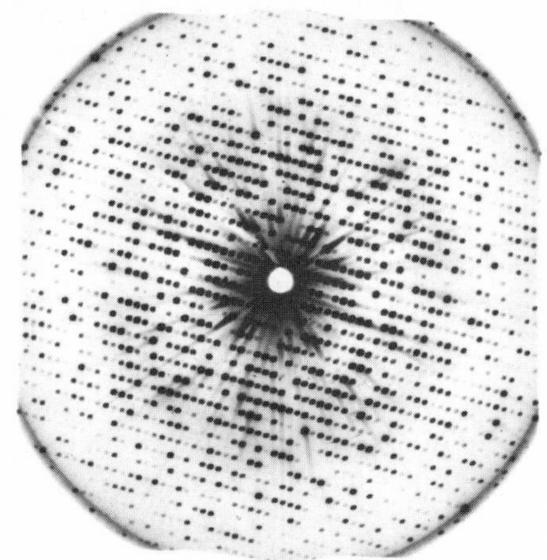

The conformation of the molecule deduced from low-resolution data (6 Å).

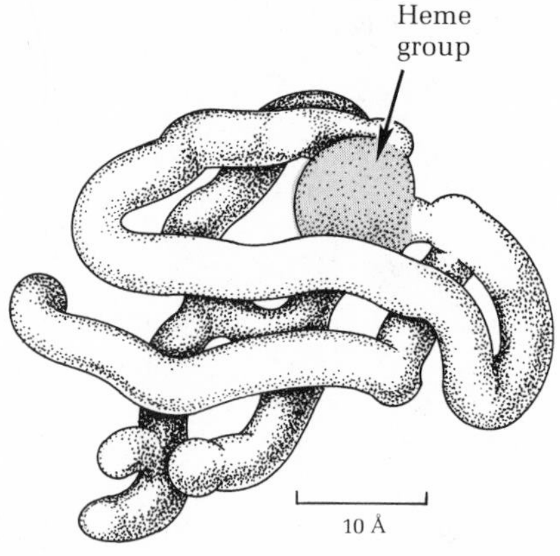

Structure of myoglobin deduced from high-resolution (2 Å) x-ray data.

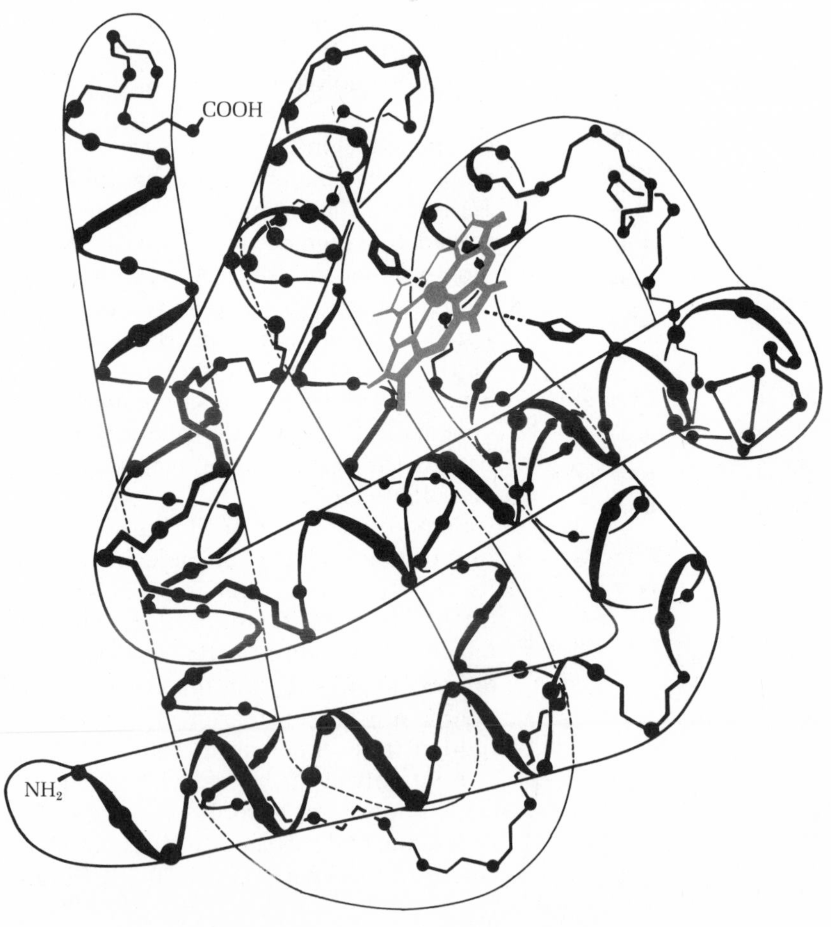

of the peptide chain is similar in myoglobins isolated from different mammalian species, despite the fact that they differ somewhat in amino acid composition. This was an especially important finding.

Other single-chain proteins have been studied by the x-ray method. Lysozyme, an enzyme from egg white that catalyzes the hydrolysis of certain glycosidic linkages in the complex polysaccharides found in the cell walls of some bacteria (Chapter 11), has 129 residues in a single chain, and four intrachain cystine cross-links. Although lysozyme has only about 25 percent of its residues in the form of α-helical regions and is a more convoluted molecule than myoglobin, it, too, is rather compactly arranged, with little space for water within it. Nearly all its polar R groups are on the outside of the molecule, and nearly all the hydrophobic R groups are on the inside. Cytochrome *c* has also been studied at high resolution. Although it is a heme protein, it shows no structural similarity to myoglobin. Cytochrome *c* contains no α-helical segments; rather, it has many residues that are in the extended or β-conformation, such as is found in the β-keratins. Chymotrypsinogen also contains few residues in α-helical configuration. All these representative crystalline proteins have highly convoluted, compactly arranged structures, with most of the hydrophobic residues inside and most of the hydrophilic residues on the surface. However, there are wide variations in the relative amounts of α-helix and β-structure among different globular proteins.

Many proteins, such as ribonuclease, contain intrachain disulfide cross-linkages. Since they are covalent, they stabilize the tertiary structure of globular proteins and greatly limit their tendency to unfold completely. It is most likely, however, that they contribute little to the actual conformation of the polypeptide chain of such proteins, since, after they are reduced, they tend to refold spontaneously so that the corresponding —SH groups "fit" each other. They do, however, greatly stabilize the tertiary conformation.

The similarity of conformation of homologous proteins from different species probably results from the presence of invariant amino acid residues in certain positions in the chain. These appear to determine the bend points and other crucial features of the conformation, such as the active site of enzymes. Amino acid residues at other positions may vary within limits since they are apparently less critical for the overall conformation (Chapter 5).

The Forces Stabilizing Tertiary Structure

We have seen that the α-helix is relatively stable, providing the R groups of the polypeptide chain are uncharged, are relatively small, and are incapable of hydrogen bonding. However, segments of α-helix in proteins do not all possess precisely the same dimensions or repeat distance, nor are they equally stable, since they differ in amino acid content and sequence. They contain local points of instability at which the helix is likely to bend in response to other forces, particularly the tendency of the entire polypeptide chain to assume that conformation in which the hydrophobic R groups are maximally shielded from water. The characteristic tertiary structure of a polypeptide chain in an aqueous system is thus the resultant of hydrogen bonding, either intrachain, as in α-helical segments, or interchain, as in the β-conformation, and the tendency of the entire chain to bend at points of instability to assume such a configuration that the surrounding water may attain the condition of maximum entropy. The number and position of disulfide cross-linkages, if present, are also very important factors in maintaining the characteristic tertiary structure.

Proteins have a characteristic temperature at which they are maximally stable. Most are maximally stable at refrigerator temperatures; a few are more stable at room temperature than in the cold. As temperatures are increased above about 40 to 50°C, nearly all proteins become unstable and tend to unfold; the higher the temperature, the more random the configuration of the unfolded chain. Curiously, proteins of the thermophilic bacteria, which can live at temperatures exceeding 70°C, are much more stable against heat denaturation than most proteins. When proteins are denatured or unfolded by heating, and then rapidly cooled, the original tertiary structure is usually not restored. However, if the heated protein solution is *annealed*, i.e., cooled very slowly to room temperature, the protein will often refold itself back to its native configuration. Annealing often restores the catalytic activity of heat-inactivated enzymes. The long annealing period is required in order to allow the polypeptide chain to "try out" many possible conformations before it finds the most stable one. As each successive residue finds its minimum-free-energy conformation, the stability of the already folded part of the chain increases very markedly, as does its rate of refolding. Such an enhancement of the stability and rate of refolding is the result of many successive cooperative interactions. Some proteins, such as trypsin, renature rapidly after heating; they literally "snap back" into their native conformation because the amino acid sequence is such that the chain can quickly find its minimum-energy conformation.

Prediction of Protein Conformation

If the secondary and tertiary conformations of protein molecules are the reflection of residue-by-residue adjustment to produce local minimum-free-energy states, it should theoretically be possible to predict the total conformation of a given protein from its amino acid sequence. Currently, attempts are being made to carry out such calculations by means of computers, guided by the known relationships between amino acid sequence and conformation in myoglobin and other proteins. At each peptide bond, the minimum-free-energy conformation must be calculated from data on electrostatic, van der Waals, and steric interactions of the adjacent R groups. In one such effort, by C. Levinthal and his colleagues, the computer output was displayed on a cathode-ray tube to indicate the conformation of the peptide-chain backbone of the molecule when viewed from different angles (Figure 6-9). These calculations are exceedingly complex, and it has

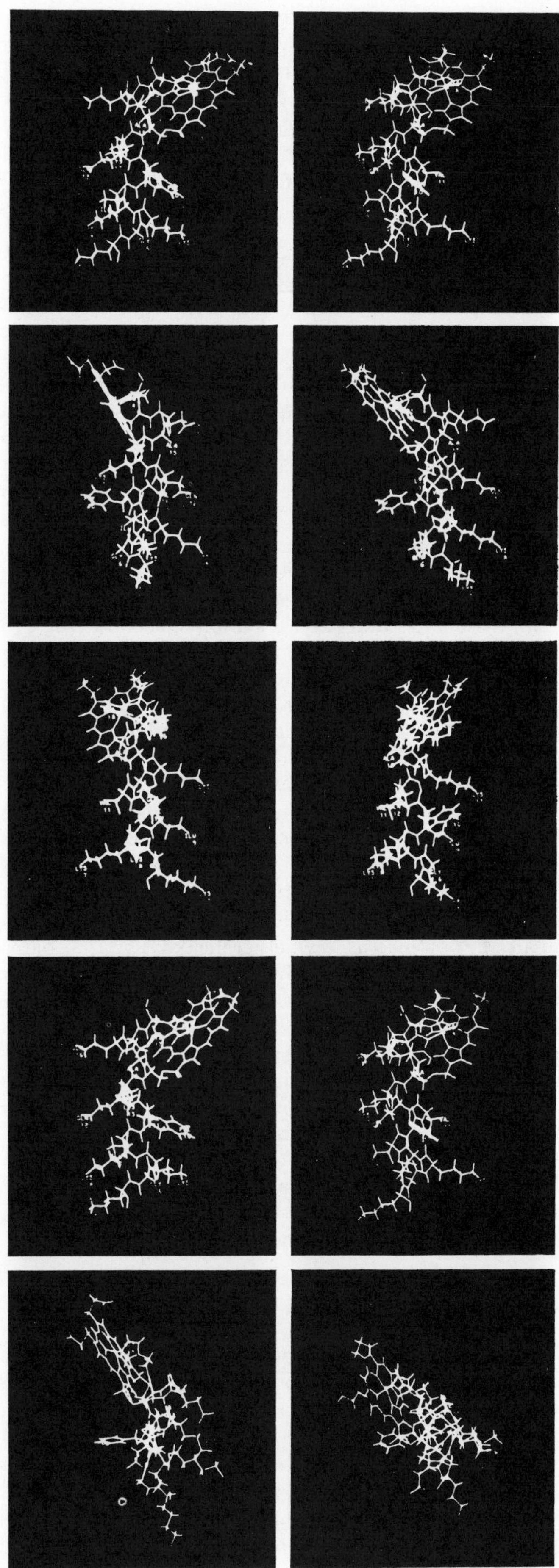

Figure 6-9
Computer representations of the backbone structure of cytochrome c as the model is rotated around its vertical axis. From C. Levinthal, Scientific American, November 1966.

not yet been possible to include all parameters of peptide-chain conformation. However, the intriguing possibility exists that one day native protein conformations may be automatically calculated on the basis of automatically collected amino acid sequence data.

The Quaternary Structure of Oligomeric Proteins

Most globular proteins having a molecular weight in excess of 50,000 are oligomeric, consisting of two or more separate polypeptide chains (protomers). The characteristic manner in which the individual polypeptide chains fit each other in the native conformation of an oligomeric protein is its quaternary structure. Oligomeric proteins may have a complex hierarchy of subunit organization. For example, the enzyme glutamate dehydrogenase of beef liver (particle weight 2.2×10^6) has eight major subunits of mol wt 280,000, into which it dissociates on dilution. Each of these subunits, in turn, consists of a number of polypeptide chains, each of mol wt ~50,000. While the term *protomer* refers to the individual polypeptide chain, the term *subunit* often is used to designate a functional portion of an oligomeric protein. Thus, on dilution, hemoglobin dissociates into two $\alpha\beta$ subunits, each having two polypeptide chains, one α and one β. The multiple chains of oligomeric proteins endow the latter with some extremely important biological advantages, which we shall consider below. The molecular weight and the number of polypeptide chains in some well-studied oligomeric proteins were given in Table 3-2.

The number of component polypeptide chains in a native protein can be established by combining information on its particle weight (Chapter 7) with the number of NH_2-terminal or COOH-terminal amino acid residues per unit weight of protein. By end-group analysis, information can also be obtained as to whether the polypeptide chains of a given oligomeric protein molecule are identical or dissimilar. The number of subunits or component polypeptide chains of enzymes can sometimes be deduced from the number of catalytic sites per molecule. For example, glyceraldehyde phosphate dehydrogenase, which has a molecular weight of 130,000, has four catalytic sites per molecule, each of which binds one molecule of its coenzyme, nicotinamide adenine dinucleotide (Chapter 15). From other analyses, the enzyme has been found to consist of four identical polypeptide chains, each of which binds a molecule of coenzyme.

The Quaternary Structure of Hemoglobin

Hemoglobin is the only oligomeric protein for which the complete tertiary and quaternary structures are known from x-ray analysis. This achievement, by M. F. Perutz and his colleagues at Cambridge, culminated some 25 years of detailed study of the structure of this important protein. The x-ray analysis of hemoglobin was carried out simultaneously with that of myoglobin, and in the same laboratory. Because of the similarity of structure and

Figure 6-10
Structure of the α-chain, the β-chain, and the hemoglobin molecule, as deduced from x-ray diffraction analysis.

α-chain

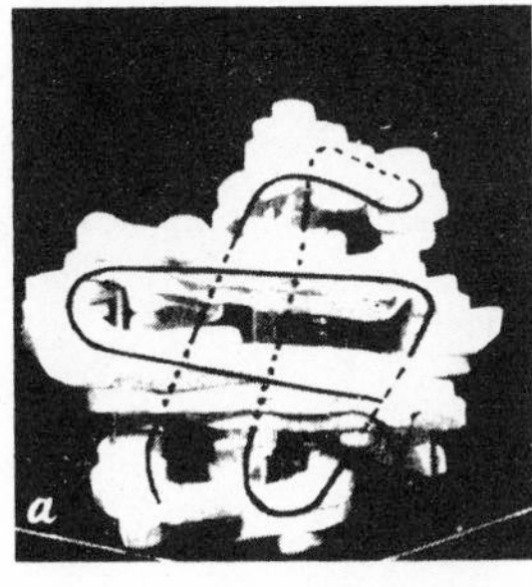

β-chain

Hemoglobin molecule from "The Hemoglobin Molecule," by M. F. Perutz. Copyright © November 1964 by Scientific American, Inc. All rights reserved.

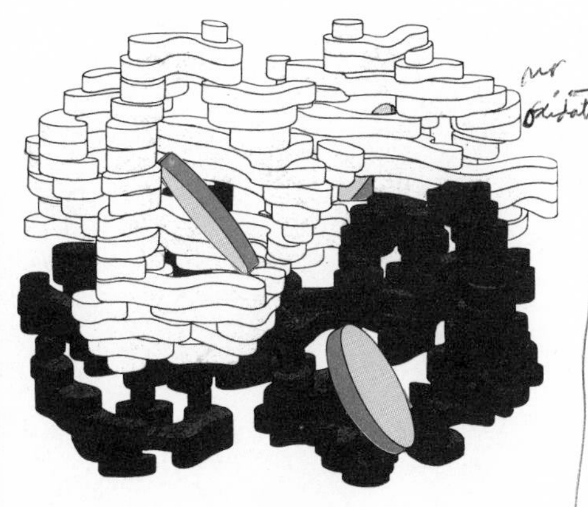

function of these two heme proteins, a number of extremely important relationships have developed from these concurrent investigations.

X-ray analysis of the hemoglobin molecule is obviously far more complex than analysis of myoglobin since hemoglobin is four times as large and has four times as many diffracting atoms. It contains four separate peptide chains—two α-chains (141 residues) and two β-chains (146 residues)—to each of which is bound a heme residue in noncovalent linkage. As in the case of myoglobin, the x-ray study of hemoglobin proceeded first at low resolution and then at higher resolution.

The results of these studies are given in Figure 6-10, which shows schematically the tertiary structure of the α- and β-chains of hemoglobin and how the chains fit together in an approximately tetrahedral configuration to yield the characteristic quaternary structure. Each of the four separate chains, it was found, has an irregularly folded conformation, in which lengths of pure α-helical regions are separated by bends. Both the α- and β-chains have about 70 percent α-helical character, as is the case for myoglobin. The α- and β-chains are very similar in their tertiary structure, consisting of similar lengths of α-helix with bends of about the same angles and directions. But most remarkable is the fact that the tertiary configuration of the α- and β-chains is very similar to that of the single chain of myoglobin. The conclusion clearly emerges that the similar biological function of these two proteins, namely, their capacity to bind oxygen reversibly, is conferred by the similar tertiary configurations of their peptide chains. This similarity is in all probability determined by the considerable number of identical amino acid residues at critical positions in the amino acid sequence (Chapter 5).

It is also a highly important finding that the quaternary structures of the oxygenated and unoxygenated forms of hemoglobin differ. On oxygenation, the distance between the two β-chains decreases, without significant change in the tertiary structure of the β-chains themselves. However, when myoglobin is oxygenated, there is no significant change in its tertiary structure. Changes in the tertiary structure or the relative positions of subunit peptide chains may be a general phenomenon in the catalytic action of many enzymes having subunits (Chapter 9).

Many oligomeric proteins dissociate at high or low pH or on exposure to high urea or salt concentrations. During denaturation of oligomeric proteins, two stages are recognized: (1) dissociation of the chains from each other, and (2) unfolding of the separated chains. The tightness of fit and the great stability of many oligomeric proteins and protein systems are guaranteed by the occurrence of many weak binding forces at each contact area between the subunits and by the cooperative nature of these weak forces. These features endow some oligomeric systems with self-assembling characteristics; for example, hemoglobin assembles itself rapidly from a mixture of α- and β-chains. Later (Chapter 35) we shall see that much larger supramolecular structures, such as viruses, also are self-assembling. These facts indicate that the amino acid sequence of a polypeptide chain of an oligomeric protein codes not only its tertiary structure but also the geometry of the contact or binding sites at which another specifically coded protomer binds. The information coded in amino acid sequence thus is meaningful at two or three or more levels of structural organization: secondary, tertiary, and quaternary.

The Biological Significance of the Subunit Structure of Proteins

The fact that large proteins usually consist of a number of individual polypeptide chains, rather than a single extremely long chain, appears to have some advantages. One is that the presence of several small chains can minimize the effect of random errors that may occur in the biosynthesis of protein molecules. Let us consider two alternative ways of constructing a very large protein molecule having 100,000 amino acid residues. In the first scheme (1), the structure is put together, residue by residue, into a single long chain. In the second scheme (2), 100 subunits, each with 1,000 amino acid residues, are built separately and then assembled to form an oligomeric protein. Let us assume that in the biosynthesis of peptide chains random mistakes happen, so that the wrong amino acid is inserted on the average of once every 100,000 times. Let us further assume that each mistake results in a biologically inactive or useless product. Under scheme 1, each complete molecule will contain on the average one wrong amino acid residue, and thus most of the molecules produced would probably be inactive. Under scheme 2, mistakes will occur in the synthesis of only 1 percent of the subunits, on the average. If the few bad subunits can be rejected in some way, then complete oligomeric protein molecules having 100,000 amino acid residues can be very easily made from the "good" subunits. This process may be compared to the assembly lines in which television sets are constructed. At each stage of assembly, defective subunits are rejected and kept from being assembled into the finished product. In the self-assembly of oligomeric protein molecules, only good subunits which fit their neighbors are likely to find their way into the final product; defective subunits that do not "fit" will be rejected because they are unable to become part of a thermodynamically stable oligomeric system. This conclusion is supported by the finding that there are some mutants of tobacco mosaic virus particles in which one specific amino acid residue in each chain is replaced. The resulting peptide chains are readily made by the host cell, but they cannot assemble into a stable sheath to yield a complete virus particle.

The subunit structure of large oligomeric protein systems can also provide considerable economy of DNA or messenger RNA. For example, the enzyme glyceraldehyde phosphate dehydrogenase consists of four identical peptide chains of about 330 residues each. A segment of DNA containing $3 \times 330 = 990$ mononucleotide units (Chapter 3) is required to code such a chain. On the other hand, if this enzyme consisted of one long polypeptide chain of

$4 \times 330 = 1{,}320$ residues, a segment of DNA containing $3 \times 1{,}320 = 3{,}960$ nucleotide units would be required to code it. It is clear that if a DNA template can be used repetitively to code identical subunits, a considerable economy of genetic material can be achieved.

Later (Chapter 9), we will see that all enzymes having regulatory or "pace-making" functions in enzyme systems belong to the class of oligomeric proteins. The rates at which such regulatory enzymes catalyze their specific reactions are modulated by the concentration of certain metabolites in the cell, particularly the end-product of the regulated enzyme system. Binding of such an end-product to the oligomeric regulatory enzyme produces physical changes in the manner in which the subunits associate together; such a change may alter the affinity of the enzyme for its substrate. Interactions between subunits of oligomeric proteins thus have many implications in the dynamics of protein function.

There is now substantial genetic evidence that each type of peptide chain in an oligomeric protein containing different chains is coded by a separate gene. The α- and β-chains of hemoglobin, for example, are coded by two different genes. Other examples, the *isozymes*, are discussed in Chapter 9.

Summary

Each protein has at least one three-dimensional conformation in which it is stable and active under biological conditions of temperature and pH; this is the native conformation. X-ray analysis of the fibrous proteins α-keratin, β-keratin, silk fibroin, and collagen have yielded important clues to their structure. The peptide chains of α-keratins, which are present in hair and wool, are right-handed α-helical coils held together by maximal intramolecular hydrogen bonding. Each peptide carbonyl oxygen is hydrogen-bonded to the —NH of the peptide bond four residues removed. The disulfide cross-linkages of cystine hold together the parallel α-helical coils in α-keratins. Silk fibroin and β-keratins possess a pleated-sheet structure, in which the polypeptide backbones are antiparallel or parallel, respectively; they are cross-linked by intermolecular hydrogen bonds. The three chains of collagen form kinked, left-handed helices, which intertwine to comprise the basic tropocollagen repeat unit of a collagen fibril.

The conformation of a polypeptide chain is automatically determined by the size, shape, and polarity of the R groups of its amino acids and by the amino acid sequence. The R groups are sufficiently close together so that they may, by interacting with each other or with the solvent, limit free rotation of the single bonds of the peptide-chain backbone. Other constraints on the conformation of the polypeptide chain are imposed by the rigid and nearly planar nature of the peptide bond and by the occurrence of covalent —S—S— cross-linkages.

X-ray analysis of globular proteins shows that their chains are compactly folded, leaving little space in the interior for water molecules. All or nearly all the polar R groups of globular proteins are on the surface and are hydrated; the hydrophobic residues remain shielded inside. Depending on their amino acid sequence, globular proteins contain widely varying amounts of α-helix or β-conformation. Proline residues cause bends to occur in α-helical coils.

Quaternary structure of oligomeric proteins is also determined by the primary amino acid sequence of the component protomers. Oligomeric proteins, such as hemoglobin and allosteric enzymes, display self-assembly properties. Construction of large proteins from a number of separate polypeptide chains minimizes the consequences of errors in the biosynthesis of proteins, conserves genetic material, and, makes possible regulatory interactions, as in the case of regulatory enzymes.

References

Books

DICKERSON, R. E. and I. GEIS: *The Structure and Action of Proteins*, Harper & Row, New York, 1969. A protein crystallographer and a scientific illustrator collaborated to produce this book, which includes a unique collection of stereo drawings of protein conformations.

WILSON, H. R.: *Diffraction of X-rays by Proteins, Nucleic Acids and Viruses*, St. Martin's Press, Inc., New York, 1966. An excellent elementary account of the x-ray technique.

WOLSTENHOLME, G. E. W. (ed.): *Principles of Biomolecular Organization*, Little, Brown and Company, Boston, 1966. Proceedings of an interesting informal symposium, with all discussion recorded.

Articles and Reviews

COHEN, C.: "Architecture of the α-Class of Fibrous Proteins," in T. Hayashi and A. G. Szent-Györgyi (eds.), *Molecular Architecture in Cell Physiology*, Prentice-Hall, Inc., Englewood Cliffs, N.J., 1966, pp. 169–190.

HARTE, R. A., and J. A. RUPLEY: "Three-dimensional Pictures of Molecular Models," *J. Biol. Chem.*, **243:**1664–1669 (1968). Startling three-dimensional "xographs" of lysozyme.

KENDREW, J. C.: "The Three-dimensional Structure of a Protein Molecule," *Sci. Am.*, **205:**96 (Dec., 1961).

KLOTZ, I. M.: "Protein Subunits: A Table," *Science*, **155:**697–698 (1967).

LEVINTHAL, C.: "Molecular Model-building by Computer," *Sci. Am.*, **214:**43 (November, 1966). Computer representation of protein conformations.

PERUTZ, M. F.: "X-ray analysis, structure, and function of enzyme molecules," The First Sir Hans Krebs Lecture, *European J. of Biochem.*, **8:** 455–466 (1969). A beautifully illustrated survey of the conformation of enzyme molecules.

PHILLIPS, D. C.: "The Three-dimensional Structure of an Enzyme Molecule," *Sci. Am.*, **215:**78–90 (Nov., 1966). Relation of structure to function in lysozyme.

SUND, H., and K. WEBER: "The Quaternary Structure of Proteins," *Angew. Chem. Intern. Ed. Engl.*, **5:**231–245 (1966). Excellent brief review.

VAN HOLDE, K. E.: "The Molecular Architecture of Multichain Proteins," in T. Hayashi and A. G. Szent-Györgyi (eds.), *Molecular Architecture in Cell Physiology*, Prentice-Hall, Inc., Englewood Cliffs, N.J., 1966, pp. 81–96.

Problems

1. Calculate the length (in Å) of a polypeptide chain containing 105 amino acid residues if (a) it exists entirely in α-helical form, or (b) it is fully extended.

2. If an *E. coli* cell contains 10^6 protein molecules, each of mol wt 40,000, calculate the total length of all the polypeptide chains of a single *E. coli* cell, assuming they are entirely α-helical.

3. In the following polypeptide: (a) Which sections would you expect to have α-helical configuration at pH 7.0? (b) Where might bend points occur? (c) Where might cross-linkages be formed?

   1 2 3 4 5 6 7 8 9 10 11 12 13 14
   Ileu-Ala-His-Thr-Tyr-Gly-Pro-Phe-Glu-Ala-Ala-Met-Cys-Lys-
   15 16 17 18 19 20 21 22 23 24 25 26 27 28
   Trp-Glu-Glu-Glu-Pro-Asp-Gly-Met-Glu-Cys-Ala-Phe-His-Arg

4. The protein sheath of the tobacco mosaic virus contains 2130 identical subunit polypeptide chains of 130 amino acids each. If each error in insertion of an amino acid results in a defective subunit which is rejected, estimate the maximum frequency of errors possible (number per 1,000,000 residues) if the final yield of intact active viral particles is to be 50 percent of all the viral polypeptide made. Repeat the calculation assuming that the entire coat is constructed of but one polypeptide chain.

5. The polypeptide chain of a given protein is α-helical in some segments and has the β-conformation in others. The protein has a mol wt of 240,000 and a contour length of 5.06×10^{-5} cm. Calculate the fraction of the molecule that exists in the α-helical configuration.

6. At low pH an enzyme of molecular weight 300,000 dissociates into two separable components, of molecular weights 100,000 and 50,000. The larger particles, which account for two-thirds of the total protein have catalytic activity; the smaller particles have none. Treatment of the larger particles with β-mercaptoethanol, which reduces disulfide linkages, caused the catalytic activity to be lost and the rate of sedimentation to decrease; only a single peak could be observed in the ultracentrifuge. What can you deduce about the structure of the enzyme?

7. There are some 25,000 ribosomes in an *E. coli* cell. If the structural proteins of these ribosomes were stretched out end to end as fully extended polypeptide chains, how many times could they encircle the *E. coli* cell? Assume that the ribosomes are 180 Å in diameter, with a specific gravity of 1.0, and that they contain 40 percent protein. Assume that the *E. coli* cell is a sphere 1 μ in diameter.

8. Calculate the density of the tightly coiled tropocollagen molecule, which may be considered to be a cylinder 2,800 Å long and 14 Å in diameter. It contains three polypeptide chains of 1,000 amino acid residues each.

CHAPTER 7 PROTEINS: BEHAVIOR IN SOLUTION

This chapter is devoted to a brief description of the physical principles underlying the behavior of proteins in solution, the methods for determining their molecular weights and shapes, and the techniques involved in their separation and purification. Although there is little discussion of biological principles in this chapter, it must be appreciated that much of our knowledge of the biological function of proteins has depended on study of highly purified preparations of globular proteins, well characterized as to their molecular weight and behavior as solutes. The isolation and characterization of pure proteins and other macromolecules have required an enormous input of painstaking and largely unsung effort in the history of biochemistry. In the last few years the techniques of protein separation have been greatly simplified and refined.

Acid-Base Properties of Proteins

The acid-base behavior of native, intact globular proteins in solution is largely determined by the relatively large number of ionizable R groups of the various amino acids; the single α-amino and α-carboxyl groups at the ends of the peptide chains make very little contribution. Since native proteins differ from each other with respect to both amino acid sequence and conformation, the extent of ionization of each type of R group will be influenced by the nature of neighboring R groups. Nevertheless, a number of important generalizations can be made from acid-base titration curves of globular proteins of known amino acid content and sequence.

Figure 7-1
Titration curve of ribonuclease.

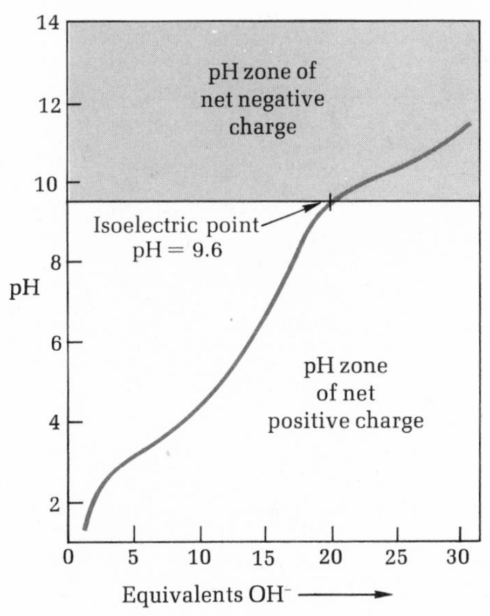

Figure 7-1 shows a titration curve of ribonuclease. Ribonuclease has 124 amino acids in known sequence and is tightly folded. It possesses 34 ionizing R groups, of which the majority are basic, in addition to the NH_2-terminal and COOH-terminal groups. Its titration curve is thus a composite, reflecting the ionization of many groups. Since the different types of ionizing groups have different heats of ionization, their quantitative contributions can be calculated by carrying out titrations at different temperatures. The results of such calculations for ribonuclease are shown in Table 7-1. These data also show that the *average* pK′ values for the different classes of R groups in ribonu-

Table 7-1 Titratable groups of ribonuclease

	Number per molecule (from amino acid composition)	*Number per molecule (from titration curve)*	*Approximate pK′*
α-COOH	1	11	
R-group–COOH (Glu, Asp)	10		4.7
Imidazole (His)	4	5	6.5
α-Amino	1		7.8
Phenolic OH (Tyr)	6	16	9.95
ε-Amino (Lys)	10		10.2
Guanidyl (Arg)	4	4	12

clease are close to the values given by the corresponding free amino acids or simple peptides.

Very similar results have been obtained with β-lactoglobulin, egg albumin, and other globular proteins. From this approach, it has been concluded that the great majority of the ionizing groups of proteins are accessible to acid-base titration. This is in agreement with the generalization from x-ray studies (Chapter 6) that nearly all the ionizing R groups of globular proteins are on the outer surface and most of the hydrophobic, or nonpolar, groups in the interior. Some globular proteins, however, possess one or more ionizing groups that are not directly titratable, presumably because they are hidden within the tertiary structure or because they participate in hydrogen bonding For example, in myoglobin 5 of the 11 histidine R groups are inaccessible to titration unless the protein is denatured.

Titration curves also show that most proteins have only a very small portion of their total buffering capacity in the range of intracellular pH, that is, pH 6 to 7. It will be recalled (Chapter 4) that the only amino acid having an R group with a pK′ in this range is histidine; moreover, most proteins contain relatively few histidine residues. Hemoglobin, which contains 8 percent histidine, is an exception; it plays a very important role as an intracellular buffer in the erythrocyte.

Proteins, like peptides and amino acids, also have characteristic isoelectric pH values at which they behave as zwitterions and carry no *net* electrical charge. At this pH, they fail to migrate when placed in an electrical field. The isoelectric pH is determined by the number and pK′ of the ionizing R groups. It will be relatively high, above pH 7.0, if the protein has a relatively high content of basic amino acids (lysine, arginine), as is the case with ribonuclease. It will be relatively low if the protein has a preponderance of acidic residues (aspartic and glutamic acids), as is the case with pepsin (Chapter 5). Most globular proteins have isoelectric points between pH 4.5 and 6.5 (Table 7-2).

The titration curve of a protein also indicates the sign and magnitude of its net electrical charge at any given pH. At any pH above the isoelectric point, a protein will have a net negative charge and will move toward the anode. Its negative charge will increase in magnitude as the pH is increased, in accordance with the shape of the titration

Table 7-2 Isoelectric points of some proteins

	Isoelectric pH
Pepsin	<1.0
Egg albumin	4.6
Serum albumin	4.9
Urease	5.0
β-Lactoglobulin	5.2
γ_1-Globulin	6.6
Hemoglobin	6.8
Myoglobin	7.0
Chymotrypsinogen	9.5
Cytochrome c	10.65
Lysozyme	11.0

curve. Similarly, at any pH below the isoelectric point, the protein will have a net positive charge and will move toward the cathode (Figure 7-1).

Both the titration curve and the isoelectric pH of a protein may change significantly in the presence of neutral salts, which influence the degree of ionization of the different types of R groups. Proteins also may bind cations such as Ca^{2+} and Mg^{2+} or anions such as chloride or phosphate. For these reasons, the observed isoelectric pH values for proteins depend on the nature of the medium in which the protein is dissolved.

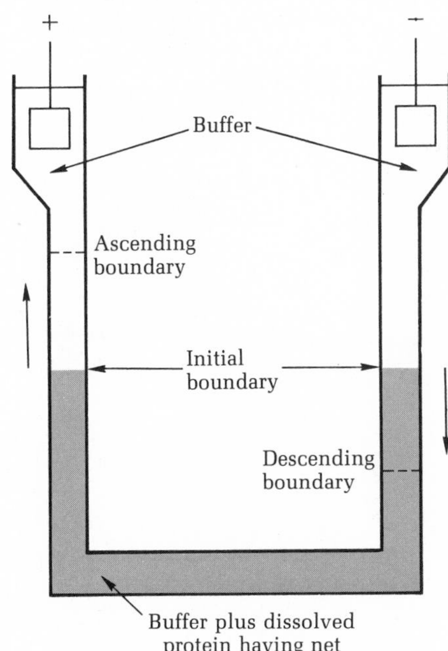

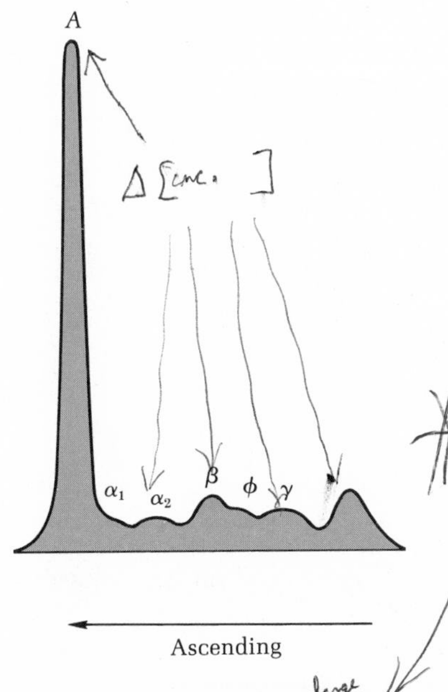

Figure 7-2
(Top) Schematic view of Tiselius moving-boundary electrophoresis apparatus. (Bottom) Electrophoretic pattern of human blood plasma proteins (pH 8.6). A = serum albumin; ϕ = fibrinogen; α_1, α_2, β, and γ are various globulins.

Separating Proteins by Acid-Base Behavior

The acid-base behavior of proteins is directly exploited in two methods for separating and analyzing protein mixtures: electrophoresis and ion-exchange chromatography.

Electrophoresis

It is possible to separate mixtures of globular proteins in solution on the basis of their different rates of migration in an electrical field at a given pH. Such separations were first carried out in a refined way by Arne Tiselius in 1937. The electrical mobility μ of a molecule is given by the ratio of the velocity of migration v to the field strength E in cm^2 per volt-sec:

$$\mu = \frac{v}{E}$$

For small ions, such as chloride, μ is between 4 and 9×10^{-4} cm^2 per volt-sec (25°C). For proteins, it is about 0.1 to 1.0×10^{-4} cm^2 per volt-sec at 25°C. Proteins therefore migrate much more slowly in an electrical field than do simple ions such as Na^+ or Cl^-; in general, they have a smaller ratio of charge to mass.

There are two general methods by which electrophoresis of protein mixtures is carried out. In *free*, or *moving boundary, electrophoresis*, a buffered solution of the protein mixture is placed in a U-shaped observation cell and columns of pure buffer are carefully layered over the protein solution (Figure 7-2). An electrical field is applied at constant temperature and under vibration-free conditions. The pH of the buffer is chosen to yield maximum separation of the proteins present. As each protein migrates from the solution into the zone of protein-free buffer, a front, or boundary, is formed and moves to the electrode. The refractive index of the solution changes sharply at this boundary because the protein molecules have an index of refraction different from that of the pure buffer alone. From measurements of the refractive-index changes along the cell, which are made by an optical technique called the *schlieren method*, electrophoretic patterns are constructed which show the direction and relative rate of migration of each protein species (Figure 7-2). Each peak in the pattern corresponds to the position of the moving boundary of a specific protein (it does not represent a peak of protein concentration). If the electrophoretic mobility of a given protein is determined at several different pH values, the isoelectric pH of the protein can be extrapolated. Actually, the titration curve of a protein is an approximate measure of its electrophoretic mobility as a function of pH. Moving-boundary electrophoresis was for many years the most valuable method for quantitative analysis of complex mixtures of proteins, such as occur in blood plasma. However, it has several disadvantages. It is slow and very large samples of protein are needed, the optical system required is complex and expensive, the moving boundaries are very prone to disturbance from vibrations and convection, and the method cannot be used for separating proteins in bulk.

The second type of electrophoresis, which has largely supplanted the moving-boundary method because of its simplicity and much greater resolving power, is zone electrophoresis. In this method, electrophoresis of the aqueous protein solution is usually carried out in a solid matrix or support, such as filter paper, starch gel, or polyacrylamide gel—materials that are hydrated and porous but which possess mechanical rigidity. The solid matrix prevents convection and vibration disturbance. No complex optical system is required to detect the boundary between protein and buffer since the position of the protein on the gel block can easily be detected by qualitative color tests. The greatest advantage is that the length of the gel block and other conditions can be so chosen as to allow the electrophoretic process to continue until the individual proteins completely separate into discrete zones. *Disk electrophoresis* is a refinement of gel electrophoresis in which the mixture of proteins is subjected simultaneously to an electrical field and to a pH gradient in a polyacrylamide gel (Figure 7-3). The proteins separate into very thin bands or disks. Disk electrophoresis permits high-resolution analysis of extremely small samples of complex mixtures of proteins. It is also used for detecting mutant forms of hemoglobin and other proteins; a difference of a single charged group per molecule is sufficient to distinguish the mutant from the normal protein.

Figure 7-3
Disk electrophoresis. In this form of zone electrophoresis, which is carried out in polyacrylamide gel columns (350 × 50 mm), a pH gradient along the column aids in separating the proteins into very narrow bands or disks.

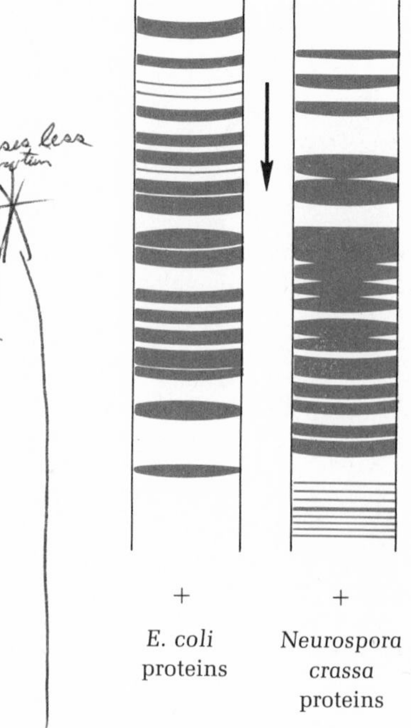

Ion-Exchange Chromatography

The same basic principles that make possible the separation and analysis of amino acid mixtures on columns of ion-exchange resins (Chapter 4) can be applied in separating protein mixtures. The most commonly used materials for chromatography of proteins are synthetically prepared derivatives of cellulose. Diethylaminoethylcellulose (abbreviated DEAE-cellulose) contains the positively charged $Et_2-NH^+-C_2H_5O-R$ group at pH 7.0 (R indicates the cellulose molecule) and is thus an anion exchanger. Carboxymethylcellulose (abbreviated CM-cellulose) contains negatively charged groups ($R-O-CH_2-COO^-$) and is a cation exchanger. The protein mixture is eluted with buffers of increasing or decreasing pH, or by keeping pH constant and varying ionic strength. The protein appearing in the eluate, which is collected in small fractions, is estimated optically by its capacity to absorb light in the ultraviolet region (Chapter 4).

Precipitation of Proteins as Salts

Most proteins can be completely precipitated from aqueous solution by the addition of certain acids, such as tri-

Figure 7-4
Effect of pH and salt concentration on the solubility of β-lactoglobulin at 25°C. Figures give the concentration of NaCl.

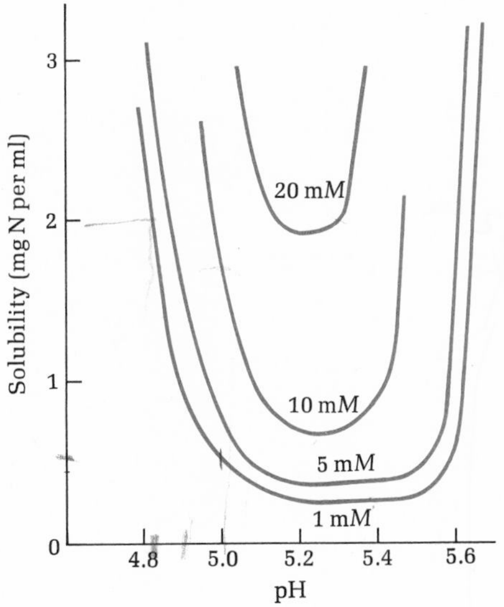

chloroacetic and perchloric acids, which form acid-insoluble salts with the protein. These reagents are widely used to "clear" biological fluids or cell extracts of proteins prior to analysis for small-molecular-weight molecules such as glucose and amino acids. Other, similar protein precipitants include tungstic acid, phosphotungstic acid, and metaphosphoric acid. Similarly, proteins may be precipitated by such cations as Zn^{2+} and Pb^{2+}.

Separation of Proteins by Solubility Differences

Globular proteins vary considerably in their solubility in aqueous systems; these differences may be exploited to bring about separation of mixtures of proteins. Four important variables influencing the solubility of proteins have been recognized: (1) pH, (2) ionic strength, (3) the dielectric properties of the solvent, and (4) temperature.

Effect of pH on Solubility

Figure 7-4 shows the effect of pH on the solubility of native β-lactoglobulin under conditions in which the NaCl concentration of the solution is varied. As you can see, solubility is minimal at pH 5.2 to 5.3, regardless of the concentration of NaCl present. On either side of this critical pH, the solubility rises sharply, and at pH 4.9 or 5.7, only a few tenths of a pH "unit" removed from the pH of least solubility, the protein may be 10 times more soluble, particularly at low NaCl concentrations.

The pH at which β-lactoglobulin is least soluble is its isoelectric pH (see Table 7-2). In fact, nearly all globular proteins are least soluble at their isoelectric pH because at this pH the molecule has no net charge and thus no electrostatic repulsions exist between neighboring protein molecules. At pH values above or below the isoelectric point, all the protein molecules will have a net charge of the same sign. They will therefore repel each other and prevent coalescence of single molecules into insoluble aggregates. Some proteins are virtually insoluble at their isoelectric pH when salt is lacking.

Since different proteins have different isoelectric pH values, they can be separated from each other by the technique known as *isoelectric precipitation*. When the pH of a protein mixture is adjusted to the isoelectric pH of one of its components, much or all of that component will precipitate, leaving behind in solution those proteins having isoelectric pH values above or below that pH.

Figure 7-5
Effect of neutral salt (K_2SO_4) on the solubility of carbonyl hemoglobin at its isoelectric pH. The ionic strength of a solution is given by $\frac{1}{2}\Sigma c_i z_i^2$, in which Σ is the sum of the products of the concentration c_i and the square of the charge z_i of each ion in the solution. At low ionic strength, the protein is salted-in, i.e., increases in solubility. At high salt concentration, it is salted-out.

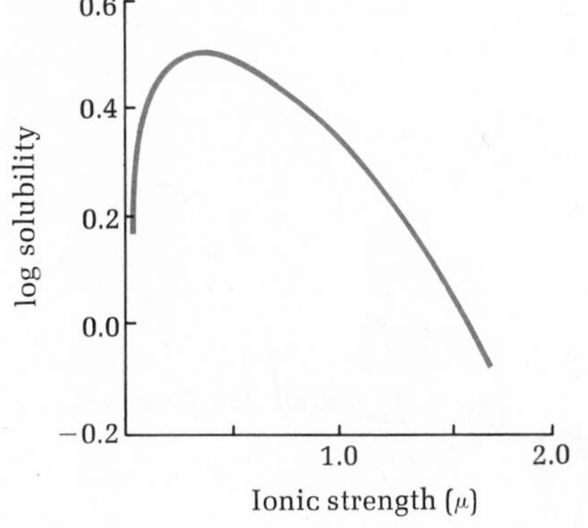

Effect of Salt Concentration on Solubility

Neutral salts have pronounced effects on the solubility of globular proteins, as shown in Figures 7-4 and 7-5. In low concentrations, they increase the solubility of many proteins, a phenomenon which is called *salting-in*. The salting-in effect is independent of the nature of the neutral salt; it is a function of both the concentration of the salt and the number of charges on each ionic species in solution. Salts containing divalent ions, such as $MgCl_2$ and $MgSO_4$, are far more effective at salting-in than salts such as NaCl, NH_4Cl, and KCl. Salting-in effects are caused by changes in the tendency of dissociable groups on the protein to ionize.

When the concentration of neutral salts is greatly increased, the solubility of proteins begins to decrease again, and at very high salt concentrations, a protein may be completely precipitated, an effect called *salting-out*. The physical-chemical basis of salting-out is not entirely clear. Salting-in and salting-out are important procedures in the separation of protein mixtures since different proteins vary in their response to neutral salt concentration.

Effect of the Solvent on Solubility

The addition of water-miscible neutral organic solvents such as ethanol and acetone decreases the solubility of most proteins in water to such an extent that they will precipitate out of solution. Quantitative study of this effect has revealed that protein solubility at a fixed pH and ionic strength is a function of the dielectric constant of the medium and of the tendency of the added solvent to decrease hydration of ionic groups. Ethanol has a lower dielectric constant than water (Table 2-2). Since a decrease in dielectric constant increases the attractive force between two opposite charges (Chapter 2), ethanol decreases the ionization of proteins and thus promotes their coalescence. Mixtures of proteins can thus be separated on the basis of quantitative differences in their loss of solubility with increasing ethanol or acetone concentration.

Effect of Temperature on Solubility

Within a limited range, from about 0° to about 40°C, most proteins will increase in solubility with increasing temperature, but there are exceptions. Above 40° to 50°C, most proteins become increasingly unstable and begin to denature, ordinarily with a loss of solubility at the neutral pH zone.

Membrane Equilibria of Proteins: Osmosis

A number of biologically important properties of proteins as solutes derive from the fact that protein molecules are very large. Protein molecules do not diffuse through certain membranes that allow passage of water and low-molecular-weight solutes. For example, cellophane membranes can be used to remove small solute molecules from solutions containing proteins by the process called *dialysis* (Figure 7-6). Dialysis is frequently used to remove protein-precipitating agents such as neutral salts and ethanol from protein solutions during purification. In general, most biological membranes are impermeable to proteins, but they do permit water and simple uncharged solutes to pass freely.

When a semipermeable membrane separates a solution of a protein in water from pure water, *osmosis* will occur. The concentration—or, more accurately, the thermodynamic activity—of water molecules in the protein solution

Figure 7-6
Dialysis. Since the membrane enclosing the protein solution is semipermeable, water and small solutes, such as glucose or NaCl, pass the membrane freely but proteins do not. By replacing the outer aqueous phase with fresh distilled H_2O several times, the concentration of small solute molecules in the protein solution can be reduced to a vanishingly small amount.

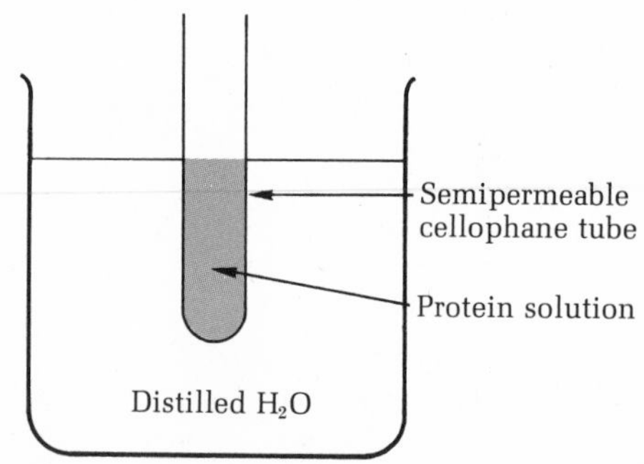

Figure 7-7
Osmosis and osmotic pressure.

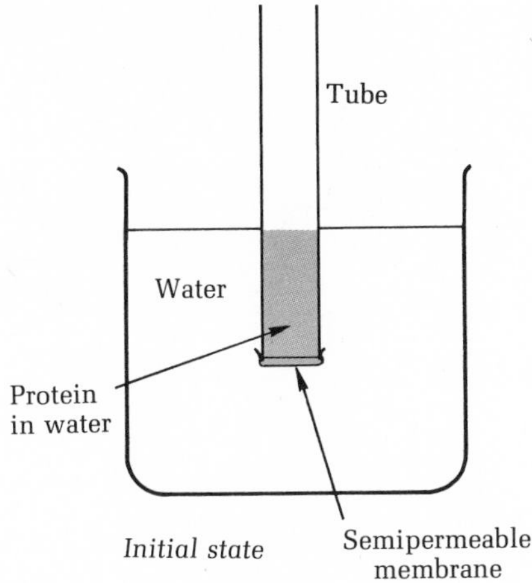

Initial state

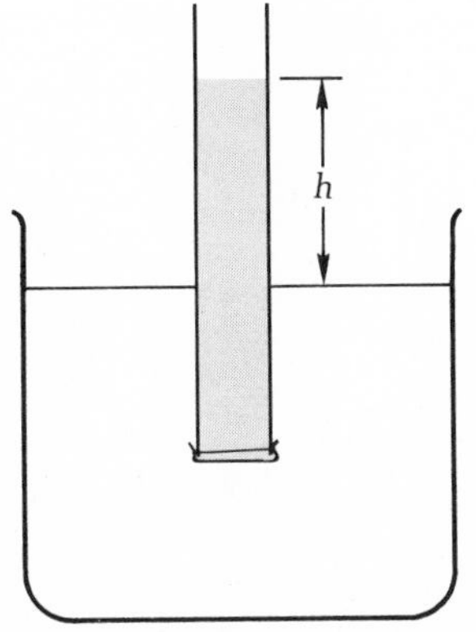

Final state. Water has moved into protein solution. At equilibrium, height of column of protein solution *h* just counterbalances osmotic pressure.

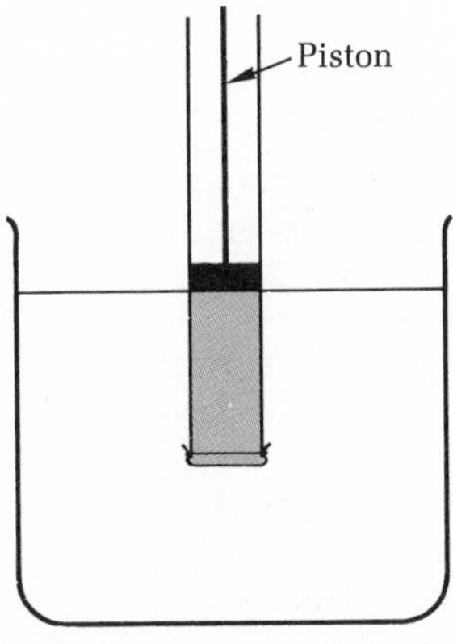

Osmotic pressure is force that must be applied to piston to exactly oppose osmotic flow. It is equal to hydrostatic head *h*.

is less than in pure water, and the system will compensate for this difference by net movement of water from the pure-water compartment into that containing the protein solution, until the concentration of the water is the same on both sides of the membrane. *Osmotic pressure* is the force that must be applied to just prevent such osmotic flow (Figure 7-7). It is one of the colligative properties of solutions and is a function of the number of solute particles per unit volume. The osmotic pressure of a solution is independent of the molecular nature of the solute. Under appropriate conditions, osmotic pressure measurements are useful in establishing the particle weight of proteins (see below).

Diffusion and the Diffusion Coefficient

In a solution at equilibrium, the distribution of the solute is statistically uniform throughout the solution, although the solute molecules are in constant thermal motion. The path in space taken by any given solute molecule over a period of time is called a *random walk*. In a solution at equilibrium, the net displacement of a solute molecule in a random walk over a period of time is zero. However, if a concentration gradient of a solute is formed—for example, by carefully layering pure water over a solution of a protein in water—then protein molecules will tend to move from the region of high concentration in the lower layer to the region of low concentration in the upper layer until an equilibrium is reached in which the protein molecules are uniformly randomized throughout the system. This net movement of solute molecules in response to a gradient is called *diffusion*. The random walk taken by any single solute molecule during such net diffusion will, at the end of a period of time, result in a net displacement of the molecule in the direction of the zone of lower concentration. Diffusion is a consequence of the second law of thermodynamics, which states that all processes tend to occur in such a direction as to increase entropy or randomness.

The rate of diffusion is given by Fick's first law of diffusion: the amount of solute ds diffusing across the area A in a period of time dt is proportional to the concentration gradient dc/dx at that point:

$$\frac{ds}{dt} = -DA\frac{dc}{dx}$$

The proportionality constant D is the *diffusion coefficient;* it is defined as the quantity of solute diffusing per second across a surface area of 1.0 cm^2 when there is a concentration gradient of unity. Since diffusion is in the direction of the lower concentration, the sign of the expression is negative. The diffusion coefficient is a function of the size and shape of the molecule and the frictional resistance offered by the viscosity of the solvent. For spherical molecules that are very large in comparison to water molecules, the diffusion coefficient is inversely proportional to the radius and thus inversely proportional to the cube root of the molecular weight.

Figure 7-8
Diffusion of Proteins.
The protein distribution in the diffusion cell at zero time and at 10 hours.

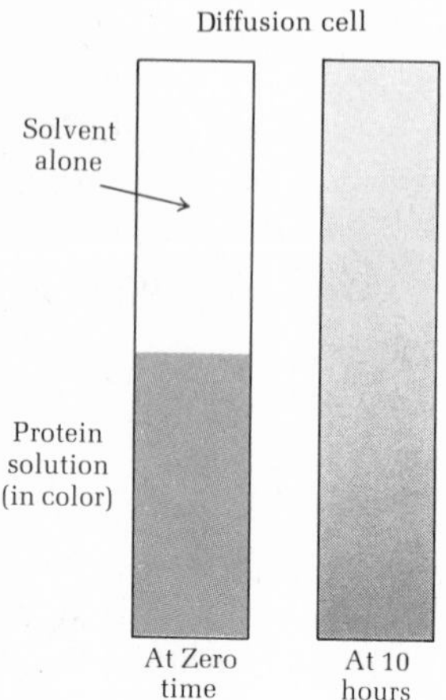

Graphical representation showing the concentration of protein in the cell at different time intervals.

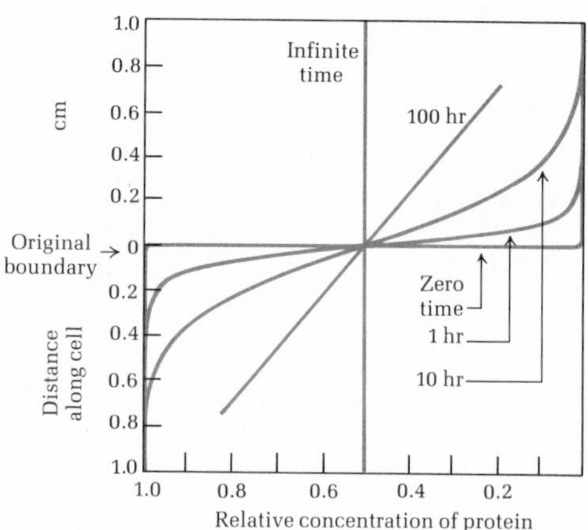

Diffusion coefficients of proteins can be determined by measuring the rate at which the boundary of protein molecules migrates upward in a diffusion cell in which pure solvent is layered over a protein solution of known concentration. The movement of the boundary is followed optically. The physical changes occurring in such a cell are diagramed in Figure 7-8. The diffusion coefficient of solutes decreases with increasing molecular weight (Table 7-3). However, for very large solute molecules, such as proteins, the diffusion coefficient is relatively insensitive to molecular weight. Serum albumin, for example, has twice the molecular weight of β-lactoglobulin, but its diffusion coefficient is only 16 percent less. This is because diffusion is opposed by the frictional resistance of the solvent, which is a very sensitive function of the radius of the particle. For this reason, the diffusion coefficient alone is not a useful measure of the molecular weight of a protein. However, combined with sedimentation measurements, it can yield quite accurate values (see below).

Diffusion is a fundamental process in all cellular transport activities. The rate of diffusion and the length of diffusion paths of various metabolites and enzymes are believed to set physical limits to the size and volume of the metabolizing mass of living cells and their organelles.

Table 7-3 Physical constants of some proteins

Protein	*Mol wt*
Cytochrome c (bovine heart)	13,370
Myoglobin (horse heart)	16,900
Chymotrypsinogen (bovine pancreas)	23,240
β-Lactoglobulin (goat milk)	37,100
Serum albumin (human)	68,500
Hemoglobin (human)	64,500
Catalase (horse liver)	247,500
Urease (jack bean)	482,700
Fibrinogen (human)	339,700
Myosin (cod)	524,800
Tobacco mosaic virus	40,590,000

Determining Molecular Weight from Chemical Composition

Since each molecule of a given protein must contain at least one molecule of its prosthetic group or at least one residue of any of its component amino acids, the mass of the protein containing one such residue is the minimum molecular weight. For example, myoglobin contains 0.335 percent iron. We may then calculate

$$\text{Minimum mol wt} = \frac{\text{atomic weight of iron}}{\text{percent iron}} \times 100$$

$$= \frac{56}{0.335} \times 100$$

$$= 16{,}700$$

The true molecular weight will be n times the minimum molecular weight, where $n =$ the number of iron atoms per molecule. Since $n = 1$ in the case of myoglobin, its true molecular weight is 16,700. Hemoglobin also contains 0.335 percent iron. However, there are four iron atoms per molecule of hemoglobin. Thus, $n = 4$ and the true molecular weight is $4 \times 16{,}700 = 66{,}800$. Such calculations are most accurate if the residue or element used as the basis for calculation has a small value of n.

Determining Molecular Weight by Physical-Chemical Methods

These methods of calculation fall into two main categories: (1) *number-average methods*, based on the colligative properties of solutions, such as osmotic pressure, which depend on the number of particles present per unit volume, and (2) *weight-average methods*, based on the actual mass of the particles. If a protein in solution is monodisperse (i.e., if all molecules have the same size), the number-average and weight-average methods will give the same molecular weight. If, however, it is polydisperse (the molecules have different sizes), the weight-average methods will give a molecular weight larger than that given by the number-average methods. Although protein molecules of a given type all have exactly the same molecular weight and can be expected to be monodisperse, a fraction of them may dissociate into subunits or associate into polymers under certain conditions. Comparison of number-average and weight-average molecular weights is one way of detecting dissociation or association phenomena.

Table 7-3 (Continued)

Diffusion coefficient ($D_{20,w} \times 10^7$)	Sedimentation coefficient ($s_{20,w}$)	Frictional ratio (f/fo)
11.4	1.17	1.19
11.3	2.04	1.11
9.5	2.54	1.19
7.48	2.85	1.26
6.1	4.6	1.29
6.9	4.46	1.16
4.1	11.3	1.25
3.46	18.6	1.19
1.98	7.63	2.34
1.10	6.43	3.63
0.46	198	2.03

Determining Molecular Weight from Osmotic Pressure

The basic relationship between molecular weight and osmotic pressure is given by

$$M = \frac{c}{\pi} RT \Big|_{c \to 0}$$

where M is molecular weight, c the concentration in grams per liter, R the gas constant (0.082 liter atm deg^{-1} mole^{-1}), T the absolute temperature, and π the osmotic pressure in atmospheres. The concentration of any solute producing an osmotic pressure equal to that of a molal solution of a perfect solute in an ideal solvent (22.4 atm at 0°C) is referred to as having an *osmolarity* of 1.00. However, because neither solutes nor solvents are ideal, this relationship holds only for very dilute solutions. In practise, osmotic-pressure measurements are made at several concentrations of solute and the data are extrapolated to zero concentration. Although the osmotic-pressure method has important theoretical advantages, it is subject to some complications. These can be avoided if the measurements are made at the isoelectric pH of the protein and if the latter is freed of low molecular weight impurities that are not permeant through the membrane of the apparatus.

Determining Molecular Weight by Sedimentation Analysis

By use of the ultracentrifuge, invented by T. Svedberg in 1925, centrifugal fields exceeding 250,000 times the force of gravity can be attained. Such a high centrifugal field causes protein molecules to sediment from solution, opposing the force of diffusion, which normally keeps them evenly dispersed in solution. Three types of sedimentation measurements are used to determine the molecular weight of proteins: *sedimentation velocity*, *sedimentation equilibrium*, and *approach-to-equilibrium*.

Sedimentation-Velocity Method

If the centrifugal force exerted on protein molecules in solution greatly exceeds the opposing diffusion force, the molecules will sediment down from the surface of the solvent (i.e., the *meniscus*), leaving behind pure solvent. A sharp boundary is thus formed. The rate of movement of this boundary down the centrifuge cell is observed by optical measurements of the index of refraction at different positions along the cell, usually by the schlieren method (also employed in free electrophoresis and diffusion measurements). The measurements are made photographically at timed intervals during the centrifugation, while the rotor is spinning. The drive system of the centrifuge is engineered to produce constant speeds without vibration.

When the sedimenting boundary of protein moves at a constant rate, the centrifugal force just counterbalances the frictional resistance of the solvent. The rate of sedimentation is expressed as the sedimentation coefficient *s*, and it is a function of both the weight and the shape of the particle:

$$s = \frac{dx/dt}{\omega^2 x}$$

where *x* is the distance from the center of rotation, ω the angular velocity in radians per second, and *t* the time in seconds. Proteins have sedimentation coefficients in the range between 1 and 200×10^{-13} sec (Table 7-3). A sedimentation coefficient of 1×10^{-13} sec is called a *Svedberg unit* or simply a Svedberg, abbreviated S. Thus, a sedimentation coefficient of 8×10^{-13} sec would be denoted 8S.

Although the sedimentation coefficient increases with molecular weight, it is not proportional to the molecular weight since it is also influenced by the frictional resistance of the solvent and by the shape of the particle. Nevertheless, with some additional data, the molecular weight *M* of a protein can be calculated from the sedimentation

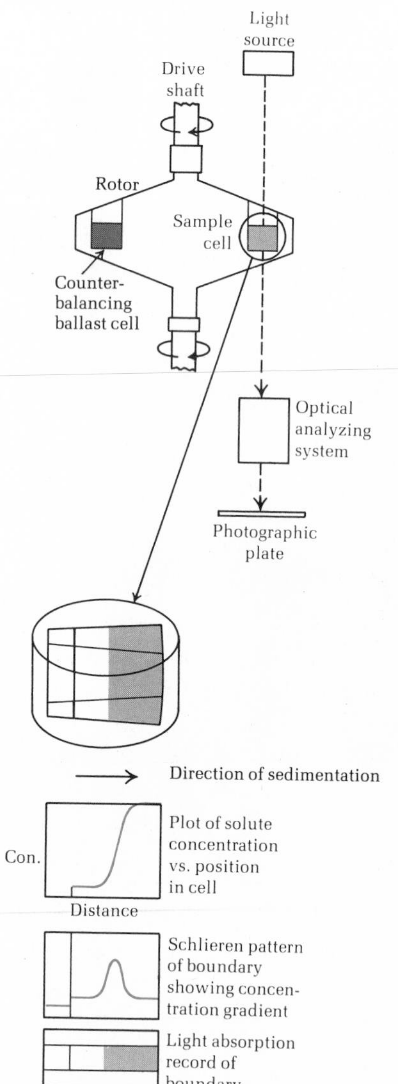

Figure 7-9
Principle of the ultracentrifuge (left), showing how optical measurements are made while sample is being centrifuged. At right are shown actual schlieren and absorption records.

coefficient by means of the Svedberg equation, which is derived by equating the centrifugal force with the opposing frictional force, the condition existing when the rate of sedimentation is constant:

$$M = \frac{RTs}{D(1 - \bar{v}\rho)}$$

where R is the gas constant in ergs per mole per degree, T the absolute temperature, s the sedimentation coefficient, $\bar{v}$ the partial specific volume of the protein, ρ the density of the solvent, and D the diffusion coefficient. The partial specific volume is the increase in volume when 1.0 gram of dry solute is added to an infinitely large volume of solvent; for most proteins in water, it is close to 0.74. Using experimentally determined values for the diffusion coefficient of the protein, obtained as described above, the molecular weight of the protein may be calculated from this equation. For the most accurate results, values of s and D must be obtained from measurements made at several different protein concentrations and extrapolated to infinite dilution.

The sedimentation-velocity method is subject to errors if the shape of the particles deviates greatly from the spherical—particularly with long, thin, rodlike molecules. Furthermore, values so calculated are very sensitive to errors in the partial specific volume, which cannot be measured accurately with small samples. On the other hand, sedimentation-velocity measurements can give valuable information about the molecular weight of a protein, its state of purity, and the composition of a protein mixture, since different proteins will sediment at different rates (Figure 7-9).

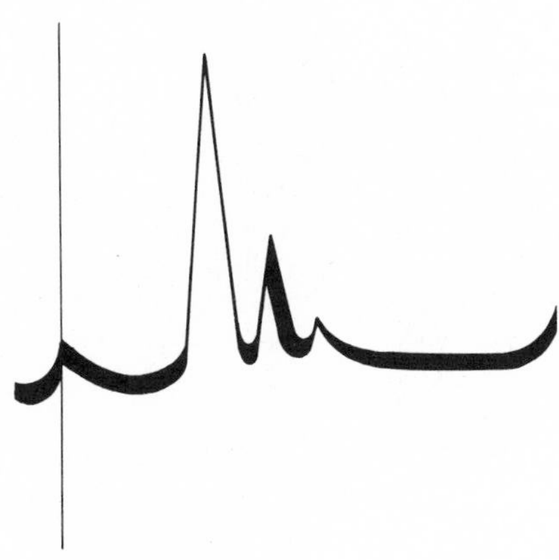

Light absorption record

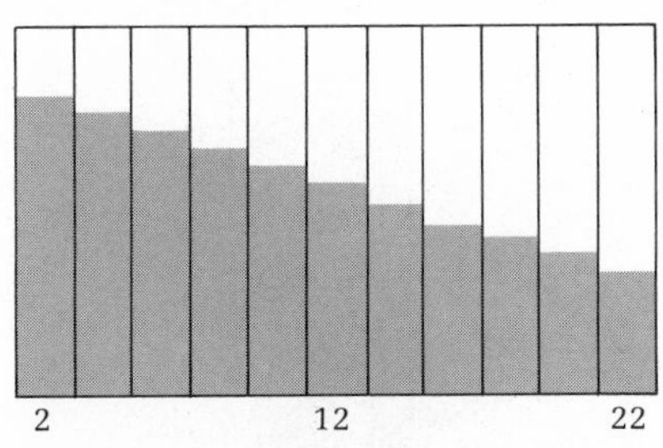

Sedimentation-Equilibrium Method

The sedimentation-equilibrium method gives molecular-weight data that are not influenced by the shape of the molecule. In this method, the ultracentrifuge is operated at a relatively low speed, just high enough so that the system comes to an equilibrium state in which the rate of sedimentation of the protein is exactly balanced by the opposing diffusion. At equilibrium no pure solvent region is present at the surface meniscus; rather, a gradient of protein molecules is formed down the centrifuge tube, in which the bottom layer may have about twice the protein concentration as the top layer. By measuring the concentration of the protein as a function of the distance from the center of rotation, data can be obtained to calculate the molecular weight from the equation

$$M = \frac{2RT \ln (c_2/c_1)}{\omega^2(1 - \bar{v}\rho)(x_2^2 - x_1^2)}$$

in which R and T have their usual meanings, c_1 and c_2 are the concentrations of the protein at two points in the tube at distances x_1 and x_2 from the center of rotation, ω is the angular velocity, ρ is the density of solvent, and $\bar{v}$ is the partial specific volume of the protein. Note that D, the diffusion coefficient, does not enter this equation. The sedimentation-equilibrium method is the most accurate of the sedimentation methods and requires no corrections for shape of the particles. It may require several days of centrifugation to attain equilibrium, a difficulty that has been solved in part by the use of cells with only a very short column of protein solution (1 to 2 mm). Furthermore, the protein must be quite pure and homogeneous.

Approach-to-Equilibrium Method

This method represents a compromise, in which some of the accuracy of the equilibrium method is sacrificed to make possible rapid measurement of molecular weight. The equilibrium method is time-consuming because of the necessity to find the precise rotor speed at which equilibrium exists. In the approach-to-equilibrium method, the rotor speed is brought to approximately the equilibrium speed over a 1 to 2 hour period by a series of adjustments. Each time, measurements of protein concentration are made near the bottom of the tube. From these, the molecular weight can be extrapolated.

Figure 7-10
Two types of density-gradient centrifugation.

Velocity type

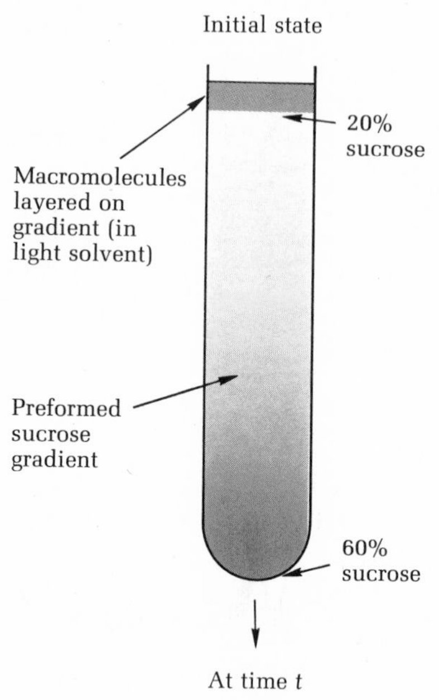

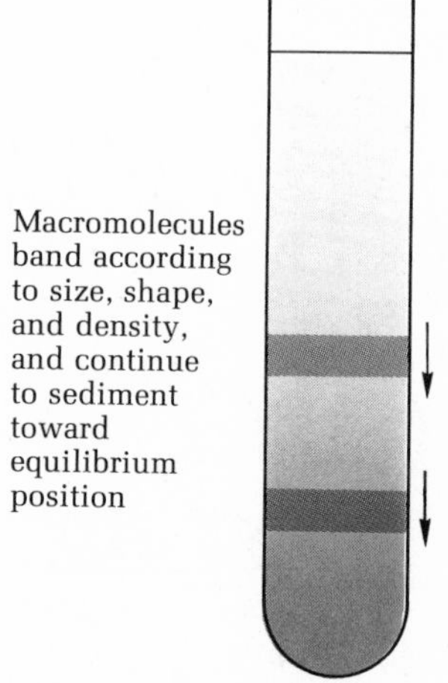

Density-Gradient Centrifugation

This relatively new and versatile procedure has become very widely used not only for determining sedimentation coefficients but also for separating all types of macromolecules, organelles, and viruses. Density-gradient centrifugation has great resolving power and simplicity.

There are two types of procedure: *velocity* and *equilibrium* (Figure 7-10). In the velocity method, a density gradient of sucrose is prepared in a centrifuge tube by means of automatically controlled pumps that mix concentrated sucrose solution and water in decreasing ratio as the tube is filled. The mixture of macromolecules, dissolved in a light solvent, is layered on top of the gradient. Centrifugation of the tube in a horizontal, or "swinging bucket," rotor causes each type of macromolecule to sediment down the density gradient at its own rate, determined primarily by its particle weight, in the form of separate bands or zones. Since the sucrose density gradient is preformed, the velocity method can yield good separations in short periods. The sedimentation coefficient of a protein may be calculated from its position in the gradient relative to the positions of bands of "marker" proteins of known sedimentation coefficient added to the same tube. An analytical ultracentrifuge is not required for such a measurement.

The equilibrium method is not used for determining molecular weight, but it is extremely useful for separating molecules on the basis of density differences. In this procedure, a preformed gradient is not employed. Instead, a 6 *M* solution of CsCl, chosen as solute because of its high solubility and low viscosity, is employed as the medium with which the macromolecules to be sedimented are mixed. When placed in a high centrifugal field, the CsCl itself will sediment slightly against the force of diffusion.

At equilibrium, which usually requires many hours or even days to attain, a stable density gradient of CsCl will be formed in the tube. The actual density at any point in the column can be calculated. The mixture of macromolecules dissolved in the CsCl solution will simultaneously separate into bands according to their density. Each component will come into equilibrium at a position where its density exactly equals that of the CsCl solution. Such equilibrium centrifugation is capable of extremely high resolution and is especially useful in separating nucleic acids (Chapter 12).

The positions of the bands of macromolecules in sucrose density gradients can be located optically or by siphoning off the contents of the tube carefully through a pinhole in the bottom of the tube and then analyzing samples. Alternatively, the plastic tube can be frozen solid and then cut into thin slices for analysis.

Equilibrium type

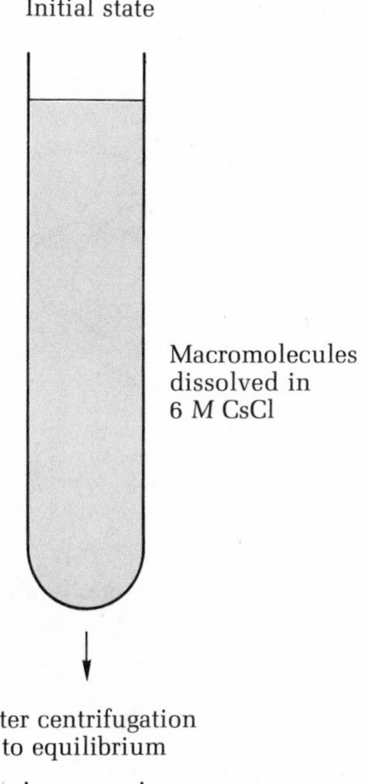
Initial state
Macromolecules dissolved in 6 M CsCl
After centrifugation to equilibrium

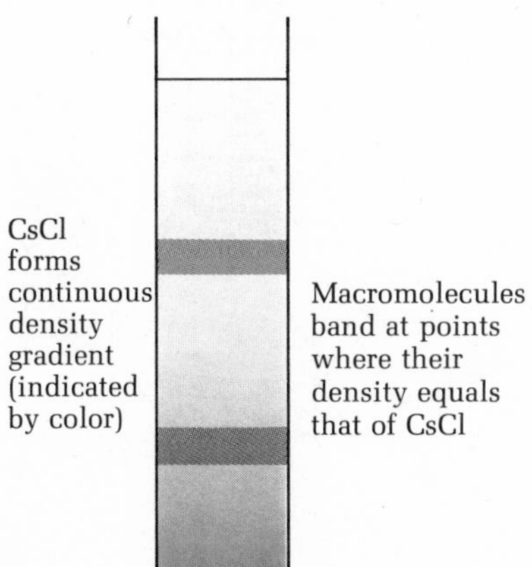
CsCl forms continuous density gradient (indicated by color)
Macromolecules band at points where their density equals that of CsCl

Determining Molecular Weight by Light Scattering

When a beam of light is passed through a protein solution in a darkened room, the path of the beam can be seen because of the scattering of the light by the protein molecules. This is called the *Tyndall effect*. From the wavelength of the incident radiation, the intensity of the scattered light, the refractive index of the solvent and solute, and the concentration of the solute, the molecular weight of the protein can be calculated. This method, which is theoretically extremely accurate, can also give information about the shape and hydration of the protein molecule. Since the measurements can be made instantaneously and recorded with time, the method can be used to study rapid changes in molecular weight (for example, by dissociation or polymerization of proteins), which no other method for measuring molecular weight permits. There are some practical difficulties. It is necessary to have extremely accurate information on the refractive-index increment of the protein solute; furthermore, extraneous dust particles produce very large errors and must be removed by careful filtration.

Molecular-Exclusion Chromatography (Gel Filtration; Molecular Sieve Chromatography)

Recently a simple, inexpensive method, requiring no elaborate instruments, has been perfected that is capable of yielding information on what is known as the *Stokes radius* (defined below) of proteins and other macromolecules. The principle of the exclusion column is best discussed on the assumption that we are dealing with spherical particles. A solution of the protein is allowed to flow by gravity through a column packed with a highly hydrated polymeric carbohydrate material which can be prepared in different particle sizes; the commercial material most widely used is Sephadex. Such a column can sort out spherical protein molecules by size because proteins of different size will differ in their ability to penetrate the hydrated pores within the particles of Sephadex. Small protein molecules, which penetrate the pores effectively, will flow more slowly down the column than proteins that are too large to penetrate the pores. The relative rates of passage are determined by measuring the concentration of the protein in successive small fractions of the eluate using light-absorption measurements at 280 nm. A pure protein capable of penetrating into the column will elute from it in a symmetrical peak. For spherical proteins, the volume of eluting buffer at which the peak appears is related to the molecular weight of the protein. The Sephadex column is first standardized by passing through it pure, approximately spherical proteins of known molecular weight and recording the volume of eluate at which their peaks appear. The unknown protein is then passed through, and its elution volume is measured and compared with those of the standards (Figure 7-11). Molecular-exclusion columns do not measure the true molecular weight of an unknown protein but rather its Stokes radius, which is most simply defined as the radius of a perfect unhydrated sphere having the same rate of passage through the column as the unknown protein in question. If the unknown and the standard are both spherical, the method yields the molecular weight directly.

Molecular-exclusion columns prepared from different materials can be used to measure the approximate molecular weights of solutes ranging in weight from as little as 500 up to many millions. The method has the unique advantage of being able to yield the Stokes radius or approximate molecular weight of a given protein even in very complex mixtures, providing the protein has a characteristic biological activity or property that can be measured. For example, crude cell extracts may contain hundreds of different enzymes. Nevertheless, it is often possible to determine the approximate molecular weight of a single type of enzyme in this extract without isolating it, simply by passing the extract through a Sephadex column and determining the position of the peak of the enzyme's catalytic activity in the eluates. The presence of other proteins is irrelevant since each protein will pass through the column independent of the others, each at a rate determined by its Stokes radius. Sephadex columns are widely used in the purification of proteins. They are also extremely useful for measuring association and dissociation of protein molecules.

Figure 7-11
Determination of molecular weight on a Sephadex column.

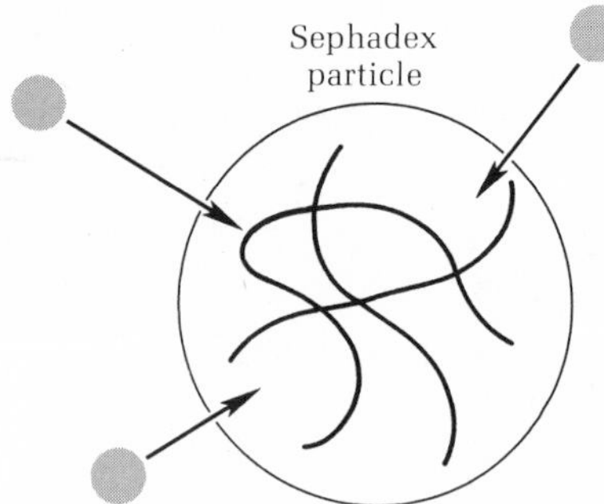

Small solute molecules penetrate into interstices of Sephadex and are retarded

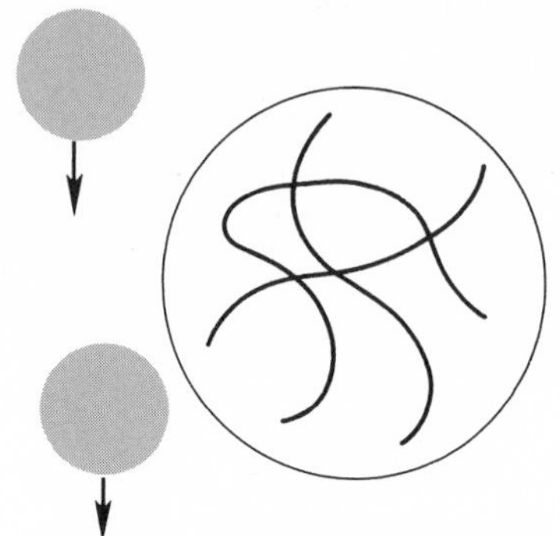

Large solute molecules cannot penetrate and are excluded

Separation of two proteins of different size on a Sephadex column.

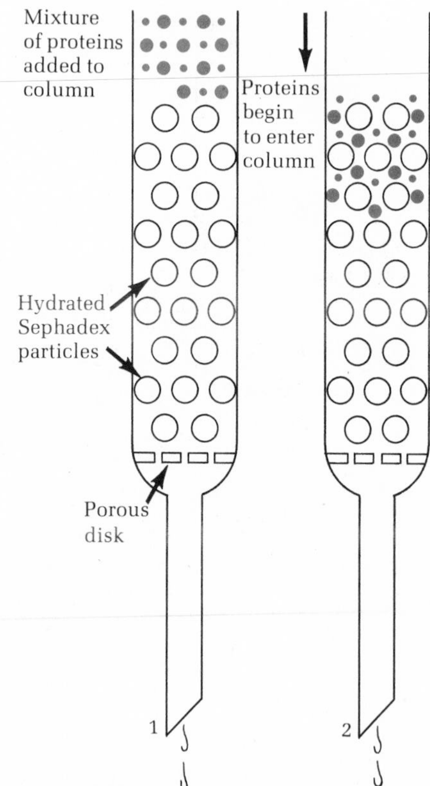

Determining the Shape of Protein Molecules

The most accurate method for determining the shape or conformation of a protein molecule, or of any molecule, is x-ray diffraction analysis (Chapter 6). However, this method gives the structure of the protein in its solid crystalline state. The shape of protein molecules in solution must be studied with rather different methods, which at best are rather indirect and can reveal only the grossest features of the shape of a protein in solution. The basic problem is that the data can be analyzed only in terms of simple symmetrical bodies such as ellipsoids of revolution. However, useful information on the shape of proteins in solution has come from diffusion data, from their light-scattering properties and particularly from viscosity measurements.

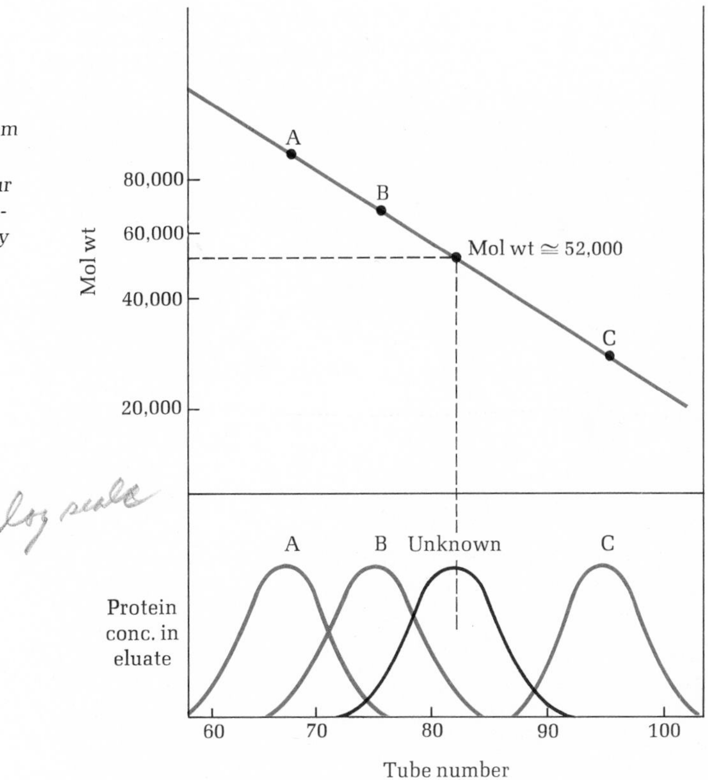

To calibrate the column, two or more proteins (A, B, and C) of known molecular weight are allowed to pass through the column and their peak elution volumes plotted against the logarithm of the molecular weight. From the elution volume of an unknown protein, its molecular weight can be extrapolated from the calibration graph. This relationship holds true only for spherical proteins. In the case of nonspherical particles, the elution volume is directly related to the Stokes radius, i.e., the radius of a spherical particle of equivalent hydrodynamic properties.

Proteins begin to separate. The smaller molecules penetrate into the Sephadex particles and are retarded. The larger protein molecules are excluded, and thus move faster down the column.

3

The two proteins are separated and may be collected in the eluate

4

If the diffusion coefficient and molecular weight of a protein are known, it is possible to calculate its *frictional ratio* (f/fo), which is the ratio of its actual frictional coefficient f and its frictional coefficient fo if it were a perfect unhydrated sphere of the same mass. We have seen that the diffusion of a particle through a liquid is opposed by the frictional resistance due to its viscosity. This resistance is dependent on the shape of the particle; the more the frictional ratio of a protein deviates from 1.0, the more the protein deviates from a perfectly spherical shape (Table 7-3). However, the precise geometrical nature of such deviations is not revealed by the frictional ratio.

The viscosity of a solution of a macromolecule is perhaps the simplest measure of its asymmetry. The rate of flow of a protein solution through a capillary tube, by gravity or under pressure, is measured and compared with that of the solvent alone. The increment in time of flow given by the protein yields its intrinsic viscosity. The intrinsic-viscosity increment is relatively small for spherical particles and relatively large for rod-shaped particles of the same molecular weight and concentration. Viscosity measurements are widely used to detect changes in shape. For example, when the rodlike muscle protein complex actomyosin is treated with ATP, its viscosity decreases because ATP causes it to dissociate into actin and myosin, whose average axial ratio is less than that of actomyosin.

The question arises as to whether proteins have a different conformation or shape in solution than in the crystalline state. It is difficult to test this question since the hydrodynamic methods employed to determine the shape of proteins in solution are relatively insensitive. However, for at least one or two proteins, there appear to be some differences in the crystal and solution conformations.

The Purification of Proteins: Tests for Homogeneity

A cell or tissue may contain hundreds or thousands of different proteins. The isolation in pure form of only one of these from such a complex mixture is a much more difficult problem than the isolation of one given amino acid from a protein hydrolyzate containing only 20 amino acids, especially in view of the fact that proteins are fragile molecules and denature readily at extremes of pH or temperature. The methods used for protein purification must be both mild, to preserve the native conformation of the molecule, and capable of very high resolution. It is also necessary to have some simple means of identifying the protein to be isolated. Enzymes are the most readily isolated class of proteins because assay of their catalytic activity provides a quick means of determining whether a given separation procedure has yielded enrichment of the enzyme in a given fraction.

The protein must first be extracted in soluble form from the cell or tissue. If the protein is known to be present exclusively in one or another organelle, it is often advantageous to isolate the organelles first by differential centrifugation (Chapters 1 and 13). For example, the enzyme succinate dehydrogenase in animal cells is completely localized in the mitochondria. If the mitochondria, which contain about 15 to 20 percent of the total protein of a cell, are first isolated, over 80 percent of all the other cell proteins may be removed. The succinate dehydrogenase may then be extracted from the mitochondria.

Once the desired protein is obtained in soluble form, the extract is subjected to fractionation procedures which exploit differences in the solubility or acid-base properties of the proteins. The first steps usually are isoelectric precipitation of the desired protein (or of the contaminating proteins), followed by fractional salting-out, or precipitation of the protein by decreasing the dielectric constant of the medium with ethanol. Selective denaturation or coagulation of unwanted proteins by careful heating is often used; for this step, the protein to be isolated must be more stable to heat than the unwanted proteins.

Following these first steps, ion-exchange chromatography, which exploits differences in acid-base properties, or adsorption chromatography on adsorbents such as hydroxyapatite, starch, or alumina gel is often used. Especially effective is molecular-exclusion chromatography on columns of Sephadex or Agarose, to sort proteins on the basis of their Stokes radius. For the final steps in purification, zone electrophoresis on starch or polyacrylamide blocks is often used. In general, the most successful isolation procedures are those involving only a few steps, since they usually give the highest yields. Often only a few percent of the protein present in the original extract is recovered in highly purified form.

Since no single physical method can give assurance of homogeneity of the isolated protein, a number of criteria must be used. Crystallinity alone is not sufficient evidence since it has been found that protein crystals often contain entrained impurities. Sedimentation analysis is useful but is relatively insensitive to minor impurities. Perhaps the most rigorous single test is provided by high-resolution disk electrophoresis. If the protein moves as a single sharp band coincident with its biological activity, it is probably homogeneous. Often highly purified proteins are directly tested for the presence of contaminating enzymes by catalytic tests, which are very sensitive.

Summary

The acid-base behavior of proteins is determined largely by the ionizable R groups of the peptide chain(s), whose tendency to ionize may be influenced by neighboring groups. The titration curves of most proteins are approximately additive functions of their ionizing groups. Each protein possesses a characteristic isoelectric pH, at which it will not move in an electrical field. Above the isoelectric pH, it has a net negative charge; below it, a net positive charge.

Mixtures of proteins can be separated on the basis of their relative rates of movement in an electrical field, either by free electrophoresis, in aqueous solution, or by zone electrophoresis, in a gel or semisolid support. Disk electrophoresis has especially great resolving power. Proteins can also be separated by ion-exchange chromatography or on the basis of solubility differences. They are least soluble at their isoelectric pH. Their solubility is increased by low ionic strength (salting-in) and decreased by high concentrations of neutral salts (salting-out). Solubility is also decreased by the addition of ethanol or acetone.

Proteins can be freed of low-molecular-weight solutes by dialysis. When a protein solution is separated from a protein-free solution by a semipermeable membrane that allows the passage of water but not of protein, water flows from the protein-free compartment into the protein solution, a process called osmosis. Diffusion is the movement of molecules in the direction of decreasing concentration. The rate of diffusion of proteins is low compared with that of small molecules.

The molecular weight of macromolecules can be determined by number-average methods or by weight-average methods. Among the most important of these methods are three different types of sedimentation procedures employing the ultracentrifuge: sedimentation velocity, sedimentation equilibrium, and approach-to-equilibrium sedimentation. Proteins may also be separated by sedimentation in density gradients of sucrose or CsCl. Proteins are easily separated and their approximate molecular weights estimated by molecular-exclusion chromatography on columns of inert hydrated polysaccharide materials, such as Sephadex, which act as molecular sieves. The approximate shape of proteins in solution can be estimated from the frictional ratio or from viscosity measurements.

References

Books

ALEXANDER, P., and H. P. LUNDGREN (eds.): *A Laboratory Manual of Analytic Methods in Protein Chemistry, Including Polypeptides,* Pergamon Press, New York, 1966.

BIER, M. (ed.): *Electrophoresis,* 2d ed., Academic Press Inc., New York, 1968. Comprehensive treatise.

DETERMANN, H. (trans. by E. Gross): *Gel Chromatography*, Springer-Verlag OHG, Berlin, 1968. Technique and theory of molecular exclusion chromatography.

SCHACHMAN, H. K.: *Ultracentrifugation in Biochemistry*, Academic Press Inc., New York, 1959. Classical monograph.

Articles

ACKERS, G.: "Molecular Sieve Studies of Interacting Protein Systems," *J. Biol. Chem.*, **242**:3026–3034 (1967). Application of molecular exclusion columns to measurement of association or dissociation of proteins.

ANDREWS, P.: "Molecular Sieve Chromatography Applied to Molecular Weight Estimation," *Lab. Pract.*, **16**:851–856 (1967).

VINOGRAD, J., and P. BRUNER: "Band Centrifugation of Macromolecules in Self-generating Density Gradients," *Biopolymers*, **4**:131–156 (1966).

Problems

1. Cytochrome *c* contains 0.426 percent Fe. Calculate its minimum molecular weight.

2. Ribonuclease is 1.65 percent leucine and 2.48 percent isoleucine by weight. Calculate its minimum molecular weight.

3. Calculate the molecular weight of a pure isoelectric protein if a 1 percent solution gives an osmotic pressure of 46 mm of H_2O at 0°C. Assume that it yields an ideal solution.

4. (*a*) Referring to Figure 7-4, if the pH of a solution of β-lactoglobulin in 1 m*M* NaCl at pH 4.0 originally containing 2 mg protein N per ml, is gradually raised, at what pH will the protein begin to precipitate?
   (*b*) At pH 5.0, what fraction of the protein originally dissolved would still remain in solution?
   (*c*) How might you bring the protein back into solution at pH 5.0?

5. Ribonuclease has a partial specific volume of 0.707 cm^3 $gram^{-1}$ and a diffusion coefficient of 13.1×10^{-7} cm^2 sec^{-1} corrected to water at 20°C. It has a sedimentation coefficient of of 2.05, also corrected to water at 20°C. The density of water at 20°C is 0.998 gram/cm^3. Calculate the molecular weight of ribonuclease using the Svedberg equation.

6. A solution contains 1 mg per ml of myosin and 10^{14} latex particles per ml. When a given volume of this solution is dried on a grid and viewed under the electron microscope, a typical field contains 122 protein molecules and 10 latex particles. Calculate the molecular weight of myosin.

7. In what direction [i.e., toward anode (A), toward cathode (C), or at origin (O)] will the following proteins migrate in an electrical field at the pH indicated? (*a*) Egg albumin at pH 5.0; (*b*) β-lactoglobulin at pH 5.0, at pH 7.0; (*c*) chymotrypsinogen at pH 5.0, at pH 9.5, at pH 11. (Use data in Table 7-2.)

8. Electrophoresis at what pH would be most effective in separating the following protein mixtures? (*a*) Serum albumin and hemoglobin, (*b*) myoglobin and chymotrypsinogen, (*c*) egg albumin, serum albumin, and urease. (Use data in Table 7-2.)

CHAPTER 8 ENZYMES: KINETICS AND INHIBITION

The enzymes make up the largest and most highly specialized class of protein molecules. They are the primary instruments for the expression of gene action since they catalyze the thousands of chemical reactions that collectively constitute the intermediary metabolism of cells.

Much of the history of biochemistry is the history of enzyme research. The discovery and early studies of enzymatic digestion in the stomach in the period 1760 to 1825 evoked the first important experiments on chemical catalysis. Although Pasteur recognized that fermentation is catalyzed by enzymes, he postulated in 1860 that these enzymes are inextricably linked with the structure and life of the yeast cell. It was therefore a major landmark in the history of enzyme research, when, in 1897, E. Büchner succeeded in extracting the enzymes catalyzing alcoholic fermentation from yeast cells. This achievement clearly demonstrated that these important enzymes, which catalyze a major energy-yielding metabolic pathway, can function independent of cell structure. However, it was not until many years later than an enzyme was for the first time isolated in pure crystalline form. This was accomplished by J. B. Sumner in 1926 for the enzyme urease, isolated from extracts of the jack bean. Sumner presented evidence that the crystals consisted of protein, and he concluded, contrary to prevailing opinion, that enzymes are proteins. His views were not immediately accepted, however, and it was not until the period 1930 to 1936, during which Northrop isolated crystalline pepsin, trypsin and chymotrypsin, that the protein nature of enzymes was firmly established.

Crystals of bovine chymotrypsin

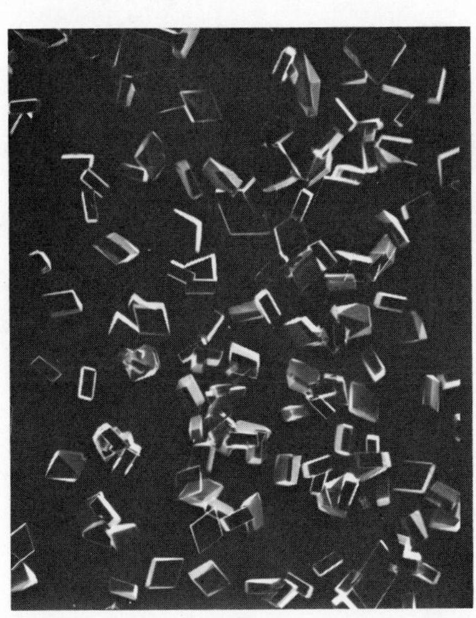

0.1 mm

Today over a thousand different enzymes have been identified. Many of these have been isolated in pure homogeneous form, and over 150 have been crystallized. Although most of the enzymes concerned with the basic metabolic housekeeping of the cell are now reasonably well known, there are genetic grounds for suspecting that many more remain to be discovered. Just within the past few years extremely important discoveries have been made which have opened whole new areas of enzyme research and have created a new understanding of the role of enzymes in cell biology. These discoveries concern the genetic control of enzyme synthesis, the self-regulating nature of many enzyme systems, and the role of enzymes in development and differentiation.

No attempt will be made in this and the following chapter to catalog and describe the large number of different enzymes known today. Rather the properties and characteristics common to most enzymes will be examined in the light of current knowledge of the structure of protein molecules. Specific enzymes participating in various metabolic cycles will be discussed in more detail in succeeding chapters.

The Classification of Enzymes

Many enzymes have been named by adding the suffix *-ase* to the name of the *substrate*, i.e., the molecule on which the enzyme exerts catalytic action. For example, urease catalyzes hydrolysis of urea to ammonia and CO_2, arginase catalyzes the hydrolysis of arginine to ornithine and urea, and phosphatase catalyzes the hydrolysis of phosphate esters. However, this nomenclature has been impractical or cumbersome in many cases, and trivial, nonsystematic, or chemically uninformative names have come into wide use (examples: pepsin, trypsin, catalase). Because of this fact and because of the rapidly increasing number of newly discovered enzymes, a systematic nomenclature and classification have been adopted on the recommendation of the International Enzyme Commission. The new system divides enzymes into six major classes, each of which is divided into subclasses and subsubclasses (Table 8-1). Each enzyme has an identifying classification number. The international nomenclature is chemically informative and is based on the nature of the chemical reaction catalyzed by the enzyme. These systematic names are used where accurate identification is

Table 8-1 International classification of enzymes (class names, code numbers, and types of reactions catalyzed)

1. Oxido-reductases
   (Oxidation-reduction reactions)
   - 1.1 Acting on $-\overset{|}{C}H-OH$
   - 1.2 Acting on $-\overset{|}{C}=O$
   - 1.3 Acting on $-CH=CH-$
   - 1.4 Acting on $-\overset{|}{C}H-NH_2$
   - 1.5 Acting on $-\overset{|}{C}H-NH-$
   - 1.6 Acting on NADH; NADPH
2. Transferases
   (Transfer of functional groups)
   - 2.1 One-carbon groups
   - 2.2 Aldehydic or ketonic groups
   - 2.3 Acyl groups
   - 2.4 Glycosyl groups
   - 2.7 Phosphate groups
   - 2.8 S-containing groups
3. Hydrolases
   (Hydrolysis reactions)
   - 3.1 Esters
   - 3.2 Glycosidic bonds
   - 3.4 Peptide bonds
   - 3.5 Other C—N bonds
   - 3.6 Acid anhydrides
4. Lyases
   (Addition to double bonds)
   - 4.1 $-\overset{|}{C}=\overset{|}{C}-$
   - 4.2 $-\overset{|}{C}=O$
   - 4.3 $-\overset{|}{C}=N-$
5. Isomerases
   (Isomerization reactions)
   - 5.1 Racemases
6. Ligases
   (Formation of bonds with ATP cleavage)
   - 6.1 C—O
   - 6.2 C—S
   - 6.3 C—N
   - 6.4 C—C

necessary, as in international research journals, abstracts, and indexes. However, since some of the systematic names are rather long, trivial names are more convenient in day-to-day reference. Two examples which illustrate the international nomenclature follow:

Trivial name	*Systematic name*	*Reaction catalyzed*
Transaminase	Glutamate: pyruvate aminotransferase	Glutamate + pyruvate $\longrightarrow$ α-ketoglutarate + alanine
Hexokinase	ATP: hexose phosphotransferase	ATP + glucose $\longrightarrow$ glucose 6-phosphate + ADP

Enzyme Cofactors

Like other proteins, enzymes may be classified on the basis of their chemical composition as either simple or conjugated. However, there is a more meaningful classification, functionally speaking. Some enzymes depend for activity only on their structure as proteins, while others require in addition nonprotein structures, or *cofactors*, for activity. The cofactor may be either a metal ion or a complex organic molecule called a *coenzyme;* sometimes both are required. Cofactors are generally stable to heat, whereas most enzyme proteins are labile to heat. The cofactor-dependent enzymes bind their cofactors with varying degrees of affinity. In most cases, the essential cofactor may be removed from the enzyme protein by dialysis or other means, but some coenzymes are covalently bound to the protein molecule. The intact enzyme-cofactor complex is called a *holoenzyme*. When the cofactor is removed, the remaining protein, which is inactive, is called an *apoenzyme*.

Table 8-2 lists some enzymes requiring metal ions as cofactors. In such enzymes the metal ion may serve one of two possible roles. It may function as a bridging group, to bind substrate and enzyme together through formation of a coordination complex. Or it may serve as the catalytic group itself. For example, the iron atoms of catalase, which catalyzes decomposition of hydrogen peroxide, are believed to be its catalytic centers. Simple iron salts possess some capacity to decompose hydrogen peroxide, which is evidently greatly enhanced by the enzyme protein.

Table 8-3 lists the principal known coenzymes and the types of enzymatic reactions in which they participate. Coenzymes usually function as intermediary carriers of electrons or of specific atoms or functional groups that are transferred in the overall enzymatic reaction. Some coenzymes are very tightly bound to the enzyme molecule, and then they are usually called *prosthetic groups*. An example is the heme group of cytochrome *c*, which is covalently bound to its peptide chain. However, in many other cases, the coenzyme is only loosely bound and has some of the characteristics of a substrate. The structure and action of various coenzymes will be described in much more detail in ensuing chapters on intermediary metabolism. Many coenzymes contain as active components certain trace substances such as riboflavin, thiamine, pantothenic acid, and nicotinamide, which are vital

Table 8-2 Some enzymes containing or requiring metal ions as cofactors

Zn^{2+}
- Alcohol dehydrogenase
- Carbonic anhydrase
- Carboxypeptidase

Mg^{2+}
- Phosphohydrolases
- Phosphotransferases

Mn^{2+}
- Arginase
- Phosphotransferases

Fe^{2+} or Fe^{3+}
- Cytochromes
- Peroxidase
- Catalase
- Ferredoxin

Cu^{2+} (Cu^{+})
- Tyrosinase
- Cytochrome oxidase

K^{+}
- Pyruvate phosphokinase (also requires Mg^{2+})

Na^{+}
- Plasma membrane ATPase (also requires K^{+} and Mg^{2+})

Table 8-3 Coenzymes in group-transferring reactions

Entity transferred	*Coenzyme*
Hydrogen atoms (electrons)	Nicotinamide adenine dinucleotide
Hydrogen atoms (electrons)	Nicotinamide adenine dinucleotide phosphate
Hydrogen atoms (electrons)	Flavin mononucleotide
Hydrogen atoms (electrons)	Flavin adenine dinucleotide
Hydrogen atoms (electrons)	Coenzyme Q
Aldehydes	Thiamine pyrophosphate
Acyl groups	Coenzyme A
Acyl groups	Lipoamide
Alkyl groups	Cobamide coenzymes
Carbon dioxide	Biocytin
Amino groups	Pyridoxal phosphate
Methyl, methylene, formyl or formimino groups	Tetrahydrofolate coenzymes

to the function of all cells, and which are required as vitamins in the nutrition of certain species.

Chemical Kinetics

Before we proceed to examine catalysis of reactions by enzymes, some relationships and terms employed in measuring and expressing the rates of chemical reactions must be outlined. Chemical reactions may be classified on the basis of the number of molecules that must ultimately react to form the reaction products. Thus, we may have *monomolecular, bimolecular,* and *termolecular* reactions.

Chemical reactions may also be classified on a kinetic basis, by *reaction order*. Thus, we may have zero-order, first-order, second-order, and third-order reactions, depending on how the reaction rate is influenced by the concentration of the reactants under a given set of conditions.

First-order reactions are those which proceed at a rate exactly proportional to the concentration of *one* reactant (Figure 8-1). The simplest example is when the rate of the reaction

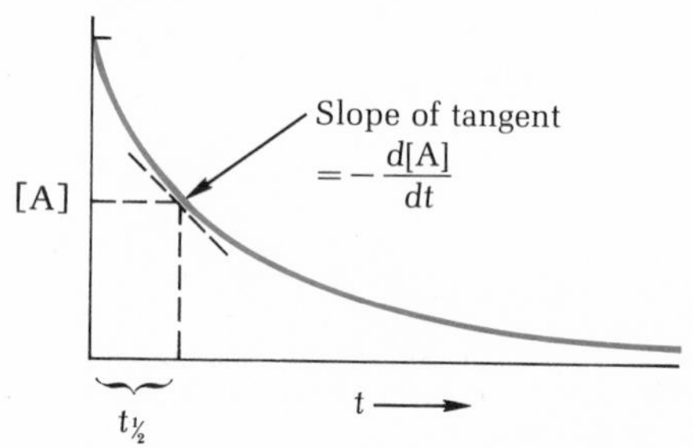

Figure 8-1
Plot of the course of a first-order reaction. The half-time ($t_{\frac{1}{2}}$) is the time required for one-half of the initial reactant to be consumed.

$$A \longrightarrow P$$

is exactly proportional to the rate of disappearance of A (or the rate of appearance of P). For such a case, the reaction rate at any time t is given by

$$\frac{-d[A]}{dt} = k[A]$$

in which [A] is the molar concentration of A and $-d[A]/dt$ is the rate at which the concentration of A decreases. The proportionality constant k is called the *rate constant* or *specific reaction rate*. First-order rate constants have the dimensions of reciprocal time, i.e., sec^{-1} or min^{-1}.

The integrated form of this equation, which is more useful for carrying out kinetic calculations, is

$$\log_{10}\frac{[A_0]}{[A]}=\frac{kt}{2.303}$$

in which $[A_0]$ is the concentration of A at zero time and [A] is the concentration at time t.

In first-order reactions, the half-time ($t\frac{1}{2}$) of the reaction is given by

$$t\tfrac{1}{2}=\frac{0.693}{k}$$

a relationship that is simply derived. Note that in first-order reactions the half-time is independent of the initial concentration of substrate.

Second-order reactions are those in which the rate is proportional to the product of the concentrations of *two* reactants or to the second power of a single reactant. The simplest example is the reaction

$$A + B \longrightarrow P$$

When the rate of this reaction, which may be designated as $-(d[A]/dt)$, $-(d[B]/dt)$, or $+(d[P]/dt)$, is proportional to the product of the concentrations of A and B, we have

$$\frac{-d[A]}{dt}=k[A][B]$$

the second-order rate equation, in which k is the second-order rate constant. If the reaction has the form

$$2A \longrightarrow P$$

and its rate is proportional to the product of the concentration of the two reacting molecules, the second-order rate equation is

$$\frac{-d[A]}{dt}=k[A][A]=k[A]^2$$

The rate constants of second-order reactions have the dimensions 1/concentration × time, or $M^{-1}\ \mathrm{sec}^{-1}$. The integrated form of the second-order expression is

$$t=\frac{2.303}{k([A_0]-[B_0])}\log_{10}\frac{[B_0][A]}{[A_0][B]}$$

where $[A_0]$ and $[B_0]$ are initial concentrations and [A] and [B] the concentrations at time t.

It is important to note that the reaction

$$A + B \longrightarrow P$$

which we have taken as an example, is not necessarily a second-order reaction under all circumstances. Under some conditions, this bimolecular reaction can be a first-order reaction. For example, if the concentration of A were very high and that of B very low, this reaction might be first-order with respect to B, since its rate is then proportional to the concentration of only one reactant (in this case, B). The order of a reaction is thus determined by the conditions under which it is taking place and is not automatically a reflection of whether the reaction is monomolecular, bimolecular, or termolecular.

Third-order reactions, which are relatively rare, are those whose velocity is proportional to the product of three concentration terms. Some chemical reactions are independent of the concentration of any reactant; these are called zero-order reactions. Many catalyzed reactions are zero-order with respect to the reactants. When this is the case, the rate of reaction depends on the concentration of catalyst or on some factor other than the concentration of the molecular species undergoing reaction. Reaction rates need not necessarily be pure first-order or pure second-order; often mixed-order reactions are observed under certain conditions.

Catalysis

A chemical reaction such as A ⟶ P takes place because a certain fraction of the population of A molecules at any given instant possesses much more energy than the rest of the population—enough energy to attain an "activated state," in which a chemical bond may be made or broken to form the product(s) P. The term *activation energy* refers to the amount of energy, in calories, required to bring all the molecules of 1 mole of a substance at a given temperature to this activated state.

Figure 8-2
Energy diagram for a chemical reaction, uncatalyzed and catalyzed.

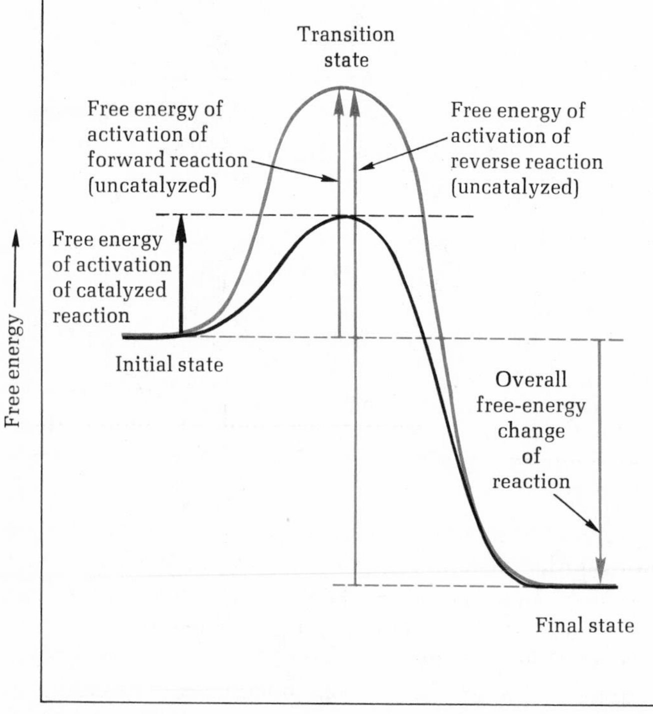

In every chemical reaction there is a *transition state*, which is defined as the energy-rich state of the interacting molecules at the top of the activation barrier (Figure 8-2):

$$\underset{\text{Reactant}}{\mathrm{A}} \rightleftharpoons [\text{transition state}] \rightleftharpoons \underset{\text{Product(s)}}{\mathrm{P}}$$

The rate of a reaction is proportional to the concentration of the transition-state species. A rise in temperature, because it increases thermal motion and energy, increases the number of molecules capable of entering the transition state; in many reactions, the reaction rate is approximately doubled by a 10°C rise in temperature.

Catalysts accelerate chemical reactions by lowering the free energy of activation. They combine with the reactants to produce a transition state having less free energy than the transition state of the uncatalyzed reaction (Figure 8-2). When the reaction products are formed, the free catalyst is regenerated.

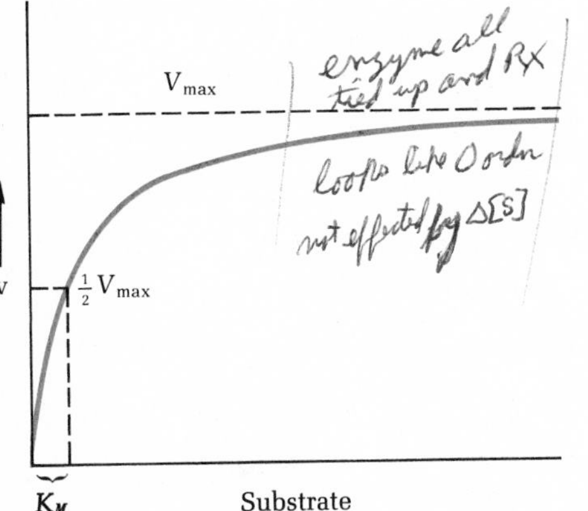

Figure 8-3
Effect of substrate concentration on the rate of an enzyme-catalyzed reaction.

Kinetics of Enzyme-Catalyzed Reactions: the Michaelis-Menten Equation

The general principles of chemical reaction kinetics described above are also applicable to enzyme-catalyzed reactions. However, the latter show a distinctive feature not usually observed in non-enzymatic reactions, namely, the phenomenon of *saturation* with substrate. In Figure 8-3, we see the effect of substrate concentration on the rate of the enzymatic reaction $\mathrm{A} \longrightarrow \mathrm{P}$. At low substrate concentration, the reaction velocity v is proportional to the substrate concentration and the reaction is thus first-order with respect to the substrate. However, as the substrate concentration is increased, the reaction rate falls off and is no longer proportional to the substrate concentration; in this zone, the reaction is mixed-order. On further increase in substrate concentration, the rate becomes constant and independent of substrate concentration. In this range of substrate concentration, the reaction is zero-order with respect to the substrate; the enzyme is then saturated with its substrate. Under these conditions, the rate-limiting factor is enzyme concentration alone. All enzymes show this saturation effect, but they vary widely with respect to the substrate concentration required to produce saturation.

The saturation effect led L. Michaelis and M. L. Menten in 1913 to a general theory of enzyme action and kinetics, which was later extended by G. E. Briggs and J. B. S. Haldane. According to this theory, which is basic to the quantitative analysis of all aspects of enzyme kinetics and inhibition, the enzyme E first reacts with the substrate S to form the enzyme-substrate complex ES, which then breaks down in a second step to form free enzyme and the product(s) P:

$$\mathrm{E} + \mathrm{S} \underset{k_2}{\overset{k_1}{\rightleftharpoons}} \mathrm{ES} \tag{1}$$

$$\mathrm{ES} \underset{k_4}{\overset{k_3}{\rightleftharpoons}} \mathrm{E} + \mathrm{P} \tag{2}$$

Both reactions are considered to be reversible; k_1, k_2, k_3, and k_4 are specific rate constants for the reactions designated.

In the following derivation of the Michaelis-Menten equation, which is that of Briggs and Haldane, [E] represents the total enzyme concentration (the sum of the free and combined enzyme), [ES] is the concentration of the enzyme-substrate complex, and [E] − [ES] represents the concentration of free, or uncombined, enzyme. [S] represents the substrate concentration, which is ordinarily far greater than [E], so that the amount of S bound by E at any given time is negligible compared with the total concentration of S. The derivation begins by considering the rates of formation and breakdown of ES. The rate of formation of ES from E + S is given by

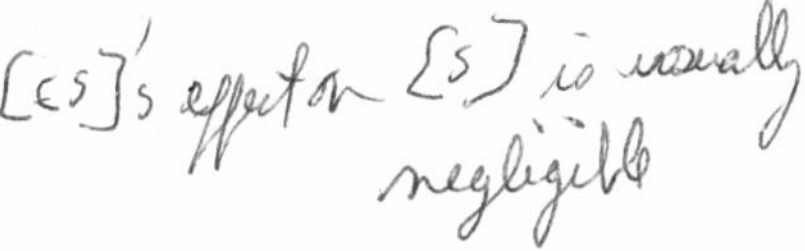

$$\frac{d[\mathrm{ES}]}{dt} = k_1([\mathrm{E}] - [\mathrm{ES}])[\mathrm{S}] \tag{3}$$

The rate of formation of ES from E + P is very small and may be neglected.

Similarly, the rate of breakdown of ES is given by

$$\frac{-d[\mathrm{ES}]}{dt} = k_2[\mathrm{ES}] + k_3[\mathrm{ES}] \tag{4}$$

When the rate of formation of ES is equal to its rate of breakdown, i.e., when the reaction system is in a steady state, with the ES concentration remaining constant,

$$k_1([\mathrm{E}] - [\mathrm{ES}])[\mathrm{S}] = k_2[\mathrm{ES}] + k_3[\mathrm{ES}] \tag{5}$$

Rearranging this expression, we have

$$\frac{[\mathrm{S}]([\mathrm{E}] - [\mathrm{ES}])}{[\mathrm{ES}]} = \frac{k_2 + k_3}{k_1} = K_M \tag{6}$$

The "lumped" constant K_M which replaces the term $(k_2 + k_3)/k_1$, is called the *Michaelis-Menten constant.* From this equation, the steady-state concentration of the ES complex may be obtained by solving for [ES]:

$$[\mathrm{ES}] = \frac{[\mathrm{E}][\mathrm{S}]}{K_M + [\mathrm{S}]} \tag{7}$$

Since the initial rate v of an enzymatic reaction is proportional to the concentration of the ES complex, we can write

$$v = k_3[\mathrm{ES}] \tag{8}$$

When the substrate concentration is so high that essentially all the enzyme in the system is present as the ES complex, we reach the *maximum velocity* $V_{\max}$, for which we can write

$$V_{\max} = k_3[\mathrm{E}] \tag{9}$$

in which [E] is the total enzyme concentration.

We can now substitute for the term [ES] in equation (8) its value from equation (7):

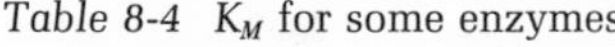

Table 8-4 K_M for some enzymes

Enzyme and substrate	K_M (mM)
Catalase	
H_2O_2	25
Hexokinase	
Glucose	0.15
Fructose	1.5
Chymotrypsin	
N-Benzoyltyrosinamide	2.5
N-Formyltyrosinamide	12.0
N-Acetyltyrosinamide	32
Glycyltyrosinamide	122
Carbonic anhydrase	
HCO_3^-	9.0
Glutamate dehydrogenase	
Glutamate	0.12
α-Ketoglutarate	2.0
NH_4^+	57
NAD_{ox}	0.025
NAD_{red}	0.018

$$v = k_3 \frac{[E][S]}{K_M + [S]} \tag{10}$$

If we now divide this equation by equation (9), we obtain

$$\frac{v}{V_{max}} = \frac{k_3 \dfrac{[E][S]}{K_M + [S]}}{k_3[E]} \tag{11}$$

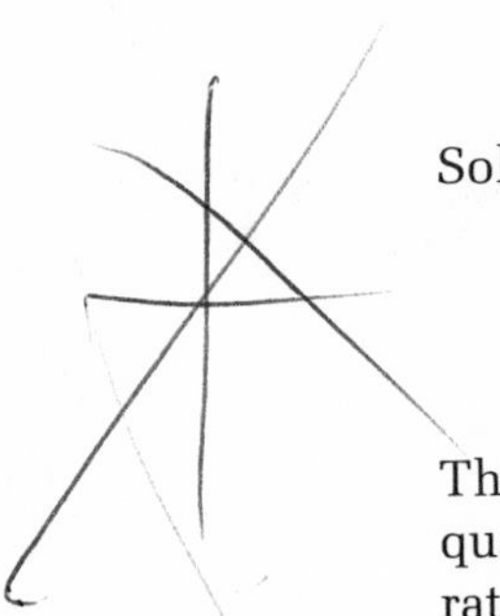

Solving for v,

$$v = \frac{V_{max}[S]}{K_M + [S]} \tag{12}$$

This is the *Michaelis-Menten equation;* it defines the quantitative relationship between the enzyme reaction rate and the substrate concentration [S] if both V_{max} and K_M are known.

An important numerical relationship emerges from the Michaelis-Menten equation in the special case when $v = \frac{1}{2}V_{max}$. We then have

$$\frac{V_{max}}{2} = \frac{V_{max}[S]}{K_M + [S]}$$

If we divide by V_{max}, we obtain

$$\frac{1}{2} = \frac{[S]}{K_M + [S]}$$

Rearranging,

$$K_M + [S] = 2[S]$$
$$K_M = [S]$$

We may therefore conclude that K_M *is equal to the substrate concentration at which the velocity is half maximal.* K_M has the dimensions moles liter^{-1}.

Figure 8-3 shows that K_M can be extrapolated graphically from data on the effect of substrate concentration on the reaction velocity; its magnitude is independent of enzyme concentration. Table 8-4 gives the K_M values for a number of enzymes. Note that K_M is not a fixed value. It may vary with the structure of the substrate, with pH, and with temperature. In those enzymes having more than one substrate, each substrate has a characteristic K_M. Under intracellular conditions, enzymes are not necessarily saturated with their substrates.

Table 8-5 Effect of substrate structure on V_{max} for D-amino acid oxidase (Data are relative to D-alanine = 100)

Substrate	*Relative* V_{max}
D-Tyrosine	297
D-Proline	231
D-Methionine	125
D-Alanine	100
D-Valine	55
D-Histidine	9.7
Glycine	0.0

The maximum velocity V_{max} varies widely from one enzyme to another. It also varies with the structure of the substrate (Table 8-5), with pH, and with temperature.

The Michaelis constant, as we noted above, is an experimentally determined quantity, which in the idealized case is represented by

$$K_M = \frac{k_2 + k_3}{k_1} \tag{6}$$

However, in many enzymatic reactions, k_2 and k_1 may be very large compared with k_3. In such reactions, the rate-limiting step in the overall reaction is the slow step, $ES \xrightarrow{k_3} P$. k_3 is then negligibly small, and equation (6) simplifies to the expression

$$K_M = \frac{k_2}{k_1}$$

Under these conditions, K_M is evidently the dissociation constant of the ES complex and is replaced by the expression K_S:

$$K_S = \frac{[E][S]}{[ES]}$$

Unfortunately, K_M and K_S are frequently used interchangeably. K_M should not be regarded as the dissociation constant of the ES complex unless specific information is available that k_3 is very low compared with k_2 and k_1.

The Michaelis-Menten equation is fundamental to all quantitative treatment of enzyme action. Its derivation from first principles, as shown above, leads to many other useful relationships. But it must be stressed that most enzymes show kinetic behavior that is much more complex than the idealized case we have just treated. For one thing, our formulation assumed that there is but one enzyme-substrate complex. However, it now appears likely that most enzyme-catalyzed reactions involve two or three enzyme-substrate complexes, acting in the following sequence:

$$E + S \rightleftharpoons ES \rightleftharpoons EZ \rightleftharpoons EP \rightleftharpoons E + P$$

in which EZ is the true transition-state complex and EP an enzyme-product complex (Figure 8-4). Furthermore, it

Figure 8-4
Energy diagram for an enzyme-catalyzed reaction. Small energy barriers exist at points 1 and 2.

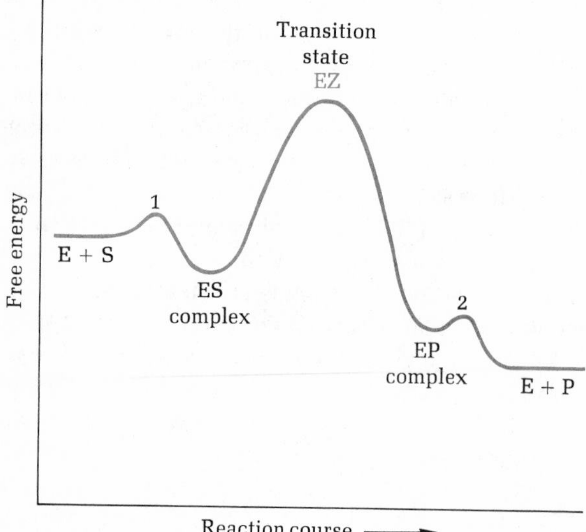

must be pointed out that in most enzymatic reactions there is more than one substrate molecule and there may be two or more products. In a reaction with two substrates S_1 and S_2, there may be three enzyme-substrate complexes, namely, ES_1, ES_2, and ES_1S_2. If the reaction has two products P_1 and P_2, there may be at least three additional complexes EP_1, EP_2, and EP_1P_2. Many intermediate steps occur in such reactions, each having its own rate constant. Kinetic analysis of enzymatic reactions involving two or more reactants can sometimes be exceedingly complex and may require computer solutions. Nevertheless, the starting point for analysis of the kinetics of all enzymatic reactions is the Michaelis-Menten relationship as derived above.

Transformations of the Michaelis-Menten Equation

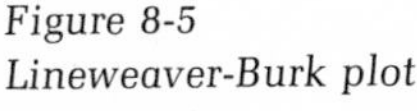

Figure 8-5
Lineweaver-Burk plot.

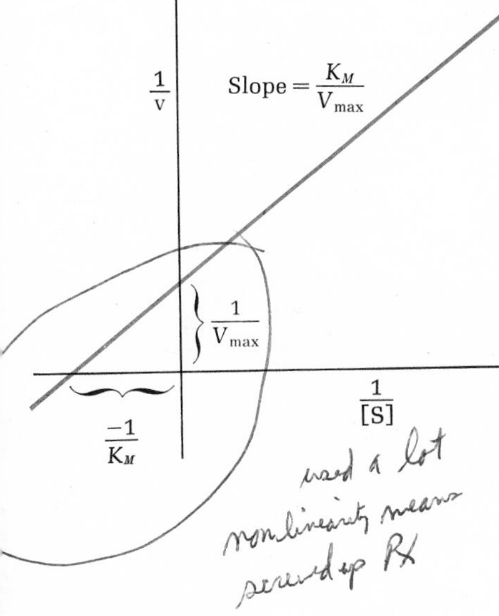

The Michaelis-Menten equation can be transformed algebraically into other forms that are more useful in plotting experimental data. One of the most widely used transformations is derived simply by taking the reciprocal of both sides of the Michaelis-Menten equation [equation (12)]:

$$\frac{1}{v} = \frac{1}{V_{max}[S]/(K_M + [S])} = \frac{K_M + [S]}{V_{max}[S]}$$

Rearranging, we have

$$\frac{1}{v} = \frac{K_M}{V_{max}[S]} + \frac{[S]}{V_{max}[S]}$$

which reduces to

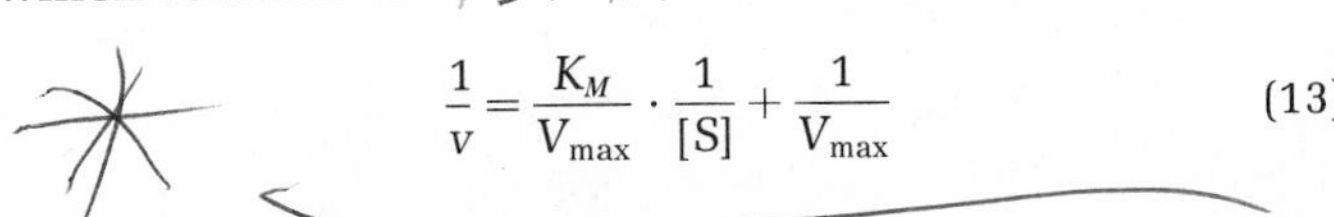

$$\frac{1}{v} = \frac{K_M}{V_{max}} \cdot \frac{1}{[S]} + \frac{1}{V_{max}} \qquad (13)$$

Figure 8-6
Eadie-Hofstee plot.

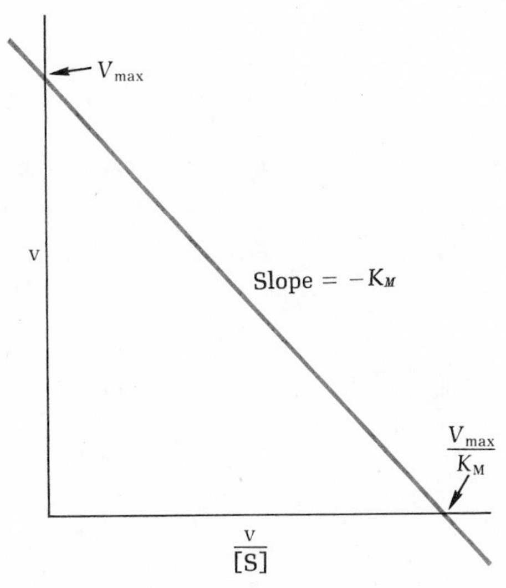

Equation (13) is the *Lineweaver-Burk equation,* which represents a straight line with a slope of K_M/V_{max} and an intercept of $1/V_{max}$ on the $1/v$ axis (Figure 8-5). This line is obtained by plotting $1/v$ vs. $1/[S]$. Such a "double-reciprocal" plot has the advantage that V_{max} can be more accurately arrived at than from the simple plot of v vs. [S]; in the latter, V_{max} is approached asymptotically and its value therefore is uncertain. The intercept on the abscissa of the Lineweaver-Burk plot is $-1/K_M$. The Lineweaver-Burk plot can also give valuable information on enzyme inhibition, as we shall see below.

Another useful transformation of the Michaelis-Menten equation is obtained by multiplying both sides of equation (13) by V_{max} (v) and rearranging to yield the equation

$$v = -K_M\left(\frac{v}{[S]}\right) + V_{max}$$

When v is plotted against $v/[S]$, the plot shown in Figure 8-6 results. This plot (the *Eadie-Hofstee plot*) not only yields V_{max} and K_M in a very simple way but also magnifies departures from linearity which might not be seen in a Lineweaver-Burk plot.

Dependence of Enzyme Reaction Rates on Cofactors

The Michaelis-Menten equation not only defines the quantitative relationship between substrate concentration and enzyme reaction rate but can also be applied to the relationship between cofactor concentration and reaction rate, in the case of those enzymes requiring a cofactor for activity. The following type of equilibrium is assumed:

$$\underset{\text{(Inactive)}}{\text{E} + \text{coenzyme}} \rightleftharpoons \underset{\text{(Active)}}{\text{E} - \text{coenzyme}}$$

The enzyme-coenzyme complex may then bind the substrate to form the enzyme-coenzyme-substrate complex

$$\text{E} - \text{coenzyme} + \text{S} \rightleftharpoons \text{S} - \text{E} - \text{coenzyme}$$

whose concentration determines the overall reaction rate. It is evident from these equilibria that such an enzyme will show a saturation phenomenon not only with its substrate but also with its cofactor.

Just as we may have a Michaelis constant K_M for substrate affinity, defined as the concentration of substrate at which half-maximal velocity is observed, we may also have a Michaelis constant to express affinity of the enzyme for its cofactor, similarly defined as the concentration of cofactor at which half-maximal activity of the enzyme is observed. To estimate the K_M for a cofactor, the substrate concentration is held constant at a saturating level and the effect of cofactor concentration on velocity is measured.

Table 8-4 lists K_M values for the enzyme glutamate dehydrogenase, which requires the cofactor NAD to accept H atoms. The reaction catalyzed by this enzyme is

$$\text{Glutamate} + \text{NAD}_{\text{ox}} \rightleftharpoons \alpha\text{-ketoglutarate} + \text{NAD}_{\text{red}} + \text{NH}_3$$

The two substrates glutamate and a-ketoglutarate have characteristic K_M values, as do the oxidized and reduced forms of NAD, the cofactor. In this and many similar enzymatic reactions involving coenzymes, the coenzyme participates in the reaction as though it were a substrate, and it can be treated by the same kinetic formalism.

Effect of pH on Enzymatic Activity

Most enzymes have a characteristic pH at which their activity is maximal (Table 8-6); above or below this pH the activity declines. However, the pH-activity profiles of enzymes are not always bell-shaped; they may even be rectilinear (Figure 8-7). The pH-activity relationship of any given enzyme depends on (1) the pK′ of the ionizing groups of the active site on the enzyme that participate in binding the substrate, (2) the pK′ of the functional groups of the substrate molecule that participate in binding to the enzyme, (3) the pK′ of the functional groups of the enzyme molecule responsible for the catalytic act, and (4) the pK′ of other groups of the enzyme molecule whose state of ionization may determine the specific, catalytically active conformation of the molecule. The pH-activity curve is usually measured with the enzyme saturated with substrate at each pH since the K_M of many enzymes changes with pH.

Table 8-6 Optimum pH of some enzymes

Enzyme and substrate	*Optimum pH*
Pepsin	
Egg albumin	1.5
Hemoglobin	2.2
Pyruvate carboxylase	
Pyruvate	4.8
Fumarase	
Fumarate	6.5
Malate	8.0
Catalase	
H_2O_2	7.6
Trypsin	
Benzoylargininamide	7.7
Benzoylarginine ethyl ester	7.0
Alkaline phosphatase	
Glycerol 3-phosphate	9.5
Arginase	
Arginine	9.7

Figure 8-7
The pH-activity profiles of some enzymes.

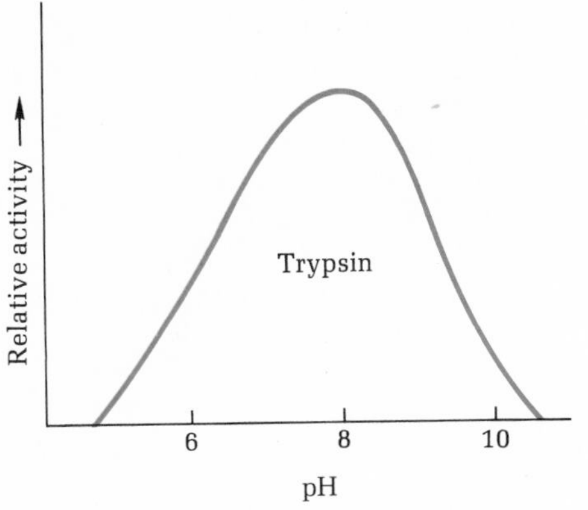

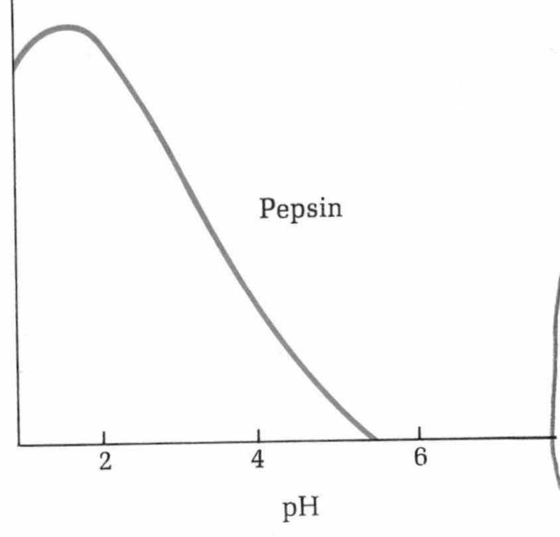

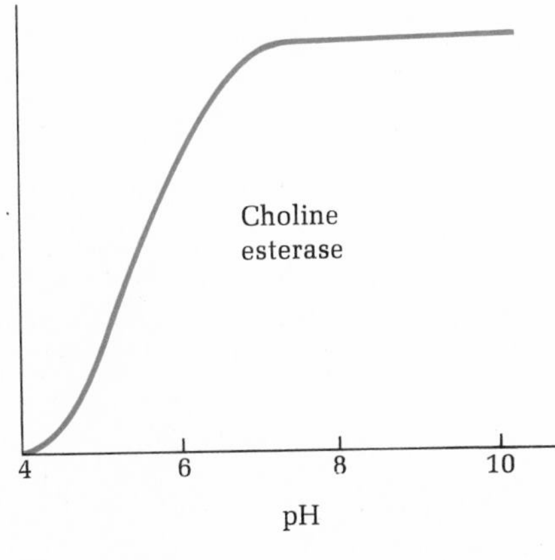

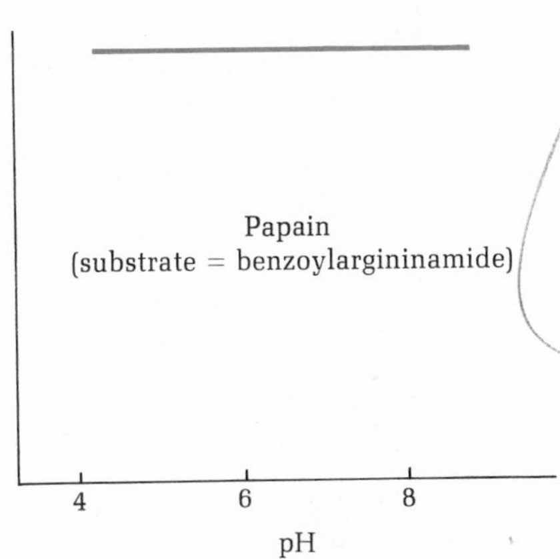

The pH-activity profiles of some enzymes acting on substrates that are electrically neutral, or in which the charge of the substrate plays no role in the catalysis, are often very simple in shape, as in the case of papain (Figure 8-7). Another example is invertase, which catalyzes the hydrolysis of the neutral molecule sucrose; it has a constant activity over the range pH 3.0 to 7.5.

The optimum pH of an enzyme is not necessarily identical with the pH of its normal intracellular surroundings, which may be on the ascending or descending slope of its pH-activity profile. This fact suggests that the pH-activity relationship of an enzyme may be a factor in intracellular control of enzymatic activity. Since cells contain hundreds of enzymes, all differently responsive to pH, the intracellular pH may represent an important element in the complex network of controls over cell metabolism.

Quantitative Assay of Enzymatic Activity

The amount of an enzyme in a given solution or tissue extract can be assayed quantitatively in terms of the catalytic effect it produces. For this purpose, it is necessary to know (1) the overall stoichiometry of the reaction catalyzed, (2) whether the enzyme requires cofactors such as metal ions or coenzymes, (3) its dependence on substrate and cofactor concentrations, i.e., the K_M for both substrate and cofactor, (4) its optimum pH, (5) a temperature zone in which it is stable and has high activity, and (6) a simple analytical procedure for determining the disappearance of the substrate or the appearance of the reaction products.

Where possible, enzymes are assayed in test systems in which the pH is optimum and the substrate concentration is above the saturating level, so that the initial reaction rate is zero-order for substrate. Under these conditions, the initial reaction rate is proportional to enzyme concentration alone. In the case of enzymes requiring cofactors, such as metal ions or coenzymes, the cofactors must also be added in concentrations that exceed saturation, so that the true rate-limiting factor in the system is the enzyme concentration. Usually, measurement of the rate of formation of the reaction product is more accurate than measurement of the disappearance of the substrate, since the substrate must often be present at relatively high concentration to preserve zero-order kinetics. The reaction product(s) may be measured by specific chemical or spectrophotometric methods. The latter are especially useful because they can yield continuous measurements of the reaction course and can be recorded on a chart.

By international agreement, 1.0 *unit* of enzyme activity is defined as that amount causing transformation of 1.0 micromole (10^{-6} mole) of substrate per minute at 25°, under optimal conditions of measurement. The *specific activity* is the number of enzyme units per mg protein. It is a measure of enzyme purity, increasing during purification of an enzyme and becoming maximal and constant when the enzyme is in the pure state. The *turnover number* is the number of substrate molecules transformed per unit time by a single enzyme molecule (or by a single active site) when the enzyme is the rate-limiting factor

(Table 8-7). The enzyme carbonic anhydrase has the highest turnover number of any known enzyme—36,000,000 per min per molecule.

By applying these quantitative assay methods to determine the enzyme activity of protein fractions isolated by various methods (described in Chapter 7), it is possible to purify enzymes and to isolate them in homogeneous form.

Table 8-7 Turnover numbers of some enzymes (per min at 20–38°C)

Carbonic anhydrase C	36,000,000
Δ^5-3-Ketosteroid isomerase	17,100,000
β-Amylase	1,100,000
β-Galactosidase	12,500
Phosphoglucomutase	1,240
Succinate dehydrogenase	1,150

Enzyme Inhibition

From the study of enzyme inhibitors, valuable information has been obtained on the substrate specificity of enzymes, the nature of the functional groups at the active site, the mechanism of enzyme action, and the participation of certain functional groups in maintaining the specific conformation of the enzyme molecule. Moreover, inhibition of certain enzymes by specific cellular components is an element in the control of enzymatic reactions in the intact cell.

Enzyme inhibition is broadly classified into two types: *irreversible* and *reversible*. Irreversible inhibition usually involves the destruction or modification of one or more functional groups of the enzyme; examples will be given later. Reversible inhibition, on the other hand, can be treated quantitatively by use of the Michaelis-Menten relationship. There are two major types of reversible inhibition: *competitive* and *noncompetitive*. Competitive inhibition can be reversed by increasing the substrate concentration, whereas noncompetitive inhibition cannot be reversed by the substrate.

Competitive Inhibition

The classic example is the inhibition of succinate dehydrogenase by malonate and other dicarboxylic acids (Figure 8-8). Succinate dehydrogenase is a member of the group of enzymes catalyzing the Krebs tricarboxylic acid cycle. It catalyzes the removal of two hydrogen atoms from the two methylene carbon atoms of succinate. (The nature of the hydrogen acceptor is not relevant to this discussion). Succinate dehydrogenase is inhibited by malonate, which resembles succinate in having two ionized carboxyl groups at pH 7.0. However, malonate is not dehydrogenated by succinate dehydrogenase. The reversibility of the inhibition by malonate is shown by the fact that if sufficient malonate is added to inhibit the dehydrogenation of a given concentration of succinate by 50 percent, increasing the succinate concentration will reduce the amount of inhibition by malonate. The inhibition is spoken of as competitive because malonate and succinate compete for the same site. In competitive inhibition, the percentage of inhibition of the enzyme is a function of the *ratio* of the concentrations of malonate and succinate rather than a function of the absolute concentration of the inhibitor alone. For example, when malonate and succinate are present in the concentration ratio 1:50, the enzyme is inhibited 50 percent regardless of their absolute concentration.

Figure 8-8
The succinate dehydrogenase reaction.

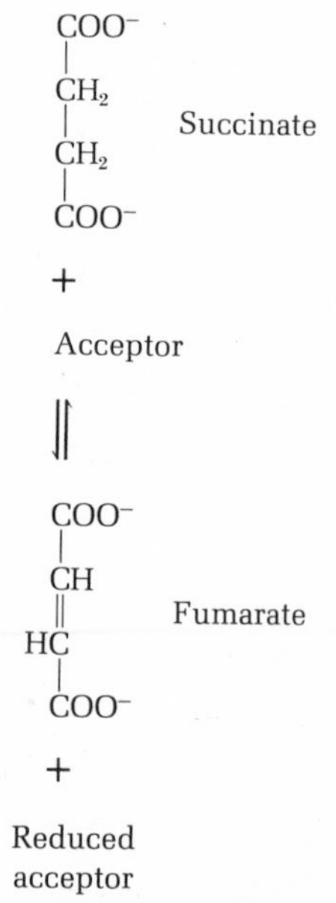

COO^- – CH_2 – CH_2 – COO^- (Succinate)

\+

Acceptor

⇅

COO^- – CH = HC – COO^- (Fumarate)

\+

Reduced acceptor

Some competitive inhibitors of succinate dehydrogenase

COO^-
|
CH_2
|
COO^- Malonate

COO^-
|
COO^- Oxalate

COO^-
|
CH_2
|
C=O
|
COO^- Oxaloacetate

O^-
|
$O{=}P{-}O^-$
|
O
|
$O{=}P{-}O^-$
|
O^- Pyrophosphate

In addition to malonate, other dibasic acids that have the proper distance between the two anionic groups may act as competitive inhibitors of succinate dehydrogenase. These findings have led to the conclusion that the catalytic site of succinate dehydrogenase has two appropriately spaced positively charged groups capable of attracting the two negatively charged carboxyl groups of the substrate. The catalytic site thus shows complementarity to the structure of the substrate.

From the study of many similar cases of competitive inhibition, it has been concluded that the competitive inhibitor I reacts with the enzyme at the normal substrate binding site to form, reversibly, an EI complex:

$$E + I \underset{k_2}{\overset{k_1}{\rightleftharpoons}} EI$$

However, the EI complex cannot break down to form reaction products as can the ES complex. Following the Michaelis-Menten formalism, an inhibitor constant K_I can be defined by the relationship

$$K_I = \frac{k_2}{k_1}$$

K_I is thus the dissociation constant of the enzyme-inhibitor complex:

$$K_I = \frac{[E][I]}{[EI]}$$

Competitive inhibition is most easily recognized by using Lineweaver-Burk plots, i.e., plots of $1/v$ vs $1/[S]$ at varying concentrations of inhibitor. In truly competitive inhibition, such plots are characterized (Figure 8-9) by straight lines of differing slope intersecting at a common intercept on the $1/v$ axis. In other words, V_{max} is not altered by the presence of a competitive inhibitor; at any inhibitor concentration, there is a substrate concentration, however high, at which full activity of the enzyme can still be evoked. Note also in Figure 8-9 that in the presence of a competitive inhibitor, the apparent K_M will be greater than the true K_M by the amount of increase in the intercept of the $1/[S]$ axis. The slope of the uninhibited reaction, we have seen, is K_M/V_{max} (Figure 8-8). The slope of the inhibited reaction is K_M/V_{max} times $(1 + [I]/K_I)$. The increase in slope in the presence of the inhibitor is thus $1 + [I]/K_I$. From this relationship, K_I can be calculated.

Noncompetitive Inhibition

This type of inhibition is not reversed by increasing the substrate concentration. Presumably, the inhibitor binds at a locus on the enzyme other than the substrate binding site; it may bind to the free enzyme, to the ES complex, or to both:

$$E + I \rightleftharpoons EI$$

$$ES + I \rightleftharpoons ESI$$

Figure 8-9
Lineweaver-Burk plots of competitive and noncompetitive inhibition.

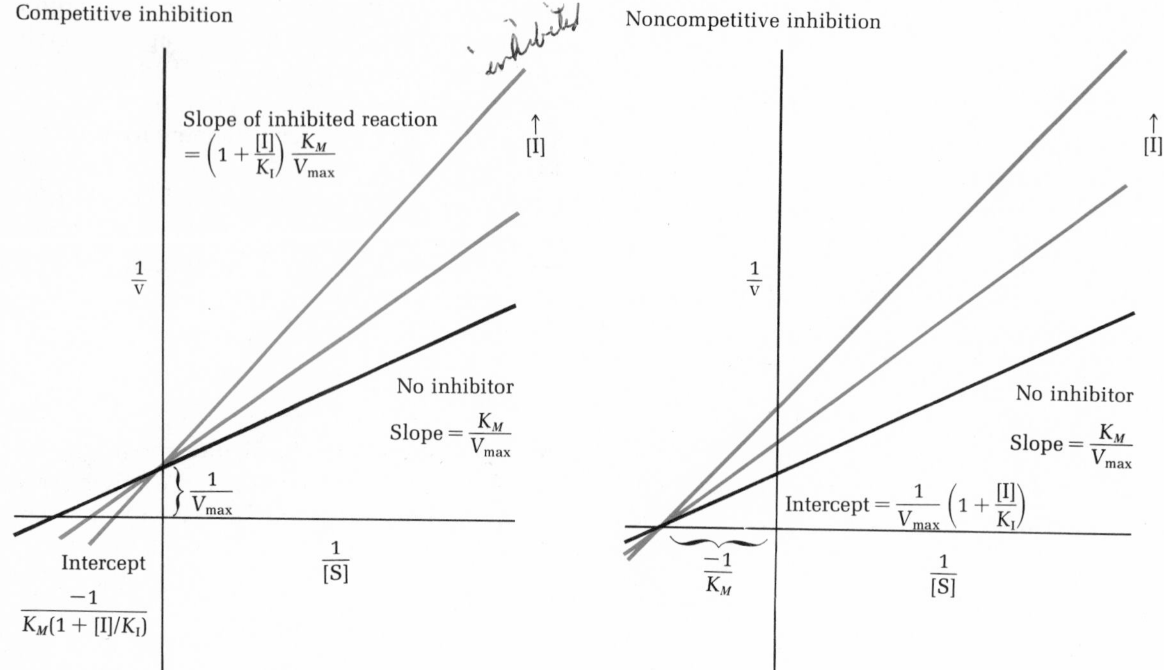

The forms EI and ESI are inactive. Noncompetitive inhibition, too, is most easily recognized from Lineweaver-Burk plots of $1/v$ vs. $1/[S]$ in the presence of various concentrations of inhibitors (Figure 8-9). In noncompetitive inhibition, the plots differ in slope but do not share a common intercept on the $1/v$ axis. The intercept on the $1/v$ axis is greater for the inhibited than the uninhibited enzyme, indicating that V_{max} is decreased by the inhibitor and cannot be restored no matter how high the substrate concentration.

The most common type of noncompetitive inhibition is that given by reagents that can combine reversibly with the —SH groups of cysteine residues that are essential for the catalytic activity of some enzymes. Heavy-metal ions (Cu^{2+}, Hg^{2+}, and Ag^{+}) or their derivatives inhibit such enzymes by forming mercaptides from —SH groups, in such a manner that the amount of enzyme in mercaptide form is in rapid equilibrium with the free metal ion:

$$E - SH + Ag^{+} \rightleftharpoons E - S - Ag + H^{+}$$

Such essential —SH groups may be located at the active catalytic site itself, or they may be located at some distance from the catalytic site. In the latter case, they may nevertheless be essential to catalytic activity because they help maintain the specific three-dimensional conformation of the enzyme molecule.

Some enzymes that require metal ions for activity may be inhibited noncompetitively by agents capable of binding to the essential metal. Cyanide inhibits some enzymes dependent on Fe^{2+} or Fe^{3+} by forming inactive complexes similar to ferrocyanide or ferricyanide. The chelating agent *ethylenediamine tetraacetate* (commonly abbreviated EDTA) reversibly binds Mg^{2+} and other divalent cations and thus inhibits enzymes requiring such ions for activity.

Mg^{2+} chelate of ethylenediamine tetraacetate

Irreversible inhibition; Enzyme Modification

It is important to distinguish between noncompetitive and irreversible inhibition. Quantitative Michaelis-Menten treatment of competitive and noncompetitive inhibition assumes that the combination of enzyme with inhibitor is reversible. When the inhibitor reacts irreversibly, the Michaelis-Menten treatment is not applicable. When an irreversible inhibitor is added in molar excess over the enzyme, inhibition may be incomplete at first but it will continuously increase with time because there is total inhibition of an increasing fraction of enzyme molecules, the remainder being completely active. However, some irreversible inhibitors act by "crippling" the enzyme molecule through chemical modification of its structure. In this case, the modified enzyme is still active but functions at a reduced rate. Special methods are required to detect this kind of inhibition.

One well-known type of irreversible inhibition is given by alkylating agents such as iodoacetamide, which may react with essential —SH groups irreversibly, i.e., in such a manner that the reaction

$$E - SH + ICH_2CONH_2 \longrightarrow E - S - CH_2CONH_2 + HI$$

proceeds far to the right, with formation of a covalent derivative of the enzyme.

Another irreversible inhibitor is diisopropylphosphofluoridate, abbreviated DFP (margin). This inhibitor is a member of a class of toxic organophosphorus compounds that are often called nerve poisons since they combine with and inactivate acetylcholinesterase, which participates in the function of the central nervous system. Some of these compounds are used as insecticides. DFP inhibits not only acetylcholinesterase but also other enzymes which possess an essential reactive serine residue at their active sites. DFP combines with the serine hydroxyl group to form a covalent derivative. This tertiary phosphate ester derivative is stable and does not readily undergo hydrolysis; the inhibition produced by DFP is thus irreversible. When enzymes that are inhibited by DFP are subjected to tryptic hydrolysis, the phosphorylated serine residue remains intact and can be found in a peptide fragment called a DFP-peptide. Analysis of DFP-peptides has given important information on the amino acid sequence near the active site of this class of enzymes (Table 8-8).

Enzyme inhibition by diisopropylphosphofluoridate

Enz—CH_2—OH

+

$(CH_3)_2CH—O—P(=O)(F)—O—CH(CH_3)_2$

Diisopropyl-phosphofluoridate

↓

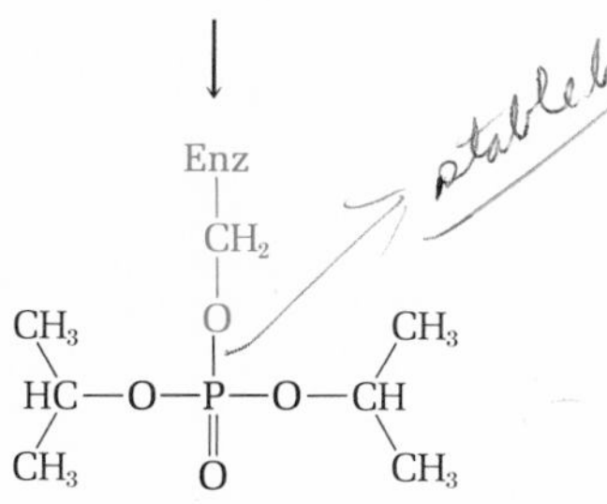

Diisopropylphosphoric ester of enzyme

+

HF

Table 8-8 Amino acid sequences around reactive serine residues of some enzymes

Enzyme	Sequence
Chymotrypsin	—Gly—Asp—Ser—Gly—Gly—
Trypsin	—Gly—Asp—Ser—Gly—Pro—
Thrombin	—Asp—Ser—Gly—
Elastase	—Asp—Ser—Gly—
Phosphoglucomutase	—Thr—Ala—Ser—His—Asp—
Phosphorylase	—Glu—Ile—Ser—Val—Arg—

Enzyme-Substrate Compounds

Although kinetic evidence of the kind outlined above strongly suggests that all enzymes combine with their substrates during the catalytic cycle, direct proof is difficult to obtain because of the instability of the ES complex, which must necessarily decompose rapidly. Nevertheless, some direct evidence of enzyme-substrate complexes has been obtained, particularly in those cases where the enzyme and substrate are linked by a covalent bond at some stage in the catalytic cycle. For example, chymotrypsin has been found to catalyze, although very slowly, the hydrolysis of the ester *p*-nitrophenyl acetate. When it is mixed with the ester, the enzyme becomes acetylated at its reactive serine hydroxyl group (margin). Although this reaction proceeds rapidly, the subsequent step—hydrolysis of acetyl chymotrypsin to form acetate and free enzyme—is relatively slow. Thus acetyl chymotrypsin accumulates in the presence of *p*-nitrophenyl acetate and is easily detected. When chymotrypsin is added to the trifluoroacetate ester of *p*-nitrophenol, the very stable trifluoroacetyl ester of chymotrypsin is formed; this enzyme-substrate complex is so stable that it can be crystallized.

Acetylation of chymotrypsin

Enz—OH
Chymotrypsin

+

$O_2N-C_6H_4-O-C(=O)-CH_3$

p-Nitrophenyl acetate

↓

$Enz-O-C(=O)-CH_3$

Acetyl chymotrypsin

+

$O_2N-C_6H_4-OH$

p-Nitrophenol

Sometimes an enzyme-substrate complex can be "trapped" in the form of a stable covalent derivative, as was found in the case of aldolase, which catalyzes the reversible reaction

$$\text{Fructose 1,6-diphosphate} \rightleftharpoons \text{dihydroxyacetone phosphate} + \text{glyceraldehyde 3-phosphate}$$

Addition of the strong reducing agent sodium borohydride to a mixture of aldolase and isotopically labeled dihydroxyacetone phosphate caused the formation of a stable, isotopically labeled (but inactive) aldolase-dihydroxyacetone phosphate complex. On hydrolysis with acid, it yielded a lysine residue whose ϵ-amino group had been converted into a stable ϵ-N-glyceryl derivative. It was concluded (margin) that the enzyme normally combines with its substrate to form a labile Schiff's base between the ϵ-amino group of a lysine residue and the carbonyl group of the substrate. By reduction with borohydride this labile complex is converted to a stable but inactive reduction product. By this reduction reaction the ES complexes of a number of enzymes acting on substrates with either an amino or carbonyl function have been successfully "trapped."

The presence of ES complexes in enzyme reaction systems can sometimes be detected by means of sensitive spectroscopic methods. Heme enzymes such as catalase, peroxidase, and cytochromes have characteristic absorption spectra in the visible range. When catalase and peroxidase react with hydrogen peroxide, characteristic changes occur in their absorption spectra which appear to reflect formation of enzyme-substrate complexes.

Reduction of enzyme-substrate complex of aldolase

Enz—NH_2
Aldolase
+
$HOCH_2—C(=O)—CH_2OPO_3H_2$
Dihydroxyacetone phosphate
⇌
Enz—N=C(CH_2OH)—$CH_2OPO_3H_2$
Unstable ES complex (Schiff's base)

2H ↓ Borohydride

Enz—NH—CH(CH_2OH)—$CH_2OPO_3H_2$
Stable reduced ES complex (inactive)

↓ Hydrolysis

COOH—CH(NH_2)—CH_2—CH_2—CH_2—CH_2—NH—CH(CH_2OH)—CH_2OH
ε-N-glyceryllysine

Summary

Enzymes are named and classified on the basis of the reaction catalyzed. Some enzymes are simple proteins; others are conjugated proteins, containing prosthetic groups of metal ions, coenzymes, or both. Coenzymes serve as intermediate carriers of electrons or of specific functional groups, such as hydrogen atoms, amino groups, methyl groups, or acetyl groups, and aid in their transfer from one substrate to another. Many coenzymes contain a molecule of a specific vitamin, an organic nutrient required in trace amounts for normal cell function.

At low substrate concentrations, the rate of an enzymatic reaction A ⇌ P is first-order, i.e., proportional to the concentration of substrate. As substrate concentration is increased, a point is reached where the reaction rate does not increase in proportion and the rate becomes independent of substrate concentration. In this zone, the enzyme is saturated and the reaction is zero-order with respect to substrate. Each enzyme has a characteristic substrate concentration (K_M, the Michaelis-Menten constant) at which the reaction velocity is one-half maximal. The quantitative relationship between K_M, the substrate concentration, and the maximum velocity of an enzyme are given by the Michaelis-Menten equation, whose derivation is based on the assumption that an enzyme-substrate complex is formed reversibly as an essential step in catalysis. Enzymes also have an optimum pH. They are usually assayed by measuring the initial reaction rate under conditions in which the enzyme is saturated with substrate and the pH is optimal. One unit of activity is that amount causing transformation of 1.0 micromole of substrate per min at 25°C; specific activity is the number of units per mg protein.

Competitive inhibitors of enzymes are those whose action can be reversed by increasing the substrate concentration. They usually have a structural resemblance to the substrate, with which they compete for the active site. They form reversible enzyme-inhibitor complexes with the enzyme. Noncompetitive inhibition cannot be reversed by the substrate; it results from the reversible interaction of the inhibitor with some other essential group of the molecule, such as an —SH group. Irreversible inhibitors usually produce a permanent, irreversible modification of some essential functional group in the enzyme molecule. Kinetic tests are used to distinguish the various types of enzyme inhibition; Lineweaver-Burk and Eadie-Hofstee plots are especially useful in plotting kinetic data.

The occurrence of enzyme-substrate complexes has been deduced from kinetic studies, from trapping experiments in which the complexes are recovered in inactive form, and from spectroscopic measurements.

References

Books

BERNHARD, S.: *The Structure and Function of Enzymes*, W. A. Benjamin, Inc., New York, 1968. Up-to-date paperback.

BOYER, P. D., H. LARDY, and K. MYRBÄCK: *The Enzymes*, 2d ed., 10 vols., Academic Press Inc., 1963. Comprehensive monograph.

BRAY, H. G., and K. WHITE: *Kinetics and Thermodynamics in Biochemistry*, 2d ed., Academic Press Inc., New York, 1967. The physical-chemical aspects of enzyme activity.

DIXON, M., and E. C. WEBB: *Enzymes*, Longmans, London, 2nd edition, 1964. Classical text on general enzyme properties.

Enzyme Nomenclature, American Elsevier Publishing Company, New York, 1965. International nomenclature and classification.

HALDANE, J. B. S.: *The Enzymes*, The MIT Press, Cambridge, Mass., 1965. An influential statement in a reprinted version.

JENCKS, W. P.: *Catalysis in Chemistry and Enzymology*, McGraw-Hill Book Company, New York, 1969. Definitive treatment of reaction mechanisms and catalysis.

WEBB, L. J.: *Enzyme and Metabolic Inhibitors*, 3 vols., Academic Press Inc., New York, 1963. Theory and kinetics of enzyme inhibition.

Articles and Reviews

CLELAND, W. W.: "The Statistical Analysis of Enzyme Kinetics," *Advan. Enzymol.*, **29**:1–32 (1967). An important review and classification of enzyme reaction pathways on the basis of kinetic behavior.

______: "Enzyme Kinetics," *Ann. Rev. Biochem.*, **36**:77–112 (1967).

INGRAHAM, L. L.: "Three-dimensional Effects in Biochemistry," *J. Chem. Educ.*, **41**:66–69 (1964). Stereospecificity and selectivity in enzyme reactions.

KOSHLAND, D. E., JR., and K. E. NEET: "The Catalytic and Regulatory properties of enzymes, *Ann. Rev. Biochem.*, **37**:359–410 (1968). An important summarizing review of catalytic mechanisms of enzymes.

Problems

1. In the first-order reaction A $\longrightarrow$ B, the concentration of A at time 0 is 0.50 m*M*. After 2 sec, it is 0.25 m*M*. What will it be after 5 sec?

2. In the second-order reaction A + B $\longrightarrow$ C, the concentrations at time 0 are, for reactant A, 5.0 m*M* and, for reactant B, 4.0 m*M*. After 1 sec, the concentration of A is 4.0 m*M* and that of B is 3.0 m*M*. After 3 sec, what will be the ratio of the concentration of A to that of B?

3. If the half-time of a first-order reaction is 0.3 sec, what is its rate constant k?

4. Show that K_M for an enzymatic reaction is equal to the substrate concentration at which the rate is half maximal.

5. Transaminase catalyzes the reaction glutamate + oxaloacetate $\longrightarrow$ α-ketoglutarate + aspartate. Pyridoxal phosphate (PP) acts as a coenzyme in this catalytic process. Calculate K_M for the apoenzyme-coenzyme complex from the following data, obtained when the concentration of PP was varied while concentrations of glutamate and oxaloacetate and other conditions were held constant:

mg glutamate disappearing per minute	0.17	0.27	0.43	0.65	0.73	0.78	0.79	0.81
PP added (μM)	0.30	0.50	1.0	2.0	3.0	4.0	5.0	10.0

6. Salicylate inhibits the catalytic action of glutamate dehydrogenase. Determine by graphical analysis of the following data whether the inhibition is competitive or noncompetitive. Assume that the salicylate concentration is held constant at 40 m*M*. Also calculate K_M for the enzyme and K_I, the dissociation constant for the enzyme-inhibitor complex.

Substrate concentration (m*M*)	1.5	2.0	3.0	4.0	8.0	16
mg Product/min (without salicylate)	0.21	0.25	0.28	0.33	0.44	0.40
mg Product/min (with salicylate)	0.08	0.10	0.12	0.13	0.16	0.18

7. From the following data on an enzymatic reaction, determine whether the inhibitor is acting competitively or noncompetitively. Also determine K_M for the enzyme and K_I for the inhibitor-enzyme complex. What is V_{max}?

Substrate concentration (m*M*)	2.0	3.0	4.0	10.0	15.0
μg Product/hr (no inhibitor)	139	179	213	313	370
μg Product/hr (6 m*M* inhibitor)	88	121	149	257	313

8. To a solution of a pure enzyme containing 1.0 mg protein per ml is added sufficient $AgNO_3$ to just completely inactivate it. A total of 0.342 micromole of $AgNO_3$ was required. Calculate the minimum molecular weight of the enzyme.

CHAPTER 9 ENZYMES: MECHANISM, STRUCTURE, AND REGULATION

This chapter is concerned with the relationships between the catalytic activity of enzymes and their 3-dimensional structure as proteins. We shall examine the physical dimensions and geometry of the catalytic site on the enzyme surface and the molecular mechanism by which the catalytic act is brought about. We shall also consider the question: why is a large protein molecule required to catalyze a reaction occurring at an active site that represents only a tiny portion of its surface?

One of the most significant advances in enzymology has been the identification of *regulatory* enzymes, which make possible the control and integration of the activity of multienzyme systems. We shall see that their regulatory properties are also reflections of their 3-dimensional structure, particularly their subunit arrangement.

Substrate Specificity

The study of the mechanism of enzyme action must begin with the substrate specificity of enzymes. It has long been a working hypothesis that the substrate molecule, or a portion of it, fits the active site in a lock-and-key relationship. Some enzymes have nearly absolute specificity for a given substrate and will not attack even very closely related molecules; others are far less specific and will act on an entire class of molecules. Among the relatively specific enzymes is aspartase, which catalyzes the reversible addition of ammonia to the double bond of fumarate to form L-aspartate (margin). Aspartase does not add ammonia to methylfumaric acid, to esters or amides of fumaric acid, or to monocarboxylic α,β-unsaturated fatty acids. It will not deaminate aminomalonic acid, glutamate, or various monocarboxylic α-amino acids. Aspartase also has rigid stereospecificity and geometrical specificity; thus, it will not deaminate D-aspartate nor will it add ammonia to maleate, the *cis* geometrical isomer of fumarate. In fact, many enzymes show rigid stereospecificity. Thus, lactate dehydrogenase is specific for L-lactate, glutamate dehydrogenase for L-glutamate, and D-amino acid oxidase for D-amino acids. At the other extreme are enzymes which have relatively broad specificity and act on many compounds having a common structural feature. Among the latter are the phosphatases, which hydrolyze many different esters of phosphoric acid, the ali-esterases, which hydrolyze various aliphatic esters, and peptidases, such as trypsin and chymotrypsin.

The aspartase reaction

COO^-
|
CH
‖ fumarate
HC
|
COO^-

+

NH_4^+

⇌

COO^-
|
CH_2
| L-aspartate
$HCNH_2$
|
COO^-

+

H^+

From studies of the substrate specificity of the less specific enzymes, particularly the peptidases, it has been found that two distinct structural features determine the specificity of an enzyme for its substrate. First, the substrate must possess the specific chemical bond or linkage that can be attacked by the enzyme. Second, the substrate usually possesses some other functional group (or groups) which binds to the enzyme and positions the substrate molecule properly on the catalytic site. This binding group usually has some specific geometrical relationship to the bond that is cleaved. In the case of acetylcholine esterase, the bond attacked is the ester linkage between choline and the acetyl group; the positively charged quaternary ammonium group is required for binding the substrate, despite the fact that it is some distance away from the bond that is attacked. The positively charged binding group is also required in the structure of competitive inhibitors of acetylcholine esterase (margin).

The positioning group and the susceptible bond in acetylcholine

$$CH_3-\overset{+}{N}(CH_3)_2-CH_2CH_2O-C(=O)-CH_3$$

The binding or positioning group — The susceptible bond

The substrate specificity of chymotrypsin, one of the most thoroughly studied enzymes, presents an instructive case history (Figure 9-1). Since chymotrypsin is secreted into the small intestine, it was thought, when it was first isolated in the 1930s, that it was specific for the hydrolysis of the large peptides that result from the action of pepsin in the stomach. However, later work revealed that chymotrypsin can also hydrolyze di- and tripeptides. Further study of various synthetic peptides as substrates showed that the enzyme is an *endopeptidase,* i.e., it can split certain peptide linkages at any point in a peptide chain, in contrast to the *exopeptidases,* which can split only terminal peptide bonds. Moreover, chymotrypsin appeared to be specific for those peptide linkages in which the carbonyl function is contributed by aromatic amino acid residues, such as tyrosine, tryptophan, and phenylalanine; it can also hydrolyze the amides of these amino acids.

It was, however, a very great surprise when later work revealed that chymotrypsin can hydrolyze not only peptides and amides of aromatic amino acids but also their esters. In fact, esters of tyrosine are the most active substrates known for chymotrypsin. Another unanticipated finding was that chymotrypsin catalyzes the transfer of the aromatic acyl group to acyl acceptors other than water, such as ammonia, certain amino acids, and certain alcohols. More recent research has shown that the aromatic rings traditionally thought to be required by chymotrypsin are also dispensable. For example, when the benzene ring of a phenylalanine peptide is replaced with the saturated cyclohexyl ring, there is no great decrease in activity. Furthermore, not even the α-amino group of the aromatic amino acid is required, since it may be replaced by a hydrogen atom, a hydroxyl group, or a chlorine atom. Chymotrypsin is thus not a simple peptidase; it is more accurately designated today as a hydrophobic acyl group transferase. Its active site has two separate and specific zones, one (a hydrophobic zone) for binding the substrate at its hydrophobic group and the other for performing the catalytic reaction at the carboxyl group (shown in Figure 9-1).

Figure 9-1
The substrate specificity of chymotrypsin. From studies of modified substrates it has been concluded that chymotrypsin is an acyl group transferase rather than strictly a peptidase. Its minimum structural requirements are shown below.

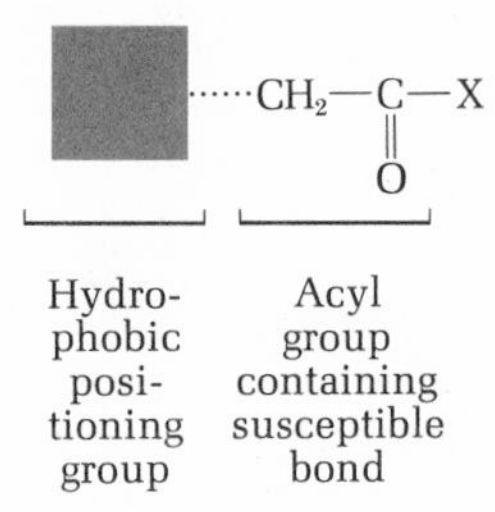

Proximity and Orientation Effects in Catalysis

Determining the molecular mechanisms by which enzymes catalyze specific chemical reactions is a major challenge in contemporary biochemical research. Much useful information has come from the study of simple organic chemical reactions that are chemical models of enzymatic reactions. One of the first questions asked of such models is whether enzymes function simply as devices to bring the sensitive bond of the substrate molecule into orientation with the specific catalytic group of the enzyme. Recent research on organic model reactions indicates that proximity and orientation effects may indeed be very important in enzyme action. For example, the carboxylate ion (R—COO$^-$), a general base, catalyzes the hydrolysis of esters; the rate of the catalyzed reaction is dependent on the concentration of the R—COO$^-$ ion. The catalytic effectiveness of the carboxylate group is greatly enhanced when the latter is covalently attached to the molecule containing the suspectible ester linkage, thus bringing catalyst and substrate close together. Table 9-1 shows, in a series of comparable intramolecular models, the influence of the proximity and orientation of the catalytic group —COO$^-$ on the hydrolysis of the ester linkage.

However, important as such proximity effects are, they alone cannot account for the reaction-rate enhancement produced by enzymes. It is now certain that much of the catalytic effectiveness of enzymes must come from direct enhancement of the bond-breaking or bond-making process itself.

Compounds hydrolyzed by chymotrypsin. The points of cleavage are shown in color.

$C_6H_5CH_2CH(\overset{+}{N}H_3)C(=O)$ + $NHCH(R)COO^-$

$C_6H_5CH_2CH(\overset{+}{N}H_3)C(=O)$ + NH_2

$C_6H_5CH_2CH(\overset{+}{N}H_3)C(=O)$ + OCH_3

$C_6H_5CH_2CH(NHC(=O)CH_3)C(=O)$ + NH_2

$C_6H_5CH_2CH(Cl)C(=O)$ + NH_2

$C_6H_5CH_2CH_2C(=O)$ + NH_2

$C_6H_5CH_2CH_2C(=O)$ + OCH_3

$C_6H_5C(=O)NHCH_2C(=O)$ + OCH_3

$C_6H_{11}CH_2CH_2C(=O)$ + OCH_3

$CH_3C(CH_3)_2CH_2CH_2C(=O)$ + OCH_3

Acid-Base Catalysis of Organic Reactions

Acids and bases, defined in the broadest sense, are the most versatile and universal catalysts of organic reactions. Acid-base catalysis of organic reactions can be divided into three major types: *specific* acid-base catalysis, *general* acid-base catalysis, and catalysis by *Lewis acids* or *Lewis bases*. Specific acid and specific base catalyses are defined as rate enhancements that are proportional only to the concentration of H^+ and OH^- ions, respectively. General acid and general base catalyses are rate enhancements that are proportional to the concentration of general acids and general bases, i.e., proton donors and proton acceptors, respectively (Chapter 2).

Specific acid-base catalysis is of relatively limited importance in organic reactions, and no enzymes are known that behave as though they act merely by enhancing the catalytic activity of free H^+ or OH^- ions in the medium. General acid-base catalysis is much more likely to be involved in the action of most enzymes because of the wide variety of organic-chemical reactions that are subject to this type of catalysis. These reactions include the addition of water to carbonyl groups, the hydrolysis of carboxylic and phosphate esters, the elimination of water from double bonds, many types of rearrangements, and also substitution reactions. Moreover, enzyme molecules contain several functional groups that are capable of acting as general acids or bases, such as amino, carboxyl, sulfhydryl, tyrosine hydroxyl, and imidazolium groups. In reactions catalyzed by general acids or bases, the catalyst at some point in the catalytic cycle functions as an acceptor or donor of protons.

Catalysis of organic-chemical reactions by Lewis acids or bases is also of general importance. A Lewis acid (or electron-pair acceptor) is electron-seeking and is thus called an *electrophilic* group. A Lewis base (electron-pair donor) is nucleus-seeking and is thus called a *nucleophilic* group. Metal ions such as Mg^{2+}, Mn^{2+}, and Fe^{3+} are examples of electrophilic groups, as are $—NH_3^+$ groups of proteins. Enzyme molecules also may contain different types of nucleophilic (electron-donating) groups, especially serine hydroxyl groups, imidazole groups, and sulfhydryl groups. Each of these contains an electron pair that is nucleus-seeking. Nucleophilic groups readily react with electrophilic groups and *vice versa*. Nucleophilic agents catalyze some chemical reactions by their capacity to form a covalent intermediate through a *nucleophilic displacement reaction*, in which the nucleophilic group of the enzyme displaces a substituent group from the susceptible carbon atom of the substrate to form a covalent compound between the enzyme and the remaining moiety of the substrate molecule. The covalent enzyme-substrate complex is extremely unstable and breaks down rapidly to form the products. Such a process is often called *covalent catalysis;* an example is given in Figure 9-2.

The imidazole group of histidine is particularly versatile as a catalyst. It is a very strong nucleophile and in its protonated form it is a general acid. Moreover, these properties are especially prominent at pH near neutrality. In many enzymes, chemical modification of specific histidine residues causes inactivation, suggesting that the histidine residues are essential in the catalytic process.

Table 9-1
Effect of proximity of the catalytic group on reaction rate. In these intramolecular models the general base $—COO^-$ is the catalyst and the ester linkage the substrate. R is a p-bromophenyl group. The cleavage of the ester is accompanied by cyclization.

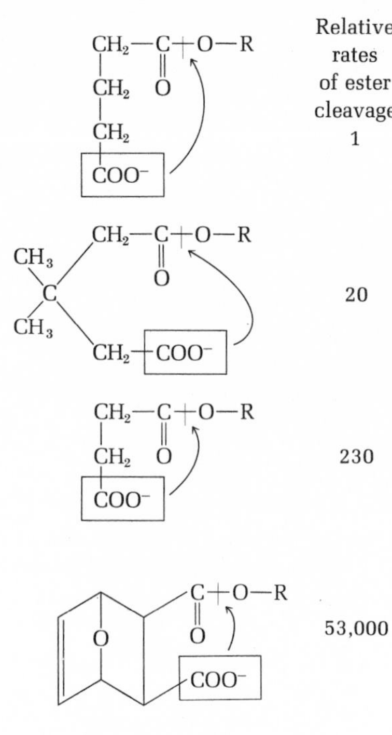

Enzyme Reaction Mechanisms

The mechanism of catalysis is not yet known in detail for any single enzyme. However, chymotrypsin, which requires both serine and histidine residues in its catalytic function, has been intensively studied and a number of mechanisms for its action have been proposed. According to one hypothesis (Figure 9-2), an imidazole group of a histidine residue, acting as a general base catalyst, promotes the nucleophilic attack of a serine hydroxyl group at the enzyme active site on the carboxyl carbon atom of the acyl group of the substrate, causing the displacement of the acyl group to the serine hydroxyl group of the enzyme. A covalent acyl derivative of the enzyme is thus formed. In a second step, which is the precise reverse of the first, the histidine residue promotes the transfer of the acyl group esterified to the serine hydroxyl of the enzyme to an external acyl group acceptor, which may be water, an alcohol, or an amino acid. This hypothesis is supported by the fact that an acyl enzyme intermediate of chymotrypsin has been isolated, namely, trifluoroacetyl chymotrypsin (Chapter 8), although it has not been proved that such acyl enzyme complexes are true catalytic intermediates.

However, this theory does not by itself account for the enormous rate enhancement produced by chymotrypsin, since covalent and general base catalysis by imidazole

Important nucleophilic groups of proteins

Ⓝ = an electrophilic nucleus

$—CH_2—\ddot{O}:—H$ → Ⓝ

serine hydroxyl group

$—CH_2—\ddot{S}:—H$ → Ⓝ

cysteine sulfhydryl group

$—CH_2—C{=}CH$ (HN, N:, C–H imidazole ring) → Ⓝ

histidine imidazole group

Figure 9-2
A proposed mechanism of chymotrypsin action.

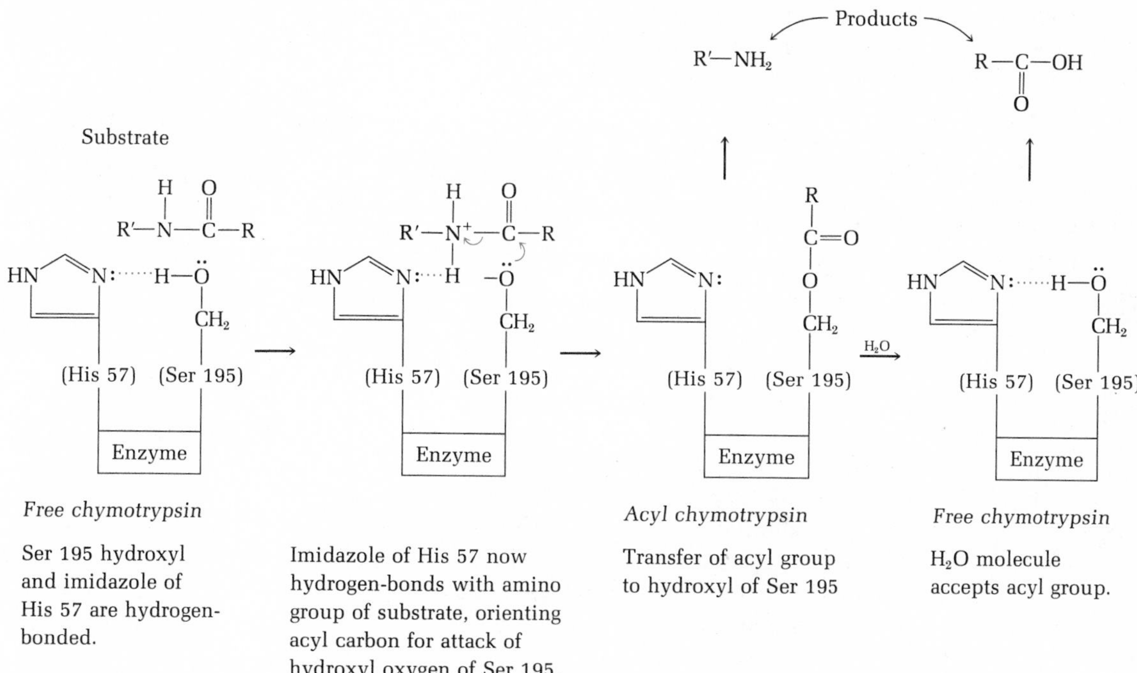
Products
R′—NH2
R—C—OH
O
Substrate
H O
R′—N—C—R
HN
N:
H—Ö
CH2
(His 57) (Ser 195)
Enzyme
R′—N+—C—R
-Ö
R
C=O
O
H2O
Free chymotrypsin
Ser 195 hydroxyl and imidazole of His 57 are hydrogen-bonded.
Imidazole of His 57 now hydrogen-bonds with amino group of substrate, orienting acyl carbon for attack of hydroxyl oxygen of Ser 195.
Acyl chymotrypsin
Transfer of acyl group to hydroxyl of Ser 195
Free chymotrypsin
H2O molecule accepts acyl group.

produces only a limited enhancement of the reaction rate in aqueous systems. Even if we also make ample allowance for the rate enhancement yielded by the proximity of the substrate to the catalytic site and by the proximity of the histidine and serine groups on the enzyme, we still fall far short of explaining the rate enhancement given by chymotrypsin, which is about 10^9 times more effective as a catalyst than any organic model known. To account for this enormous superiority of the enzyme as catalyst, it has been suggested that the microscopic environment at the catalytic site of chymotrypsin is not that of a dilute aqueous system, but rather a much less polar region possessing a lower dielectric constant than water. In such a low-dielectric region, the interacting groups are more reactive, since they would not be stabilized by hydration.

Ribonuclease also appears to involve imidazole groups in its catalytic mechanism since it contains two essential histidine residues. The enzyme phosphoglucomutase, which catalyzes the overall reaction

$$\text{Glucose 1-phosphate} \rightleftharpoons \text{glucose 6-phosphate}$$

involves participation of a serine residue acting as a nucleophile in a displacement reaction, with the formation of a phosphoric acid ester of the serine. The phosphorylated form of phosphoglucomutase has been isolated and shown to contain a phosphoserine residue; this reaction will be discussed in more detail in Chapter 15. In other phosphate-transferring enzymes, it has been found that specific histidine residues become phosphorylated. Still another class of enzymes, those represented by the proteolytic enzyme papain from the latex of the papaya plant, requires the participation of the thiol group of a specific cysteine residue as a nucleophile, probably in displacement reactions similar to those in Figure 9-2. The pathway and mechanism of a number of different enzymatic reactions will be described in later chapters, particularly those dealing with intermediary metabolism.

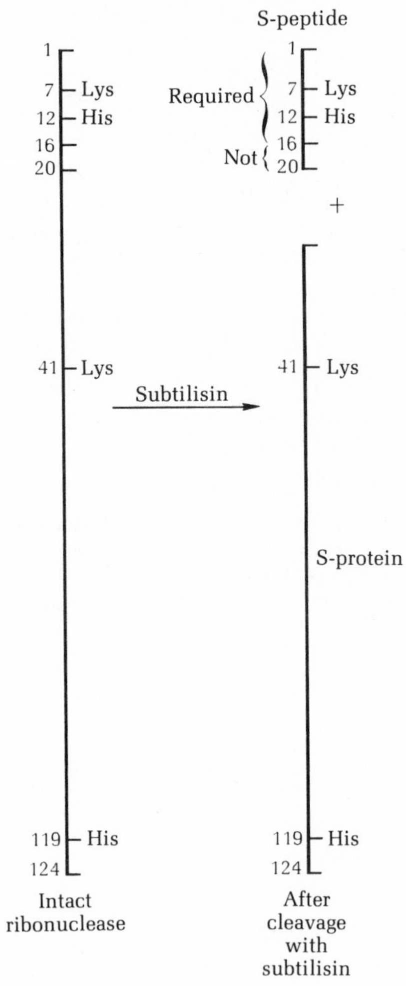

Figure 9-3
Requirement of S-peptide and S-protein for ribonuclease activity. The fragments need not be covalently joined for restoration of activity—merely mixed.

Relationship of the Conformation of Enzyme Molecules to Catalytic Activity

We have seen that the catalytic site of an enzyme contains specific functional groups that can bind the substrate and then bring about the catalytic event. Our discussion did not indicate, however, why enzyme molecules are so large in relation to their substrates or why the rest of the enzyme molecule is required for catalysis. That enzyme activity is dependent in a general way on a specific three-dimensional conformation of the molecule has long been known, since denaturation of enzyme proteins causes loss of activity. However, recent research on some enzymes of known amino acid sequence and conformation is beginning to provide more specific clues.

One question that has been considered is whether the entire peptide-chain backbone of an enzyme is required for catalytic activity. Although some enzymes lose their activity on the cleavage of only one or a few peptide bonds, others still retain activity after removal of a number of residues. Ribonuclease, which has a chain of 124 residues, may be cleaved between residues 20 and 21 by action of the bacterial protease subtilisin (Figure 9-3). The long fragment, called the S-protein, is inactive by itself, as is the short fragment, the S-peptide. When the separated S-peptide and S-protein are simply mixed again at pH 7.0, enzymatic activity is restored, even though the covalent linkage between them is not reformed. The S-peptide is evidently bound to the S-protein through weak forces, such as hydrogen bonding and hydrophobic interactions, to restore the specific three-dimensional conformation necessary for activity. The S-peptide has been synthesized in the laboratory. Amino acids 16 through 20 of the S-peptide are not required for activity. However, two histidine residues, one at position 12 and the other at position 119, are indispensable; they are believed to participate in the catalytic process. Furthermore, two of the four intrachain —S—S— linkages of ribonuclease are required for activity. These observations indicate that specific amino acid residues which are rather far apart in the peptide chain are essential for activity, even though the chain between them may be interrupted. They also suggest that the chain must be held in a folded configuration by the cross-links in such a way as to bring together such essential groups from different parts of the molecule into the structure of the active site.

Recent work on chymotrypsin has also yielded important information on the relationship of structure to catalytic activity (Figure 9-4). This enzyme is secreted in an inactive form, chymotrypsinogen, which has been crystallized. Chymotrypsinogen consists of a single peptide chain of 245 residues held together by five intrachain disulfide bridges. It is converted into active α-chymotrypsin following hydrolysis of four peptide linkages by trypsin or by free chymotrypsin, with the release of two dipeptides. The α-chymotrypsin so produced consists of three peptide chains held together by two —S—S— bonds. Its structure has been determined by x-ray analysis to 2-Å resolution (Figure 9-5). The size of the molecule is 45 × 35 × 38 Å. Contrary to the case of myoglobin, chymotrypsin has very little α-helix; only eight residues are in α-helical configuration. The histidine residue at position 57 and the serine residue at position 195 of chymotrypsin have been

Figure 9-4
Conversion of chymotrypsinogen to α-chymotrypsin. After excision of the two dipeptides, Ser-Arg *and* Thr-Asn, *the* A, B, *and* C *chains of α-chymotrypsin are connected only by —S—S— bridges. The catalytically active residues come from two chains.*

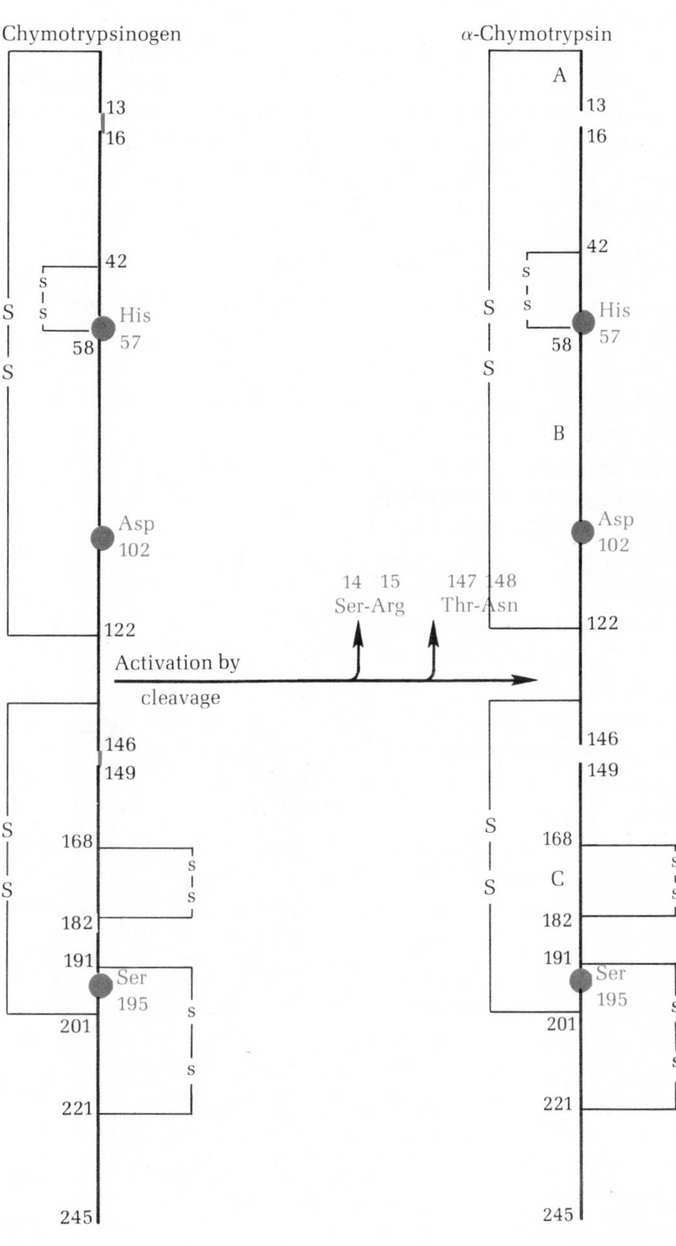

Folded representation

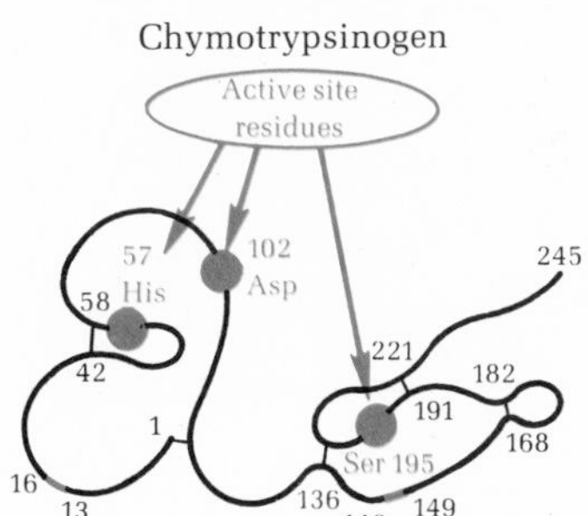

identified as participating in catalysis, and it appears probable that the aspartic acid at 102 is also necessary. The x-ray analysis shows that His 57 and Ser 195 are indeed close together in the tertiary structure, as predicted from kinetic and chemical modification studies.

It is therefore clear that essential functional groups in enzymes are often far removed from each other in the peptide chain and that the chain must be coiled in such a manner as to bring them together at the active site. We may now ask: why is such a molecular arrangement of the active site of any advantage in enzyme functions? One hypothesis suggests that this arrangement makes it possible for the large enzyme molecule to exert stress on the substrate molecule by means of a conformational change in the enzyme structure. Actually, it has been found that some enzymes undergo a change in three-dimensional conformation as they bind their substrates; these changes can be detected by optical-rotation measurements. The "induced fit" of the enzyme to the substrate, it is proposed, produces the precise alignment and orientation of the catalytic and binding groups needed to cause reaction. The change in conformation may also result in strain or compression of the substrate molecule, rendering it more susceptible to catalytic attack. The conformational "flexibility" of the large enzyme molecule may thus be a device to enhance or amplify catalysis. Very recently, x-ray diffraction analysis of the structure of carboxypeptidase and

Figure 9-5
Three-dimensional model of α-chymotrypsin as determined by x-ray analysis. Residues His 57 *and* Ser 195 *function in the catalytic cycle;* Asp 102 *probably also participates.*

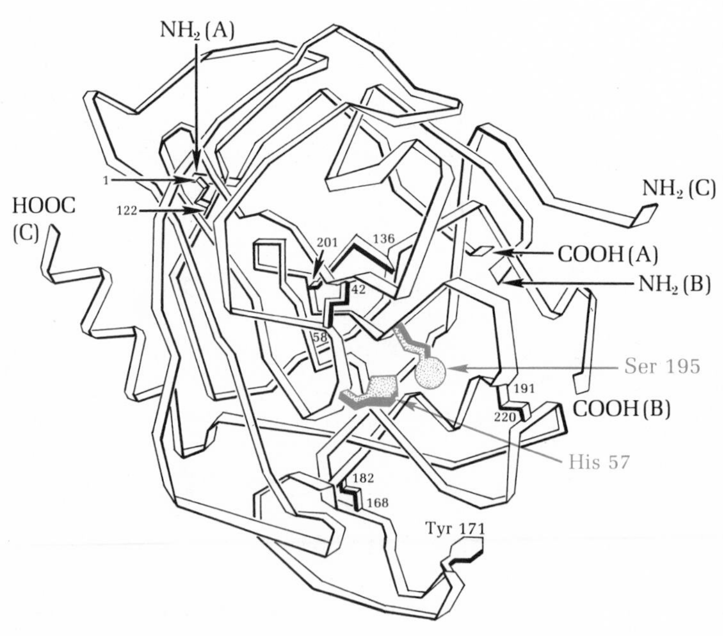

of carboxypeptidase saturated with a "sluggish" substrate, such as glycyltyrosine, has revealed that binding of the substrate does indeed change the structure of the catalytic site. Another function of the induced conformational change is to make possible unloading of the reaction products from the active site, after which the conformation may revert to its initial state.

X-ray diffraction research on the structure of lysozyme has also yielded important information. This enzyme, which contains 129 amino acid residues, catalyzes the hydrolysis of specific glycosidic linkages between residues of the amino sugars N-acetylglucosamine and N-acetylmuramic acid, which are arranged in an alternating fashion in the long polysaccharide chains found in some bacterial cell walls. Lysozyme, which is found in tears and in egg white, causes the lysis of such bacteria. Very recently, x-ray diffraction patterns were obtained, not only of free lysozyme, but also of lysozyme crystals to which an oligosaccharide substrate was bound; the substrate is actually a very poor one and functions as a competitive inhibitor. Two important conclusions resulted from this investigation. First, it was found that the three-dimensional conformation of the lysozyme molecule is altered significantly when it contains bound substrate, confirming the hypothesis that the substrate induces a change in enzyme structure. Second, the precise location of the substrate molecule on the surface of the enzyme could be deduced. This finding made it possible to locate the functional groups in the lysozyme molecule that are in the appropriate positions to exert catalytic action on the sensitive glycosidic bond of the polysaccharide molecule. Figure 9-6 shows schematically a projection of the enzyme-substrate complex of lysozyme and, below it, a diagram illustrating the hypothesis that the glutamic acid residue at position 35 and the aspartic acid residue at position 52 in the peptide chain of lysozyme cooperate in bringing about hydrolysis of the glycosidic linkage of the substrate.

Multienzyme Systems

In the intact cell, enzymes usually work together in sequential chains in which the product of the first enzyme becomes the substrate of the next, and so on. Three levels of complexity of molecular organization of multienzyme systems can be discerned. In the simplest multienzyme system, the individual enzymes are in solution in the cytoplasm as independent molecular entities; presumably they are not physically associated with each other at any time during their action. The small substrate molecules, which have high rates of diffusion, find their way from one enzyme molecule to the next very rapidly (Figure 9-7).

Other multienzyme systems are more highly organized, so that the individual enzymes are physically associated and function together as *enzyme complexes*. For example, the fatty acid synthetase system of yeast, which catalyzes

Figure 9-6
Structure and postulated action of the lysozyme-substrate complex. The drawing at the upper right shows the backbones of the lysozyme and substrate molecules in the crystalline complex. (From Atlas of Protein Sequence and Structure 1967–68, *Margaret O. Dayhoff and Richard V. Eck, National Biomedical Research Foundation, Silver Spring, Maryland, 1968. See* Acknowledgments, *page 810.) The large drawing shows a magnification of the portion of the structure near the catalytic site. It is proposed that a hydrogen ion* H^+ *leaves the carboxyl group of residue* 35 *(glutamic acid) and combines with the oxygen joining rings* D *and* E *of the substrate, thus breaking the bond. The carbonium ion so formed at carbon* 1 *of the* D *ring is stabilized by the negative carboxyl group of residue* 52 *(aspartic acid). A water molecule supplies the* OH^- *ion to react with the carbonium ion and an* H^+ *ion to replace that lost by residue* 35. *The two parts of the substrate then leave the enzyme, which is thus free to bind another substrate molecule. (Redrawn from* "The Three-Dimensional Structure of an Enzyme Molecule," *by David C. Phillips. Copyright © November 1966 by Scientific American, Inc. All rights reserved.)*

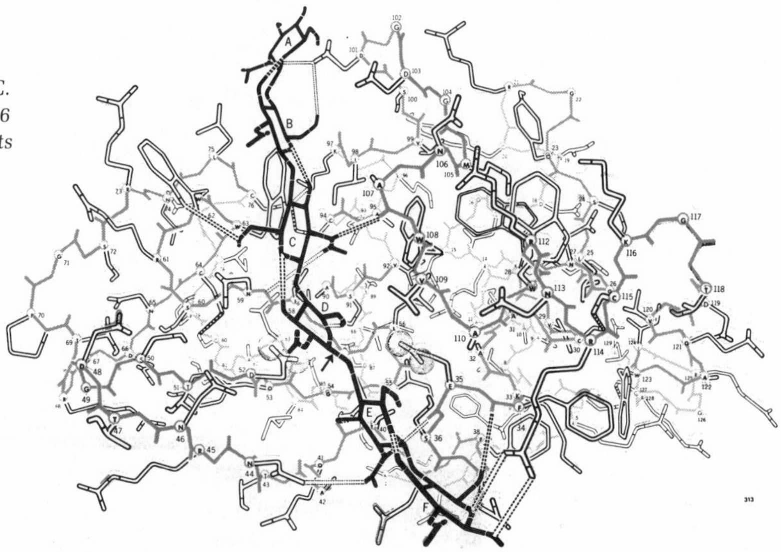

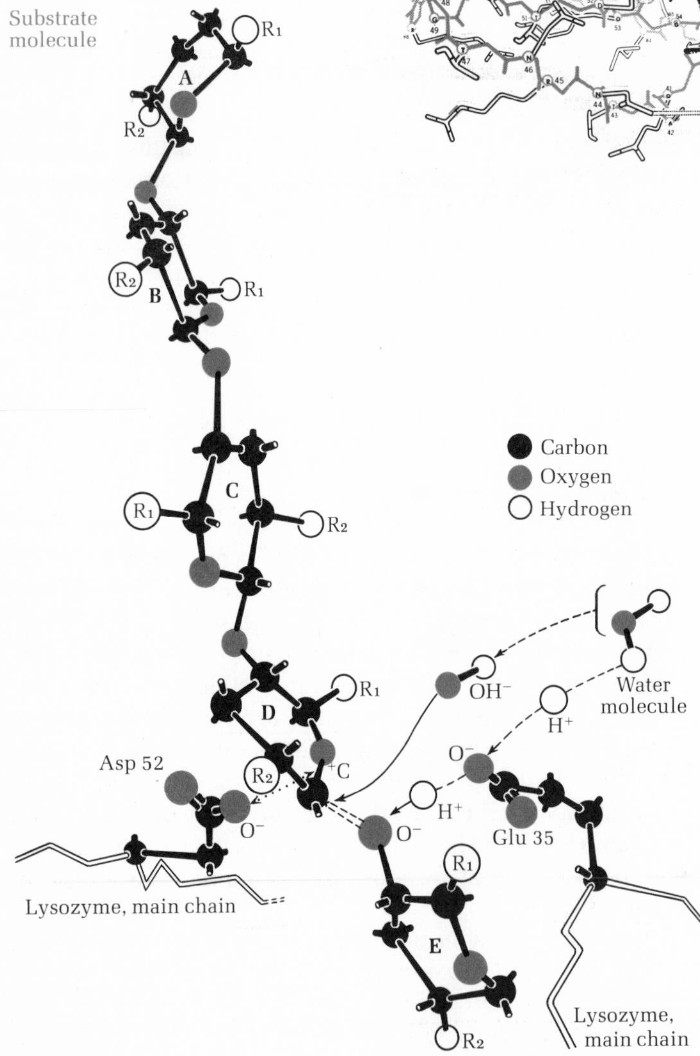

Figure 9-7
Types of multienzyme systems.

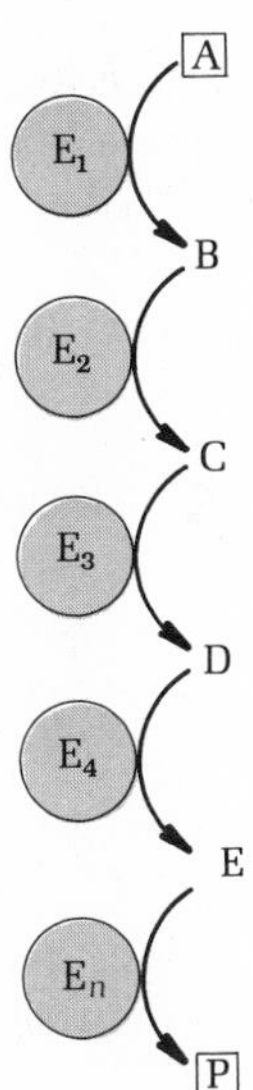

A soluble or dissociated multienzyme system with diffusing intermediates (B, C, D, E···)

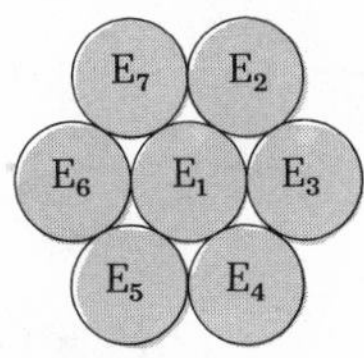

A multienzyme complex

Usually its intermediates do not diffuse away from the complex

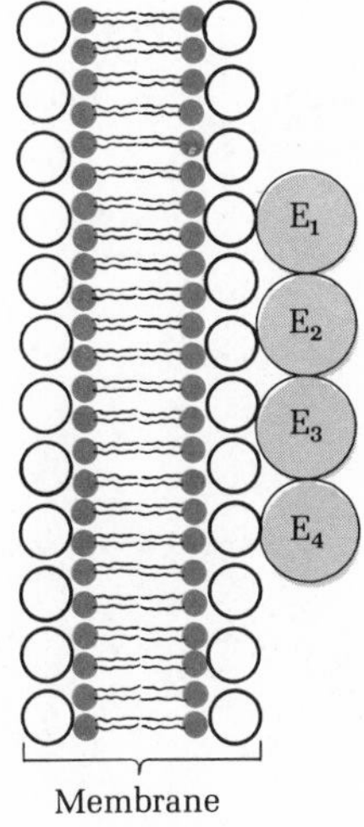

A membrane-bound enzyme system

the synthesis of fatty acids from small-molecular-weight precursors, consists of seven different types of enzyme molecules arranged in a tightly bound cluster. This complex does not readily dissociate into separate enzyme molecules; in fact, the separated molecules are inactive. Presumably the arrangement of enzyme molecules of a system into nondissociating complexes is biologically advantageous in that it limits the distance through which the substrate molecules must diffuse during the course of the reaction sequence. Actually, in the fatty acid synthetase system the intermediate substrates never leave the complex (Chapter 23).

The most highly organized enzyme systems are those associated with large supramolecular structures such as membranes or ribosomes (Figure 9-7). An important example is the chain of respiratory enzymes that is responsible for transferring electrons from substrates to oxygen; the individual enzyme molecules are attached to the inner membrane of the mitochondrion and, indeed, form part of its structure (Chapters 17 and 18). The more complex the enzyme system, the more likely it is to be associated with some organelle or other intracellular structure.

The kinetic behavior of a multienzyme system is obviously much more difficult to analyze quantitatively than the kinetics of a single enzyme. Each member of a multienzyme sequence has its own characteristic K_M for its substrate(s) and for its cofactor(s). The rates of the individual steps are determined by the steady-state concentration of each intermediate in the metabolic sequence, as well as by the concentration of each enzyme. Usually there is a single reaction in the sequence that sets the rate for the whole system because either the enzyme concentration or the substrate concentration is rate-limiting. Considerable success has been achieved in simulating the kinetics of multienzyme systems with electronic computers, starting from known data on the K_M and V_{max} values for each enzyme and the steady-state concentration of intermediates.

Self-Regulating Properties of Enzyme Systems

Many multienzyme systems possess the capacity for self-regulation of their overall reaction rate. In most such systems, the end product of the sequence of reactions can inhibit the first enzyme, with the result that the rate of the entire sequence is determined by the steady-state concentration of the end product. An example is the multienzyme sequence catalyzing the conversion of L-threonine to L-isoleucine, which occurs in five enzyme-catalyzed steps (Figure 9-8). The first enzyme of the sequence, L-threonine deaminase, is strongly inhibited, even in highly purified form, by L-isoleucine, the end product of the sequence, but not by any other intermediate. The inhibition by isoleucine is atypical in that it is not competitive with the substrate L-threonine nor is it noncompetitive. Isoleucine is quite specific as an inhibitor; other amino acids or related compounds do not inhibit. It is clear that if L-isoleucine accumulates to too high a level in the system, the first step in the series of enzymatic reactions leading to its own formation will be inhibited. This type of end-product inhibition is called *feed-back inhibition* or *retro-inhibition*.

In most self-regulating enzyme systems, it is the first enzyme of the sequence that is inhibited by the end product of the sequence. This enzyme is called a *regulatory* or *allosteric enzyme*, and the inhibitory metabolite is the *effector* or *modulator*. If the latter is inhibitory, it is a negative effector or modulator. Although the regulatory enzyme is usually the first member of a multienzyme sequence, it may also occur at a point where a multienzyme system undergoes branching. The example in Figure 9-8 represents the simplest type of regulatory enzyme system in which the regulatory enzyme is *monovalent*, i.e., has only one modulator molecule. In many self-regulating systems, the regulatory enzyme is *polyvalent*, i.e., it responds to more than one specific modulator molecule. The additional modulators may be end products of some other, but related, metabolic sequences. In this manner, two or more multienzyme systems may be connected by a control network. Specific examples of such networks will be described later (Chapters 18, 22–25). A regulatory enzyme may also possess a specific positive modulator; most often the positive modulator is the substrate of the regulatory enzyme. Some regulatory enzymes may possess one or more specific positive modulators and one or more specific negative modulators simultaneously, each being bound to a specific site on the enzyme. Most regulatory enzymes appear to share another common property; they usually catalyze reactions that are essentially irreversible under intracellular conditions. The first step in a multienzyme reaction sequence is often called the *committed step;* once it takes place, all the ensuing reactions take place. Strategically, inhibition of the first step in a sequence by an allosteric modulator yields maximum economy of metabolites.

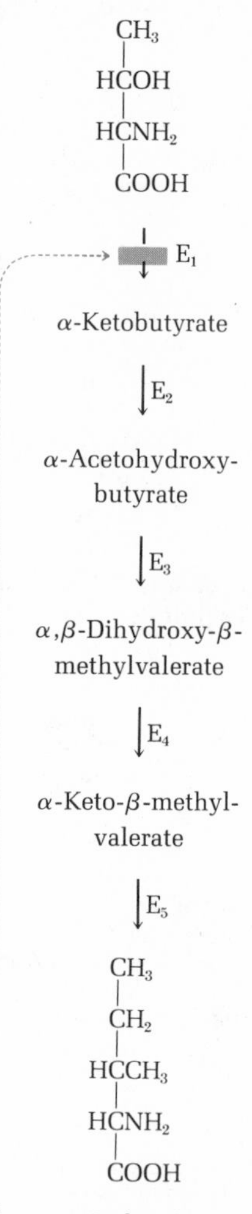

Figure 9-8
Feedback inhibition of L-*threonine deaminase, the first enzyme* (E_1) *in the sequence, by* L-*isoleucine, the end product of the sequence.* E_2, E_3, E_4, *and* E_5 *symbolize enzymes catalyzing the intermediate steps.*

Properties of Regulatory Enzymes

Regulatory enzymes are usually much larger, more complex, and more difficult to purify than enzymes not endowed with regulatory properties. Often they show anomalous properties; some regulatory enzymes are unstable at 0° but stable at room temperature. All known regulatory enzymes have more than one polypeptide chain; some contain many chains. In most cases, regulatory enzymes possess an atypical dependence of reaction velocity on substrate concentration, not easily treated by the simple Michaelis-Menten relationship; they also show atypical inhibition by the modulating substance.

Three major classes of regulatory enzymes are now recognized: (1) *homotropic*, (2) *heterotropic*, and (3) *homotropic-heterotropic*. In homotropic regulatory enzymes, the substrate molecule is not only a substrate but also a modulator which usually accelerates the catalytic activity, depending on its concentration. Heterotropic regulatory enzymes are stimulated or inhibited by a specific, naturally occurring effector or modulator other than the substrate, such as the end product isoleucine in the example of Figure 9-8. Some multivalent regulatory enzymes are *both* homotropic and heterotropic; in these, the substrate is one of two or more modulators to which the enzyme responds.

Homotropic regulatory enzymes are believed to contain two or more binding sites for the substrate, at least one of which is catalytic. Heterotropic enzymes possess not only a binding or catalytic site for the substrate but also a second site, believed to be physically separate from the catalytic site, at which the modulator molecule binds. The heterotropic enzyme threonine deaminase, for example, is believed to have one site specific for the substrate L-threonine and another site specific for the modulator L-isoleucine. The term allosteric means "other space" or "other site." However, the more general term "regulatory enzyme" is now preferred for all enzymes having a regulatory function since it avoids the need to specify whether or not a separate modulator site is involved in the action of the enzyme.

Many regulatory enzymes are very complex in behavior. To date only one, aspartate transcarbamylase, has been proved by direct experimental approaches to have separate binding sites for substrates and other modulators, which reside in separate subunits (Chapter 25). The existence of multiple binding sites in other regulatory enzymes must still be regarded as hypothetical and largely based on indirect kinetic evidence.

Figure 9-9
Substrate concentration-velocity curves for two types of homotropic regulatory enzymes. The sigmoid curve (top) *shows that the binding of one substrate molecule enhances the binding of the second. Inhibition by excess substrate* (bottom) *is observed in other cases.*

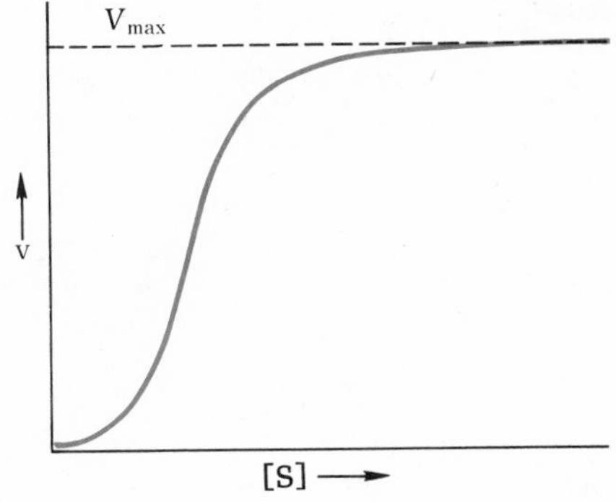

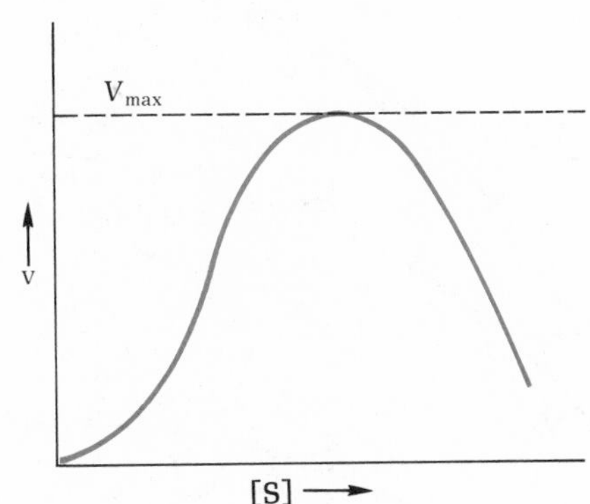

Kinetics of Regulatory Enzymes

Most regulatory enzymes have atypical substrate-saturation curves, which appear to be at variance with classic Michaelis-Menten behavior. The shape of such substrate-concentration-velocity curves seems to depend on whether the regulatory enzyme is homotropic or heterotropic, but generalizations are still somewhat dangerous. Homotropic regulatory enzymes usually show a sigmoid dependence on substrate concentration (Figure 9-9) rather than the hyperbolic Michaelis-Menten relationship. The sigmoid nature of the curve implies that the binding of the first substrate molecule to the enzyme enhances the binding of a second substrate molecule and thus enhances activity. Sometimes such sigmoid curves are very steep; a small increase in substrate concentration can cause a very large acceleration of the rate of catalysis, much more than is the case in the hyperbolic Michaelis-Menten curve of a simple, nonregulatory enzyme.

Some homotropic regulatory enzymes respond to rising substrate concentration to yield an increase in the affinity of the enzyme for its substrate without a change in the maximum velocity. In these cases, there is a decrease in the apparent K_M, defined as the substrate concentration at which the rate is half-maximal, but no change in V_{max}. Other regulatory enzymes show a change in V_{max} without a change in affinity; however, these are less common.

Some homotropic enzymes are inhibited by excess substrate (Figure 9-9); in such cases, it is evident that maximum velocity is yielded by only a limited range of substrate concentration.

The curves shown in Figure 9-10 illustrate typical substrate-concentration curves of heterotropic enzymes. The effector molecule may either inhibit or stimulate the reaction at any given substrate concentration; the inhibition or stimulation may result from changes in either K_M or V_{max} of the enzyme. Again, we should emphasize that it is difficult to generalize, since each regulatory enzyme has its own characteristic kinetic behavior. The study of heterotropic enzymes has shown that their specificity for the modulator molecule, whether positive or negative, may be just as great as their specificity for their normal substrates.

The capacity of a regulatory enzyme to be activated or inhibited by its specific modulators can sometimes be abolished without damaging its catalytic activity. Often this can be brought about by treating the enzyme with an agent that produces a chemical modification of the modulator site. The enzyme is then spoken of as being desensitized; desensitization by such chemical modification is irreversible. Genetic mutation sometimes results in the synthesis of a regulatory enzyme in which the sensitivity to the effector molecule is lost. It has therefore been concluded that the amino acid sequence of a regulatory enzyme specifies not only its catalytic activity but also its capacity to act as a pacemaker or regulatory enzyme.

Figure 9-10
Effects of modulators on substrate-velocity curves of heterotropic regulatory enzymes. In some (left), the presence of a stimulatory or an inhibitory effector causes an increase or a decrease, respectively, in the affinity of the enzyme for its substrate without influencing V_{max}. In other cases (right), the effectors change V_{max} without influencing the affinity.

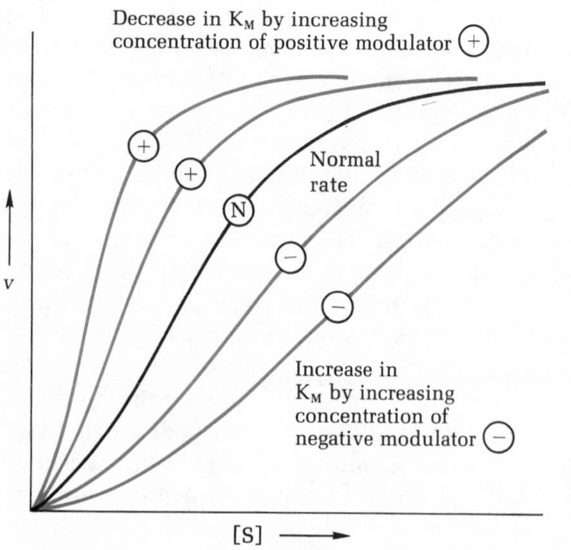

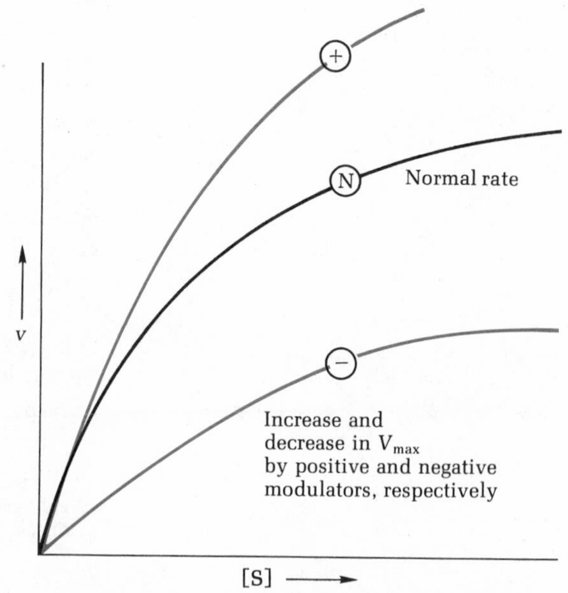

Figure 9-11
Oxygen-saturation curves for myoglobin and hemoglobin.

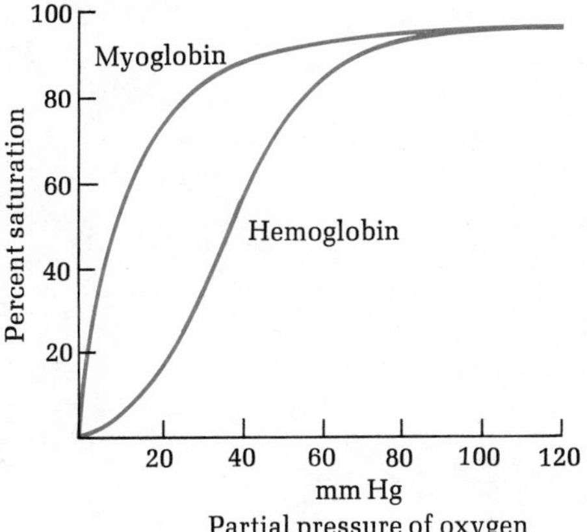

Mechanism of Regulation

How can the binding of the modulator molecule to its specific binding site modulate the catalytic activity of a regulatory enzyme when the binding site may be distant from the catalytic site and may even reside on a different polypeptide chain? Several theories have been developed, all of which ultimately postulate that the binding of the modulator to its specific site causes a conformational change in the three-dimensional structure of the regulatory enzyme molecule. The form that results is intrinsically either more active or less active catalytically than the form with the modulator site unoccupied.

An important model for the action of allosteric enzymes is the oxygen-binding protein hemoglobin. Although hemoglobin is not an enzyme, it has long been known that its saturation by oxygen shows a sigmoid relationship with oxygen partial pressure (Figure 9-11) that resembles the sigmoid substrate curve of homotropic regulatory enzymes. In contrast, the oxygen-saturation curve for myoglobin is hyperbolic, resembling the classic Michaelis-Menten curve for a simple enzyme. Hemoglobin has four peptide chains and four hemes, each of which can bind an oxygen molecule, whereas myoglobin has only a single chain and a single heme and can bind only one oxygen molecule. Hemoglobin may be regarded as a model of a homotropic regulatory enzyme and myoglobin as a model of a simple, nonregulatory enzyme.

The sigmoid saturation curve of hemoglobin shows that the binding of the first oxygen molecule to one heme group enhances the binding of succeeding oxygen molecules to the three remaining heme groups. The mechanism of this effect has long been a mystery since x-ray diffraction analysis shows that the four heme groups of hemoglobin are spaced far apart and cannot react with each other directly. One recent theory is as follows: It has been found that hemoglobin dissociates reversibly into half-molecules, each of which contains an α- and a β-chain, to give the equilibrium

$$\underset{\text{Hemoglobin}}{\alpha\alpha\beta\beta} \rightleftharpoons \underset{\text{Half-molecules}}{\alpha\beta + \alpha\beta}$$

This fact, and much other evidence, indicates that the $\alpha\beta$ half-molecules are the *functional* subunits of hemoglobin. When one molecule of oxygen [designated below by an asterisk (*)] combines with one of the hemes of hemoglobin, it may be envisaged as combining with one of the two hemes in an $\alpha\beta$ half-molecule, for example, the α-heme. As this combination takes place, the α-polypeptide chain undergoes a change in conformation from the form designated ○ to the form designated □:

$$O_2 + \begin{matrix}(\alpha)(\beta)\\(\beta)(\alpha)\end{matrix} \rightleftharpoons \begin{matrix}\overset{*}{[\alpha]}(\beta)\\(\beta)(\alpha)\end{matrix}$$

As this occurs, the conformational change in the α-chain is mechanically transmitted to the tightly bound β-chain, which now also undergoes a conformational change to the □ form:

$$\begin{matrix}\overset{*}{[\alpha]}(\beta)\\(\beta)(\alpha)\end{matrix} \rightleftharpoons \begin{matrix}\overset{*}{[\alpha]}[\beta]\\(\beta)(\alpha)\end{matrix}$$

Since the β-chain in its new conformation $\boxed{\beta}$ has a higher affinity for oxygen than the form $\textcircled{\beta}$, the β heme also becomes oxygenated:

$$\begin{array}{c}\overset{*}{\boxed{\alpha}}\boxed{\beta}\\ \textcircled{\beta}\textcircled{\alpha}\end{array} + O_2 \rightleftharpoons \begin{array}{c}\overset{*}{\boxed{\alpha}}\overset{*}{\boxed{\beta}}\\ \textcircled{\beta}\textcircled{\alpha}\end{array}$$

In this way, the binding of one molecule of oxygen enhances the binding of the second. With the complete oxygenation of the first $\alpha\beta$ functional subunit and the consequent change in its conformation, new internal stresses are developed among the subunits of the hemoglobin molecule which cause the other $\alpha\beta$ subunit to change from the $\textcircled{\beta}\textcircled{\alpha}$ conformation, which has a relatively low affinity for oxygen, to the form $\boxed{\beta|\alpha}$, which has a relatively high affinity for oxygen:

$$\begin{array}{c}\overset{*}{\boxed{\alpha}}\overset{*}{\boxed{\beta}}\\ \textcircled{\beta}\textcircled{\alpha}\end{array} \rightleftharpoons \begin{array}{c}\overset{*}{\boxed{\alpha}}\overset{*}{\boxed{\beta}}\\ \boxed{\beta}\boxed{\alpha}\end{array}$$

Two additional molecules of oxygen now are bound to the second $\alpha\beta$ subunit, probably sequentially, to yield ultimately the fully oxygenated oxyhemoglobin

$$\begin{array}{c}\overset{*}{\boxed{\alpha}}\overset{*}{\boxed{\beta}}\\ \boxed{\beta}\boxed{\alpha}\end{array} + 2O_2 \longrightarrow \begin{array}{c}\overset{*}{\boxed{\alpha}}\overset{*}{\boxed{\beta}}\\ \underset{*}{\boxed{\beta}}\underset{*}{\boxed{\alpha}}\end{array}$$

This mechanism for hemoglobin oxygenation is directly applicable to regulatory enzymes. The binding of the first substrate molecule to one subunit of a homotropic enzyme enhances the binding of a second substrate molecule to a second subunit because there is a conformational change in the first subunit which is transmitted mechanically or sterically to the second subunit. In all cases studied to date, regulatory enzymes have been found to be rather large molecules containing subunits; presumably, the existence of interacting subunits is necessary for their function.

Note that the term "subunit" is ambiguous and may have two different meanings when applied to oligomeric proteins. Hemoglobin contains four *structural* subunits or protomers i.e., the two α and two β chains, but two *functional* subunits, i.e., the two $\alpha\beta$ half-molecules.

Isozymes

Recent research has revealed another way in which the activity of some enzymes may be controlled through features of their molecular structure. A number of different enzymes have been found to exist in multiple molecular forms *within a single species, or even within a single cell.* Such multiple forms can be detected and separated by gel electrophoresis of cell extracts; they are therefore distinct molecular species differing in net electrical charge. Multiple forms within a single species or cell are called *isozymes* (or *isoenzymes*).

Lactate dehydrogenase, one of the first enzymes in this class to have been studied intensively, exists in five different major forms, or isozymes, in the tissues of the rat

Figure 9-12
Relative amounts of lactate dehydrogenase isozymes in the tissues of an adult white rat, as determined by zone electrophoresis of tissue extracts in a starch block. The extracts are applied at the line marked "Origin." Four of the isozymes move to the anode and one to the cathode at the pH chosen. The size and density of the spots reflect the amount of each isozyme. The lactate isozymes are also designated as $A_4(=M_4)$, A_3B, A_2B_2, AB_3, *and* $B_4(=H_4)$.

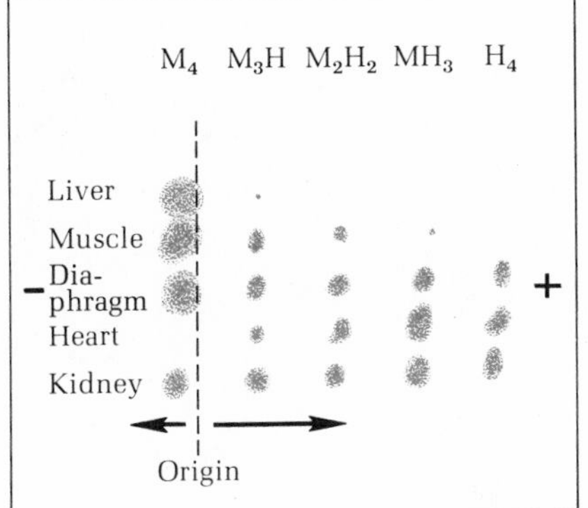

(Figure 9-12). These have been obtained in pure form. Although all five isozymes of lactate dehydrogenase catalyze the same overall reaction, they have distinctly different K_M values for their substrates; the biological significance of these differences will be described in Chapters 15 and 18. The five isozymes all have the same particle weight, about 134,000, and all contain four polypeptide chains, each of mol wt 33,500. They have been found to consist of five different combinations of two different types of polypeptide chains, designated M and H chains. One of the isozymes, which predominates in muscle, has four identical M chains and is designated M_4; another, which predominates in heart, has four identical H chains and is designated H_4. The other three isozymes consist of the different possible combinations of M and H chains, i.e., M_3H, M_2H_2, and MH_3 forms. The single M and H chains, which have been isolated and found to be enzymatically inactive, differ significantly in amino acid content and sequence. When the M and H chains are mixed in appropriate proportions, all the different isozymes of lactate dehydrogenase can be made to form spontaneously in the test tube.

Recent research indicates that the two different peptide chains M and H of lactate dehydrogenase are coded by two different genes and that the relative amounts of the two types of chains, and thus the type of lactate dehydrogenase isozyme in a given cell type, are under genetic regulation. Figure 9-12 shows that the isozymes of lactate dehydrogenase exist in different proportions in different tissues. Later we will see that the relative proportions of the different lactate dehydrogenase isozymes may change during embryological development (Chapters 18, 32).

Many different enzymes are now known to exist in the form of isozymes. In each case, so far as has been investigated, the isozymes have been found to consist of various combinations of different polypeptide chains. Usually the isozymes of a given enzyme differ from each other with respect to kinetic characteristics.

The study of isozymes has come to be of fundamental significance in the investigation of the molecular basis of cellular differentiation and of morphogenesis. It is believed that many proteins in cells, not only those with catalytic activity, may exist in multiple forms that consist of mixtures of different subunits coded by different genes.

Summary

Detailed studies have been made of the substrate specificity of many enzymes; the study of chymotrypsin has been especially instructive. From these studies, it has been deduced that the substrate molecule must possess not only the specific chemical bond or functional group involved in the reaction catalyzed but also, in most cases, another functional group essential for its binding to the enzyme, so that the susceptible bond is properly positioned in proximity with the catalytic group.

Organic model reactions have shown that acids and bases are very potent catalysts, particularly general acids and general bases. Usually the general acid or general base donates or accepts protons during catalysis. Enzymes contain functional groups that may act as general-acid catalysts, such as $—NH_3^+$ or tyrosine hydroxyl groups, or as general-base catalysts, such as carboxylate groups. Catalysis is also promoted by Lewis acids, defined as electron-pair acceptors or electrophilic groups, and Lewis bases, which are electron-pair donors or nucleophilic groups. Enzymes contain electrophilic groups, such as metal ions, and nucleophilic groups, such as serine hydroxyl groups, sulfhydryl groups, and imidazole groups. The imidazole group of histidine, which is involved in the action of many enzymes, is especially versatile since it can function as a general acid, a general base, or a strong nucleophile. Catalytic activity also requires a specific three-dimensional conformation of the enzyme molecule, which may undergo a significant change during the catalytic cycle, suggesting that the substrate molecule is subjected to conformational stress during or following its combination with the enzyme. Such a conformational change induced by the substrate may also function to allow rapid release of the products.

Enzymes usually function in sequential multienzyme systems. Often such a system is organized into a complex, which may be located in a membrane or in a cell organelle. Multienzyme systems usually have a rate-limiting step catalyzed by an allosteric, or regulatory, enzyme. The activity of the regulatory enzyme may be stimulated or inhibited by the binding of another molecule, often a product of the sequence, at a second site on the enzyme molecule. Regulatory enzymes usually possess subunits which can interact with each other. Some enzymes exist in multiple forms, called isozymes, which consist of various mixtures of two or more peptide chains. Isozymes are believed to be important in the regulation of enzyme activity and in differentiation and development of cells.

References

(Also see references in Chapter 6 (particularly those on enzyme conformation) and Chapter 8.)

Books

BERNHARD, S.: *The Structure and Function of Enzymes*, W. A. Benjamin, Inc. New York, 1968. Paperback stressing structure-function-mechanism relationships.

BRUICE, T. C., and S. J. BENKOVIC: *Bioorganic Mechanisms*, 2 vols., W. A. Benjamin, Inc., New York, 1966. Comprehensive review of organic model reactions for enzyme reactions.

BRESLOW, R.: *Organic Reaction Mechanisms*, W. A. Benjamin, Inc., New York, 1965. Useful paperback review of the organic chemistry background.

GOODWIN, T. W., J. I. HARRIS, and B. S. BENTLEY (eds.): *Structure and Activity of Enzymes*, Academic Press, Inc., New York, 1964. A symposium.

GUTFREUND, H.: *Introduction to the Study of Enzymes*, Wiley, New York, 1965. A standard text book.

JENCKS, W. P.: *Catalysis in Chemistry and Enzymology*, McGraw-Hill Book Company, New York, 1969. A definitive, up-to-date treatment of catalytic mechanisms.

WILKINSON, J. H.: *Isoenzymes*, J. B. Lippincott Company, Philadelphia, 1966. A survey of the literature on isozymes.

Articles and Reviews

ATKINSON, D. E.: "Regulation of Enzyme Activity," *Ann. Rev. Biochem.*, **35**:85–124 (1966). Excellent survey of the biochemical and biological implications of enzyme regulation.

BLOW, D. M., J. J. BIRKTOFT, and B. S. HARTLEY: "Role of a Buried Acid Group in the Mechanism of Action of Chymotrypsin," *Nature*, **221**:337–340 (1969).

FINE, I. H., N. O. KAPLAN, and D. KUFTINEC: "Developmental Changes of Mammalian Lactic Dehydrogenases," *Biochemistry*, **2**:116–121 (1963). Isozyme changes during development.

KOSHLAND, D. E., JR., and K. E. NEET: "The Catalytic and Regulatory Properties of Enzymes," *Ann. Rev. Biochem.*, **37**:359–410 (1968). Superb review of important factors in mechanisms of catalysis and control.

MONOD, J., J. P. CHANGEUX, and F. JACOB: "Allosteric Proteins and Cellular Control Systems," *J. Mol. Biol.*, **6**:306–329 (1963). Classical statement of the molecular theory of enzyme regulation.

PHILLIPS, D. C.: "The Three-dimensional Structure of an Enzyme Molecule," *Sci. Am.*, **215**:78–90 (Nov., 1966). Structure of lysozyme and its complex with substrate.

REED, L. J., and D. J. COX: "Macromolecular Organization of Enzyme Systems," *Ann. Rev. Biochem.*, **35**:57–84 (1966). Review of enzyme complexes.

SHANNON, L. M.: "Plant Isoenzymes," *Ann. Rev. Plant Physiol.*, **19**:187–210 (1968).

STADTMAN, E. R.: "Allosteric Regulation of Enzyme Activity," *Advan. Enzymol.*, **28**:41–154 (1966). Outstanding review of regulatory mechanisms.

STRYER, L.: "Implications of X-ray Crystallographic Studies of Protein Structure," *Ann. Rev. Biochem.*, **37**:25–50 (1968). Excellent review of the most recent work on conformation of enzyme molecules.

CHAPTER 10 LIPIDS, LIPOPROTEINS, AND MEMBRANES

Lipids are water-insoluble organic substances found in cells which are extractable by nonpolar solvents such as chloroform, ether, and benzene. There are several major classes and subclasses of lipids, most of which may occur in different molecular species, depending on the structure of their fatty acid components. Lipids appear to serve four general functions: (1) as structural components of membranes, (2) as intracellular storage depots of metabolic fuel, (3) as a transport form of metabolic fuel, and (4) as protective components of the cell walls of many bacteria, of the leaves of higher plants, of the exoskeleton of insects, and of the skin of vertebrates. Some substances classified among the lipids have intense biological activity; they include some vitamins and their precursors, as well as a number of hormones.

Until only a few years ago, lipid biochemistry was considered an uninteresting and hopelessly complex field. However, the perfection of new chromatographic methods for high-resolution separation and analysis of lipids has been an important factor in opening this field to more penetrating investigation. It appears probable, from the tempo of recent research, that we are now on the eve of important discoveries regarding the role of lipids in the structure of cell membranes.

Examples of Fatty Acids

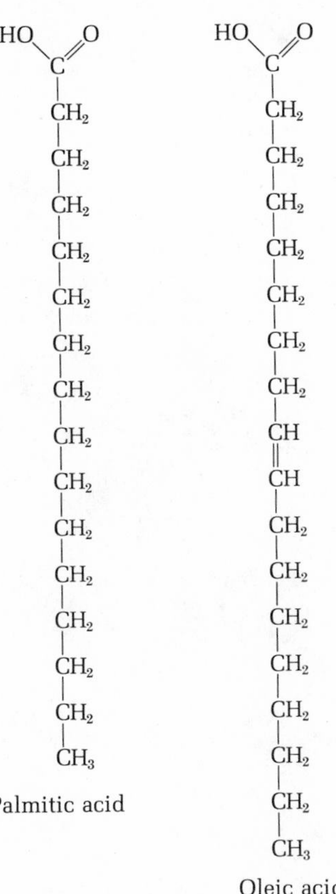

Palmitic acid

Oleic acid

Fatty Acids

Although fatty acids occur in the free state in only trace amounts in most cells and tissues, we shall discuss them in some detail since they are the building blocks of several classes of lipids, including the neutral fats, phosphoglycerides, glycolipids, cholesterol esters, and some waxes. Over 70 different fatty acids have been isolated from various cells and tissues. All possess a long hydrocarbon chain and a terminal carboxyl group (margin). The chain may be saturated, or it may have one or more double bonds; a few fatty acids contain triple bonds. Fatty acids differ primarily in chain length and in the number and position of their unsaturated bonds. Table 10-1 gives the structures of some important naturally occurring saturated and unsaturated fatty acids.

Table 10-1 Some naturally occurring fatty acids

Carbon atoms	*Structure*	*Systematic name*	*Common name*	*Melting point (°C)*
Saturated fatty acids				
12	$CH_3(CH_2)_{10}COOH$	*n*-Dodecanoic	Lauric acid	44.2
14	$CH_3(CH_2)_{12}COOH$	*n*-Tetradecanoic	Myristic	53.9
16	$CH_3(CH_2)_{14}COOH$	*n*-Hexadecanoic	Palmitic	63.1
18	$CH_3(CH_2)_{16}COOH$	*n*-Octadecanoic	Stearic	69.6
20	$CH_3(CH_2)_{18}COOH$	*n*-Eicosanoic	Arachidic	76.5
24	$CH_3(CH_2)_{22}COOH$	*n*-Tetracosanoic	Lignoceric	86.0
Unsaturated fatty acids				
16	$CH_3(CH_2)_5CH{=}CH(CH_2)_7COOH$		Palmitoleic	− 0.5
18	$CH_3(CH_2)_7CH{=}CH(CH_2)_7COOH$		Oleic	13.4
18	$CH_3(CH_2)_4CH{=}CHCH_2CH{=}CH(CH_2)_7COOH$		Linoleic	− 5
18	$CH_3CH_2CH{=}CHCH_2CH{=}CHCH_2CH{=}CH(CH_2)_7COOH$		Linolenic	−11
20	$CH_3(CH_2)_4CH{=}CHCH_2CH{=}CHCH_2CH{=}CHCH_2CH{=}CH(CH_2)_3COOH$		Arachidonic	−49.5
Some unusual fatty acids				
18	$CH_3(CH_2)_5CH{=}CH(CH_2)_9COOH$ (*trans*)		*trans*-Vaccenic acid	44
19	$CH_3(CH_2)_5HC{-}CH(CH_2)_9COOH$ (the two CH carbons bridged by CH_2)		Lactobacillic	
19	$CH_3(CH_2)_7CH(CH_3)(CH_2)_8COOH$		Tuberculostearic	
24	$CH_3(CH_2)_{21}CH(OH)COOH$		Cerebronic	

Some generalizations may be made on the fatty acids present in lipids of higher plants and animals. Nearly all have an even number of carbon atoms and have chains that are between 14 and 22 carbon atoms long; those having 16 or 18 carbons are by far the most abundant. In general, unsaturated fatty acids predominate over the saturated type, particularly in the neutral fats and in cells of poikilothermic organisms living at lower temperatures. Unsaturated fatty acids have lower melting points than saturated fatty acids (Table 10-1); most neutral fats rich in unsaturated fatty acids are liquid down to 5°C or lower. In most of the unsaturated fatty acids in higher organisms, there is a double bond between carbon atoms 9 and 10; additional double bonds usually occur between C_{10} and the methyl-terminal end of the chain. In fatty acids containing two or more double bonds, the double bonds are never found in conjugation (that is, $-CH{=}CH-CH{=}CH-$) but are separated by one methylene group (that is, $-CH{=}CH-CH_2-CH{=}CH-$). The double bonds of nearly all the naturally occurring unsaturated fatty acids are in the *cis* geometrical configuration. The most abundant unsaturated fatty acids in higher organisms are oleic, linoleic, linolenic, and arachidonic acids.

In general, bacteria contain fewer and simpler types of lipids than the cells of higher organisms. The fatty acids

Stearic acid

Oleic acid (*cis*)

Linoleic acid

of *E. coli* lipids consist of C_{12} to C_{18} saturated acids (some of which contain a substituted methyl group or a cyclopropyl group) and C_{16} or C_{18} monounsaturated acids. Fatty acids with more than one double bond have not been found in bacteria.

Properties of Fatty Acids

Saturated and unsaturated fatty acids differ significantly in structural configuration. In saturated fatty acids, the hydrocarbon tails can exist in an infinite number of conformations because each single bond in the backbone has complete freedom of rotation. Actually, however, the extended form shown in Figure 10-1, which is the minimum-energy form, is the most probable configuration. Unsaturated fatty acids, on the other hand, have a rigid kink in their hydrocarbon chains contributed by the nonrotating double bond(s). The *cis* configuration of the double bonds in naturally occurring fatty acids produces a bend of about 30° in the aliphatic chain (Figure 10-1), whereas the *trans* forms have nearly the same conformation as that of the saturated chains. The *cis* forms are less stable than the *trans* forms; they may be converted into the latter by heating with certain catalysts. In this way oleic acid can be readily converted to its *trans* isomer elaidic acid, which has a much higher melting point. There is only one naturally occurring *trans* fatty acid of any abundance, namely, vaccenic acid. In fatty acids with multiple double bonds, their *cis* configuration causes the hydrocarbon chain to become kinked and shortened. Presumably, these structural features of unsaturated fatty acid chains are biologically significant, particularly in membranes.

Long-chain fatty acids (C_{16} to C_{18}) are essentially insoluble in water; however, their Na^+ and K^+ salts, called *soaps*, form micelles in water that are stabilized by hydrophobic interactions (see Chapter 2).

Naturally occurring fatty acids, whether saturated or unsaturated, show no absorption of light in the visible and near-ultraviolet range. However, those unsaturated fatty acids having more than one double bond may be isomerized by heating with KOH into fatty acids in which the

Figure 10-1
Configuration of double bonds (below). At the left are shown space-filling models of saturated and unsaturated fatty acids (anionic forms).

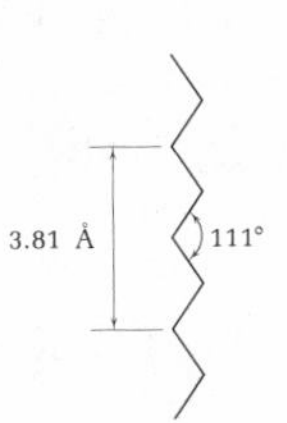

Saturated chain

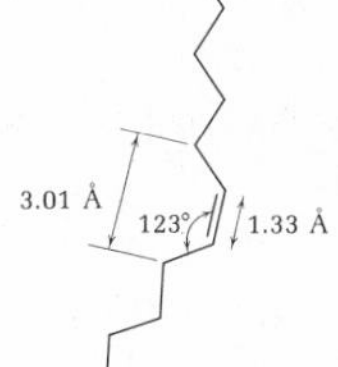

cis double bond (in most naturally occurring unsaturated fatty acids)

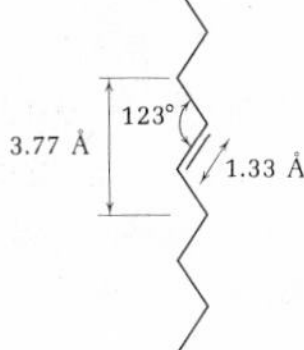

trans double bond (rare)

double bonds are in conjugation (that is, —CH═CH—CH═CH—). Since conjugated double bonds have characteristic light absorption in the zone 230 to 260 nm, polyunsaturated fatty acids may be quantitated by spectrophotometry after isomerization.

Unsaturated fatty acids undergo addition reactions at their double bonds. For example, they readily add halogens such as iodine or chlorine. Quantitative titration with halogens thus yields information on the relative number of double bonds in a given sample of fatty acids or lipid.

Table 10-2 Fatty acid composition of lipids of mouse liver (percent)

	Phosphoglycerides	*Triacylglycerols*
Saturated		
Myristic	0	0
Palmitic	28	24
Stearic	20	4
Unsaturated		
Palmitoleic	4	6
Oleic	17	43
*Linoleic	12	20
*Linolenic	1	1
Arachidonic	18	2

* Of dietary origin (plants).

Gas-Liquid Chromatography of Fatty Acids

Analysis of complex fatty acid mixtures obtained on hydrolysis of natural lipids was once an extremely difficult problem. However, precise analysis of fatty acid mixtures (as in Table 10-2) can now be carried out by *gas-liquid chromatography*. In this procedure, an inert "carrier" gas, such as nitrogen, is used to sweep the vaporized methyl esters of the fatty acid mixture at a high temperature through a long, heated capillary tube whose inner surface is coated with a stationary liquid phase of a high-melting paraffin or silicone grease. The methyl esters of the various fatty acids partition themselves between the gas phase and the liquid phase, depending on their individual gas-liquid partition coefficients. The separated methyl esters in the gas phase leaving the column can be detected by extremely sensitive physical methods. In one of these, the changes in the ionization properties of the gas phase when it is exposed to a source of β-rays are recorded on a chart, which shows a series of separate peaks, each corresponding to a separate fatty acid. Gas-liquid chromatography may also be used to analyze mixtures of sterols and hydrocarbons, as well as any compounds that are volatile at reasonable temperatures (up to 300°C) or that can be converted chemically into volatile derivatives.

Neutral Fats (Acylglycerols)

Fatty acid esters of the alcohol glycerol are called *acylglycerols, neutral fats,* or *glycerides*. They are the major components of depot, or storage, fats in plant and animal cells, especially in the adipose (or fat) cells of vertebrates. When all three hydroxyl groups of glycerol are esterified with fatty acids, the structure is called a *triacylglycerol*. (Although the term "triglyceride" has been widely used to designate these compounds, an international nomenclature commission has recently recommended that this term, which is chemically inaccurate, no longer be used.) Triacylglycerols make up the great bulk of the neutral fats in nature; however, *diacylglycerols* (also called diglycerides) and *monoacylglycerols* (or monoglycerides) are also found (margin).

Triacylglycerols occur in many different types, depending on the identity and position of the three fatty acid components esterified to glycerol. Those containing a single kind of fatty acid in all three positions are called *simple* triacylglycerols; they are named after the fatty acids they contain. Examples are tristearoylglycerol, tripalmitoylglycerol, and trioleoylglycerol; the trivial and

Acylglycerols

Glycerol

```
     H
     |
  H—C—OH   1
     |
  H—C—OH   2
     |
  H—C—OH   3
     |
     H
```

1-Monoacylglycerol

```
     H
     |
  H—C—O—C—R1
     |     ||
     |     O
  H—C—OH
     |
  H—C—OH
     |
     H
```

1,2-Diacylglycerol

```
     H
     |
  H—C—O—C—R1
     |     ||
     |     O
  H—C—O—C—R2
     |     ||
     |     O
  H—C—OH
     |
     H
```

Triacylglycerol

```
     H
     |
  H—C—O—C—R1
     |     ||
     |     O
  H—C—O—C—R2
     |     ||
     |     O
  H—C—O—C—R3
     |     ||
     H     O
```

Table 10-3 Occurrence of simple and mixed triacylglycerols in depot fat of white rat (S = saturated; U = unsaturated)

Type	*Symbol*	*Mole percentage*
Trisaturated	SSS	0.3
Disaturated	SSU	4.1
	SUS	1.6
Monosaturated	SUU	19.5
	USU	12.8
Triunsaturated	UUU	61.8

more commonly used names are tristearin, tripalmitin, and triolein, respectively. Those containing two or more different fatty acids are called *mixed* triacylglycerols. Mixed triacylglycerols containing two different fatty acids A and B can exist in six different molecular species: AAA, AAB, ABA, ABB, BAB, and BBB. Those containing three different fatty acids can exist as 18 different molecular species. The naming of mixed triacylglycerols is simple, as the following examples show: 1-palmitoyldistearoylglycerol (trivial or common name: 1-palmitodistearin), 2-stearoyldipalmitoylglycerol (trivial name: 2-stearodipalmitin), and 1-palmitoyl-2-stearoyl-3-lauroylglycerol (trivial name: 1-palmito-2-stearomonolaurin). Most natural fats are extremely complex mixtures of simple and mixed triacylglycerols.

Although there have been many attempts to discover the biological "ground rules" determining the mode of distribution of different fatty acids in natural triacylglycerols, no simple, all-encompassing generalizations can yet be made. Table 10-3 shows the distribution of various types of triacylglycerols in the depot fat of the rat. The fatty acid composition of depot fat in vertebrates in part reflects the composition of ingested lipids.

Tripalmitin

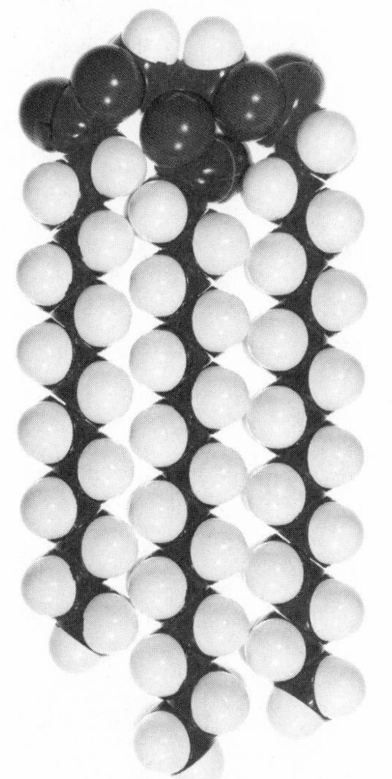

Properties of Acylglycerols

The melting point of neutral fats is determined by their fatty acid components. In general, the melting point increases with the number and length of the saturated fatty acid components. Tristearin and tripalmitin are solids at 20°C, whereas triolein and trilinolein are liquids. All triacylglycerols are relatively insoluble in water and do not tend by themselves to form highly dispersed micelles. However, diacylglycerols, and monoacylglycerols do have appreciable polarity and, because of their free hydroxyl groups, readily form micelles. Acylglycerols are soluble in ether, chloroform, and benzene, as well as in hot ethanol. They are lighter than water.

Although glycerol itself is optically inactive, its β- or two-carbon atom becomes asymmetric whenever the fatty acid substituents on carbon atoms 1 and 3 are different. Naturally occurring triacylglycerols having an asymmetric carbon atom have been found to possess a configuration related to L-glyceraldehyde.

Glycerides undergo hydrolysis when boiled with acids or bases or by the action of lipases, such as are present in pancreatic juice. Hydrolysis with alkali, which is called *saponification*, yields a mixture of fatty acid soaps and glycerol.

Hydrolysis of triacylglycerols

$$\begin{array}{l} \mathrm{H_2C{-}O{-}C({=}O){-}R_1} \\ \mathrm{HC{-}O{-}C({=}O){-}R_2} \\ \mathrm{H_2C{-}O{-}C({=}O){-}R_3} \end{array} \xrightarrow{3H_2O} \begin{array}{l} \mathrm{H_2C{-}OH} \\ \mathrm{HC{-}OH} \\ \mathrm{H_2C{-}OH} \end{array} + \begin{array}{c} R_1{-}COOH \\ + \\ R_2{-}COOH \\ + \\ R_3{-}COOH \end{array}$$

Thin-Layer Chromatography

Acylglycerols are separated and identified by the technique of thin-layer chromatography (Figure 10-2), which is extremely versatile and can be used for the separation and analysis of many other classes of compounds. A glass plate of about 10 × 10 cm is covered with an aqueous slurry of an inert absorbent material, such as silica gel or cellulose; the slurry also contains a binder such as plaster of paris. The plate is dried and then baked to remove the water, leaving a thin, uniform layer of firmly bound adsorbent. The mixture to be analyzed is "spotted" at the bottom of the plate, whose lower edge dips vertically into a solvent pool in a closed chamber. The solvent rises by capillary action, as in paper chromatography, and the mixture of glycerides is resolved into discrete zones, or spots, as it rises. When the solvent reaches the top, which requires only 20 to 30 min, the plate is dried and the positions of the separated components are determined by spraying with a suitable indicator. The spots remain very small, and the separated lipids can be recovered by scraping the patches of adsorbent off the plate and eluting the lipid. This method can separate minute quantities of acylglycerols; if the layers are made relatively thick, it can be used to separate much larger amounts. Two-dimensional thin-layer methods are also used.

Figure 10-2
Thin-layer chromatography of acylglycerols on silica gel. A = synthetic mixture, B = lard, C = cocoa butter, D = cottonseed oil, E = peanut oil. The spots are (1) tristearin, (2) 2-oleodistearin, (3) 1-oleodistearin, (4) 1-stearodiolein, (5) 1-linoleodistearin, (6) triolein, (7) trilinolein, and (8) monostearin.

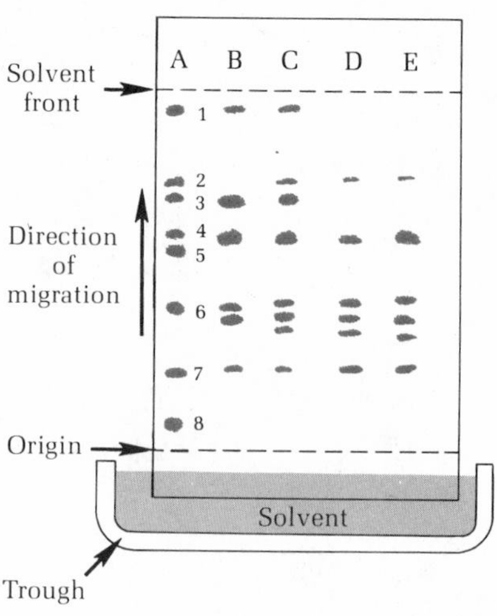

Phosphoglycerides

These lipids, also called glycerol phosphatides, are found almost entirely in cellular membranes; only very small amounts of phosphoglycerides occur in depot fats. In phosphoglycerides, one of the primary hydroxyl groups of glycerol is esterified to phosphoric acid instead of a fatty acid. The parent compound of the series is thus glycerol phosphoric acid rather than glycerol. This compound has an asymmetric carbon atom and can be designated as either D-glycerol 1-phosphate or L-glycerol 3-phosphate. Because of this ambiguity, the convention has been adopted that the stereochemistry of glycerol derivatives is based on the stereospecific numbering (abbreviated sn) of the carbon atoms, as is shown below. This assumes that the secondary hydroxyl group is to the left in the projection formula. The isomer of glycerol phosphoric acid found in phosphoglycerides is called sn-glycerol 3-phosphoric acid. It belongs to the L-stereochem-

sn-Glycerol 3-phosphoric acid

1 CH_2OH
2 HO—C—H
3 CH_2—O—P(=O)(OH)—OH

Phosphatidic acid

CH_2—O—C(=O)—R_1
R_2—C(=O)—O—C—H
CH_2—O—P(=O)(OH)—OH

General structure of phosphoglycerides. The moiety X is contributed by an alcohol (see Table 10-4).

CH_2—O—C(=O)—R_1
R_2—C(=O)—O—C—H
CH_2—O—P(=O)(OH)—O—X

General structure of phosphoglycerides, in a form emphasizing their amphipathic nature. Usually the fatty acid in the 2-position is unsaturated.

```
                    X
                    |
                    O
                    |
                 O=P—O⁻
                    |
    H       H       O          Polar
    |       |       |          head
H—¹C————²C————³CH2
    |       |
    O       O
    |       |
    C=O     C=O
    |       |
    CH2     CH2
    CH2     CH2
    CH2     CH2
    CH2     CH2
    CH2     CH2
    CH2     CH2
    CH2     CH2
    CH2     CH
    CH2     ||         Nonpolar
    CH2     CH         tails
    CH2     CH2
    CH2     CH2
    CH2     CH2
    CH2     CH2
    CH2     CH2
    CH2     CH2
    CH3     CH3
```

ical series. In addition to the two fatty acid residues esterified to the hydroxyl groups at carbon atoms 1 and 2, most phosphoglycerides contain an alcohol component, X–OH, whose hydroxyl group is esterified to the phosphoric acid to form a phosphodiester (margin).

All phosphoglycerides possess a polar head and two nonpolar hydrocarbon tails. For this reason, they are called *amphipathic* (Chapter 2), or *polar*, lipids. The names of the common phosphoglycerides and the structures of their polar head groups are given in Table 10-4; space-filling models of these lipids are shown in Figure 10-3. As you can see in the figure, the phosphoglycerides differ from each other primarily in the size, shape, polarity, and net charge of the X-groups of their polar heads. Each type of phosphoglyceride can exist in many different species, depending on the two fatty acid substituents. Usually there is one saturated and one unsaturated fatty acid, the latter in the 2 position of glycerol.

The simplest type of phosphoglyceride is *phosphatidic acid*, which contains no X-group esterified to the phosphoric acid. It occurs in only very small amounts in cells, but it is an important intermediate in the biosynthesis of other phosphoglycerides (margin).

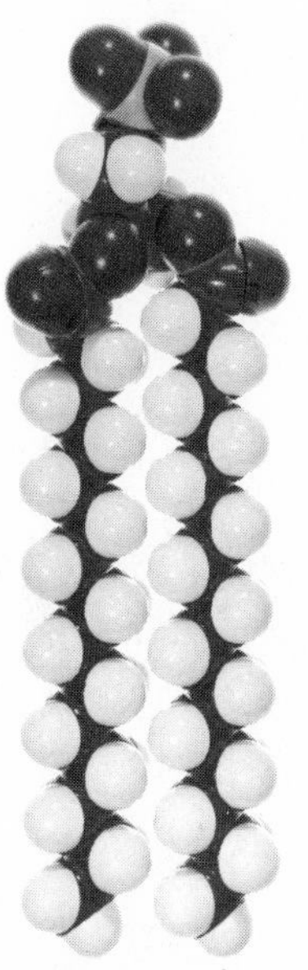

Phosphatidic acid

The most abundant phosphoglycerides in higher plants and animals are *phosphatidyl ethanolamine* and *phosphatidyl choline*, which contain as X-groups the amino alcohols ethanolamine and choline, respectively. (The new names recommended for these phosphoglycerides are *ethanolamine phosphoglyceride* and *choline phosphoglyceride*, but they have not yet gained wide use. The old trivial names cephalin and lecithin, respectively, although still often used, are considered unsatisfactory and should be abandoned.) These two phosphoglycerides are metabolically related and are the major lipid components of most membranes in animal cells.

In phosphatidyl serine, the hydroxyl group of serine is esterified to the phosphoric acid. In phosphatidyl inositol, the X-group is the six-carbon sugar alcohol inositol. In phosphatidyl glycerol, the X-group is a molecule of glycerol. Phosphatidyl glycerol is often found in bacterial membranes as an amino acid derivative, particularly of L-lysine, which is esterified at the 3′ position of the glycerol X-group. This type of amino-acid-containing lipid is called a *lipoamino acid* or, more accurately, an O-aminoacyl phosphatidyl glycerol. Closely related to phosphatidyl glycerol is the more complex lipid cardiolipin, which consists of a molecule of phosphatidyl glycerol in which the 3′-hydroxyl group of the second glycerol moiety is esterified to the phosphate group of a molecule of phosphatidic acid. The backbone of cardiolipin thus consists of three molecules of glycerol joined in 1,3 fashion by two phosphodiester bridges; the hydroxyl groups of the two external glycerol molecules are esterified with fatty acids. Phosphatidic acid, phosphatidyl glycerol, cardiolipin, and O-aminoacyl phosphatidyl glycerol are therefore structurally related. They are characteristically abundant in the cell membranes of bacteria; cardiolipin is also present in the membranes of mitochondria and of chloroplasts.

Figure 10-3
Space-filling models of the major phosphoglycerides. For convenience all the fatty acid components are shown as palmitic acid. Sphingomyelin, although it is not a phosphoglyceride, is included to show its structural similarity. The electrical charges shown assume pH = 7.0.

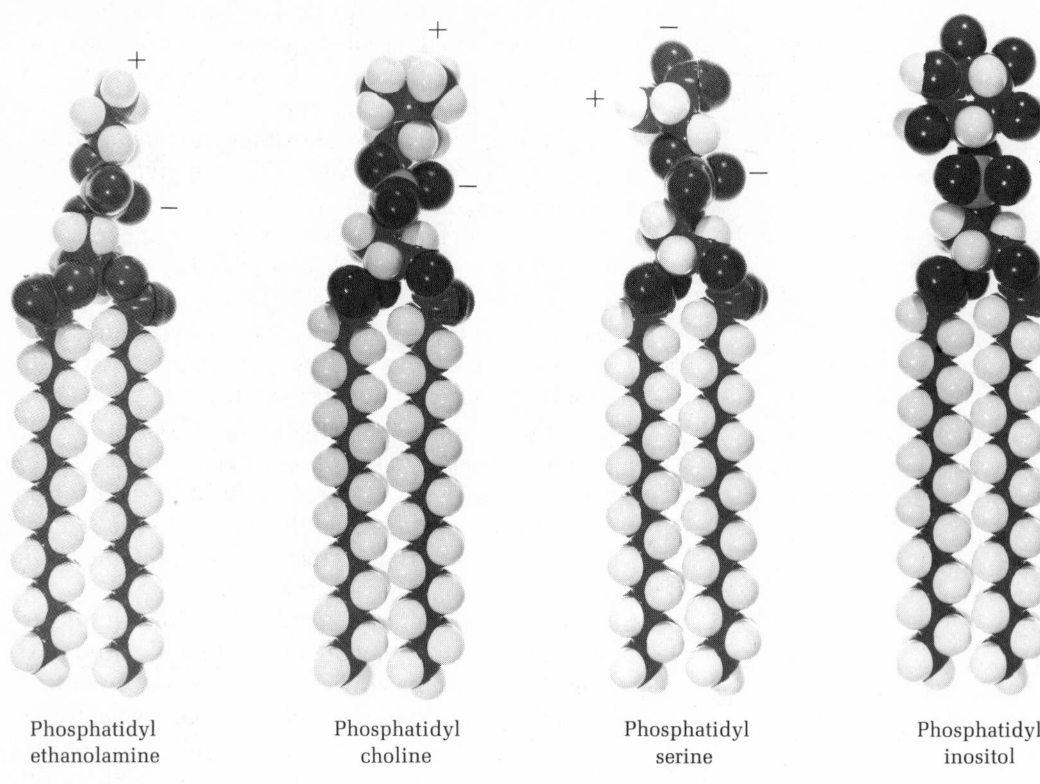

Table 10-4 The alcohols contributing the polar X groups in the major phosphoglycerides. (The hydroxyl group esterified to phosphoric acid is given in color.)

Phosphoglyceride	*Alcohol component*
Phosphatidyl ethanolamine	$HOCH_2CH_2NH_2$
Phosphatidyl choline	$HOCH_2CH_2\overset{+}{N}(CH_3)_3$
Phosphatidyl serine	$HOCH_2CHNH_2COOH$
Phosphatidyl inositol	OH OH H H OH H H OH H HO H H OH
Phosphatidyl glycerol	$HOCH_2CHOHCH_2OH$
Phosphatidyl 3′-O-aminoacyl glycerol	$HOCH_2CHOHCH_2O{-}\overset{O}{\overset{\Vert}{C}}{-}CH(R){-}NH_2$
Cardiolipin	$HOCH_2CHOHCH_2{-}O{-}\overset{O}{\overset{\Vert}{P}}(OH){-}O{-}CH_2CH(O{-}C(=O){-}R_1){-}CH_2{-}O{-}C(=O){-}R_2$

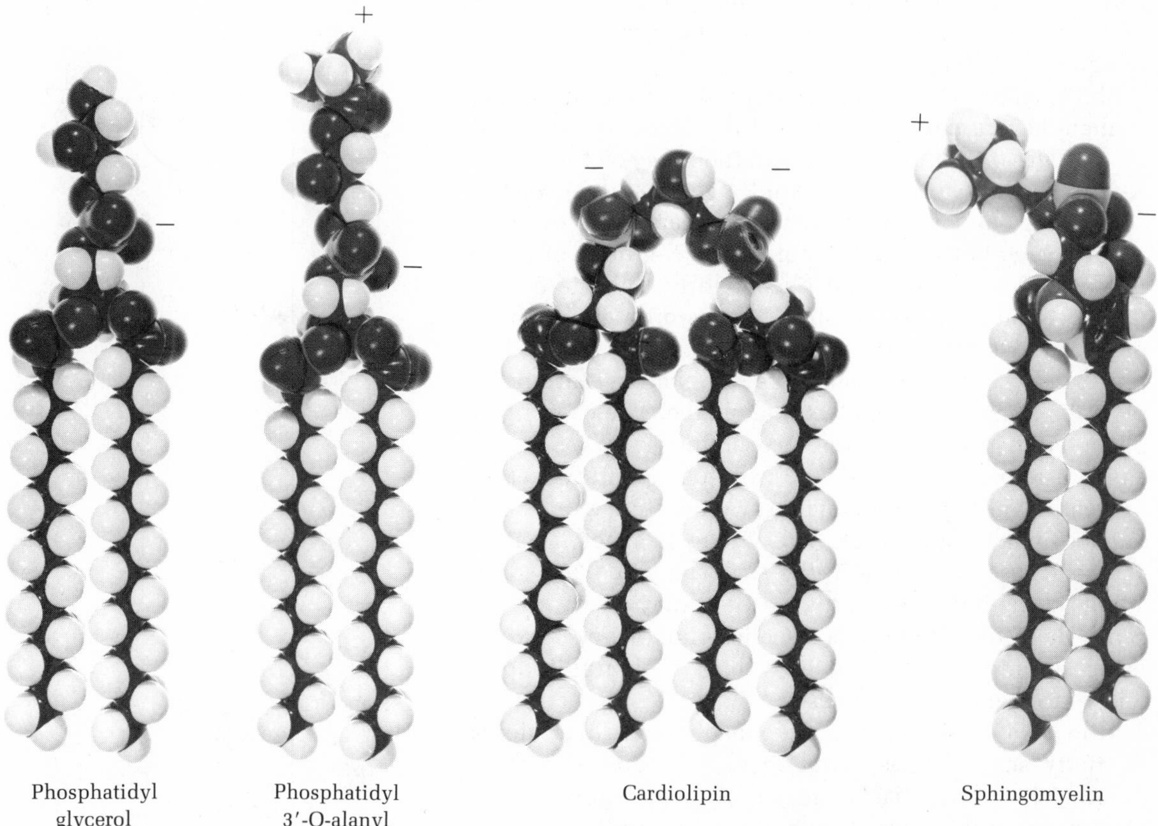

Phosphatidyl glycerol

Phosphatidyl 3′-O-alanyl glycerol

Cardiolipin

Sphingomyelin

The polar X-groups of phosphatides may also be contributed by a sugar molecule. Such glycophosphoglycerides (or phosphatidyl sugars) are found in plants and microorganisms. They are not to be confused with the glycolipids (see below), which also contain sugars but no phosphoric acid.

Plasmalogens, a subgroup of phosphoglycerides, differ from the phosphoglycerides discussed above in that their hydrocarbon tails consist of one molecule of a long-chain fatty acid esterified to one hydroxyl group of the glycerol moiety and a long aliphatic chain in an α,β-unsaturated ether linkage with the other hydroxyl group. On complete hydrolysis, plasmalogens yield one molecule of fatty acid and one molecule of a long-chain fatty aldehyde, such as palmitaldehyde or stearaldehyde, in addition to glycerol, phosphoric acid, and the alcohol X–OH. Plasmalogens are more systematically designated as *phosphatidal* derivatives. They are especially abundant in the membranes of muscle and nerve cells. (See margin on page 198.)

Properties of Phosphoglycerides

Pure phosphoglycerides are white waxy solids, but on exposure to air they darken and undergo complex chemical changes because of the tendency of their unsaturated fatty acid components to be peroxidized by atmospheric oxygen. Phosphoglycerides are soluble in most nonpolar solvents containing some water and are best extracted from cells and tissues by chloroform-methanol mixtures. They are not readily soluble in anhydrous acetone. When phosphoglycerides are placed in water, they appear to dissolve. However, only very minute amounts go into true solution; most of the "dissolved" lipid is in the form of micelles in aqueous systems (see below).

Phosphoglycerides are the most polar of the lipids. All of them have a negative charge at the phosphate group at pH 7.0; the pK′ of this group is in the range of 1 to 2. The X-groups of phosphatidyl inositol, phosphatidyl glycerol, cardiolipin, and the phosphatidyl sugars have no electrical charge but are highly polar. The X-groups of phosphatidyl ethanolamine and phosphatidyl choline have a positive charge at pH 7.0 since their amino groups have pK′ values of about 10 and 13, respectively. These two phosphoglycerides are therefore dipolar zwitterions at pH 7.0 and have no *net* electrical charge. The X-group of phosphatidyl serine contains an α-amino group (pK′ = 10) and a carboxyl group (pK′ = 3); the phosphatidyl serine molecule thus contains a total of two negative groups and one positive group at pH 7.0, giving it a net negative charge. These variations in the size, shape, polarity, and charge of the polar heads (Figure 10-3) play a very significant role in the structure of micelles, monolayers, and bilayers of lipids (see below), as well as in natural lipoproteins and membrane systems.

Mild alkaline hydrolysis of phosphoglycerides yields the fatty acids as soaps but leaves the glycerol–phosphoric acid–alcohol backbone of the molecule intact; mild alkaline hydrolysis of phosphatidyl choline thus yields glycerol 3-phosphorylcholine. Hydrolysis of phosphoglycerides with strong alkali causes cleavage of both fatty acids and the alcohol X–OH. Since the linkage between phosphoric acid and glycerol is relatively stable to alkaline hydrolysis, glycerol 3-phosphate is the other product of strong alkaline hydrolysis. It can be cleaved by acid hydrolysis.

Phosphoglycerides may also be hydrolyzed by specific phospholipases, which have become important tools in the determination of phosphoglyceride structure (Figure 10-4). Phospholipases of the A class (found in some snake venoms) specifically hydrolyze the fatty acid from the 2 position. The resulting product is called a *lysophosphatide*. Lysophosphatides are not normally found in cells or tissues in any quantity; they are toxic and injurious to membranes. Phospholipase B is specific for removing the second (or both) fatty acids; phosphatidyl choline on treatment with phospholipase B yields glycerol 3-phosphorylcholine. Phospholipase C hydrolyzes the bond between phosphoric acid and glycerol, while phospholipase D removes the X-group to leave a phosphatidic acid.

Phosphoglycerides, as well as other complex lipids described below, are readily separated and identified by thin-layer chromatography or by chromatography on silicic acid columns.

A plasmalogen (phosphatidal choline)

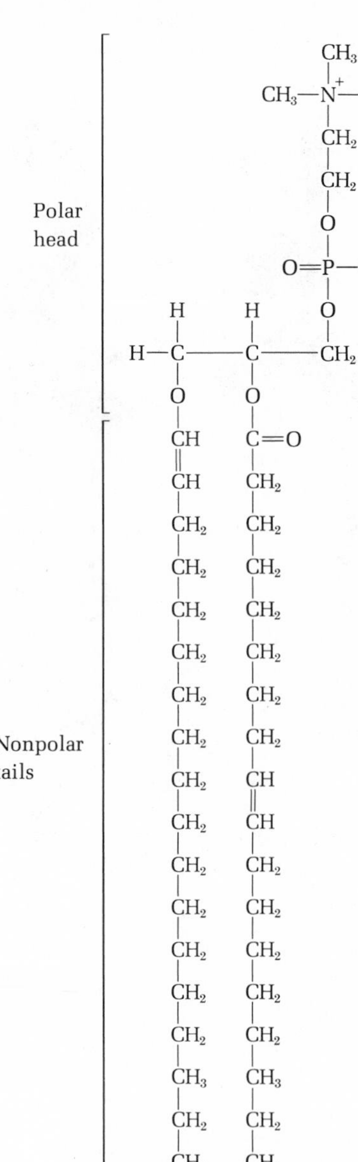

Sphingolipids and Glycolipids

Some of the lipids belonging to these two groups are difficult to classify since they can be put in either category.

Figure 10-4
Sites of action of phospholipases on phosphatidyl choline.

Phospholipase B → H_2CO—|—C(=O)—R_1

Phospholipase A → R_2—C(=O)—|—OCH

H_2CO—|—P(=O)(O^-)—|—$OCH_2CH_2N^+(CH_3)_3$

Phospholipase C (arrow to the H_2CO–P bond); Phospholipase D (arrow to the P–OCH_2 bond)

Sphingolipids are found in the membranes of both plants and animals; they are present in especially large amounts in brain and nerve tissue. Only minor amounts are found in depot fat. On hydrolysis, sphingolipids yield one molecule of a fatty acid, one molecule of the long-chain unsaturated amino alcohol *sphingosine* or its saturated analog *dihydrosphingosine* (margin), one molecule of phosphoric acid, and one molecule of an alcohol (X–OH). Sphingolipids contain no glycerol.

Sphingomyelin, which contains choline as its X-group, is the most abundant sphingolipid. The most important structural feature of sphingomyelin and all sphingolipids is that the long aliphatic chain of the sphingosine component represents one of the two hydrocarbon tails of these lipids; the esterified fatty acid represents the other (see Figure 10-3). The conformation of the sphingolipids is thus very similar to that of the phosphoglycerides, in that they contain a polar head and two nonpolar tails.

The glycolipids contain polar, hydrophilic carbohydrate head groups, most often D-galactose; unlike the sphingolipids, however, they contain no phosphoric acid. The simplest glycolipids are the *glycosyldiacylglycerols,* found in plants and microorganisms. Another group, the *cerebrosides,* may be classified either as glycolipids or as sphingolipids since they contain both a sugar and sphingosine. They are especially abundant in the membranes of brain and nerve cells, particularly in the myelin sheath. The fatty acids found in cerebrosides are unusual in that they contain 24 carbon atoms; the most abundant of these fatty acids are nervonic acid, cerebronic acid, and lignoceric acid. The fatty acid amide of sphingosine alone, without the sugar, is known as *ceramide.* Sulfate esters of cerebrosides have also been found; the sulfuric acid is esterified to carbon atom 2 of the galactose residue. Many galactose-containing glycolipids have been found in plants. (See following page.)

Another major class of glycolipid is the group of *gangliosides,* which are carbohydrate-rich complex lipids of extremely large size and complexity (Figure 10-5). They are usually found on the outer surface of cell membranes,

	Sphingosine (systematic name, 4-sphingenine)	Dihydrosphingosine (systematic name, sphinganine)
Polar head	CH_2OH	CH_2OH
	H—C—NH_2	H—C—NH_2
	H—C—OH	H—C—OH
Nonpolar tail	CH	CH_2
	‖ HC	CH_2
	$(CH_2)_{12}$	$(CH_2)_{12}$
	CH_3	CH_3

In sphingosine the double bond is *trans*.

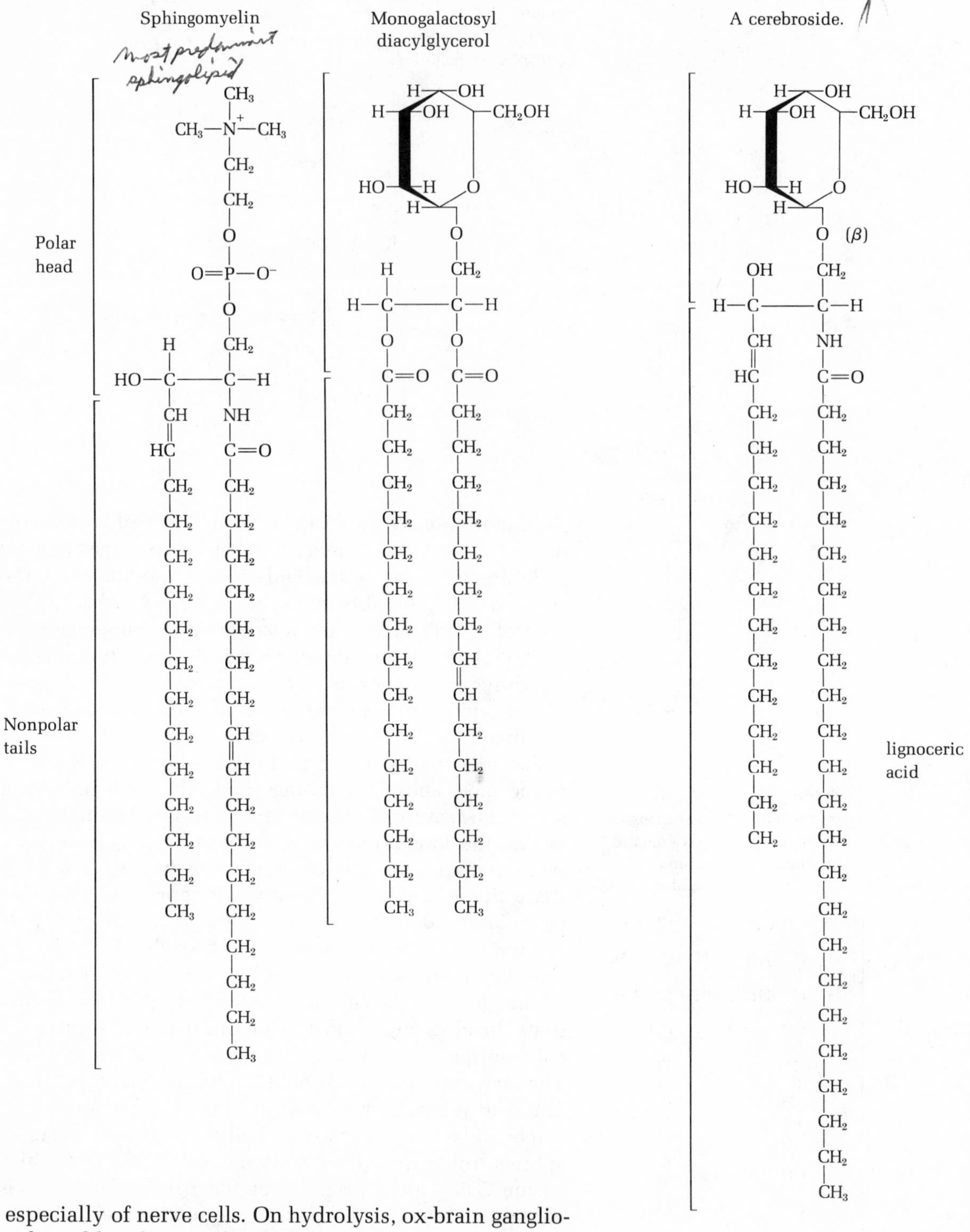

Sphingomyelin

Monogalactosyl diacylglycerol

A cerebroside.

Polar head

Nonpolar tails

lignoceric acid

especially of nerve cells. On hydrolysis, ox-brain ganglioside yields a fatty acid, sphingosine, the sugars D-glucose and D-galactose, and the amino sugar derivatives N-acetylgalactosamine and N-acetylneuraminic acid (Chapter 11). They are similar to the cerebrosides in structure; instead of a single galactose residue, they contain a complex oligosaccharide.

Waxes

Closely related to the acylglycerols in structure and properties are the waxes, which are esters of higher fatty acids with long-chain monohydroxylic alcohols. Waxes are found as protective coatings on skin, fur, and feathers,

Figure 10-5
A ganglioside. The hydrophilic head (in color) of gangliosides is relatively large and complex.

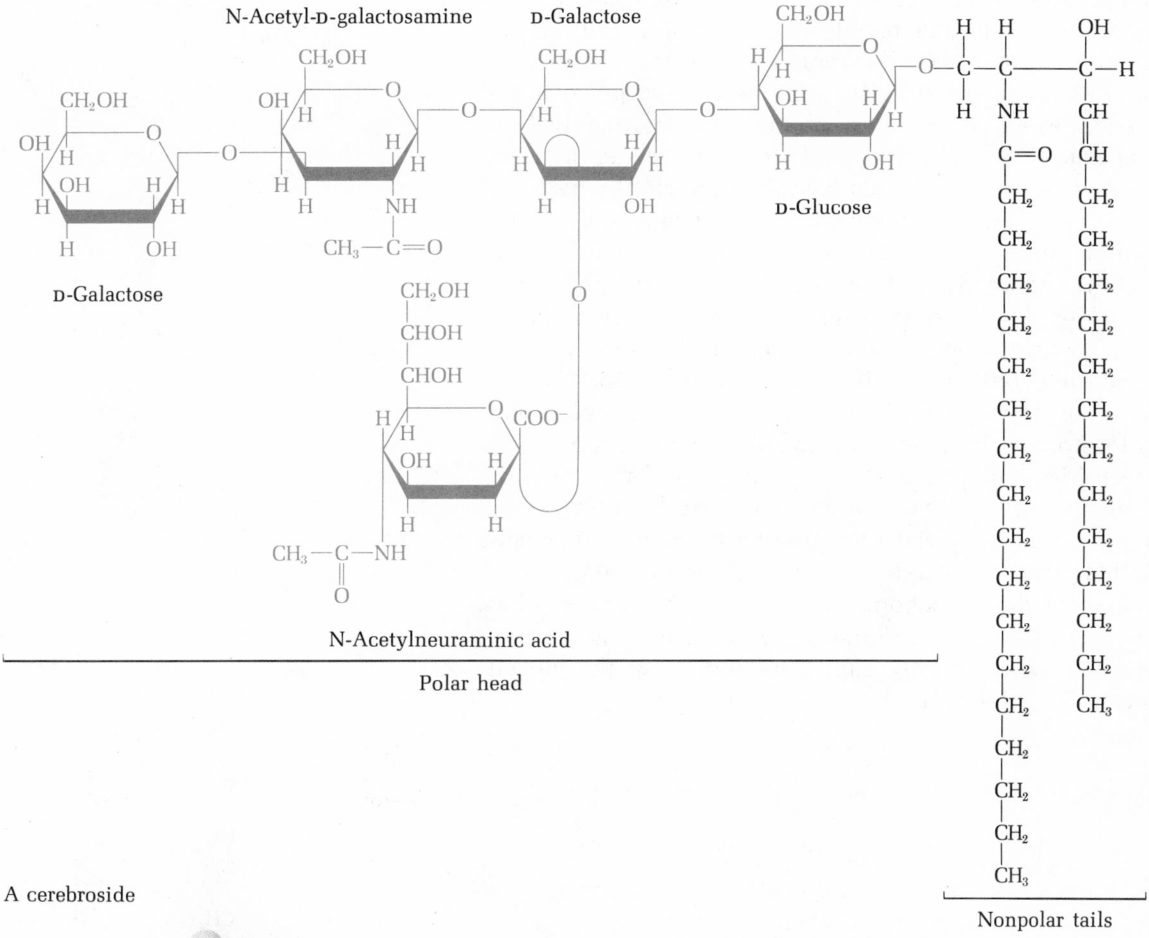

D-Galactose
N-Acetyl-D-galactosamine
D-Galactose
D-Glucose
N-Acetylneuraminic acid
Polar head
Nonpolar tails

A cerebroside

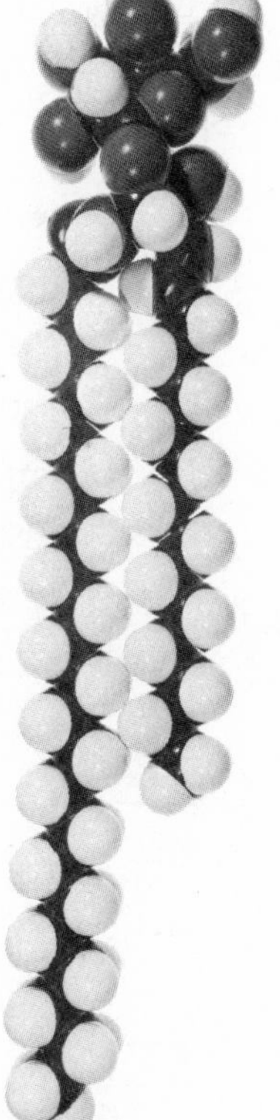

on leaves and fruits of higher plants, and on the cuticle of the exoskeleton of many insects. Lanolin or wool fat is a mixture of fatty acid esters of the sterols lanosterol and agnosterol (see below). The major components of beeswax are palmitic acid esters of long-chain fatty alcohols.Leaf waxes consist of esters of fatty acids and alcohols having from 26 to 34 carbon atoms.

Saponifiable and Non-Saponifiable Lipids

The lipids discussed to this point are often called *saponifiable,* since they may be hydrolyzed by heating with alkali to yield soaps of the fatty acid compounds. Cells also contain another class of lipids, quantitatively minor, termed *non-saponifiable* lipids, since they do not undergo hydrolysis to yield fatty acids. There are two major types of non-saponifiable lipids, *steroids* and *terpenes.* Although it is convenient to consider the steroids and terpenes as two distinct classes, actually they are closely related since they derive from common 5-carbon building blocks.

Steroids

Steroids are derivatives of the perhydrocyclopentanophenanthrene nucleus, which contains three fused cyclohexane rings in the phenanthrene arrangement. Among the important naturally occurring steroids are the bile acids, the male and female sex hormones, the adrenocortical hormones, and various other steroids that have intense biological activity, such as cardiac poisons and toad poisons. While most of these occur in only trace amounts in cells, one class of steroids, the sterols, is extremely abundant. Sterols contain an alcoholic hydroxyl group at C_3 and a branched aliphatic chain of 8 or more carbon atoms at C_{17}. They occur either as free alcohols or as long-chain fatty acid esters of the hydroxyl group at C_3. Cholesterol is the most abundant sterol in animal tissues and occurs in both free and combined form. A white, crystalline, optically active solid, it melts at 150°C and is insoluble in water but is readily extracted from cells with chloroform, ether, benzene, or hot alcohol. It mixes with glycerides and phospholipids, and it appears to endow lipid mixtures with the property of absorbing water. It is abundant in the plasma membranes of many animal cells and is present, but in much smaller amounts, in the membranes of the mitochondria and endoplasmic reticulum. Lanosterol, which is found in the fatty coating of wool, also serves as an important intermediate in the biosynthesis of cholesterol.

Perhydrocyclopentanophenanthrene nucleus

Cholesterol

Lanosterol

Space-filling model of cholesterol.

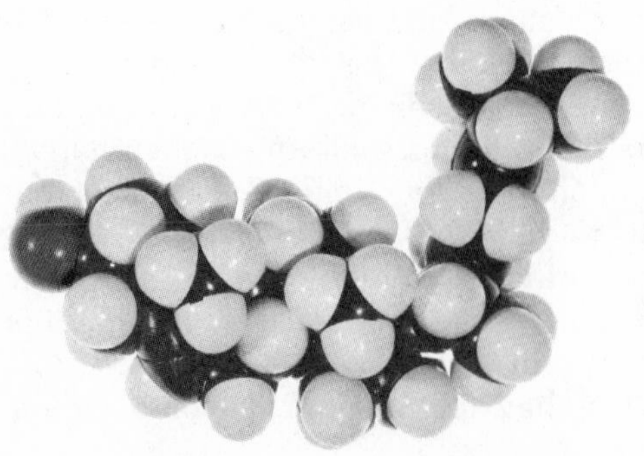

Cholesterol is not present in plants, which contain other types of sterols known collectively as *phytosterols*. Among these are stigmasterol and sitosterol. Fungi and yeasts contain still other types of sterols, the *mycosterols*. Among these is ergosterol, which is converted to vitamin D on irradiation by sunlight. Sterols are not present in bacteria.

Terpenes

Among the minor lipid components of cells are the terpenes, which are constructed of multiples of the 5-carbon hydrocarbon *isoprene* or 2-methyl-1,3 butadiene (Figure 10-6). Terpenes containing 2 isoprene units are called *monoterpenes*, those containing 3 isoprene units are called *sesquiterpenes*, and those containing 4, 6, and 8 units are called *diterpenes, triterpenes*, and *tetraterpenes*, respectively. Terpenes may be either linear or cyclic molecules; some terpenes contain both linear and cyclic structures. The successive isoprene units of terpenes are usually linked in a head-to-tail arrangement, particularly in the linear segments, but in some terpenes the isoprene units are in tail-to-tail or irregular arrangement. The double bonds in the linear segments of most terpenes are in the stable *trans* configuration, but in some, particularly Vitamin A and its precursor carotenes (below), some of the double bonds are *cis*.

A very large number of mono- and sesquiterpenes have been identified in plants. Many of these impart characteristic odors or flavors and are major components in "essential oils" derived from such plants. Thus the monoterpenes geraniol, limonene, menthol, pinene, camphor, and carvone are major components of oil of geranium, lemon

Figure 10-6
Isoprene and some simple terpenes. See also the margin of the following page. The colored lines delineate the isoprene units.

Isoprene

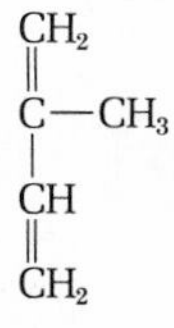

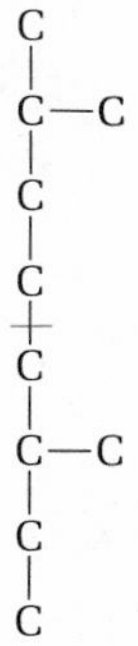

Head-to-tail or regular arrangement of isoprene units

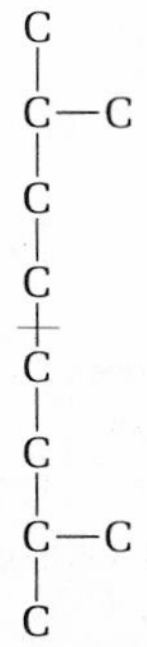

Tail-to-tail or irregular arrangement of isoprene units

Geraniol, a linear monoterpene

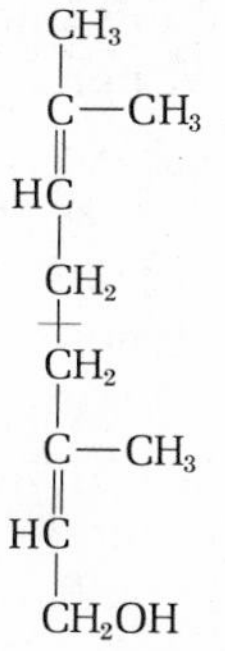

Limonene, a cyclic monoterpene

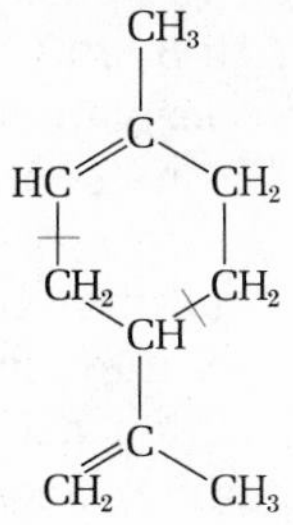

Farnesol, a linear sesquiterpene

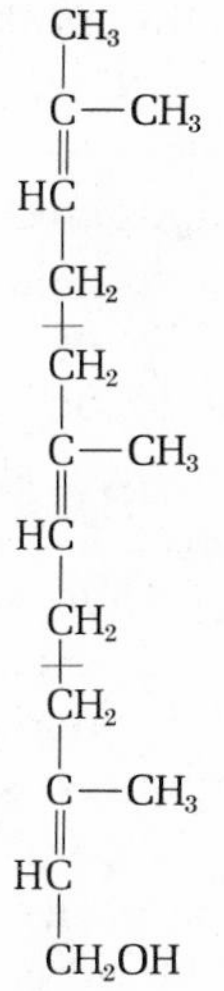

oil, mint oil, turpentine, camphor, and caraway oil, respectively. Farnesol is an example of a sesquiterpene. The diterpenes include phytol, a linear terpenoid alcohol which is a component of the photosynthetic pigment chlorophyll, and Vitamin A (below). The triterpenes include squalene and lanosterol, which are important precursors in the biosynthesis of cholesterol. Other higher terpenes include the carotenoids, which are tetraterpenes. Natural rubber is a polyterpene; it consists of long hydrocarbon chains containing thousands of isoprene units in regular linear order. Examples of terpenes are shown in the margin.

Fat-Soluble Vitamins

Vitamins were first defined as substances required in trace amounts in the diet for normal maintenance, growth, or reproduction of a given species. Some are essential because they are important precursors of certain coenzymes, as in the case of riboflavin, thiamine, pantothenic acid, and nicotinamide (Chapters 8, 12). Others, not as well understood, are required for certain specialized activities of higher organisms. It is now reasonably certain that a given vitamin performs the same function in all species, even though it may not be required in the diet. For example, the vitamin ascorbic acid (Vitamin C) is required in the diet of man, monkeys, guinea pig, and the Indian fruit bat, but other animal species do not require ascorbic acid in the diet because they are genetically capable of manufacturing it from simple precursors. Nevertheless, all higher species appear to employ ascorbic acid as a cofactor in certain specific enzymatic reactions. For this reason the term vitamin is now more loosely and generally employed to denote a vital trace substance required in normal cell function which some species are unable to synthesize and must obtain from exogenous sources.

The vitamins are divided into two classes: *water-soluble* and *fat-soluble*. The water-soluble vitamins include ascorbic acid. nicotinamide, pantothenic acid, thiamine and riboflavin, among others; in most cases they serve as components of various coenzymes (Chapter 8). The fat-soluble vitamins include Vitamin A, Vitamin E, Vitamin K, and Vitamin D; the molecular basis of their function is not as well known. Although they are present in natural sources in only small amounts, they are considered to be lipids, since they are insoluble in water but extractable with organic solvents. The fat-soluble vitamins have a second common denominator. They are all ultimately derived from isoprenoid building blocks. The isoprenoid structure is most apparent in Vitamins A, E, and K, which are readily seen to consist of multiples of isoprene units (Figures 10-7, 10-8, and 10-9). Vitamin D, on the other hand, is a steroid derivative but we shall see later that steroids are derived from isoprenoid precursors (Chapter 23).

Vitamin A occurs only in animal tissues. Although plants are devoid of Vitamin A they contain a group of substances called *carotenes*, which act as precursors of Vitamin A in mammals. Vitamin A occurs in two major

Phytol, a diterpene

CH_3
$HC—CH_3$
CH_2
CH_2
CH_2
$HC—CH_3$
CH_2
CH_2
CH_2
$HC—CH_3$
CH_2
CH_2
CH_2
$C—CH_3$
HC
CH_2OH

Squalene, a triterpene

CH_3
$C—CH_3$
HC
CH_2
CH_2
$C—CH_3$
HC
CH_2
CH_2
$C—CH_3$
HC
CH_2
CH_2
HC
$C—CH_3$
CH_2
CH_2
HC
$C—CH_3$
CH_2
CH_2
HC
$C—CH_3$
CH_3

The isoprene units are set apart by colored bars.

Figure 10-7
Vitamin A and β-carotene. The isoprene units are set apart by colored bars.

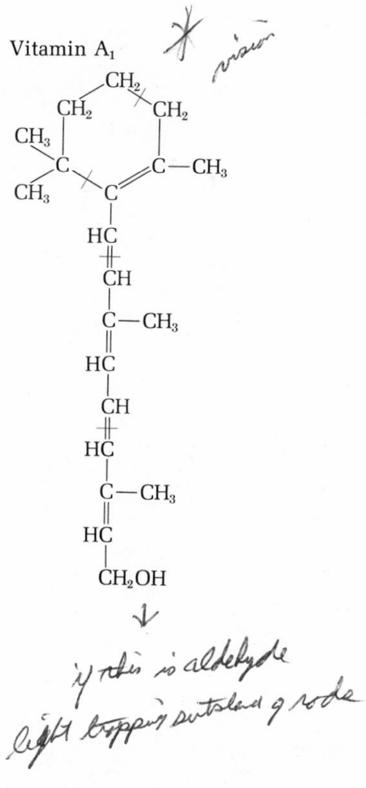

Vitamin A_2

β-carotene. Oxidative cleavage at the jagged line yields two molecules of Vitamin A_1

Space-filling model of Vitamin A_1

chemical forms, Vitamin A_1 and A_2; multiple forms of vitamins are called vitamers. Vitamins A_1 and A_2 (also called retinol$_1$ and retinol$_2$) are alcohols containing 6-membered alicyclic rings bearing side-chains consisting of two isoprene units; they differ only in that Vitamin A_2 has one more double bond than Vitamin A_1 (Figure 10-7). Vitamin A_1 is the predominant form in most higher animals, whereas Vitamin A_2 predominates in fish liver oils. Vitamin A_1 has about twice the potency of Vitamin A_2 when fed to rats. The major forms of Vitamins A_1 and A_2 have all their double bonds in the *trans* configuration, but in some forms one or more of the double bonds are *cis*.

Certain carotenoid pigments found in plants, particularly α- and β-, and γ-carotene, which have about twice the molecular weight of Vitamin A, can yield Vitamin A in animal tissues by oxidative cleavage of a central double bond (Figure 10-7).

Deficiency of Vitamin A results in impaired growth and the condition known as *xerophthalmia*, a disturbance of epithelial tissues. In man, an early symptom of Vitamin A deficiency is "night blindness," a condition in which the

retinal rods, the light receptors sensitive to dim light, fail to respond normally.

The various molecular steps in visual excitation have been studied in penetrating detail by Wald and his colleagues. Vitamin A, also called retinol, must first be oxidized to its physiologically active form, Vitamin A aldehyde, or *retinal*, which was formerly known as *retinene*. Retinal normally has a *cis* double bond at position 11; in this form, called 11-*cis*-retinal, it combines with a rod protein called *opsin* to yield *rhodopsin*, or *visual purple*, which has an absorption maximum at about 500 nm. When rhodopsin absorbs light energy, its retinal component undergoes photo-isomerization to the more stable all-*trans* retinal, a reaction which is accompanied by a change in conformation of the retinal and its dissociation from opsin, which is accompanied by bleaching. This light-induced conformational change is a trigger which excites the nerve cells of the retinal rods. The all-*trans* retinal is then enzymatically converted back to the 11-*cis* isomer by retinal isomerase, to complete a sequence of reactions called the visual cycle (Figure 10-8).

Vitamin E consists of a group of closely related vitamers, abundant in vegetable oils, which are called *tocopherols*. These compounds contain a hydroxyl-bearing aromatic ring system and an isoprenoid side-chain. The most abundant are α-, β-, and γ-tocopherols (Figure 10-9). Nutritional deficiency of Vitamin E in rodents leads to sterility and muscular weakness and atrophy. The specific molecular function of the Vitamin E compounds is not known with certainty but there is some good evidence that they prevent the destructive, non-enzymatic attack of molecular oxygen on the double bonds of the polyunsaturated fatty acid components of tissue lipids. They are therefore known as "antioxidants."

Vitamin K consists of two major forms, Vitamins K_1 and K_2, which are naphthoquinones possessing long isoprenoid side-chains of different length (Figure 10-9). They are broadly distributed in plants, but are required in the diet of most higher animals. Deficiency of Vitamin K results in faulty coagulation of the blood, due to failure to synthesize *prothrombin*, a protein required in blood clotting. However, the precise molecular basis for the action of Vitamin K is not known.

Figure 10-8
Outline of the visual cycle in retinal rods. Similar cycles occur in retinal cones, which are color sensitive.

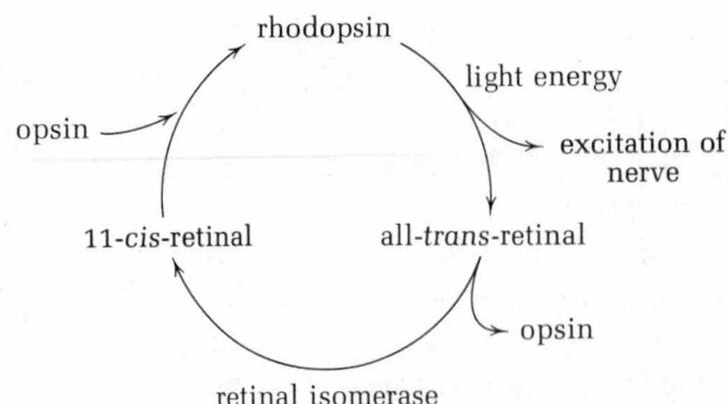

Figure 10-9
Vitamin E and Vitamin K.

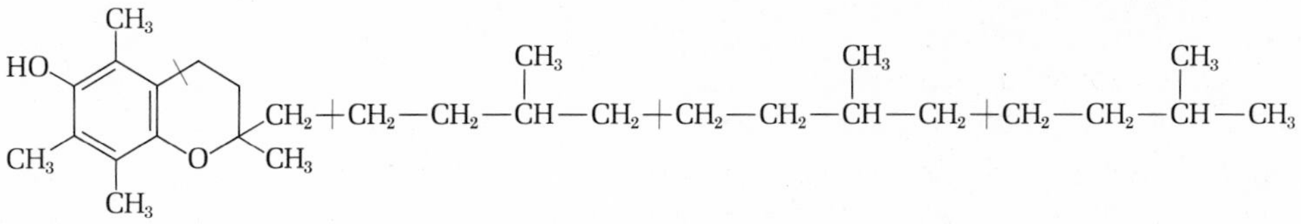

Vitamin E (α-tocopherol)

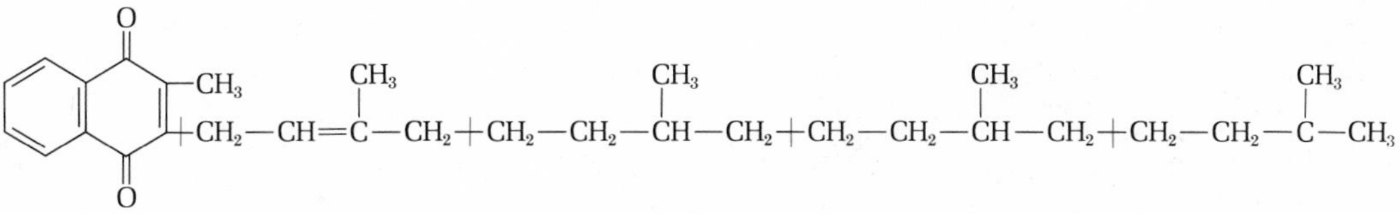

Vitamin K_1

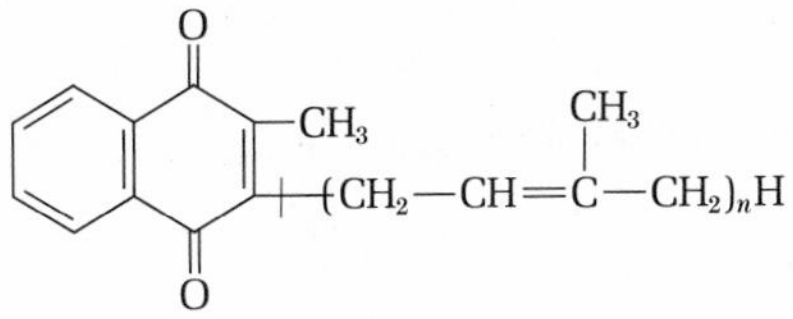

Vitamin K_2 (n may be 6, 7, or 9)

Figure 10-10
Vitamins D_2 and D_3 and their precursors.

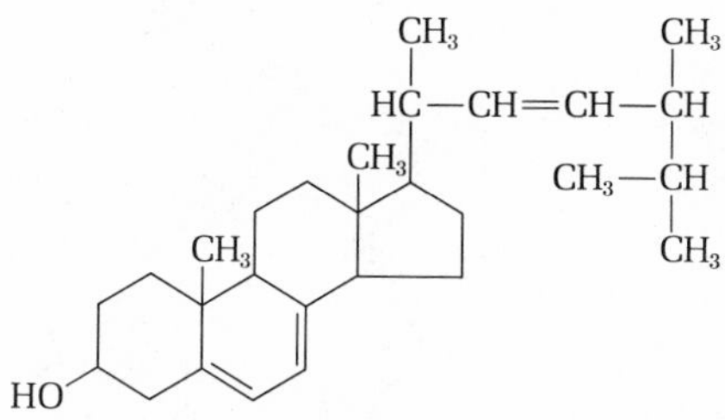

ergosterol

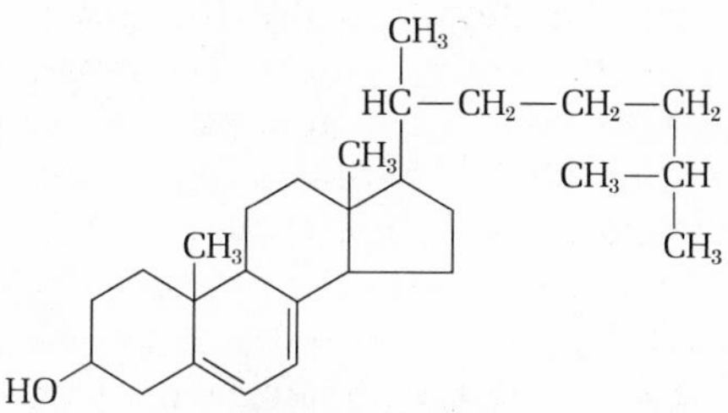

7-dehydrocholesterol

irradiation

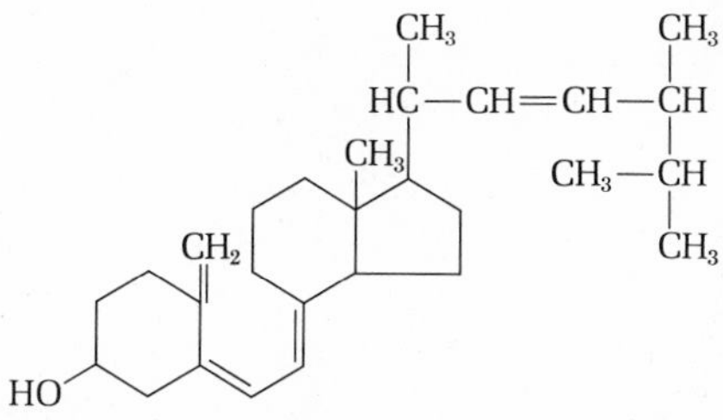

Vitamin D_2
(calciferol)

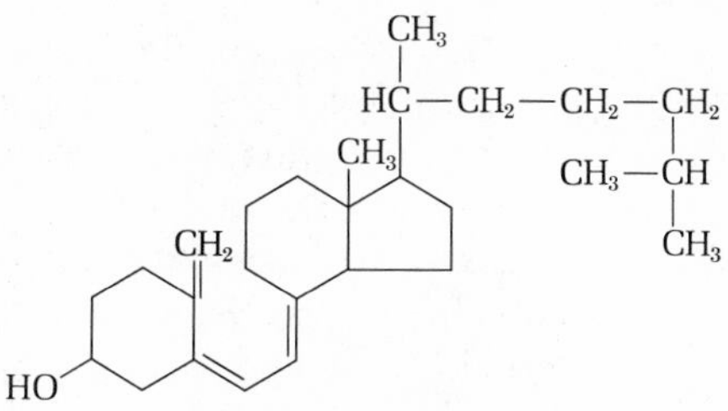

Vitamin D_3

Vitamin D differs from Vitamins A, E, and K in being a steroid derivative (Figure 10-10). It actually consists of a group of vitamers, of which the most important are Vitamin D_2, or calciferol, which is produced in animal tissues from the ingested plant sterol ergosterol by irradiation, and Vitamin D_3, which is derived from 7-dehydrocholesterol in the liver of various fishes, in which Vitamin D is present in high concentration. Deficiency of Vitamin D in the rat and the human results in abnormalities in calcium and phosphate metabolism, causing changes in the structure of bones and teeth. In children this condition is known as *rickets* and in adults, *osteomalacia*. Vitamin D stimulates the absorption of Ca^{++} from the small intestine; recent research suggests it evokes the synthesis of a Ca^{++}-transporting protein.

Vitamin D is formed from ergosterol on irradiation by ultraviolet light, which causes cleavage of ring B between carbon atoms 9 and 10.

Prostaglandins

These recently discovered substances were first found in the prostate glands of sheep and other mammals. They are now known to be present in small amounts in many organs and tissues. Prostaglandins apparently function as modulators of hormone activity. Different members of this group of compounds stimulate contraction of smooth muscle, lower the blood pressure, and oppose the action of such hormones as vasopressin.

Prostaglandins are formed from polyunsaturated fatty acids by oxidative closure of a cyclopentane or cyclopentene ring in the middle of the fatty acid chain (margin).

Formation of prostaglandin

8,11,14-Eicosatrienoic acid

10 11 9 12 8 14 15 COOH 20

$\downarrow 2O_2$

Prostaglandin (PGE$_1$)

HO 11 10 9 O 12 8 13 14 HO COOH 20

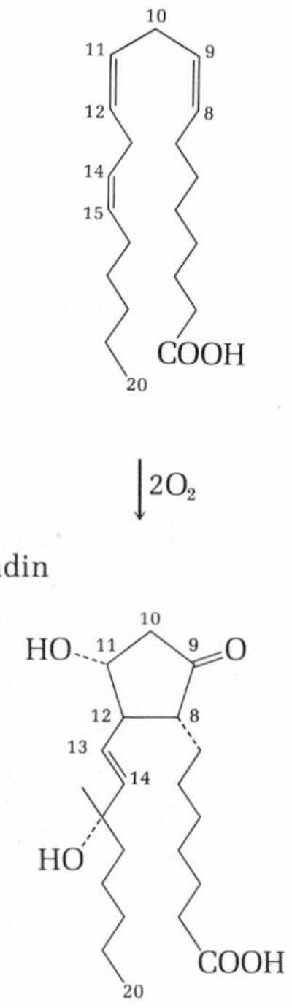

Lipid Micelles, Monolayers, and Bilayers

In aqueous systems, the polar lipids, like the simple fatty acid soaps (Chapter 2), disperse to form micelles in which the hydrocarbon tails of the lipids are hidden from the aqueous environment and form an internal hydrophobic phase, with the hydrophilic heads exposed on the surface. Such micelles may contain thousands of lipid molecules and thus have rather high particle weights. Although triacylglycerols and cholesterol do not *per se* disperse readily to form micelles, they can associate into the structure of micelles of polar lipids to form mixed micelles.

Polar lipids may be spread on the surface of aqueous solutions to form a layer one molecule thick, with the hydrocarbon tails exposed to air, which has relatively hydrophobic properties, and the hydrophilic heads extending into the aqueous phase (Figure 10-11). When such a monolayer of a phosphoglyceride is maximally compressed, each molecule occupies an area of about 75 Å^2.

Bimolecular layers of phosphoglycerides also form readily, particularly in apertures separating two aqueous compartments (Figure 10-11). In such bilayers, the hydrocarbon tails extend inward to form a continuous hydrocarbon phase and the hydrophilic heads face outward, extending into the aqueous phases. These structures are about 70 Å thick. Phospholipid bilayers of this sort have

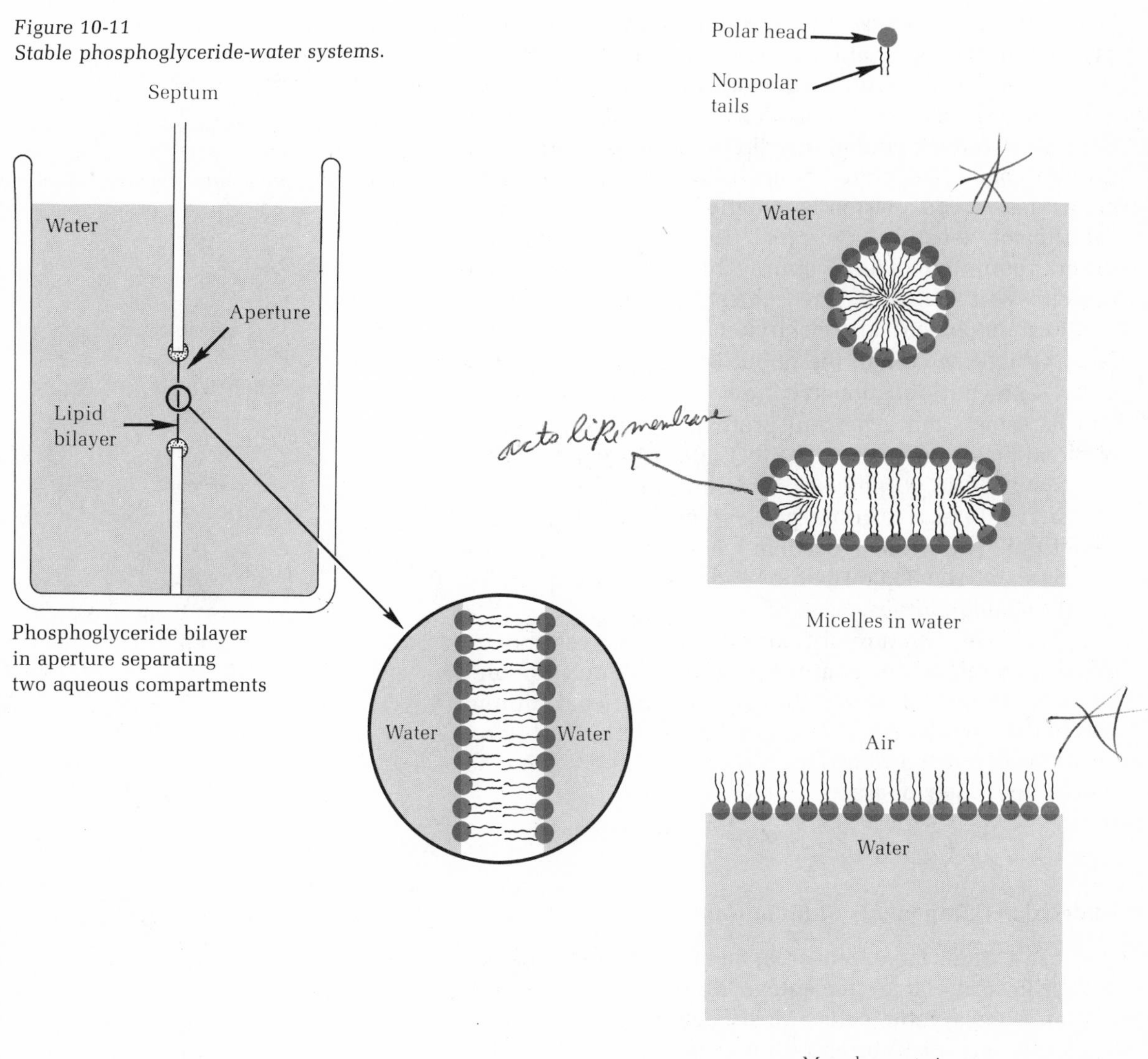

Figure 10-11
Stable phosphoglyceride-water systems.

Phosphoglyceride bilayer in aperture separating two aqueous compartments

been extensively studied since their properties are very similar to those of natural cellular membranes. They are freely permeable to water but relatively impermeable to simple cations (Na^+, K^+) and anions (Cl^-). They have a very high electrical capacitance and resistance since the continuous hydrocarbon layer has a low dielectric constant and is an extremely poor conductor. Because phospholipids readily form such bilayers spontaneously, it has been suggested that natural membranes may contain a lipid bilayer "core."

Lipoproteins

Polar lipids associate with certain specific proteins to form lipoproteins, of which the best known are the transport lipoproteins of mammalian blood plasma. In these conjugated proteins, no covalent linkages exist between the lipid(s) and the protein components. Lipoproteins usually contain both polar and neutral lipids, as well as cholesterol and its esters. They serve as vehicles for the transport of lipids from the small intestine to the liver and from the liver to the fat depots and various other tissues. Several classes of lipoproteins are found in blood plasma; their classification is based on their density.

Because lipids have low densities (0.95 gram per cm^3) and proteins relatively high densities (~ 1.20 grams per cm^3), lipoproteins containing different ratios of lipid and protein can be separated from each other in the ultracentrifuge. Blood plasma is usually mixed with an NaCl solution of density 1.05 grams per cm^3; in such a medium, lipoproteins will float upwards and normal, simple proteins will sediment. The lightest lipoproteins (density < 1.00 gram per cm^3) are the chylomicrons, which are very large structures containing about 80 percent triacylglycerols, 7 percent phosphoglycerides, 8 percent cholesterol and its esters, and 2 percent protein. The β-lipoproteins of blood plasma (density, 1.01 to 1.06 grams per cm^3) contain about 80 to 90 percent lipid, and the α-lipoproteins (density, 1.06 to 1.20 grams per cm^3) contain 40 to 70 percent lipid. The average particle weight of the β-lipoproteins is about 10,000,000 daltons and that of α-lipoproteins about 300,000 daltons.

The precise structure of lipoproteins is not yet known, but the protein chain is apparently located on the outer surface, where it forms a thin hydrophilic coat around part of the micellar lipid structure. Presumably, the hydrophilic heads of the phospholipid molecules are oriented toward the water phase.

Molecular Components of Membranes

Because of their large total area, membranes may make up a significantly large percentage of the total dry mass of some eucaryotic cells. Most membranes consist of about 40 percent lipid and 60 percent protein. The lipid portion of the membrane contains predominantly polar lipids of different types; actually, nearly all the polar lipid of cells is present in their membranes. Most membranes contain relatively little sterol or triacylglycerol with the exception of the plasma membrane of cells of higher animals, which are characteristically rich in cholesterol. The ratio of different kinds of polar lipids in each membrane is characteristic for the type of membrane, the cell type, and the species. Figure 10-12 shows the distribution of the major lipids in the plasma membranes of the erythrocytes of different species. Since the erythrocytes of these species differ in their permeability to various small molecules, it has been suggested that their permeability is a function of the ratio of the lipid components.

The ratio of the different lipids is constant in any given type of membrane and thus appears to be genetically determined; this ratio cannot be altered, for example, by feeding vertebrates different mixtures of lipids. However, the fatty acid components of the individual membrane lipids are not fixed; they may vary with nutritional state and with environmental temperature.

The proteins of membranes are now under intensive study. Early investigations led to the view that each type of membrane contains only one species of noncatalytic monomeric membrane protein, called structure protein,

Figure 10-12
Lipid composition of erythrocyte membranes of different mammals. Note that the proportions of cholesterol and phosphatidyl ethanolamine are approximately constant but that the ratio of phosphatidyl choline to sphingomyelin varies greatly with the species.

Key
C = cholesterol
PE = phosphatidyl ethanolamine
PC = phosphatidyl choline
SP = sphingomyelin

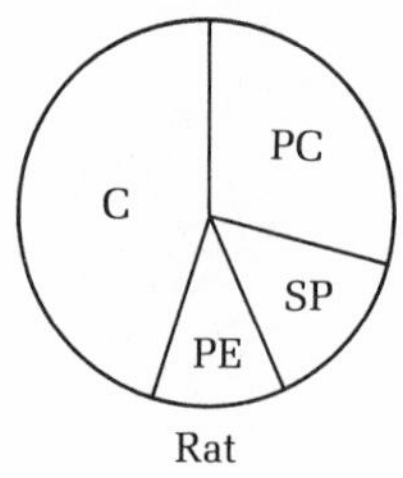

Rat

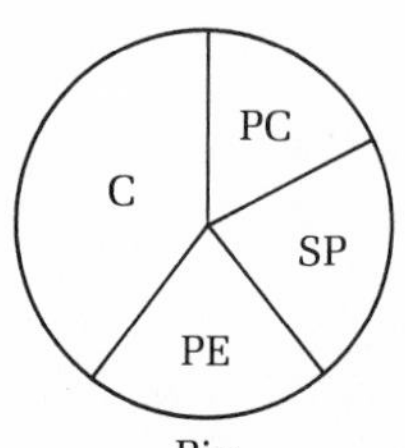

Pig

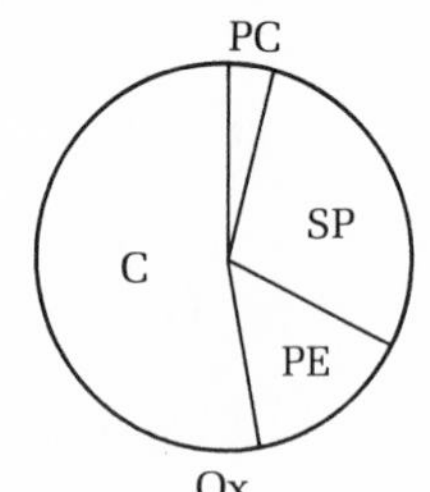

Ox

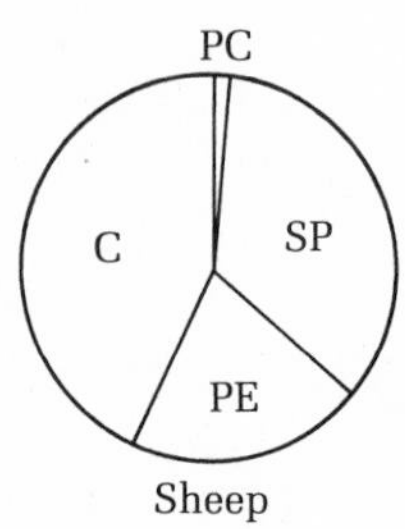

Sheep

which forms into polymeric sheets, similar to the protein sheaths of viruses. However, more recent work indicates that membranes contain several or many species of protein that are separable by disk electrophoresis. Membrane proteins appear to have molecular weights of about 23,000 to 60,000 in mitochondria and about 50,000 in erythrocytes. Such membrane proteins are insoluble in aqueous systems near pH 7.0 and are exceedingly difficult to separate.

The Unit Membrane Hypothesis

For many years it was assumed that all biological membranes have the same basic molecular structure, because they have many common properties. Most membranes contain about the same proportion of lipid and protein. Almost all membranes are freely permeable to water and to neutral lipophilic molecules but are much less permeable to polar molecules such as sugars and amides and are usually only slightly permeable to small ions, such as Na^+ and Cl^-. Furthermore, most membranes have a high electrical resistance. These common properties formed the basis of the first important hypothesis of the structure of biological membranes, proposed by H. Davson and J. Danielli in 1935, which postulated that membranes contain a continuous hydrocarbon phase contributed by the lipid components of the membrane. Some years later this hypothesis was modified and refined, particularly by Robertson, into the *unit membrane hypothesis* (Figure 10-14). According to this hypothesis, the unit membrane consists of a bilayer of mixed polar lipids, with their hydrocarbon chains oriented inward to form a continuous hydrocarbon phase and their hydrophilic heads oriented outward. Each surface is coated with a monomolecular layer of protein molecules, with the polypeptide chains in extended form, or β-configuration. The total thickness of the unit membrane was suggested to be about 90 Å; the thickness of the lipid bilayer alone is about 60–70 Å.

Figure 10-13
High-magnification electron micrograph of erythrocyte plasma membrane, showing the trilaminar image yielded by fixation in osmium tetroxide. Usually the two electron-dense lines separate a clear space of about 25 Å.

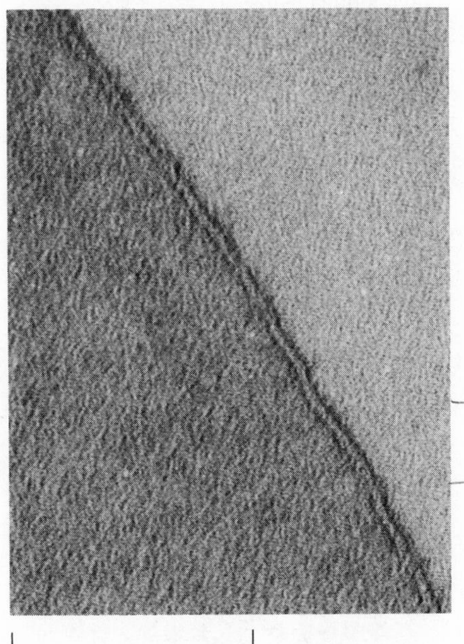

This membrane model accounts for many properties of natural membranes. For example, a bimolecular layer of closely packed lipid molecules would account for the fact that most membranes contain about 40 percent lipid by weight. Secondly, phospholipids tend to form bilayer systems quite spontaneously in aqueous systems; the bilayer is one of the minimum-energy configurations of phospholipids in water and requires no input of work to maintain it. The continuous hydrocarbon phase of the unit membrane would also account for the high electrical resistance of natural membranes, since hydrocarbons are very poor conductors. It would account for the characteristically high permeability of natural membranes to nonpolar molecules, which dissolve readily in the hydrocarbon layer, and their relative impermeability to charged ions, which do not. The unit-membrane model also is consistent with the characteristically paired, electron-dense lines representing the images of membranes as observed by electron microscopy of cell sections following fixation with osmium tetroxide or potassium permanganate (Figure 10-13). For these reasons, it was postulated that all membrane systems of cells consist of such unit membranes, which may occur singly, as in the plasma membrane, or in closely associated pairs, as in the endoplasmic reticulum or the cristae of mitochondria.

Other Models of Membrane Structure

Although the unit-membrane hypothesis accounts satisfactorily for many observations on natural membranes, recent research has raised some doubts and evoked new hypotheses of membrane structure. For one thing, more refined electron microscopy has revealed that different membranes vary quite significantly in thickness. For example, very recent work suggests that the inner mitochondrial membrane may be only 50 to 60 Å thick and may contain only about 20 percent lipid. Many membranes have also been found to possess a surface pattern consistent with the presence of recurring globular subunits of diameter 60 Å in some membranes and as large as 90 Å in others. These findings, in addition to the fact that membranes vary considerably in their functions and enzymatic activities, have led to the conclusion that there is much more structural differentiation among membranes than was earlier supposed. The long-accepted view that the electron-dense lines observed in electron micrographs of membranes fixed with osmium tetroxide correspond to the polar heads of lipids in bilayer array has also been challenged. New fixation and staining techniques are now being employed to examine membrane structure more closely, particularly negative contrast methods.

As a result of these developments, other models of membrane structure have recently been proposed (Figure 10-14). Two of these models are variants of the unit-membrane model. One of them proposes that the membrane structure protein is arranged *within* the lipid bilayer, so that the hydrocarbon tails of the lipids intertwine in interstices of the folded polypeptide chain of the protein. Another proposes that structure protein molecules extend across the entire bilayer at regular intervals. Presumably, the segments of the polypeptide chain that lie within the hydrocarbon phase consist of sequences of the more hydrophobic amino acids. These two models share a common feature with the unit-membrane model, namely, an essentially continuous hydrophobic layer. They satisfactorily account for the fact that natural membranes behave as though the protein and lipid components are held together largely by hydrophobic rather than ionic interactions.

Globular models of membrane structure have also been proposed (Figure 10-14). In these, the recurring structural units are small globular lipoproteins or alternating lipid micelles and globular proteins, to account for the observation that some membranes have a surface pattern suggesting a globular-subunit structure. However, globular packing arrangements appear to be less compatible with the high electrical resistance of membranes, which is best accounted for by a completely continuous hydrocarbon phase.

Figure 10-14
Some models of membrane structure.

Two unit-membrane models

Polypeptide chains in β-form

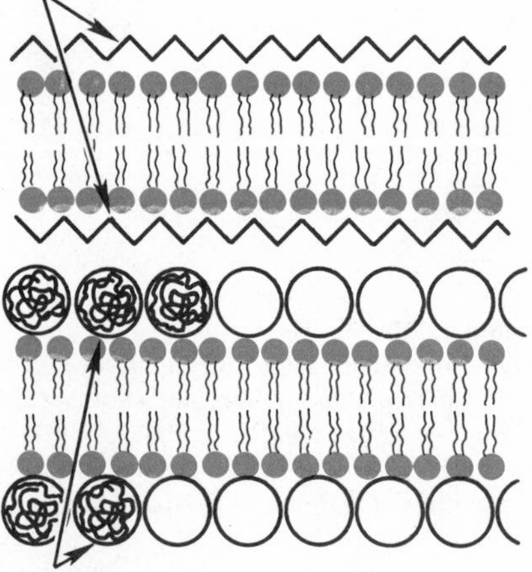

Polypeptide chains in globular form

A bilayer model with the polypeptide chain in the hydrocarbon phase

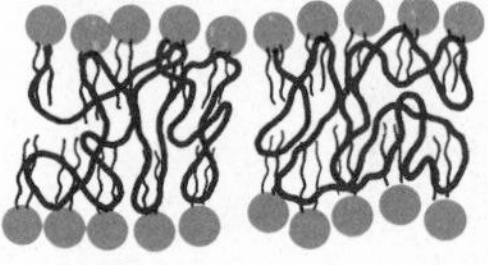

A bilayer model with penetration of the polypeptide chain

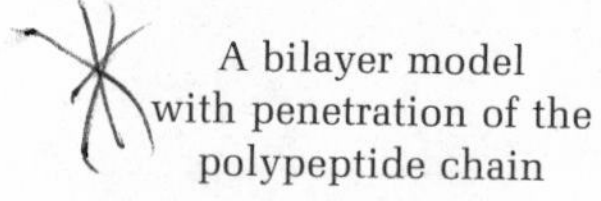

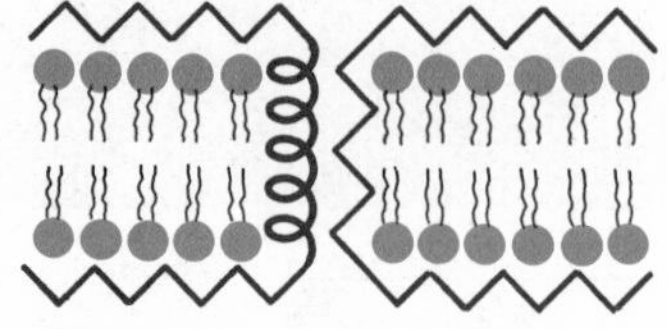

A globular model in which polypeptide chains coat lipid micelles

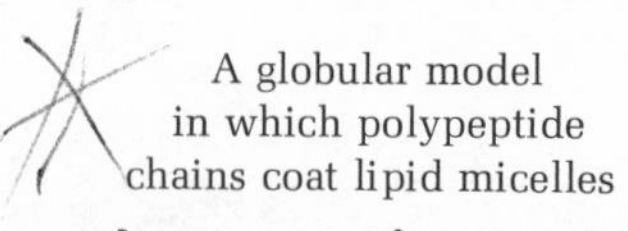

Since different membranes have characteristic ratios of various lipids, in which polar lipids predominate, it appears likely that the lipids occur in specific and characteristic two-dimensional arrangements. The phosphoglycerides, sphingolipids, and glycolipids possess polar heads of widely different geometry, size, polarity, and electrical charge, which might be arranged in different patterns in different membranes. Such patterns might be specified by the membrane structure proteins, which are, of course, genetically coded. These considerations suggest that the various types of polar head groups of the complex lipids of membranes constitute an "alphabet" of membrane structure and properties, just as the R groups of amino acids comprise an alphabet of protein structure and properties.

It appears highly probable that membranes are asymmetrical, i.e., that they possess "sidedness." The asymmetry may be contributed by chemically different protein layers on either side or by chemically different lipid layers. Such asymmetry can, in fact, be observed in some cellular membranes with the electron microscope, as in the case of the inner mitochondrial membrane (Chapter 18). Asymmetry of the membrane is an important element in the mechanism of directional or vectorial transport processes across membranes (Chapter 27).

Whatever the details of the molecular organization of membranes, it is remarkable that these extremely thin structures, no more than a few molecules thick, are held together entirely by hydrophobic and polar interactions. There is no evidence whatsoever for the occurrence of covalent linkages between successive lipid molecules, between successive protein molecules, or between adjacent lipids and proteins in membranes. The lipids can in some cases be nearly completely extracted from membranes with chloroform-methanol mixtures. When such lipids are added back to the solvent-extracted membranes, they reassociate into the membrane structure. Membranes are very probably minimum-energy, self-assembling systems.

Summary

Lipids are water-insoluble components of cells that can be extracted by nonpolar solvents. Their fatty acid components usually have an even number of carbon atoms and are from 12 to 22 carbon atoms long. Fatty acids may be saturated or unsaturated; the double bonds of unsaturated fatty acids have the *cis* configuration. In most unsaturated fatty acids, one double bond is at the 9,10 position. Fatty acids can be separated and analyzed by gas-liquid partition chromatography.

Triacylglycerols (neutral fats) contain three fatty acid molecules esterified to the three hydroxyl groups of glycerol. Simple triacylglycerols contain a single type of fatty acid; mixed triacylglycerols contain at least two different types. Triacylglycerols serve primarily to store fuel in the form of fat droplets in cells. Waxes are esters of long-chain fatty acids with high-molecular-weight alcohols. The amphipathic, or polar, lipids include the phosphoglycerides, which contain two fatty acid molecules esterified to the two free hydroxyl groups of glycerol 3-phosphate and an alcohol esterified to the phosphoric acid. Naturally occurring phosphoglycerides are optically active and belong to the L series. Sphingolipids contain no glycerol but possess two long hydrocarbon chains, one contributed by a fatty acid and the other by sphingosine, a long-chain aliphatic amino alcohol. They also contain phosphoric acid, usually esterified with choline. Glycolipids contain sphingosine, a fatty acid, and one or more carbohydrate molecules. Gangliosides are glycolipids that contain one or more residues of an acidic nine-carbon acylated amino sugar, N-acetylneuraminic acid. The polar lipids spontaneously form micelles, monolayers, and bilayers; they function as structural elements in cell membranes.

Steroids are derivatives of perhydrocyclopentanophenanthrene. Many steroids, such as the adrenal cortical and sex hormones, possess intense biological activity. Cholesterol is an important component of plasma membranes. Lipids are transported in the blood in the form of lipoproteins, of which there are three different classes that differ in lipid content and thus in density.

Cell membranes of different species are from 60 to 100 Å thick and contain about 60 percent protein and 40 percent lipid, although these proportions may vary. Each type of membrane contains characteristic types of polar lipids in fixed molar ratios, which are probably genetically determined. Membranes also contain several species of proteins serving a structural role. Several models of membrane structure have been proposed. Much evidence supports a structure containing a continuous hydrocarbon layer as a core, with proteins on either side. However, there are probably many specialized variations in membrane structure, in some of which the proteins may penetrate into the hydrocarbon phase.

References

Books

ANSELL, G. B., and J. N. HAWTHORNE: *Phospholipids: Chemistry, Metabolism, and Function*, American Elsevier Publishing Company, New York, 1964. Comprehensive treatise covering all aspects of phospholipid biochemistry.

CHAPMAN, D.: *The Structure of Lipids by Spectroscopy and X-ray Techniques*, Methuen & Co., Ltd., London, 1965. The physical-chemical aspects of lipids and membranes.

Articles and Reviews

FREEMAN, N. K., F. T. LINDGREN, and A. V. NICHOLS: "The Chemistry of Serum Lipoproteins," *Progr. Chem. Fats Lipids*, **6**:215–250 (1963).

HOLMAN, R. T.: "Chromatography," *Progr. Chem. Fats Lipids*, **8**:301–420 (1966). Comprehensive review of the chromatography of lipids and fatty acids.

IUPAC-IUB COMMISSION ON BIOCHEMICAL NOMENCLATURE: "The Nomenclature of Lipids," *Biochem. J.* **105**:897–902 (1967). Newly approved nomenclature.

KORN, E. D.: "Structure of Biological Membranes," *Science*, **153**: 1491–1498 (1966). A critique of the unit membrane hypothesis.

NORTHCOTE, D. H. (ed.): "Structure and Function of Membranes," *Brit. Med. Bull.*, **24**:99–186 (1968). A series of excellent brief articles on membranes.

ROTHFIELD, L., and A. FINKELSTEIN: "Membrane Biochemistry," *Ann. Rev. Biochem.*, **37**:463–496 (1968). Excellent and stimulating review of recent advances.

VAN DEENEN, L. L. M.: "Phospholipids and Biomembranes," *Progr. Chem. Fats Lipids*, **8**:1–127 (1966). Comprehensive review of the chemical relationship of phospholipids to membrane structure.

WIEGANDT, H.: "The Structure and Function of Gangliosides," *Angew. Chem. Intern. Ed. Engl.*, **7**:87–96 (1968). A short review of these complex substances.

Problems

1. How many isomers of a triacylglycerol containing palmitic, stearic, and oleic acid are possible? Include both positional isomers and stereoisomers.

2. A sample of triacylglycerols from the depot fat of the rat was found to contain palmitic (P), oleic (O), and stearic (S) acids. Indicate the various molecular species of L-triacylglycerols that could conceivably be present.

3. Most membranes of animal cells contain about 60 percent protein and 40 percent phosphoglycerides.
   (*a*) Calculate the average density of a membrane, assuming that protein has a density of 1.2 grams cm^{-3} and phosphoglyceride a density of 0.92 gram cm^{-3}.
   (*b*) If a sample of membrane material were centrifuged in NaCl solution of 1.05 specific gravity, would it sediment or float?

4. A mixture of (*a*) 1-palmitoyl-2-stearoyl-3-lauroylglycerol and (*b*) phosphatidic acid in benzene is shaken with an equal volume of water. After the two phases are allowed to separate, which lipid will be in higher concentration in the aqueous phase?

5. Electrophoresis at pH 7.0 was carried out on a mixture of lipids containing (*a*) cardiolipin, (*b*) phosphatidyl glycerol, (*c*) phosphatidyl ethanolamine, and (*d*) phosphatidyl serine. Indicate how you would expect these compounds to move [toward the anode (A), toward the cathode (C), or remain at origin (O)].

6. Name the products of mild alkaline hydrolysis of (*a*) 1-stearoyl-2,3-dipalmitoylglycerol, (*b*) 1-stearoyl-2-elaidoylphosphatidyl inositol, (*c*) 1-palmitoyl-2-oleyl phosphatidyl choline.

7. Name the products of the following: (*a*) hydrolysis of 1-stearoyl-2-oleyl phosphatidyl serine by strong base, followed by acid hydrolysis; (*b*) treatment of 1-palmitoyl-2-linoleyl phosphatidyl choline with phospholipase D.

8. How many isoprene units are contained in the structure of (*a*) squalene, (*b*) β-carotene, (*c*) vitamin A?

9. If a membrane contains 40 percent by weight of lipids and 60 percent protein, calculate the molar ratio of lipids to proteins. Assume that the lipid molecules have an average molecular weight of 800 and the proteins an average molecular weight of 50,000.

CHAPTER 11 SUGARS, STORAGE POLYSACCHARIDES, AND CELL WALLS

The carbohydrates or saccharides are polyhydroxy aldehydes or ketones that have the empirical formula $(CH_2O)_n$, and their derivatives. *Monosaccharides*, or simple sugars, consist of a single polyhydroxy aldehyde or ketone unit. The most abundant monosaccharide is the six-carbon sugar D-glucose; it is the primordial or parent monosaccharide from which all others are derived. D-Glucose is the most important fuel molecule for most organisms, and it is also the basic building block or a precursor of the most abundant polysaccharides.

Oligosaccharides contain from two to ten monosaccharide units joined in glycosidic linkage. *Polysaccharides* contain very long chains of monosaccharide units; they may be linear or branched. Most polysaccharides contain recurring monosaccharide units of only a single kind or two alternating kinds; they are therefore not informational macromolecules.

In the biosphere, there is probably more carbohydrate than all other organic matter combined, largely because of the abundance of two polymers of D-glucose, namely cellulose and starch. Cellulose is the predominant extracellular structural component of the fibrous and woody tissues of plants. Starch is also found in immense quantities in plants, where it is the chief form of fuel storage.

Polysaccharides are also important components in the rigid cell walls of bacteria and plants and in the soft cell coats in animal tissues. The structure and function of cell walls and coats are currently the subject of much research, not only because of their complexity, but also because of newly discovered biological implications.

Glyceraldehyde

```
     H
     |
     C=O
     |
  H—C—OH
     |
  H—C—OH
     |
     H
```

Dihydroxyacetone

```
     H
     |
  H—C—OH
     |
     C=O
     |
  H—C—OH
     |
     H
```

Families of Monosaccharides

Monosaccharides have the empirical formula $(CH_2O)_n$, where $n = 3$ or some larger number. The carbon skeleton of monosaccharides is unbranched, and each carbon atom except one contains a hydroxyl group; at the remaining carbon atom, there is a carbonyl oxygen. If the carbonyl group is at the end of the chain, the monosaccharide is an aldehyde and is called an *aldose;* if it is at any other position, the monosaccharide is a ketone and is called a *ketose.* The simplest monosaccharides are the three-carbon *trioses*

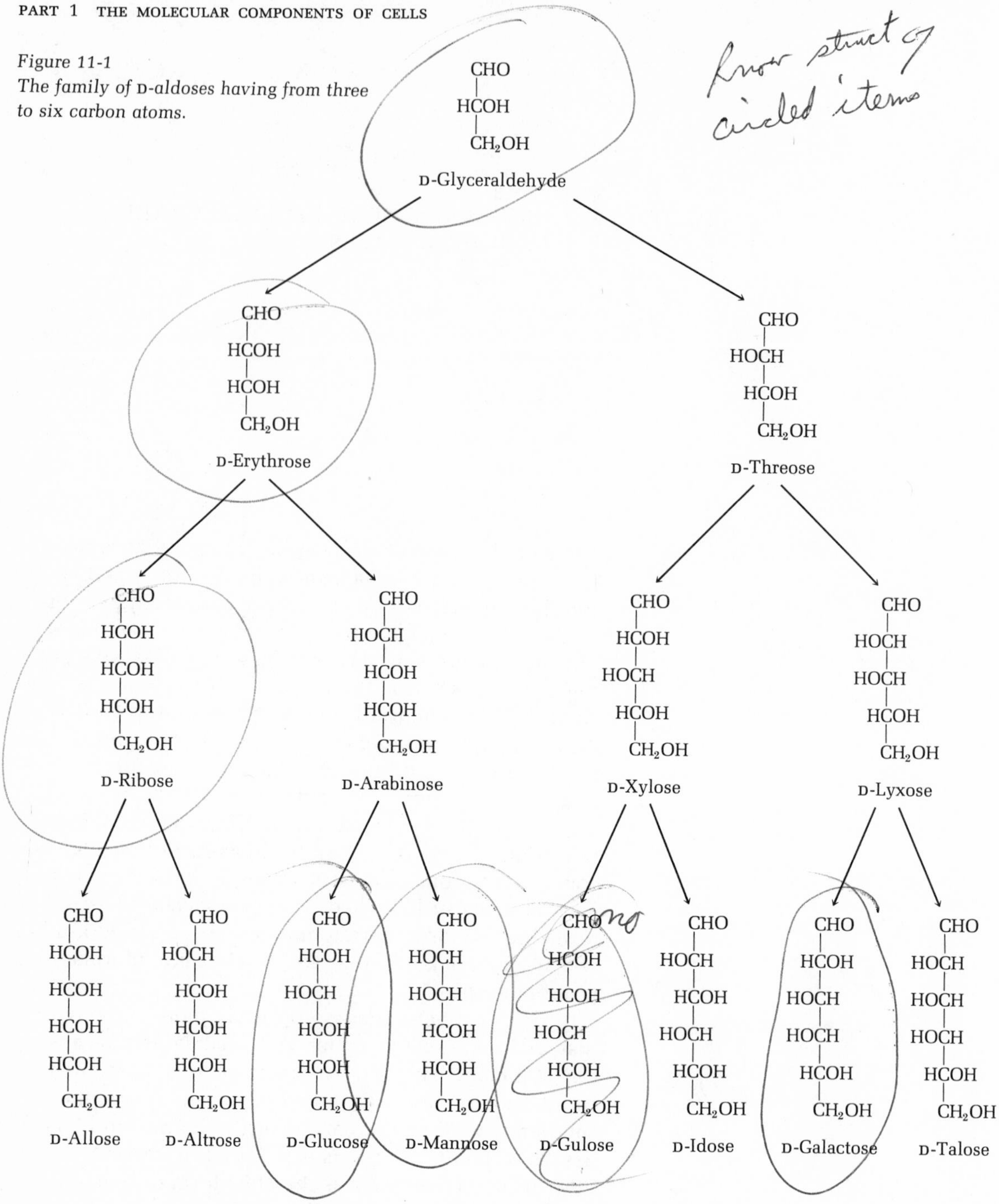

Figure 11-1
The family of D-aldoses having from three to six carbon atoms.

D-Glyceraldehyde: CHO / HCOH / CH_2OH

D-Erythrose: CHO / HCOH / HCOH / CH_2OH

D-Threose: CHO / HOCH / HCOH / CH_2OH

D-Ribose: CHO / HCOH / HCOH / HCOH / CH_2OH

D-Arabinose: CHO / HOCH / HCOH / HCOH / CH_2OH

D-Xylose: CHO / HCOH / HOCH / HCOH / CH_2OH

D-Lyxose: CHO / HOCH / HOCH / HCOH / CH_2OH

D-Allose: CHO / HCOH / HCOH / HCOH / HCOH / CH_2OH

D-Altrose: CHO / HOCH / HCOH / HCOH / HCOH / CH_2OH

D-Glucose: CHO / HCOH / HOCH / HCOH / HCOH / CH_2OH

D-Mannose: CHO / HOCH / HOCH / HCOH / HCOH / CH_2OH

D-Gulose: CHO / HCOH / HCOH / HOCH / HCOH / CH_2OH

D-Idose: CHO / HOCH / HCOH / HOCH / HCOH / CH_2OH

D-Galactose: CHO / HCOH / HOCH / HOCH / HCOH / CH_2OH

D-Talose: CHO / HOCH / HOCH / HOCH / HCOH / CH_2OH

glyceraldehyde and dihydroxyacetone. Glyceraldehyde is an *aldotriose;* dihydroxyacetone is a *ketotriose.*

If the carbon chains of the trioses are extended by the addition of carbon atoms, we have, successively, *tetroses, pentoses, hexoses, heptoses,* and *octoses.* Each of these exists in two series, i.e., aldotetroses and ketotetroses, aldopentoses and ketopentoses, aldohexoses and ketohexoses, etc. The structures of some representative D-aldoses and D-ketoses are shown in Figures 11-1 and 11-2. In both classes of monosaccharides, the hexoses are by far the most abundant. However, aldopentoses are important components of nucleic acids, and derivatives of trioses and heptoses are intermediates in carbohydrate metabolism. All the simple monosaccharides are white crystalline solids that are freely soluble in water but insoluble in nonpolar solvents. Most have a sweet taste.

D-glyceraldehyde

CHO / HOH_2C—C—OH / H

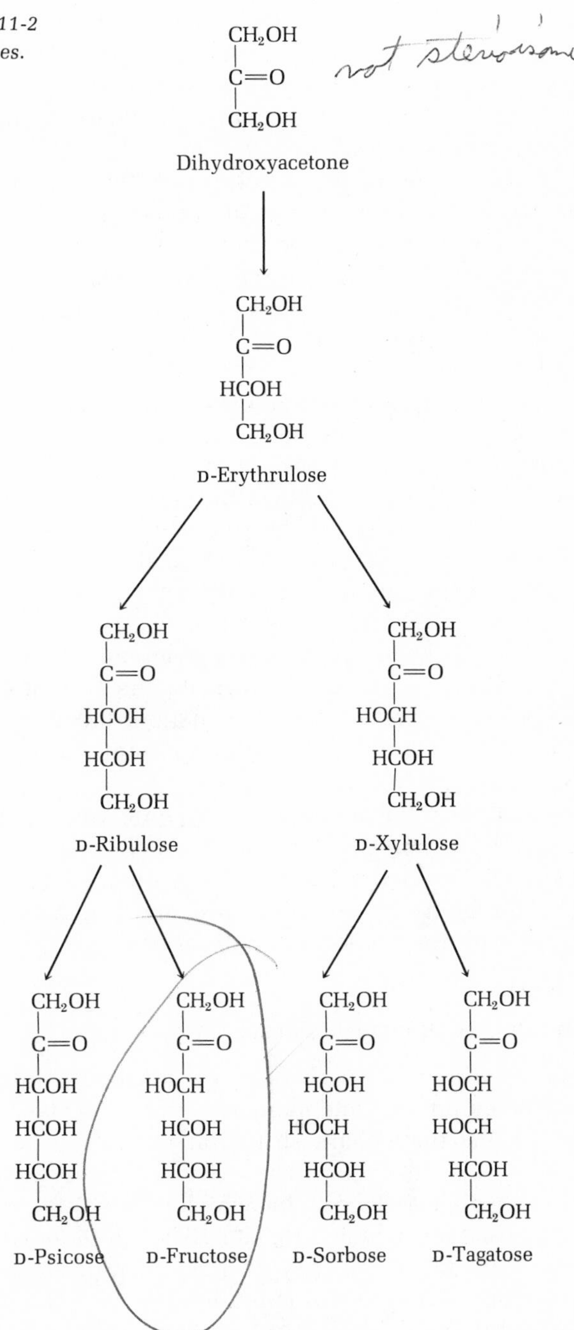

Figure 11-2
D-Ketoses.

L-glyceraldehyde

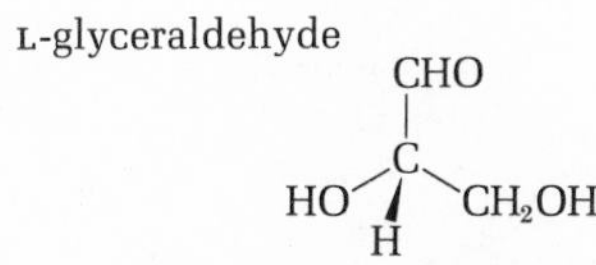

Stereoisomerism of Monosaccharides

All the monosaccharides except dihydroxyacetone contain one or more asymmetric carbon atoms. The simplest aldose, glyceraldehyde, contains only one asymmetric carbon atom and thus is capable of existing in the form of two different stereoisomers (margins). However, the aldohexoses have four asymmetric carbon atoms and can exist in the form of $2^n = 2^4 = 16$ different stereoisomers.

Naturally occurring monosaccharides show optical activity. For example, the usual form of glucose found in nature is dextrorotatory ($[\alpha]_D^{20} = +52.7°$), while the usual form of fructose is levorotatory ($[\alpha]_D^{20} = -92.4°$). Actually, both are members of the D series since their absolute configurations are related to D-glyceraldehyde (Chapter 4). For those sugars having two or more asymmetric carbon atoms, the convention has been adopted that the prefixes D- and L- refer to the asymmetric carbon atom farthest removed from the carbonyl carbon atom. The absolute configurations of all the common monosaccharides are now known with certainty.

Figure 11-1 shows the structures of the D-aldoses. All have the same configuration at the asymmetric carbon atom farthest from the carbonyl carbon, but because most have two or more asymmetric carbon atoms, a number of isomeric D-aldoses exist. Those of greatest biological importance are D-glyceraldehyde, D-ribose, D-glucose, D-mannose, and D-galactose.

Figure 11-2 shows the D-ketoses, which share the same configuration at the asymmetric carbon atom farthest from the carbonyl group. Ketoses are sometimes designated by inserting "ul" into the name of the corresponding aldose; for example, D-ribulose is the ketopentose corresponding to the aldopentose D-ribose. Biologically, the most important ketoses are dihydroxyacetone, D-ribulose, and D-fructose.

Aldoses and ketoses of the L series are mirror images of their D counterparts, as is shown for the case of D- and L-glucose. L-Sugars are found in nature, but they occur infrequently. Among the most important are L-fucose, L-rhamnose, (p. 226) and L-sorbose.

Two sugars differing only in the configuration around one specific carbon atom are called *epimers* of each other. Thus, D-glucose and D-mannose are epimers with respect to carbon atom 2, and D-glucose and D-galactose are epimers with respect to carbon atom 4.

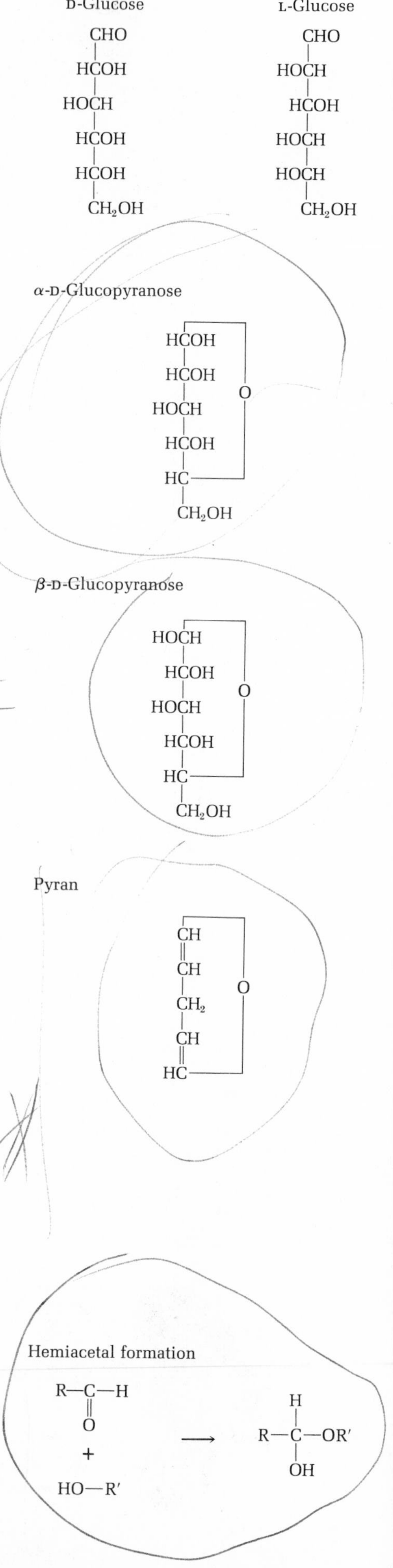

Mutarotation; Anomeric Forms

Many monosaccharides behave in aqueous solution as though they possess one more asymmetric center than is given by the open-chain structural formulas in Figures 11-1 and 11-2. D-Glucose may exist in two different isomeric forms—α-D-glucose, for which $[\alpha]_D^{20} = +112.2°$, and β-D-glucose, for which $[\alpha]_D^{20} = +18.7°$. Both have been isolated in pure form; they do not differ in elementary composition. When the α- and β-isomers of D-glucose are dissolved in water, the optical rotation of each gradually changes with time and approaches a final equilibrium value of $[\alpha]_D^{20} = +52.7°$. This change, called *mutarotation*, is due to the formation of an equilibrium mixture consisting of about one-third α-D-glucose and two-thirds β-D-glucose at 25°C. From various chemical considerations, it has been deduced that the α- and β-isomers of D-glucose are not open-chain structures, as shown in Figure 11-1, but rather six-membered ring structures formed by the reaction of the alcoholic hydroxyl group at carbon atom 5 with the aldehydic carbon atom 1. Such six-membered ring forms of sugars are called *pyranoses* because they are derivatives of the heterocyclic compound pyran. The systematic name for the ring form of α-D-glucose is α-D-glucopyranose (margin).

The formation of pyranoses is a special case of a more general type of reaction between an aldehyde and an alcohol to form a *hemiacetal*, which contains an asymmetric

β-D-Fructofuranose

HOC—CH_2OH
HOCH
O
HCOH
HC
CH_2OH

Furan

CH
CH O
CH
HC

Haworth Projection Formulas

α-D-Glucopyranose

6 CH_2OH
5 H H O H
4 OH H 1
HO OH
3 2
H OH

β-D-Glucopyranose

CH_2OH
H H O OH
OH H
HO H
H OH

α-D-Fructofuranose

6 $HOCH_2$ O 1 CH_2OH
5 H HO 2
H OH
4 3
OH H

β-D-Fructofuranose

6 $HOCH_2$ O OH
5 H HO 2
H CH_2OH 1
4 3
OH H

carbon atom and thus may exist in two stereoisomeric forms. D-Glucopyranose is an intramolecular hemiacetal in which the free hydroxyl group at carbon atom 5 has reacted with the aldehydic carbon atom 1, rendering the latter asymmetric (margin). D-Glucopyranose therefore can exist as two different stereoisomers, designated α- and β-. Isomeric forms of monosaccharides that differ from each other only in their configuration about the hemiacetal carbon atom are *anomers,* and the hemiacetal carbon atom is called the *anomeric carbon.* Only monosaccharides having five or more carbon atoms can form stable rings and exist in anomeric forms. Tetroses and trioses therefore occur in open-chain form in aqueous solution.

Ketohexoses also occur in α- and β-anomeric forms. In these compounds, the alcoholic hydroxyl group on carbon atom 5 reacts with the carbonyl group at carbon atom 2, forming a five-membered ring called a *furanose* (since it is a derivative of furan). Aldohexoses may exist in aldofuranose forms; however, since the six-membered aldopyranose ring is much more stable than the furanose ring, it predominates in aldohexose solutions. It is generally assumed that the open-chain form of hexoses is an intermediate in the interconversion of α- and β-forms during mutarotation.

Haworth projection formulas are commonly used to indicate the configuration in space of the ring forms of monosaccharides; the edge of the ring nearest the reader is usually represented by bold lines. Such projections are somewhat misleading, however, since they suggest that the five- and six-membered furanose and pyranose rings are planar, which is not the case. The pyranose ring may exist in two configurations, the *chair form* and the *boat form.* The chair form is much more stable than the boat form and presumably predominates in most natural sugars. The substituent groups in the chair form are not geometrically and chemically equivalent; they fall into two classes, designated *axial* and *equatorial.* Equatorial hydroxyl groups of pyranoses are more readily esterified than axial groups. (See next page.)

β-D-Fructofuranose

α-D-Glucopyranose

Conformations of pyranose ring.

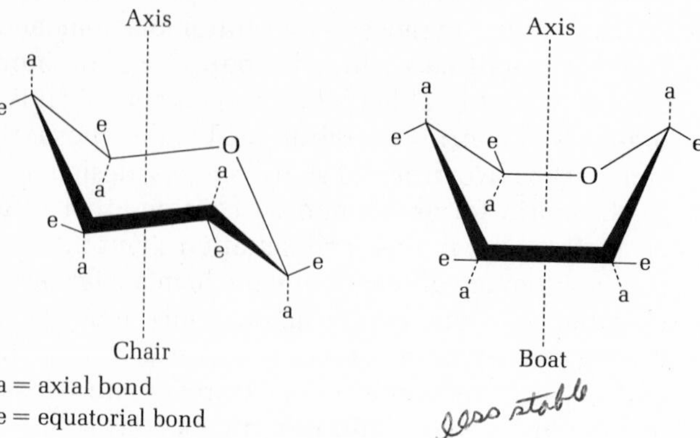

a = axial bond
e = equatorial bond

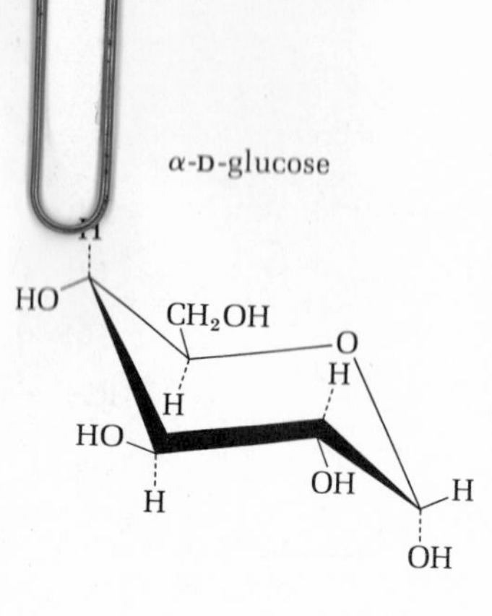

Action of Acids and Bases on Monosaccharides

The fact that monosaccharides are stable to hot dilute mineral acids makes possible the quantitative recovery of most monosaccharides in intact form after the hydrolysis of polysaccharides. Concentrated acids, however, cause dehydration of sugars to yield *furfurals*, which are aldehyde derivatives of furan. For example, D-glucose heated with strong HCl yields 5-hydroxymethylfurfural (margin). Furfurals condense with phenols to give characteristic colored products often used for colorimetric analysis of sugars.

Dilute aqueous bases at room temperature cause rearrangements about the anomeric carbon atom and its adjacent carbon atom, without affecting substituents at other carbon atoms. For example, treatment of D-glucose with dilute alkali yields an equilibrium mixture of D-glucose, D-fructose, and D-mannose. These reactions are believed to involve enol forms, called *enediols*, of the hydroxyaldehyde and hydroxyketone structures of carbon atoms 1 and 2. (See below.)

At high temperatures or high concentrations, alkalis cause free monosaccharides to undergo further rearrangements, fragmentation, and also polymerization. As we shall see later, however, glycosides and some polysaccharides are stable to alkali.

Furfural formation

HC=O
HCOH
HOCH
HCOH
HCOH
CH_2OH

D-Glucose

↓ H^+

HC=O
C
HC
HC
C
CH_2OH
O

5-Hydroxymethylfurfural

+

3 H_2O

Isomerization by dilute alkali

D-Glucose		*trans*-Enediol		D-Fructose		*cis*-Enediol		D-Mannose
HC=O		HOCH		$HOCH_2$		HOCH		O=CH
HCOH		COH		C=O		HOC		HOCH
HOCH	⇌	HOCH	⇌	HOCH	⇌	HOCH	⇌	HOCH
HCOH		HCOH		HCOH		HCOH		HCOH
HCOH		HCOH		HCOH		HCOH		HCOH
CH_2OH		CH_2OH		CH_2OH		CH_2OH		CH_2OH

Important Derivatives of Monosaccharides and Glycosides

Aldohexoses readily react with alcohols in the presence of a mineral acid to form anomeric α- and *β-glycosides*. The glycosides are asymmetric mixed acetals, formed by the reaction of the aldehydic carbon atom of the intramolecular hemiacetal or pyranose form of the aldohexose with a

Methyl α-D-glucoside

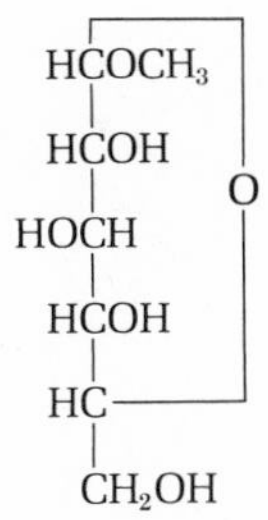

Methyl β-D-glucoside

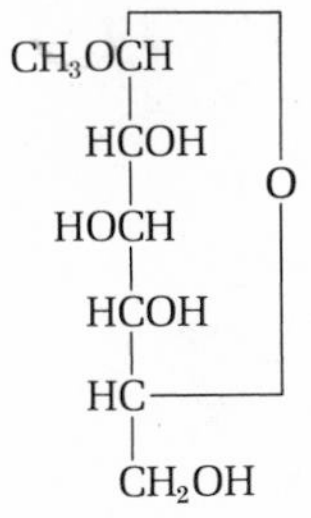

second alcoholic hydroxyl group furnished by the alcohol. The aldehydic carbon in glycosides is asymmetric. D-Glucose yields, with methanol, methyl α-D-glucoside ($[\alpha]_D^{20} = +158.9°$) and methyl β-D-glucoside ($[\alpha]_D^{20} = -34.2°$).

The glycosidic linkage is also formed by the reaction of a monosaccharide with the hydroxyl groups of other monosaccharides to form *disaccharides*. Polysaccharides are chains of monosaccharides joined by these glycosidic linkages. The glycosidic linkage is stable to bases but is hydrolyzed by boiling with acid, to yield the free monosaccharide and free alcohol. Glycosides are also hydrolyzed by enzymes, which differ in their specificity, depending on the nature of the monosaccharide unit(s) and the alcohol.

Whether a given glycoside exists in furanose or pyranose form can be ascertained by oxidative degradation with periodate in acid solution. Periodic acid cleaves α-glycols to yield characteristic products which serve to identify the ring form. Oxidation of methyl α-D-glucopyranoside, for example, cleaves the pyranose ring to yield a dialdehyde and formic acid (Figure 11-3). Periodate cleavage of methyl α-D-arabinofuranoside yields the same dialdehyde, but no formic acid, as can be seen by writing out the full structures. Periodate oxidation is a valuable tool in the investigation of the structure of oligosaccharides.

Figure 11-3
Action of periodate. Furanosides can be distinguished from pyranosides, since the latter yield formic acid.

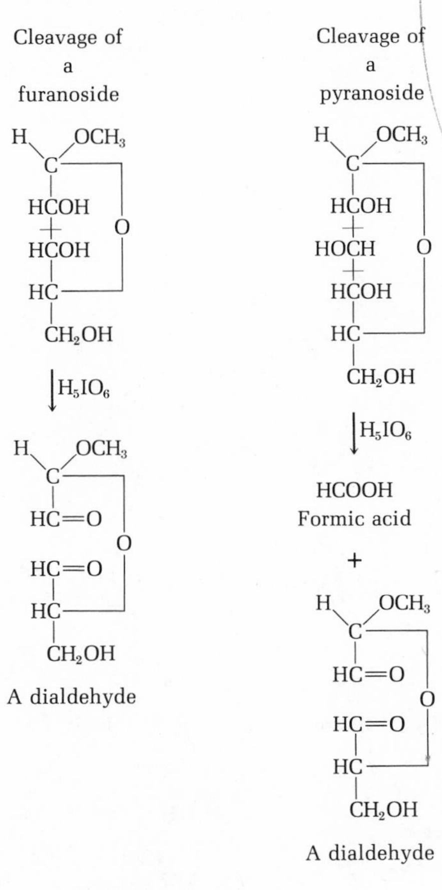

O-Acyl Derivatives

The free hydroxyl groups of monosaccharides and polysaccharides can be acylated to yield O-acyl derivatives, which are sometimes useful in structure determination. For example, treatment of α-D-glucose with excess acetic anhydride yields penta-O-acetyl-α-D-glucose. All the hydroxyl groups of a monosaccharide can be acylated, although they differ somewhat in reactivity. The resulting esters can be hydrolyzed again (margin below).

O-Methyl Derivatives

The hydroxyl groups of monosaccharides can also be methylated. The hydroxyl group on the anomeric carbon atom reacts readily with methanol in the presence of acid to yield methyl glycosides, which are acetals, as we have seen. The remaining hydroxyl groups of monosaccharides require much more drastic conditions for methylation, such as treatment with dimethyl sulfate or methyl iodide plus silver oxide. In this case, methyl ethers are formed, not methyl acetals. Methyl acetals are easily hydrolyzed by boiling with acid; methyl ethers are not. Methylation of all the free hydroxyl groups of a carbohydrate is called *exhaustive methylation*. It is commonly used to establish the positions of substituents in which the hydroxyl group is no longer free to form an ether, such as amino groups, phosphate groups, or glycosidic linkages (see below), and also to determine whether a given monosaccharide is a furanose or a pyranose. Methylation of methyl α-D-glucopyranoside, for example, yields methyl-2,3,4,6-tetra-O-methyl-D-glucopyranoside.

Penta-O-acetyl-α-D-glucose

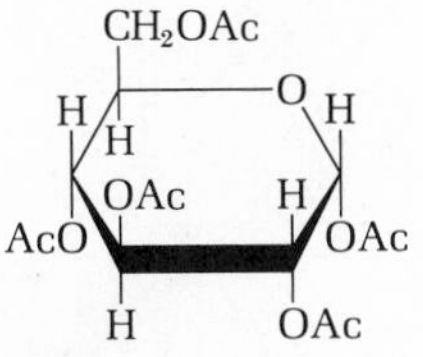

Exhaustive methylation

Methyl α-D-glucopyranoside

HCOCH$_3$
HCOH
HOCH
HCOH
HC
CH$_2$OH

$\xrightarrow{CH_3I}$

Methyl-2,3,4,6-tetra-O-methyl-D-glucopyranoside

HCOCH$_3$
HCOCH$_3$
CH$_3$OCH
HCOCH$_3$
HC
CH$_2$OCH$_3$

Phenylosazones

Monosaccharides in slightly acid solution at 100°C react with excess phenylhydrazine to form *phenylosazones,* which are insoluble in water and easily crystallized. The structure of D-glucose phenylosazone is given in the margin. Glucose, fructose, and mannose yield the same phenylosazone since the differences in configuration about carbon atoms 1 and 2 are abolished. Phenylosazones or the analogous 2,4-dinitrophenylosazones (formed by reaction with 2,4-dinitrophenylhydrazine) are sometimes used to identify sugars.

D-Glucose phenylosazone

HC=N—NH—C$_6$H$_5$
C=N—NH—C$_6$H$_5$
HOCH
HCOH
HCOH
CH$_2$OH

Sugar Alcohols

The carbonyl group of monosaccharides can be reduced by H_2 gas in the presence of metal catalysts or by Na amalgam in water to form the corresponding sugar alcohols. D-Glucose, for example, yields the sugar alcohol *sorbitol,* and D-mannose yields *mannitol*. These reductions can also be carried out by enzymes.

Two other sugar alcohols occur in nature in some abundance. One is *glycerol,* an important component of some lipids. The other is the cyclohexane derivative *inositol,* which exists in several stereoisomeric forms. The latter is found not only in the lipid phosphatidyl inositol but also as phytic acid, the hexaphosphoric ester of inositol. The calcium and magnesium salt of phytic acid is called phytin; it is abundant in the extracellular supporting material in higher-plant tissues. The structures of some sugar alcohols are shown in the margin.

Sugar alcohols

Sorbitol

CH$_2$OH
HCOH
HOCH
HCOH
HCOH
CH$_2$OH

D-Mannitol

CH$_2$OH
HOCH
HOCH
HCOH
HCOH
CH$_2$OH

Glycerol

CH$_2$OH
HCOH
CH$_2$OH

myo-Inositol

The most abundant stereoisomer of inositol

Sugar Acids

There are three important types of sugar acids: aldonic, aldaric, and uronic acids. The aldoses are oxidized at the aldehydic carbon atom by weak oxidizing agents (such as sodium hypoiodite) or by specific enzymes to form the corresponding carboxylic acids, which are called generically *aldonic acids*. D-Glucose, for example, yields D-gluconic acid, which in phosphorylated form is an important intermediate in carbohydrate metabolism.

If a stronger oxidizing agent is employed, such as nitric acid, both the aldehydic carbon atom and the carbon atom bearing the primary hydroxyl group are oxidized to carboxyl groups, yielding *aldaric acids* (also called *saccharic*

Sugar acids and lactones

D-Gluconic acid

COOH
HCOH
HOCH
HCOH
HCOH
CH_2OH

D-Glucaric acid

COOH
HCOH
HOCH
HCOH
HCOH
COOH

D-Glucuronic acid

CHO
HCOH
HOCH
HCOH
HCOH
COOH

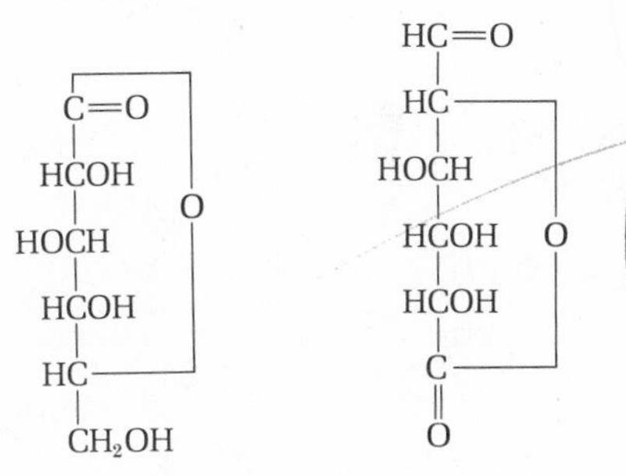

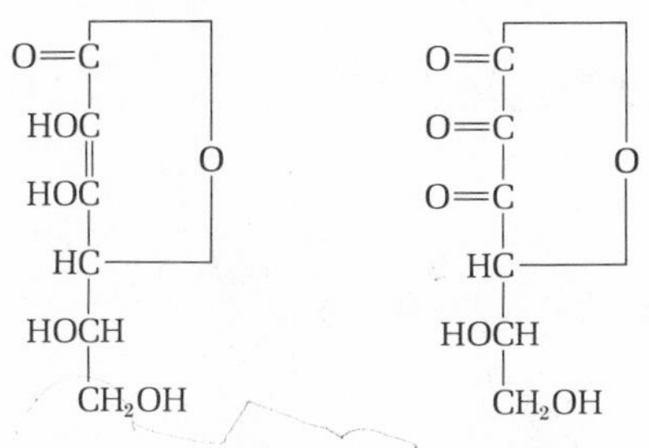

acids). In the case of D-glucose, the product is called D-glucaric acid. Aldaric acids are sometimes useful for the identification of sugars, but they are of no great biological significance.

However, the third class of sugar acids, the uronic acids, are biologically very important. In uronic acids, only the carbon atom bearing the primary hydroxyl group is oxidized, to a carboxyl group. The uronic acid derived from D-glucose is D-glucuronic acid. Other important uronic acids are D-galacturonic acid and D-mannuronic acid. The uronic acids are components of many polysaccharides.

Aldonic and uronic acids usually exist in lactone forms if a five- or six-membered ring can form. Examples are D-δ-gluconolactone and D-δ-glucuronolactone.

One of the most important sugar acids is ascorbic acid, or vitamin C, the γ-lactone of a hexonic acid having an enediol structure at carbon atoms 2 and 3. It is a very unstable compound and readily undergoes oxidation to dehydroascorbic acid. Lack of ascorbic acid in the diet of humans results in the deficiency disease scurvy. Ascorbic acid is present in large amounts in citrus fruit.

Monosaccharides are often estimated quantitatively on the basis of their oxidation in alkaline solution by Cu^{2+}, Ag^{2+}, or ferricyanide; a mixture of sugar acids results. Some sugar acids are shown in the margin.

Phosphoric Acid Esters

Phosphoric acid esters of monosaccharides are found in all cells, in which they serve as important intermediates in carbohydrate metabolism. Representative sugar phosphates are shown below.

Deoxy Sugars

The most abundant deoxy sugar found in nature is 2-deoxy-D-ribose, the sugar component of deoxyribonucleic

Phosphoric acid esters

α-D-Glucose 1-phosphoric acid

α-D-Glucose 6-phosphoric acid

α-D-Fructose 1,6-diphosphoric acid

α-D-Fructose 6-phosphoric acid

acid. L-*Rhamnose* (6-deoxy-L-mannose) and L-*fucose* (6-deoxy-L-galactose) are important components of some bacterial cell walls (margin).

Deoxy sugars

2-Deoxy-D-ribose

HC=O
CH_2
HCOH
HCOH
CH_2OH

L-Rhamnose

HC=O
HCOH
HCOH
HOCH
HOCH
CH_3

L-Fucose

HC=O
HOCH
HCOH
HCOH
HOCH
CH_3

Amino Sugars

Two amino sugars of wide distribution are D-glucosamine and D-galactosamine, in which the hydroxyl group at carbon atom 2 is replaced by an amino group. D-Glucosamine occurs in many polysaccharides of vertebrate tissues and is also a major component of chitin, a structural polysaccharide found in the exoskeletons of insects and crustaceans. D-Galactosamine is a component of glycolipids and of the major polysaccharide of cartilage, chondroitin sulfate. These amino sugars are shown in the margin.

Amino sugars

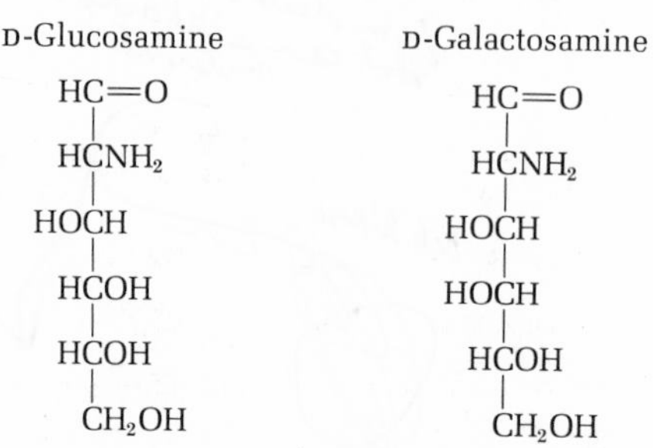

Muramic Acid and Neuraminic Acid

These sugar derivatives are important building blocks in the structural polysaccharides found in the cell walls of bacteria and the cell coats of higher animal cells, respectively. Both are nine-carbon sugar acid derivatives; they may be visualized as consisting of a six-carbon amino sugar linked to a three-carbon sugar acid. The amino groups are usually acetylated, to yield N-acetylmuramic acid and N-acetylneuraminic acid. N-Acetylmuramic acid is a major building block of the polysaccharide backbone of bacterial cell walls. It consists of the six-carbon amino sugar D-glucosamine in ether linkage with the three-carbon acid lactic acid. N-Acetylneuraminic acid is derived from D-mannosamine and pyruvic acid. It is an important building block in the polysaccharide chains found in the glycoproteins and glycolipids of the cell coats of animal tissues. N-Acyl derivatives of neuraminic acid are generically called *sialic acids* (margin).

N-Acetylneuraminic acid

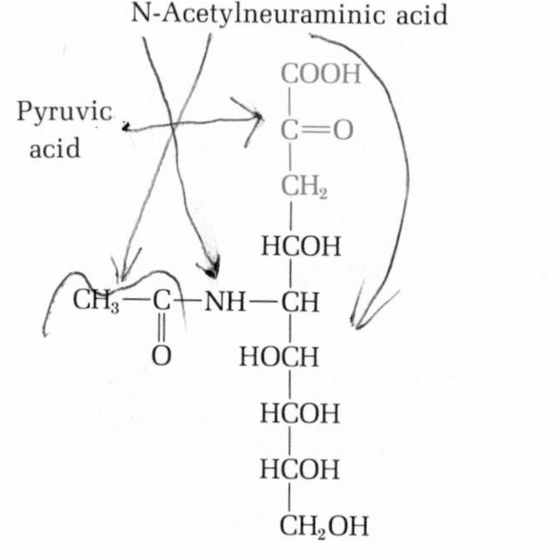

Disaccharides

The most common disaccharides are maltose, lactose, and sucrose. *Maltose*, which is formed as an intermediate product of the action of amylases on starch, contains two D-glucose residues. It is a mixed acetal of the anomeric carbon atom 1 of D-glucose; one hydroxyl group is furnished intramolecularly by carbon atom 5 and the other by carbon atom 4 of a second D-glucose molecule. Both glucose moieties are in pyranose form, and the configuration at the anomeric carbon atom in glycosidic linkage is α. Maltose may therefore be called 4-O-α-D-glucopyranosyl-β-D-glucopyranose. The second glucose residue of maltose thus possesses a free anomeric carbon atom that is capable of existing in α- and β-forms, of which the β-form shown is predominant. The glycosidic linkage between the glucose residues is symbolized $\alpha(1 \longrightarrow 4)$. That the linkage in maltose involves carbon atom 1 of the first residue and carbon atom 4 of the second glucose unit was

N-Acetylmuramic acid

HC=O
COOH HC—NH—C—CH_3 (C=O)
CH—O—CH
CH_3 HCOH
Lactic acid HCOH
CH_2OH

Maltose (β-form)
(4-O-α-D-glucopyranosyl-β-D-glucopyranose)

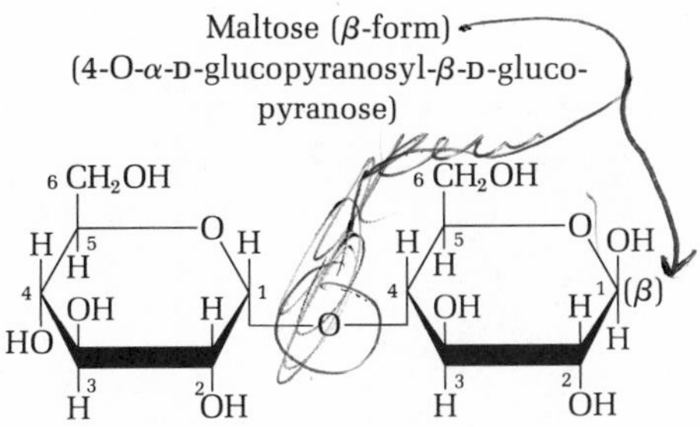

Model of maltose

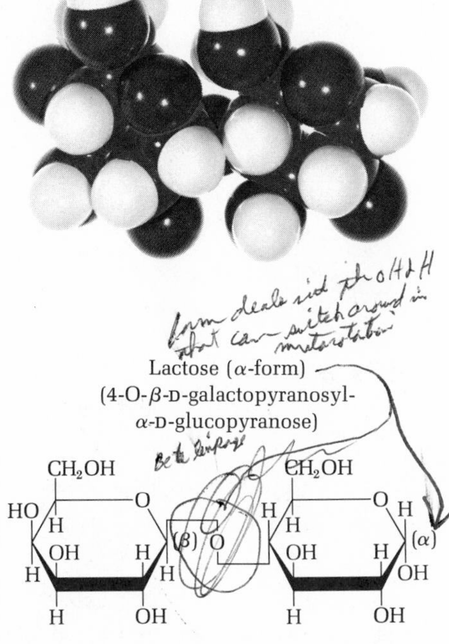

Lactose (α-form)
(4-O-β-D-galactopyranosyl-α-D-glucopyranose)

proved by exhaustive methylation of all the free hydroxyl groups, followed by hydrolysis of the glycosidic linkage. The two methylated fragments resulting were 2,3,4,6-tetra-O-methyl-D-glucose and 2,3,6-tri-O-methyl-D-glucose.

Two other common disaccharides that contain two D-glucose units are cellobiose and gentiobiose. Cellobiose, the repeating disaccharide unit of cellulose, has the glycosidic linkage $\beta(1 \longrightarrow 4)$; its full name is thus 4-O-β-D-glucopyranosyl-D-α-glucopyranose. In gentiobiose, the linkage is $\beta(1 \longrightarrow 6)$. Each of these disaccharides has a free anomeric carbon.

The disaccharide lactose is found in milk but otherwise does not occur in nature. It yields D-galactose and D-glucose on hydrolysis. Since it possesses a free anomeric carbon on the glucose residue, lactose is a reducing disaccharide (margin).

Sucrose, or cane sugar, is a disaccharide of glucose and fructose. It is extremely abundant in the plant world. In contrast to most disaccharides and oligosaccharides, sucrose contains no free anomeric carbon atom; the anomeric carbon atoms of the two sugars are linked to each other. Sucrose is therefore neither a hemiacetal nor a hemiketal. It does not undergo mutarotation, it does not react with phenylhydrazine to form osazones, and it does not act as a reducing sugar. It is much more readily hydrolyzed than other disaccharides. The hydrolysis of sucrose ($[\alpha]_D^{20} = +66.5°$) to D-glucose ($[\alpha]_D^{20} = +52.5°$) and D-fructose ($[\alpha]_D^{20} = -92°$) is often called *inversion* since it is accompanied by a net change in optical rotation from dextro to levo as the equimolar mixture of glucose and fructose is formed; this mixture is often called *invert sugar*. The hydrolysis of sucrose, which is also catalyzed by the enzyme invertase, can therefore be followed with a polarimeter.

Trehalose, which contains two D-glucose residues, is another example of a nonreducing disaccharide in which the two anomeric carbon atoms are joined; it is the major sugar found in the hemolymph of many insects.

Sucrose
(α-D-glucopyranosyl-β-D-fructofuranoside)

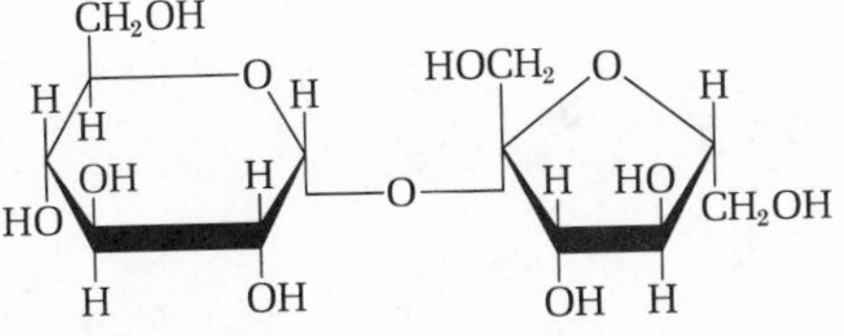

Model of sucrose

Trisaccharides

A number of trisaccharides occur free in nature. *Raffinose* (fructose, glucose, galactose) is found in abundance in sugar beets and many other higher plants. *Melezitose* (glucose, fructose, glucose) is found in the sap of some coniferous trees.

Identification and Analysis of Monosaccharides and Oligosaccharides

Chromatographic procedures have revolutionized the art of isolating, separating, and identifying sugars and sugar derivatives. Paper chromatography and thin-layer chromatography are very widely employed. For most effective separation and analysis, sugar mixtures are chromatographed on columns of ion-exchange materials in the presence of excess boric acid, which converts neutral sugars into their weakly acid borate complexes and allows them to be more effectively separated on the basis of differences in acid-base properties. The structure of such borate complexes is not known with certainty; they dissociate readily to form the free sugar and boric acid. Automated systems similar to amino acid analyzers have been devised for analysis of sugar mixtures resulting from hydrolysis of oligosaccharides and polysaccharides.

Polysaccharides (Glycans)

Most of the carbohydrates found in nature occur as polysaccharides of high molecular weight. On complete hydrolysis with acid or specific enzymes, these polysaccharides yield monosaccharides and/or simple monosaccharide derivatives. D-Glucose is the most prevalent monosaccharide unit in polysaccharides, but polysaccharides of D-mannose, D-fructose, D- and L-galactose, D-xylose, and D-arabinose are also common. Monosaccharide derivatives commonly found as hydrolysis products of natural polysaccharides are D-glucosamine, D-galactosamine, D-glucuronic acid, N-acetylmuramic acid, and N-acetylneuraminic acid.

Polysaccharides, which are also called *glycans*, differ in the nature of their recurring monosaccharide units, in the length of their chains, and in the degree of branching. They are divided into *homopolysaccharides*, which consist of only a single type of monomeric unit, and *heteropolysaccharides*, which contain two or more different monomeric units. Starch, which contains only D-glucose units, is a homopolysaccharide. Hyaluronic acid consists of alternating residues of D-glucuronic acid and N-acetyl-D-glucosamine and is thus a heteropolysaccharide. Often homopolysaccharides are given class names indicating the nature of their building blocks. For example, those containing D-glucose units, such as starch and glycogen, are called *glucans* and those consisting of mannose units are *mannans*. The important polysaccharides are best described in terms of their biological function.

Storage Polysaccharides

These polysaccharides, of which starch is the most abundant in plants and glycogen in animals, are usually deposited in the form of large granules in the cytoplasm of cells. Such granules have a diameter of 100–400 Å and consist of a number of polysaccharide molecules in close association. Proteins are also present in the granules, as well as certain enzymes participating in the synthesis and breakdown of the polysaccharides (Chapter 23). The granules may be isolated from cell extracts by differential centrifugation. In times of glucose surplus, glucose units are enzymatically linked to the ends of starch or glycogen chains; in times of metabolic need, they are released again enzymatically.

Starch

Starch occurs in two forms, α-amylose and amylopectin. *α-Amylose* consists of long unbranched chains in which all the D-glucose units are bound in $\alpha(1 \longrightarrow 4)$ linkages. The chains are polydisperse and vary in molecular weight

Electron micrograph of glycogen granules in a liver cell of the hamster. They consist of clusters, called α-particles, of many small granules, about 150 to 300 Å in diameter, called β-particles. They are usually associated with the smooth surfaced endoplasmic reticulum, as shown here.

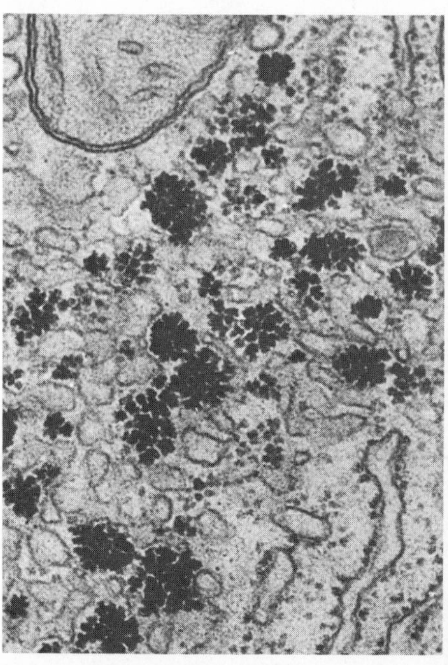

1.0 μ

The helical coil of amylose.

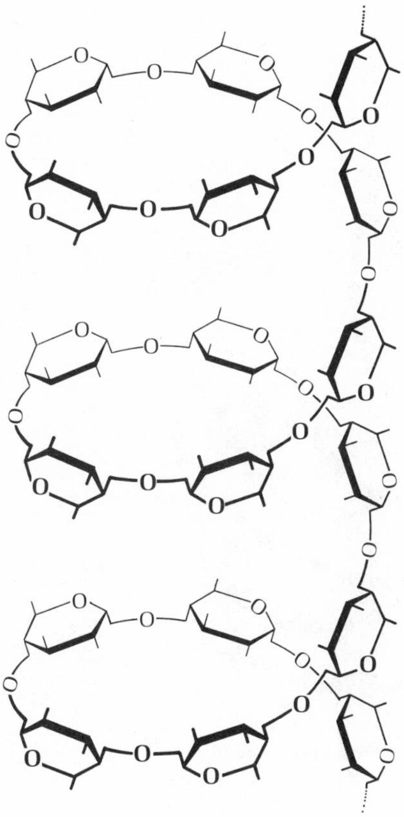

from a few thousand to 500,000. Amylose is not truly soluble in water but forms hydrated micelles, which give a blue color with iodine. In such micelles, the polysaccharide chain is twisted into a helical coil. *Amylopectin* is highly branched. The branches are about 12 glucose residues long and occur on the average at every twelfth glucose residue. The backbone glycosidic linkage is $\alpha(1 \longrightarrow 4)$, but the branch points are $\alpha(1 \longrightarrow 6)$ linkages. Amylopectin, too, yields colloidal or micellar solutions, which give a red-violet color with iodine. Its molecular weight may be as high as 1 million.

The major components of starch can be enzymatically hydrolyzed in two different ways (Figure 11-4). Amylose may be hydrolyzed by the enzyme traditionally known as α-amylase, which is more precisely called $\alpha(1 \longrightarrow 4)$ glucan 4-glucano-hydrolase. This enzyme, which is present in pancreatic juice and saliva, participates in the digestion of starch in the gastrointestinal tract. It hydrolyzes $\alpha(1 \longrightarrow 4)$ linkages throughout the amylose chain in such a way as to yield ultimately a mixture of glucose and maltose. Amylose may also be hydrolyzed by β-amylase, more precisely called $\alpha(1 \longrightarrow 4)$ glucan maltohydrolase. This enzyme, which is present in malt, cleaves away successive maltose units beginning from the nonreducing end. The polysaccharides of intermediate chain length that are formed during amylase action are called *dextrins*. Amylopectin is also attacked by the α- and β-amylases, but since neither amylase can hydrolyze the $\alpha(1 \longrightarrow 6)$ linkages at the branch points of amylopectin, the end product of exhaustive amylase action on amylopectin is a large, highly branched "core" called a *limit dextrin*. Debranching enzymes [$\alpha(1 \longrightarrow 6)$-glucosidases] hydrolyze the $\alpha(1 \longrightarrow 6)$ linkages at the branch points. The combined action of an α-amylase and an $\alpha(1 \longrightarrow 6)$-glucosidase can therefore completely degrade amylopectin to glucose and maltose. The branched structure of amylopectin is shown below.

An $\alpha(1 \longrightarrow 6)$ branch point in amylopectin

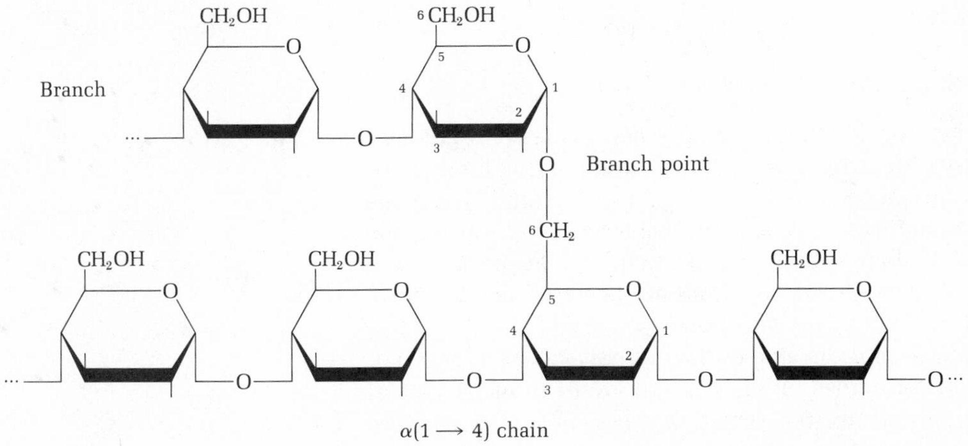

Branch

Branch point

$\alpha(1 \longrightarrow 4)$ chain

Figure 11-4
Action of β-amylase on amylopectin. Successive maltose residues are hydrolyzed until the α(1 ⟶ 6) branch points are reached. The remaining "core," which represents about 40 percent of the molecule, is the limit dextrin.

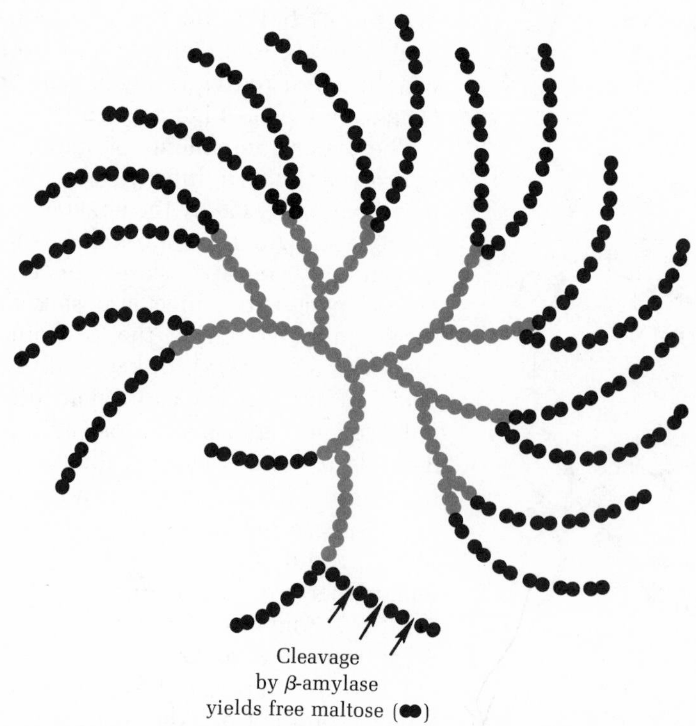

Glycogen

This storage polysaccharide is found in animal tissues; it is especially abundant in liver and muscle. Like amylopectin, glycogen is a polysaccharide of D-glucose in α(1 ⟶ 4) linkage. However, it is more highly branched than amylopectin; the branches occur about every 8 to 10 glucose residues. The branch linkages are α(1 ⟶ 6). Glycogen can be isolated from animal tissues by digesting them with hot KOH solutions, in which the nonreducing α(1 ⟶ 4) and α(1 ⟶ 6) linkages are stable. Glycogen is readily hydrolyzed by α- and β-amylases to form glucose and maltose, respectively; it also forms a limit dextrin.

Other Storage Polysaccharides

Dextrans, too, are branched polysaccharides of D-glucose, but they differ from glycogen and starch in that their major backbone linkage is α(1 ⟶ 6). They are found as storage polysaccharides in yeasts and bacteria. They vary in the nature of their branch points, which may be 1 ⟶ 2, 1 ⟶ 3, or 1 ⟶ 4 in different species. Dextrans form highly viscous, slimy solutions.

Fructans and levans are homopolysaccharides composed of D-fructose units; they are found in many plants. Inulin, found in the artichoke, consists of D-fructose residues in $\beta(2 \longrightarrow 1)$ linkage. Mannans are mannose homopolysaccharides found in bacteria, yeasts, molds, and higher plants. Similarly, xylans and arabinans are homopolysaccharides found in plant tissues.

Structural Polysaccharides

Cellulose makes up more than 50 percent of the total organic carbon in the biosphere. It is the simplest and most abundant structural and cell-wall polysaccharide in the plant world. Wood is about 50 percent cellulose, and cotton is nearly pure cellulose. Cellulose is also found in some lower invertebrates. It is almost entirely of extracellular occurrence.

Figure 11-5
Electron micrograph of the cell wall of an alga (Chaetomorpha). The wall consists of successive layers of cellulose fibers in parallel arrangement.

On complete hydrolysis with strong acids, cellulose yields only D-glucose, but partial hydrolysis yields the reducing disaccharide *cellobiose*, in which the linkage between the D-glucose units is $\beta(1 \longrightarrow 4)$. When cellulose is exhaustively methylated and then hydrolyzed, it yields only 2,3,6-tri-O-methylglycose, showing that its glycosidic linkages are all $1 \longrightarrow 4$ and that there are no branch points. Enzymes capable of hydrolyzing these $\beta(1 \longrightarrow 4)$ linkages are not secreted in the digestive tract of most mammals; cellulose is therefore not available to them as a nutrient. However, the ruminants, such as the cow, can utilize cellulose as food since bacteria present in the rumen form *cellulases*, which hydrolyze cellulose to D-glucose.

The minimum molecular weight of cellulose has been estimated to vary from 50,000 to 500,000, equivalent to 300 to 3,000 glucose residues. X-ray diffraction analysis indicates that cellulose molecules are organized in bundles of parallel chains, or fibrils, which are cross-linked by hydrogen bonding (Figure 11-5). Such fibrils are completely insoluble in water.

Cellulose is the major structural component of the cell walls of plants. Some plant cells, particularly in aquatic plants, must be able to withstand extremely hypotonic or hypertonic conditions and thus require rigid cell walls. In other plants, especially in trees, the cell walls not only must contribute rigidity but also must be able to sustain tremendous weight. In all plant cell walls, densely packed cellulose fibrils surround the cell in a regular, near-crystalline arrangement. These fibrils are cemented together by a matrix of three other polymeric materials: hemicellulose, pectin, and extensin. The most abundant of these materials are the *hemicelluloses*, which are not related structurally to cellulose but are D-xylans, polymers of D-xylose in $\beta(1 \longrightarrow 4)$ linkage, with side-chains of arabinose and other sugars. *Pectin* is a polymer of methyl D-galacturonate. *Extensin*, which is a protein, is attached covalently to the cellulose fibrils. Extensin resembles its animal-tissue counterpart collagen in being rich in hydroxyproline residues. The cell walls of higher plants can be compared to cases of reinforced concrete, in which the cellulose fibrils correspond to the steel rods and the matrix material to the concrete. These walls are capable of withstanding enormous stresses. Wood contains another polymeric substance, called *lignin*, which makes up nearly

25 percent of its dry weight. The structure of lignin is not yet known with certainty; it consists of polymerized aromatic alcohols.

The polysaccharide *chitin* forms a major structural element in the hard, horny exoskeletons of insects and crustaceans. It is a homopolymer of N-acetyl-D-glucosamine and it is structurally a close relative of cellulose; the hydroxyl group at position 2 in the glucose residues of cellulose is replaced by an N-acetylamino group in chitin. Like cellulose, chitin is insoluble in water and forms crystalline arrays of parallel chains.

Other polysaccharides serving as cell-wall or structural components include *agar* of seaweeds, which contains D- and L-galactose residues, some of which are esterified with sulfuric acid; *alginic acid* of algae and kelp, which contains D-mannuronic acid units; and *gum arabic*, or vegetable gum, which contains D-galactose and D-glucuronic acid residues, as well as arabinose and rhamnose.

Bacterial Cell Walls

The cell walls of bacteria are rigid, porous, boxlike structures which provide physical protection to the cell. Since free-living bacteria may often be exposed to hypotonic conditions (in contrast to the cells of a higher animal, which are always bathed by extracellular fluids of constant osmotic pressure), they must have a rigid cell wall to prevent swelling and rupture of the cell membrane.

Recent research indicates that the walls of bacteria participate in many other aspects of bacterial physiology. Sexual conjugation of bacteria is made possible through the contact of certain pili or fimbriae, which are elaborations of the cell wall. Some viruses gain entry into bacteria by attaching to specific wall components. Similarly, the *bacteriocins*, a group of toxic agents that can inhibit metabolic processes in bacteria, attach to specific target sites on the wall. The bacterial cell wall also contains materials that act as antigens in vertebrates, stimulating them to develop immunity to the bacteria. Portions of the cell wall structure may communicate with the interior of the cell, through the membrane.

Bacteria are classically divided into *Gram-positive* and *Gram-negative* organisms, according to their reaction to the Gram stain, an empirical procedure in which the cells are treated successively with the dye crystal violet, with iodine, and with safranine. Gram-positive cells have cell walls that contain very little lipid (examples, *Streptococcus albus* and *Micrococcus lysodeikticus*), whereas Gram-negative cell walls are rich in lipid (example, *E. coli*). Both Gram-positive and Gram-negative cell walls have one molecular feature in common: the rigid structural framework in both consists of covalently linked polysaccharide and peptide chains. To this frame are attached characteristic accessory components, which are different in Gram-negative and Gram-positive cells, as we shall see below.

The rigid, covalently linked framework surrounding the bacterial cell is actually one large sacklike molecule (spoken of as a *sacculus*), a complex polysaccharide-peptide called a *peptidoglycan* or *murein*, from the Latin *murus*, meaning "wall." The murein sacculus of some bacterial walls can be isolated after the accessory molecules have been stripped off. It consists of parallel polysaccharide chains cross-linked by short peptide chains. The basic recurring unit in the polysaccharide chains is the *muropeptide* (Figure 11-6). It consists of a disaccharide of N-acetyl-D-glucosamine in $\beta(1 \longrightarrow 4)$ linkage with N-acetylmuramic acid. To the hydroxyl group of the lactic acid substituent of muramic acid is attached a tetrapeptide side-chain containing L-alanine, D-alanine, D-glutamic acid, and either diaminopimelic acid or its decarboxylation product L-lysine.

Further study of murein hydrolysis products reveals that the long parallel polysaccharide chains are, in turn, cross-linked by their peptide side-chains. The terminal D-alanine residue of the peptide side-chain of one polysaccharide chain is joined covalently with the peptide side-chain in an adjacent polysaccharide chain, either directly or through another short peptide. In *Staphylococcus aureus*, (Figure 11-7) a pentapeptide of glycine serves as the cross-link. The basic structure of the murein sacculus thus consists of a network of parallel polysaccharide chains with many peptide cross-linkages. The net is closed on all sides to make a completely continuous,

Figure 11-6
Recurring muropeptide of bacterial cell walls. It consists of a disaccharide to which is attached a tetrapeptide side-chain. The linkage between successive units is 1 ⟶ 4.

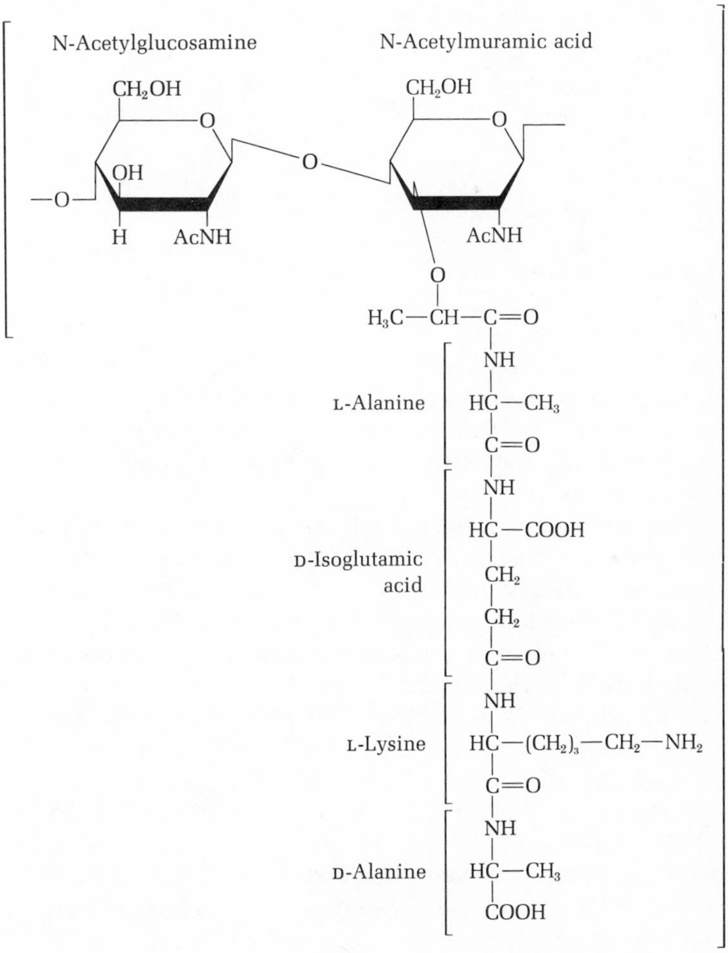

Figure 11-7
Manner of cross-linking of murein (peptidoglycan) chains in S. aureus cell walls. The backbones are in color. X is an N-acetylglucosamine residue, and Y an N-acetylmuramic acid residue. The tetrapeptide side-chains of each disaccharide unit are cross-linked to those of adjacent chains by a glycine pentapeptide.

Y — Ala — D—Gln — Lys — D—Ala—Gly—Gly—Gly—Gly—Gly—Lys

Y — Ala — D—Gln — Lys — D—Ala—Gly—Gly—Gly—Gly—Gly—Lys

Y — Ala — D—Gln — Lys — D—Ala—Gly

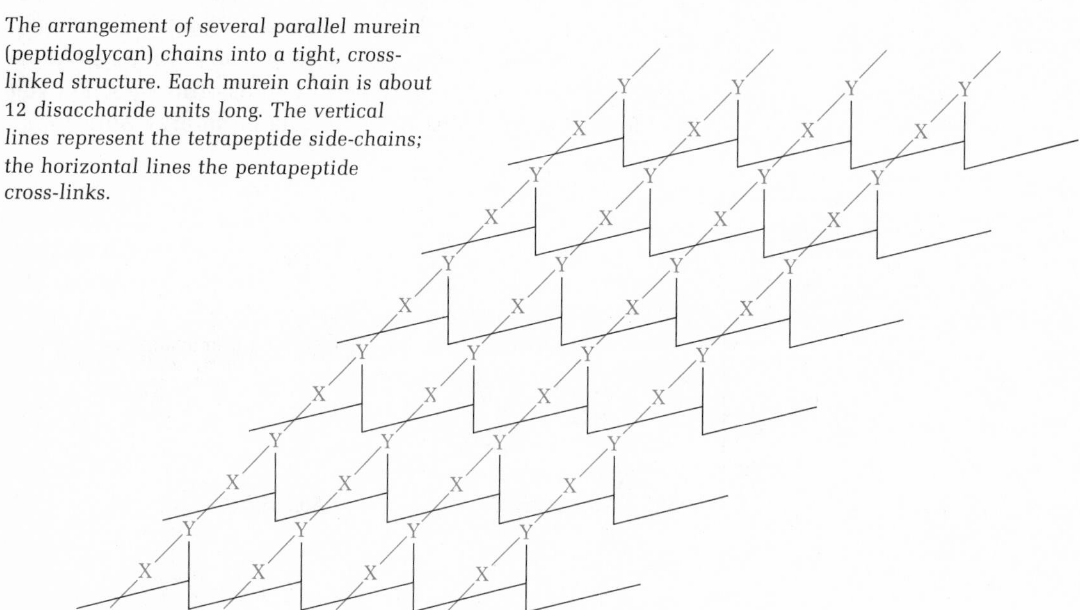

The arrangement of several parallel murein (peptidoglycan) chains into a tight, cross-linked structure. Each murein chain is about 12 disaccharide units long. The vertical lines represent the tetrapeptide side-chains; the horizontal lines the pentapeptide cross-links.

covalent structure around the entire cell. The murein sacculus may be a tight net, as in S. *aureus* (Figure 11-7), or a loose net, as in *E. coli*, depending on the number of cross-linkages.

The enzyme lysozyme (Chapter 9) causes lysis of many Gram-positive bacteria by "dissolving" the cell wall. It catalyzes hydrolysis of the 1 ⟶ 4 glycosidic linkages of the polysaccharide backbone of mureins, yielding disaccharides of N-acetyl-D-glucosamine and N-acetylmuramic acid, to which are attached the peptide side-chains, i.e., muropeptides. When Gram-positive bacteria are treated with lysozyme in the presence of high concentrations of an impermeant solute such as sucrose, the wall is removed, to yield a *protoplast*, the term applied to a naked Gram-positive bacterial cell surrounded only by its membrane. Protoplasts remain viable so long as the medium is hypertonic to prevent swelling and rupture of the membrane.

Segment of a teichoic acid containing alternating residues (in color) of D-alanine and N-acetylglucosamine

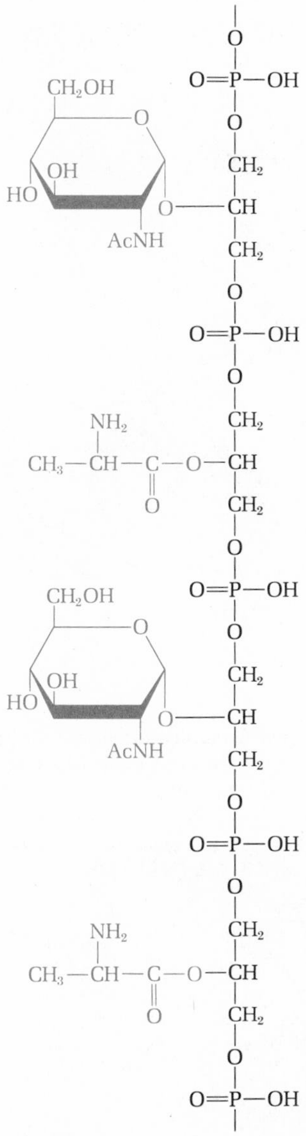

Bacterial cell walls contain, in addition to the murein or peptidoglycan framework described above, a number of accessory components, which differ from one species to another. The major accessories of Gram-positive bacteria are polymers, and they are usually intricately interwoven into the murein framework. There are three types of accessory polymers: (1) teichoic acids, (2) polysaccharides, and (3) polypeptides or proteins. *Teichoic acids* consist of a long chain of glycerol or ribitol molecules linked to each other by phosphodiester bridges. In one type of teichoic acid, alternating free hydroxyl groups of the backbone are occupied by D-alanine and D-glucose or N-acetyl-D-glucosamine residues. Accessory polysaccharides may contain recurring residues of rhamnose, glucose, and galactose (or their amines) or of mannose. Both the teichoic acids and the polysaccharides of the cell walls of Gram-positive bacteria have antigenic activity.

The walls of Gram-negative cells, such as *E. coli*, have somewhat more accessory material attached to the murein framework. Their accessory components consist of polypeptides, lipoproteins, and complex lipopolysaccharides whose structure is just now beginning to be understood. These materials contribute to the complex antigenic specificity of certain Gram-negative cells, as well as to their acceptor specificity for viruses and bacteriocins.

In general, the cell wall of Gram-positive organisms can be thought of as a rigid, brittle box, like the shell of a crustacean, whereas the cell wall of Gram-negative organisms has a smooth, soft, lipid-rich skin, with the murein skeleton buried underneath. The murein skeleton of many Gram-negative bacteria can be broken by treatment with lysozyme or other enzymes, but the wall material usually remains attached to the cell, which is then called a *spheroplast*.

The biosynthesis of the cell walls of bacteria occurs outside the cell membrane. The precursors are generated inside the cell, pass to the membrane, and are then assembled outside the cell by the action of enzymes attached to the cell membrane. The remarkable reactions by which they are formed are shown in Chapter 22.

Cell Coats and Ground Substance in Animal Tissues

Cells of higher-animal tissues are not surrounded by rigid walls. However, many of them do possess an outer coat that is in some respects comparable to a cell wall. Electron microscopy often reveals the presence of a filamentous or "fuzzy" surface coating the cell membrane, in certain animal cells. Such coats are soft and flexible and in many tissues have adhesive properties. (See next page.)

Although the chemical nature of some of the major components of animal cell coats is known, there is still little information about how these components are arranged on the outer surface of the cell. This is an important field of study since cells of vertebrates engage in biologically significant contacts with neighboring cells. Cell surfaces are evidently highly ordered structures containing specific recognition sites. For example, when kidney cells are separated from each other and then grown in tissue culture, they will reassociate and will even seek each other out from a mixture of liver and kidney cells. Furthermore, the growth of normal animal cells in tissue culture is very orderly because of the phenomenon called *contact inhibition*, which permits the growth of cells in monocellular layers but prevents a disorderly "piling-up" of cells. Cell coats also are the site of cell and tissue antigens such as are involved in the rejection of grafted or transplanted tissues by a given organism. Cell surfaces are, of course, involved in many other types of intercellular reactions, such as the synaptic contacts between neurons of the nervous system.

The major components of the cell coats of higher organisms consist of (1) the carbohydrate moieties of glycolipids, particularly the cerebrosides and gangliosides, (2) glycoproteins, and (3) acid mucopolysaccharides. The glycolipids and gangliosides are thought to be present in the outer lipid layer of the plasma membrane. Their oligosaccharide "heads" are hydrophilic and may extend outward from the cell surface. The glycoproteins of cell coats are presumably present in the outer protein layer of the plasma membrane. Their structures are not yet known in detail. In one class of glycoproteins, serine residues in the peptide chain are linked in glycosidic bonds to oligosaccharides containing N-acetyl-D-galactosamine residues, which terminate in N-acetylneuraminic acid residues.

The acid mucopolysaccharides are highly hydrated. They are jellylike, sticky, or slippery substances that provide intercellular lubrication and act as a flexible cement. The most abundant and ubiquitous acid mucopolysaccharide is *hyaluronic acid*, which is present in most of the extracellular ground substance of connective tissues of vertebrates, in or surrounding cell coats, and is also abundant in the synovial fluid in joints and the vitreous humor of the eye. The repeating unit of hyaluronic acid is a disaccharide composed of D-glucuronic acid and N-acetyl-D-glucosamine in $\beta(1 \longrightarrow 3)$ linkage. Each disaccharide unit is attached to the next by $\beta(1 \longrightarrow 4)$ linkages; thus hyaluronic acid contains alternating $\beta(1 \longrightarrow 3)$ and $\beta(1 \longrightarrow 4)$ linkages. Hyaluronic acid is a linear polymer. Because its carboxyl groups are completely ionized and thus have negative charges at pH 7.0, it is soluble in water, in which it forms highly viscous solutions. The enzyme hyaluronidase catalyzes hydrolysis of the $\beta(1 \longrightarrow 4)$ linkages of hyaluronic acid; this hydrolysis is accompanied by a decrease in viscosity.

Repeating unit of hyaluronic acid

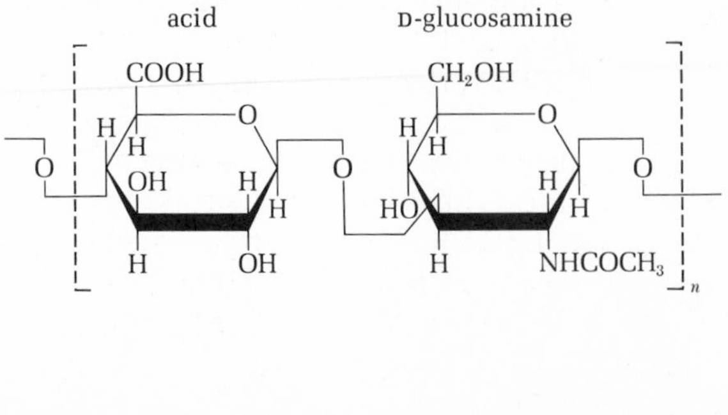

Electron micrograph of the absorptive surface of an epithelial cell in the small intestine of the cat, showing the polysaccharide cell coat or glycocalyx on the tips of the villi.

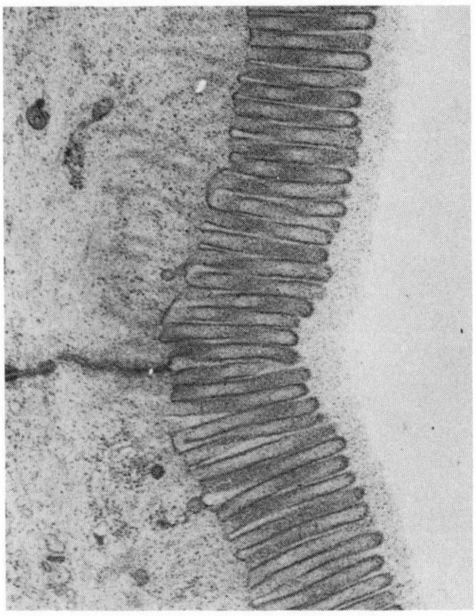

1.0 μ

The higher magnification below shows its filamentous mesh-like structure, often called a "fuzzy coat."

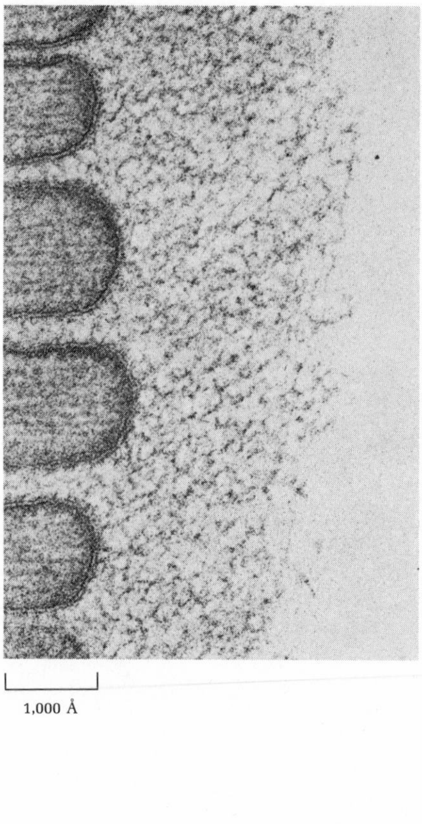

1,000 Å

Chondroitin is another mucopolysaccharide found in extracellular ground substance and also in cell coats. It is nearly identical in structure to hyaluronic acid; the only difference is that it contains N-acetyl-D-galactosamine instead of N-acetyl-D-glucosamine residues. Chondroitin itself is only a minor component of extracellular material, but its sulfate ester derivatives, namely, chondroitin sulfate A and chondroitin sulfate C, are major structural components of cartilage, bone, cornea, and other connective tissue structures in vertebrates. Chondroitin sulfate A contains a sulfate ester group at carbon atom 4 of the N-acetylgalactosamine residue, and chondroitin sulfate C, at carbon atom 6. The related mucopolysaccharide *heparin* is also found in the extracellular space of some tissues (liver, lung, arterial walls).

Summary

Carbohydrates are polyhydroxylic aldehydes or ketones that have the empirical formula $(CH_2O)_n$. Pentoses $(C_5H_{10}O_5)$ and hexoses $(C_6H_{12}O_6)$ are the most abundant simple carbohydrates, or sugars. Most sugars have at least one asymmetric carbon atom and thus exist in the form of stereoisomers. Most naturally occurring sugars, such as ribose, glucose, fructose, and mannose, are of the D series. Sugars having five or more carbon atoms may exist in two anomeric forms, which are stereoisomeric intramolecular hemiacetals formed between the hydroxyl group of carbon atom 4 or 5 and the carbonyl group at C_1 or C_2. The five- and 6-membered rings thus formed are called furanoses and pyranoses, respectively. Such rings exist in boat and chair conformations.

Anomeric glycosides result from the treatment of pentoses and hexoses with alcohols and acid. The free hydroxyl groups of sugars can be completely acetylated or methylated; their rings can also be cleaved by periodic acid. Such reactions permit determination of the position of free hydroxyl groups and the nature of the ring forms. Sugars may be reduced to sugar alcohols. They may be oxidized at the aldehydic carbon to aldonic acids, at the primary hydroxyl group to uronic acids, and at both terminal carbon atoms to aldaric acids. Sugars may be separated and identified by chromatographic methods.

Disaccharides consist of two monosaccharides joined in glycosidic linkage. Maltose contains two glucose residues in $\alpha(1 \longrightarrow 4)$ linkage, cellobiose contains two glucose residues, lactose contains galactose and glucose, and sucrose contains glucose and fructose. In sucrose, the anomeric carbon atoms of both monosaccharides are bonded to each other and thus cannot undergo oxidation.

Polysaccharides (glycans) are classified chemically as homopolysaccharides, which contain a single recurring monosaccharide unit (example: glycogen, a polymer of glucose), and heteropolysaccharides, which contain two or more recurring monosaccharide units (example: hyaluronic acid, an alternating polymer of D-glucuronic acid and N-acetyl-D-glucosamine). They are also classified functionally as either storage or structural polysaccharides. The most important storage polysaccharides are starch and glycogen; these are branched structures having $\alpha(1 \longrightarrow 4)$ linkages in the chains and $\alpha(1 \longrightarrow 6)$ linkages at branch points. The most important structural polysaccharide is cellulose, with D-glucose units in $\beta(1 \longrightarrow 4)$ linkages.

The walls of bacterial cells contain peptidoglycans (mureins), heteropolysaccharides of N-acetyl muramic acid and N-acetylhexosamine, with short cross-linking peptides containing D-amino acids. Animal cells possess cell coats containing glycoproteins, glycolipids, and acid mucopolysaccharides. The walls of plant cells are composed largely of cellulose, but they contain other polysaccharides as well.

References

Books

BAILEY, R. W.: *Oligosaccharides,* The Macmillan Company, New York, 1965. Comprehensive reference work on structure, preparation, and chemistry.

BRIMACOMBE, J. S., and J. M. WEBBER: *Mucopolysaccharides,* American Elsevier Publishing Company, New York, 1964. Structure and distribution of chitin, hyaluronic acid, chondroitin, heparin, and blood-group substances.

DAVIDSON, E. A.: *Carbohydrate Chemistry,* Holt, Rinehart and Winston, Inc., New York, 1967. An excellent survey.

DAVIS, B., and L. WARREN (eds.): *The Specificity of Cell Surfaces,* Prentice-Hall, Inc., Englewood Cliffs, N.J., 1967. A collection of papers on biological and chemical aspects of cell surfaces.

FLORKIN, M., and E. H. STOTZ (eds.): *Carbohydrates,* vol. 5 of *Comprehensive Biochemistry,* American Elsevier Publishing Company, New York, 1963. Reference treatise.

GOTTSCHALK, A. (ed.): *Glycoproteins,* American Elsevier Publishing Company, New York, 1966. Comprehensive reference work.

JEANLOZ, B. W., and E. A. BALASZ (eds.): *Amino Sugars,* vols. I and II, Academic Press Inc., New York, 1965.

OTT, F., H. M. SPURLIN, and M. W. GRAFFIN: *Cellulose and Cellulose Derivatives,* 2d ed., pts. 1–3, vol. 5 of *High Polymers,* Interscience Publishers, Inc., New York, 1955. Reference work.

STACEY, M., and S. A. BARKER: *Carbohydrates of Living Tissues,* D. Van Nostrand Company, Inc., Princeton, N.J., 1962. Excellent short book.

Articles

STROMINGER, J. L., and J. M. GHUYSEN: "Mechanisms of Enzymatic Bacteriolysis," *Science,* **156**:213–221 (1967). Interesting brief account of bacterial cell-wall biochemistry.

WEIDEL, W., and H. PELZER: "Bag-shaped Macromolecules—A New Outlook on Bacterial Cell Walls," *Advan. Enzymol.,* **26**:193–232 (1964). A review stressing the essentially continuous nature of the covalently-linked wall polymer.

Problems

1. 80 ml of a freshly prepared 10 percent solution of α-D-glucose is mixed with 20 ml of a freshly prepared solution of β-D-glucose. Estimate (*a*) the initial specific rotation ($[\alpha]_D^{20}$) of the resulting solution and (*b*) the rotation after several hours have elapsed. (*c*) Do the same for a mixture of 50 ml of methyl-α-D-glucoside and 50 ml of methyl-β-D-glucoside.

2. Name the products of (*a*) treatment of α-D-galactose with excess acetic anhydride and (*b*) treatment of α-D-glucose with dimethyl sulfate, followed by gentle hydrolysis.

3. Name the products of (*a*) treatment of D-galactose with Na amalgam in water, (*b*) oxidation of L-mannose with nitric acid, and (*c*) exhaustive methylation of D-galactosamine.

4. (*a*) Lactose is exhaustively methylated and then hydrolyzed. Name the products. (*b*) What are the products of the exhaustive methylation of sucrose followed by hydrolysis?

5. On acid hydrolysis, a trisaccharide yields D-glucose and D-galactose in a 2:1 ratio. Exhaustive methylation, followed by hydrolysis yields 2,3,6-tri-O-methylgalactose, 2,3,4,6-tetra-O-methylglucose, and 2,3,4-tri-O-methylglucose. Name the trisaccharide.

6. After exhaustive methylation and hydrolysis, a polysaccharide yields equimolar amounts of 2,3,4-tri-O-methylglucose and 2,3,6-tri-O-methylglucose. The polysaccharide has one reducing terminus. Indicate its structure.

7. A 10.0-gram sample of glycogen yields 6 millimoles of 2,3-di-O-methylglucose on methylation and hydrolysis. (*a*) What percentage of the glucose residues occur at $1 \longrightarrow 6$ branch points? (*b*) What is the average number of glucose residues per branch? (*c*) How many millimoles of 2,3,6-tri-O-methylglucose were formed? (*d*) If the molecular weight of the polysaccharide is 2×10^6, how many glucose residues does it contain?

8. On treatment with periodate, a 100-mg sample of amylose yielded 0.005 millimole of formic acid. What is the approximate chain length of the amylose?

9. On treatment with periodate, a 100-mg sample of cellulose gave 0.0015 millimole of formic acid. What is the approximate chain length?

CHAPTER 12 NUCLEOTIDES AND POLYNUCLEOTIDES

The most prominent function of mononucleotides is to serve as building blocks of the nucleic acids and thus to participate in the molecular mechanisms by which genetic information is stored, replicated, and transcribed—matters which we shall discuss in Part IV of this book. However, mononucleotides play a number of other vital roles in the cell, particularly in intermediary metabolism and in energy-transforming reactions. Different nucleotides serve as energy-carrying coenzymes, as coenzymes in the transfer of acetic acid, sugars, amines, and other biomolecules, and as coenzymes in oxidation-reduction reactions. This remarkable diversity of function lends much support to the view that nucleotides are not only the most versatile biomolecules but also the most fundamental to the molecular logic of living cells.

In this chapter we shall be concerned with the common features in the molecular structures and properties of the various types of nucleotides and polynucleotides. We shall also examine the structure of the phosphodiester linkages between mononucleotide residues of polynucleotides, the cleavage of these linkages, and the determination of base sequence in polynucleotides.

Components of Mononucleotides

Mononucleotides contain three characteristic components: (1) a nitrogenous base, (2) a five-carbon sugar, and (3) phosphoric acid. These components are released in equimolar amounts on complete hydrolysis of mononucleotides.

Pyrimidines and Purines

Two classes of nitrogenous bases are found in nucleotides; they are derivatives of the aromatic heterocyclic compounds *pyrimidine* and *purine*. Purine is itself a derivative of pyrimidine; it consists of fused pyrimidine and imidazole rings (margin).

Pyrimidine

Purine

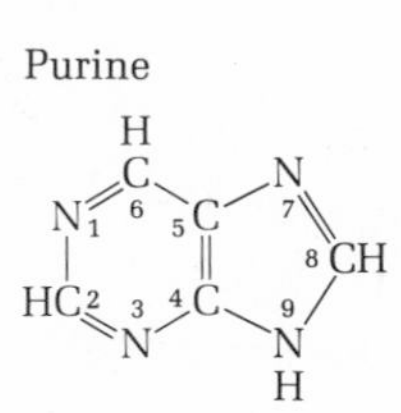

Three pyrimidine bases are commonly found in nucleotides, namely, *uracil, thymine,* and *cytosine,* designated as U, T, and C, respectively. In addition, there are a number of minor pyrimidines of lesser occurrence, such as

5-methylcytosine and 5-hydroxymethylcytosine. The two major purines found in nucleotides are adenine and guanine, designated A and G, respectively. Some minor purines, such as 2-methyladenine and 1-methylguanine, are also found as components of nucleotides.

Two minor purines

2-Methyladenine

1-Methylguanine

Two minor pyrimidines

5-Methylcytosine

5-Hydroxymethylcytosine

The precise three-dimensional structure of various pyrimidines and purines has been studied by x-ray diffraction analysis. Pyrimidines are planar molecules. Purines are nearly planar, but they possess a very slight pucker. The structures of some purines and pyrimidines are shown in Figure 12-1.

The properties of the free pyrimidine and purine bases are very similar. They have only limited solubility in water. All of them exist in tautomeric forms. For example, uracil occurs in lactim and lactam forms. At pH ~ 7.0, the lactam form of uracil predominates. The structures of the other purines and pyrimidines shown are those predominating at pH 7.0. The ring nitrogen atoms in pyrimidines and purines are weakly basic, having p*K*′ values in the range of 9 to 10, above which they lose their protons. The 6-amino group of adenine has a p*K*′ of 4.2, and the 2-amino group of guanine a p*K*′ of 3.2. Therefore, at pH 7.0 these amino groups are not protonated.

All the purine and pyrimidine bases of nucleic acids strongly absorb ultraviolet light in the zone 260 to 280 nm; the wavelength of maximum absorption of mixtures of the common bases is about 260 nm. This property is of

Tautomeric forms of uracil

Lactim ⇌ Lactam

The major purines

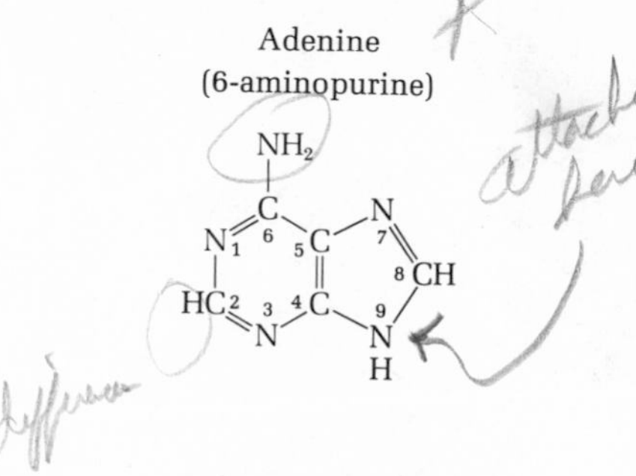

Guanine
(2-amino-6-oxypurine)

The major pyrimidines

Cytosine
(2-oxy-4-aminopyrimidine)

Uracil
(2,4-dioxypyrimidine)

Thymine
(5-methyl-2,4-dioxypyrimidine)

Figure 12-1
The spatial configuration of purines and pyrimidines.

Adenine

Guanine

Uracil

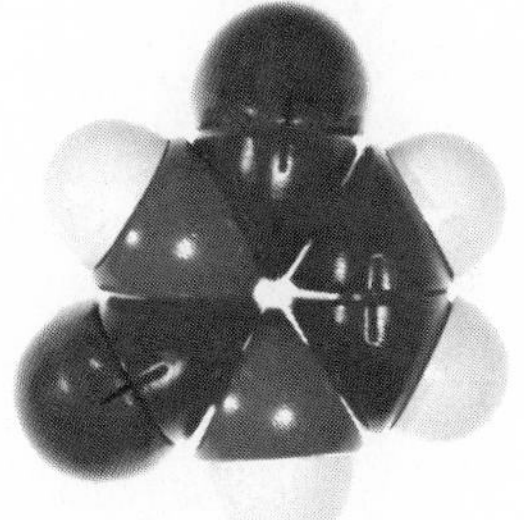

Thymine

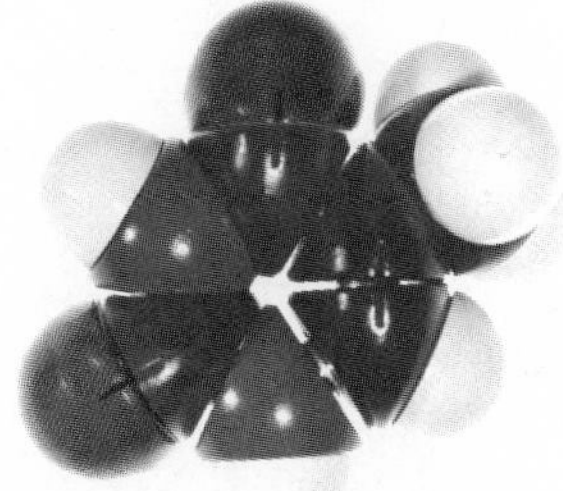

Cytosine

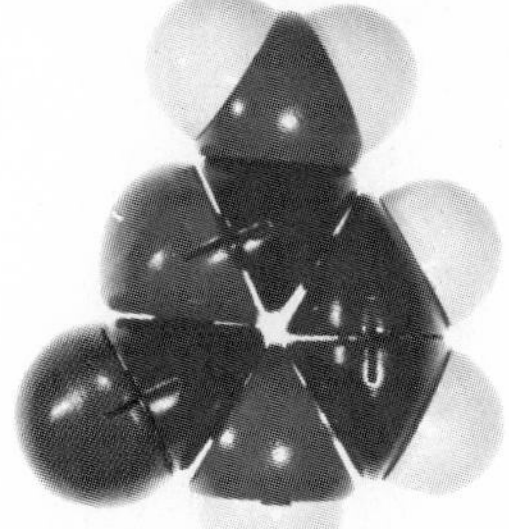

Dimensions of the adenine molecule.

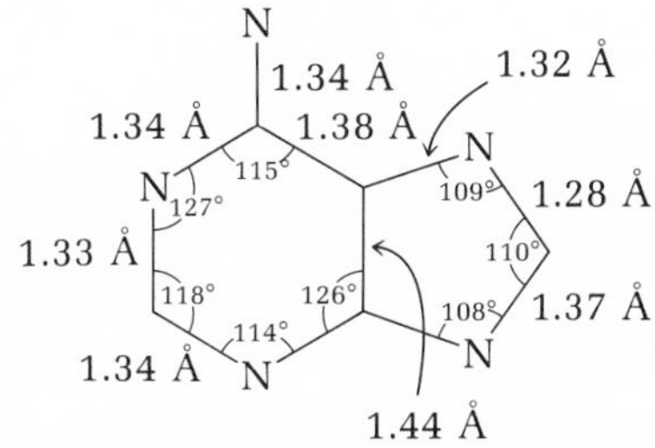

great utility in the detection and quantitative analysis not only of the free bases but also of nucleosides, nucleotides, and intact nucleic acid molecules (Figure 12-2).

The free purine and pyrimidine bases are easily separated and identified by paper chromatography or thin-layer chromatography.

Nucleosides

When nucleotides are subjected to partial hydrolysis in such a manner that only the phosphate group is lost, *nucleosides* are formed. Nucleosides are N-glycosides of the pyrimidine or purine bases, in which carbon atom 1 of the pentose is glycosidically linked to nitrogen atom N_1 of a pyrimidine or to nitrogen atom N_9 of a purine. The glycosidic linkage in natural nucleotides is always β-, and the pentoses are always present in the furanose form. There are two series of nucleosides: the *ribonucleosides*, which contain D-ribose as the sugar component, and the *2′-deoxyribonucleosides*, which contain 2-deoxy-D-ribose. The trivial names of the four major ribonucleosides are adenosine, guanosine, cytidine, and uridine, and those of the four major deoxyribonucleosides are 2′-deoxyadenosine, 2′-deoxyguanosine, 2′-deoxycytidine, and 2′-deoxythymidine.

Nucleosides are much more soluble in water than the parent bases. They are readily separated and identified by means of paper chromatography or thin-layer chromatography. Like all glycosides, the nucleosides are relatively stable in alkali but readily undergo hydrolysis when heated in acid; the products of hydrolysis are the free bases and the free pentoses. Pyrimidine nucleosides are significantly more resistant to hydrolysis than purine nucleosides. Both types of nucleosides are hydrolyzed by specific nucleosidases.

Two nucleosides

Adenosine
(9-β-D-ribofuranosyladenine)

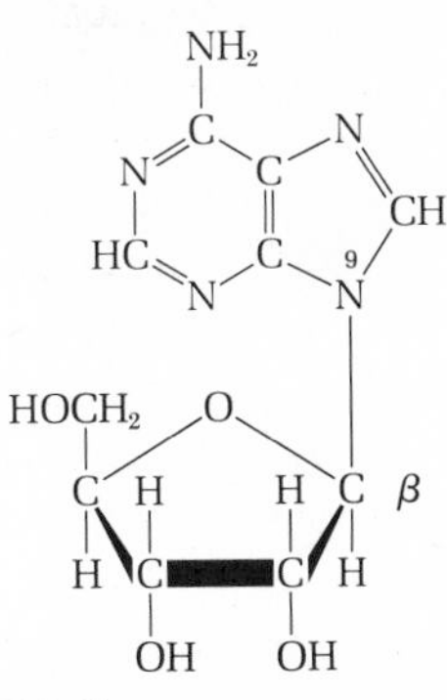

2′-Deoxyadenosine
(9-β-2′-deoxy-D-ribofuranosyladenine)

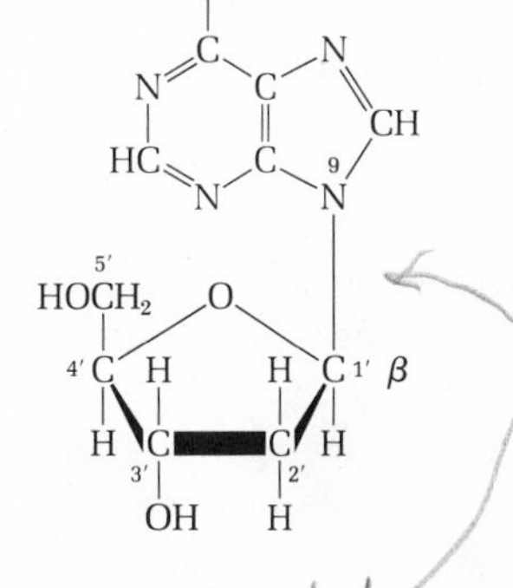

Figure 12-2
The Lambert-Beer law (below), the absorption spectra of the common bases, and the molar absorbancy indexes of the bases.

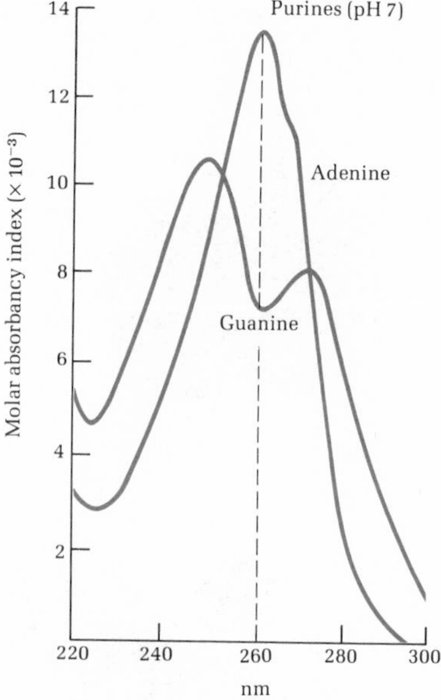

Measurement of light absorption is an extremely important tool for analysis of nucleotides and nucleic acids (see also Chapters 29 and 30). The fraction of the incident light absorbed by a solution at a given wavelength is related to the thickness of the absorbing layer and to the concentration of the absorbing species. These two relationships are combined into the Lambert-Beer law, given in integrated form as

$$\log \frac{I_o}{I} = acl$$

where I_o is the intensity of the incident light, I is the intensity of the transmitted light, a is the molar absorbancy index (also given as ϵ, the molar extinction coefficient), c the concentration of the absorbing species in moles per liter, and l the thickness of the light-absorbing sample, which is arbitrarily set at 1.0 cm. The Lambert-Beer law assumes that the incident light is parallel and monochromatic and that the solvent and solute molecules are randomly oriented. The expression $\log I_o/I$ is called the absorbancy (A) or optical density (O.D.); the former designation is preferred.

It is important to note that the Lambert-Beer law is not a linear relationship. Each mm thickness of absorbing solution in a 1.0 cm cell does not absorb a constant amount but rather a constant fraction of the incident light. However, with an absorbing layer of fixed thickness, the absorbancy A is directly proportional to the concentration of the absorbing solute.

The molar absorbancy index varies with the nature of the absorbing compound, with the solvent, with the wavelength, and may also vary with pH if the light-absorbing species is one which is in equilibrium with another species having a different spectrum through gain or loss of protons.

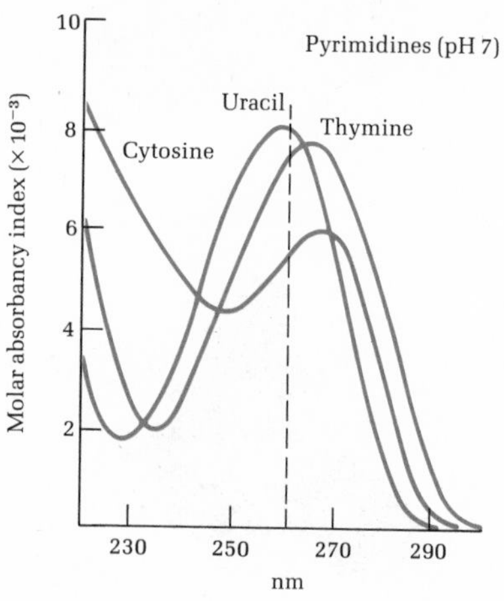

Base	*Molar absorbancy index at 260 nm. M^{-1} cm^{-1}*
Adenine	13.4×10^3
Guanine	7.2×10^3
Cytosine	5.55×10^3
Uracil	8.2×10^3
Thymine	7.4×10^3

Nucleotides

Nucleotides are phosphoric acid esters of nucleosides in which the phosphoric acid is esterified to one of the free pentose hydroxyl groups. Nucleotides occur in free form in significant amounts in all cells. They are also formed on partial hydrolysis of nucleic acids, particularly by the action of enzymes called, generically, *nucleases*. Nucleotides containing 2-deoxy-D-ribose are *deoxyribonucleotides;* those containing D-ribose are *ribonucleotides*.

Since there are two or more free hydroxyl groups in nucleosides, the phosphate group of nucleotides can potentially occur in more than one position on the sugar ring. In the case of deoxyribonucleotides, there are only two possible positions in 2-deoxyribose that can be esterified with phosphoric acid, namely, the 3′ and 5′ positions. Both 3′- and 5′-deoxyribonucleotides occur biologically. In the case of ribonucleotides, the phosphate group may be at the 2′, 3′, or 5′ position; all 3 types of ribonucleotides have been found as hydrolysis products of RNA, depending on conditions. Cyclic monophosphates of adenosine are also known. However, the nucleotides that occur in the free form in cells are predominantly those having

The adenine ribonucleoside monophosphates

Adenosine 5′-phosphoric acid (adenylic acid; 5′-adenylic acid)

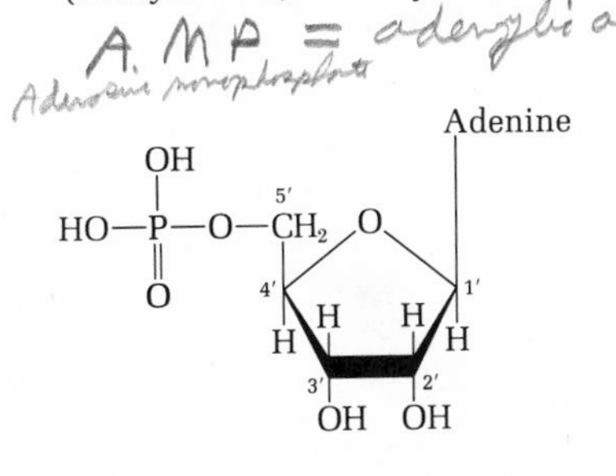

Adenosine 3′-phosphoric acid (3′-adenylic acid)

Adenine
HO—CH₂ O
H H H H
3′
O OH
HO—P—OH
O

Adenosine 2′-phosphoric acid (2′-adenylic acid)

Adenine
HO—CH₂ O
H H H H
2′
OH O
HO—P—OH
O

Model of 5′-adenylic acid

Adenosine 3′,5′-phosphoric acid (cyclic adenylic acid)

5′
O—CH₂ O Adenine
H H H H
O=P——O 3′ OH
OH

the phosphate group in the 5′ position, since the enzymatic reactions normally involved in nucleic acid synthesis and breakdown in cells proceed via the nucleoside 5′-phosphates as intermediates. Figure 12-3 gives the basic structures and nomenclature of the major ribonucleoside 5′-monophosphates (also called 5′-ribonucleotides) and deoxyribonucleoside 5′-monophosphates (also called 5′-deoxyribonucleotides). The trivial names adenylic acid, guanylic acid, uridylic acid, etc., are also in common use.

The mononucleotides of both series are strong acids since the pK′ values of the two dissociable protons of the phosphoric acid group are about 1.0 and 6.2. At pH 7.0, the free nucleotides thus exist primarily in the form R—O—PO_3^{2-}, where R is the nucleoside group.

Due to their content of pyrimidine or purine bases, all the mononucleotides show strong light absorption at 260 nm. They are easily separated from each other by paper electrophoresis or by chromatography on ion-exchange columns; paper chromatography and thin-layer chromatography are also useful.

The 5′-phosphate group of mononucleotides is relatively stable to acid hydrolysis. However, the enzyme 5′-nucleotidase can hydrolyze the phosphate group at the 5′ position without attacking the N-glycosidic linkage.

Figure 12-3
The major ribonucleotides and dexoyribonucleotides.

Ribonucleoside 5′-monophosphates	2′-Deoxyribonucleoside 5′-monophosphates
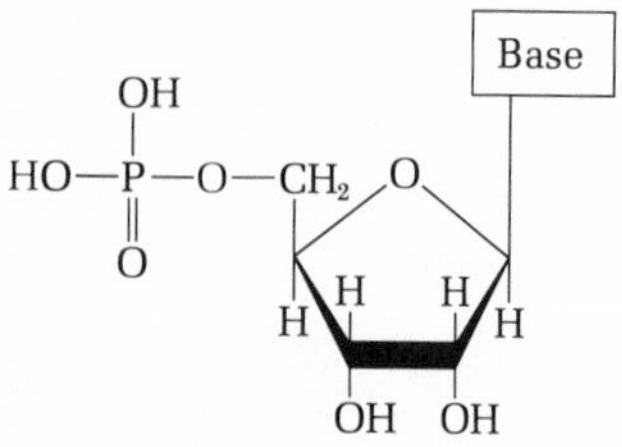	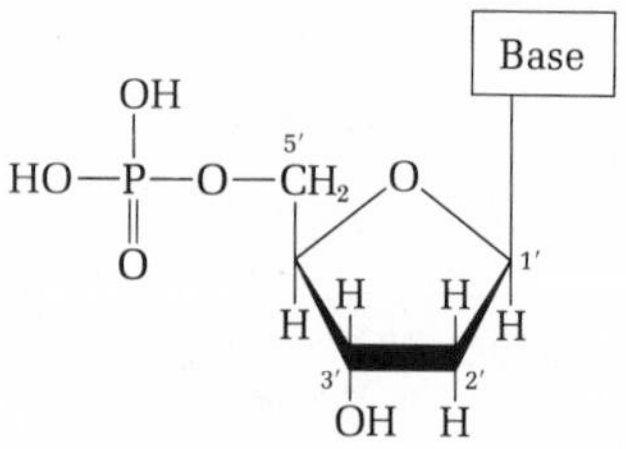
General structure	General structure
Names	Names
Adenosine 5′-phosphoric acid (adenylic acid; AMP)	Deoxyadenosine 5′-phosphoric acid (deoxyadenylic acid; dAMP)
Guanosine 5′-phosphoric acid (guanylic acid; GMP)	Deoxyguanosine 5′-phosphoric acid (deoxyguanylic acid; dGMP)
Cytidine 5′-phosphoric acid (cytidylic acid; CMP)	Deoxycytidine 5′-phosphoric acid (deoxycytidylic acid; dCMP)
Uridine 5′-phosphoric acid (uridylic acid; UMP)	Deoxythymidine 5′-phosphoric acid (deoxythymidylic acid; dTMP)

Nucleoside 5′-Diphosphates and 5′-Triphosphates (NDPs and NTPs)

All the common ribonucleosides and 2′-deoxyribonucleosides shown in Figure 12-3 also occur in cells as the 5′-diphosphates and the 5′-triphosphates, i.e., the 5′-pyrophosphoric and the 5′-triphosphoric acid esters of the nucleosides. Their general structures and abbreviations are shown on the opposite page. The specific phosphate groups of these compounds are designated by the symbols α, β, and γ, as shown in the figure.

The nucleoside 5′-diphosphoric acids and 5′-triphosphoric acids dissociate three and four protons, respectively, from their condensed phosphate groups. NDPs have pK's of about 0.9, 1.5, and 7.2; NTPs have 3 pK's below 2.0 and one at 6.5. The condensed phosphate groups of the NDPs and NTPs form complexes with divalent cations such as Mg^{2+} and Ca^{2+}. Under intracellular conditions, the NDPs and NTPs exist primarily as the Mg^{2+} complexes. The significance of these complexes will be discussed in Chapter 14. The second and third phosphate groups of the NDPs and NTPs may be selectively hydrolyzed by specific enzymes without cleavage of other bonds. They are also hydrolyzed completely by boiling the NDPs or NTPs in 1 *N* HCl for 7 min, without cleaving the α-phosphate linkage, but this procedure also hydrolyzes the N-glycosidic linkage.

All the NDPs and NTPs shown here occur in cells and can be extracted with acid. They can be quantitatively analyzed by means of paper electrophoresis, thin-layer chromatography, or ion-exchange chromatography.

The general structures and abbreviations of the NMPs, NDPs, and NTPs.

General structure

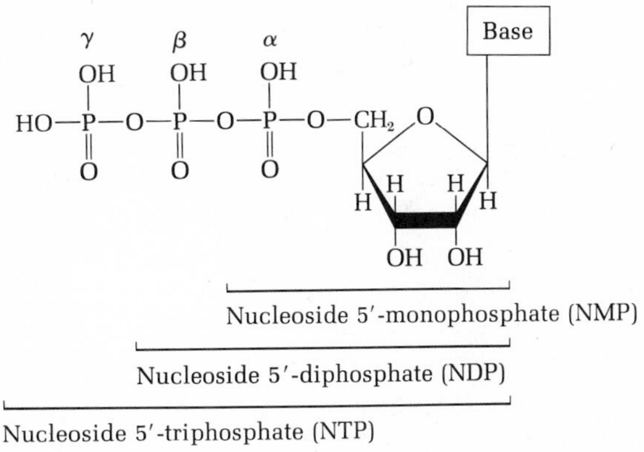

γ β α

Base

Nucleoside 5′-monophosphate (NMP)

Nucleoside 5′-diphosphate (NDP)

Nucleoside 5′-triphosphate (NTP)

Abbreviations

Ribonucleoside 5′-mono-, di-, and triphosphates

Base	Abbreviations		
Adenine	AMP	ADP	ATP
Guanine	GMP	GDP	GTP
Cytosine	CMP	CDP	CTP
Uracil	UMP	UDP	UTP

Deoxyribonucleoside 5′-mono-, di-, and triphosphates

Base			
Adenine	dAMP	dADP	dATP
Guanine	dGMP	dGDP	dGTP
Cytosine	dCMP	dCDP	dCTP
Thymine	dTMP	dTDP	dTTP

Uridine diphosphate glucose
UDPG

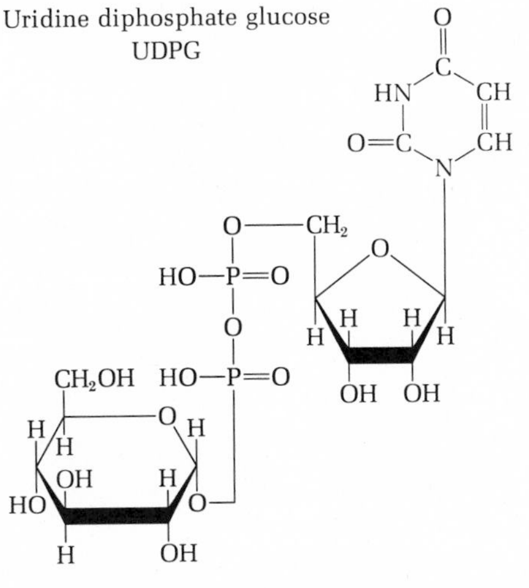

Cytidine diphosphate choline

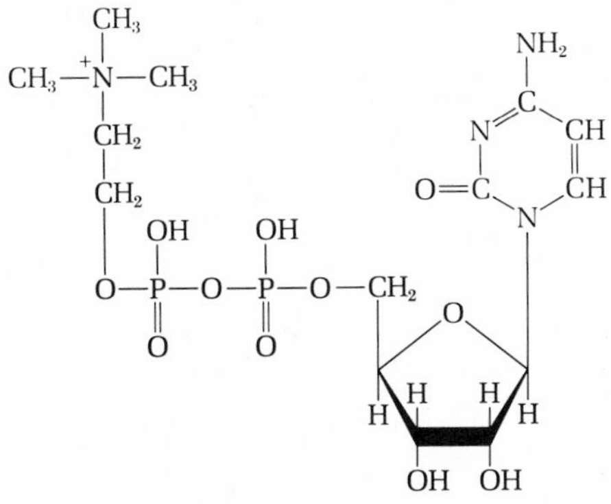

The NTPs have a number of important functions. ATP is the primary carrier of chemical energy in the cell, serving to transfer high energy phosphate groups from energy-yielding to energy-requiring processes. After dephosphorylation of ATP, the ADP and AMP formed are rephosphorylated to ATP during respiration. Although the ATP-ADP couple is the primary, or "main-line," phosphate-transferring system in the cell, other NTPs channel or distribute phosphate bond energy in biosynthetic reactions (Chapter 14).

A second major function of the NTPs and NDPs is to serve as coenzymelike carriers of specific types of building-block molecules. Thus uridine diphosphate (UDP) is a specific carrier of sugar residues in the synthesis of polysaccharides. An example is uridine diphosphate glucose, which is a donor of a glucose residue in the biosynthesis of glycogen. Similarly, cytidine diphosphate choline is a donor of choline in the biosynthesis of choline-containing phosphoglycerides (margin).

The third major function of NTPs is to serve as energy-rich precursors of mononucleotide units in the enzymatic synthesis of DNA and RNA. During these reactions, the various NTPs lose the terminal pyrophosphate group to become the nucleoside monophosphate residues of the nucleic acids.

Other Mononucleotides

There are a number of other important mononucleotides, and these sometimes contain nitrogenous bases other than those found in nucleic acids. Nicotinamide mononucleotide and coenzyme A, which have a nitrogenous base in β-N-glycosidic linkage at the 1 position of D-ribose, are shown in Figure 12-4, as is the misnamed flavin mononucleotide. Nicotinamide mononucleotide and flavin mononucleotide contain nicotinamide and 6,7-dimethylisoalloxazine, respectively, as their nitrogenous bases. Nicotinic acid is a vitamin required in the nutrition of man and many other mammals; its deficiency in the diet causes the nutritional diseases pellagra in man and blacktongue in dogs. Nicotinamide mononucleotide is a precursor of nicotinamide adenine dinucleotide (abbreviated NAD), which is described below. Flavin mononucleotide (FMN) is the 5′-phosphoric acid ester of riboflavin, or vitamin B_2, also required in the nutrition of man and other vertebrates. FMN, which contains the five-carbon

Nicotinic Acid

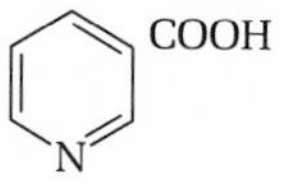

COOH

N

Figure 12-4
Mononucleotide coenzymes. Each contains a vitamin of the B complex (shown in color).

Nicotinamide mononucleotide (NMN)

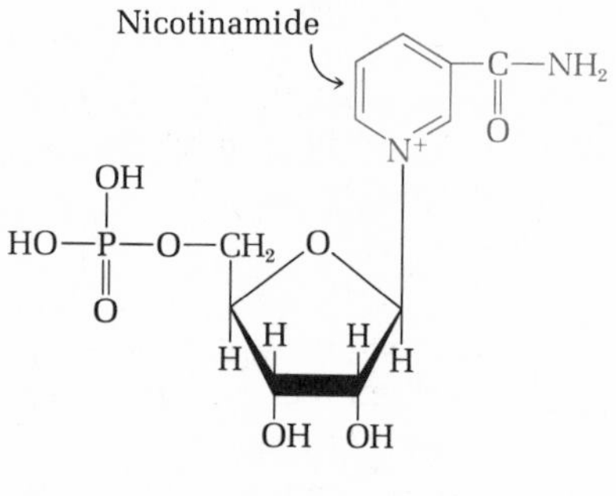

Nicotinamide

Flavin mononucleotide (FMN)
(riboflavin phosphate)

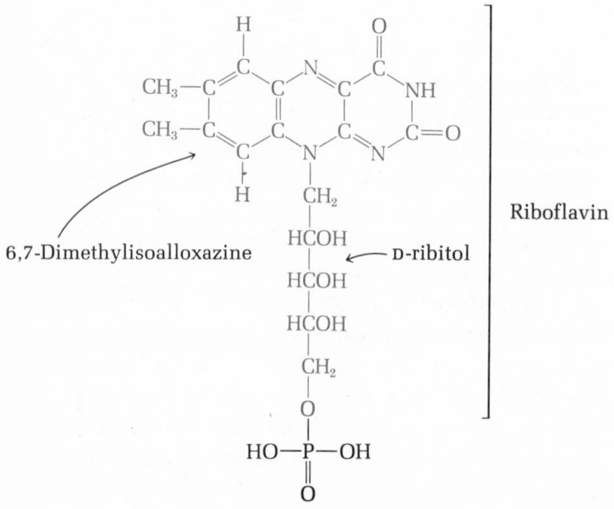

6,7-Dimethylisoalloxazine

D-ribitol

Riboflavin

Coenzyme A

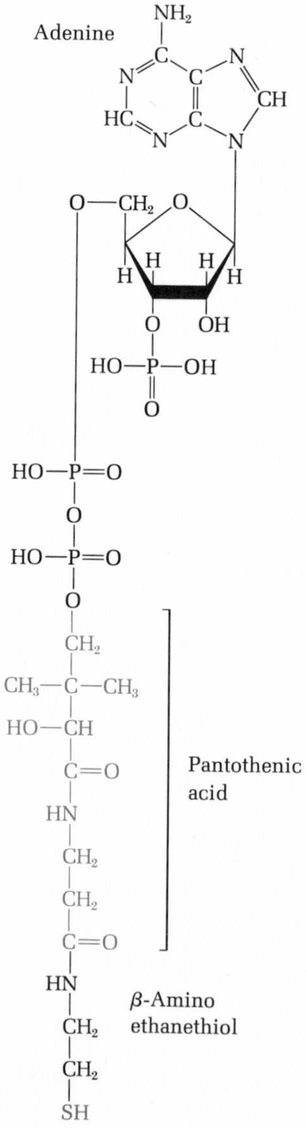

Adenine

Pantothenic acid

β-Amino ethanethiol

sugar alcohol D-ribitol rather than D-ribose, is an important oxidation-reduction coenzyme participating in cellular respiration (Chapters 16 and 17); the isoalloxazine ring undergoes reversible oxidation-reduction. FMN is also a precursor in the synthesis of *flavin adenine dinucleotide* (abbreviated FAD), another important oxidation-reduction coenzyme (below).

Coenzyme A contains adenine in β-glycosidic linkage with the 1 position of D-ribose. At the 5′ position of D-ribose, there is a pyrophosphoric acid group to which is esterified the peptidelike compound pantothenyl-β-aminoethanethiol. Pantothenic acid is another vitamin of the B complex; it is required in the nutrition of most vertebrates. The function of coenzyme A is to carry acetyl and fatty acyl groups, which are esterified to the thiol group.

Dinucleotides

Dinucleotides consist of two mononucleotide units joined by a phosphoric acid bridge. Most dinucleotides are products of the enzymatic hydrolysis of nucleic acids; in such dinucleotides the bridging group is a phosphodiester linkage joining the 5′ position of the D-ribose (or 2-deoxy-D-ribose) of one mononucleotide and the 3′ position of the other. An example of a dinucleotide derived from RNA is shown in the margin.

A 3′,5′-dinucleotide

Only a few dinucleotides are known in which the bridging phosphate group is other than the 3′,5′-phosphodiester linkage. These do not derive from nucleic acids but occur free in the cell. The best-known examples are the three oxidation-reduction coenzymes (Figure 12-5) nicotinamide adenine dinucleotide (NAD), nicotinamide adenine dinucleotide 2′-phosphate (NADP), and flavin adenine dinucleotide (FAD). Each contains adenosine 5′-monophosphate; NAD and NADP also contain nicotinamide mononucleotide. In all three coenzymes, the two mononucleotide units are joined by an anhydride linkage between their phosphate groups to form a 5′,5′-pyrophosphate bridge. NADP is a derivative of NAD in which another molecule of phosphoric acid is esterified to the 2′ position of the adenine mononucleotide moiety. NAD and NADP are coenzymes in enzymatic oxidation-reduction reactions; the pyridine ring of nicotinamide may undergo reversible oxidation (Chapters 15–17).

FAD similarly consists of one molecule of adenine ribonucleotide and one of flavin mononucleotide, joined by an anhydride linkage between their 5′-phosphate groups. The isoalloxazine ring of FMN and FAD undergoes reversible oxidation-reduction (Chapter 17). FMN and FAD serve as the prosthetic groups of the class of oxidation-reduction enzymes known as flavin dehydrogenases.

Polynucleotides

The mononucleotides are the recurring monomeric units of *oligonucleotides*, which contain several mononucleotide units, and of *polynucleotides*, which contain many.

Figure 12-5
Dinucleotide coenzymes.

Flavin adenine dinucleotide (FAD). *The riboflavin portion is in color.*

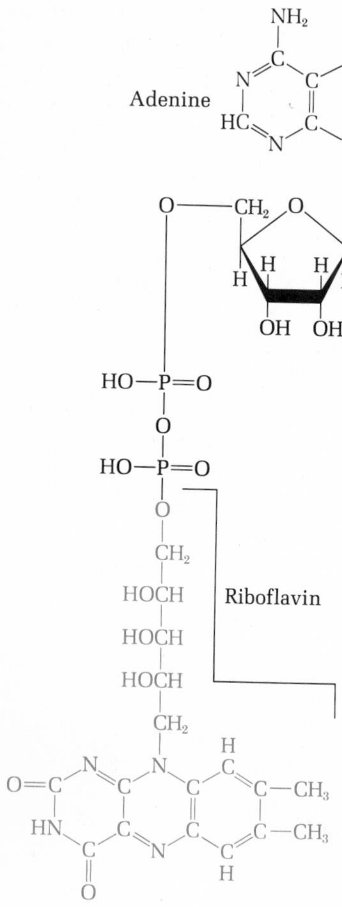

Adenine

Riboflavin

Nicotinamide adenine dinucleotide (NAD), *which is also called diphosphopyridine nucleotide* (DPN). *In nicotinamide adenine dinucleotide phosphate* (NADP), *also called triphosphopyridine nucleotide* (TPN), *there is a third phosphate group as shown. The nicotinamide portion is in color.*

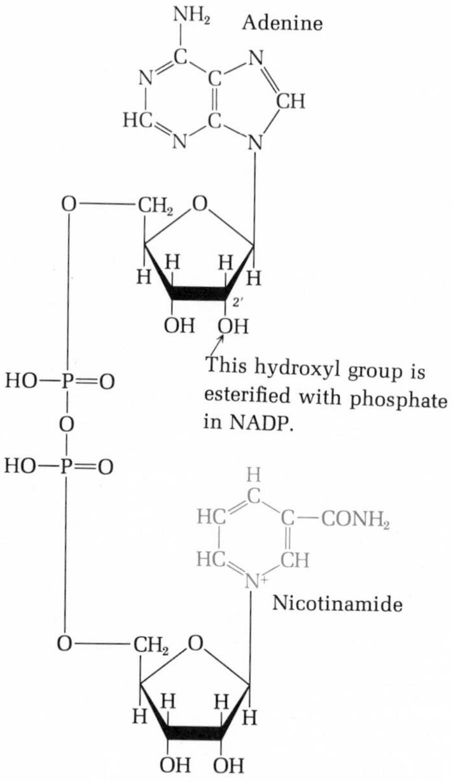

Adenine

This hydroxyl group is esterified with phosphate in NADP.

Nicotinamide

Polynucleotides consisting of covalently linked chains of deoxyribonucleotide units are *deoxyribonucleic acids* (DNAs); those consisting of chains of ribonucleotides are *ribonucleic acids* (RNAs) (Figure 12-6). DNA and RNA share a number of chemical and physical properties because in both the successive mononucleotide units are covalently linked in a similar fashion, i.e., through phosphodiester bridges between the 3′ position of one mononucleotide unit and the 5′ position of the next. The nucleic acids are not readily soluble in aqueous acids. However, they may be extracted from cells with neutral salt solutions or with phenol.

DNA

DNA was first isolated (from leucocytes and fish sperm) and intensively studied by Friedrich Miescher, a German, in a series of remarkable investigations beginning in 1869. However, it required many years of research before the major building-block components of nucleic acids were

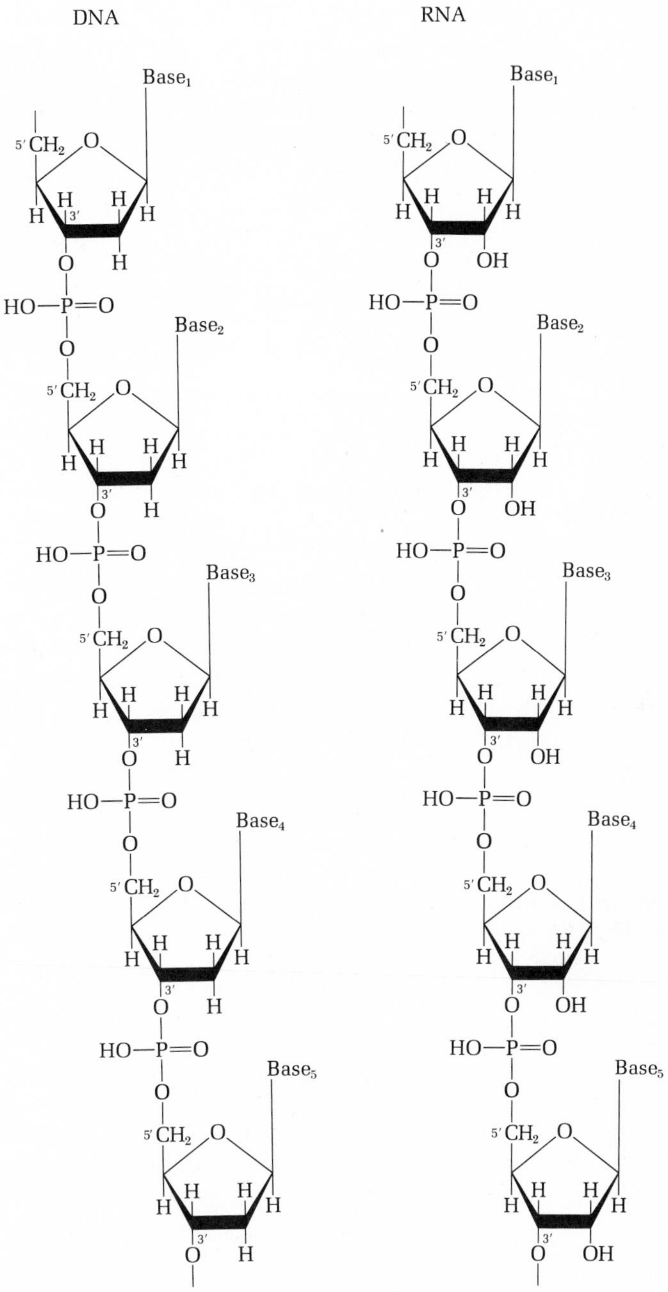

Figure 12-6
Polynucleotide structure. In DNA and RNA, the phosphodiester bridges link the 3′-hydroxyl of one nucleotide to the 5′-hydroxyl of the next.

identified; our present picture of DNA structure did not emerge until the early 1950s.

All DNA molecules, from all types of cells, contain four major mononucleotide units, namely, dAMP, dGMP, dTMP, and dCMP, linked in various sequences by 3′,5′-phosphodiester bridges. The DNAs isolated from different species of organism vary in the ratio and sequence of these four mononucleotide units; they also vary in molecular weight. In addition to the major bases adenine, guanine, thymine, and cytosine found in all specimens of DNA, small amounts of methylated derivatives of these bases are also present. These are especially conspicuous in the DNA found in some viruses. DNA molecules have a definite molecular weight, but in most cells they are so large that they are not easily isolated in intact form. In procaryotic cells, which contain only a single chromosome, essentially all the DNA is present as a single macromolecule exceeding 2×10^9 in molecular weight. In eucaryotic cells, which contain several or many chromosomes, there are, correspondingly, several or many DNA molecules, which are also of extremely high molecular weight.

In bacteria, the single DNA molecule, which makes up about 1 percent of the cell weight, is found in the nuclear zone; it is often attached to an infolding of the cell membrane called a *mesosome*. Apparently no protein is associated with DNA in bacteria. Sometimes molecules of extrachromosomal DNA occur in the cytoplasm of bacteria; these molecules, which are much smaller than the chromosome, are called either *plasmids* or *episomes*, depending on their genetic relationship to the chromosomal DNA.

In diploid eucaryotic cells, nearly all the DNA is present in the cell nucleus, where it is combined with basic proteins called *histones* and divided among the chromosomes. In addition to the nuclear DNA, eucaryotic cells contain very small amounts of cytoplasmic DNA, often called satellite DNA, which differs in base composition and molecular weight from nuclear DNA. One type of satellite DNA is present in the mitochondria, which contain about 0.1 to 0.2 percent of the total cellular DNA. Some plastids of plant cells, particularly the chloroplasts, also contain small amounts of a distinctive type of DNA. The structure and function of DNA are considered in more detail in Chapters 28 and 29.

RNA

The three major types of ribonucleic acid in cells are messenger RNA (mRNA), ribosomal RNA (rRNA), and transfer RNA (tRNA). Each has a characteristic molecular weight and base composition (Table 12-1). All consist of a single polyribonucleotide strand. The three major types of RNA occur in multiple molecular species. Ribosomal RNA exists in 3 major species, transfer RNA in as many as 60 species, and messenger RNA in hundreds and perhaps thousands of species. In most cells, there is from 5 to 10 times as much RNA as DNA.

In bacterial cells, nearly all the RNA is found in the cytoplasm. In the liver cell, approximately 11 percent of the total RNA is in the nucleus (largely mRNA), about 15 percent in the mitochondria (both rRNA and tRNA), over 50 percent in the ribosomes (largely rRNA), and about 24 percent in the cytosol (largely tRNA). RNA is present in the structure of all the plant viruses, of which tobacco mosaic virus is the best known. RNA is also found in some bacterial viruses, such as bacteriophage Qβ of *E. coli*, and some animal viruses, such as the poliomyelitis virus.

Messenger RNA

Messenger RNA contains only the four bases A, G, C, and U. It is synthesized in the nucleus during the process

Table 12-1 Properties of E. coli RNAs

Type	Sedimentation coefficient	Mol wt	No. of nucleotide residues	Percent of total cell RNA
mRNA	6S–25S	25,000–1,000,000	75–3,000	~2
tRNA	~4S	23,000–30,000	75–90	16
rRNA	5S	~35,000	~100	82
	16S	~550,000	~1,500	
	23S	~1,100,000	~3,100	

of *transcription*, in which the sequence of bases in one strand of the chromosomal DNA is enzymatically transcribed in the form of a single strand of mRNA. The bases of the mRNA strand are complementary to those of the DNA strand. After transcription, mRNA passes to the ribosomes, where it serves as the template for the sequential ordering of amino acids during protein synthesis. Triplets of nucleotides (codons) along the mRNA strand specify the amino acid sequence in colinear fashion. Although mRNA molecules make up only a very small fraction of the total RNA of the cell, they occur in many species, which may vary greatly in molecular weight and in base sequence. Each of the thousands of different proteins synthesized by cells is coded by a specific mRNA or segment of an mRNA molecule.

Two unusual nucleotides found in tRNA's. In pseudouridylic acid the glycosidic linkage is at position 5 of uracil, rather than the usual position 1. Ribothymidylic acid is also unusual in that thymine is normally found in DNA but not in RNA.

Pseudo-uridylic acid

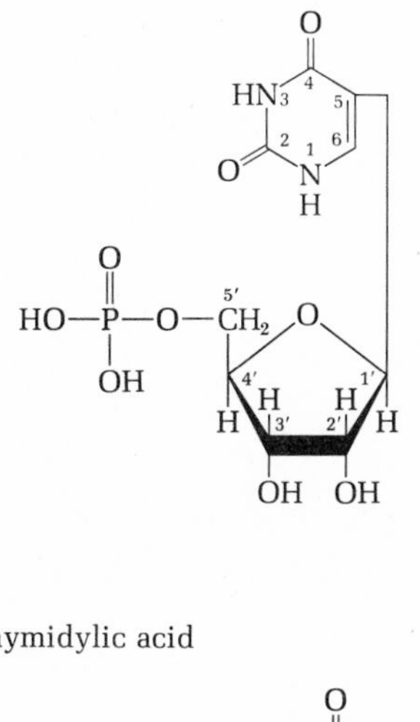

Ribothymidylic acid

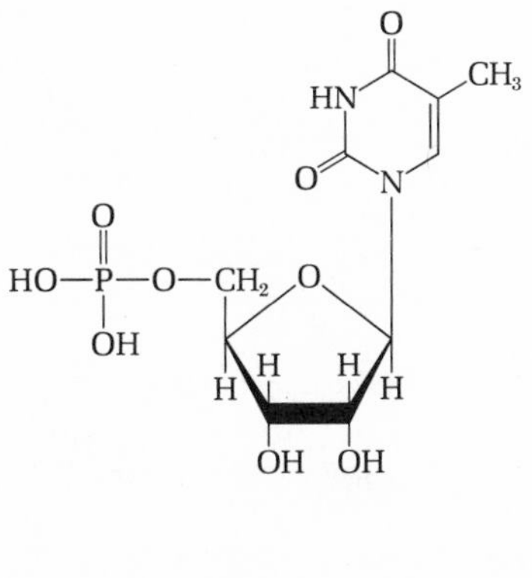

Transfer RNA

Transfer RNAs are relatively small molecules that act as carriers of specific amino acids during protein synthesis on the ribosome. They have molecular weights in the range of 23,000 to 30,000 and sedimentation coefficients of about 4S. They contain from 75 to 90 mononucleotide units. Each of the 20 amino acids found in proteins has at least one corresponding tRNA, and some have multiple tRNAs. For example, there are five distinctly different tRNA molecules specific for the transfer of leucine and five for serine in *E. coli* cells. tRNA molecules may exist either in free form or "charged" with their specific amino acids. In the charged form of tRNA, the carboxyl group of the amino acid is esterified to the 2′- or 3′-hydroxyl group of the terminal adenylic acid residue at one end of the polynucleotide chain of the tRNA. Transfer RNAs characteristically contain a rather large number of minor or "odd" bases, up to 10 percent of the total, in addition to the major bases A, G, C, and U. The minor bases are largely methylated forms of the normal major bases or their derivatives. In addition, tRNA's also contain unusual mononucleotides such as pseudouridylic and ribothymidylic acids (margin). Transfer RNA molecules share other identifying features. At one end of the polynucleotide chain, all transfer RNA's contain a guanylic acid residue, linked by its 3′-hydroxyl group to the penultimate nucleotide residue. The terminal guanylic acid residue contains an extra phosphate group at its 5′-hydroxyl group. At the other end of the chain, all transfer RNA molecules contain a common trinucleotide sequence, namely pCpCpA. The 5′-hydroxyl group of the terminal adenylic acid residue is linked to the preceding cytidylic acid residue, but its 2′ and 3′ positions are open. The general structure of tRNA's may thus be written as

$$pG(pN)_{75\text{-}90}pCpCpA\text{-}OH$$

The free 2′ or 3′-hydroxyl group of the terminal adenylic acid residue of the pCpCpA sequence in tRNA molecules is enzymatically esterified with a specific α-amino acid, to yield the active or transfer form, namely amino acyl-tRNA:

$$pG(pN)_{75\text{-}90}pCpCpA{-}O{-}\underset{\underset{O}{\|}}{C}{-}CH(NH_2)R$$

This amino acid residue is enzymatically transferred to the end of the growing peptide chain on the surface of the ribosome (Chapter 30). Many tRNAs have been isolated in homogeneous form and some have recently been crystallized. Moreover, the nucleotide sequences of a number of tRNA's have been established (below).

Ribosomal RNA

Ribosomal RNA constitutes up to 65 percent of the weight of ribosomes. It can be extracted from *E. coli* ribosomes with phenol in the form of linear, single-stranded molecules which appear in three characteristic forms, sedimenting at 23S, 16S, and 5S, respectively. Although rRNA makes up a large fraction of total cellular RNA, its function in the ribosome is not yet clear. It contains the four major bases A, G, C, and U; a few of the bases are methylated.

The structure and function of RNA's are further developed in Chapters 29–33.

The Covalent Backbone of Nucleic Acids

DNA and the three different forms of RNA are linear polymers of successive mononucleotide units, in which one mononucleotide is linked to the next by a phosphodiester bridge between the 3′-hydroxyl group of the pentose moiety of one nucleotide and the 5′-hydroxyl group of the pentose of the next (Figure 12-6). The covalent backbone of nucleic acids thus consists of alternating pentose and phosphoric acid groups; the purine and pyrimidine bases represent side-chains attached to the pentose units of the backbone.

The backbone structure of polynucleotides is often schematized as shown in Figure 12-7; such diagrams are useful in indicating the specific bonds that are cleaved during enzymatic and nonenzymatic hydrolysis of nucleic acids, as we shall see below. Another way of symbolizing nucleic acid structure is by a shorthand notation to indicate base sequence. The bases of RNA, for example, are symbolized by A, U, G, and C; p designates the phosphate group. When p appears to the left of the base, it designates

Figure 12-7
Site of action of nucleases. In both DNA and RNA, snake venom phosphodiesterase hydrolyzes only a linkages, whereas bovine spleen phosphodiesterase hydrolyzes only b linkages.

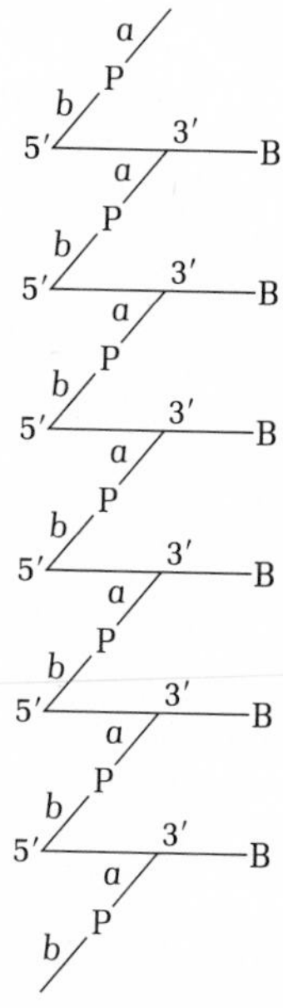

the 5′ position; a p to the right of the base designates the 3′ position. Thus, pApU designates a dinucleotide in which the 5′ position of the adenosine bears a free phosphate group and in which the phosphate bridge involves the 3′ position of the adenosine and the 5′ position of the uridine. ApUp designates a dinucleotide in which there is a phosphodiester bridge between the 3′ position of the adenosine and the 5′ position of the uridine and a free phosphate group at the 3′ position of the uridine. To symbolize DNA sequence, the base symbols are prefixed by d, as in the example d-ApTpGpAp.

Enzymatic Hydrolysis of Internucleotide Linkages

That 3′,5′-phosphodiester bonds are the sole linkage between mononucleotide units in nucleic acids is supported by much evidence. Partial hydrolysis of either DNA or RNA yields many simple dinucleotides joined by such 3′,5′ bridges. The other possible phosphodiester linkages between 2′-deoxyribonucleotides, namely 5′,5′ or 3′,3′ linkages, have never been found in hydrolyzates of DNA. Similarly, no dinucleotides containing other than 3′,5′ bridges have ever been found in hydrolyzates of RNA.

The second line of evidence for the 3′,5′ linkage comes from the use of certain nucleases and phosphodiesterases having known substrate specificities. The phosphodiester bridges of DNA and RNA are attacked by two classes of enzymes, *a* and *b*. The *a* enzymes specifically hydrolyze the ester linkage between the 3′-hydroxyl and the phosphoric acid (site *a* in Figure 12-7), and the *b* enzymes hydrolyze the ester linkage between the phosphoric acid and the 5′-hydroxyl end of the phosphodiester bridges (site *b*). The best known of the *a* enzymes is a phosphodiesterase from the venom of the rattlesnake or Russell's viper, which hydrolyzes all the bonds of class *a* in either RNA or DNA, liberating all the nucleotide units as nucleoside 5′-phosphates. The enzyme requires a free 3′-hydroxyl group and proceeds stepwise from that end of the polynucleotide chain. This enzyme and all other nucleases attacking only at the ends of polynucleotide chains are called *exonucleases*. The *b* enzymes are represented by a phosphodiesterase from bovine spleen, also an exonuclease, which hydrolyzes all the *b* linkages of both DNA and RNA and thus liberates only nucleoside 3′-phosphates. It begins its attack at the end of the chain having a free 5′-hydroxyl group.

Endonucleases do not require a free 3′- or 5′-hydroxyl group at the end of the chain; they attack certain *a* or *b* linkages wherever they occur in the polynucleotide chain. Deoxyribonuclease I of bovine pancreas catalyzes hydryolsis of all the class-*a* linkages of DNA between adjacent pyrimidine-purine pairs, regardless of their position in the chain. Deoxyribonuclease II, isolated from spleen, thymus, or from various bacteria, is also an endonuclease; it hydrolyzes some but not all of the *b* linkages.

RNA can similarly be degraded by RNA-specific nucleases. Crystalline ribonuclease from bovine pancreas is

Exonucleases	*Nucleic acid attacked*	*Linkage attacked*
Snake venom phosphodiesterase	DNA and RNA	*a*, starting from 3′-end.
Bovine spleen phosphodiesterase	DNA and RNA	*b*, starting from 5′-end.
Endonucleases		
Deoxyribonuclease I (bovine pancreas)	DNA	all *a* linkages
Deoxyribonuclease II	DNA	some *b* linkages
Ribonuclease (bovine pancreas)	RNA	*b* linkages in which the *a* linkage is to a pyrimidine nucleotide
Ribonuclease T_1 (mold)	RNA	*b* linkages in which the *a* linkage is to a purine nucleotide

an endonuclease and hydrolyzes only those *b* linkages of RNA in which the *a* linkage is attached to a pyrimidine nucleotide (Figure 12-7). The end products of ribonuclease action are thus pyrimidine-containing nucleoside 3′-phosphates and oligonucleotides terminating in a pyrimidine nucleotide with a 3′-phosphate group. These enzymes are extremely important tools in analyzing the base sequence of nucleic acids, just as trypsin and chymotrypsin are important in amino acid sequence analysis.

Hydrolysis of Nucleic Acids by Acids and Bases

Mild-acid hydrolysis of DNA at pH 3.0 is very selective in its action, causing cleavage of the β-glycosidic bonds between the purine bases and the deoxyribose; the pyrimidine-deoxyribose bonds and the backbone bonds remain intact. The resulting DNA derivative, which is devoid of purine bases, is called an *apurinic acid*. Treatment of DNA under somewhat different conditions produces *apyrimidinic acids*.

DNA is not hydrolyzed by bases, whereas RNA is. This finding indicates that the 2′-hydroxyl group of D-ribose is required for alkaline hydrolysis of RNA. Dilute NaOH produces from RNA a mixture of nucleoside 2′- and 3′-phosphates and small amounts of nucleoside 2′,3′-cyclic monophosphates. The latter are actually the first products of alkaline hydrolysis of RNA. They are further hydrolyzed in the presence of base, which attacks the P—O—C_2 and the P—O—C_3 linkages equally, to yield an equimolar mixture of 2′- and 3′-nucleoside monophosphates. The cyclic monophosphate appears to be an obligatory intermediate in alkaline hydrolysis of RNA since DNA, which has no 2′-hydroxyl groups and therefore cannot form 2′,3′-cyclic monophosphates, is not hydrolyzed by base. Nucleoside 2′,3′-cyclic monophosphates are also readily hydrolyzed by pancreatic ribonuclease.

Selective hydrolytic cleavage of polynucleotides by the methods described above is an essential step in determining the base sequence of nucleic acids, which in principle is approached with the same logic as that employed in the sequence analysis of proteins.

Sequence Analysis of Nucleic Acids

We have seen that selective hydrolysis of peptide bonds makes possible the analysis of amino acid sequence in protein molecules. In a similar way selective hydrolysis of internucleotide linkages has made possible analysis of nucleotide sequence of nucleic acids. However, the problem is generally more difficult in the case of nucleic acids. Because there are usually only four major bases in nucleic acids whereas proteins contain 20 amino acids, recognition of distinctive sequences of bases in nucleic acids is not easy and the chances of ambiguity greater. Since tRNA's are relatively small molecules and contain a significant number of minor bases which may serve as useful "markers," this class of nucleic acids is clearly experimentally more approachable than other nucleic acids.

In 1965, Holley and his colleagues deduced the entire base sequence of a yeast alanine tRNA, a remarkable experimental achievement. The experimental approach taken was in principle that used for determination of amino acid sequence of peptide chains (Figure 12-8). The 77-member polynucleotide chain of this tRNA was cleaved into a series of small oligonucleotide fragments by means of nucleases. These were separated and the sequence of bases in each fragment determined. The overall sequence was pieced together by using a second fragmentation method to provide "overlaps." Since tRNA contains up to 10 percent of its bases in methylated forms, which can serve as very distinctive markers of different parts of the polynucleotide chain, the base sequence of tRNA is fortunately easier to solve than that of polynucleotides possessing only A, G. C, and U. The base sequence of yeast alanine tRNA is given in Figure 12-9. The sequences of a number of other tRNA molecules, as well as that of a 5S ribosomal RNA, have since been solved.

Figure 12-8
Analysis of the nucleotide sequence of yeast alanine tRNA. Yeast alanyl tRNA was first isolated from all other tRNA's by countercurrent distribution. The intact tRNA chain (77 residues) was then fragmented into two series of oligonucleotides by action of two ribonucleases, one from pancreas (a, b, c, d) the other from a mold (e, f, g). These fragments were separated by column chromatography. Each fragment was then completely hydrolyzed to determine its base content. To analyze the base sequence of the single fragment shown, snake venom phosphodiesterase was used for successive removal of mononucleotides from one end of the chain (right). Chromatography of the resulting complex mixture (lower right) permitted identification of the base sequence in this fragment. Many repetitive cleavage and chromatographic steps were required.

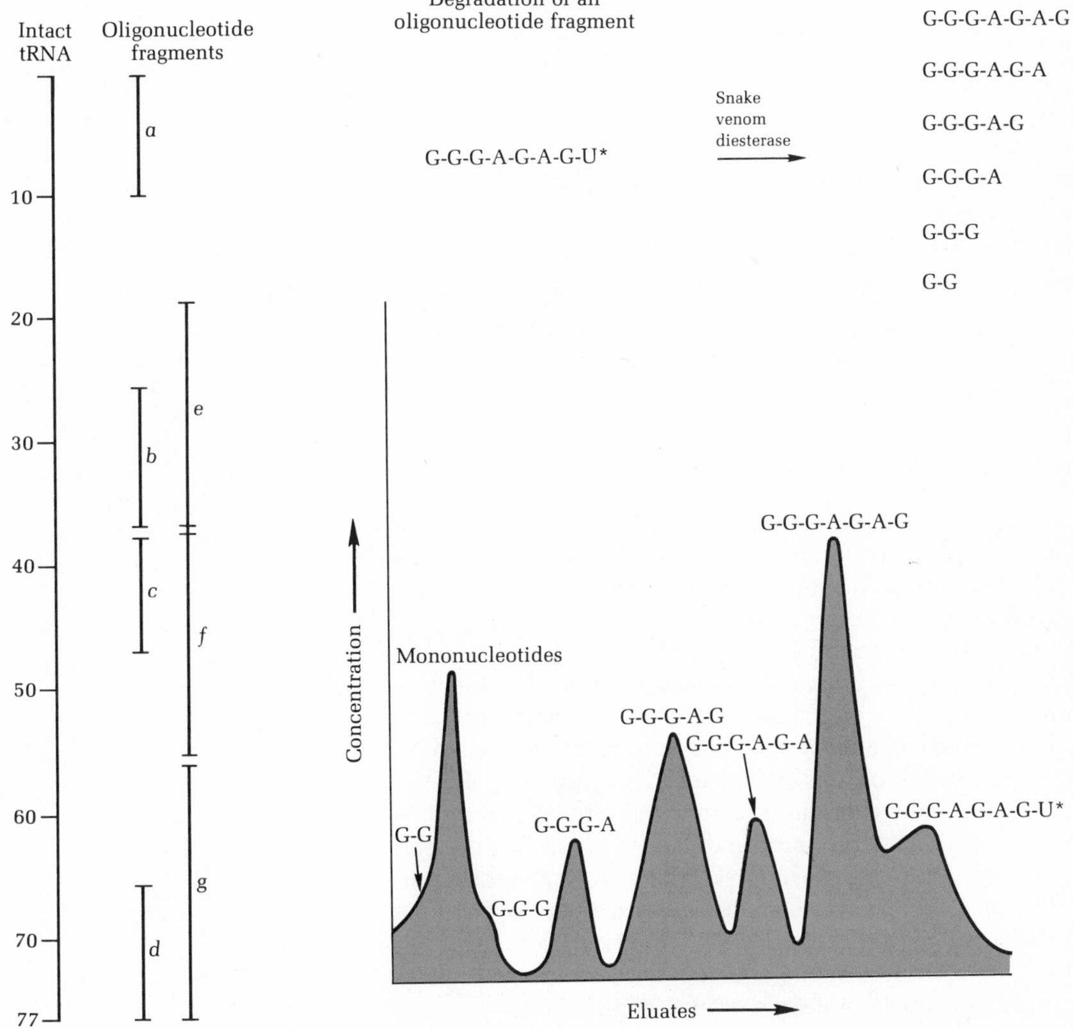

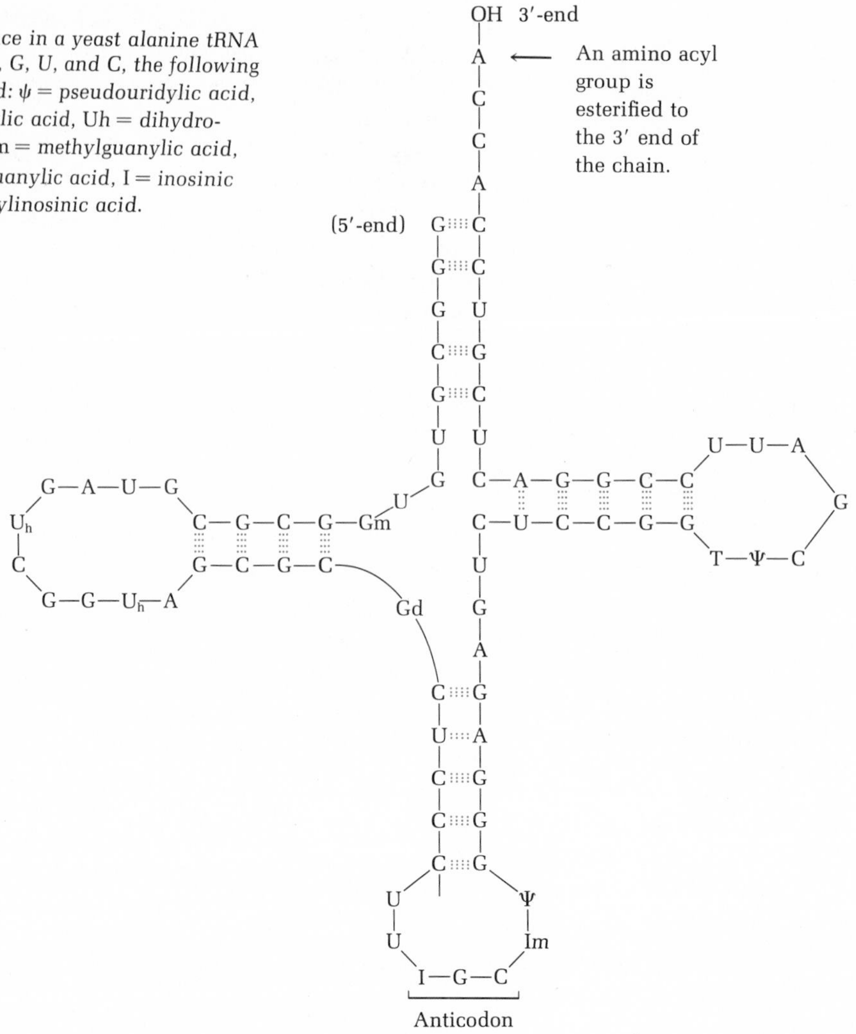

Figure 12-9
The base sequence in a yeast alanine tRNA In addition to A, G, U, and C, the following symbols are used: ψ = pseudouridylic acid, T = ribothymidylic acid, Uh = dihydrouridylic acid, Gm = methylguanylic acid, Gd = dimethylguanylic acid, I = inosinic acid, Im = methylinosinic acid.

Nucleic Acid–Protein Complexes

Some nucleic acids are characteristically associated with specific proteins to form systems having very complex structures and functional activities. Chief among these are the ribosomes and viruses.

Ribosomes

Ribosomes of procaryotic cells consist of 60 to 65 percent rRNA and about 35 to 40 percent protein; in eucaryotic cells, they contain about 50 percent rRNA and 50 percent protein. In *E. coli* cells, ribosomes occur in free form in the cytoplasm and may make up about 25 percent of the total cell weight. An *E. coli* cell possesses about 15,000 ribosomes, each having a particle weight of about 2,800,000 daltons and a diameter of 180 Å (Figure 12-10). The ribosomes in eucaryotic cells are somewhat larger, and most of them are in the cytoplasm, associated with the endoplasmic reticulum. Ribosomes are also found within the cell nucleus and within organelles such as mitochondria and chloroplasts. Many ribosomes are associated in beadlike strings called polyribosomes or, more simply, polysomes, which are formed by the attachment of a number of ribosomes to a single molecule of messenger RNA.

Figure 12-10
Subunit structure of 70s ribosomes of E. coli.

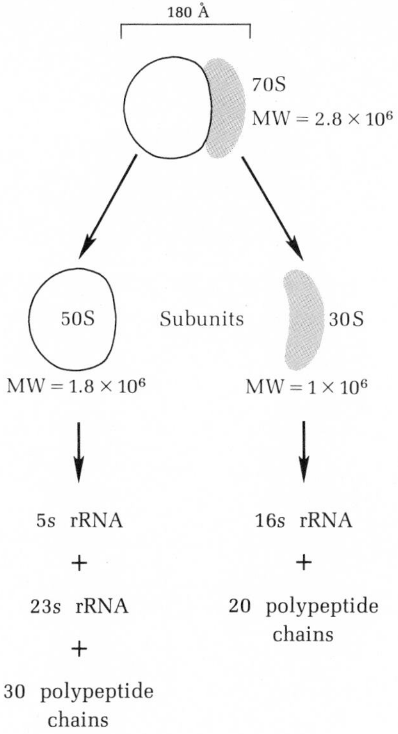

The ribosomes of all cells are constructed according to the same architectural plan, with only minor variations in size and rRNA content. They consist of two subunits of unequal size (Figure 12-10). *E. coli* ribosomes, which have a sedimentation coefficient of 70S, contain subunits having sedimentation coefficients of 30S and 50S (mol wt ~ 1.0 million and ~ 1.8 million, respectively). The 50S subunit contains a molecule of 23S rRNA, and the 30S subunit contains a molecule of 16S rRNA. Both subunits contain a large number of separate polypeptide chains. Ribosomes are stable in solutions containing relatively high Mg^{2+} concentration but may dissociate into their subunits when the Mg^{2+} concentration is reduced. Ribosomal structure and function are considered in more detail in Chapter 30.

Viruses

Viruses, which have aptly been described as structures "at the threshold of life," are stable supramolecular complexes containing a nucleic acid molecule and many protein subunits organized into a characteristic three-dimensional arrangement. Although viruses have extremely large particle weights, they can be isolated in homogeneous form and many have been crystallized. Viruses in pure, isolated form have no power to reproduce themselves. However, when a viral particle (also called a *virion*) gains access to the interior of a specific host cell, it has the capacity to direct its own replication. The viral nucleic acid, which is the infective part of a virion, can monopolize the biosynthetic machinery of the host cell, forcing it to synthesize the molecular components of virus molecules rather than the normal host cell components. The RNA of the RNA viruses is bound to the host-cell ribosomes, in preference to the host-cell mRNA molecules. It then acts as a template for the synthesis of viral coat proteins and for those additional enzymes required to replicate other component parts of the virus structure—in particular, the viral RNA itself. The DNA of DNA-containing viruses similarly serves as the template for transcription of complementary mRNA molecules, which can, in turn, usurp the ribosomal apparatus and cause it to synthesize viral proteins and those enzymes required to synthesize viral DNA.

Viruses vary considerably in size, shape, and chemical composition (Table 12-2). In some viruses (for example, the tobacco mosaic virus), only a single type of protein subunit is present; in others (for example, the *E. coli* bacteriophage T_2), there may be many types of subunits. The protein coat, or *capsid*, of the more complex viruses is made up of many clusters of protein subunits, called *capsomeres*. The nucleic acids of viruses frequently possess methylated bases.

All plant viruses contain RNA and are either rodlike helices, as in the case of the tobacco mosaic virus, or icosahedral (20-sided), as in bushy stunt virus, which consists of 60 capsomeres, each containing three subunits arranged in a symmetrical manner. Animal viruses may

Table 12-2 Composition of some viruses

	Particle weight (daltons)	*Nucleic acid and no. of chains*	*Percent nucleic acid*	*Shape*	*Long dimension (Å)*
E. coli bacteriophages					
T_2,T_4,T_6	~220,000,000	DNA (2)	61	Tadpole	180
T_7	38,000,000	DNA (2)	41	Tadpole	60
ϕx-174	6,000,000	DNA (1 or 2)	26	Polyhedral	150
λ	50,000,000	DNA (2)	64	Tadpole	200
MS2	3,600,000	RNA (1)	32	Polyhedral	175
Plant viruses					
Tobacco mosaic	40,000,000	RNA (1)	5	Rod	3,000
Tomato bushy stunt	10,600,000	RNA (1)	15	Polyhedral	280
Tobacco necrosis	1,970,000	RNA (1)	20	Polyhedral	210
Animal viruses					
Poliomyelitis	6,700,000	RNA (1)	28	Polyhedral	300
Polyoma	21,000,000	DNA (2)	13.4	Polyhedral	450
Adenovirus	200,000,000	DNA (2)	5.0	Polyhedral	700
Vaccinia	2,000,000,000	DNA (?)	7.5	Brick	2,300

contain either DNA or RNA. Although some, such as the poliomyelitis virus, are very small, most are larger than plant viruses. Bacterial viruses (called bacteriophages) are the most convenient to study because they replicate in large numbers in bacterial suspensions and are easily isolated. The most important bacterial viruses are those of *E. coli* cells, such as the bacteriophages T_2, T_4, T_6, ϕX-174, and λ.

The structure of viruses has been studied in great detail by means of electron microscopy and x-ray diffraction. The structures of several viruses are given in Figure 12-11. The biosynthesis of viruses will be considered in detail in Chapter 33.

Figure 12-11
Electron micrographs of viruses.

Tobacco mosaic virus

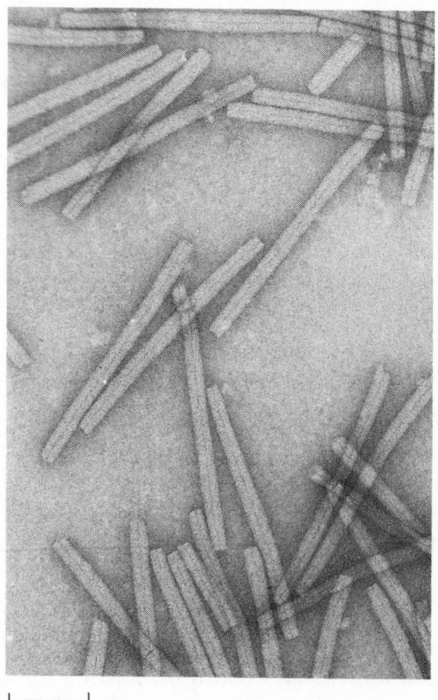

Bacteriophage T_4

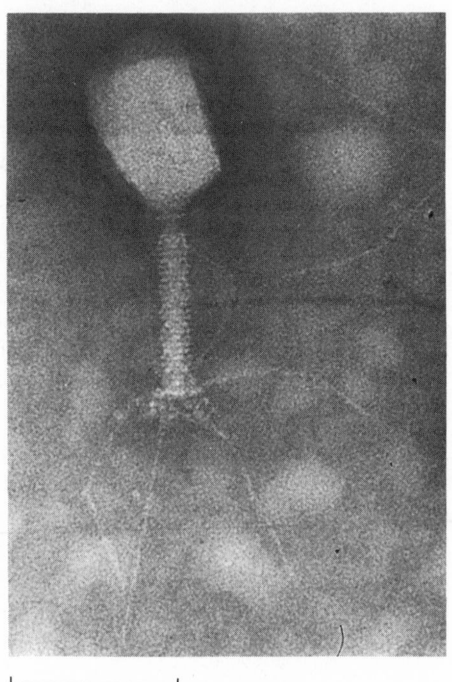

Summary

Mononucleotides contain one molecule of a purine or pyrimidine base, one of D-ribose or 2-deoxy-D-ribose, and one of phosphoric acid. The purine or pyrimidine bases are covalently bonded in β-glycosidic linkage to carbon atom 1 of D-ribose or 2-deoxy-D-ribose to form ribonucleosides or deoxyribonucleosides, respectively. The most common mononucleotides are phosphorylated at the 5′-hydroxyl group of the pentose. Ribonucleotides contain one of the pyrimidines cytosine and uracil or one of the purines adenine and guanine, and deoxyribonucleotides contain one of the pyrimidines cytosine and thymine or one of the purines adenine and guanine. All ribonucleotides and deoxyribonucleotides also occur in the form of pyrophosphoric and triphosphoric acid esters, which are called nucleoside (or deoxyribonucleoside) 5′-diphosphates and 5′-triphosphates. Mononucleotides have many functions. ATP serves as an energy-carrying coenzyme, UDP as a sugar-carrying coenzyme, and CDP as an amine-carrying coenzyme. Other mononucleotides serve as coenzymes in oxidation-reduction reactions of nucleic acids (polynucleotides). The most prominent function of mononucleotides is to serve as building blocks of the nucleic acids.

Nucleic acids are chains of mononucleotides joined by phosphodiester bridges between the 3′-hydroxyl group of one nucleotide and the 5′-hydroxyl group of the next. Deoxyribonucleic acids contain only deoxyribonucleotides; they serve to store genetic information. Most have extremely high molecular weight; they vary in base composition and sequence. There are three major types of ribonucleic acids: messenger RNA, transfer RNA, and ribosomal RNA.

The internucleotide linkages of DNA and RNA may be hydrolyzed by enzymes or acids. Some enzymes, such as rattlesnake venom phosphodiesterase, hydrolyze either DNA or RNA in such a way as to yield only 5′-phosphorylated nucleosides. Others, such as spleen phosphodiesterase, cleave the other side of the phosphodiester linkage to yield only 3′-phosphorylated nucleosides. Deoxyribonucleases specific for the linkages between certain pairs of mononucleotides also are known; they are important tools in degrading DNA. Pancreatic ribonuclease hydrolyzes RNA in such a way as to yield pyrimidine-containing nucleoside 3′-phosphates, as well as oligonucleotides. Dilute acids cleave purines from DNA to yield apurinic acids. DNA is not hydrolyzed by bases, but RNA is, suggesting that the 3′-hydroxyl group of ribose is necessary for alkaline cleavage of phosphodiester bridges.

Nucleic acids are frequently associated with specific proteins to form high-molecular-weight supramolecular nucleoprotein complexes, such as ribosomes and viruses.

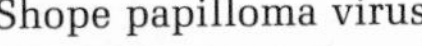

Shope papilloma virus

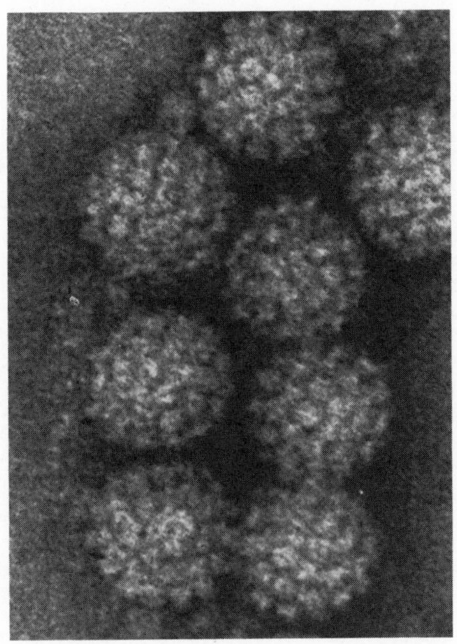

0.1 μ

References

Books

CANTONI, G. L., and D. DAVIES (eds.): *Procedures in Nucleic Acid Research,* Harper & Row, Publishers, Inc., New York, 1966. A useful compendium of laboratory methods.

DAVIDSON, J. N. (ed.): *Biochemistry of Nucleic Acids,* Wiley, New York, 1969. Complete and comprehensive treatise on all aspects of nucleic acid chemistry.

FLORKIN, M., and E. H. STOTZ (eds.): *Nucleic Acids*, vol. 8 of *Comprehensive Biochemistry*, American Elsevier Publishing Company, New York, 1963. Authoritative articles on the chemical and biological aspects of the nucleic acids.

FRAENKEL-CONRAT, H.: *Design and Function at the Threshold of Life: The Viruses*, Academic Press Inc., New York, 1962. An elementary account of virus structure and function.

MICHELSON, A. M.: *The Chemistry of Nucleosides and Nucleotides*, Academic Press Inc., New York, 1963. Structure, laboratory synthesis, and chemical and physical properties are considered in detail.

Articles and Reviews

ANDERSON, T. F.: "The Molecular Organization of Virus Particles," in J. M. Allen (ed.), *Molecular Organization and Biological Function*, Harper & Row, Publishers, Inc., New York, 1967, pp. 37–64. The Structure of the T-bacteriophages of *E. coli.* are given special emphasis.

BURTON, K.: "Sequence Determination in Nucleic Acids," in P. N. Campbell and G. D. Greville (eds.), *Essays in Biochemistry*, vol. I, Academic Press, New York, 1965, p. 57. The chemical problems in sequence analysis of nucleic acids.

HOLLEY, R. W., J. APGAR, G. A. EVERETT, J. T. MADISON, M. MARGUISEE, S. H. MERRILL, J. R. PENSWICK, and A. ZAMIR: "The base sequence of yeast alanine transfer RNA," *Science*, **147:**1462–1465 (1965). The first determination of the base sequence of an RNA.

LASKOWSKI, M., SR.: "DNA-ases and Their Uses in the Study of Primary Structure of Nucleic Acids." *Advan. Enzymol.*, **29:**165–257 (1968).

MADISON, J. T.: "Primary structure of RNA," *Ann. Rev. Biochem.*, **37:**137–148 (1968). Summary of known base sequences of RNA's and methodology of sequence analysis.

THOMAS, C. A., and L. A. MACHATTIE: "The Anatomy of Viral DNA Molecules," *Ann. Rev. Biochem.*, **36:**485–518 (1967). A comprehensive review of the chemical, physical, and biological properties of viral DNA's.

UEDA, T., and J. J. FOX: "The Mononucleotides," *Advan. Carbohydrate Chem.*, **22:**307–419 (1967).

Problems

1. Calculate A, the absorbancy index ($\log I_0/I$), of the following solutions in 1.0 cm cells at pH 7.0. Use data in Figure 12-2.
   (a) 3.2×10^{-5} M adenine at 260 nm
   (b) 47.5 μM cytosine at 260 nm
   (c) 6.0 μM uracil at 260 nm

2. Calculate the concentration in moles per liter of the following solutions at pH 7.0, using data in Figure 12-2.
   (a) A guanine solution of $A_{260\,\mathrm{nm}} = 0.325$ (optical path, 1.0 cm)
   (b) A thymine solution of $A_{260\,\mathrm{nm}} = 0.090$ (optical path, 1.0 cm)

3. Calculate the absorbancy index of an aqueous solution containing 4.8×10^{-5} M adenine and 3.2×10^{-5} molar uracil at 260 nm.

4. A solution containing a mixture of AMP and GMP gave an absorbancy index of 0.652 at 260 nm and 0.284 at 280 nm. Given the molar absorbancy indexes below, calculate the concentrations of AMP and GMP in the solution.

   AMP: $\epsilon_{260} = 15.4 \times 10^3\ M^{-1}\ cm^{-1}$
   AMP: $\epsilon_{280} = 2.5 \times 10^3\ M^{-1}\ cm^{-1}$
   GMP: $\epsilon_{260} = 11.7 \times 10^3\ M^{-1}\ cm^{-1}$
   GMP: $\epsilon_{280} = 7.7 \times 10^3\ M^{-1}\ cm^{-1}$

5. Indicate the products of the action of (*a*) snake venom phosphodiesterase on ApUpApApCpU, (*b*) bovine pancreatic ribonuclease on ApUpApApCpU, (*c*) snake venom phosphodiesterase on d-TpApGpGpCp, (*d*) mild acid hydrolysis on d-TpApCpGpGpCpA, (*e*) mild basic hydrolysis on d-TpApCpGpGpCpA.

6. An oligoribonucleotide of base composition $A_2C_4G_2U$ was incubated with various enzymes. Treatment with pancreatic ribonuclease yielded 2 moles of Cp, a dinucleotide containing adenine and uracil, a dinucleotide containing guanosine and cytosine, and a trinucleotide containing adenine, cytosine and guanine. Treatment with takadiastase yielded one molecule each of free cytosine, Ap, and pGp, a trinucleotide containing adenine and cytosine, and a trinucleotide containing cytosine, guanine, and uracil. Snake venom phosphodiesterase treatment for a limited time yielded some pC. Takadiastase is an enzyme preparation from a mold which hydrolyzes those *b* linkages of oligonucleotides in which the *a* linkage is attached to purine containing nucleotides. From these data deduce the base sequence of the oligonucleotide.

7. An oligoribonucleotide of base composition $A_2C_4G_4U_2$ was treated with certain enzymes and the base composition of the products determined following their hydrolysis. Pancreatic ribonuclease gave three Cp, a dinucleotide containing adenine and uracil, another containing only guanine, a third containing guanine and uracil, and a trinucleotide containing adenine, cytosine and guanine. Takadiastase gave Ap, 2 Gp, and three trinucleotides, one containing adenine, cytosine and uracil, the second containing cytosine and guanine, and the third containing cytosine, guanine and uracil. What may be deduced about the base sequence of the oligonucleotide?

PART 2 CATABOLISM AND THE GENERATION OF PHOSPHATE-BOND ENERGY

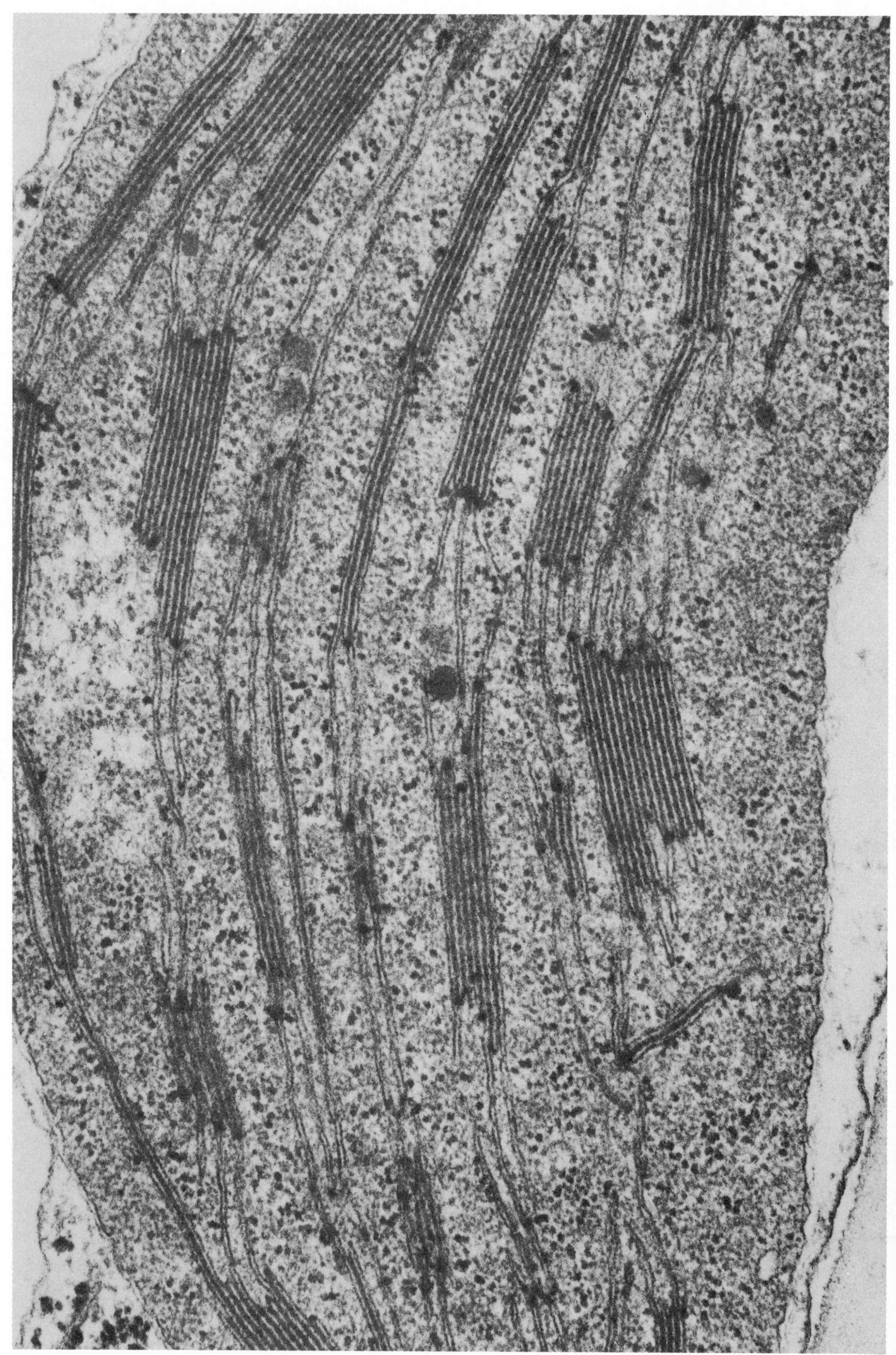

Thin-section of a chloroplast of Phleum pretense *(timothy).*

CHAPTER 13 METABOLIC AND ENERGY-TRANSFER PATHWAYS: A SURVEY

Intermediary metabolism is often briefly defined as the sum total of all the enzymatic reactions occurring in the cell. Although this is not an inaccurate statement, it is incomplete as a definition, since it does not indicate that metabolism is a highly integrated, purposeful activity in which many sets of multienzyme systems participate for the purpose of exchanging matter and energy between the cell and its environment. There are four specific functions of metabolism: (1) to extract chemical energy from the environment, either from organic nutrients or from sunlight, (2) to convert exogenous nutrients into the building blocks, or precursors, of the macromolecular components of cells, (3) to assemble the building blocks into proteins, nucleic acids, lipids, and other characteristic cell components, and (4) to form and degrade those biomolecules required in specialized functions of cells.

The reaction sequences of metabolism are remarkably similar in all forms of life, particularly in what are known as the *central metabolic pathways*. Although metabolism involves hundreds of different enzyme-catalyzed reactions and is often depicted in immensely detailed charts or metabolic maps, which give an impression of hopeless complexity, the form and function of the central metabolic pathways are easy to understand. In this chapter we shall survey the sources of matter and energy for cellular life, the major routes by which cell components are synthesized and degraded, the pathway of cellular energy transfers, and the experimental approaches used in the study of cell metabolism.

Sources of Carbon and Energy for Cellular Life

Cells can be divided into two large groups on the basis of the chemical form of carbon they require from the environment. *Autotrophic* ("self-feeding") cells can utilize carbon dioxide as the sole source of carbon and construct from it all their carbon-containing biomolecules. *Heterotrophic* ("feeding on others") cells, on the other hand, cannot utilize carbon dioxide and must obtain carbon from their environment in a relatively complex, reduced form, such as glucose. Autotrophs are relatively self-sufficient cells, whereas heterotrophs, with their requirement for carbon in a fancier form, must subsist on the products formed by other cells. Photosynthetic cells and some bacteria are autotrophic, whereas the cells of higher animals and most microorganisms are heterotrophic.

The second dimension in which cells may be classified is in terms of their energy sources. Cells using light as energy source are *phototrophs;* those using oxidation-reduction reactions are *chemotrophs.* Chemotrophs can be further subdivided on the basis of the nature of the electron donors they oxidize to obtain energy. Recall that oxidation-reduction reactions are those in which electrons are transferred from an electron donor (reducing agent) to an electron acceptor (oxidizing agent). Chemotrophs requiring complex organic molecules as their electron donors, such as glucose, are called *chemoorganotrophs.* Organisms that can employ simple inorganic electron donors, such as hydrogen, hydrogen sulfide, ammonia, or sulfur, are called *chemolithotrophs* (Greek, *lithos,* stone). Table 13-1 shows the classification of all cells into four major groups: chemoorganotrophs, chemolithotrophs, photoorganotrophs, and photolithotrophs, according to their energy and carbon sources.

The great majority of organisms are either photolithotrophs or chemoorganotrophs, the other two groups containing relatively few species. However, the latter groups should not be regarded as rare curiosities. Some of them play extremely important roles in the biosphere, particularly the soil microorganisms that fix molecular nitrogen or oxidize ammonia to nitrate. Recall that nearly half the living matter on the earth is microbial and that most microbial life occurs in the soil and seas.

Chemoorganotrophs, which are more generally called heterotrophs, can in turn be divided into two major classes, *aerobes,* which use molecular oxygen as the ultimate acceptor of electrons from their organic electron donors, and *anaerobes,* which instead of oxygen use some other molecule as electron acceptor. Many cells can live either aerobically or anaerobically, i.e., can use either oxygen or an organic compound as electron acceptor; such organisms

Table 13-1 Classification of organisms according to carbon and energy source

Type of organism	*Carbon source*	*Energy source*	*Electron donors*	*Examples*
1. Photolithotrophs	CO_2	Light	Inorganic compounds (H_2O, H_2S, S)	Green cells of higher plants, blue-green algae, photosynthetic bacteria
2. Photoorganotrophs	Organic compounds (as well as CO_2)	Light	Organic compounds	Nonsulfur purple bacteria
3. Chemolithotrophs	CO_2	Oxidation-reduction reactions	Inorganic compounds (H_2, S, H_2S, Fe II, NH_3)	Hydrogen, sulfur, iron, and denitrifying bacteria
4. Chemoorganotrophs	Organic compounds	Oxidation-reduction reactions	Organic compounds (glucose)	All higher animals, most microorganisms, nonphotosynthetic plant cells

are called *facultative*. Anaerobes that cannot utilize oxygen are called *strict anaerobes*; many strict anaerobes are poisoned by oxygen. Most heterotrophic cells, particularly those of higher organisms, are facultative, and if oxygen is available to them, they prefer to use it.

It is important to note that not all cells of a given organism are of the same class and that some types of cells have great metabolic flexibility. For example, in higher plants the green chlorophyll-containing cells of leaves are photosynthetic autotrophs, whereas the root cells are heterotrophs. Moreover, most green leaf cells function as photosynthetic autotrophs in the sunlight but as heterotrophs in the dark.

Figure 13-1
The carbon and oxygen cycles in the biosphere.

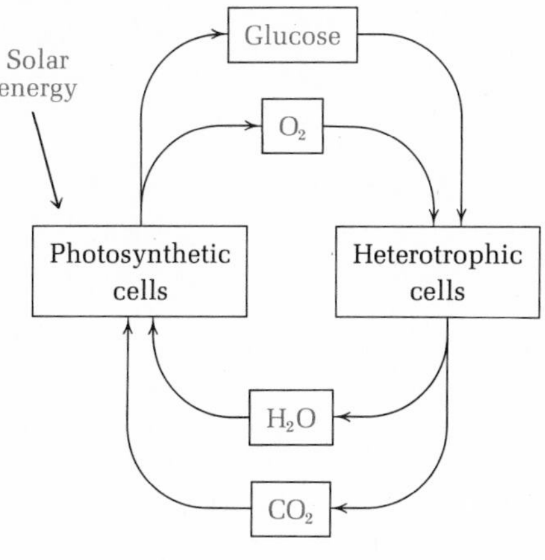

The Carbon and Energy Cycle; Syntrophy

Living organisms in nature are nutritionally interdependent. If we consider the biosphere broadly, we see that photosynthetic cells and heterotrophic cells feed each other. The former produce organic compounds such as glucose from atmospheric CO_2 and evolve oxygen. The latter utilize the oxygen and glucose produced by photosynthetic cells and return CO_2 to the atmosphere again (Figure 13-1). Coupled to the carbon cycle in the biosphere is an energy cycle. Solar energy is transformed during photosynthesis into the chemical energy of glucose and other photoreduction products, which is then utilized by heterotrophs to perform all their energy-requiring activities (Figure 13-2). It is therefore clear that solar light is the ultimate source of energy for all cells, whether they are autotrophic or heterotrophic. Ultimately, however, biological energy is dissipated into the environment and increases its entropy.

The biological energy cycle involves massive amounts of energy. Annually, some 10^{21} cal of solar energy are captured by photosynthetic cells, and some 33×10^9 tons of carbon flow through the biological carbon cycle on the face of the earth. In contrast, the annual energy flow through all man-made machines is only a small percentage of that in the biological energy cycle. Nutritional interdependence between living organisms in nature, exemplified here by the carbon and energy cycles, is called *syntrophy* ("feeding together"). Syntrophy occurs at many levels in the biosphere, from the global level just described to the microscopic level. It is characteristic of all ecological systems.

Figure 13-2
The flow of energy in the biosphere. Solar energy is the origin of all cellular energy. Glucose and other photosynthetic products are utilized in both plants and animals to provide energy for vital cell activities. Ultimately solar energy is dissipated into a useless form.

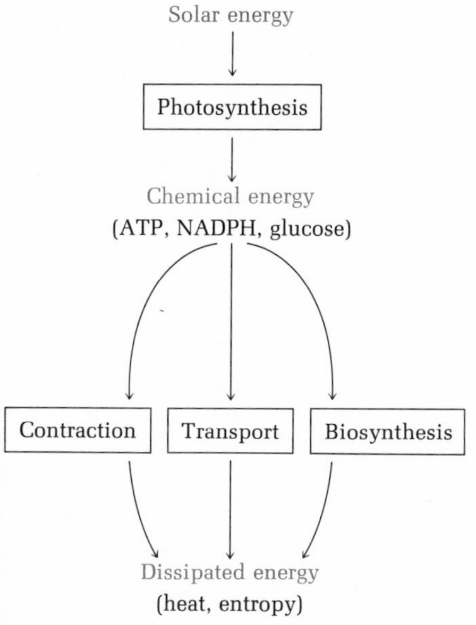

The Nitrogen Cycle

Nitrogen is another important element that cycles through living organisms via syntrophy; it is of course required for synthesis of proteins and nucleic acids. Although molecular nitrogen (N_2) occurs in vast amounts in the atmosphere, it is chemically inert and cannot be used by most organisms, which must obtain nitrogen from the environment in some combined form such as nitrate, ammonia, or more complex compounds such as amino acids. However, combined nitrogen is rather scarce in surface water and the soil, and it is continuously cycled (Figure 13-3). In the nitrogen cycle, plants obtain much of their nitrogen from the soil as nitrate, which they reduce to form ammonia, amino acids, and other reduced products. These are used by animals and are then returned to the soil, still in reduced form. Soil microorganisms in turn can reoxidize NH_3 to form nitrite and nitrate, which can then be utilized again by plants. Nitrogen-fixing bacteria can reduce atmospheric N_2 and thus supplement the available supply of combined nitrogen.

The most self-sufficient cells known are the nitrogen-fixing photosynthetic blue-green algae, procaryotes found in soil, fresh water, and the oceans. These organisms obtain their energy from sunlight, their carbon from CO_2, their nitrogen from atmospheric N_2, and their electrons for reduction of CO_2 from water. Blue-green algae are believed to be the first organisms that colonized land during evolution, a hypothesis given support by an interesting observation made many years ago. After the eruption of Mt. Krakatoa in 1883 had caused complete destruction of all life in a large surrounding oceanic area, the first organisms to reestablish themselves were the nitrogen-fixing blue-green algae.

Specialized Nutritional Requirements for Nitrogenous Compounds: Vitamins

Many organisms have become nutritionally dependent on very specific chemical forms of exogenous combined nitrogen. Although some bacteria, e.g., *E. coli*, can utilize the simple compound ammonia as sole precursor of all their amino acids, nucleotides, and other nitrogenous components, others, e.g., the lactic acid-forming bacterium *Leuconostoc mesenteroides*, cannot live on ammonia alone but requires a total of 32 different nitrogenous nutrients, including most of the common amino acids (Table 13-2).

Figure 13-3
The nitrogen cycle.

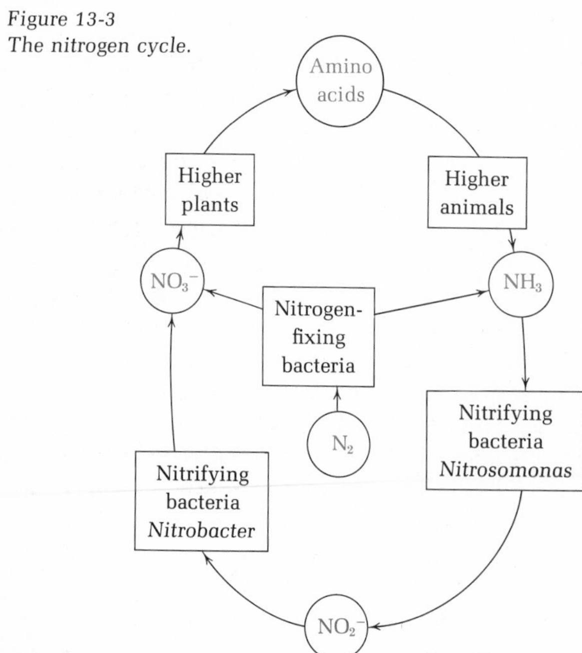

Table 13-2 Comparison of minimal growth requirements for two bacteria

	Escherichia coli	*Leuconostoc mesenteroides*
Carbon and energy source	Glucose	Glucose
Nitrogen source	NH_4^+	NH_4^+
		Amino acids:
		Ala, Arg, Asp, Asn, Cys, Glu, Gly, His, Ile, Leu, Lys, Met, Phe, Pro, Ser, Thr, Trp, Tyr, Val
		Bases:
		Adenine, Guanine, Uracil, Xanthine
		Vitamins:
		Thiamine, Pyridoxine, Pantothenic acid, Riboflavin, Nicotinic acid, *p*-Aminobenzoic acid, Biotin, Folic acid
Minerals	Na^+, K^+, Mg^{2+}, HPO_4^{2-}, SO_4^{2-}	Na^+, K^+, Mg^{2+}, HPO_4^{2-}, SO_4^{2-}, Fe^{2+}, Mn^{2+}

Many vertebrates, including man, also lack the ability to synthesize a number of amino acids from ammonia as nitrogen source and therefore require them preformed in the diet. The 10 nutritionally essential amino acids for the albino rat are lysine, tryptophan, histidine, phenylalanine, leucine, isoleucine, threonine, methionine, valine, and arginine.

Other organisms have similarly developed nutritional dependence on other forms of combined nitrogen, such as purine and pyrimidine bases, which are building blocks in nucleic acid synthesis, or choline, an essential building block of the choline glycerophosphatides.

Some organisms require from exogenous sources one or more of a group of complex organic substances known as *vitamins*, which are needed in only trace amounts, in contrast to most nutrients, such as glucose or amino acids, which are required in bulk amounts. Actually the vitamins are present in and perform similar vital functions in nearly all organisms, since most are precursors of important coenzymes (Chapter 8). Some organisms do not require them in the diet, because they can synthesize them from simpler precursors, whereas others must obtain them from exogenous sources.

Since coenzymes exist in cells in relatively small concentrations, the nutritional requirements for the vitamins can be satisfied by trace amounts. For example, the amount of the vitamin biotin required by some bacteria is so small (about 1 picogram, or 10^{-12} mg, per ml of culture medium) that the traces of biotin present in tap water or even in the purified glucose introduced into the culture medium are often sufficient for maximal growth. Table 13-3 lists the major known water-soluble vitamins and the coenzymes of which they are precursors (Chapter 8). Most of the water-soluble vitamins contain nitrogen. The group of fat-soluble vitamins, required only by higher animals, is also believed to participate in coenzymelike functions, but the action of most vitamins of this class is still unknown in molecular terms (Chapter 10). The nutritional requirements of the albino rat are shown in the margin.

Within a given multicellular organism, one type of cell may become nutritionally dependent on the products of metabolism of another type of cell. Syntrophy is in fact an organizing principle in the evolution of multicellular organisms and in the evolution of tissues and organs. In general, the cells of higher animals require many exogenous components for growth; in fact, the complex nutritional requirements for culturing some mammalian cells in vitro have only recently been chemically identified.

Table 13-3 Some water-soluble vitamins and growth factors†

Name	*Precursor of*
Thiamine (vitamin B_1)	Thiamine pyrophosphate
Riboflavin (vitamin B_2)	Flavin coenzymes (FAD, FMN)
Nicotinic acid	Nicotinamide coenzymes (NAD, NADP)
Pantothenic acid	Coenzyme A
Pyridoxine (vitamin B_6)	Pyridoxal phosphate
Biotin	Biocytin
Folic acid	Tetrahydrofolate coenzymes
Cobalamine (vitamin B_{12})	Cobamide coenzymes
Lipoic acid	Prosthetic group of lipoic reductase-transacetylase
myo-Inositol	Essential lipids (phosphatidyl inositol)
Ascorbic acid (vitamin C)	Cofactor in hydroxylations; tyrosine oxidation
Carnitine	Fatty acid–carrying coenzyme

† See Table 8-3. The structure and function of the vitamins and their coenzyme derivatives will be considered in chapters to follow.

Flexibility and Economy in Nutritional Requirements

Living organisms have considerable metabolic flexibility and can adjust to the type and amount of the various nutrients available from the environment within the bounds of their basic metabolic classification. *E. coli* cells always are chemoorganotrophs, but within this classification they have much metabolic versatility. For example, *E. coli* can use as sole carbon source not only glucose but also other sugars, glycerol, amino acids, or even such simple molecules as ethanol or acetate. This flexibility is possible because all these carbon sources are ultimately converted by *E. coli* cells into compounds that can be accepted as fuels by the central metabolic pathways.

E. coli cells can also utilize sources of nitrogen other than ammonia, namely, various amino acids, singly or in combination, purines, pyrimidines, choline, and other nitrogenous compounds. Actually, *E. coli* cells grow much faster if instead of ammonia alone the medium contains a complete mixture of the different amino acids, purines, and pyrimidines required in synthesis of their proteins and nucleic acids. Under these circumstances the cells are spared the complex job of making all these compounds from ammonia. When *E. coli* cells subsisting on ammonia as sole nitrogen source are suddenly provided with an ample supply of exogenous amino acids, they stop using the ammonia and use the preformed amino acids instead. The latter act as a signal to turn off the genes responsible for making the enzymes required to catalyze the synthetic reactions leading from ammonia to the amino acids, thus saving the cell the metabolic work of making these now superfluous enzymes. This turning-off process is called *repression*. However, if the concentration of preformed amino acids in the environment falls below a critical level, the genes for these enzymes are derepressed, with the result that the necessary enzymes are made again and the

Nutritional requirements of the albino rat

Amino acids
- Arginine
- Histidine
- Isoleucine
- Leucine
- Lysine
- Methionine
- Phenylalanine
- Threonine
- Tryptophan
- Valine

Vitamins
- Water-soluble
  - Thiamine
  - Riboflavin
  - Nicotinic acid
  - Pantothenic acid
  - Pyridoxine
  - Biotin
  - Vitamin B_{12}
  - Folic acid
- Fat-soluble
  - Vitamin A
  - Vitamin D
  - Vitamin E
  - Vitamin K

Other organic compounds
- Polyunsaturated fatty acids
- Choline
- Inositol

Minerals
- Ca
- Mg
- Mn
- P
- K
- Na
- Fe
- Cu
- Cl
- I
- Mo
- Zn
- Se

cell begins to manufacture its own amino acids from exogenous ammonia. As we shall see, economy in the use of energy and matter by cells is assured by various types of regulatory systems.

Catabolism, and Anabolism

Metabolism is divided into *catabolism* and *anabolism*. Catabolism is the enzymatic degradation, largely by oxidative reactions, of relatively large nutrient molecules (carbohydrates, lipids, and proteins) coming either from the environment of the cell or from its own nutrient storage depots into a series of smaller, simpler molecules, e.g., lactic acid, acetic acid, CO_2, ammonia, or urea. Catabolism is accompanied by release of the free energy inherent in the complex structure of large organic molecules and its conservation in the form of the phosphate-bond energy of adenosine triphosphate (ATP).

Anabolism is the enzymatic synthesis of relatively large molecular components of cells, e.g., polysaccharides, nucleic acids, proteins, and lipids, from simple precursor molecules. Since the synthetic process results in increased size and complexity of structure and thus a decrease in entropy, it requires input of free energy, which is furnished by the phosphate-bond energy of ATP. Catabolism and anabolism take place concurrently in cells.

Both catabolism and anabolism consist of two simultaneous and interdependent processes which may be analyzed separately. One process comprises the sequential enzymatic reactions by which the covalent backbone of a given biomolecule is degraded or synthesized. The chemical intermediates in this process are called *metabolites*, and this side of the metabolic coin is spoken of as *intermediary metabolism*. Accompanying each chemical reaction of intermediary metabolism is a characteristic energy change. At certain steps in catabolic sequences the chemical energy of metabolites may be conserved, usually as phosphate bond energy, and at certain steps in anabolic sequences phosphate bond energy may be utilized. This phase of metabolism is spoken of as *energy-coupling* Intermediary metabolism and energy coupling are obligatorily interconnected and interdependent. Therefore, as we examine metabolic pathways, we must analyze (1) the reaction steps by which the covalent structure of the precursor is altered to form the product and (2) the exchanges of chemical energy that accompany this conversion.

Catabolic, Anabolic, and Amphibolic Pathways

The enzymatic degradation of each of the bulk nutrients of cells, namely, carbohydrates, lipids, and proteins, proceeds through a number of consecutive enzymatic reactions. The enzymes catalyzing these steps and the various chemical intermediates that are formed in such stepwise fragmentation of nutrient molecules are for the most part rather well understood. The catabolism of these major nutrients takes place in three major stages (Figure 13-4). In stage I, large nutrient molecules are degraded to

Figure 13-4
The three stages of catabolism and anabolism. The catabolic pathways are shown in black arrows and the anabolic pathways in color. Stage III is amphibolic. It not only is the final pathway for degradation of foodstuffs to CO_2, but also can furnish small molecular weight precursors for anabolism.

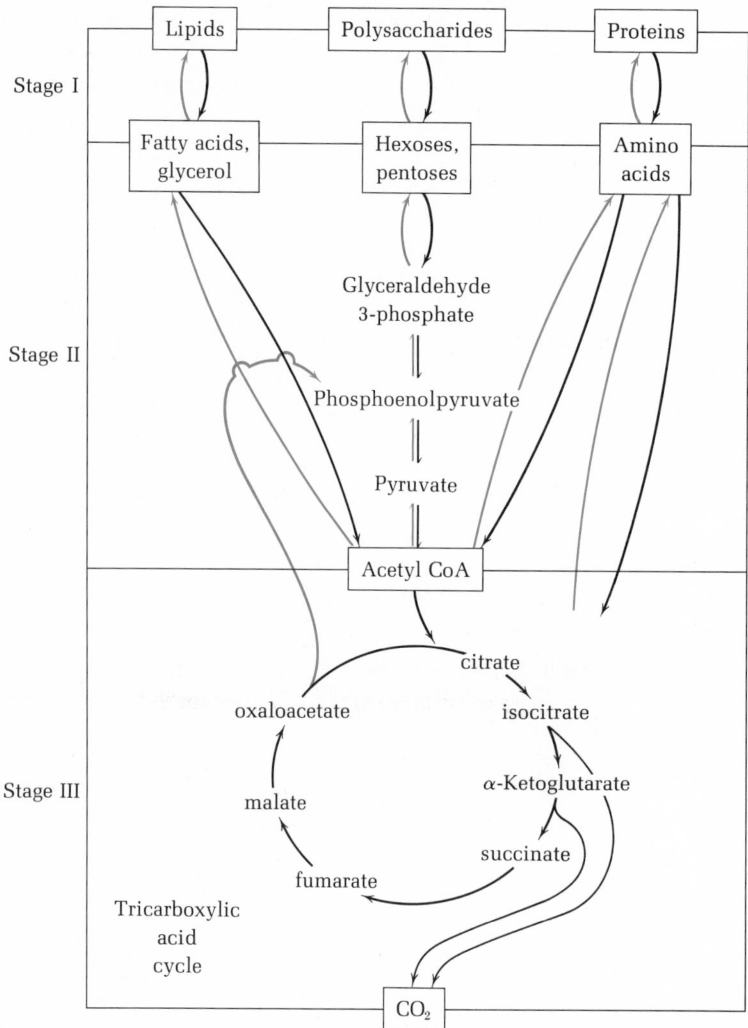

their major building blocks. Polysaccharides are degraded to hexoses or pentoses, lipids to fatty acids, glycerol, and other components, and proteins to their 20 component amino acids. In stage II, the many different products of stage I are collected and then converted into a smaller number of simpler molecules. Thus, the hexoses, pentoses, and glycerol are degraded into the three-carbon phosphorylated sugar glyceraldehyde 3-phosphate and then to a single two-carbon species, the acetyl group of acetyl CoA. Similarly, the various fatty acids are broken down to form acetyl CoA. The 20 different amino acids are also degraded to a few end products, namely, acetyl CoA, α-ketoglutarate, succinate, fumarate, and oxaloacetate. These products of stage II are then channeled into stage III, the final common pathway in which they are ultimately oxidized to carbon dioxide and water.

Anabolism also takes place in three stages, beginning with small building blocks originating from stage III of catabolism. For example, protein synthesis begins in stage III from α-keto acids, which are precursors of the α-amino acids. In stage II the α-keto acids are aminated by amino group donors to form α-amino acids, and in stage I the amino acids are assembled into peptide chains (Figure 13-4). As we shall see, stage III is common to both catabolism and anabolism.

Although intermediary metabolism is one of the oldest and most thoroughly investigated fields of biochemistry, only within the past decade has it been clearly recognized that the catabolic and the anabolic pathways between a given precursor and a given product are usually not identical. For example, a sequence of 12 well-characterized enzymes catalyzes the sequential steps responsible for the degradation of glycogen into lactic acid. Although it would seem logical and economical for the anabolic synthesis of glycogen from lactic acid to occur by simple reversal of the 12 enzymatic steps involved in the catabolic breakdown, it is now known that the biosynthesis of glycogen from lactic acid utilizes only 9 of the 12 enzymatic steps involved in degradation; the other 3 steps are replaced by entirely different enzyme-catalyzed reactions that are used only in the direction of biosynthesis. Similarly, the catabolic and anabolic pathways between proteins and amino acids or between fatty acids and acetyl CoA are dissimilar. Although it seems wasteful to have two metabolic pathways, one for catabolism and one for anabolism, such parallel routes are an absolute necessity, since the pathway taken in catabolism is energetically impossible for anabolism. Degradation of a complex organic molecule is energetically a "downhill" process and its synthesis an "uphill" process. We can develop the hill analogy further. A boulder dislodged at the top of a hill rolls downhill in a fairly direct pathway, following the line of least resistance. To haul the boulder back up to its original position by precisely the same pathway taken in its descent may be quite impossible for a tractor of a given horsepower, but the tractor can haul it back up the hill if it follows another pathway with a less precipitous slope. However, some parts of the uphill path may be identical to parts of the downhill path if they are energetically feasible for the tractor.

Catabolic and anabolic pathways, particularly in eucaryotic cells, may differ in a second way, namely, in their intracellular location. For example, the oxidation of fatty acids to the stage of acetate takes place by the action of a set of enzymes localized in the mitochondria, whereas the synthesis of fatty acids from acetate takes place by another set of enzymes located in the extramitochondrial cytoplasm. Separate compartmentation of parallel catabolic and anabolic pathways in the cell allows them to take place independently and simultaneously. Still another way in which catabolic and anabolic routes may differ is in their genetic and allosteric regulation. For example, the rate of breakdown of glycogen to lactic acid is regulated by different mechanisms than the conversion of lactic acid to glycogen. In fact, this is a general principle: the rates of the parallel but opposite flows of metabolites between a specific nutrient and its product(s) are usually regulated independently.

Although the pathways of catabolism and anabolism are not identical, stage III (Fig 13-4) constitutes a central meeting ground or pathway which is accessible to both. This central route, which is called an *amphibolic* pathway, has a dual function (*amphi*, both). The amphibolic route can be used catabolically, to bring about completion of the degradation of small molecules derived from stage II of catabolism, or it can be used anabolically, to furnish small molecules as precursors for stage II of anabolism.

Nearly all the reactions of metabolism are linked to each other because the product of one enzymatic reaction becomes the substrate of the next in consecutive sequences. Such sequences are made possible by enzymatic reactions in which specific functional groups of metabolite molecules are removed and transferred to acceptor molecules. Most of the consecutive reactions of intermediary metabolism involve the sequential transfer of amino, acetyl, phosphate, methyl, formyl, or carboxyl groups, or of hydrogen atoms.

The Energy Cycle in Cells

Complex organic molecules, such as glucose, contain much potential energy because of their high degree of structural order; they have relatively little randomness, or entropy (defined more exactly in Chapter 14). When the glucose molecule is oxidized by molecular oxygen to form six molecules of CO_2 and six of water, its atoms undergo an increase in randomness; they become separated from each other and may assume many different locations in relation to each other. As a result of this transformation, the glucose molecule undergoes a loss of free energy, which is useful energy capable of doing work at constant temperature and pressure (Chapter 14).

The free energy of glucose so released is harnessed by the cell to do work. Biological oxidations are in essence flameless or low-temperature combustions. As we have seen (Introduction), heat cannot be used as energy source by living organisms, which are essentially isothermal, since heat can do work at constant pressure only when it can flow from a warmer to a cooler body. Instead, the free energy of cellular fuels is conserved as chemical energy, specifically the phosphate-bond energy of adenosine triphosphate (ATP) (Chapters 12 and 14). ATP is enzymatically generated from adenosine diphosphate (ADP) and inorganic phosphate in enzymatic phosphate-group transfer reactions that are coupled to specific oxidation steps during catabolism. Since the ATP so formed can now diffuse to those sites in the cell where its energy is required, it is thus also a transport form of energy. The chemical energy of ATP is then released during transfer of its terminal phosphate group(s) to certain specific acceptor molecules, which become energized and can do work. The ATP-ADP energy cycle is shown in Figure 13-5 and discussed in more detail in Chapter 14.

A second way of carrying chemical energy from oxidation-reduction reactions of catabolism to the energy-requiring reactions of anabolism or synthesis is in the form of electrons. In the synthesis of some hydrogen-rich biomolecules, such as fatty acids and cholesterol, electrons and hydrogen are required for the reduction of double bonds to single bonds. In the cell, electrons are transported enzymatically from the electron-yielding oxidations of catabolism to such electron-requiring groups as carbon-carbon or carbon-oxygen double bonds, by means of electron-carrying coenzymes, the most important of which is *nicotinamide adenine dinucleotide phosphate* (NADP) (Chapters 12 and 16). NADP thus serves as a carrier of energy-rich electrons from catabolic reactions to electron-requiring anabolic reactions (Figure 13-6), just as ATP is a carrier of energy-rich phosphate groups from reactions of catabolism to those of anabolism.

Figure 13-5
The ATP-ADP cycle. The high-energy phosphate bonds of ATP are used in coupled reactions for carrying out energy-requiring functions; ultimately, inorganic phosphate is released. ADP is rephosphorylated to ATP during energy-yielding reactions of catabolism.

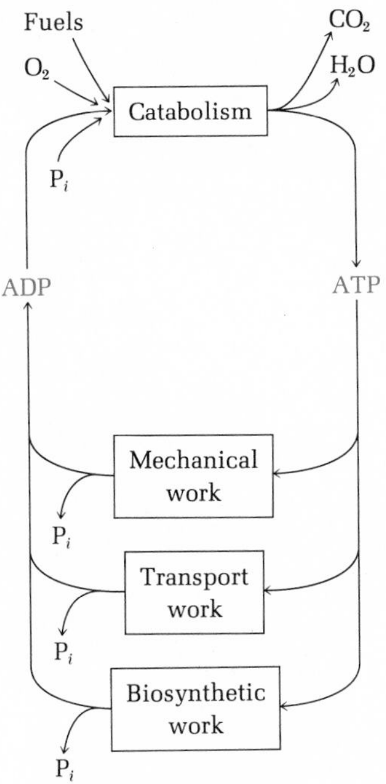

Experimental Approaches to Intermediary Metabolism

There are two major goals in the experimental analysis of a given metabolic pathway. (1) The identification of the stoichiometry and mechanism of each reaction step in the sequence involves the extraction of each enzyme from the cell, its purification, and study of its kinetics, inhibition, and specificity. It culminates in the reconstruction of the enzyme system in the test tube, starting from highly purified known components. (2) The identification of the genetic, allosteric, and endocrine mechanisms by which the rate of a given metabolic pathway is dynamically regulated in the intact cell involves, in one way or another, a return to study of the metabolic pathway in the intact cell or organism. The elucidation of a metabolic pathway is approached experimentally by a succession of methods beginning with the intact organism.

Figure 13-6
Transfer of reducing power via the nicotinamide adenine dinucleotide phosphate (NADP) cycle. Other electron-carrying coenzymes, such as flavin nucleotides, also participate in reductive biosynthesis.

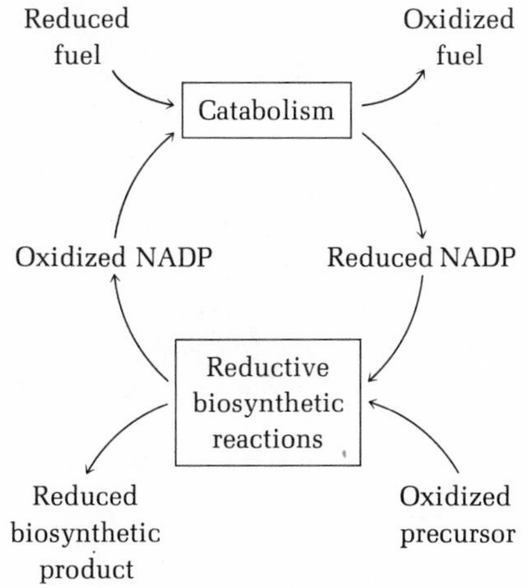

Metabolic Studies on Intact Organisms

The beginning and end of some major metabolic pathways have been identified from balance studies of the metabolic input and output of intact organisms. In this way carbon dioxide, which can be quantitatively recovered in the expired air and the urine of animals, was recognized to be the final end product of oxidation of carbohydrate. Similarly, ethanol and carbon dioxide were found to be the major products of glucose fermentation in yeast, and urea was identified in the urine of some mammals as the major end product of protein nitrogen catabolism. However, the intermediate steps in carbohydrate and protein catabolism are not easily recognized by such balance-sheet approaches.

The chemical intermediates in metabolic processes normally exist in cells in low steady-state concentrations. However, under the stress or imbalance created by dysfunction or disease, certain metabolites may accumulate and yield important clues as to the chemical pathway taken in metabolism. During violent physical exercise, lactic acid appears in the blood as glycogen of the muscle disappears. In fasting animals or in people with the disease *diabetes mellitus*, fatty acids are incompletely oxidized, and intermediates of fatty acid metabolism known as the *ketone bodies* (β-hydroxybutyric acid, acetoacetic acid, and acetone) appear in the blood and urine. From diabetic animals, which excrete large amounts of glucose in the urine because its utilization is defective, it was found that certain amino acids, e.g., alanine, glutamic acid, and serine, cause increased excretion of glucose and thus may function as its metabolic precursors. Under similar conditions, tyrosine and phenylalanine were found to increase the excretion of ketone bodies and thus were identified as precursors of acetoacetic acid. Treatment of intact organisms with certain drugs or inhibitors may also cause a specific metabolite to accumulate in the blood and tissues. For example, administration of *fluorocitrate* causes citrate to accumulate in the liver of some animals because it competitively inhibits citrate oxidation.

Perfusion of the vascular system of isolated organs such as the liver or kidney with blood or buffered saline containing a metabolic precursor, followed by chemical analysis of the perfusate, also gives valuable information about the sites of major metabolic pathways. In this manner it was established that the liver is the major site of formation of the ketone bodies and urea and of the conversion of certain amino acids into glucose.

Surviving-Slice and Manometric Methods

Another important technique used for study of intermediary metabolism in animal or plant tissues is the *surviving-slice* technique, introduced by Warburg in the 1920s. Solid animal or plant tissues are sliced or minced to yield preparations in which most of the cells are intact but the slices are sufficiently thin (< 0.4 mm) for the rate of diffusion of oxygen and metabolities into and out of the cells from the aqueous suspending medium not to be rate-limiting for the metabolic exchanges occurring within the cells. Such suspensions of sliced tissue can be incubated with a given metabolite to study its conversion to a product which may accumulate in the medium. The rate of many metabolic events, e.g., the conversion of glucose to lactic acid by animal tissues, can be determined with surprisingly great accuracy by simple chemical measurements of the changes occurring in the medium in which tissue slices are suspended. This approach is especially successful for measurement of the rate of oxygen consumption of tissues; the decrease in partial pressure of oxygen over the suspension is measured in a manometric device called the Warburg-Barcroft apparatus (Figure 13-7). The manometric technique was very important in elucidation of the reactions of the tricarboxylic acid cycle in muscle (Chapter 16).

Figure 13-7
Warburg-Barcroft apparatus for measurement of oxygen consumption of sliced or minced tissue suspensions. The incubation is carried out in a special reaction vessel (left) attached to a manometer for recording the decrease in oxygen pressure as respiration takes place. The reaction vessel is shaken in a constant-temperature bath. The carbon dioxide generated during respiration is continuously absorbed from the gas phase by KOH in the center well. In this way, the partial pressure of CO_2 in the gas phase is kept at or near zero, and the pressure changes observed are due only to changes in oxygen pressure. Consumption or production of metabolites can be determined by chemical measurements on the suspending medium.

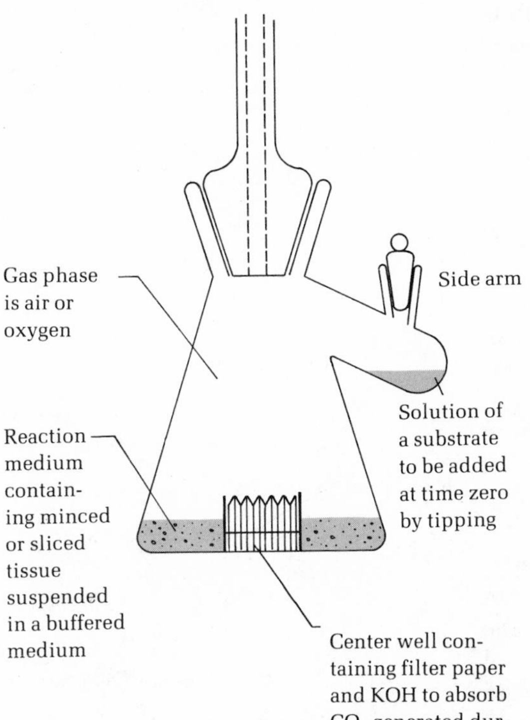

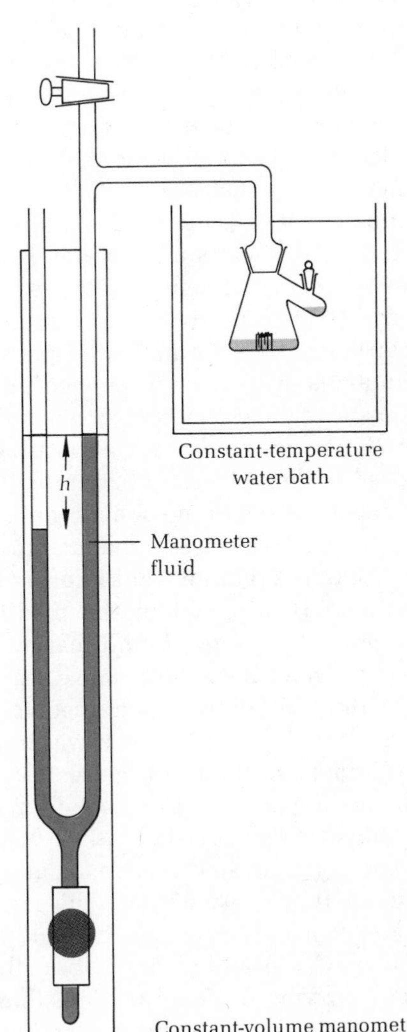

Genetic Defects in Metabolism; Auxotrophic Mutants

One of the most revealing experimental approaches to the study of intermediary metabolism in intact cells and organisms is afforded by genetic mutations in which a given enzyme fails to be synthesized in active form. Such defects, if they are not lethal, result in the accumulation and excretion of the normal substrate of the defective enzyme; in normal animals, of course, the intermediate would not accumulate. One such genetic defect in human patients leads to the excretion of *homogentisic acid* in the urine (Chapter 20). Since the excretion of this acid is increased by feeding phenylalanine and tyrosine and is decreased by withholding them from the diet, it was concluded that homogentisic acid is formed as an intermediate during oxidative catabolism of these amino acids. Many other genetic defects in human amino acid metabolism are known; they have provided important evidence for the nature of the intermediate reaction steps.

Nonlethal genetic defects involving major metabolic pathways are relatively rare in mammals and not easily recognized, but they can be produced at will in microorganisms and are powerful tools for studying metabolic pathways. In 1941 the "one gene–one enzyme" relationship was postulated by Beadle and Tatum on the basis of their studies of nutritional or biochemical mutants of the mold *Neurospora crassa*. The approaches they developed were extremely important, not only for analysis of the gene–enzyme relationship but also for the study of the pathways of intermediary metabolism. Wild type, i.e., unmutated, *Neurospora* can grow on a simple medium containing glucose as sole carbon source and only ammonia as nitrogen source. Treatment of *Neurospora* spores with mutagenic agents, such as x-rays, yields some mutant cells no longer capable of growing on this simple medium. However, such mutants often grow if the medium is supplemented with a specific metabolite, e.g., an amino acid such as arginine. From such studies it was postulated that an enzyme required in the synthesis of arginine from ammonia was genetically defective in such mutants, and for lack of arginine the cell could not manufacture those proteins which contain arginine, and thus could not grow. When arginine is supplied in the medium, the mutant cells can grow. It was also found that mutants of *Neurospora* defective in the capacity to make arginine are not all identical; they differ in which specific step in arginine biosynthesis is defective. Thus it was found that the growth of *argineless* mutant I (Figure 13-8) can be sustained only by adding arginine to the medium and not by adding any known precursor such as A, B, C, or D, indicating that this mutant is defective in enzyme E_4. *Arginineless* mutant II will grow when the medium is supplied with precursor D or with arginine but not when precursors A, B, or C are added, indicating that it is blocked by lack of enzyme E_3. Such mutants, blocked at different points in a metabolic pathway, can be used to test suspected precursors of a given product and to determine the sequence in which such precursors are converted to the product.

Such sets of mutants can be used in another way to identify intermediates in a biochemical sequence. For example, when mutant I (Figure 13-8) is grown in the presence of small, limiting amounts of arginine, the blocked precursor D will accumulate in the growth medium since it cannot be converted into arginine. After removal of the mutant I cells by filtration, this medium will support the growth of mutant II in the absence of arginine, since it supplies the precursor D. The filtrate of mutant II, however, will not support the growth of mutant I. This type of experiment is known as *cross-feeding*. The precursor generated by mutant I that can feed mutant II can then be isolated and identified; mutant II is used to bioassay for the precursor. Mutants defective in a biosynthetic pathway whose growth can be restored by providing

Figure 13-8
Mutants of Neurospora crassa *with defective enzymes (color) at different points in the biosynthesis of arginine from precursor A.*

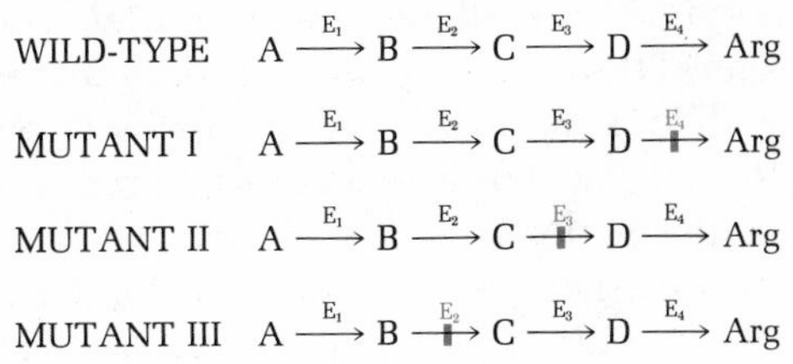

WILD-TYPE	$A \xrightarrow{E_1} B \xrightarrow{E_2} C \xrightarrow{E_3} D \xrightarrow{E_4} Arg$
MUTANT I	$A \xrightarrow{E_1} B \xrightarrow{E_2} C \xrightarrow{E_3} D \not\xrightarrow{E_4} Arg$
MUTANT II	$A \xrightarrow{E_1} B \xrightarrow{E_2} C \not\xrightarrow{E_3} D \xrightarrow{E_4} Arg$
MUTANT III	$A \xrightarrow{E_1} B \not\xrightarrow{E_2} C \xrightarrow{E_3} D \xrightarrow{E_4} Arg$

them with the normal product of the pathway are called *auxotrophic mutants.*

Mutants can also be used to analyze catabolic pathways. For example, wild-type *E. coli* cells are able to grow on lactose, glucose, or galactose as carbon source. In some *E. coli* mutants, the capacity to grow on lactose is lost, but the cells are still able to grow on the other sugars. The genetic defect in this case involves the enzyme that can hydrolyze lactose to its component hexoses, glucose and galactose. By these approaches many intermediate steps in metabolism have been established, particularly in the biosynthesis of amino acids, purines, and pyrimidines.

Isotopic Labeling Methods

Another powerful method applicable to intact organisms is the use of a compound labeled so that its metabolic fate can be traced. This approach was first used as long ago as 1904, when Knoop found that a phenyl group substituted onto the terminal methyl carbon of a fatty acid remained attached to this carbon atom throughout its metabolism. From the urine of animals fed such phenyl-substituted fatty acids, Knoop recovered phenyl-substituted degradation products from whose structure he deduced that fatty acids were degraded by successive removal of two-carbon fragments (Chapter 19). This primitive chemical-labeling method has been superseded by the use of isotopes to label a given metabolite so that it is chemically indistinguishable from normal molecules but can easily be detected and measured (Table 13-4). An extraordinary range of important observations have been made with the isotope tracer technique applied to intact animals, among them the discovery that the carbon atoms of acetic acid are metabolic precursors of all the carbon atoms of cholesterol and that glycine is a precursor in the synthesis of purines.

The isotope tracer method can also be used to determine the rate of metabolic processes in intact organisms and whether a given metabolic pathway is a major or minor route for a given metabolite. It has also been used to determine whether a metabolic pathway postulated by study of isolated enzymes in the test tube actually occurs in the intact cell (see Chapter 16).

Table 13-4 Some isotopes useful as tracers†

Isotope	*Relative natural abundance, %*	*Type of radiation*	*Half-life*
$^{2}_{1}H$	0.0154		Stable
$^{3}_{1}H$		β^-	12.1 years
$^{13}_{6}C$	1.1		Stable
$^{14}_{6}C$		β^-	5,700 years
$^{15}_{7}N$	0.365		Stable
$^{18}_{8}O$	0.204		Stable
$^{24}_{11}Na$		β^-,γ	15 hours
$^{32}_{15}P$		β^-	14.3 days
$^{35}_{16}S$		β^-	87.1 days
$^{36}_{17}Cl$		β^-	3.1×10^5 years
$^{42}_{19}K$		β^-	12.5 hours
$^{45}_{20}Ca$		β^-	152 days
$^{59}_{26}Fe$		β^-,γ	45 days
$^{131}_{53}I$		β^-,γ	8 days

† The superscript before the symbol of the element designates the mass number, the subscript the atomic number. β^- radiation is due to negative electrons. Radioactivity is expressed in terms of the *curie*, the quantity undergoing the same number of disintegrations per second as 1.0 gram of radium (3.7×10^{10} sec^{-1}); the millicurie and microcurie are more convenient units. Stable isotopes are measured in atoms percent excess over the natural abundance.

One of the most significant advances made with the isotope tracer method is the discovery that the components of some cells undergo metabolic turnover, first observed by Schoenheimer in the 1930s. Before then it was thought that once cell components, such as proteins or membrane lipids, were synthesized, they remained intact and stable for the lifetime of the cell. By feeding amino acids enriched with ^{15}N in their amino nitrogen atoms, Schoenheimer and others found that the labeled amino acid was incorporated into the peptide chains of liver proteins at an unexpectedly high rate, even though the total amount of protein in the liver did not change. He concluded that the proteins of the liver cell exist in a dynamic steady state, in which a relatively high rate of synthesis is exactly counterbalanced by a relatively high rate of degradation. The proteins of rat liver were found to have a half-life of about 5 to 6 days, whereas the liver cell itself has a much longer lifetime of several months (Table 13-5). On the other hand, most of the proteins and lipids of muscle tissue or the brain do not turn over rapidly, nor do those of bacteria grown on a medium of constant composition. Metabolic turnover is conspicuous only in cells or tissues which must adapt themselves rapidly to changes in the chemical composition of their exogenous nutrients, such as the liver and the intestinal mucosa. The rapid synthesis and degradation of enzyme proteins in such cells makes possible rapid changes in the concentration of different enzymes in the cell in response to changes in the incoming nutrient mixture.

Table 13-5 Turnover of some components of rat tissues

Tissue	*Half-life, days*
Liver:	
Total protein	5.0–6.0
Glycogen	0.5–1.0
Phosphoglycerides	1–2
Triacylglycerols	1–2
Cholesterol	5–7
Mitochondrial proteins	9.7
Muscle:	
Total protein	30
Glycogen	0.5–1.0
Brain:	
Triacylglycerols	10–15
Phospholipid	200
Cholesterol	>100

Cell-Free Systems

The most direct experimental approach to a metabolic sequence is the study of the pathway in preparations or extracts free of intact cell structure and the isolation of the enzymes catalyzing the process. Thus, modern knowledge of the details of the conversion of glucose to ethanol and carbon dioxide arose from the discovery of Büchner and Büchner in 1892 that cell-free extracts of yeast catalyze alcoholic fermentation. Similarly, it was shown later that conversion of glucose to lactic acid occurs in cell-free extracts of muscle. Once such preparations have been obtained, metabolic intermediates can be made to accumulate by use of specific enzyme inhibitors, by inactivation of specific enzymes, or by removal or inactivation of essential coenzymes. Chemical identification of intermediates accumulating after such treatments then permits identification of the enzymatic reactions forming and utilizing the intermediate and, ultimately, the isolation of the enzymes from the extract. The final goal is the reconstruction of part or all of the enzyme system *in vitro* (Latin, in glass, i.e., in the test tube), starting from highly purified enzymes, coenzymes, and other components. Since many enzymatic reactions are complex and may themselves consist of two or more steps, complete elucidation of a given metabolic sequence may require examination of the reaction steps occurring on the active site of the enzymes participating.

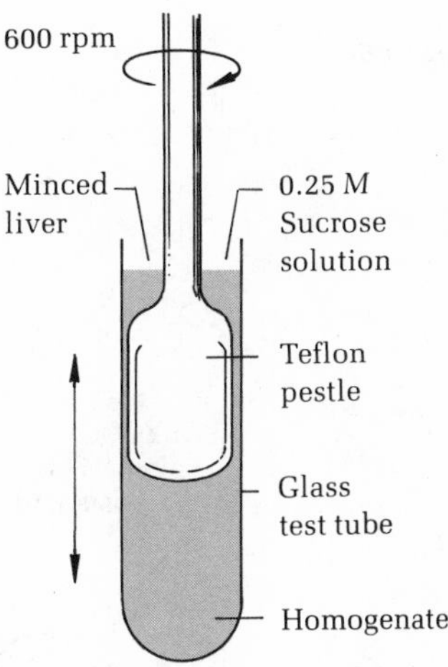

Figure 13-9
Isolation of intracellular structures by differential centrifugation. The cell membrane is ruptured by the shearing forces developed by the rotating homogenizer pestle. Following removal of connective tissue and fragments of blood vessels and bile ducts by a stainless steel sieve, the cell extract is centrifuged at a series of increasing rotor speeds.

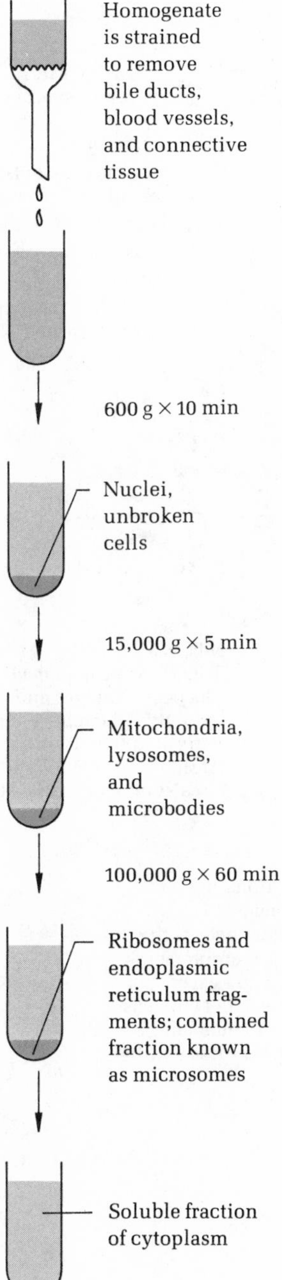

If cell structure is disrupted by homogenization in isotonic sucrose solution, the subcellular organelles and structures, such as nuclei, mitochondria, and ribosomes, can be isolated by differential centrifugation from the homogenate (Figure 13-9). These fractions can then be tested in vitro for their capacity to catalyze a given metabolic sequence. In this way it was shown that isolated mitochondria catalyze the oxidative reactions of the tricarboxylic acid cycle. Extracts prepared from isolated mitochondria also formed the starting point for tracing the enzymatic steps in fatty acid oxidation and for isolating the enzymes participating in this process. Similarly, isolated ribosomes are used to study the pathway and mechanism of protein synthesis.

Intracellular Compartmentation of Enzymes and Enzyme Systems

Different enzymes and enzyme systems are characteristically located in one or another organelle or intracellular structure of eucaryotic cells (Figure 13-10). The entire glycolytic enzyme system is located in the soluble portion of the cytoplasm, whereas the enzymes concerned in oxidation of pyruvate, fatty acids, and some amino acids are located in the mitochondria, as are the enzymes of electron transport and phosphorylation of ADP. It appears probable that some multienzyme systems are so located in the structure of an organelle that each enzyme is physically oriented adjacent to the next in the pathway, presumably to limit the diffusion paths, so that the entire sequence can function in a high degree of spatial and temporal coordination. This is true of the enzymes of electron transport, which are located in the inner membrane of mitochondria, and the enzymes and templates concerned in protein synthesis, which takes place on the ribosomes.

Compartmentation of enzyme systems also permits control and integration of some intracellular activities. For example, the biosynthesis of glucose from pyruvate involves a complex interplay of a series of enzymes, some

Figure 13-10
Compartmentation of some important enzymes and metabolic sequences in the liver cell of the rat. The electron micrograph from which the cell drawing was traced is shown in Figure 1-8.

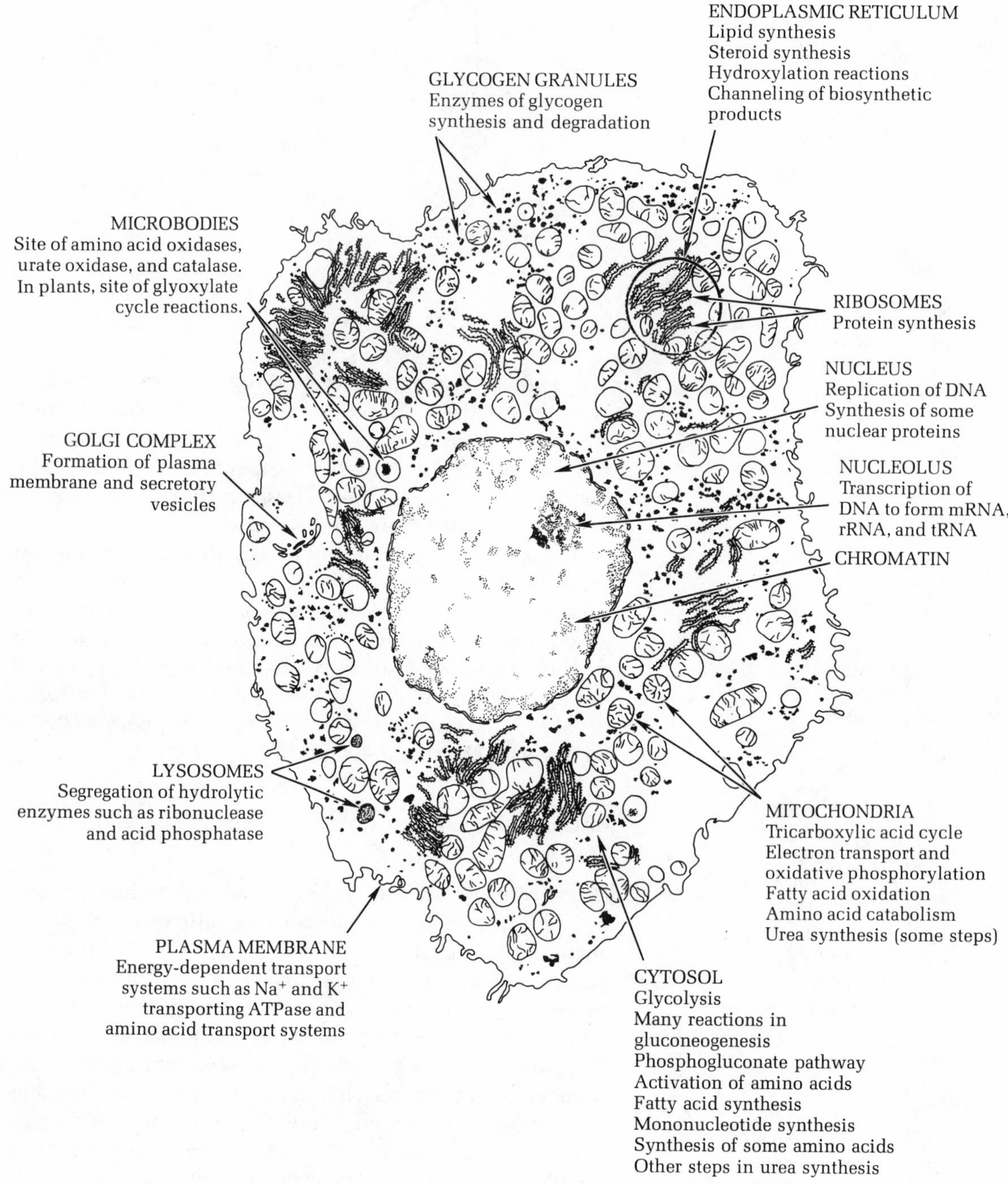

located in the mitochondria and some in the soluble phase of the cytoplasm. The rate of this overall reaction depends not only on the activity of allosteric enzymes in both compartments but also on the exchanges of essential intermediates across the mitochondrial membranes.

Still another advantage of compartmentation is that it segregates chemically incompatible reactions. For example, at one and the same time a cell may be oxidizing long-chain fatty acids to the stage of acetic acid and carrying out the reverse process, reduction of acetic acid to form long-chain fatty acids. These chemically incompatible processes occur in different parts of the cell: net oxidation in the mitochondria and net reduction in the extramitochondrial cytoplasm.

Cellular Regulation of Metabolic Pathways

In general, the rate of catabolism of a cell is controlled not by the concentration of its nutrients in the environment, but rather by its second-to-second needs for energy in the form of ATP. In short, cells utilize only so much fuel as to produce the amount of energy required for its current activities. Similarly, the rate of biosynthesis of cell components is also adjusted to immediate needs. For example, cells synthesize amino acids at such a rate as to just provide themselves with the minimum necessary supply of building blocks for protein synthesis. The principle of maximum economy pervades all aspects of cellular metabolism.

The regulation of a metabolic pathway may occur at several levels, increasing in complexity. The simplest type of regulation involves the basic parameters affecting the rates of enzymatic reactions. Each enzyme of a multienzyme sequence has a characteristic optimum pH, a characteristic affinity, or Michaelis constant, for its substrate(s) and product(s), as well as a characteristic affinity for its coenzyme or metal-ion activator. The overall rate of such a sequence in the cell is therefore a function of the concentration of each enzyme, the intracellular pH, the intracellular concentration of each intermediate, and the concentration of all essential metal ions and coenzymes. Since the intracellular pH is a function of the relative rates of all proton-releasing and proton-absorbing reactions in the cell, it is clear that the rate of a given metabolic pathway can be influenced by any intracellular process that can alter intracellular pH. Similarly, the steady-state concentration of each metabolic intermediate in the cell is the resultant of the rates of its formation and utilization, which may be determined not only by the activity of the enzyme system under consideration but also by the rates of other enzymatic reactions capable of using or forming that intermediate. Similar considerations apply to the available concentration of essential metal ions, such as Mg^{2+}, and of essential coenzymes, for which many enzymes may compete.

The second general mechanism regulating metabolic sequences is by the action of regulatory enzymes (Chapter

9), which usually are located at or near the beginning of a multienzyme sequence. Most regulatory enzymes are inhibited by the end-product of the sequence; such inhibition is called *feed-back inhibition*, *end-product inhibition*, or *retroinhibition*. In those enzyme systems concerned with the generation of ATP from ADP coupled to catabolic reactions, the end-product ATP usually functions as the allosteric inhibitor. In enzyme systems leading to biosynthesis the biosynthetic end product usually functions as an allosteric inhibitor. Moreover, some allosteric enzymes are activated or stimulated by specific modulators; thus an allosteric enzyme regulating a catabolic sequence may be stimulated by ADP. Some allosteric enzymes are multivalent, i.e., they can respond to two or more activators or inhibitors which may be the products of two or more different metabolic sequences. Thus, multivalent allosteric enzymes may integrate the rates of two or more enzyme systems. Furthermore, because the anabolic and catabolic sequences between a given precursor and a given product have different regulatory enzymes, the rates of biosynthesis and degradation of a given cell component can be regulated independently.

The third level at which metabolic regulation is exerted is through genetic control of the rate of enzyme synthesis. The rate of a given metabolic sequence must depend on the concentration of the active form of each enzyme in a sequence, which in turn is the result of a balance between the rates of its synthesis and its degradation. The rate of synthesis of a given enzyme in a cell may vary widely, depending on conditions. Enzymes that are always present in nearly constant amounts in a given cell are called *constitutive*. Others that are synthesized only in response to the presence of certain substrates are called *adaptive* or *induced* enzymes. The genes specifying the synthesis of induced enzymes are usually under repression and come into play, i.e., undergo *derepression*, only in response to the presence of the inducing agent. An entire sequence of enzymes may be repressed or induced as a group because their synthesis is coded by a set of consecutive genes in DNA, called an *operon*, which can be repressed or derepressed together. These processes are called *coordinate* repression or depression (Chapter 33).

Metabolic control is exerted at still another level in higher multicellular organisms that have endocrine systems. Hormones elaborated by an endocrine gland are chemical messengers that stimulate or inhibit specific metabolic activities in other tissues or organs. Deficiency of insulin secretion by the pancreas results in impaired transport of glucose into cells, which leads to a number of secondary metabolic effects, e.g., a decrease in the biosynthesis of fatty acids from glucose and an excessive formation of ketone bodies by the liver. Administration of trace amounts of insulin repairs these defects. Opposed to the action of insulin is *somatotrophin*, elaborated by the anterior pituitary gland. How hormones control metabolic activity is not yet known. Some may operate by changing the permeability or transport activity of cell membranes;

others may function by altering the rate at which messenger RNA is transcribed for the synthesis of specific enzymes.

Summary

Organisms can be classified on the basis of their exogenous carbon requirements. Autotrophs require only carbon dioxide, whereas heterotrophs require carbon in a more complex reduced form, such as glucose. They can also be classified by energy source: phototrophs obtain their energy from light, whereas chemotrophs obtain energy from oxidation-reduction reactions. Cells using inorganic reductants or electron donors are called lithotrophs; those using organic molecules are organotrophs. Most species of cells can be classified as photolithotrophs, which include most photosynthetic cells, or chemoorganotrophs, which include animal cells, many microorganisms, and nonphotosynthetic plant cells. Photosynthetic autotrophs and chemoorganotrophs "feed" each other: photosynthetic cells use atmospheric carbon dioxide and solar energy to synthesize glucose and evolve oxygen, whereas animal cells use the glucose so formed at the expense of oxygen to yield carbon dioxide. Solar energy is the ultimate source of energy for nearly all forms of life.

In the biological nitrogen cycle, plants obtain their nitrogen as nitrate and reduce it to ammonia and amino acids; these are then utilized by animals and returned to the soil as ammonia, which is reoxidized to nitrate. Only nitrogen-fixing bacteria can utilize the molecular nitrogen of the atmosphere. Some organisms require exogenous preformed amino acids, purines, or pyrimidines as nitrogen sources, as well as trace amounts of vitamins or growth factors as precursors of essential coenzymes.

Intermediary metabolism can be divided into catabolic pathways, responsible for the degradation of energy-rich nutrient molecules, anabolic pathways, for the synthesis of cellular components, and amphibolic or central, pathways, which serve in both capacities. Anabolic and catabolic pathways are not enzymatically identical and are often located in different parts of the cell. Catabolism of nutrient molecules is accompanied by conservation of some of the energy of the nutrient in the form of the phosphate-bond energy of adenosine triphosphate (ATP). The energy for anabolic pathways is provided by dephosphorylation of ATP, which serves as a carrier of chemical energy. Chemical energy is also carried from catabolic to anabolic pathways in the form of coenzymes, particularly NADPH.

Metabolic pathways are studied in intact organisms by means of input-output studies on normal, pathological, stressed, or poisoned organisms, by perfusion of intact organisms, and by study of surviving slices of tissue. Genetically defective microorganisms, called auxotrophs, provide a powerful tool for analysis of metabolic pathways, as does the isotope tracer technique. Once a given metabolic conversion can be demonstrated in a cell-free system, the individual enzymes catalyzing the separate reactions can be isolated and identified. Metabolism is regulated through the intrinsic properties of enzymes, through the action of regulatory, or allosteric, enzymes, through genetic repression and depression of enzymes, and by endocrine control.

References

Books

BAKER, J. J. W., and G. E. ALLEN, *Matter, Energy and Life: An Introduction for Biology Students*, Addison-Wesley Publishing Company, Inc., Reading, Mass., 1965.

CHASE, G. D., and J. L. RABINOWITZ, *Principles of Radioisotope Methodology*, 2d ed., Burgess Publishing Company, Minneapolis, Minn., 1962. Application of isotopic techniques to biochemical problems.

COLOWICK, S. P., and N. O. KAPLAN, *Methods in Enzymology*, vols. I–XII, Academic Press Inc., New York, 1955 to present. Detailed and extensive treatise on experimental approaches to study of intermediary metabolism.

GUNSALUS, I. C., and R. Y. STANIER (eds.), *The Bacteria*, vols. II and III, Academic Press Inc., New York, 1961. The metabolic classification of microorganisms is described in detail, as are many metabolic pathways.

KREBS, H. A., and H. L. KORNBERG, *Energy Transformations in Living Matter*, Springer-Verlag OHG Berlin, 1957. A classical and readable analysis of metabolism in terms of energy exchanges; it has had a wide influence.

LEHNINGER, A. L., *Bioenergetics*, W. A. Benjamin, Inc., New York, 1965. An elementary treatment of the molecular basis of biological energy transformations.

MOROWITZ, H. J., *Energy Flow in Biology*, Academic Press Inc., New York, 1968. A theoretical analysis of some more profound aspects of bioenergetics.

ROODYN, D. B. (ed.), *Enzyme Cytology*, Academic Press Inc., New York, 1967. Comprehensive discussion of the intracellular location and function of enzymes and enzyme systems, in terms of cell structure.

Reviews and Articles

DE DUVE, C., R. WATTIAUX, and P. BAUDHUIN, "Distribution of Enzymes between Subcellular Fractions in Animal Tissues," *Advan. Enzymol.*, **24**:291–358 (1962).

KORNBERG, H. L., "The Coordination of Metabolic Routes," *Symp. Soc. Gen. Microbiol.*, **15**:8–31 (1965). A brief review of regulatory aspects of metabolism, particularly in *E. coli* and other bacteria.

CHAPTER 14 BIOENERGETIC PRINCIPLES AND THE ATP CYCLE

The ATP-ADP system functions as a carrier of chemical energy because ADP is able to accept a phosphate group during coupled energy-yielding reactions of catabolism and the ATP so formed is able to donate its terminal phosphate group in coupled energy-requiring reactions. In this chapter we shall examine the chemical and thermodynamic principles underlying the function of the ATP-ADP system.

Occurrence and Properties of ATP and ADP

ATP was first isolated from acid extracts of muscle in 1929 by Fiske and Subbarow. Its structure (Chapter 12 and Figure 14-1) was deduced some years later by degradation experiments and ultimately confirmed by total chemical synthesis by Todd and his colleagues in 1948. From its first discovery ATP was suspected to play a role in cellular energy transfer, but it was not until 1939–1941 that Lipmann proposed it serves as a principal means of transfer of chemical energy in the cell. ATP, ADP, and AMP are not trace substances; the sum of their concentrations in the aqueous phase of various types of intact cells is between 2 and 15 m*M*. The concentration of ATP usually greatly exceeds the sum of the concentrations of the other two; the AMP concentration is usually much the lowest of the three. These nucleotides are present not only in the soluble cytoplasm but also within organelles such as mitochondria and nuclei. The intracellular compartmentation of the ATP system is an important feature in cellular regulation of metabolism.

At pH 7.0, both ATP and ADP are highly charged anions. ATP has four ionizable protons in its triphosphoric acid group. Three have low pK' values of about 2 to 3 and are thus completely dissociated at pH 7.0; the fourth has a pK' of 6.50 and therefore is about 75 percent dissociated at pH 7.0. ADP has three ionizable protons; two are completely dissociated at pH 7.0 and the third, which has a pK' of 7.2, is about 39 percent dissociated at pH 7.0. The high concentration of negative charges around the triphosphate group of ATP is an important factor in its high-energy nature, as will be seen. In the intact cell, very little ATP and ADP exist as free anions; they are largely present as the 1:1 $MgATP^{2-}$ and $MgADP^{-}$ complexes, because of the high affinity of the pyrophosphate groups for binding divalent cations and the high concentration of Mg^{2+} in intracellular fluid. The affinity of ATP for Mg^{2+} is about 10 times as great as that of ADP. In most enzymatic reactions in which ATP participates as phosphate donor, its active form is the $MgATP^{2-}$ complex (Figure 14-2). In other reactions, however, the MnATP complex appears to be the more active substrate.

ADP and ATP are easily separated and measured by paper electrophoresis or thin-layer chromatography. Both show the characteristic ultraviolet absorption peak at 260 nm given by the adenine moiety (Chapter 12). The last two phosphate groups of ATP and the terminal phosphate group of ADP can be hydrolyzed by boiling in 1 *N* HCl for 7 min; the ester linkage between the remaining phosphate group and ribose is stable to this treatment. Specific enzymes hydrolyzing or transferring the terminal phosphate group of ATP are discussed below.

Figure 14-1
Structures of ATP and ADP.

ATP

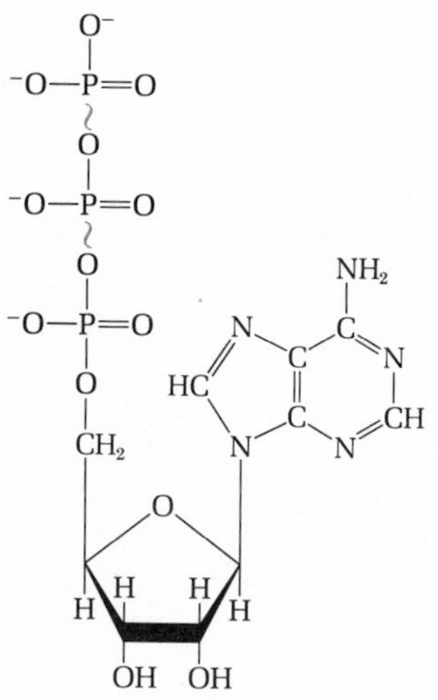

ADP

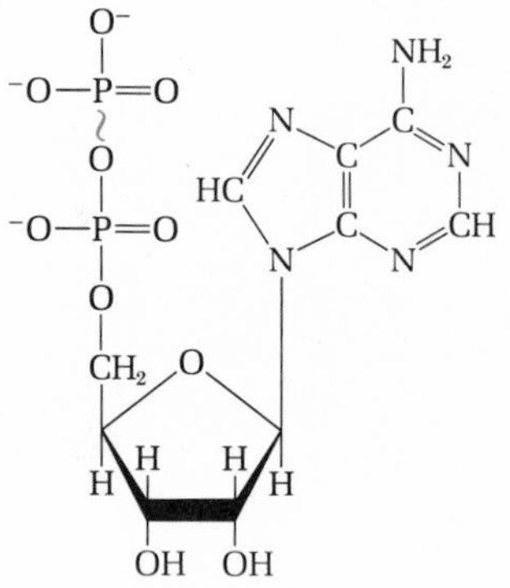

Principles of Chemical Thermodynamics

A description of the physicochemical basis of the function of ATP in the energy cycle of the cell requires a brief review of some relevant principles of equilibrium thermodynamics. Thermodynamic analysis of energy exchanges begins by specifying a *system,* the collection of matter under study. Since thermodynamics is a statistical science, the predictive value of its principles increases in proportion to the size of the collection of matter analyzed. All

Figure 14-2
Metal complexes of ATP and ADP. In the Mg^{2+} complexes the two terminal phosphate groups are the ligands. In the Mn^{2+} complexes the 7-nitrogen atom of the adenine ring is also a ligand.

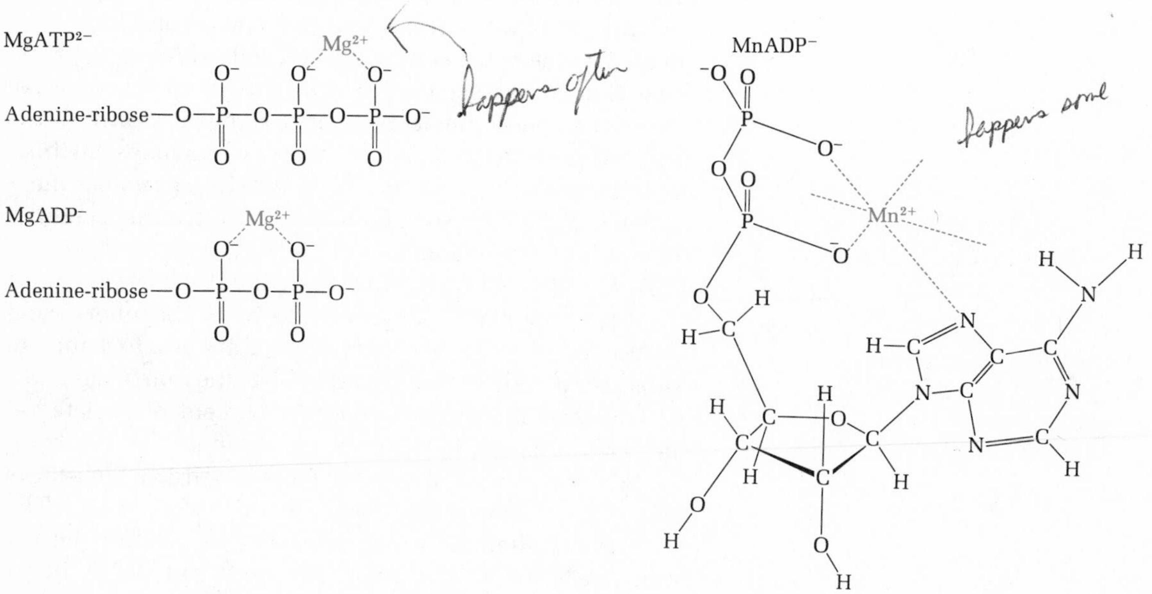

$MgATP^{2-}$

$MgADP^{-}$

$MnADP^{-}$

ATP

ADP

other matter in the universe apart from the specified system is called the *surroundings*. During the process under study, energy may pass from the system to the surroundings or from the surroundings to the system. Processes are analyzed in terms of the energy content of the *initial state* of the system and surroundings and the *final state*, after equilibrium has been reached. The energy content of each state is a function of various measureable attributes—temperature, pressure, volume, mass, etc.—formulated into an *equation of state*. From measurements of the changes in energy content of the system and the surroundings as the system proceeds from its initial to its final state, an energy balance sheet can be prepared. Since the analysis of energy exchanges by thermodynamics is made by considering properties of matter in the bulk, such as temperature or pressure, it requires no knowledge of the molecular composition of the system or its surroundings, or of the molecular mechanism by which a process takes place. Furthermore, thermodynamic analysis of energy exchanges is independent of the rates of processes; it depends only on the initial and final states of the system.

The First law of thermodynamics is the principle of the conservation of energy: in any process the total energy of the system plus surroundings remains constant. Although energy is neither created nor destroyed during chemical or physical processes, it may undergo transformation from one form to another, such as heat, light, electrical, mechanical, and chemical energy.

The Second law places some limitations on the kinds of energy transformation that may take place in physical or chemical processes and predicts in what direction a given process is likely to occur. It states that all processes tend to proceed in such a direction that the *entropy* of the system plus surroundings, i.e., the entropy of the universe, increases until an equilibrium is reached at which the entropy is the maximum that can be attained under the prevailing conditions of temperature and pressure. Entropy is defined (for the moment) as the degree of disorder, or randomness. An equilibrium is defined as a state in which no further net chemical or physical change is taking place and in which temperature, pressure, and concentration are uniform throughout the system. A system at equilibrium has exhausted its capacity for doing work on its surroundings. Once a process has occurred with an increase in entropy and has attained a condition of equilibrium, it cannot spontaneously reverse and return to its initial state, which would require a decrease in entropy. A randomized system never unrandomizes itself spontaneously, as is seen in Figure 14-3. Processes proceeding with an increase in entropy are termed *irreversible*. Processes occurring without change in entropy are called *reversible*. All "real" processes occurring in our physical world, including the process of life, are irreversible.

Although entropy may be visualized qualitatively in verbal or material terms, as illustrated in Figure 14-3, a more rigorous definition and its expression in quantitative terms is much more difficult, particularly for chemical

Figure 14-3
The increase of entropy or randomness in two physical systems. Such flows never reverse spontaneously.

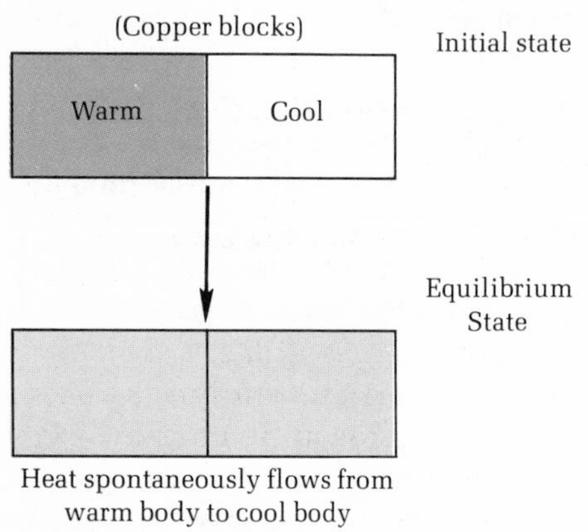

Heat spontaneously flows from warm body to cool body

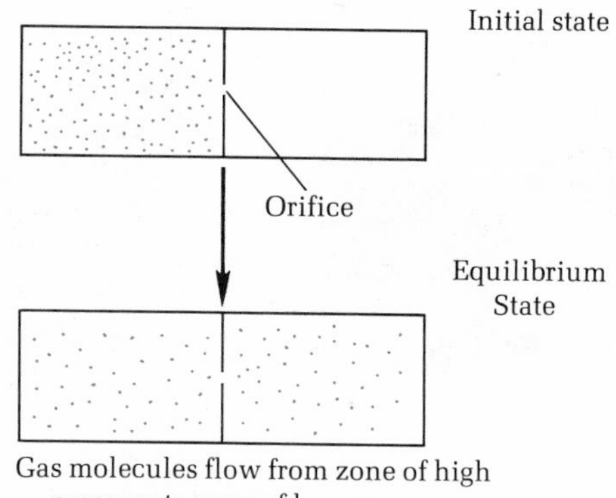

Gas molecules flow from zone of high pressure to zone of low pressure

reactions. Entropy is actually a complex mathematical function of a number of variables, such as temperature and pressure, and its amount is expressed in entropy units, which have the dimensions of calories per degree. At any given temperature, solids possess relatively low entropy, liquids intermediate entropy, and gases relatively high entropy. In solids, individual atoms and molecules are usually present in an ordered arrangement, particularly when they are crystalline; in the gaseous state individual molecules are moving randomly.

Entropy changes during chemical reactions are not always easily measured or calculated. However, the change in entropy during a process is quantitatively related to changes in total energy of the system by a third function, called the free energy, through an equation that combines the First and Second laws. Since changes in free energy of chemical reactions can be measured relatively easily, this equation is extremely useful for predicting the direction and final equilibrium of chemical reactions in dilute aqueous systems. It defines the change in free energy ΔG, when temperature and pressure are constant, as

$$\Delta G = \Delta H - T\Delta S \qquad (1)$$

in which ΔH is the change in the function termed enthalpy, T is the absolute temperature, and ΔS the change in entropy. The change in enthalpy, ΔH, which is also called the heat change, is defined by the equation

$$\Delta H = \Delta E + \Delta PV \qquad (2)$$

in which ΔE is the change in total energy of the system, P is the pressure, and V the volume. We can now introduce an important simplification in our treatment. In biological systems chemical reactions take place in dilute aqueous solutions in which temperature, pressure and volume remain constant. Under these conditions the term ΔPV in equation (2) becomes zero, and ΔH now is equal to ΔE, the

Figure 14-4
Summary of free energy and entropy relationships between a system and its surroundings when the temperature, pressure and volume of the system are constant. The entropy of the system + surroundings, or the free energy of the system alone, are the criteria for predicting the direction of chemical reactions under these conditions.

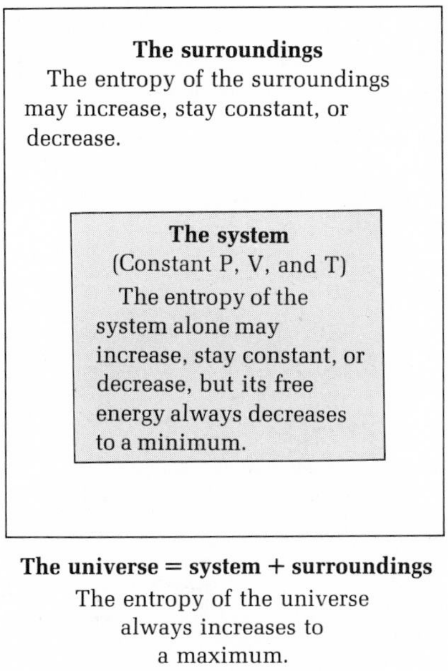

The surroundings
The entropy of the surroundings may increase, stay constant, or decrease.

The system
(Constant P, V, and T)
The entropy of the system alone may increase, stay constant, or decrease, but its free energy always decreases to a minimum.

The universe = system + surroundings
The entropy of the universe always increases to a maximum.

change in total energy of the system. We can therefore substitute in equation (1)

$$\Delta G = \Delta E - T\Delta S$$

no pV work

If this equation is rearranged to give

$$\Delta E = \Delta G + T\Delta S$$

we see that at constant temperature and pressure the change in total energy of a system ΔE, which is equivalent to the change in heat, is the sum of the term $T\Delta S$ and the change in free energy ΔG. The free-energy change can be defined as that portion of the total energy change which is available to do work as the system proceeds on its way to the condition of equilibrium at constant temperature and pressure. As the system approaches equilibrium, the free energy decreases to a minimum.

With the assistance of Figure 14-4 we can now summarize the relationships between changes in free energy and entropy in a system and its surroundings under the special conditions when temperature and pressure *in the system* are constant, recalling that the system is free to exchange energy with its surroundings but does not exchange mass. When the system undergoes a change leading to an equilibrium, the total energy of the system plus surroundings remains constant, although the total energy of the system alone may increase, stay constant, or decrease. During this change, the system may either gain heat from its surroundings or yield it to them. Next, we note that the entropy of the system plus surroundings increases during a given process, to attain a maximum at the point of equilibrium; it is the tendency to maximize entropy in the universe that is the real driving force of any process. Note, however, that the entropy of the system *alone* need not increase during a process leading to equilibrium; it may increase, stay constant, or actually decrease. However, if the entropy of the system alone decreases, then the Second law says that the entropy of the surroundings must increase by such an amount so that the sum of the entropy changes in the system *and* surroundings increases. (In fact, this is what happens when a living organism grows: the entropy of the organism, i.e., the system, decreases whereas that of the surroundings increases.) Entropy measurements are not always useful for predicting the direction of a chemical process, since it is difficult to measure entropy changes in both the system and surroundings. On the other hand, the free energy change is a more useful criterion because it is an attribute of the system alone, so long as temperature and pressure are constant. Under these conditions the free energy of the system always decreases to a minimum at equilibrium, it never increases. The free energy change of chemical reactions can be measured relatively easily, as we shall now see.

The Standard Free-Energy Change of Chemical Reactions

The free-energy change occurring during chemical reactions is calculated using an equation which can be derived from the law of chemical equilibrium. For the generalized reaction

$$aA + bB \rightleftharpoons cC + dD \tag{3}$$

where a, b, c, and d are the number of molecules of A, B, C, and D participating in the reaction, the free-energy change ΔG is given by the equation

$$\Delta G = \Delta G^{\circ} + RT \ln \frac{[C]^c[D]^d}{[A]^a[B]^b} \tag{4}$$

in which the terms [A], [B], [C], and [D] are the molar concentrations of A, B, C, and D, and a, b, c, and d now are exponents of their concentrations, R is the gas constant (1.987 cal mole^{-1} degree^{-1}), T the absolute temperature, and ΔG°, the *standard free-energy change*, to be defined below.

When reaction (3) is at equilibrium, regardless of the starting concentrations of A, B, C, and D, the condition of minimum free energy exists and no further change is possible; ΔG is therefore 0.0. We then obtain

$$0 = \Delta G^{\circ} + RT \ln \frac{[C]^c[D]^d}{[A]^a[B]^b} \tag{5}$$

which becomes

$$\Delta G^{\circ} = -RT \ln \frac{[C]^c[D]^d}{[A]^a[B]^b} \tag{6}$$

Since the apparent equilibrium constant K'_{eq} for equation (3) is

$$K'_{eq} = \frac{[C]^c[D]^d}{[A]^a[B]^b} \tag{7}$$

we can substitute K'_{eq} in equation (6) and obtain the general equation

$$\Delta G^{\circ} = -RT \ln K'_{eq}$$

or

$$\Delta G^{\circ} = -2.303RT \log_{10} K'_{eq} \tag{8}$$

This equation shows us that ΔG°, the standard free-energy change of a chemical reaction, can be calculated from its equilibrium constant K'_{eq} at any given temperature. The standard free-energy change is thus a characteristic thermodynamic constant for any given chemical reaction. It can be defined in another way which clearly indicates its true meaning. The standard free-energy change of a reaction is in reality the *difference* in the *standard free energy* of the reactants and the *standard free energy* of the products, each term being adjusted to the stoichiometry of the reaction equation:

$$\Delta G^{\circ} = \sum G^{\circ}_{\text{products}} - \sum G^{\circ}_{\text{reactants}}$$

For reaction (3) it is

$$\Delta G^\circ = (cG^\circ_C + dG^\circ_D) - (aG^\circ_A + bG^\circ_B)$$

The standard free energy of a compound is a measure of the total amount of free energy it can yield on complete decomposition. As we shall see later, approximate values for standard free energies of formation have been calculated and from them standard free energy *changes* of chemical reactions can be arrived at.

It is extremely important to understand the difference between ΔG°, the *standard* free-energy change, and ΔG, the *actual* or *measured* free-energy change. This difference is best explained in terms of an analogy. ΔG° is a constant for any given reaction at a given temperature, just as the pK' of a weak acid is a constant at a given temperature. On the other hand, ΔG varies with the concentrations of the reactants and products, just as the pH of a solution of a weak acid varies with the concentrations of the proton donor and proton acceptor. ΔG equals ΔG° only when all reactants and products are present at 1.0 *M* concentration, in the same way that the pH of a solution of a weak acid is equal to its pK' when the proton donor and acceptor species are 1.0 *M*. It is ΔG that determines whether a chemical reaction will occur in the direction written starting from given concentrations of reactants. Remember that a chemical reaction will occur only if ΔG is negative, i.e., if the free energy of the system decreases. On the other hand, a chemical reaction whose *standard* free-energy change ΔG° is positive can still go forward as written providing that the initial concentrations of the reactants and products are such that ΔG will be negative.

Equation (8) enables us to calculate the standard free-energy change ΔG° of any chemical reaction from its equilibrium constant, which in turn can be estimated from analytical measurements. If the equilibrium constant for a reaction is 1.0, then $\Delta G^\circ = 0.0$ and no change in free energy occurs when 1 mole of reactant(s) is completely converted to product(s), all at a concentration of 1.0 *M*. If the equilibrium constant is greater than 1.0, the standard free-energy change ΔG° is negative. If the equilibrium constant is less than 1.0, ΔG° is positive. Chemical reactions with a negative standard free-energy change are termed *exergonic*; such reactions proceed spontaneously in the direction written starting from 1.0 *M* concentrations of all components. Reactions with a positive standard free-energy change are called *endergonic*; they do not proceed spontaneously in the direction written starting from 1.0 *M* concentrations of all reactants and products; in fact, they proceed in the reverse direction. Table 14-1 shows the quantitative relationship between the standard free-energy change ΔG° and the magnitude of the equilibrium constant K'_{eq}.

Three important conventions relevant to thermodynamic analysis of biochemical systems must now be specified.

1 Whenever water is a reactant or product, its thermodynamic activity or concentration is arbitrarily set at

Table 14-1 Relationship between the equilibrium constant and the standard free-energy change at 25°

K'_{eq}	ΔG°, *cal*
0.001	+4089
0.01	+2726
0.1	+1363
1.0	0
10.0	−1363
100.0	−2726
1,000.0	−4089

1.0, even though the molar concentration of water in dilute aqueous systems is actually about 55.5 *M*.

2 In biochemical energetics, pH 7.0 is designated as the reference state, rather than a hydrogen-ion activity of 1.0, that is, pH = 0.0, as normally used in physical chemistry. The standard free-energy change at pH 7.0 is designated by $\Delta G^{\circ\prime}$.

3 The $\Delta G^{\circ\prime}$ values used in biochemical energetics assume that the standard state of each reactant and product capable of ionization is that mixture of its un-ionized and ionized forms which exists at pH 7.0. Therefore $\Delta G^{\circ\prime}$ values based on pH = 7.0 may not necessarily be used at pH values other than 7.0, because the extent of ionization of one or more components may change with pH. The variation of ΔG° with pH for some biochemical reactions is quite large and sometimes difficult to calculate.

A sample calculation of the standard free-energy change can now be made from equilibrium data on the enzyme *phosphoglucomutase*, which catalyzes the reversible reaction

$$\text{Glucose 1-phosphate} \rightleftharpoons \text{glucose 6-phosphate} \qquad (9)$$

Chemical analysis shows that if we start with 0.020 *M* glucose 1-phosphate in the presence of excess enzyme and allow the reaction to go in the forward direction, or if we start with 0.020 *M* glucose 6-phosphate and go in the reverse direction, the final equilibrium mixture in either case contains 0.001 *M* glucose 1-phosphate and 0.019 *M* glucose 6-phosphate at 25°C and pH 7.0. We can then calculate the equilibrium constant

$$K'_{eq} = \frac{[\text{glucose 6-phosphate}]}{[\text{glucose 1-phosphate}]} = \frac{0.019}{0.001} = 19$$

From this value of K'_{eq}, the standard free-energy change $\Delta G^{\circ\prime}$ is calculated from equation (8)

$$\begin{aligned} \Delta G^{\circ\prime} &= -RT \ln K'_{eq} \\ &= -1.987 \times 298 \ln 19 \\ &= -1.987 \times 298 \times 2.303 \log 19 \\ &= -1745 \text{ cal} \\ &= -1.745 \text{ kcal} \end{aligned}$$

Since the sign of the standard free-energy change is negative, the conversion of glucose 1-phosphate to glucose 6-phosphate is an exergonic process. When 1.0 mole of glucose 1-phosphate is converted to 1.0 mole of glucose 6-phosphate at 25° and pH 7.0, under conditions in which the concentration of each is maintained at 1.0 *M*, a decline in free energy of 1745 cal, or 1.745 kcal, occurs. It is usually more convenient to express thermodynamic data in kilocalories, a practice we shall follow.

Another important point must be made. When a chemical reaction at constant temperature and pressure proceeds with a decline in free energy, it can theoretically do an amount of work that is energetically equivalent to the decrease in free energy. Actually, however, a chemical reaction performs work only if it can be harnessed in some way so as to utilize the energy. The $\Delta G^{\circ\prime}$ of a chemical reaction represents the *maximum* work it can do; the amount actually performed may be much less or zero.

The standard free-energy changes of chemical reactions have another valuable property; they are additive. As an example, we may consider the following consecutive reactions, each having a characteristic standard free-energy change.

Reaction	*Standard free-energy change*
$A \longrightarrow B$	$\Delta G_1^{\circ\prime}$
$B \longrightarrow C$	$\Delta G_2^{\circ\prime}$
$C \longrightarrow D$	$\Delta G_3^{\circ\prime}$

The sum of these reactions is $A \longrightarrow D$, whose standard free-energy change $\Delta G_s^{\circ\prime}$ is the algebraic sum of the $\Delta G^{\circ\prime}$ values of the individual steps, each being given its proper sign:

$$\Delta G_s^{\circ\prime} = \Delta G_1^{\circ\prime} + \Delta G_2^{\circ\prime} + \Delta G_3^{\circ\prime}$$

This property is extremely useful for calculating the standard free-energy change of a reaction when its equilibrium constant cannot be determined directly. In such a case the reaction may be coupled to one or more reactions of known equilibrium constants, to yield a sequence whose overall equilibrium can more readily be measured. In the above example, if we know the values of $\Delta G_1^{\circ\prime}$, $\Delta G_2^{\circ\prime}$, and $\Delta G_s^{\circ\prime}$, we can calculate $\Delta G_3^{\circ\prime}$.

Another way of arriving at the $\Delta G^{\circ\prime}$ for a given chemical reaction is to calculate it from the standard free energy of formation of its substrates and products. The results of many thermodynamic measurements have shown that each type of organic functional group has a characteristic free energy of formation from its elements and that such values are additive. The standard free energies of formation $\Delta G_f^{\circ\prime}$ for many biologically occurring compounds have been calculated (Table 14-2).

Table 14-2 Standard free energies of formation†

Substance	$\Delta G_f^{\circ\prime}$ *kcal/mole*
Acetate$^-$	− 88.99
cis-Aconitate^{3-}	−220.51
L-Alanine	− 88.75
NH_4^+	− 19.00
L-Aspartate$^-$	−166.99
HCO_3^-	−140.33
Carbon dioxide (gas)	− 94.45
Ethanol	− 43.39
Fumarate^{2-}	−144.41
α-D-Glucose	−219.22
Glycerol	−116.76
OH^-	− 37.60
H^+ (reference standard)	0
α-Ketoglutarate^{2-}	−190.62
Lactate$^-$	−123.76
L-Malate^{2-}	−201.98
Oxaloacetate^{2-}	−190.53
Pyruvate$^-$	−113.44
Succinate^{2-}	−164.97
Water (liquid)	− 56.69

† The values given are for 1 *M* aqueous solutions at pH 7.0 and 25°.

The ΔG° of a chemical reaction is equal to the difference between the sum of the standard free energies of formation of the products and the sum of those of the reactants, taking into account the actual stoichiometry of the reaction

$$\Delta G^\circ = \sum \Delta G^\circ_{f,\text{products}} - \sum \Delta G^\circ_{f,\text{reactants}}$$

For example, we can calculate the standard free-energy change $\Delta G^{\circ\prime}$ of the reaction catalyzed by the enzyme fumarase

$$\text{Fumarate} + H_2O \rightleftharpoons \text{malate}$$

From data in Table 14-2

$$\Delta G^{\circ\prime} = -201.98 - (-144.41 - 56.69) = -0.88 \text{ kcal}$$

Although the errors in such calculations can be rather large, because they represent small differences between two large terms, this approach often represents the only convenient way of obtaining the $\Delta G^{\circ\prime}$ of a reaction.

Table 14-3 gives the standard free-energy changes for a number of biologically important reactions calculated from equilibrium measurements or standard free energies of formation. Note that two types of reactions proceed with especially large decreases in standard free energy: hydrolysis of anhydrides and oxidation reactions. Such reactions are prominent in cellular energy transformations.

The Standard Free Energy of Hydrolysis of ATP

In principle, the simplest way to determine $\Delta G^{\circ\prime}$ for the reaction

$$\text{ATP} + \text{HOH} \longrightarrow \text{ADP} + \text{phosphate} \qquad (10)$$

is to determine its equilibrium constant and calculate $\Delta G^{\circ\prime}$ from the relationship [equation (8)]

$$\Delta G^{\circ\prime} = -2.303RT \log K'_{eq}$$

Direct measurement of the equilibrium constant for ATP hydrolysis is not practical. One reason, and the most important, is that available analytical methods are not precise or sensitive enough to determine exactly when equilibrium has been reached and what the exact equilibrium concentrations of ATP, ADP, and phosphate are, because at equilibrium ATP is almost completely hydrolyzed to ADP and phosphate. In fact, this is a serious

Table 14-3 Standard free-energy changes of some chemical reactions (pH = 7.0; T = 25°)

Reaction	$\Delta G^{\circ\prime}$, *kcal*
Hydrolysis:	
Acid anhydrides:	
Acetic anhydride + $H_2O \longrightarrow$ 2 acetate	−21.8
Pyrophosphate + $H_2O \longrightarrow$ 2 phosphate	− 8.0
Esters:	
Ethyl acetate + $H_2O \longrightarrow$ ethanol + acetate	− 4.7
Glucose 6-phosphate + $H_2O \longrightarrow$ glucose + phosphate	− 3.3
Amides:	
Glutamine + $H_2O \longrightarrow$ glutamate + NH_4^+	− 3.4
Glycylglycine + $H_2O \longrightarrow$ 2 glycine	− 2.2
Glycosides:	
Sucrose + $H_2O \longrightarrow$ glucose + fructose	− 7.0
Maltose + $H_2O \longrightarrow$ 2 glucose	− 4.0
Rearrangement:	
Glucose 1-phosphate $\longrightarrow$ glucose 6-phosphate	− 1.7
Fructose 6-phosphate $\longrightarrow$ glucose 6-phosphate	− 0.4
Elimination:	
Malate $\longrightarrow$ fumarate + H_2O	+ 0.75
Oxidation:	
Glucose + $6O_2 \longrightarrow 6CO_2 + 6H_2O$	−686
Palmitic acid + $23O_2 \longrightarrow 16CO_2 + 16H_2O$	−2338

problem for most reactions having large negative $\Delta G^{\circ\prime}$ values.

The $\Delta G^{\circ\prime}$ for ATP hydrolysis, which is −7.30 kcal at pH 7.0, 37°, and in the presence of excess Mg^{2+}, has been arrived at by exploiting the additive nature of the $\Delta G^{\circ\prime}$ values of consecutive reactions. Thus $\Delta G^{\circ\prime}_{ATP}$ can be calculated from the $\Delta G^{\circ\prime}$ values of two consecutive reactions in which the phosphate group of ATP is transferred to H_2O via an intermediate; in principle, the large standard free-energy change of the hydrolysis of ATP, which cannot be measured accurately, is broken up into a number of smaller steps, which can be measured more easily. Let us illustrate by an example. ATP is first allowed to react with glucose in the presence of hexokinase to yield ADP and glucose 6-phosphate. The equilibrium constant is measured and from the latter the standard free-energy change is calculated

$$\text{ATP} + \text{glucose} \xrightarrow{\text{hexokinase}} \text{ADP} + \text{glucose 6-phosphate} \qquad K'_{eq} = 661 \qquad \Delta G^{\circ\prime}_1 = -4.00 \text{ kcal} \quad (11)$$

This is now followed by a measurement of the equilibrium constant and standard free-energy change $\Delta G^{\circ\prime}$ for the hydrolysis of glucose 6-phosphate catalyzed by a *phosphatase*

$$\text{Glucose 6-phosphate} + \text{HOH} \xrightarrow{\text{phosphatase}} \text{glucose} + \text{phosphate} \qquad K'_{eq} = 171\ M \qquad \Delta G^{\circ\prime}_2 = -3.30 \text{ kcal} \quad (12)$$

The sum of reactions (11) and (12) is the equation for hydrolysis of ATP

$$\text{ATP} + \text{HOH} \longrightarrow \text{ADP} + \text{phosphate}$$

Since the $\Delta G^{\circ\prime}$ values of the two reactions are additive, the standard free energy of hydrolysis of ATP can be calculated

$$\Delta G^{\circ\prime}_{ATP} = \Delta G^{\circ\prime}_1 + \Delta G^{\circ\prime}_2 = -4.00 + (-3.30) = -7.30 \text{ kcal}$$

From many such measurements on different sets of enzyme-catalyzed reactions in which ATP donates a phosphate group, the value $\Delta G^{\circ\prime}_{ATP} = -7.30$ kcal is now considered to be the most accurate. It is important to note that this value is based on the following assumptions: pH = 7.0, $T = 37°$, an excess of Mg^{2+} ions, and 1.0 M concentrations of reactants and products. For some years there has been uncertainty about the precise value of $\Delta G^{\circ\prime}_{ATP}$, and published values show considerable variation. Some of the variations are due to the inherent analytical difficulties in determining the equilibrium concentrations in a strongly exergonic reaction, as mentioned above, and some are due to the fact that measurements have not always been made under precisely the same conditions of temperature, pH, and Mg^{2+} concentration, each of which can influence $\Delta G^{\circ\prime}_{ATP}$ markedly, as will be seen below.

Since the $\Delta G^{\circ\prime}$ values for the hydrolysis of most other phosphate esters are based on the value for ATP, there is a correspondingly large variation in published values for the other phosphate compounds. However, there is substantial agreement regarding the relative values of ATP and the other phosphate compounds. The values used in this book are believed to be the most reliable available at present (see the references for this chapter).

The terminal phosphate group of ADP also has a relatively large standard free energy of hydrolysis at pH7.0

$$\mathrm{ADP} + \mathrm{H_2O} \rightleftharpoons \mathrm{AMP} + \mathrm{P}_i \qquad \Delta G^{\circ\prime} = -7.3\ \mathrm{kcal}$$

However, the single phosphate group of AMP has a much lower value

$$\mathrm{AMP} + \mathrm{H_2O} \rightleftharpoons \mathrm{adenosine} + \mathrm{P}_i \qquad \Delta G^{\circ\prime} = -3.40\ \mathrm{kcal}$$

Note that the bonds between adjacent phosphate groups are anhydride linkages, whereas the bond between phosphate and ribose in AMP is an ester linkage.

The Structural Basis of the Free-Energy Change During Hydrolysis of ATP

What structural features of the ATP molecule give it a more negative standard free energy of hydrolysis at pH 7.0 than the simple ester ethyl acetate, for example? This is tantamount to asking why the equilibrium of hydrolysis lies farther in the direction of completion for ATP than it does for ethyl acetate. The answer to this question can be found in the properties of *both* the substrate and the reaction products, since the standard free energy of hydrolysis is a measure of the *difference* in free energy of the reactants and products.

At pH 7.0, ATP molecules have on the average about 3.8 closely spaced negative charges, which repel each other strongly. When the terminal phosphate bond is hydrolyzed, some of this electrical stress is removed. The resulting products, the anions HPO_4^{2-} and ADP^{3-}, have little tendency to approach each other again because of charge repulsion and thus do not readily recombine to form ATP. In contrast, when ethyl acetate undergoes hydrolysis, one product, ethanol, has no net charge and the other, the acetate anion, has but a single charge. Since they do not repel each other, they have a greater tendency to recombine.

The second major feature contributing to the more negative $\Delta G^{\circ\prime}$ of ATP hydrolysis is the fact that the two products ADP^{3-} and HPO_4^{2-} are stabilized as *resonance hybrids*. The large number of electrons around the phosphorus and oxygen atoms of the terminal phosphate bond of ATP compete with each other for orbitals having the lowest energy content. Because of this competing, or opposed, resonance, not all the electrons in the terminal pyrophosphate linkage of the intact ATP can attain as low an energy level as they can when ADP^{3-} and HPO_4^{2-} are separated from each other. In contrast, when ethyl acetate hydrolyzes, one product, ethanol, does not undergo significant resonance stabilization. Acid anhydrides, of which ATP is an example, characteristically show opposed resonance and tend to have rather negative $\Delta G^{\circ\prime}$ values for hydrolysis.

The term phosphate-bond energy used by the biochemist must not be confused with the term bond energy used by the physical chemist, which denotes the energy required to *break* a bond between two atoms. Actually, relatively large energies are required to break chemical bonds, which would not exist if they were not quite stable. The term phosphate-bond energy specifically denotes the *difference* in the free energy of the reactants and products when a phosphorylated compound is hydrolyzed to yield inorganic phosphate.

Factors Affecting the Standard Free Energy of Hydrolysis of ATP

Figure 14-5
Effect of pH on free energy of hydrolysis of ATP (25°C).

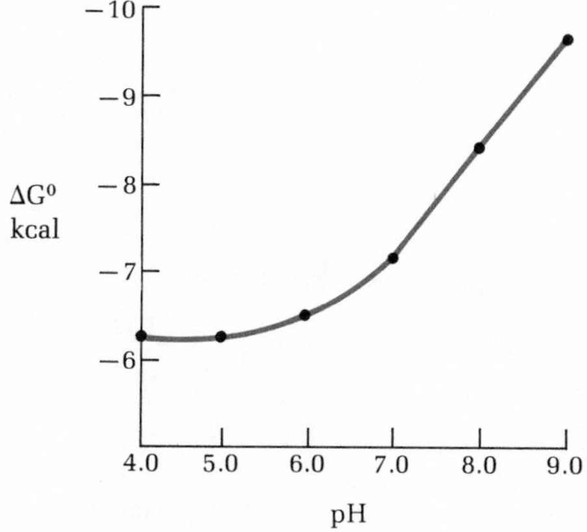

The variation of ΔG°_{ATP} with pH in the zone pH 5 to 9 is the consequence of the fact that three components of the overall equation, namely, ATP, ADP, and phosphate, have an ionization step with pK' near 7.0. As pH is varied in this zone, the ratio of the ionized to un-ionized species of each of these components varies, as is evident from their ionization equations:

$$HATP^{3-} \rightleftharpoons ATP^{4-} + H^+ \qquad pK_1' = 6.50$$
$$HADP^{2-} \rightleftharpoons ADP^{3-} + H^+ \qquad pK_2' = 7.20$$
$$H_2PO_4^- \rightleftharpoons HPO_4^{2-} + H^+ \qquad pK_3' = 7.20$$

Figure 14-5 shows how ΔG°_{ATP} varies with pH.

We have already seen that free ATP, ADP, and phosphate form complexes with Mg^{2+} by reversible reactions

$$Mg^{2+} + ATP^{4-} \rightleftharpoons MgATP^{2-}$$
$$Mg^{2+} + ADP^{3-} \rightleftharpoons MgADP^-$$
$$Mg^{2+} + HPO_4^{2-} \rightleftharpoons MgHPO_4$$

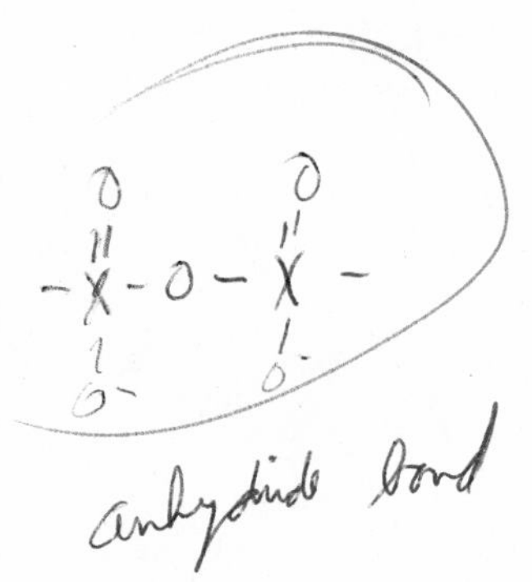

Since the affinity of Mg^{2+} for each of the three phosphate compounds differs, and since this affinity in turn increases with pH, it is clear that the effect of pH and Mg^{2+} concentration on ΔG°_{ATP} can be quite complex.

Finally, it must be pointed out that the concentrations of ATP, ADP, and phosphate in intact cells are far from the arbitrarily defined standard concentrations of 1.0 *M* on which $\Delta G^{\circ\prime}$ values are based. After appropriate corrections are made for intracellular pH, Mg^{2+} concentration, and the steady-state concentrations of ATP, ADP, and phosphate in the intracellular water phase, the free energy of hydrolysis of ATP in the cell can be approximated as −12.5 kcal. For consistency in thermodynamic calculations, the *standard* free-energy change of chemical reactions must be used, but it is quite clear that rather large corrections must be applied to such calculations if they are to be related to actual intracellular conditions and processes. Furthermore, it is also evident that the free energy of hydrolysis of ATP in the cell is not necessarily constant; it can vary from time to time or even from place to place in the cell, depending on the pH, Mg^{2+} concentration, and the concentration of ATP, ADP, and phosphate.

High-Energy and Low-Energy Phosphate Compounds

The phosphorylated compounds found in cells were originally classified into high-energy and low-energy compounds, according to the magnitude of the $\Delta G^{\circ\prime}$ values for their hydrolysis, but these terms are rather misleading since they fail to indicate an important and fundamental energetic relationship between ATP and other phosphorylated compounds in the cell. Table 14-4 shows the $\Delta G^{\circ\prime}$ values for the hydrolysis of a number of important phosphate compounds, arranged in order of increasingly positive values. Compounds with the more negative values undergo more complete hydrolysis at equilibrium, i.e., have a higher equilibrium constant, than those lower in the scale; in other words, those high in the scale tend to lose phosphate groups readily, and those low in the scale tend to hold on to them.

We see from these data that no sharp line divides high-energy and low-energy compounds; moreover, a number of phosphorylated compounds have a much more negative $\Delta G^{\circ\prime}$ value than ATP itself. ATP is unique because it has an *intermediate* value in this thermodynamic scale. It is the whole function of the ATP-ADP system to serve as an obligatory intermediate carrier of phosphate groups originating from high-energy phosphate compounds above ATP on the thermodynamic scale to acceptor molecules that form low-energy phosphate compounds below ATP on the scale. We shall continue to call ATP a high energy compound, in accordance with long usage, but its crucial intermediate position in the scale must always be kept in mind.

High-Energy Phosphate Compounds

Two classes of phosphorylated compounds have a standard free energy of hydrolysis substantially more negative than that of ATP: (1) phosphate compounds generated during enzymatic breakdown of fuel molecules and (2) phosphate compounds serving as storage reservoirs of phosphate-bond energy.

The two most important members of the first class are *1,3-diphosphoglycerate* and *phosphoenolpyruvate*, which are formed during anaerobic fermentation of glucose (Chapter 15). In the intact cell, 1,3-diphosphoglycerate does not undergo hydrolysis; instead its 1-phosphate group is transferred to ADP to form ATP and 3-phosphoglycerate. This reaction (margin) is catalyzed by the enzyme *3-phosphoglycerate kinase* (systematic name *ATP:3-phosphoglycerate phosphotransferase*). Since the $\Delta G^{\circ\prime}$ of ATP hydrolysis is known, that for the hydrolysis of the 1-phospho group of 1,3-diphosphoglycerate can be

Table 14-4 Standard free energy of hydrolysis of some phosphorylated compounds

	$\Delta G^{\circ\prime}$, *kcal*	*Phosphate group transfer potential*†
Phosphoenolpyruvate	−14.80	14.8
1,3-Diphosphoglycerate	−11.80	11.8
Phosphocreatine	−10.30	10.3
Acetyl phosphate	−10.10	10.1
Phosphoarginine	− 7.70	7.7
ATP	− 7.30	7.3
Glucose 1-phosphate	− 5.00	5.0
Fructose 6-phosphate	− 3.80	3.8
Glucose 6-phosphate	− 3.30	3.3
Glycerol 1-phosphate	− 2.20	2.2

† Defined as $-\Delta G^{\circ\prime} \times \text{kcal}^{-1}$.

Phosphoglycerate kinase reaction

O^-
$^-O—P{=}O$
O
CH_2
HCOH O^-
$C—O\sim P—O^-$
‖   ‖
O   O

1,3-diphosphoglycerate

+

ADP^{3-}

⇌

O^-
$^-O—P{=}O$
O
CH_2
HCOH
C—OH
‖
O

3-phosphoglycerate

+

ATP^{4-}

Pyruvate phosphokinase reaction

phosphoenolpyruvate

+

ADP^{3-}

⇌

pyruvate

+

ATP^{4-}

Conversion of enol to keto form of pyruvate

enol form

+

H^+

↓

keto form

Phosphocreatine

calculated if we know the equilibrium constant of the phosphate-transferring reaction. Such data have in fact been obtained. At pH 7.0 this reaction has an equilibrium constant K'_{eq} of 2,070 and a calculated $\Delta G^{\circ\prime}$ of -4.50 kcal. From this value it follows, by the principle of additivity applied to the reaction sequence

$$\text{1,3-Diphosphoglycerate} + \text{ADP} \rightleftharpoons \text{3-phosphoglycerate} + \text{ATP} \qquad \Delta G^{\circ\prime} = -4.50 \text{ kcal}$$

$$\text{ATP} + H_2O \longrightarrow \text{ADP} + P_i \qquad \Delta G^{\circ\prime} = -7.30 \text{ kcal}$$

that the free energy of hydrolysis of the 1-phosphate group of 1,3-diphosphoglycerate must be

$$\Delta G^{\circ\prime} = -7.30 + (-4.50) = -11.8 \text{ kcal}$$

The very negative standard free energy of hydrolysis of the acyl phosphate linkage of 1,3-diphosphoglycerate, which is a mixed anhydride of phosphoric acid and a carboxylic acid, is contributed by the negative charges of its hydrolysis products and the large amount of opposed resonance in its anhydride structure.

Phosphoenolpyruvate, also formed during breakdown of glucose, donates its phosphate group to ADP in a reaction (margin) catalyzed by *pyruvate phosphokinase* (systematic name *ATP:pyruvate phosphotransferase*). This reaction also has a large positive equilibrium constant and thus a large negative $\Delta G^{\circ\prime}$ value. From this value, and the $\Delta G^{\circ\prime}$ for ATP, the $\Delta G^{\circ\prime}$ for hydrolysis of phosphoenolpyruvate is -14.8 kcal (Table 14-4). This large negative value may be attributed to the fact that phosphoenolpyruvate is also an anhydride of two acids, namely, phosphoric acid and the enol form of pyruvic acid, which can be regarded as a dibasic acid (margin). As phosphopyruvate undergoes hydrolysis, the ionized enol form of pyruvate first formed reverts to the stabler keto form at pH 7.0, giving a large extra "pull" to the overall equilibrium.

The high-energy phosphate compounds serving as reservoirs of phosphate-bond energy are often called *phosphagens*. The two major phosphagens, *phosphocreatine*, found in most vertebrates, and *phosphoarginine*, found in many invertebrates, are guanidine derivatives in which the phosphorus atom is bonded directly to nitrogen (margin). The energy-rich nature of these two compounds is due to the constraints on the normal resonance stabilization of the guanidino group and the phosphate group; this constraint is relieved when the phosphate group is hydrolyzed and the reaction products form stable resonance hybrids. Phosphocreatine and phosphoarginine are formed from creatine (methylguanidoacetic acid) and arginine by transfer of phosphate groups from ATP, catalyzed by creatine phosphokinase and arginine phosphokinase, respectively. These reactions are reversible, but the equilibria favor formation of ATP

$$\text{Phosphocreatine} + \text{ADP} \rightleftharpoons \text{creatine} + \text{ATP} \qquad \Delta G^{\circ\prime} = -3.0 \text{ kcal}$$

High-energy phosphate bonds are universally symbolized by the squiggle ~ and high-energy phosphate groups as ~P. For example, ATP can be designated as A—R—P~P~P, ADP as A—R—P~P, and phosphocreatine as Cr~P. Many experiments on the mechanism and pathway of enzymatic phosphate-transferring reactions between ATP and various phosphate acceptors, particularly with the use of isotopic oxygen as tracer, have proved that it is not the phosphate group (—O—P(=O)(O^-)O^-) that is transferred, but the phosphoryl group (—P(=O)(O^-)O^-), as is seen in the margin. Although "phosphate-group transfer" is a commonly used term referring to such reactions, they are more accurately designated as phosphoryl-group transfers.

Phosphoarginine

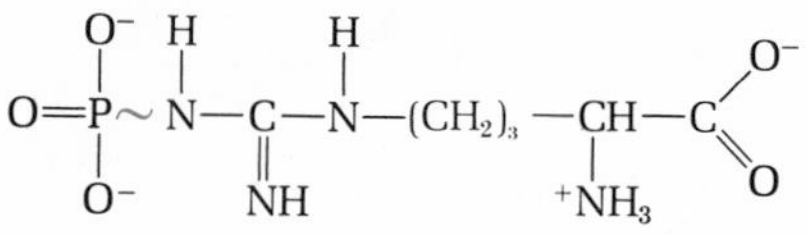

$$O=P(O^-)_2\sim NH—C(=NH)—NH—(CH_2)_3—CH(^+NH_3)—COO^-$$

Low-Energy Phosphate Compounds

Some examples of the large number of low-energy phosphate compounds found in cells are shown in Table 14-4. Most low-energy phosphate compounds are phosphoric acid esters of organic alcohols. When they undergo hydrolysis, the free alcohol formed as one of the products has no net charge at pH 7.0 and undergoes little or no resonance stabilization. Many enzymes are known that catalyze transfer of phosphate groups from ATP to specific phosphate acceptors to form low-energy phosphate compounds, among them the enzymes *glycerol kinase* and *hexokinase,* which catalyze phosphate transfer from ATP to glycerol and from ATP to D-glucose, respectively

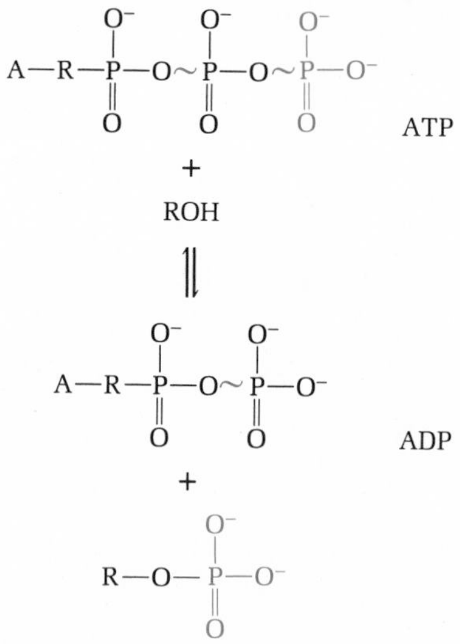

$$\text{ATP} + \text{glycerol} \rightleftharpoons \text{ADP} + \text{L-glycerol 3-phosphate} \qquad \Delta G^{\circ\prime} = -5.10 \text{ kcal}$$

$$\text{ATP} + \text{D-glucose} \rightleftharpoons \text{ADP} + \text{D-glucose 6-phosphate} \qquad \Delta G^{\circ\prime} = -4.00 \text{ kcal}$$

Since the $\Delta G^{\circ\prime}$ for hydrolysis of glycerol 3-phosphate and glucose 6-phosphate is less negative than for ATP, these reactions tend to go to the right as written.

Phosphoryl group transfer

A—R—P(=O)(O^-)—O~P(=O)(O^-)—O~P(=O)(O^-)—O^- ATP

\+

ROH

⇌

A—R—P(=O)(O^-)—O~P(=O)(O^-)—O^- ADP

\+

R—O—P(=O)(O^-)—O^-

The Enzymatic Pathways of Phosphate Transfers

Figure 14-6 is a flow sheet of enzymatic phosphate transfer reactions in the cell. An important feature is that the ATP-ADP system is the obligatory connecting link between high- and low-energy phosphate compounds. Phosphate groups are first transferred by action of specific phosphotransferases from high-energy compounds to ADP, as in the example

$$\text{Phosphoenolpyruvate} + \text{ADP} \xrightleftharpoons{\text{pyruvate kinase}} \text{pyruvate} + \text{ATP}$$

The ATP so formed then becomes the specific phosphate donor in a second enzymatic reaction to form a low-energy phosphate compound

$$\text{ATP} + \text{D-glucose} \xrightleftharpoons{\text{hexokinase}} \text{ADP} + \text{D-glucose 6-phosphate}$$

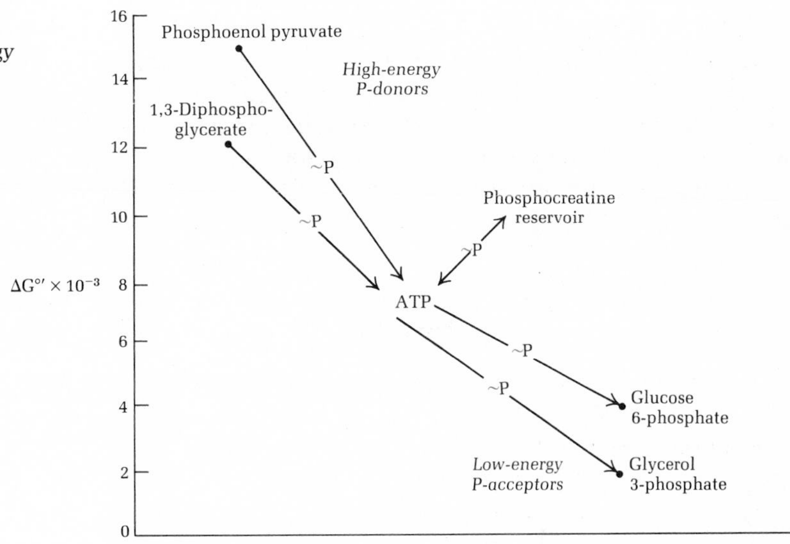

Figure 14-6
Flow of phosphate groups from high-energy phosphate donors to low-energy acceptors via ATP-ADP *system.*

The overall reaction is

$$\text{Phosphoenolpyruvate} + \text{D-glucose} \rightleftharpoons \text{pyruvate} + \text{D-glucose 6-phosphate}$$

the net result being the transfer of a phosphate group from a high-energy donor to a low-energy acceptor through the ATP-ADP system as mediator. The energy content of the D-glucose has been raised by its phosphorylation; glucose 6-phosphate may be regarded as an energized form of glucose, which is at the same energy level as the glucosyl residues of glycogen (Chapter 15). From the standard free energies of hydrolysis of phosphoenolpyruvate and glucose 6-phosphate we can calculate the concentrations of all components in the overall reaction when it has reached equilibrium, given the initial concentrations.

In the mainstream of energy-transferring reactions of the cell, phosphate transfer never occurs *directly* from a high-energy compound like 1,3-diphosphoglycerate to a low-energy phosphate acceptor like glycerol; enzymes catalyzing such direct phosphate transfers are uncommon. Furthermore, cells generally do not contain enzymes that can catalyze *direct* phosphate transfers from one high-energy compound, such as 1,3-diphosphoglycerate, to another high-energy acceptor, such as pyruvate, to form phosphoenolpyruvate, or from one low-energy phosphate compound like glycerol 3-phosphate to another low-energy acceptor like D-glucose. Essentially all phosphate-transferring reactions in the cell must take place through the ATP-ADP system.

Figure 14-6 also shows the reservoir role of phosphocreatine, which is formed by direct enzymatic transfer of a phosphate group from ATP to creatine at the expense of ATP; there is no other pathway for its formation. Furthermore, the only known major pathway for its dephosphorylation is the reversal of the reaction by which it is formed. The phosphocreatine reservoir system is especially important in skeletal muscle (Chapter 26). It is also found in smooth muscle and nerve cells but only in small amounts in liver, kidney, and other mammalian tissues and not at all in bacteria.

Some microorganisms store high-energy phosphate groups in the form of insoluble granules containing polymetaphosphate, a linear polymer of indefinite size (Figure 14-7). These granules stain in a characteristic way with basic dyes and are called *metachromatic granules*. Phosphate groups can be released from polymetaphosphate by specific enzymes.

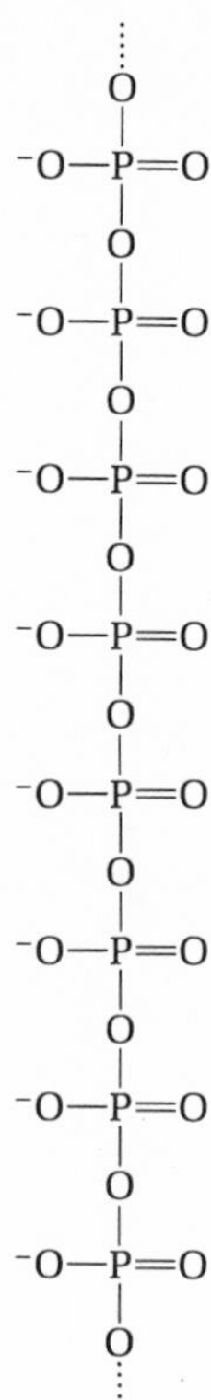

Figure 14-7
The structure of polymetaphosphate.

The Common-Intermediate Principle

In two consecutive reactions in which a product of the first is a substrate of the second, such as the consecutive reactions

$$A + B \longrightarrow C + D$$
$$D + E \longrightarrow F + G$$

the reactions are linked or coupled by a *common intermediate*, in this case the component D. The only way chemical energy can be transferred from one reaction to another under isothermal conditions (apart from fluorescence phenomena) is for the two reactions to have such a common reaction intermediate. Nearly all metabolic reactions in the cell proceed in sequences of this sort. In consecutive reactions responsible for energy transfers via ATP, chemical energy is transferred from a high-energy phosphate donor to ADP and is conserved in the form of ATP as a reaction product. In the succeeding reaction ATP becomes a substrate; when it loses its terminal phosphate group to the acceptor molecule, the latter increases in energy content. ATP is thus the common intermediate. Actually, the transfer of energy through common intermediates is a general attribute of consecutive chemical reactions and does not necessarily require either phosphate groups or ATP. In fact, we shall see that many functional groups other than phosphate, e.g., hydrogen atoms, amino groups, and acetyl groups, are enzymatically transferred by means of consecutive reactions having common intermediates. We shall also see that such reactions can be analyzed thermodynamically by the same means developed for the special case of phosphate-group transfers.

Channeling of Phosphate Groups Via Other Nucleoside 5′-Triphosphates

Although the ATP-ADP system is the obligatory phosphate carrier in the mainstream of energy transfers in the cell, the 5′-diphosphates and 5′-triphosphates of other ribonucleosides and 2-deoxyribonucleosides (Chapter 12) also participate in cellular energy transfers. The 5′-di- and triphosphates of the various ribonucleosides not only serve as precursors in RNA synthesis but also channel high-energy phosphate groups into specific biosynthetic reactions (Figure 14-8). These channels all connect with ATP though the enzyme *nucleoside diphosphokinase*,

Figure 14-8
Channeling of high-energy phosphate groups into different biosynthetic pathways via the ribonucleoside and deoxyribonucleoside 5′-triphosphates.

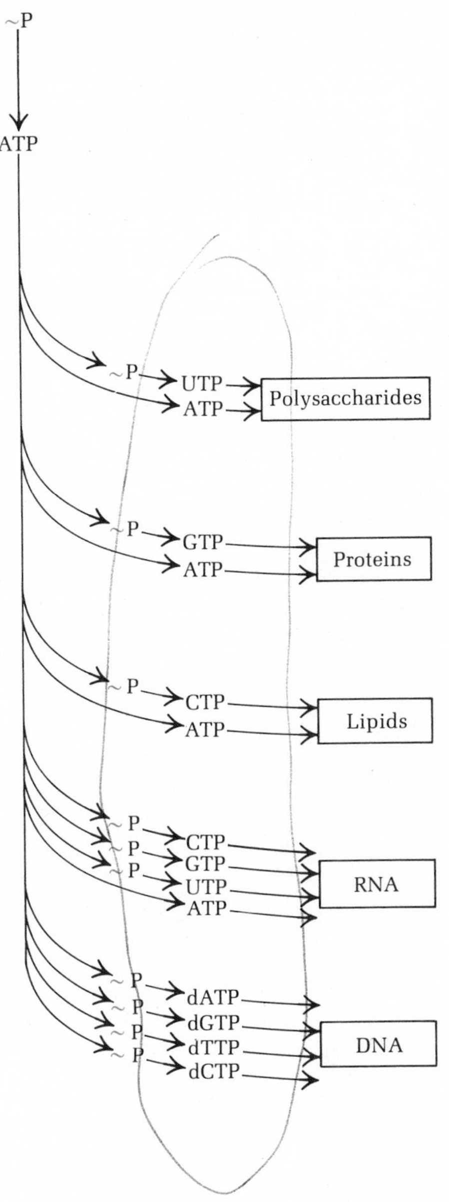

which is found in mitochondria and in the soluble cytoplasm of cells; it catalyzes reversible reactions of the type shown in the margin. This enzyme is relatively nonspecific with respect to its substrates. It not only transfers phosphate between ATP and any XDP but also between any XTP and any XDP. The equilibrium constant for all such phosphate-group transfers is approximately 1.0 at pH 7.0, since the free energy of hydrolysis of the terminal phosphate group of all the ribonucleoside and deoxyribonucleoside 5′-triphosphates is approximately the same.

Figure 14-8 also shows that each type of nucleoside 5′-triphosphate has a specialized function. Uridine triphosphate (UTP) is the immediate phosphate donor, and thus the energy donor, for many reactions in animal tissues leading to polysaccharide synthesis. Similarly, cytidine triphosphate (CTP) is the energy donor for several reactions of lipid biosynthesis.

Nucleoside diphosphokinase reactions

$$\text{ATP} + \text{UDP} \rightleftharpoons \text{ADP} + \text{UTP}$$

$$\text{ATP} + \text{GDP} \rightleftharpoons \text{ADP} + \text{GTP}$$

$$\text{ATP} + \text{CDP} \rightleftharpoons \text{ADP} + \text{CTP}$$

$$\text{GTP} + \text{UDP} \rightleftharpoons \text{GDP} + \text{UTP}$$

$$\text{ATP} + \text{dCDP} \rightleftharpoons \text{ADP} + \text{dCTP}$$

$$\text{GTP} + \text{dADP} \rightleftharpoons \text{GDP} + \text{dATP}$$

The Role of AMP and Pyrophosphate

Although ADP is the product of many ATP-utilizing reactions in the cell and ADP is the direct phosphate acceptor in the energy-yielding reactions of glycolysis and of oxidative phosphorylation in mitochondria, in many ATP-utilizing reactions in the cell the two terminal phosphate groups of ATP are removed in one piece as pyrophosphate, leaving AMP as the product. An example is the enzymatic activation of a fatty acid to form its CoA ester (Chapter 19); such CoA esters are important energized intermediates in the biosynthesis of triacylglycerols and phosphoglycerides

$$\underset{\text{Fatty acid}}{\text{ATP} + \text{RCOOH}} + \text{CoA—SH} \rightleftharpoons \text{AMP} + \text{PP}_i + \underset{\text{Fatty acyl CoA}}{\text{RCO—S—CoA}}$$

This reaction proceeds by what is termed a *pyrophosphate cleavage* of ATP, in contrast to the usual *orthophosphate cleavage*, in which ATP loses a single orthophosphate group. The two types of cleavage may be written:

Orthophosphate cleavage:

$$\text{A—R—P}{\sim}\text{P}{\sim}\text{P} \longrightarrow \text{A—R—P}{\sim}\text{P} + \text{P}_i$$

Pyrophosphate cleavage:

$$\text{A—R—P}{\sim}\text{P}{\sim}\text{P} \longrightarrow \text{A—R—P} + \text{P}{\sim}\text{P}$$

Inorganic pyrophosphate is a high-energy phosphate compound with a $\Delta G^{\circ\prime}$ of hydrolysis comparable to that of the terminal phosphate bond of ATP.

The question now arises: By what mechanism can ATP be regenerated from AMP and pyrophosphate, the products of pyrophosphate cleavage? Two important auxiliary enzymes allow AMP and pyrophosphate to return to the mainstream, *inorganic pyrophosphatase* and *adenylate kinase*. The former catalyzes the hydrolysis of inorganic pyrophosphate (PP_i) to form two molecules of inorganic orthophosphate (P_i)

$$PP_i + H_2O \longrightarrow 2P_i$$

This reaction, which proceeds with a large decrease in free energy, appears to be wasteful of phosphate-bond energy, but we shall see (Chapters 22 and 23) that the secondary hydrolysis of pyrophosphate is a valuable step in assuring the completeness of certain biosynthetic reactions. The orthophosphate so formed can then be utilized in the regeneration of ATP from ADP. Adenylate kinase, which is also called myokinase, catalyzes the rephosphorylation of AMP to ADP in the reaction

$$\text{ATP} + \text{AMP} \rightleftharpoons \text{ADP} + \text{ADP}$$

which has an equilibrium constant of approximately 0.8. Other nucleoside monophosphokinases make possible the formation of other XDPs from the corresponding XMPs and ATP

$$\text{ATP} + \text{XMP} \rightleftharpoons \text{ADP} + \text{XDP}$$

The ATP, ADP, and AMP of the cell exist in constant steady-state concentrations. As will be seen in Chapter 18, the ratio of their concentrations serves as a means of communication between ATP-utilizing and ATP-generating reactions. When a muscle cell begins a series of contractions, it uses up ATP and forms ADP, thus decreasing the molar ratio of ATP to ADP. This change is a signal that automatically causes the rate of enzymatic oxidation of fuels to be increased, which in turn causes an increase in the rate of the phosphorylation of ADP to ATP, thus restoring the ratio of ATP to ADP to its normally high value.

Dynamics and Turnover of the Terminal Phosphate Group of ATP

If ATP is the mediator of all phosphate-transferring reactions in the cell, and thus of most of the energy transfers, the terminal phosphate group of ATP must undergo very rapid turnover. This prediction has been verified by the use of the radioactive isotope of phosphorus as a tracer. Introduction of inorganic phosphate labeled with ^{32}P into the cell is followed by extremely rapid incorporation of the labeled phosphate into the terminal phosphate group of the intracellular ATP; in a very short time the specific radioactivity of the terminal phosphate group and the inorganic phosphate pool become identical. In fact, the turnover rate of the terminal phosphate group of the intracellular ATP is so high that it cannot be measured accurately. The half-time of turnover of ATP in a rapidly respiring bacterial cell, such as *E. coli*, has been calculated to be less than 1 sec, and that of the larger, more slowly respiring eucaryotic cells, such as a liver cell, less than 1 min.

Energetics of Open Systems

The principles of classical or equilibrium thermodynamics we have used in analyzing energy changes in isolated chemical reactions in this chapter are applicable only to *closed systems*, i.e., systems that do not exchange matter with their surroundings. Analysis of closed systems is relatively simple since we need consider only the initial and final states of a given system or collection of matter, after it has come to equilibrium. From such approaches much important information is available on the energetics of individual enzymatic reactions. But when we now attempt to apply this information to analysis of energy exchanges in intact living cells, we face great difficulties, since living cells are *open systems;* i.e., they *do* exchange matter with their surroundings. Furthermore, they are never totally in equilibrium. A living cell at any given moment exists in a steady state in which the rate of input of matter equals the rate of output of matter.

The analysis of the magnitude and the efficiency of energy exchanges in open systems is much more complex than in closed systems, but an extension of classical thermodynamic theory, called *nonequilibrium* or *irreversible thermodynamics,* has been developed for the analysis of nonequilibrium open systems. The application of these principles is beyond the scope of this book, but at least two general attributes of open systems existing in steady states have considerable significance in biology. An open system in a steady state is capable of doing work precisely because it is away from the condition of equilibrium; systems already at equilibrium can do no work. Moreover, only a system away from equilibrium can be subjected to control and regulation. But the most profound implication is this: in the formalism of nonequilibrium thermodynamics, the steady state, which is a characteristic of all smoothly running machinery, may be considered to be the *orderly* state of an open system, the state in which the rate of entropy production is at a *minimum.* The significance of this relationship has been aptly commented on by A. Katchalsky, a pioneer in the application of nonequilibrium thermodynamics to biology.

> This remarkable conclusion sheds new light on the wisdom of living organisms. Life is a constant struggle against the tendency to produce entropy. The synthesis of large and information-rich macromolecules, the formation of intricately structured cells, the development of organization, all these are powerful antientropic forces. But since there is no possibility of escaping the entropic doom imposed on all natural phenomena under the Second Law of thermodynamics, living organisms choose the least evil—they produce entropy at a minimum rate by maintaining a steady-state.

Summary

Energy changes of chemical reactions can be analyzed quantitatively in terms of the First and Second laws of thermodynamics, which are combined into the equation $\Delta G = \Delta H - T\,\Delta S$. Under conditions in which biological reactions occur, i.e., at constant temperature and pressure, chemical reactions proceed in such a direction that at equilibrium the entropy S of the system plus surroundings is at a maximum and the free energy G of the system alone is at a minimum. Every chemical reaction has a characteristic standard free-energy change $\Delta G^{\circ\prime}$ at standard temperature and pressure, with all reactants and products at 1 M concentration and pH = 7.0. It can be calculated from the equilibrium constant for the reaction by the equation $\Delta G^{\circ\prime} = -2.303RT \log K'_{eq}$. Standard free-energy changes can also be calculated from equilibrium data of a consecutive series of reactions or from the difference in the standard free energy of formation of reactants and products. The $\Delta G^{\circ\prime}$ of hydrolysis of ATP to ADP and phosphate is −7.30 kcal at pH 7.0 and 37° in the presence of excess Mg^{2+}. This relatively negative value is the result of electrostatic repulsion between the products of hydrolysis, namely, ADP^{3-} and HPO_4^{2-}, and the resonance stabilization of the products. However, $\Delta G^{\circ\prime}_{ATP}$ varies with pH, Mg^{2+} concentration, and ionic strength, as well as temperature. Under intracellular conditions it is approximately −12.5 kcal. Some phosphorylated compounds, e.g., phosphoenolpyruvate and 1,3-diphosphoglycerate, which are generated in glycolysis, have much more negative $\Delta G^{\circ\prime}$ values for their hydrolysis than ATP, whereas others, e.g., glucose 6-phosphate, have more positive values. The intermediate position of ATP in the thermodynamic scale of phosphate-bond energy and the specificity of the phosphate-transferring enzymes for ADP or ATP as phosphate acceptor or donor, respectively, mean that the ADP-ATP system is the obligatory common intermediate, or carrier, of phosphoryl ($-PO_3^{2-}$) groups from high-energy phosphate compounds generated during catabolism to low-energy phosphate acceptors, which thus become energized. Phosphocreatine, phosphoarginine, and polymetaphosphate are reservoirs of high-energy phosphate groups.

ATP may undergo loss of either an orthophosphate or a pyrophosphate group during its utilization in biosynthetic reactions, to form ADP or AMP, respectively. AMP is rephosphorylated to ADP by the adenylate kinase reaction, $ATP + AMP \rightleftharpoons 2ADP$. Other nucleoside 5′-triphosphates such as GTP, UTP, CTP, dATP, dTTP, etc., also participate as carriers of high-energy phosphate groups, which they channel into specific biosynthetic routes by the action of nucleoside diphosphokinase. The terminal phosphate group of ATP undergoes extremely rapid replacement by inorganic phosphate in intact respiring cells. Living cells are open systems which exchange both matter and energy with their surroundings; they exist in steady states, far from equilibrium.

References

Books

BRAY, H. G., and K. WHITE, *Kinetics and Thermodynamics in Biochemistry*, 2d ed., Academic Press Inc., New York, 1966.

FLORKIN, M., and E. H. STOTZ (eds.), *Bioenergetics*, vol. 22 of *Comprehensive Biochemistry*, American Elsevier Publishing Company, New York, 1967.

KALCKAR, H. M., *Biological Phosphorylations. Development of Concepts*, Prentice-Hall, Englewood Cliffs, N.J., 1969. A collection of reprinted papers describing classical investigations in bioenergetics, with an accompanying narrative.

KAPLAN, N. O., and E. P. KENNEDY (eds.), *Current Aspects of Biochemical Energetics*, Academic Press Inc., New York, 1966. Volume of essays and papers dedicated to Fritz Lipmann.

KATCHALSKY, A., and P. F. CURRAN, *Non-equilibrium Thermodynamics in Biophysics*, Harvard University Press, Cambridge 1965.

KLOTZ, I., *Energy Changes in Biochemical Reactions*, Academic Press Inc., New York, 1967. Excellent elementary treatment stressing thermodynamic principles.

KREBS, H. A., and H. L. KORNBERG, *Energy Transformations in Living Matter*, Springer-Verlag OHG, Berlin, 1957. A classical analysis of the energetics of metabolism.

LEHNINGER, A. L., *Bioenergetics*, W. A. Benjamin, Inc., New York, 1965. Elementary treatment stressing biochemical aspects.

WALL, F. T., *Chemical Thermodynamics*, W. H. Freeman and Company, San Francisco, 1965. A standard textbook of equilibrium thermodynamics.

Reviews and Articles

ALBERTY, R. A., "Effect of pH and Metal Ion Concentration on the Equilibrium Hydrolysis of Adenosine Triphosphate to Adenosine Diphosphate," *J. Biol. Chem.*, **243**:1337–1343 (1968). Important paper on effect of pH and Mg^{2+} on $\Delta G^{\circ\prime}$ of ATP hydrolysis.

GEORGE, P., and R. J. RUTMAN, "The High Energy Phosphate Bond Concept," *Progr. Biophys. Biophys. Chem.*, **10,** 1–53 (1960). Rigorous physicochemical treatment.

INGRAHAM, L. L., and A. B. PARDEE, "Free Energy and Entropy in Metabolism," in D. M. Greenberg (ed.), *Metabolic Pathways*, 3d ed., vol. 1, pp. 2–45, Academic Press Inc., New York, 1967. Excellent review article.

JENCKS, W. P., "Free Energies of Hydrolysis and Decarboxylation," in *Handbook of Biochemistry*, The Chemical Rubber Co., Cleveland, Ohio, pp. J144–J149 (1968). Authoritative compilation of thermodynamic data, the source of many values used in this book.

LIPMANN, F., "Metabolic Generation and Utilization of Phosphate Bond Energy," *Advan. Enzymol.*, **1**:99–162 (1941). Classical statement of the ATP-ADP cycle.

Problems

1. Calculate the percent dissociation of (*a*) the third ionizable proton of ADP and (*b*) the fourth ionizable proton of ATP at the pH of the intracellular fluid of muscle (pH 6.0).

2. Calculate the ΔG° value for the alcoholic fermentation of glucose (D-glucose $\longrightarrow$ 2 ethanol + $2CO_2$) from data on the standard free energies of formation of reactants and products (Table 14-2).

3. Calculate the equilibrium constants for the following reactions at pH = 7.0 and $T = 25°C$, using the $\Delta G^{\circ\prime}$ values of Table 14-3:
   (*a*) Glucose 6-phosphate + $H_2O \longrightarrow$ glucose + phosphate
   (*b*) Glutamine + $H_2O \longrightarrow$ glutamate + NH_4^+

4. Calculate the standard free-energy changes of the following reactions at 25°C from the equilibrium constants given (pH 7.0):
   (*a*) Glutamate + oxaloacetate $\rightleftharpoons$ asparate + α-ketoglutarate $\quad K'_{eq} = 6.8$
   (*b*) $H_2O \longrightarrow H^+ + OH^-$ $\quad K'_{eq} = 6.31 \times 10^{-15}$ M
   (*c*) Isopropanol + $NAD^+ \longrightarrow$ acetone + NADH + H^+ $\quad K'_{eq} = 7.2 \times 10^{-9}$ M
   (*d*) Malate + $NAD^+ \longrightarrow$ oxaloacetate + NADH + H^+ $\quad K'_{eq} = 7.5 \times 10^{-13}$ M

5. Calculate $\Delta G'$ (pH 7.0; $T = 25°$) for the hydrolysis of ATP to ADP and phosphate, assuming that ATP and ADP are present in equimolar concentrations and that the phosphate concentration is (a) 1.0 M, (b) 0.1 M, (c) 0.01 M, and (d) 1.0 mM.

6. Calculate the free energy of hydrolysis of ATP to ADP + P_i under conditions existing in a resting muscle cell, namely, ATP = 5.0 mM, ADP = 0.5 mM, P_i = 5.0 mM, pH = 6.0, and $T = 25°C$. Start from data in Figure 14-5.

7. A spherical cell of radius 10 μ and pH 7.0 originally contained ATP at 6.0 mM concentration. All the ATP was then hydrolyzed to ADP and P_i. If the free energy lost during the phosphate transfer is used to heat the water in the cell (assume it is 100 percent H_2O), what is the increase in temperature?

8. At what minimum concentration must malate be present to make the fumarase reaction (malate $\longrightarrow$ fumarate + H_2O) proceed to the right at pH = 7.0 and $T = 25°C$ if the fumarate is present at a concentration of 10^{-3} M?

9. Glucose 1-phosphate is converted to fructose 6-phosphate in two successive reactions

Glucose 1-phosphate $\longrightarrow$ glucose 6-phosphate
Glucose 6-phosphate $\longrightarrow$ fructose 6-phosphate

Using the $\Delta G°'$ values of Table 14-3, determine the $\Delta G°'$ value for the overall reaction.

10. The standard free-energy change for the reaction phosphoenolpyruvate + ADP $\longrightarrow$ pyruvate + ATP is -7.50 kcal. If phosphoenolpyruvate and ADP are originally present at 10 mM concentrations but no ATP or pyruvate are present, what will the equilibrium concentrations of the products and reactants be? Repeat the calculation, assuming the reaction is initiated with 6.0 mM ADP, 6.0 mM phosphoenolpyrurate, and 6.0 mM ATP.

11. A mixture of 10 mM 1,3-diphosphoglycerate and 10 mM pyruvate is incubated at pH 7.0 with 3-phosphoglycerate kinase, pyruvate phosphokinase, and a small amount of ATP, until equilibrium occurs. Calculate the concentration of phosphoenolpyruvate at equilibrium.

CHAPTER 15 GLYCOLYSIS

We now begin consideration of the mechanisms by which fuel molecules are degraded and their energy conserved as the phosphate-bond energy of ATP. For three reasons it is useful to begin with the processes known generically as *fermentations*, by which many organisms extract chemical energy from glucose or other fuels in the absence of molecular oxygen. (1) Since living organisms probably first arose in an atmosphere lacking oxygen, anaerobic fermentation is the simplest and most primitive type of biological mechanism for obtaining energy from nutrient molecules. (2) Most present-day aerobic organisms have retained the capacity to conserve energy from glucose by means of the primitive pathway, which has become a preparatory step for the further oxidation of fermentation products by oxygen. (3) The enzymatic steps in the anaerobic degradation of glucose and the recovery of its energy as ATP are now known in great detail. Fermentation processes, and particularly that known as glycolysis, thus serve as important prototypes for the study of the much more complex and incompletely understood processes of respiration and photosynthesis.

Fermentation and Respiration

All heterotrophic organisms ultimately obtain their energy from oxidation-reduction reactions, i.e., reactions in which electrons are transferred from one compound, the *electron donor*, or reducing agent, to an *electron acceptor*, or oxidizing agent. In anaerobic fermentation, the final oxidant, or acceptor of electrons, is some organic molecule, usually generated in the fermentation process itself. There is no *net* oxidation of the fuel molecule in fermentation but an internal oxidoreduction, so that the net oxidation state of the fermentation products is the same as that of the fuel.

Organisms that can live anaerobically are divided into two classes. The strict anaerobes are the more primitive and comprise relatively few species of bacteria and lower invertebrates living in environments having little or no oxygen, as in deep soils, deep waters, and marine mud. The strict anaerobic bacteria include the *Clostridia*, the denitrifying bacteria, and the methane-forming bacteria. Facultative anaerobes, however, include a great many different species. When they live anaerobically, they obtain energy from fermentation of glucose by the same or similar processes as strict anaerobes. When they live aerobically, they usually continue to degrade their fuels by the anaerobic pathway but then oxidize the products of the anaerobic pathway at the expense of molecular oxygen. In facultative cells, therefore, the anaerobic pathway of glucose breakdown has become an obligatory first stage for the aerobic phase of respiration which follows it (Figure 15-1). This pattern is characteristic not only of many bacteria, yeasts, and fungi but also of the aerobic cells of most higher animals and plants.

Figure 15-1
Glucose utilization in facultative organisms. The fermentation pathway is common to both the aerobic and anaerobic utilization of glucose.

Anaerobic conditions

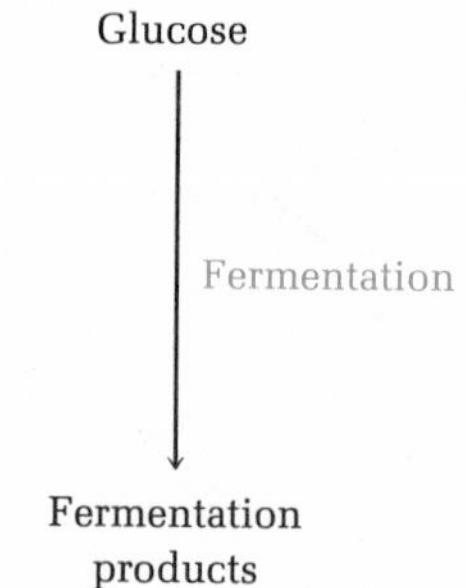

Aerobic conditions

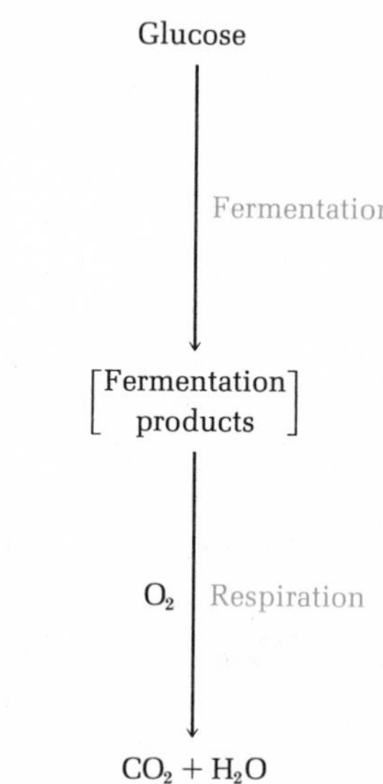

The most commonly employed fuels for anaerobic fermentations are the six-carbon sugars, particularly D-glucose, but some bacteria can obtain their metabolic energy by carrying out anaerobic fermentation of pentoses, fatty acids, or amino acids. Of the many kinds of glucose fermentation two closely related types (Figure 15-2) predominate. (1) In *homolactic fermentation* the six-carbon glucose molecule is degraded to two molecules of the three-carbon lactic acid as sole end product. This type of glucose breakdown occurs in many microorganisms and in the cells of most higher animals, including mammals. It is usually called *glycolysis,* meaning the dissolution of sugar. (2) In *alcoholic fermentation* the six-carbon glucose is broken down into two molecules of the two-carbon ethanol (C_2H_5OH) and two molecules of CO_2. Alcoholic fermentation occurs by the same enzymatic pathway as glycolysis but requires two additional enzymatic steps, which break down both three-carbon fragments resulting from glucose cleavage into ethanol and CO_2 (Figure 15-2). Most of the other types of glucose fermentation are variations on the basic pathway of glycolysis. Since each species of organism usually has a single, characteristic, genetically determined fermentation pathway, many microorganisms can be classified on the basis of their fuel molecule specificity and their fermentation mechanism.

The equations for glycolysis and alcoholic fermentation in Figure 15-2 do not involve molecular oxygen, yet in both fermentations oxidoreduction reactions have taken place. This is most evident in the end products of alcoholic fermentation; ethanol is a relatively reduced molecule, i.e., hydrogen-rich, and CO_2 a relative oxidized molecule, i.e., hydrogen-poor. The occurrence of oxidoreduction is less immediately evident in the end products of glycolysis, but it may be noted that one end of the lactic acid molecule, the methyl group, is more reduced than the other end, the carboxyl group. In contrast, the hydrogen atoms are rather evenly distributed over the carbon skeleton of the glucose molecule.

The equations for glycolysis and alcoholic fermentation in Figure 15-2 are incomplete statements, since ATP is formed from ADP and phosphate during both processes. In fact, they cannot occur without the simultaneous phosphorylation of ADP. The complete balanced equations for glycolysis and alcoholic fermentation are:

Figure 15-2
Path of carbon atoms in glycolysis and alcoholic fermentation. The numbers indicate the origin of the carbon atoms from glucose.

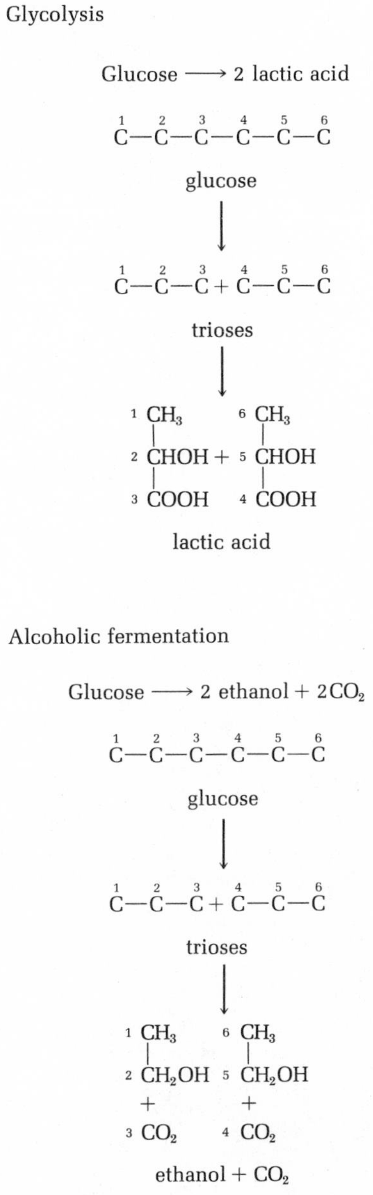

Glycolysis

Glucose ⟶ 2 lactic acid

$$\overset{1}{C}-\overset{2}{C}-\overset{3}{C}-\overset{4}{C}-\overset{5}{C}-\overset{6}{C}$$

glucose

↓

$$\overset{1}{C}-\overset{2}{C}-\overset{3}{C}+\overset{4}{C}-\overset{5}{C}-\overset{6}{C}$$

trioses

↓

1 CH_3 | 2 CHOH | 3 COOH + 6 CH_3 | 5 CHOH | 4 COOH

lactic acid

Alcoholic fermentation

Glucose ⟶ 2 ethanol + $2CO_2$

$$\overset{1}{C}-\overset{2}{C}-\overset{3}{C}-\overset{4}{C}-\overset{5}{C}-\overset{6}{C}$$

glucose

↓

$$\overset{1}{C}-\overset{2}{C}-\overset{3}{C}+\overset{4}{C}-\overset{5}{C}-\overset{6}{C}$$

trioses

↓

1 CH_3 | 2 CH_2OH + 3 CO_2 and 6 CH_3 | 5 CH_2OH + 4 CO_2

ethanol + CO_2

Glycolysis:

$$C_6H_{12}O_6 + 2P_i + 2ADP \longrightarrow \underset{\text{Lactic acid}}{2CH_3CHOHCOOH} + 2ATP + 2H_2O$$

Alcoholic fermentation:

$$C_6H_{12}O_6 + 2P_i + 2ADP \longrightarrow \underset{\text{Ethanol}}{2CH_3CH_2OH} + 2CO_2 + 2ATP + 2H_2O$$

To analyze the energetics of glycolysis we break its overall equation down into two processes, the conversion of glucose to lactate, which is exergonic, and the formation of ATP from ADP and phosphate, which is endergonic.

$$\text{Glucose} \longrightarrow 2\ \text{lactate} \qquad \Delta G_1^{\circ\prime} = -47.0\ \text{kcal}$$

$$2P_i + 2ADP \longrightarrow 2ATP + 2H_2O \qquad \Delta G_2^{\circ\prime} = 2 \times 7.30 = +14.6\ \text{kcal}$$

Sum:

$$\text{Glucose} + 2P_i + 2ADP \longrightarrow 2\ \text{lactate} + 2ATP + 2H_2O$$

$$\Delta G_s^{\circ\prime} = \Delta G_1^{\circ\prime} + \Delta G_2^{\circ\prime} = -47.0 + 14.6 = -32.4\ \text{kcal}$$

From the free-energy data it is clear that the breakdown of glucose to lactate provides more than sufficient energy to cause the phosphorylation of two molecules of ADP to ATP. We can calculate that 14.6/47.0 × 100, or about 31 percent, of the free-energy decrease during breakdown of glucose to lactate is conserved as the phosphate-bond energy of ATP. Actually if we adjust such calculations, which are based on 1.0 *M* concentrations, to take account of the actual intracellular concentrations of reactants and products, the true efficiency of glycolysis is much higher than 31 percent (see below).

The overall process of glycolysis, even after making allowance for the coupled formations of ATP, still proceeds with a very large net decrease in free energy, −32.4 kcal. Glycolysis is thus an essentially irreversible reaction, with its equilibrium overwhelmingly in the direction of lactate formation. We shall see later, however, that most of its reaction steps have a relatively small standard free-energy change and are employed in the biosynthesis of glucose from lactate and other precursors (Chapter 22).

The Stages of Glycolysis

Glycolysis is catalyzed by the consecutive action of a group of 11 enzymes, most of which have been crystallized and thoroughly studied. They are easily extracted in soluble form from cells and thus are believed to be localized in the soluble portion of the cytoplasm. It is also thought that the individual enzymes catalyzing the steps in glycolysis have no physical dependence on each other; i.e., they appear not to be associated into a multienzyme complex (Chapter 9). There is some evidence, however, that certain specific individual enzymes of the sequence may be loosely associated with the plasma membrane, with myofibrils, or with the mitochondria in different types of cells.

In the two major stages of glycolysis (Figure 15-3), glucose is first phosphorylated and cleaved to form the three-carbon sugar glyceraldehyde 3-phosphate, which is then converted into lactic acid in the second stage. The first stage of glycolysis serves as a preparatory, or collection, process, in which a number of different hexoses enter the scheme following their phosphorylation at the expense of ATP and are collected in the form of a common product, glyceraldehyde 3-phosphate. The second stage of glycolysis is the common pathway for all sugars and in it occur the oxidoreduction steps and the energy-conserving mechanisms in which ADP is phosphorylated to

Figure 15-3
The two stages of glycolysis.

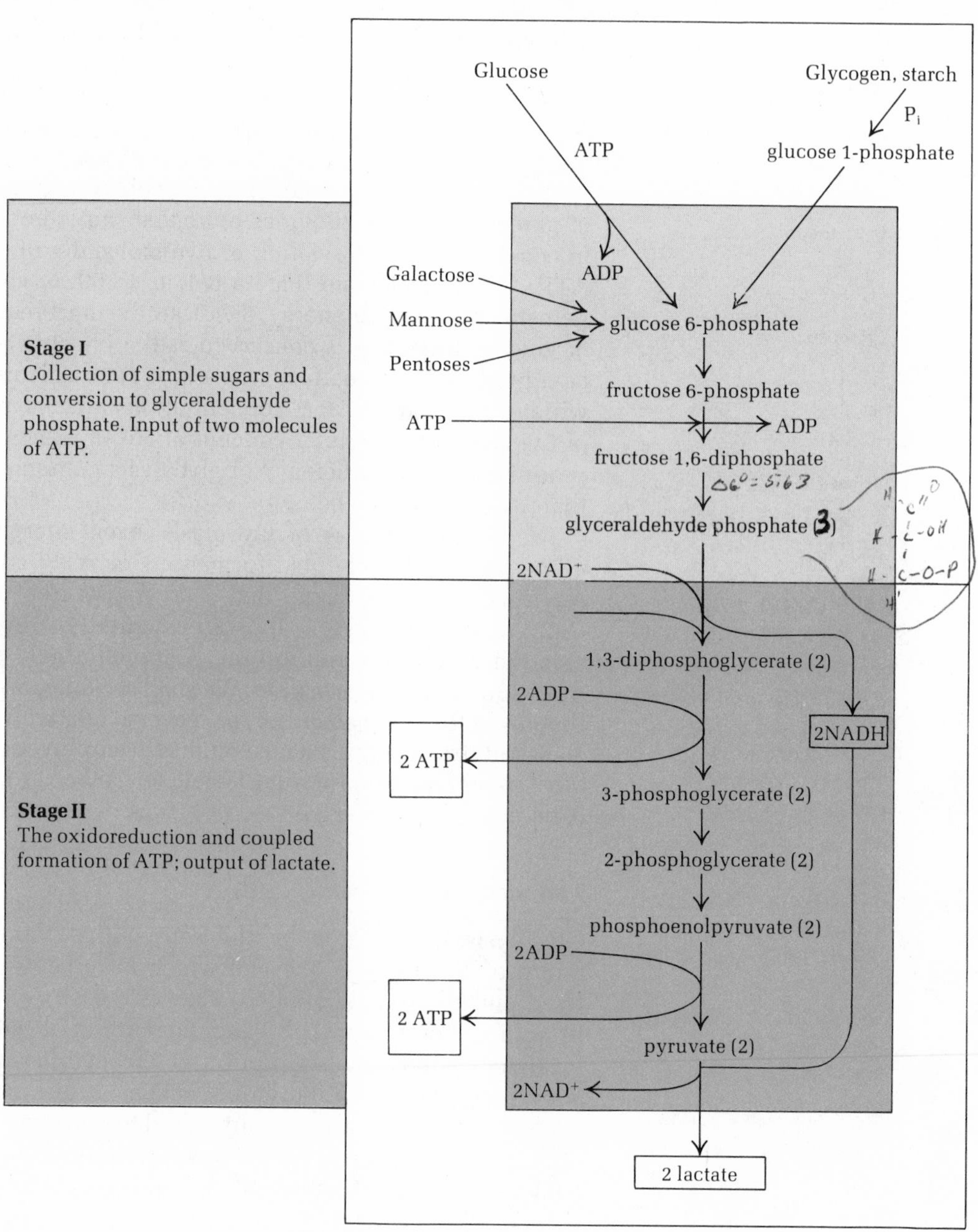

ATP. Three different types of chemical transformation take place during glycolysis; their pathways are interconnected: (1) the sequence of reactions by which the carbon skeleton of glucose is degraded to form the lactic acid end product, i.e., the pathway of the carbon atoms, (2) the sequence of reactions by which inorganic phosphate becomes the terminal phosphate group of ATP, i.e., the pathway of phosphate, and (3) the sequence of oxidoreductions, i.e., the pathway of electrons.

Experimental History

The mechanisms of glycolysis and alcoholic fermentation were elucidated over the course of many years of research. Some important landmarks illustrate what experimental and conceptual approaches have been taken in the investigation of this fundamental metabolic pathway.

Büchner and Büchner first discovered in 1892 that an extract of macerated yeast, freed of intact cells by filtration, retained the ability to ferment glucose to ethanol. This observation demonstrated that the enzymes of fermentation not only could function independently of cell structure but also that they were quite stable. Some years later Meyerhof found that cell-free extracts of skeletal muscle could catalyze all the reactions leading from glucose to lactic acid.

A second major landmark was Harden's and Young's discovery in England (1905) that alcoholic fermentation in yeast extracts requires phosphate and that a hexose diphosphate, later identified as fructose 1,6-diphosphate, accumulates in fermenting yeast extracts under some conditions but is utilized in others, suggesting that it is an intermediate in the overall fermentation process. Harden and Young also found that the enzyme system responsible for alcoholic fermentation consisted of a heat-labile fraction, called *zymase*, presumably containing the heat-labile enzymes required for the process, and a heat-stable fraction (*cozymase*) required for activity of zymase. The heat-stable fraction was later shown to contain two essential components, the oxidation-reduction coenzyme *nicotinamide adenine dinucleotide* (Chapter 12), to be discussed further below, and a mixture of adenine nucleotides (AMP, ADP, ATP).

Another important set of observations revealed that in the presence of the inhibitor fluoride, fermenting yeast extracts showed an accumulation of two phosphate esters, 3-phosphoglycerate and 2-phosphoglycerate. On the other hand, the inhibitor iodoacetate caused an accumulation of both fructose 1,6-diphosphate and the triose phosphates. Once these intermediates were identified, it became possible to study the enzymatic reactions by which they were formed or utilized.

These basic observations served as the starting point for more intensive investigations in Germany in the middle 1930s, which led to our present understanding of glycolysis. Among the most important contributors to this phase were Gustav Embden, who postulated the manner of cleavage of fructose 1,6-diphosphate and suggested the overall pattern of the oxidoreduction steps, and Otto Meyerhof, who isolated some of the enzymes, demonstrated the sequence leading from 3-phosphoglycerate to lactate and studied the energetics of glycolysis. The glycolytic sequence is often called the Embden-Meyerhof pathway. Other important contributions were made by Otto Warburg, in Germany, who worked out the mechanism of the triose oxidation step and the accompanying phosphorylation of ADP, as well as the structure of NAD, and by Cori and Cori, in the United States, who isolated the enzymes catalyzing the pathway from glycogen to glucose 6-phosphate. Although the individual steps of glycolysis have been known since about 1940, research on glycolysis has by no means ceased. In fact, only recently has closer study revealed some of the mechanisms by which specific enzymes of the glycolytic sequence participate in the regulation of this process in the intact cell.

α-D-Glucose 6-phosphate

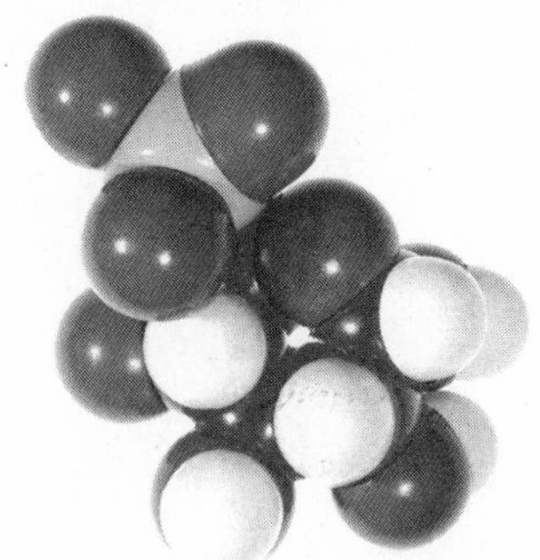

The Enzymatic Steps in the First Stage of Glycolysis

Although glycolysis proceeds by the same pathway in all cells having this type of fermentation, there are sometimes significant differences in the properties of the homologous enzymes of the sequence from one species or cell type to another. Presumably such variations relate to cellular differentiation and control of this pathway. Most of the detailed work on purified glycolytic enzymes has been done on enzymes from skeletal muscle of the rabbit.

Phosphorylation of D-Glucose by ATP

This is a priming step, in which the neutral D-glucose molecule is mobilized and made ready for the subsequent steps by its phosphorylation to a negatively charged molecule at the expense of ATP. There is relatively little free D-glucose in cells, most intracellular glucose existing in phosphorylated form. The phosphorylation of D-glucose at the 6 position by ATP to yield D-glucose 6-phosphate (margin) is catalyzed by two types of enzyme, which differ in their sugar specificity, hexokinase and glucokinase. The reaction for both enzymes is

$$\text{ATP} + \alpha\text{-D-glucose} \xrightarrow{Mg^{2+}} \text{ADP} + \alpha\text{-D-glucose 6-phosphate} \qquad \Delta G^{\circ\prime} = -4.0 \text{ kcal}$$

Hexokinase is the more important and is the enzyme normally employed by most cells. It catalyzes the phosphorylation not only of D-glucose but also of many other hexoses, e.g., D-fructose, D-mannose, and D-glucosamine; it has a higher affinity for aldohexoses than for ketohexoses. Hexokinases are found in yeast and bacteria and in many animal and plant tissues. Yeast hexokinase has been crystallized (mol wt 96,000). The hexokinase of brain and other animal tissues exists in multiple molecular forms, i.e., isozymes (Chapter 9), which can be separated from each other by zone electrophoresis.

At normal concentrations of blood glucose, hexokinase is fully saturated. When blood glucose concentration becomes very high, as in diabetes, in which it may rise several-fold, glucokinase becomes significantly active.

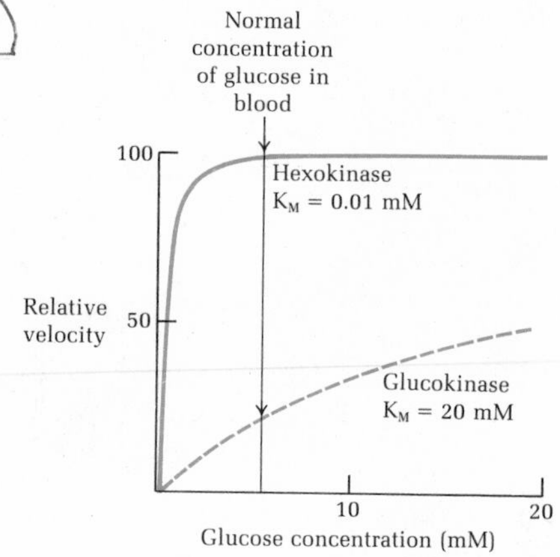

α-D-Fructose 6-phosphate

The second class of glucose-phosphorylating enzymes are the *glucokinases*, which phosphorylate only D-glucose. Glucokinase has a much lower affinity for D-glucose ($K_M = 2 \times 10^{-2}$ *M*) than hexokinase ($K_M = 1 \times 10^{-5}$ *M*). Glucokinase is present in liver but not in muscles. It comes into play only in emergencies when the blood glucose concentration is very high. Both kinases require a divalent cation (Mg^{2+} or Mn^{2+}), which first combines with ATP to form the true substrate, $MgATP^{2-}$ or $MnATP^{2-}$. Hexokinase is inhibited by certain sulfhydryl reagents, especially arsenicals.

The large standard free-energy decrease of the hexokinase reaction in the forward direction indicates that it is not reversible under intracellular conditions. The enzymatic dephosphorylation of D-glucose 6-phosphate to regenerate free D-glucose (a reaction of great importance in the liver since it delivers free glucose to the blood) occurs through the action of an entirely different enzyme, *D-glucose 6-phosphatase* (Chapter 22).

$$\text{D-Glucose 6-phosphate} + H_2O \longrightarrow \text{D-glucose} + \text{phosphate} \qquad \Delta G^{\circ\prime} = -3.30 \text{ kcal}$$

α-D-Fructose 1,6-diphosphate

Open-chain form

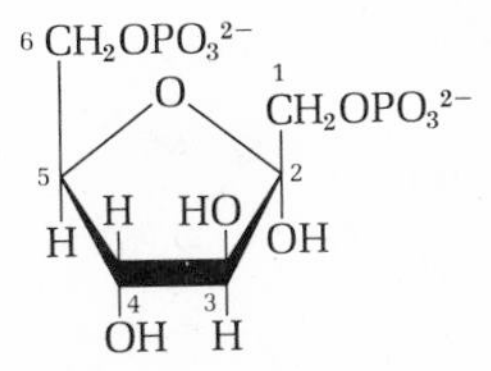

Furanose form

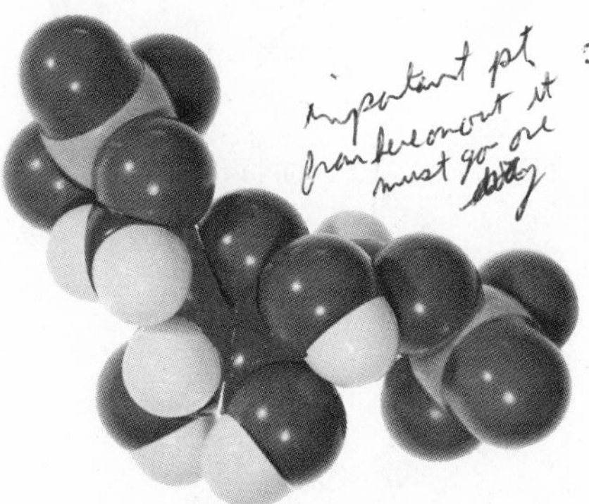

Conversion of Glucose 6-Phosphate to Fructose 6-Phosphate

Phosphoglucoisomerase, which has been isolated in highly purified form from muscle tissue, catalyzes isomerization of glucose 6-phosphate to fructose 6-phosphate (margin)

$$\alpha\text{-D-Glucose 6-phosphate} \rightleftharpoons \alpha\text{-D-fructose 6-phosphate} \qquad \Delta G^{\circ\prime} = +0.4 \text{ kcal}$$

The reaction proceeds readily in either direction. Phosphoglucoisomerase does not require Mg^{2+} or Mn^{2+}; it is specific for glucose 6-phosphate and fructose 6-phosphate.

Phosphorylation of D-Fructose 6-Phosphate to Fructose 1,6-Diphosphate

In this, the second of the two priming reactions of glycolysis, a second molecule of ATP is invested to phosphorylate fructose 6-phosphate in the 1 position (margin) by action of *phosphofructokinase (ATP:D-fructose 6-phosphate 1-phosphotransferase)*

$$\text{ATP} + \text{D-fructose 6-phosphate} \longrightarrow \text{ADP} + \text{D-fructose 1,6-diphosphate} \qquad \Delta G^{\circ\prime} = -3.40 \text{ kcal}$$

Mg^{2+} is required, presumably because the true substrate is MgATP. Although fructose 6-phosphate is the specific phosphate acceptor in the reaction, UTP and ITP may replace ATP as phosphate donors.

The phosphorylation of fructose 6-phosphate is an important control point in the glycolytic sequence; phosphofructokinase is an allosteric, or regulatory, enzyme

(Chapter 9). Like most allosteric enzymes, it has a rather high molecular weight (~360,000), is not easy to purify, and shows a complex dependence of its reaction velocity on substrate concentration. Since phosphofructokinase is inhibited by high concentrations of either ATP or citrate and is stimulated by ADP or AMP, it is a multivalent allosteric enzyme. Its role in control of glycolysis will be described in more detail in Chapter 18. The strongly negative $\Delta G^{\circ\prime}$ value for the phosphofructokinase reaction indicates that it is essentially irreversible in the cell; most regulatory enzymes catalyze irreversible reactions (Chapter 9).

By a separate enzymatic pathway D-fructose 1,6-diphosphate is converted back to fructose 6-phosphate, through a hydrolytic reaction catalyzed by the enzyme *diphosphofructose phosphatase*; the properties of this allosteric enzyme and its role in glucose synthesis and regulation will be considered in Chapters 18 and 22.

Fructose 1,6-diphosphate + $H_2O \longrightarrow$
fructose 6-phosphate + P_i $\qquad \Delta G^{\circ\prime} = -4.0$ kcal

Cleavage of Fructose 1,6-Diphosphate to Glyceraldehyde 3-Phosphate and Dihydroxyacetone Phosphate

This reaction is catalyzed by the well-studied enzyme *aldolase* (*D-fructose 1,6-diphosphate:D-glyceraldehyde 3-lyase*), which is easily isolated in crystalline form from rabbit muscle extracts. The reaction catalyzed is a reversible aldol condensation; no metal ion is required by the muscle enzyme

D-Fructose 1,6-diphosphate $\rightleftharpoons$
dihydroxyacetone phosphate + D-glyceraldehyde 3-phosphate
$\Delta G^{\circ\prime} = +5.73$ kcal

The structures of the products are shown in the margin.

Since $\Delta G^{\circ\prime}$ in this reaction is strongly positive, it may seem unlikely that the reaction occurs in the forward direction. However, the concentration of fructose 1,6-diphosphate in the intact cell is usually quite low (< 0.1 m*M*) in comparison with the standard concentration of 1.0 *M* assumed for calculation of $\Delta G^{\circ\prime}$. Under these conditions, a significantly large fraction of fructose 1,6-diphosphate is cleaved before equilibrium is reached. The position of equilibrium in this type of reaction, in which one molecule of reactant is cleaved into two products, is strongly influenced by the reactant concentration. As a calculation will show (see Problems), the lower the initial fructose 1,6-diphosphate concentration, the greater the fraction that is cleaved before equilibrium is attained.

Skeletal muscle aldolase has a molecular weight of 150,000 and contains four major subunits. Acidification of the enzyme causes it to dissociate into the subunits, which are inactive; upon neutralization the subunits reassemble quickly and spontaneously to reform the active enzyme. Aldolase contains free —SH groups, some of which are essential for catalytic activity. In the forward direction,

Dihydroxyacetone phosphate

1 $CH_2OPO_3^{2-}$ (6)
2 C=O (5)
3 CH_2OH (4)

D-Glyceraldehyde 3-phosphate

H
4 C=O (3)
5 HCOH (2)
6 $CH_2OPO_3^{2-}$ (1)

Non-specificity of aldehydes in aldolase reaction. Below, normal reaction. Right, the reaction with acetaldehyde.

Dihydroxyacetone phosphate

+

H
C=O
HCOH $\quad$ D-Glyceraldehyde
CH_2OH

$\Downarrow\Uparrow$

$CH_2OPO_3^{2-}$
C=O
HOCH
HCOH
HCOH
CH_2OH

D-Fructose 1-phosphate

Figure 15-4
Enzyme-substrate complex of aldolase and dihydroxyacetone-phosphate. The substrate molecule is shown in color.

$HOCH_2-C-CH_2OPO_3^{2-}$
‖
N
|
CH_2
|
CH_2
|
CH_2
|
CH_2
|
CH
HN   C=O
Aldolase

Lysine derivative of dihydroxyacetone (in color) isolated from hydrolyzate of reduced aldolase-substrate complex.

H
|
$HOCH_2-C-CH_2OH$
|
NH
|
CH_2
|
CH_2
|
CH_2
|
CH_2
|
$HCNH_2$
|
COOH

muscle aldolase cleaves not only fructose 1,6-diphosphate but also a number of different ketose 1-phosphates. In the reverse direction it is absolutely specific for dihydroxyacetone phosphate but will accept a variety of aldehydes, e.g., acetaldehyde or free glyceraldehyde, instead of glyceraldehyde 3-phosphate (margin). From this and other observations it was postulated that aldolase forms an enzyme-substrate complex with dihydroxyacetone phosphate and other ketose 1-phosphates. This hypothesis was confirmed when incubation of crystalline aldolase with dihydroxyacetone phosphate in the presence of the reducing agent sodium borohydride caused a stable covalent bond to form between the enzyme and dihydroxyacetone phosphate. Hydrolysis of the trapped enzyme-substrate complex, which is catalytically inactive, yielded a derivative of a lysine residue of the enzyme, in which the ε-amino group is covalently bonded with dihydroxyacetone (Chapter 8). From this experiment it was concluded that the enzyme-substrate complex between aldolase and dihydroxyacetone phosphate involves a labile Schiff's base with the ε-amino group of a lysine residue of the enzyme (Figure 15-4).

The aldolases found in bacteria, yeasts, and fungi are distinguished by having a requirement for specific divalent metal ions, usually Zn^{2+}, Ca^{2+}, or Fe^{2+}; they also require K^+. Their molecular weight is about 65,000, or one-half that of the animal enzymes.

The Interconversion of the Triose Phosphates

Only one of the two triose phosphates, namely, glyceraldehyde 3-phosphate, can be directly degraded in the further reactions of glycolysis. The other, dihydroxyacetone phosphate, is reversibly converted to glyceraldehyde 3-phosphate by the enzyme *triose phosphate isomerase*

Dihydroxyacetone phosphate $\rightleftharpoons$
D-glyceraldehyde 3-phosphate $\qquad \Delta G^{\circ\prime} = +1.83$ kcal

Note that by this reaction carbon atoms 1, 2, and 3 of the starting glucose now have become indistinguishable from carbon atoms 6, 5, and 4, respectively. Dihydroxyacetone phosphate constitutes over 90 percent of the equilibrium mixture of the two triose phosphates.

This reaction completes the first stage of glycolysis, in which the glucose molecule has been prepared by two phosphorylation steps and cleavage for the second stage. The collecting reactions by which glycogen, starch, and hexoses other than glucose are fed into the first stage are described later.

Dihydroxyacetone phosphate
+
H
|
C=O   Acetaldehyde
|
CH_3
⇅
$CH_2OPO_3^{2-}$
|
C=O
|
HOCH
|
HCOH
|
CH_3

5-Deoxyketopentose 1-phosphate

The Second Stage of Glycolysis

This stage comprises the oxidoreductions and the phosphorylation steps in which ATP is generated. Since one molecule of glucose forms two of glyceraldehyde 3-phosphate, both halves of the glucose molecule follow the same pathway.

Oxidation of Glyceraldehyde 3-Phosphate to 1,3-Diphosphoglycerate

This is one of the most important steps of the glycolytic sequence, since it conserves the energy of oxidation of the aldehyde group of glyceraldehyde 3-phosphate in the form of a high-energy phosphate compound formed as oxidation product, namely, 1,3-diphosphoglycerate (Chapter 14). The elucidation of the pathway of this and the following reaction, carried out by Warburg and his colleagues in 1937–1938, is considered one of the most important discoveries in modern biology, since it demonstrated for the first time an enzymatic and chemical mechanism by which energy yielded on oxidation of an organic molecule could be conserved in the form of ATP.

The enzyme catalyzing this step, *glyceraldehyde 3-phosphate dehydrogenase*, is easily isolated in crystalline form (mol wt = 140,000) from rabbit muscle or yeast. It contains four identical subunits, each consisting of a single polypeptide chain of some 330 residues, the amino acid sequence of which has just recently been deduced. The overall reaction catalyzed by the enzyme is

$$\text{D-Glyceraldehyde 3-phosphate} + NAD^+ + P_i \longrightarrow$$
$$\text{1,3-diphosphoglycerate} + NADH + H^+ \qquad \Delta G^{\circ\prime} = +1.5 \text{ kcal}$$

Figure 15-5
Nicotinamide adenine dinucleotide. The nicotinamide moiety, which is the portion undergoing reversible reduction, is shown in color.

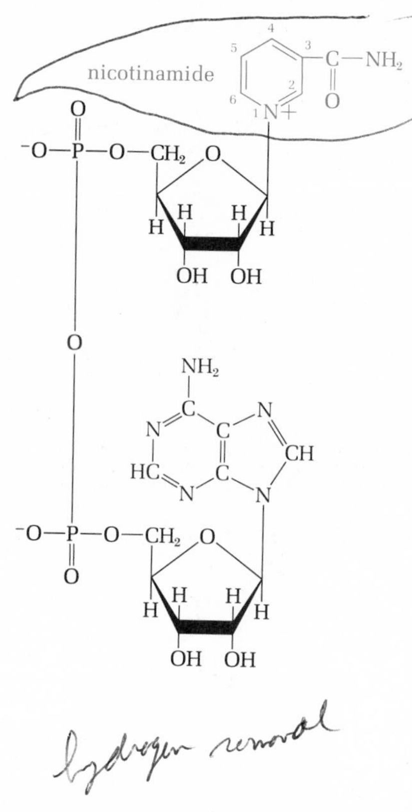

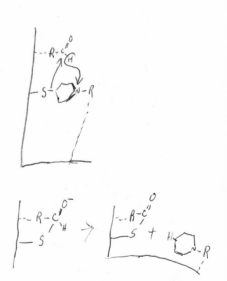

In this reaction the aldehyde group of D-glyceraldehyde 3-phosphate is oxidized to the oxidation level of a carboxyl group. However, instead of a free carboxylic acid, the reaction yields a mixed anhydride of phosphoric acid and the carboxyl group of 3-phosphoglyceric acid, 1,3-diphosphoglycerate, which, as we have seen, is a high-energy phosphate compound having a more negative standard free energy of hydrolysis than ATP (Chapter 14).

The other important component of this reaction is the oxidizing agent, designated as NAD^+, which accepts electrons from the aldehyde group of D-glyceraldehyde 3-phosphate. NAD is the symbol for the oxidoreduction coenzyme *nicotinamide adenine dinucleotide* (Figure 15-5), whose structure, properties, and reactions are more fully described in Chapters 12 and 16. NAD is now known to be a component of cozymase, the heat-stable fraction required for alcoholic fermentation in the early experiments of Harden and Young. It serves as a carrier of electrons from the electron donor D-glyceraldehyde 3-phosphate to pyruvate, which is formed later in the glycolytic sequence. NAD^+, the oxidized form of NAD, contains a positively charged substituted pyridine derivative, *nicotinamide*, which is in turn derived from the vitamin nicotinic acid. When NAD^+ is reduced to NADH (Fig. 15-6), a hydride ion ($:H^-$) is transferred from the substrate molecule to the 4-position of the nicotinamide ring, ultimately leading to reduction at positions 1 and 4. The other hydrogen atom of the substrate is lost to the medium as a H^+ ion.

The overall reaction has a slightly positive value of $\Delta G^{\circ\prime}$ (+1.5 kcal $mole^{-1}$) and thus proceeds readily in either direction depending on the concentration of the reactants

Figure 15-6
Reduction of the pyridine ring in NAD^+ by substrate (SH_2). The two reducing equivalents are transferred to NAD^+ in the form of a hydride ion ($:H^-$).

Figure 15-7
Postulated mechanism for action of glyceraldehyde 3-phosphate dehydrogenase. A molecule of NAD remains bound to the active site throughout the cycle. Its reduced form is reoxidized by free NAD^+ from the medium.

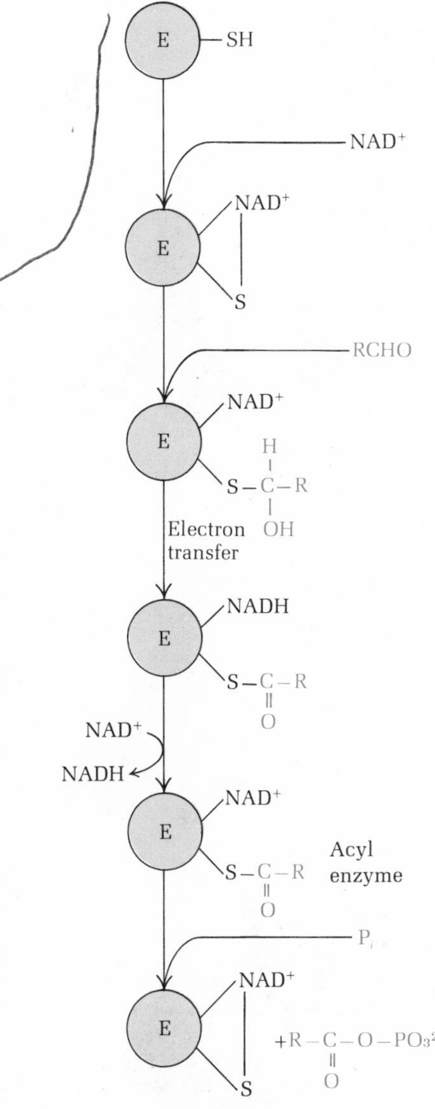

and products. We already know (Chapter 14) that oxidation reactions are usually highly exergonic and that the formation of 1,3-diphosphoglycerate from inorganic phosphate and 3-phosphoglycerate is a highly endergonic reaction. The overall reaction may be broken down into two separate processes for analysis of the energy changes, using RCHO to designate glyceraldehyde 3-phosphate; $RCOO^-$, 3-phosphoglycerate; and $RCOOPO_3^{2-}$, 1,3-diphosphoglycerate.

$$R{-}CHO + H_2O + NAD^+ \longrightarrow RCOO^- + NADH + 2H^+ \qquad \Delta G_1^{\circ\prime} = -10.3\ \text{kcal}$$

$$R{-}COO^- + P_i \longrightarrow R{-}\underset{\underset{O}{\|}}{C}{-}O{-}PO_3^{2-} + H_2O \qquad \Delta G_2^{\circ\prime} = +11.8\ \text{kcal}$$

Sum:

$$R{-}CHO + P_i + NAD^+ \rightleftharpoons R{-}\underset{\underset{O}{\|}}{C}{-}O{-}PO_3^{2-} + NADH + H^+ \qquad \Delta G_S^{\circ\prime} = \Delta G_1^{\circ\prime} + \Delta G_2^{\circ\prime} = -10.3 + 11.8 = +1.5\ \text{kcal}$$

The oxidation of RCHO to $RCOO^-$ by NAD^+ is thus a highly exergonic process which would normally proceed far in the direction of completion as written, whereas the formation of 1,3-diphosphoglycerate is highly endergonic and would not normally proceed as written. In the overall enzymatic reaction, the endergonic process is coupled to the exergonic process: the energy released on oxidation of the aldehyde is thus conserved in the form of the high-energy phosphate group of 1,3-diphosphoglycerate.

The mechanism of this important oxidoreduction has been studied in detail (Figure 15-7). Each of the enzyme's four identical subunits contains a molecule of bound NAD^+ and presumably also an active catalytic site. Since glyceraldehyde 3-phosphate dehydrogenase is inhibited by heavy metals, such as Hg^{2+}, as well as by alkylating agents, such as iodoacetate, it has been concluded that a sulfhydryl group in the active site is an essential functional group in catalysis. It is believed that the enzyme binds the oxidized form of the coenzyme NAD^+ first, in a reaction in which the essential sulfhydryl group becomes chemically or sterically masked (Figure 15-7). In the next step the aldehyde group of the substrate forms a *thiohemiacetal* linkage with the sulfhydryl group. The enzyme then catalyzes hydrogen transfer from the covalently bound glyceraldehyde 3-phosphate to the bound NAD^+, forming a thioester between the enzyme sulfhydryl group and the carboxyl group of the substrate. The reduced NAD does not leave the enzyme but passes its hydrogen atom and electron to a molecule of free NAD^+ in the medium, leaving the bound NAD in oxidized form. This form is called the *acyl enzyme*. The acyl group is then transferred from the sulfhydryl group of the enzyme to inorganic phosphate to form 1,3-diphosphoglycerate, the oxidation product. The free oxidized form of the enzyme can now initiate another catalytic cycle.

The enzyme requires NAD^+ specifically as oxidant. Although it is most active with glyceraldehyde 3-phosphate, it also oxidizes D- or L-glyceraldehyde or even acetaldehyde, but at very low rates. The enzyme can also utilize arsenate instead of phosphate, presumably forming 1-arseno-3-phosphoglycerate (margin), a highly unstable compound which immediately and spontaneously decomposes into 3-phosphoglycerate and arsenate. Note that in the presence of arsenate, no high-energy phosphate group is generated by the dehydrogenase, although the overall oxidoreduction takes place. In this way arsenate uncouples oxidation and phosphorylation in the triose oxidation step.

Hydrolysis of 1-arseno-3-phosphoglycerate

$$\begin{array}{c} O^- \\ | \\ {}^-O{-}As{=}O \\ | \\ O \\ | \\ C{=}O \\ | \\ HCOH \\ | \\ CH_2OPO_3^{2-} \end{array}$$

$$+$$

$$H_2O$$

$$\downarrow \text{nonenzymatic}$$

$$HAsO_4^{2-} \quad \text{Arsenate}$$

$$+$$

3-Phosphoglycerate

3-Phosphoglycerate

$$\begin{array}{c} CH_2OPO_3^{2-} \\ | \\ HCOH \\ | \\ COO^- \end{array}$$

Transfer of Phosphate from 1,3-Diphosphoglycerate to ADP

Warburg and his colleagues showed that the 1,3-diphosphoglycerate formed in the preceding reaction now reacts enzymatically with ADP, with transfer of the 1-phosphate group to ADP and formation of 3-phosphoglycerate, catalyzed by *phosphoglycerate kinase*

$$\text{1,3-Diphosphoglycerate} + \text{ADP} \rightleftharpoons \text{3-phosphoglycerate} + \text{ATP} \qquad \Delta G^{\circ\prime} = -4.50 \text{ kcal}$$

This reaction is highly exergonic and serves to pull the preceding reaction equilibrium to completion. The phosphate-transferring enzyme has an extremely high affinity for 1,3-diphosphoglycerate. The overall equation for the two reactions involving oxidation of the aldehyde group of glyceraldehyde 3-phosphate to the carboxyl group of 3-phosphoglycerate, with coupled formation of ATP from ADP and phosphate, is

$$\text{Glyceraldehyde 3-phosphate} + P_i + \text{ADP} + NAD^+ \rightleftharpoons \text{3-phosphoglycerate} + \text{ATP} + \text{NADH} + H^+ \qquad \Delta G^{\circ\prime} = -3.0 \text{ kcal}$$

By the action of these two enzymes the energy of oxidation of an aldehyde group to a carboxylate group has been conserved as the phosphate-bond energy of ATP.

2-Phosphoglycerate

$$\begin{array}{c} CH_2OH \\ | \\ HCOPO_3^{2-} \\ | \\ COO^- \end{array}$$

Conversion of 3-Phosphoglycerate to 2-Phosphoglycerate

This reaction is catalyzed by the enzyme phosphoglyceromutase

$$\text{3-Phosphoglycerate} \rightleftharpoons \text{2-phosphoglycerate} \qquad \Delta G^{\circ\prime} = +1.06 \text{ kcal}$$

Mg^{2+} is essential for this reaction, which involves transfer of the phosphate group from the 3 to the 2 position of glyceric acid (margin). Since the reaction has only a small standard free-energy change, it is freely reversible. There are two forms of the enzyme; one requires 2,3-diphosphoglycerate as an intermediate and is analogous in its mechanism to phosphoglucomutase (see below).

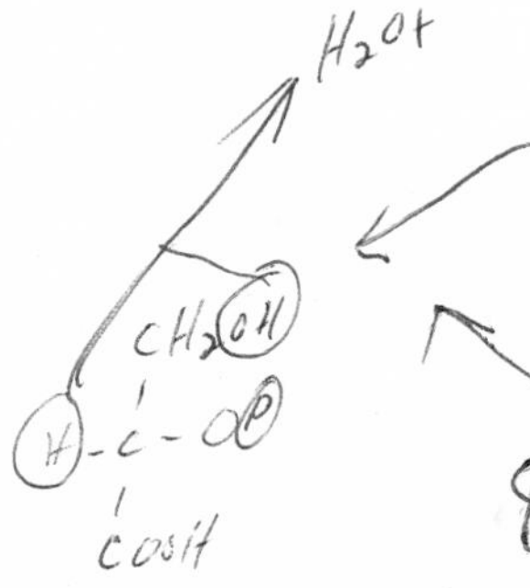

Dehydration of 2-Phosphoglycerate to Phosphoenolpyruvate

This is the second reaction of the glycolytic sequence in which a high-energy phosphate bond is generated; it is catalyzed by *enolase*

$$\text{2-Phosphoglycerate} \rightleftharpoons \text{phosphoenolpyruvate} + H_2O \qquad \Delta G^{\circ\prime} = +0.44 \text{ kcal}$$

Phosphoenolpyruvate

$$\begin{array}{l} CH_2 \\ \| \\ C{-}O{-}PO_3^{2-} \\ | \\ COO^- \end{array}$$

Enolase has been obtained in pure crystalline form from several sources (mol wt 85,000). It has an absolute requirement for a divalent cation (Mg^{2+} or Mn^{2+}), which makes a complex with the enzyme before the substrate is bound. The enzyme is strongly inhibited by fluoride, particularly if phosphate is present; the inhibitory species is the Mg^{2+}-fluorophosphate complex. Although the reaction catalyzed by enolase is formally an elimination of a molecule of water from the two- and three-carbon atoms of 2-phosphoglycerate, it may also be regarded as an intramolecular oxidoreduction, since the removal of water causes carbon atom 2 to become more oxidized and carbon atom 3 more reduced. Despite the relatively small standard free-energy change in this reaction, there is a very large change in the standard free energy of hydrolysis of the phosphate group of the reactant and product, that of 2-phosphoglycerate being about -4.2 kcal and that of phosphoenolpyruvate about -14.8 kcal. Evidently there is a large change in the distribution of energy within the 2-phosphoglycerate molecule when it is dehydrated to phosphopyruvate.

Pyruvate

$$\begin{array}{l} CH_3 \\ | \\ C{=}O \\ | \\ COO^- \end{array}$$

Transfer of Phosphate from Phosphopyruvate to ADP

The transfer of the phosphate group from phosphopyruvate to ADP is catalyzed by the enzyme *pyruvate kinase (ATP:pyruvate phosphotransferase)*

$$\text{Phosphoenolpyruvate} + \text{ADP} \rightleftharpoons \text{pyruvate} + \text{ATP} \qquad \Delta G^{\circ\prime} = -7.5 \text{ kcal}$$

which has been obtained in pure crystalline form (mol

wt 250,000). The enzyme requires Mg^{2+} or Mn^{2+}, with which it must form a complex before binding the substrate. Ca^{2+} competes with Mn^{2+} or Mg^{2+} and forms an inactive complex. The enzyme also requires an alkali-metal cation, which may be K^+, Rb^+, or Cs^+; K^+ is of course the physiological activator. It is believed that the binding of K^+ causes a conformational change of the enzyme to produce a more active form. The reaction is highly exergonic (see Chapter 14) and is essentially irreversible under intracellular conditions.

Lactate

$$\begin{array}{c} CH_3 \\ | \\ HC{-}OH \\ | \\ COO^- \end{array}$$

Reduction of Pyruvate to Lactate

In the last step of glycolysis, pyruvate is reduced to lactate at the expense of electrons originally donated by glyceraldehyde 3-phosphate. These electrons are carried by NADH. The reaction is catalyzed by *lactate dehydrogenase*, which has been isolated in crystalline form.

$$\text{Pyruvate} + \text{NADH} + \text{H}^+ \rightleftharpoons \text{lactate} + \text{NAD}^+ \qquad \Delta G^{\circ\prime} = -6.0 \text{ kcal}$$

The overall equilibrium of this reaction is far to the right, as shown by the large negative value of $\Delta G^{\circ\prime}$. Lactate dehydrogenase exists in at least five different molecular forms, or isozymes, in higher animals (Chapter 9), forms which differ in their affinity for the substrates; their role in glycolysis will be described in Chapter 18. This reaction completes the internal oxidoreduction cycle of glycolysis.

Lactate is the end product of the glycolytic sequence under anaerobic conditions and diffuses through the plasma membrane of the cell to the surroundings as waste. When muscle cells of higher animals function anaerobically during short bursts of exceptionally vigorous activity, lactate escapes from muscle cells into the blood in large quantities and is rebuilt to glucose in the liver during recovery (Chapter 26). Fatigue and rigor of muscle fibers is in part due to their acidification; glycolytic breakdown of the neutral D-glucose molecule results in formation of two molecules of a monocarboxylic acid.

The Overall Balance Sheet

A balance sheet for glycolysis can now be constructed to account for the fate of the carbon skeleton of glucose, the oxidoreduction reactions, and the input and output of phosphate, ADP, and ATP. The left-hand part of the following equation shows all the inputs of the glycolytic sequence and the right, all the outputs, adjusted for the fact that each molecule of glucose yields two molecules of glyceraldehyde 3-phosphate:

$$\text{Glucose} + 2\text{ATP} + 2\text{NAD}^+ + 2\text{P}_i + 4\text{ADP} + 2\text{NADH} + 2\text{H}^+ \longrightarrow 2\text{ lactate} + 2\text{ADP} + 2\text{NADH} + 2\text{H}^+ + 2\text{NAD}^+ + 4\text{ATP} + 2\text{H}_2\text{O}$$

By canceling out common terms on both sides of the equation we get

$$\text{Glucose} + 2\text{P}_i + 2\text{ADP} \longrightarrow 2\text{ lactate} + 2\text{ATP} + 2\text{H}_2\text{O}$$

Table 15-1 The steady-state concentrations of intermediates of glycolysis in the human erythrocyte

Intermediate	*Concentration, μM*
Glucose	5000
Glucose 6-phosphate (G6P)	83
Fructose 6-phosphate (F6P)	14
Fructose 1,6-diphosphate (FDP)	31
Dihydroxyacetone phosphate (DHP)	138
Glyceraldehyde 3-phosphate (GAP)	18.5
3-Phosphoglycerate (3PG)	118
2-Phosphoglycerate (2PG)	29.5
Phosphoenolpyruvate (PEP)	23
Pyruvate (Pyr)	51
Lactate (Lact)	2900
ATP	1850
ADP	138
Phosphate	1000

In the overall process D-glucose is converted to two molecules of lactate, two molecules of ADP and phosphate are converted to ATP, and four electrons have been transferred from glyceraldehyde 3-phosphate to pyruvate in the form of $2NADH + 2H^+$. Although two oxidoreduction steps have taken place in the sequence, there is no net change in oxidation-reduction state.

Energetics of Glycolysis in the Intact Cell

Much interest attaches to finding the magnitude of the free-energy changes of the separate steps of glycolysis as they occur in intact cells. This has recently been accomplished for the human erythrocyte, which obtains all its energy from glycolysis. From chemical analysis of erythrocytes, the actual steady-state concentrations of all intermediates of glycolysis have been determined (Table 15-1). From these values one can easily calculate the free-energy change ($\Delta G'$, not $\Delta G^{\circ\prime}$) of each step in the intact erythrocyte, with the general equation (see Chapter 14)

$$\Delta G' = \Delta G^{\circ\prime} + RT \ln \frac{[C][D]}{[A][B]}$$

From the data so obtained, a free-energy profile of glycolysis in the erythrocyte has been constructed (Figure 15-8), which shows that eight of the reactions of glycolysis are at or very close to equilibrium, whereas three reactions occur with large decreases in free energy and are thus far from equilibrium, namely, the hexokinase, phosphofructokinase, and pyruvate kinase reactions. From such data it can also be calculated that the free energy of hydrolysis of ATP is about −13.3 kcal under intracellular conditions and that the actual efficiency of

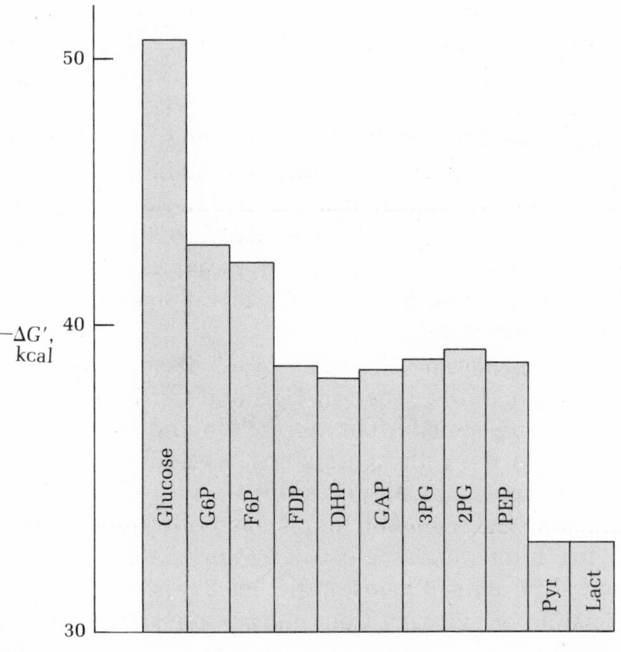

Figure 15-8
Energy profile of glycolysis in human erythrocyte. All the reactions are at or near equilibrium except those catalyzed by hexokinase, phosphofructokinase, and pyruvate phosphokinase, at which large decreases in ΔG′ occur. The abbreviations used are defined in Table 15-1.

energy recovery in erythrocyte glycolysis is about 53 percent, or much greater than the efficiency calculated from standard free-energy data.

There is now good evidence that the phosphofructokinase reaction is the rate-limiting reaction in glycolysis. Allosteric regulation of the glycolytic rate will be detailed in Chapter 18.

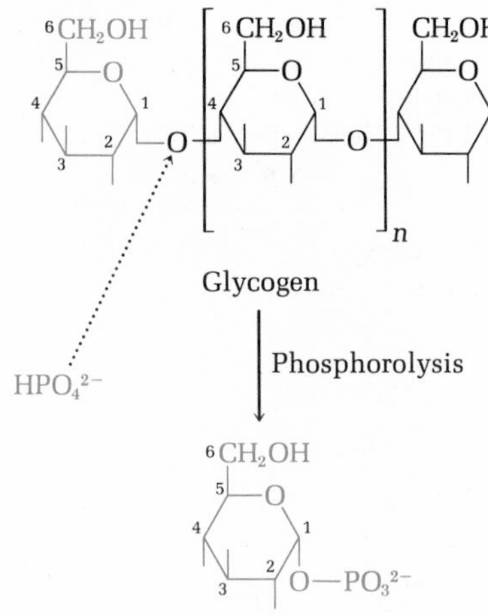

Figure 15-9
Phosphorolytic removal of a glucose residue from the nonreducing end of a glycogen chain by phosphorylase.

Entry of Other Carbohydrates into the Glycolytic Sequence

The storage polysaccharides, glycogen and starch, and simple sugars other than D-glucose are brought into the first stage of glycolysis by several auxiliary enzymes, whose action will now be described.

Glycogen and Starch

The D-glucose units of glycogen and starch gain entrance into the glycolytic sequence through the sequential action of two enzymes *glycogen phosphorylase* (or *starch phosphorylase* in plants) and *phosphoglucomutase*. Glycogen phosphorylase and starch phosphorylase are members of a class of enzymes designated as $\alpha(1 \longrightarrow 4)$ glucan phosphorylases. Widely distributed in animal, plant, and microbial cells, they catalyze the general reaction shown, in which $(\text{glucose})_n$ designates the glucan chain and $(\text{glucose})_{n-1}$ the shortened glucan chain.

$$(\text{Glucose})_n + HPO_4^{2-} \rightleftharpoons (\text{glucose})_{n-1} + \text{glucose 1-phosphate} \qquad \Delta G^{\circ\prime} = +0.73 \text{ kcal}$$

In this reaction the terminal nonreducing $\alpha(1 \longrightarrow 4)$ glycosidic linkage of a glycogen side-chain undergoes *phosphorolysis*, i.e., removal of the terminal glucose residue by attack of phosphate to yield glucose 1-phosphate, leaving behind a glycogen chain with one less glucose unit (Figure 15-9). The enzyme acts repetitively on the nonreducing ends of glycogen chains until it meets the $\alpha(1 \longrightarrow 6)$ branch points, which it cannot attack. Exhaustive action of glycogen phosphorylase can thus produce a limit dextrin (Chapter 11), further degradation of which by glycogen phosphorylase can occur only after the action of a debranching enzyme, a hydrolytic *$\alpha(1 \longrightarrow 6)$ glucosidase*, which hydrolyzes the $1 \longrightarrow 6$ linkage at the branch point, thus making available another length of the polysaccharide chain to the action of glycogen phosphorylase.

Although glycogen phosphorylase, discovered and studied in penetrating detail by Cori and Cori, seemed at first to be responsible for both formation and breakdown of glycogen in the cell, it has since been found that its primary function is to catalyze the breakdown of glycogen. Under intracellular conditions, the equilibrium greatly favors the formation of glucose 1-phosphate. Another enzyme, *glycogen synthetase* (Chapter 22) is responsible for formation of glycogen from glucose phosphate units.

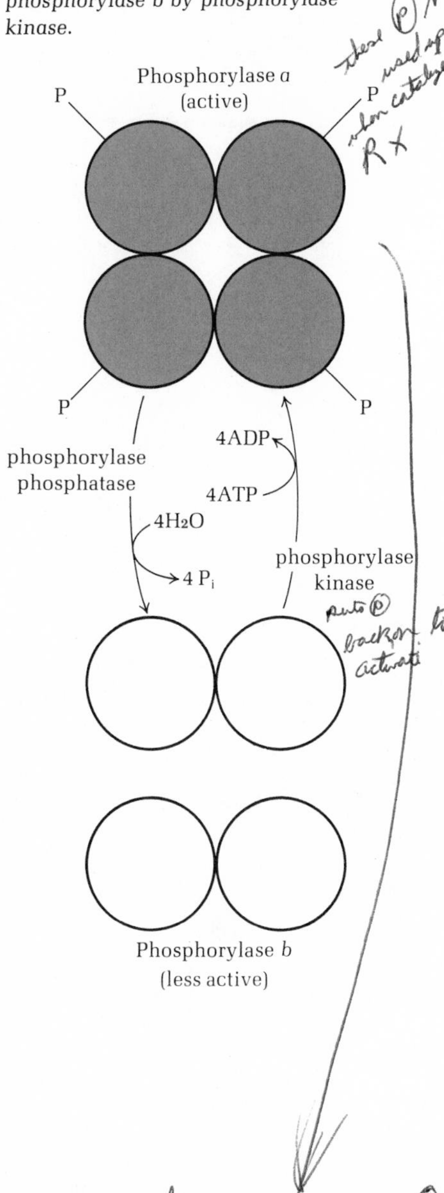

Figure 15-10
Conversion of phosphorylase a to phosphorylase b by phosphorylase phosphatase and reactivation of phosphorylase b by phosphorylase kinase.

Phosphorylase is situated at an important point between the fuel reservoir, i.e., glycogen or starch, and the enzymatic apparatus for utilizing the fuel. Its activity in muscle and liver has been found to be under regulation by an elaborate set of controls. The glycogen phosphorylase of skeletal muscle occurs in two forms, the active form (phosphorylase *a*) and a much less active form (phosphorylase *b*). Phosphorylase *a* has been crystallized; it has a molecular weight of 380,000 and consists of four identical subunits. Each subunit contains a phosphoserine residue that is essential for catalytic activity and a molecule of the coenzyme pyridoxal phosphate (Chapter 20), which is covalently bound to a lysine residue. The active form of phosphorylase *a* can be attacked by another enzyme, *phosphorylase phosphatase*, which hydrolyzes the phosphate groups from the serine phosphate residues (Figure 15-10). This reaction causes phosphorylase *a* to dissociate into two half-molecules of phosphorylase *b*, the less active form. Phosphorylase *b* is converted back to active phosphorylase *a* molecules not by simple reversal of the above reaction, which is irreversible, but by an alternate pathway in which four molecules of ATP act on two molecules of phosphorylase *b* in the presence of the enzyme *phosphorylase kinase*. In this manner, the ratio of the active phosphorylase *a* and the less active phosphorylase *b* in the cell may shift, thus varying the rate of conversion of glycogen into glucose 1-phosphate. Actually, the activity of phosphorylase kinase can itself be controlled, since it in turn occurs in active and inactive forms (Chapter 22).

Liver also contains active and inactive forms of phosphorylase, the ratio of which can also be controlled by the rate of the interconversion between the active and inactive forms. However, in the liver these enzymes have a distinctly different architecture than in muscle and they are controlled in a different fashion, in harmony with the differences in the dynamics of glucose metabolism in liver and muscle.

Glucose 1-phosphate, the end product of the glycogen and starch phosphorylase reactions, is converted into glucose 6-phosphate by the interesting enzyme *phosphoglucomutase*, which has been obtained in pure form from many sources. It catalyzes the reaction

$$\text{Glucose 1-phosphate} \rightleftharpoons \text{glucose 6-phosphate}$$

Although it can also catalyze the conversion of D-mannose 1-phosphate to D-mannose 6-phosphate, the rate of this reaction is only $\frac{1}{100}$ of the rate of conversion of D-glucose 1-phosphate.

Phosphoglucomutase contains a serine residue that is essential for catalytic activity; its hydroxyl group becomes esterified with phosphoric acid during the catalytic cycle. The hydroxyl group of the serine can also be esterified by the inhibitor diisopropyl phosphofluoridate (DFP) to yield an inactive form. This enzyme is a member of the serine class of enzymes (Chapters 8 and 9). Phosphoglucomutase requires not only Mg^{2+} but also an organic cofactor, glucose 1,6-diphosphate, which plays a role indicated by the following sequence of intermediate steps in the action of the enzyme:

Phosphoenzyme + glucose 1-phosphate $\rightleftharpoons$
dephosphoenzyme + glucose 1,6-diphosphate

Dephosphoenzyme + glucose 1,6-diphosphate $\rightleftharpoons$
phosphoenzyme + glucose 6-phosphate

The conversion of glucose 1-phosphate to glucose 6-phosphate requires the phosphoglucomutase to be in its phosphorylated form, which can be produced by reaction of the dephosphorylated form with glucose 1,6-diphosphate. In turn, glucose 1,6-diphosphate is a product of another reaction

Glucose 1-phosphate + ATP $\rightleftharpoons$
glucose 1,6-diphosphate + ADP

catalyzed by the enzyme *phosphoglucokinase*. Glucose 6-phosphate formed as the product of the phosphoglucomutase reaction now may enter the glycolytic cycle.

Entry of Simple Sugars Other than Glucose

D-Mannose and D-fructose can be phosphorylated at the 6-position by hexokinase, which is relatively nonspecific

D-Mannose + ATP $\rightleftharpoons$ D-mannose 6-phosphate + ADP

D-Fructose + ATP $\rightleftharpoons$ D-fructose 6-phosphate + ADP

The D-fructose 6-phosphate so formed is an intermediate in the glycolytic sequence. D-Mannose 6-phosphate is enzymatically isomerized into D-fructose 6-phosphate by the action of *phosphomannoisomerase*

D-Mannose 6-phosphate $\rightleftharpoons$ D-fructose 6-phosphate

In the liver of vertebrates, fructose may gain entry into glycolysis by another pathway. *Fructokinase* catalyzes the phosphorylation of fructose not at carbon atom 6 but at carbon atom 1

D-Fructose + ATP $\rightleftharpoons$ D-fructose 1-phosphate + ADP

The resulting fructose 1-phosphate is then cleaved into D-glyceraldehyde and dihydroxyacetone phosphate

Fructose 1-phosphate $\rightleftharpoons$
D-glyceraldehyde + dihydroxyacetone phosphate

by *fructose 1-phosphate aldolase*, which is abundant in liver but lacking in muscle. The free D-glyceraldehyde so formed is phosphorylated to 3-phosphoglyceraldehyde in the reaction

D-Glyceraldehyde + ATP $\longrightarrow$ 3-phosphoglyceraldehyde + ADP

Epimerization of D*-galactose 1-phosphate.*

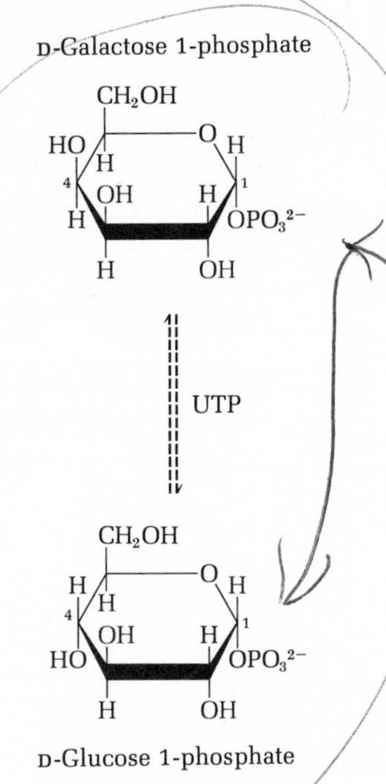

The hexose D-galactose, a component of milk sugar (D-lactose), enters the glycolytic cycle following phosphorylation at the expense of ATP by galactokinase

$$\text{ATP} + \text{D-galactose} \longrightarrow \text{ADP} + \text{D-galactose 1-phosphate}$$

D-Galactose 1-phosphate is now converted into its epimer at carbon atom 4, namely D-glucose 1-phosphate (margin), through a sequence of reactions requiring as a coenzyme uridine triphosphate (UTP). The details of this and other UTP-requiring sugar transformations will be described in Chapter 22.

Pentoses may also enter the glycolytic cyle, following degradation by other mechanisms to be described in Chapter 16. Glycerol and L-glycerol 3-phosphate, which are derived from triacylglycerols and phosphoglycerides, respectively, may also enter the glycolytic sequence, a major pathway for both the formation and degradation of glycerol. Free glycerol is phosphorylated at the expense of ATP by glycerol kinase

$$\text{ATP} + \text{glycerol} \longrightarrow \text{ADP} + \text{glycerol 3-phosphate}$$

Glycerol 3-phosphate may undergo oxidation to dihydroxyacetone phosphate, either by cytoplasmic glycerophosphate dehydrogenase, an enzyme that also requires the coenzyme NAD as electron acceptor, or by mitochondrial glycerophosphate dehydrogenase, a flavoprotein (Chapter 18)

$$\text{L-Glycerol 3-phosphate} + \text{NAD}^+ \rightleftharpoons \text{dihydroxyacetone phosphate} + \text{NADH} + \text{H}^+$$

The dihydroxyacetone phosphate formed is then enzymatically converted into glyceraldehyde 3-phosphate and enters the second stage of glycolysis.

Figure 15-11
The concluding steps in glycolysis and alcoholic fermentation.

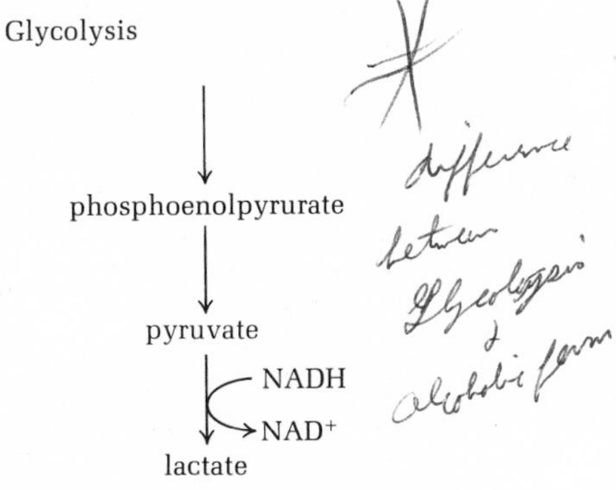

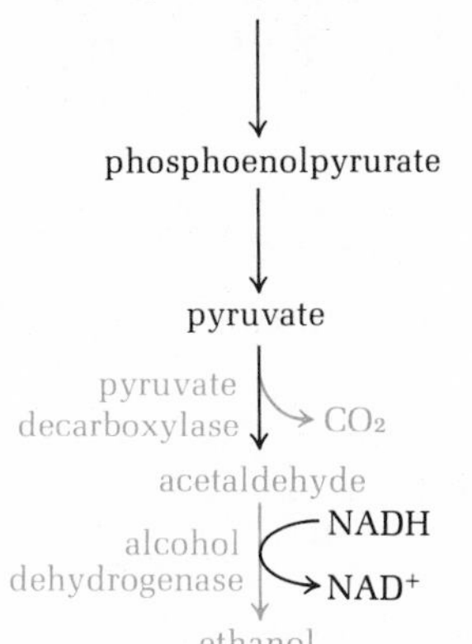

Alcoholic Fermentation

In organisms like brewer's yeast, which ferment glucose to ethanol and CO_2 rather than to lactic acid, the fermentation pathway is identical to that described for glycolysis except for the terminal step catalyzed by lactate dehydrogenase, which is replaced by two other enzymatic steps (Figure 15-11), catalyzed by *pyruvate decarboxylase* and *alcohol dehydrogenase.*

In the first step, pyruvate is decarboxylated to acetaldehyde and CO_2

$$\text{Pyruvate} \longrightarrow \text{acetaldehyde} + CO_2$$

The decarboxylation of pyruvate to form acetaldehyde and CO_2 is essentially irreversible. Pyruvate decarboxylase requires Mg^{2+} and has a tightly bound coenzyme, *thiamine pyrophosphate* (formerly called cocarboxylase), which is the pyrophosphoric acid ester of thiamine, or vitamin B_1, a necessary growth factor for many microorganisms and most vertebrate species. Deficiency of thiamine in the diet leads to the deficiency disease *beriberi*

Figure 15-12
Thiamine and thiamine pyrophosphate. The thiazole ring (color) is the active portion.

Thiamine (vitamin B1)

Thiamine pyrophosphate

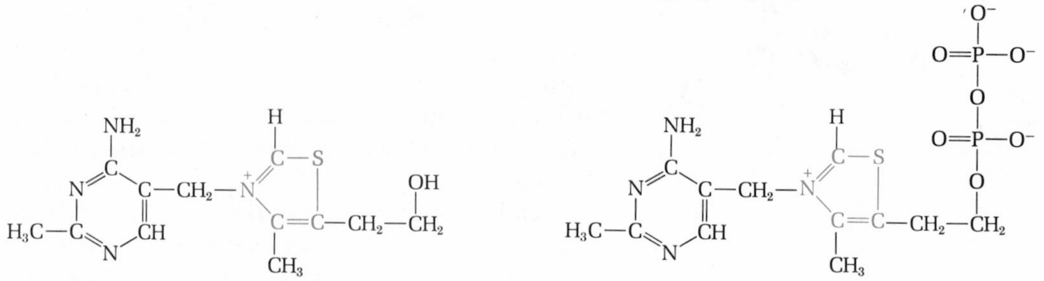

in man and polyneuritis in birds. The structures of thiamine and its pyrophosphate are shown in Figure 15-12. Thiamine pyrophosphate is the coenzyme for a number of enzymes that catalyze either nonoxidative or oxidative decarboxylation of α-keto acids such as pyruvate. The decarboxylation of pyruvate proceeds through a series of intermediate steps on the enzyme (Figure 15-13). First the α carbon atom of pyruvate is attacked by the strongly nucleophilic carbon atom 2 of the thiazole ring of the enzyme-bound thiamine pyrophosphate, to form a 2-α-lactyl derivative. This undergoes decarboxylation with loss of CO_2; the coenzyme is left in the form of a 2-hydroxyethyl derivative, which may be viewed as an activated, or coenzyme-bound, form of acetaldehyde. In the last step, the hydroxyethyl group leaves as free acetaldehyde, regenerating the free enzyme-TPP complex. Thiamine pyrophosphate is a carrier of active aldehyde groups, in the same sense that ATP is a carrier of active phosphate groups. In thiamine-deficient animals pyruvate accumulates in the tissues and blood.

In the final step of alcoholic fermentation, acetaldehyde is reduced to ethanol, with NADH + H^+ furnishing the reducing power, through the enzyme alcohol dehydrogenase

$$\text{Acetaldehyde} + \text{NADH} + \text{H}^+ \rightleftharpoons \text{ethanol} + \text{NAD}^+$$

Ethanol and CO_2 are thus the end products of alcoholic fermentation, instead of lactate. The overall equation of alcoholic fermentation can therefore be written

$$\text{Glucose} + 2\text{P}_i + 2\text{ADP} \longrightarrow 2\ \text{ethanol} + 2\text{CO}_2 + 2\text{ATP} + 2\text{H}_2\text{O}$$

The energy-conserving steps leading to ATP formation are identical in both glycolysis and alcoholic fermentation.

Other Types of Anaerobic Fermentation

Although homolactic and alcoholic fermentations are the most common fermentation mechanisms, other pathways

Figure 15-13
Steps in the action of thiamine pyrophosphate in decarboxylation of pyruvate.

Thiazole ring of thiamine pyrophosphate

Pyruvate

α-Hydroxyethyl derivative

Acetaldehyde

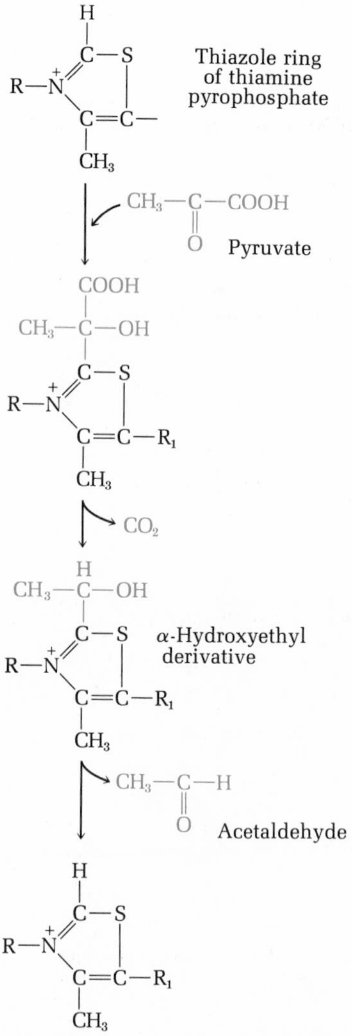

are known; most of them are variations of the Embden-Meyerhof scheme. In heterolactic, or mixed lactic, fermentations, one molecule each of lactic acid, ethanol, and carbon dioxide constitute the end products. In other types of sugar fermentations, propionic acid, butyric acid, succinic acid, and acetone are end products. Fatty acids and amino acids undergo fermentation by rather different mechanisms.

Summary

Anaerobic fermentation is the most primitive pathway for obtaining energy from fuels such as glucose. In anaerobic cells, it is the sole energy-producing process. In facultative cells it is an obligatory first stage in glucose catabolism, which is followed by aerobic oxidation of the fermentation products. The two most common types of fermentation are glycolysis and alcoholic fermentation. Both utilize identical energy-conserving mechanisms, and differ only in their terminal steps. The overall equation for glycolysis is glucose + 2ADP + $2P_i \longrightarrow$ 2 lactic acid + 2ATP + $2H_2O$ and for alcoholic fermentation is glucose + 2ADP + $2P_i \longrightarrow$ 2 ethanol + $2CO_2$ + 2ATP + $2H_2O$. Both fermentations are essentially irreversible.

Glycolysis takes place in two stages. In the first, D-glucose is enzymatically phosphorylated by ATP and ultimately cleaved to yield two molecules of D-glyceraldehyde 3-phosphate. Other hexoses, pentoses and glycerol are also collected and converted into glyceraldehyde 3-phosphate, following their phosphorylation.

In the second stage of glycolysis, the glyceraldehyde 3-phosphate is oxidized by NAD^+, with uptake of inorganic phosphate, by the action of glyceraldehyde phosphate dehydrogenase, to form 1,3-diphosphoglycerate. The latter donates its high-energy phosphate group to ADP to yield ATP and 3-phosphoglycerate, which is then isomerized to 2-phosphoglycerate. After dehydration of the latter by enolase, the phosphoenolpyruvate formed donates its high-energy phosphate group to ADP. The free pyruvate formed is reduced to lactate by NADH from the triose phosphate dehydrogenation. Two molecules of ATP enter the first stage of glycolysis, and four are formed from ADP in the second stage, giving a net yield of two ATP from one molecule of glucose. The efficiency of energy recovery by glycolysis in the intact erythrocyte is over 50 percent. There are three essentially irreversible steps in glycolysis, catalyzed by hexokinase, phosphofructokinase, and pyruvate phosphokinase. Phosphofructokinase, a regulatory enzyme, is rate-limiting for glycolysis. The entry of glucose residues of glycogen and starch into glycolysis is made possible by glycogen (starch) phosphorylase and phosphoglucomutase. Glycogen phosphorylase, which is responsible for converting glycogen to glucose 1-phosphate, is a regulatory enzyme existing in active (phosphorylase *a*) and less active (phosphorylase *b*) forms. In alcoholic fermentation, the reaction sequence is identical, but instead of being reduced to lactate, pyruvate is decarboxylated to acetaldehyde, which is in turn reduced to ethanol.

References

See also References in Chapter 14.

Books

Ciba Foundation Symposium, *Control of Glycogen Metabolism*, Little, Brown and Company, Boston, 1964.

COLOWICK, S. P., and N. O. KAPLAN (eds.), *Carbohydrate Metabolism*, vol. IX of *Methods in Enzymology*, Academic Press Inc., New York, 1966. Compendium of experimental methods and approaches.

DICKENS, F., P. J. RANDLE, and W. J. WHELAN, *Carbohydrate Metabolism and Its Disorders*, 2 vols., Academic Press Inc., New York, 1968. A series of papers on metabolism and control mechanisms.

FLORKIN, M., and E. H. STOTZ (eds.), *Carbohydrate Metabolism*, vol. 17 of *Comprehensive Biochemistry*, American Elsevier Publishing Company, New York, 1967.

Reviews and Articles

AXELROD, B., "Glycolysis," in D. M. Greenberg (ed.), *Metabolic Pathways*, 3d ed., vol. 1, pp. 112–145, Academic Press Inc., New York, 1967.

FISCHER, E. H., and E. G. KREBS, "Relationship of Structure to Function of Muscle Phosphorylase," *Fed. Proc.*, **25:**1511–1520 (1966).

KREBS, E. G., and E. H. FISCHER, "Molecular Properties and Transformations of Glycogen Phosphorylase in Animal Tissues," *Advan. Enzymol.*, **24:**263–290 (1962).

MANNERS, D. J., "Enzymatic Synthesis and Degradation of Starch and Glycogen," *Advan. Carbohyd. Chem.*, **17:**371–430 (1962).

MINIKAMI, S., and H. YOSHIKAWA, "Thermodynamic Considerations of Erythrocyte Glycolysis," *Biochem. Biophys. Res. Commun.*, **18:**345–349 (1965). Determination of the steady-state concentrations of intermediates and $\Delta G^{\circ\prime}$ of ATP hydrolysis in intact cell.

MORSE, D. E., and G. L. HORECKER, "The Mechanism of Action of Aldolases," *Advan. Enzymol.*, **31:**125–181 (1968), Interscience Publishers, Inc., New York.

PASSONEAU, J. V., and O. H. LOWRY, "Phosphofructokinase and the Pasteur Effect," *Biochem. Biophys. Res. Commun.* **7:**10–15 (1962). This and the following paper were important in demonstrating the important regulatory role of this enzyme.

PASSONEAU, J. V., and O. H. LOWRY, "Phosphofructokinase and the Control of the Citric Acid Cycle," *Biochem. Biophys. Res. Commun.*, **13:**372–379 (1963).

STADTMAN, E. R. "Allosteric Regulation of Enzyme Activity," *Advan. Enzymol.*, **28**:42–154 (1966). Pages 71 to 117 deal with enzymes of carbohydrate metabolism.

WALKER, D. G., "The Nature and Function of Hexokinases in Animal Tissues," in P. N. Campbell and G. D. Greville (eds.), *Essays in Biochemistry*, vol. 2, pp. 33–68, Academic Press Inc., New York, 1966. An informative and wide-ranging article.

Problems

1. Calculate the overall free-energy change when glycolysis occurs under conditions similar to those existing in the intact cell, i.e., glucose = 5 m*M*, phosphate = 1.0 m*M*, ADP = 0.5 m*M*, ATP = 3.0 m*M*, and lactate = 3.0 m*M*. What is the effect of raising the lactate concentration to 100 m*M*?

2. Write a balanced equation for the conversion of free D-fructose to lactic acid in the liver, including all associated phosphorylation steps.
3. Write balanced equations for the following, including all phosphorylation steps: (a) Conversion of free glycerol to lactic acid. (b) Conversion of L-glycerol 3-phosphoric acid to ethanol and CO_2. (c) Conversion of D-mannose to phosphoenolpyruvate. (d) Conversion of glucose 1,6-diphosphate to ethanol and CO_2.
4. Predict the effect of a shift in pH from 7 to 9 on the standard free energy of hydrolysis of phosphoenolpyruvate.
5. Name the compounds present at equilibrium when pure muscle aldolase acts on a mixture of fructose 1,6-diphosphate, D-glyceraldehyde, and acetaldehyde.
6. Calculate what percentage of the starting concentration of fructose 1,6-diphosphate is cleaved by pure aldolase at equilibrium, when the initial concentration of the fructose 1,6-diphosphate is (a) 1.0 M, (b) 0.1 M, (c) 0.01 M, (d) 0.001 M, and (e) 10^{-4} M. Assume $\Delta G^{\circ\prime}$ for the aldolase reaction is +5.73 kcal.
7. Write the overall equation for the conversion of fructose 1,6-diphosphate to phosphoenolpyruvate in the presence of NAD^+, phosphate, ADP, and arsenate.
8. A yeast extract containing all the enzymes required in the alcoholic fermentation of glucose is incubated with 200 mmoles of D-glucose, 20 mmoles of ATP, 2.0 mmoles of NAD^+, and 20 mmoles of phosphate. The incubation is continued until the system comes into equilibrium. Predict the amounts of glucose and ethanol in the equilibrium mixture. How can the fermentation be made to go to completion?

CHAPTER 16 THE TRICARBOXYLIC ACID CYCLE AND THE PHOSPHOGLUCONATE PATHWAY

Aerobic cells obtain most of their energy by respiration, the transfer of electrons from organic fuel molecules to molecular oxygen. Respiration is far more complex than glycolysis; it has been aptly said that respiration is to the process of glycolysis what a modern jet turbine is to a one-cylinder reciprocating engine.

This chapter outlines the overall plan of respiration and then considers in detail the Krebs tricarboxylic acid cycle, the final common pathway into which all the fuel molecules of the cell—carbohydrate, fatty acids, and amino acids—are ultimately degraded in catabolism. The phosphogluconate pathway for oxidation of glucose, a mechanism that generates reducing power for biosynthetic reactions is also described.

The Energetics of Fermentation and Respiration

Glycolysis releases only a very small fraction of the chemical energy potentially available in the structure of the glucose molecule. Much more energy is released when the glucose molecule is oxidized completely to CO_2 and H_2O, as is shown by comparing the standard free-energy changes for the anaerobic conversion of glucose to lactate and for its oxidation to CO_2 and water (Chapter 14):

$$\text{Glucose} \longrightarrow 2\ \text{lactate} \qquad \Delta G^{\circ\prime} = -47.0\ \text{kcal}$$

$$\text{Glucose} + 6O_2 \longrightarrow 6CO_2 + 6H_2O \qquad \Delta G^{\circ\prime} = -686.0\ \text{kcal}$$

When cells ferment glucose anaerobically, the products, which cannot be utilized further and thus leave the cell, still contain most of the energy of the original glucose molecule. Cells living anaerobically must therefore consume much more glucose than when they are living aerobically, in order to obtain an equal amount of useful energy.

Why does respiration yield so much more energy than glycolysis? In the first place, the glycolysis product lactic acid is almost as complex a molecule as glucose, and its carbon atoms are still in the same oxidation state, retaining on the average the same number of hydrogen atoms per carbon. Carbon dioxide, the product of respiration, is a much simpler and smaller molecule than glucose, and its carbon atoms are fully oxidized. Second, the amount of energy that becomes available when a pair of electrons is transferred from a given fuel molecule to an electron acceptor varies considerably depending on the nature of the acceptor (Chapter 17). Much more energy can be delivered when molecular oxygen is the electron acceptor, as is true in respiration, than when pyruvate serves as acceptor, as in glycolysis.

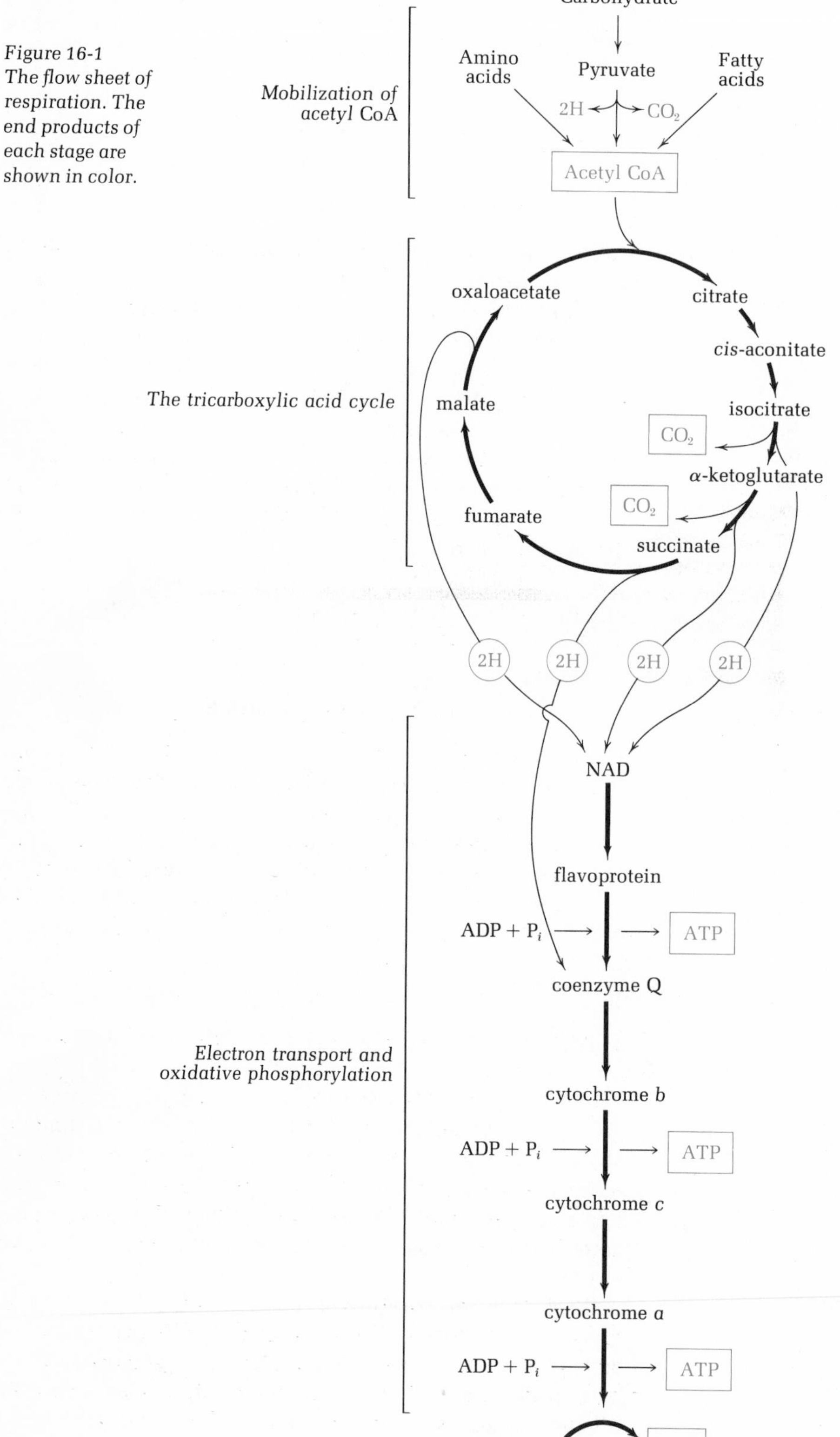

Figure 16-1
The flow sheet of respiration. The end products of each stage are shown in color.

The Organizational Plan of Respiration

The flow sheet of respiration is shown in Figure 16-1. Acetyl groups derived from carbohydrates, lipids, and amino acids in stage II of catabolism (Chapter 13) now enter stage III, the Krebs tricarboxylic acid cycle, which is the final common pathway of oxidative catabolism of all fuel molecules in aerobic cells. In this cycle acetyl groups are dismembered to form CO_2 and hydrogen atoms. The latter (or their equivalent electrons) are then fed into the *respiratory chain*, a series of electron carriers. The ensuing process of electron transport to molecular oxygen proceeds with a very large decline in free energy, much of which is conserved as ATP by the coupled oxidative phosphorylation of ADP.

The overall reaction catalyzed by the Krebs tricarboxylic acid cycle is

$$CH_3COOH + 2H_2O \longrightarrow 2CO_2 + 8H$$

As can be seen from this equation, neither molecular oxygen, inorganic phosphate, nor ATP participate in the cycle. Its primary function is the dehydrogenation of acetic acid to form ultimately two molecules of CO_2 and four pairs of hydrogen atoms. This process is catalyzed in a series of consecutive reactions that is cyclic, in contrast to the reaction sequence of glycolysis, which is linear. In each turn of the Krebs cycle (Figure 16-2) a molecule of acetic acid (two carbon atoms) enters by condensation with a molecule of the four-carbon compound oxaloacetic acid to form the six-carbon citric acid. The citric acid is

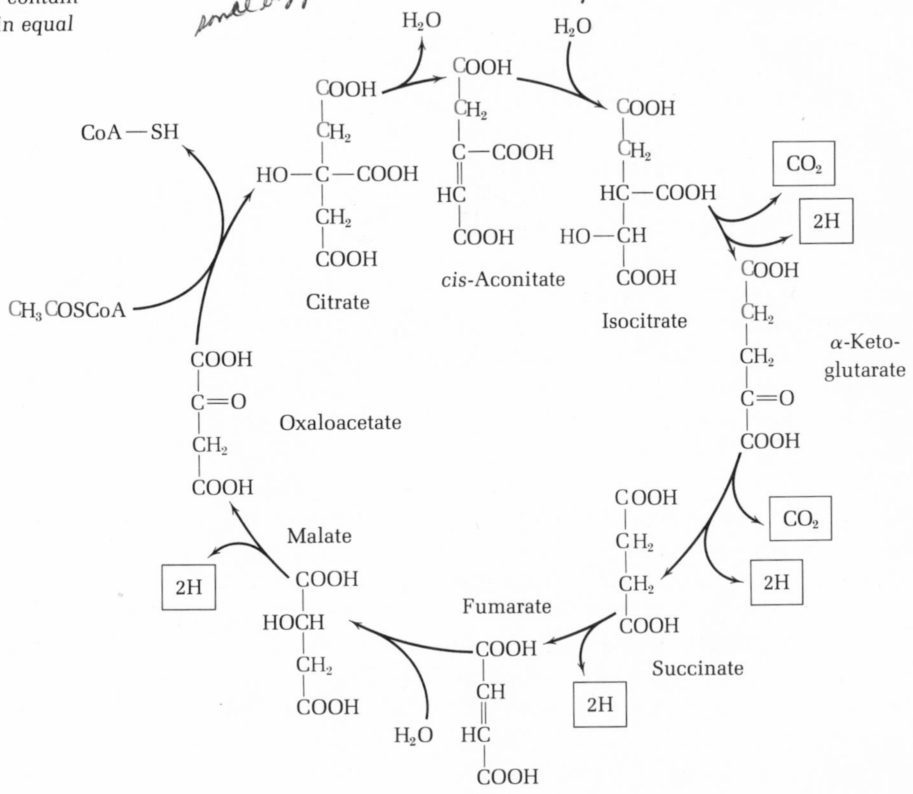

CoA—SH
$CH_3COSCoA$
Citrate
cis-Aconitate
Isocitrate
α-Keto-glutarate
Succinate
Fumarate
Malate
Oxaloacetate
H_2O H_2O H_2O
CO_2 2H CO_2 2H 2H 2H

Figure 16-2
The tricarboxylic acid cycle. The end products ($2CO_2$ plus four pairs of H atoms) are shown in boxes. The carbon atoms entering as acetyl CoA are in color, and their incorporation into the cycle intermediates is given to the stage of succinate. Since succinate is symmetrical, all its carbon atoms, and those of fumarate, malate, and oxaloacetate contain carbon from acetyl CoA in equal amount.

then degraded to yield two molecules of CO_2 and the four-carbon compound succinic acid. The latter is ultimately oxidized to oxaloacetic acid, which may then start another turn of the cycle. For each turn, one molecule of acetic acid enters and two molecules of CO_2 come out. In each turn, a molecule of oxaloacetate is used up to form citrate but is regenerated at the end of the cycle. There is therefore no net removal of oxaloacetate when the cycle operates; one molecule of oxaloacetate can suffice to bring about oxidation of an infinite number of acetate molecules. The Krebs cycle is thus catalytic in two senses: each separate step of the cycle is of course catalyzed by a specific enzyme, as is true in all enzyme systems, but superimposed on this level of catalysis is the catalytic effect of the cycle intermediates themselves: one molecule of any of the intermediates catalyzes the utilization of many acetate molecules.

The Experimental Origin of the Tricarboxylic Acid Cycle

The postulation of the tricarboxylic acid cycle by Krebs and Johnson in 1937, under its original name citric acid cycle, was a brilliant and ingenious piece of experimentation and reasoning which ranks among the classical investigations of modern biology. Their investigation will be reconstructed briefly since it is an instructive model for the analysis of other metabolic pathways in the cell.

First, some background must be sketched. It had been known from the work of Thunberg and of Batelli and Stern in the period 1910–1920 that anaerobic suspensions of minced animal tissues contained enzymes capable of transferring hydrogen atoms from certain organic acids known to occur in cells—especially succinic, fumaric, malic, and citric acids—to the reducible dye *methylene blue*, to produce its *leuco*, or colorless, reduced form (Figure 16-3). Such enzymes were called *dehydrogenases*. Later, in the early 1930s, several investigators using manometric measurement of the oxygen-utilization rate of minced-tissue suspensions (Chapter 13) found that succinate, fumarate, malate, and citrate are also rapidly oxidized to CO_2 and water by molecular oxygen.

Then, in 1935, Szent-Györgyi made the extremely important discovery that addition of small amounts of fumarate, malate, or succinate to minced-muscle suspensions evoked utilization of an amount of oxygen far beyond that required to oxidize the added dicarboxylic acid to CO_2 and water (Table 16-1). He concluded that each of these acids greatly stimulates the oxidation of some endogenous carbohydrate substrate in the tissue, presumably glycogen, and that this effect is catalytic, one molecule of succinate being able to promote the oxidation of many molecules of the endogenous substrate. Szent-Györgyi also showed that the oxidation of succinate by the action of succinate dehydrogenase must be in the mainstream of the oxidative metabolism of muscle, since the competitive inhibitor malonate, which blocks succinate dehydrogenase (Chapter 8), also inhibited the respiration of muscle suspensions almost completely.

Figure 16-3
The oxidized and reduced forms of methylene blue. Since the reduced form is rapidly oxidized by molecular oxygen, the reduction of methylene blue by tissue suspensions must be observed under anaerobic conditions.

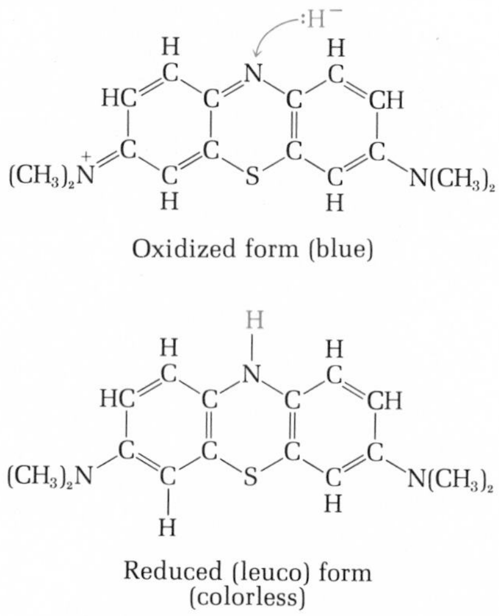

Oxidized form (blue)

Reduced (leuco) form (colorless)

Table 16-1 Catalytic effect of fumarate on the respiration of minced pigeon breast muscle

Fumarate added, µmoles	*Oxygen uptake calculated for oxidation of fumarate added, µatoms*	*Total oxygen uptake observed, µatoms*
1.0	6.0	47.2
2.0	12.0	69.4

Figure 16-4
Position of the malonate block. When succinate dehydrogenase is blocked, the oxidation of citrate, cis-aconitate, isocitrate, and α-ketoglutarate leads to accumulation of succinate. Inhibition by malonate also blocks the reverse action of succinate dehydrogenase. In order for fumarate to be converted to succinate in the presence of malonate another pathway must exist.

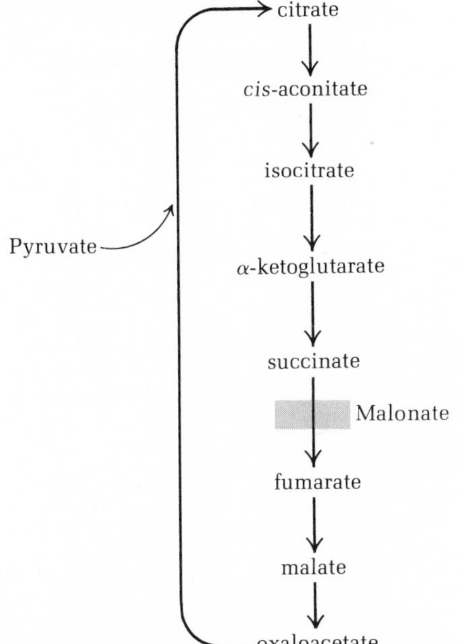

Starting with these observations, Krebs studied the interrelationships in the oxidative metabolism of various organic acids, using as experimental material suspensions of the minced flight muscles of the pigeon, which have a very high respiration rate. His observations are summarized in the following paragraphs.

1 The muscle suspensions were found to oxidize at a very high rate only certain specific dicarboxylic acids, namely, succinic, fumaric, malic, oxalacetic, and α-ketoglutaric acids, and only certain tricarboxylic acids, namely, citric, isocitric, and *cis*-aconitic acids. Although many other organic acids, e.g., tartaric acid, were also oxidized by muscle, the rate was relatively very slow. Thus the specific acids enumerated above are sharply different in their oxidation rate from other organic acids tested.

2 The oxidation of endogenous carbohydrate or of added pyruvate by muscle suspensions was found to be catalytically stimulated not only by small amounts of succinate, fumarate, malate, and oxalacetate, but also by citrate, *cis*-aconitate, isocitrate, and α-ketoglutarate. On the other hand, tartrate and the anions of other organic acids did not stimulate respiration catalytically.

3 Malonate completely inhibited the stimulation of the oxidation of pyruvate by any of the specific tricarboxylic and dicarboxylic acids enumerated above. Since malonate inhibits succinate dehydrogenase specifically and does not inhibit the dehydrogenases attacking the other dicarboxylic and tricarboxylic acids, it was concluded that the oxidation of succinate to fumarate by succinate dehydrogenase is an essential link in a chain of reactions involving all the specific dicarboxylic and tricarboxylic acids that can stimulate respiration. If this link is blocked, none of the other acids stimulate pyruvate oxidation. (At this point it is useful to refer to Figure 16-4.)

4 When oxaloacetate and pyruvate were incubated with the muscle suspension under anaerobic conditions, small amounts of citrate were formed. Krebs postulated that the condensation of pyruvate and oxaloacetate to form citrate was the missing link by which the various known enzymatic reactions of the dicarboxylic and tricarboxylic acids could be arranged in a cycle (Figure 16-4). The subsequent experiments put this hypothesis to critical tests.

5 When malonate was added to muscle suspensions to block succinate dehydrogenase, it was found that succinate accumulated quantitatively following oxidation of added citrate, isocitrate, *cis*-aconitate, or α-ketoglutarate, the most immediate precursors of succinate, as expected from the cyclic formulation in Figure 16-4.

6 Moreover, in malonate-poisoned muscle the oxidation of fumarate, malate, or oxaloacetate also led to quantitative accumulation of succinate. This important observation clearly established that an oxidative pathway must exist for fumarate to be converted to succinate in a system in which succinate dehydrogenase is poisoned by malonate and in which formation of succinate from fumarate by reversal of the action of succinate dehydro-

genase would therefore be impossible. These observations thus strongly supported Krebs' hypothesis of a pathway from fumarate to succinate via oxaloacetate and citrate, a pathway which established that the overall sequence of reactions was cyclic in nature.

7 Krebs also found that the inhibition of pyruvate utilization by malonate could be relieved or overcome by raising the concentration of oxaloacetate or of its precursors fumarate or malate. Under these circumstances, one molecule of dicarboxylic acid disappeared for each molecule of pyruvate consumed. He explained this finding as follows. In the uninhibited cycle, one molecule of oxaloacetate can stimulate the oxidative removal of many molecules of pyruvate, as would be expected if oxaloacetate is regenerated at each turn of the cycle. However, when the cycle is poisoned by malonate, oxaloacetate can no longer be regenerated. Under these circumstances one molecule of oxaloacetate is required to remove each molecule of pyruvate. Oxidation of the citrate so formed yields succinate, which then accumulates before the malonate block. In malonate-poisoned muscle the following overall reaction therefore takes place:

$$\text{Fumarate} + \text{pyruvate} + 2O_2 \longrightarrow \text{succinate} + 3CO_2 + H_2O$$

These experiments conclusively proved that the entire sequence of reactions is cyclic.

From these simple yet elegant experiments and reasoning Krebs postulated what he called the citric acid cycle as the main pathway for oxidation of carbohydrate in muscle. Because for some years there was uncertainty whether citric acid or some other tricarboxylic acid was the first product of condensation of pyruvate and oxaloacetate, the name of the cycle was changed to "tricarboxylic acid cycle," As it turned out, citric acid is in fact the first one formed, but over 10 years were to pass before this was proved conclusively. It is now certain that the tricarboxylic acid cycle is virtually universal; it represents the major if not sole pathway for oxidation of acetic acid residues in all tissues of higher animals, in most aerobic microorganisms, and in many plant tissues. In some microorganisms and in the seeds and other tissues of higher plants, the tricarboxylic acid cycle has undergone a modification that allows these cells to utilize acetic acid or fatty acids as sole carbon source (see below).

Intracellular Location of the Enzymes of the Tricarboxylic Acid Cycle

Before detailing the enzymatic steps of the cycle, we must consider another aspect of the organization of the tricarboxylic acid cycle. In 1948 Kennedy and Lehninger discovered that when mitochondria are separated from rat liver homogenates by differential centrifugation (Chapter 13) and are suspended in a buffered medium provided with phosphate, adenine nucleotides and Mg^{2+}, they catalyze the oxidation of pyruvate and all the intermediates of the tricarboxylic acid cycle at the expense of molecular oxygen. The overall rate of oxygen consumption and pyruvate utilization by the isolated mitochondria was sufficient to account for the rate of respiration of the entire intact liver cell. The nuclei, the microsomes, and the soluble fraction of the cytoplasm (Chapter 13) were found to be essentially inactive. Because only Mg^{2+} and an adenine nucleotide had to be added to the mitochondrial suspension, it was concluded that the mitochondria must contain all the enzymes required for not only the tricarboxylic acid cycle but also for electron transport to oxygen. It has since been found that mitochondria isolated from many different animal and plant tissues, as well as from yeasts, protozoa, and other microorganisms, can carry out the oxidations of the tricarboxylic acid cycle.

Some of the enzymes of the cycle are found not only in the mitochondria but also in the extramitochondrial cytoplasm, particularly aconitase, fumarase, and malate dehydrogenase (see below). These extramitochondrial enzymes function in other metabolic pathways. The enzymatic reactions of the tricarboxylic acid cycle take place within the inner compartment of the mitochondrion. This and other aspects of the compartmentation of oxidative reactions in mitochondria will be described in Chapter 18. One other important consequence of the location of the enzymes of the cycle in the mitochondria, however, remains to be mentioned. Since some of the tricarboxylic acid cycle enzymes appear to be firmly attached to the mitochondrial membranes and are not easily extracted in soluble form, their isolation and the elucidation of their reaction mechanisms has been more difficult than for the glycolytic enzymes, which are easily extracted from cells.

The Oxidation of Pyruvate to Acetyl CoA

After the tricarboxylic acid cycle was postulated, the pathway of formation of citrate from pyruvate and oxaloacetate became the subject of much speculation and study. One hypothesis held that pyruvate condenses directly with oxaloacetate to yield a seven-carbon compound, which becomes the precursor of the six-carbon citric acid, but tests of various seven-carbon acids failed to reveal any with the expected properties of an intermediate. It was not until 1948–1950 that the problem was solved. Pyruvate is first oxidized to acetic acid, in the form of the acetyl derivative of coenzyme A, which then reacts directly with oxaloacetate to form citrate.

The oxidation of pyruvate to acetyl CoA, catalyzed by the *pyruvate dehydrogenase system*, is in fact a very complex process, which has been studied in detail by Reed and his colleagues. The overall equation is

$$\text{Pyruvate} + \text{NAD}^+ + \text{CoA-SH} \longrightarrow \text{acetyl-S-CoA} + \text{NADH} + \text{H}^+ + \text{CO}_2 \qquad \Delta G^{\circ\prime} = -8.0\ \text{kcal} \qquad (1)$$

Because of the large decrease in the standard free energy, this reaction is essentially irreversible. Although it is not itself part of the tricarboxylic acid cycle, it is an obligatory step by which carbohydrates (via pyruvate) enter the cycle. Before analyzing this reaction sequence, we should examine the properties of two coenzymes participating in it, namely, CoA, the structure of which was discussed in Chapter 12, and lipoic acid, which has yet to be considered.

Lipmann and his colleagues, in the period 1947–1950, found that a heat-stable coenzyme was required in many enzymatic reactions involving transfer of acetyl groups and that acetate combined with this coenzyme to form an active acetyl-group donor. They isolated and determined the structure of CoA (A for acetyl), which was later proved by synthesis (Figure 16-5). CoA serves as a carrier of acyl groups, analogous to the function of ATP as a carrier of phosphate groups. The acetylated form of CoA (designated acetyl coenzyme A, acetyl CoA, or acetyl-S-CoA) is the thioester of acetic acid with the thiol group of the β-mercaptoethylamine moiety. The thioester linkage is a high-energy bond; i.e., it has a strongly negative standard free energy of hydrolysis

$$\text{Acetyl-S-CoA} + H_2O \longrightarrow \text{acetate} + \text{CoA-SH} \qquad \Delta G^{\circ\prime} = -7.52 \text{ kcal}$$

Lipoic acid, a growth factor for some microorganisms, is an eight-carbon saturated fatty acid in which carbons 6 and 8 are joined by a disulfide group, forming a five-membered ring (Figure 16-6). It is readily reduced, with cleavage of the disulfide group, to *dihydrolipoic acid*, which has free thiol groups at carbon atoms 6 and 8. Lipoic acid is covalently attached to the enzyme *lipoyl reductase-transacetylase* (see below) by a peptide linkage between its carboxyl group and the ϵ-amino group of a lysine residue of the enzyme protein (Figure 16-6); this dipeptidelike structure is known as *lipoamide* or *lipoyllysine*.

Figure 16-5
Coenzyme A. The free thiol group is in color. In acetyl CoA the —SH group is esterified to acetic acid.

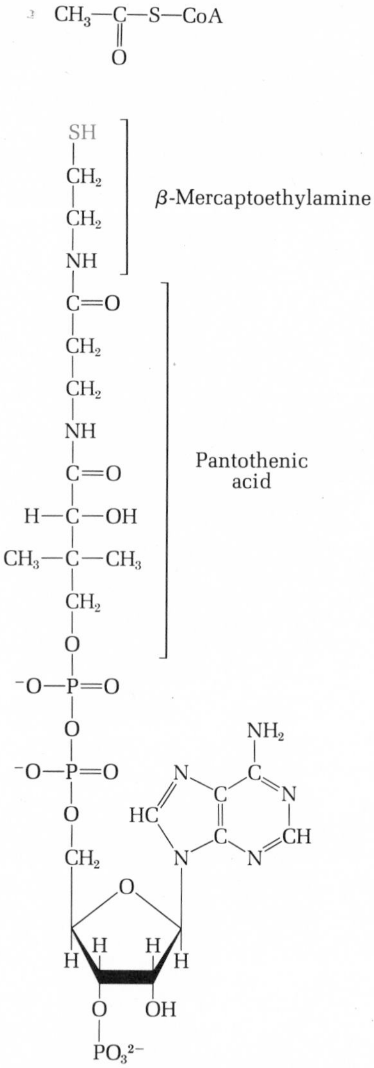

$CH_3—C(=O)—S—CoA$

β-Mercaptoethylamine

Pantothenic acid

Figure 16-6
Forms of lipoic acid.

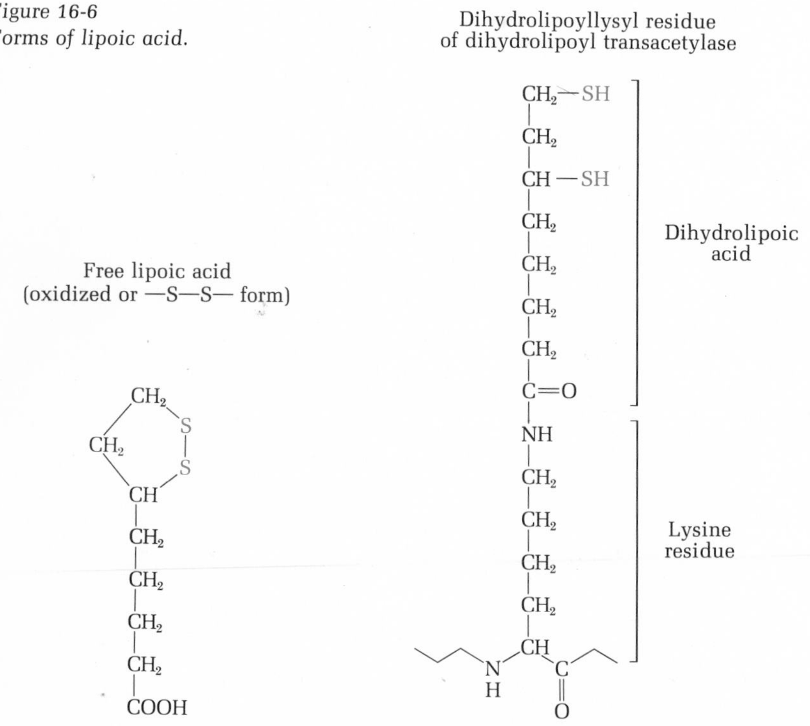

Free lipoic acid (oxidized or —S—S— form)

Dihydrolipoyllysyl residue of dihydrolipoyl transacetylase

Dihydrolipoic acid

Lysine residue

Space-filling model of coenzyme A.

The oxidative decarboxylation of pyruvate to acetyl CoA and CO_2 requires three different enzymes and five different coenzymes organized into a multienzyme complex, the *pyruvate dehydrogenase system*, whose interactions are schematized in Figure 16-7. Step I in the dehydrogenation of pyruvate to acetyl CoA and CO_2 is catalyzed by *pyruvate dehydrogenase* (E_1—TPP in Figure 16-7). In this reaction a hydroxyethyl derivative of the thiazole ring of enzyme-bound thiamine pyrophosphate (E_1—TPP—CHOH—CH_3) is formed from pyruvate in reactions that are identical to those involved in the nonoxidative decarboxylation of pyruvate during alcoholic fermentation (Chapter 15). In step II the hydroxyethyl group of the E_1—TPP—CHOH—CH_3 complex is transferred to one of the sulfur atoms of the cyclic disulfide group of lipoic acid, which is covalently bound to the second enzyme of the complex, *dihydrolipoyl transacetylase* (E_2). When the hydroxyethyl group is transferred from thiamine pyrophosphate to the lipoic acid group, an oxidoreduction occurs; the hydroxyethyl group becomes an acetyl group by loss of hydrogen atoms to the disulfide bond of lipoic acid, which is reduced to its dithiol form.

In step III, the acetyl group is enzymatically transferred from the lipoyl group of dihydrolipoyl transacetylase to the thiol group of CoA; the acetyl CoA so formed then leaves the enzyme complex in free form. In step IV, the free dithiol form of dihydrolipoyl transacetylase is reoxidized to its disulfide form by the third enzyme, *dihydrolipoyl dehydrogenase* (E_3—FAD), which contains a tightly bound reducible coenzyme, *flavin adenine dinucleotide* (FAD), which acts as a hydrogen acceptor. The structure of FAD was shown in Chapter 12, and its properties will be described in Chapter 17. The FAD becomes reduced to $FADH_2$, which remains bound to the enzyme (E_3—$FADH_2$). In the final reaction (step V), E_3—$FADH_2$ is reoxidized by NAD^+, to regenerate the oxidized form E_3—FAD, with formation of NADH. The overall reaction [equation (1)] is strongly exergonic ($\Delta G^{\circ\prime} = -8.00$ kcal) and essentially irreversible under intracellular conditions.

The pyruvate dehydrogenase complex has been isolated from pig heart mitochondria and *E. coli*. From the latter source, the complex has a particle weight of 4.0 million.

Figure 16-7
Oxidation of pyruvate to acetyl CoA by the pyruvate dehydrogenase complex of enzymes. The fate of pyruvate is traced in color.
E_1 = pyruvate dehydrogenase
TPP = thiamine pyrophosphate
E_2 = dihydrolipoyl transacetylase
E_3 = dihydrolipoyl dehydrogenase

yes

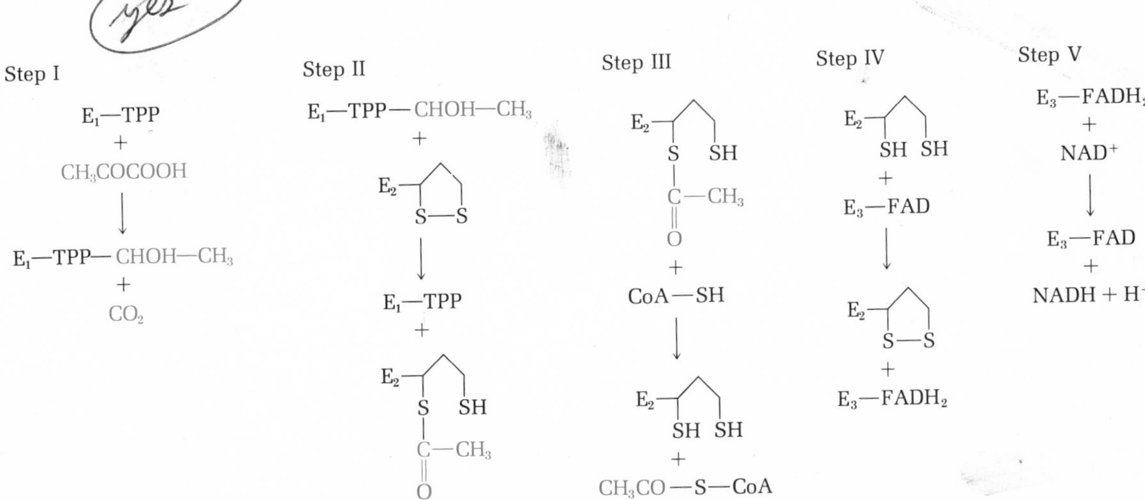

It consists of 24 molecules of pyruvate dehydrogenase (mol wt 90,000), each containing a molecule of bound thiamine pyrophosphate, 1 molecule of dihydrolipoyl transacetylase containing 24 polypeptide chains, each of mol wt 36,000 and each containing one molecule of lipoic acid, and 12 molecules of dihydrolipoyl dehydrogenase (mol wt 55,000), each containing one molecule of FAD. The complex has a diameter of 350 ± 50 Å and a height of 225 ± 25 Å, as shown by the electron microscope. The long lipoyllysine side-chain of E_2 has been postulated to serve as a "swinging arm" to transfer the electron pair from E_1 to E_2 and the acetyl group from E_2 to E_3 (Figure 16-8).

The pyruvate dehydrogenase complex is characteristically inhibited by trivalent arsenicals or by arsenite, which can react with both thiol groups to yield an inactive cyclic derivative. Recent research has shown that the pyruvate dehydrogenase system is also inhibited by ATP, which thus is a negative modulator. Whenever the ATP level in the cell exceeds a certain point, the pyruvate dehydrogenase system, which provides fuel for the tricarboxylic acid cycle, "turns off."

The acetyl CoA formed as the end product of the complex pyruvate dehydrogenase system is now ready to enter the tricarboxylic acid cycle.

At the top is shown an electron micrograph of the pyruvate dehydrogenase complex of E. coli. Below are shown top and side views of a model of the complex. The black spheres represent pyruvate dehydrogenase and the colored spheres, dihydrolipoyl dehydrogenase molecules, which are clustered around a central core of dihydrolipoyl transacetylase.

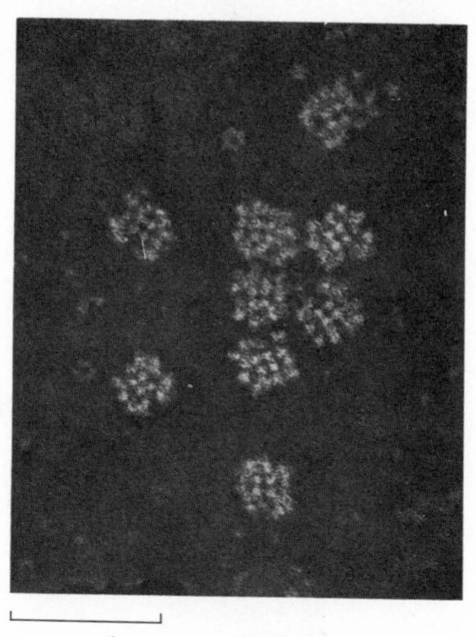

Top view

Side view

Figure 16-8
The long lipoyllysine side-chain of dihydrolipoyl transacetylase (E_2) serves as a swinging arm to transfer electrons from pyruvate dehydrogenase (E_1) to dihydrolipoyl dehydrogenase (E_3).

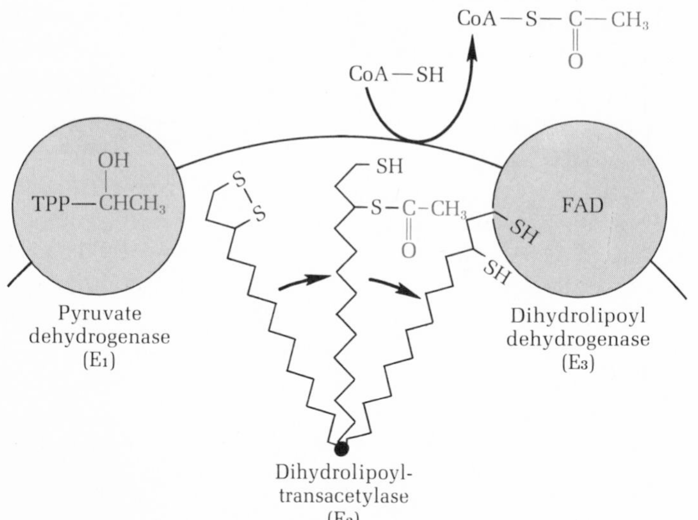

Individual Reactions of the Tricarboxylic Acid Cycle

The cycle originally postulated in 1937 was a skeleton. It has since been filled in with many details from the study of highly purified preparations of the enzymes catalyzing the following individual steps.

Citrate Synthase

The condensation of acetyl CoA with oxaloacetate to form citrate is catalyzed by *citrate synthase* (earlier called condensing enzyme), which has been obtained in crystalline

The citrate synthase reaction. The carbon atoms originating from acetate are in color.

O=C—S—CoA
|
CH_3
+
O
||
C—COOH
|
CH_2 Oxaloacetic acid
|
COOH

⇌

[O=C—S—CoA, CH_2, HO—C—COOH, CH_2, COOH] Citryl CoA (enzyme-bound)

⇌

COOH
|
CH_2
|
HO—C—COOH Citric acid
|
CH_2
|
COOH

form. In this reaction, the methyl group of acetyl CoA condenses with the carbonyl carbon atom of oxaloacetate, with hydrolysis of the thioester bond and formation of free CoA—SH (margin). The reaction proceeds far in the direction of citrate formation because of the exergonic hydrolysis of the high-energy thioester linkage ($\Delta G^{\circ\prime} = -7.7$ kcal). Citryl CoA (margin) is formed as an intermediate at the active site but does not leave before it is hydrolyzed to yield free citrate and free CoA—SH. The enzyme also catalyzes conversion of monofluoroacetyl CoA to *monofluorocitrate*, a potent inhibitor of *aconitase*, the next enzyme in the cycle. Citrate synthase is a regulatory enzyme; it catalyzes the ratesetting step of the tricarboxylic acid cycle in liver and other mammalian tissues. It is strongly inhibited by ATP in most organisms and by NADH in *E. coli*.

The Aconitase Equilibrium

The enzyme *aconitase* catalyzes the reversible equilibria shown in the margin. The equilibrium mixture at pH 7.4 and 25° contains about 91 percent citrate, 6 percent isocitrate, and 3 percent *cis*-aconitate. These reactions involve the reversible addition of water to the α,β double bond of *cis*-aconitate. Aconitase is activated and stabilized by Fe(II) and cysteine. Its stereochemistry and mechanism of action have been the subject of much study. For one thing, the enzyme can catalyze addition of H_2O to the double bond of *cis*-aconitic acid in two directions, one leading to citric and the other to isocitric acid. Because isocitric acid has a specific stereochemical configuration about its asymmetric carbon atoms, and because aconitic acid has a *cis* double bond, there are steric restrictions on how the elements of water can add to the double bond. From cleverly designed experiments with deuterium-labeled substrates, it has been deduced that H and OH are added to the double bond of *cis*-aconitate *trans* to each other (Figure 16-9).

The aconitase equilibrium.

COOH
|
CH_2
|
HO—C—COOH Citric acid (91%)
|
CH_2
|
COOH

⇌

COOH
|
CH_2
|
C—COOH *cis*-Aconitic acid (3%)
||
HC
|
COOH

⇌

COOH
|
CH_2
|
HC—COOH Isocitric acid (6%)
|
HO—CH
|
COOH

Figure 16-9
The stereospecific trans addition of water (color) to cis-aconitate in two directions, leading to citrate and isocitrate.

The mechanism of the aconitase reaction has also attracted much attention because the ferrous ion, which is known to form a stable chelate complex with citric acid, is required in the action of the enzyme. Recent x-ray crystallographic studies of the three-dimensional structure of citric, isocitric, and *cis*-aconitic acids and their ferrous complexes have led to an interesting hypothesis of the structure of the aconitase—Fe(II)-substrate complex, which is shown in Figure 16-10. The Fe(II) atom, which is bound to the enzyme by two of its six coordination bonds, forms a tridentate complex with citrate, i.e., one with three points of attachment. The entire Fe(II)-citrate complex is bound to the active site in a highly specific manner, involving at least three points of attachment. The enzyme is believed to function by abstracting a hydrogen ion from carbon atom 2 of citrate, thus leaving the latter as a carbanion, which then allows the hydroxyl group at carbon 3 to leave, coordinated to Fe(II). Following rotation of the Fe(II) complex about the axis of two of its coordination bonds (Figure 16-10) and a conformational change of the *cis*-aconitate, the hydroxyl group is transferred from the Fe(II) to carbon atom 2. The hydrogen atom earlier abstracted by the enzyme is then returned to carbon atom 3 to yield isocitrate. This hypothesis also suggests that *cis*-aconitate is an enzyme-bound intermediate in the conversion of citrate to isocitrate; free *cis*-aconitate forms by dissociation of the intermediate from the enzyme.

Later we shall see that citrate, a symmetrical molecule, behaves in the Krebs cycle as though it were asymmetrical, i.e., in such a way that the two terminal carboxyl groups of citrate are not equivalent. The reaction mechanism in Figure 16-10 allows for such asymmetric behavior, as we shall also see.

Figure 16-10
Crystallographic models of the structures of the aconitase-iron-citrate (top) and the aconitase-iron-isocitrate complexes (bottom). It is postulated that the iron atom rotates around the bonds shown to transfer the —OH groups from one carbon atom to another. Simultaneously, the cis-aconitate undergoes a change in conformation.

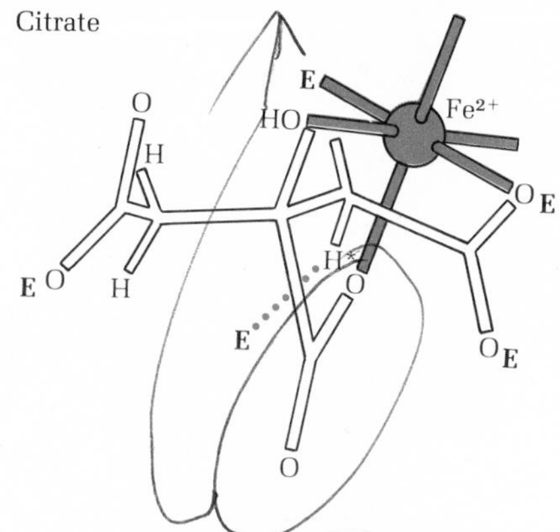

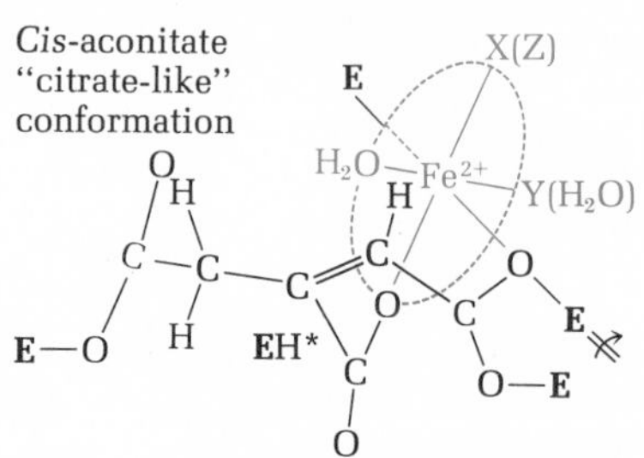

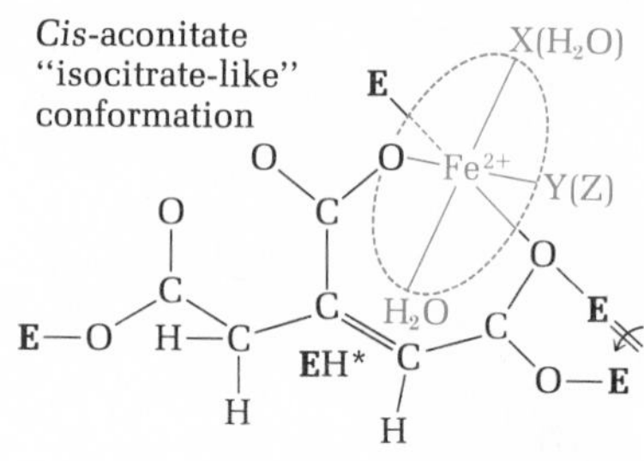

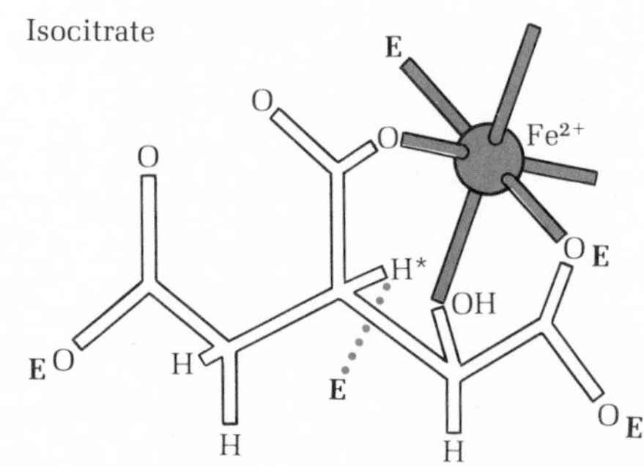

NAD-*Linked Isocitrate Dehydrogenase*

This enzyme is of special interest because of its unusual experimental history, because it is catalyzed by an allosteric enzyme, and because it is a secondary control point of the tricarboxylic acid cycle in the liver and probably the primary control point in some muscles.

Most microorganisms and higher animal and plant tissues contain two types of isocitrate dehydrogenase. For years a controversy has raged over which type is responsible for the oxidation of isocitrate to α-ketoglutarate in the tricarboxylic acid cycle. One type of isocitrate dehydrogenase requires NAD^+ as electron acceptor and the other $NADP^+$ (Chapters 12 and 17). The overall reactions catalyzed by the two types of isocitrate dehydrogenase are identical

$$\text{Isocitrate} + NAD^+ \; (NADP^+) \rightleftharpoons \alpha\text{-ketoglutarate} + CO_2 + NADH \; (NADPH) + H^+$$

Both the NAD-linked and NADP-linked isocitrate dehydrogenases have been found in mitochondria of many higher animal tissues, but the former is found only in mitochondria whereas the latter is found both in mito-

Space-filling models of tricarboxylic acid cycle intermediates.

Citric acid

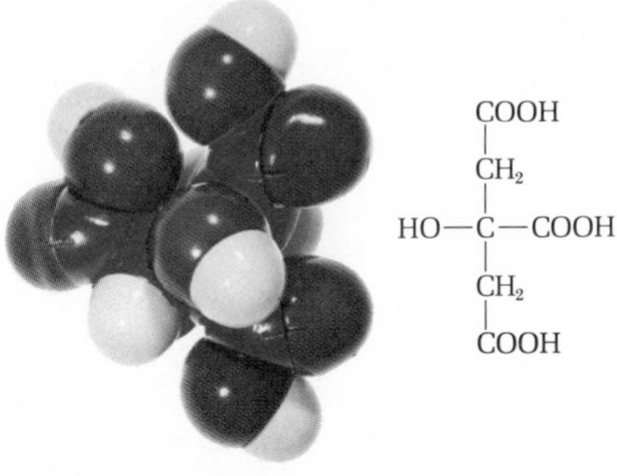

Isocitric acid

α-Ketoglutaric acid

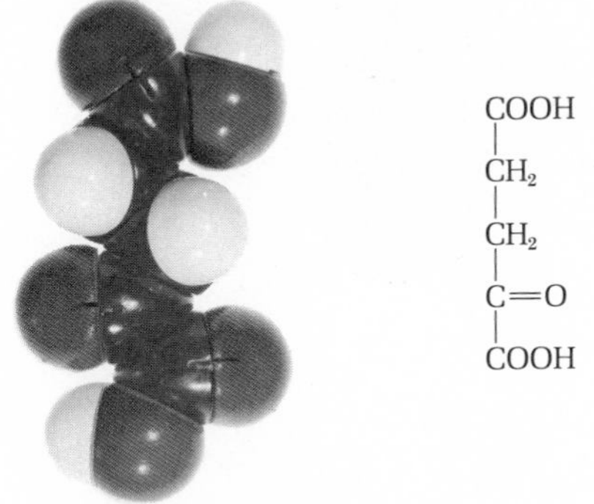

chondria and in the extramitochondrial cytoplasm. Recent research has shown that the NAD-linked isocitrate dehydrogenase is the normal catalyst for isocitrate oxidation in the tricarboxylic acid cycle; the NADP-linked enzyme is primarily concerned with auxiliary biosynthetic reactions of the cycle. This distinction between the NAD- and NADP-specific isocitrate dehydrogenases was obscured for years because the NAD-linked enzyme is an allosteric enzyme which requires ADP as a specific activator. In the absence of ADP, the NAD-linked enzyme has very little activity. Until the stimulating effect of ADP on the NAD-linked enzyme was discovered, it was thought that the latter was feebly active and played some minor role.

The NAD-specific isocitrate dehydrogenase of mitochondria requires Mg^{2+} or Mn^{2+} for activity. The reaction proceeds with a large decrease in $\Delta G^{\circ\prime}$ because the simultaneous loss of the β-carboxyl group as CO_2 is a highly exergonic reaction. When the NAD-specific isocitrate dehydrogenase of animal tissues is stimulated by ADP, the latter undergoes no enzymatic alteration and can be recovered again at the end of the reaction. No other nucleoside 5′-diphosphate (except dADP) can activate the enzyme from heart or liver, nor can ADP or ATP. The activation by ADP appears to be the result of a positive allosteric modulation. The stimulating effect of ADP is maximal at low isocitrate concentration, an observation which led to the finding that the binding of ADP to the regulatory site of the enzyme decreases the value of the K_m for isocitrate, i.e. increases the affinity of the enzyme for its substrate, without change in the maximum velocity (V_{max}) of the enzyme, as is shown in Figure 16-11.

The activity of isocitrate dehydrogenase is also influenced by ATP and by NADH, which strongly inhibit the enzyme, largely by competition with NAD^+. In any metabolic condition in which the ADP concentration rises in the cell, presumably because of an excessively high rate of breakdown of ATP in energy-requiring reactions, the increase in ADP concentration will automatically stimulate the rate of isocitrate oxidation. An increase in the rate of the tricarboxylic acid cycle reactions will cause an increased rate of electron transport and thus

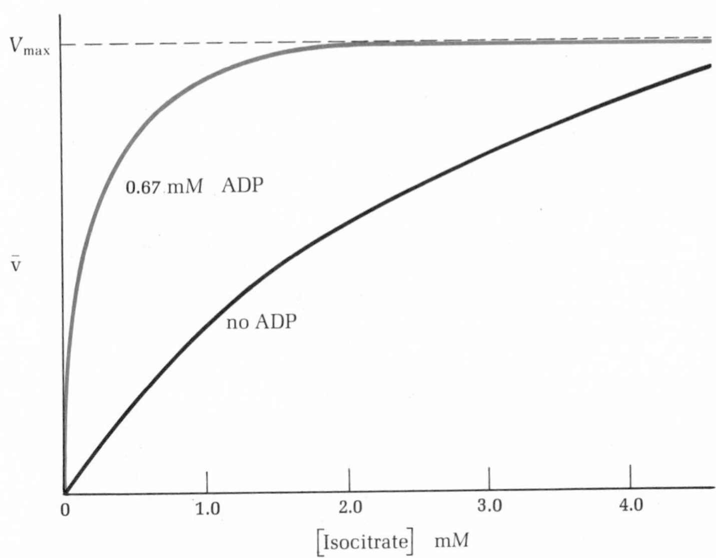

Figure 16-11
Allosteric stimulation of NAD-linked isocitrate dehydrogenase by ADP. In the presence of ADP the Km for isocitrate is about 0.15 mM, in its absence K_m is about 1.5 mM. The apparent affinity for isocitrate thus is increased about 10-fold by ADP.

of oxidative phosphorylation of ADP to ATP. As the concentration of ATP in the cell then increases, that of ADP must decrease, a change which tends to "turn off" isocitrate dehydrogenase. In the same way accumulation of NADH in the mitochondria can also turn off oxidation of isocitrate; as the excess NADH is consumed by respiration, the inhibition of isocitrate oxidation will be gradually relieved.

The purified NAD-specific isocitrate dehydrogenase of beef heart mitochondria occurs in a monomeric form of molecular weight 330,000 and a dimeric form. In the presence of the positive modulator ADP the monomeric form aggregates to form the dimer. Such ADP-induced aggregation is prevented by NADH, a negative modulator. Although both the monomeric and dimeric forms are enzymatically active, the dimer is apparently significantly more active at low ADP concentrations.

The above description refers largely to isocitrate dehydrogenase of heart and liver mitochondria; in other mammalian tissues, in plants, and in microorganisms the enzyme has significantly different regulatory properties. Although the citrate synthase reaction is believed to be the primary control point of the tricarboxylic acid cycle in the liver and other mammalian tissues, the isocitrate dehydrogenase reaction may represent an important secondary regulatory step in these tissues. In the flight muscles of some insects, however, isocitrate dehydrogenase appears to represent the primary regulatory reaction of the tricarboxylic acid cycle.

Figure 16-12
The monomeric form of heart isocitrate dehydrogenase is converted to the dimeric form by ADP.

The monomeric form of heart isocitrate dehydrogenase is converted to the dimeric form by ADP.

Monomers

ADP

Dimeric form

Oxidation of α-Ketoglutarate to Succinate

The oxidation of α-ketoglutarate to succinate, which is irreversible in heterotrophs, occurs in two stages. In the first step, α-ketoglutarate undergoes oxidative decarboxylation to form succinyl-S-CoA (margin) and CO_2:

$$\alpha\text{-Ketoglutarate} + NAD^+ + \text{CoA-SH} \rightleftharpoons \text{succinyl-S-CoA} + CO_2 + NADH + H^+ \qquad \Delta G^{\circ\prime} = -8.0 \text{ kcal}$$

like Pyruvate dehydrogenase

This reaction is comparable to that for the oxidation of pyruvate to acetyl CoA and CO_2 (see above) and occurs by the same mechanism, with thiamine pyrophosphate, lipoic acid, CoA, NAD^+, and FAD participating as required enzyme-bound cofactors. The α-ketoglutarate dehydrogenase complex is very similar in structure and properties to the pyruvate dehydrogenase complex. It has been isolated from animal tissues and from *E. coli*, in which it has a particle weight of 2.1×10^6.

The end product of this reaction is succinyl CoA, a high-energy thioester of one carboxyl group of succinic acid. Succinyl CoA then undergoes loss of its CoA group, not by simple hydrolysis, but by an energy-conserving reaction with guanosine diphosphate (GDP) and phosphate.

$$\text{Succinyl CoA} + P_i + GDP \rightleftharpoons \text{succinate} + GTP + \text{CoA—SH} \qquad \Delta G^{\circ\prime} = -0.7 \text{ kcal}$$

The enzyme catalyzing this reaction, succinyl thiokinase, or succinyl CoA synthetase, causes the formation of the

Succinyl-S-CoA

COOH
|
CH_2
|
CH_2
|
O=C—S—CoA

3-Phosphohistidine

COOH
|
HC—NH_2
|
CH_2
|
H C=C (4, 5)
O^- | O=P—N3 2 1N
| C H
O^-

Space-filling models of tricarboxylic acid cycle intermediates.

Succinic acid

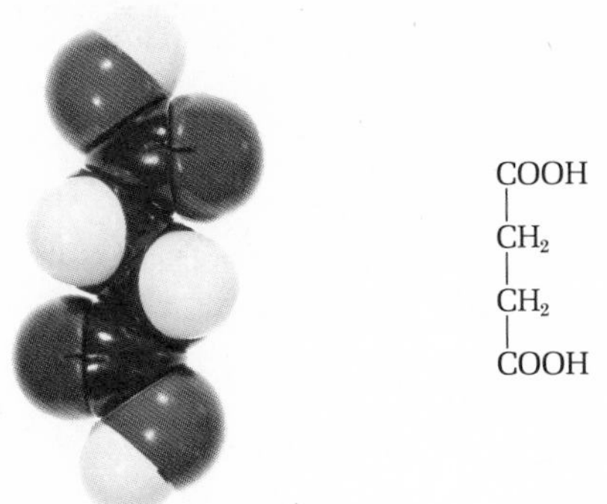

$$\begin{array}{c} COOH \\ | \\ CH_2 \\ | \\ CH_2 \\ | \\ COOH \end{array}$$

Fumaric acid

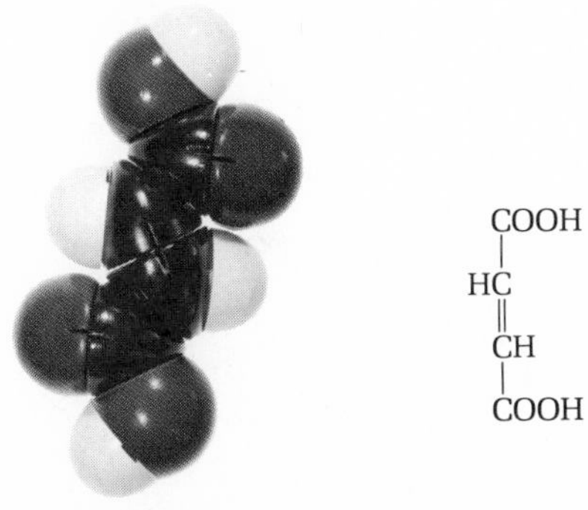

$$\begin{array}{c} COOH \\ | \\ HC \\ \| \\ CH \\ | \\ COOH \end{array}$$

L-Malic acid

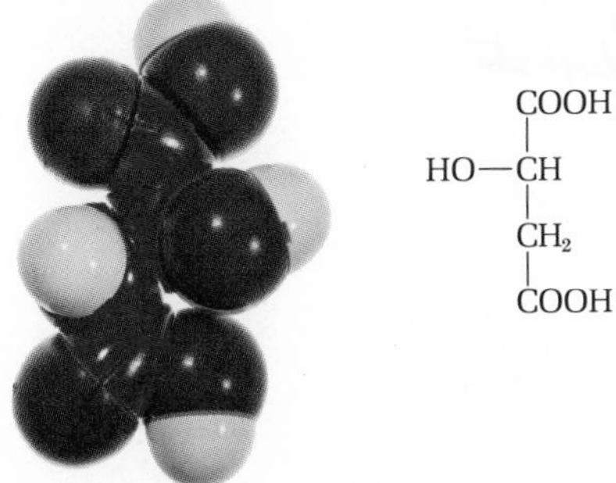

$$\begin{array}{c} COOH \\ | \\ HO-CH \\ | \\ CH_2 \\ | \\ COOH \end{array}$$

Oxaloacetic acid

$$\begin{array}{c} COOH \\ | \\ C{=}O \\ | \\ CH_2 \\ | \\ COOH \end{array}$$

high-energy phosphate bond of GTP from GDP and P_i at the expense of the high-energy thioester bond of succinyl CoA. The enzyme from animal tissues is specific for GDP as phosphate acceptor. It has been postulated that at the active site some functional group of the enzyme displaces CoA from succinyl CoA to form enzyme-bound CoA, from which CoA—SH is in turn displaced by phosphate to yield the phosphorylated form of the enzyme. The latter then donates its phosphate group to GDP

$$\text{Succinyl-S-CoA} + \text{E} \rightleftharpoons \text{CoA-S-E} + \text{succinate}$$

$$\text{CoA-S-E} + P_i \rightleftharpoons \text{P}{\sim}\text{E} + \text{CoA-SH}$$

$$\text{P}{\sim}\text{E} + \text{GDP} \rightleftharpoons \text{E} + \text{GTP}$$

Sum:

$$\text{Succinyl-S-CoA} + P_i + \text{GDP} \rightleftharpoons \text{succinate} + \text{CoA-SH} + \text{GTP}$$

Recent research has revealed direct evidence that a phosphorylated form of the enzyme results. A histidine residue of the enzyme protein becomes phosphorylated when the enzyme is incubated with ^{32}P, succinyl CoA, and Mg^{2+} in the absence of GDP or with ^{32}P-labeled GTP in the presence of Mg^{2+}. The 3-phosphohistidine residue (opposite margin) is believed to donate its phosphate group to GDP in the last step of the overall reaction.

The GTP formed in this reaction then donates its terminal phosphate group to ADP to form ATP in the nucleoside diphosphokinase reaction (Chapter 14)

$$\text{GTP} + \text{ADP} \rightleftharpoons \text{GDP} + \text{ATP}$$

The formation of GTP (or ATP) during the oxidation of α-ketoglutarate to succinate is not inhibited by 2,4-dinitrophenol, the characteristic inhibitor or uncoupling agent for oxidative phosphorylation associated with the process of electron transport (Chapter 18). The generation of ATP coupled to deacylation of succinyl CoA is often called a *substrate-level* phosphorylation, to distinguish it from respiratory-chain-linked phosphorylations.

Succinyl CoA can be deacylated to succinate by other reactions, which are important in certain auxiliary functions of the Krebs cycle. They will be described in Chapters 19 and 24.

Succinate Dehydrogenase

Succinate is oxidized to fumarate by the flavoprotein *succinate dehydrogenase*, which contains covalently bound flavin adenine dinucleotide (Chapter 12). This reducible coenzyme functions as hydrogen acceptor in the following reaction,

$$\text{Succinate} + \text{E—FAD} \rightleftharpoons \text{fumarate} + \text{E—FADH}_2$$

The reduced enzyme can donate electrons to various artificial electron acceptors, e.g., reducible dyes; the normal acceptor is not known with certainty (Chapter 17).

Succinate dehydrogenase is tightly bound to the mitochondrial membrane. Although it has been extracted from the membrane and highly purified, it probably has a complex subunit organization. As isolated from beef heart, the enzyme has a molecular weight of about 175,000 and contains one molecule of covalently bound FAD, which can be released only by tryptic digestion of the enzyme, as well as four atoms of iron. In addition, the enzyme contains four atoms of sulfur in an unknown chemical form which, when acidified, yields H_2S. It appears probable that the iron atoms undergo Fe(II)-Fe(III) valence changes during the action of succinate dehydrogenase. Since the enzyme contains no heme group, such as is found in cytochrome, the iron of this enzyme is spoken of as *nonheme iron*. The nonheme iron and labile sulfur atoms are present in distinct subunits of succinate dehydrogenase, designated as *nonheme iron proteins*. A number of nonheme iron proteins are known; some of them, called *ferredoxins*, function in the light reactions of photosynthesis, and others are catalysts in the hydrogenase system of some bacteria.

The stereochemistry of the removal of hydrogen atoms from succinate by succinate dehydrogenase has been studied in detail. An important clue has come from analysis of the action of the enzyme on L-chlorosuccinate, which it dehydrogenates, and D-chlorosuccinate, which it does not. From this fact, as well as isotopic experiments with deuterium (^2_1H) as tracer, it has been concluded that the dehydrogenase removes *trans* hydrogen atoms from the methylene carbon atoms of succinate (margin).

Succinate dehydrogenase has some of the attributes of an allosteric enzyme: it is activated by phosphate, succinate, and fumarate, and it is competitively inhibited by very low concentrations of oxaloacetate (Chapter 8). Accumulation of oxaloacetate, the last dicarboxylic acid of the Krebs cycle, can thus inhibit its own formation from succinate. Oxaloacetate is a far more potent competitive inhibitor of succinate dehydrogenase than malonate.

Stereochemistry of the succinate dehydrogenase reaction.

Succinate dehydrogenase removes at equal rates the *trans* pairs of H atoms a + d and b + c to yield fumaric acid, a *trans* compound. The enzyme does not remove the *cis* pairs a + b or c + d. In fumaric acid the carboxyl groups and the remaining H atoms are in one plane perpendicular to the page.

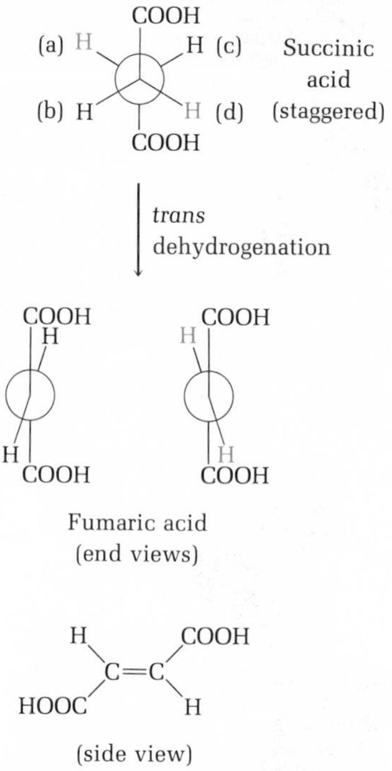

COOH
(a) H H (c)
(b) H H (d)
COOH
Succinic acid (staggered)

trans dehydrogenation

COOH H / H COOH   COOH H / H COOH

Fumaric acid (end views)

H COOH
C=C
HOOC H

(side view)

Fumarase

The reversible hydration of fumarate to L-malate is catalyzed by the enzyme *fumarase*, which has been obtained in crystalline form from pig heart

$$\text{Fumarate} + H_2O \rightleftharpoons \text{L-malate}$$

The standard free-energy change is relatively small, and the reaction is freely reversible (Chapter 14). Fumarase has a molecular weight of about 200,000 and contains four polypeptide-chain subunits, which are inactive in separated form. It requires no coenzyme. ATP decreases the affinity of fumarase for fumarate, causing the reaction to be inhibited if the concentration of fumarate is less than saturating. The kinetics of fumarase action has been very extensively studied, and from this work some of the most important experimental and mathematical approaches to enzyme kinetics have been developed.

Fumarase also acts stereospecifically, since it forms (and

Stereochemistry of the fumarase reaction.

The D^+ and OD^- groups of D_2O approach the double bond of fumaric acid, whose 4 substituent groups are in the plane of the page, from behind and from forward of the plane, respectively. Since only one stereoisomer is formed, the OD group can be added to only one side of the double bond, to yield the stereoisomer shown.

erythro-3-Monodeutero-L-malic acid

dehydrates) only the L-stereoisomer of malate. Stereochemical studies on the mechanism, using water labeled with deuterium, have revealed that fumarase catalyzes *trans* addition of H and OH to the double bond of fumarate. Although fumarate is a symmetrical molecule, the OH group can be added to only one side of the double bond to yield the L-stereoisomer of malate (margin).

Oxidation of Malate to Oxaloacetate

In the last reaction of the cycle, the NAD-linked L-malate dehydrogenase catalyzes the oxidation of L-malate to oxaloacetate

$$\text{L-Malate} + NAD^+ \rightleftharpoons \text{oxaloacetate} + NADH + H^+ \qquad \Delta G^{\circ\prime} = 7.1 \text{ kcal}$$

Although the reaction is endergonic as written (Chapter 17), it goes in the forward direction very readily in the cell because of the rapid removal of the reaction products oxaloacetate and NADH in subsequent steps. $NADP^+$ is only feebly reduced by the enzyme.

Cells of higher animals contain two forms of L-malate dehydrogenase, one in the mitochondria and the other in the extramitochondrial cytoplasm. They have the same molecular weight but differ in amino acid composition, electrophoretic, and kinetic properties. The crystalline mitochondrial enzyme consists of at least five multiple forms, which appear to have identical catalytic characteristics but differ in conformation.

We can now sum up the output of one turn around the tricarboxylic acid cycle. Two carbon atoms appear as carbon dioxide, equivalent to, but not identical with, the two carbon atoms of the acetyl group entering the cycle. Four pairs of hydrogen atoms are yielded by enzymatic dehydrogenation; three pairs have been used to reduce NAD and one to reduce the FAD of succinate dehydrogenase. Ultimately these four pairs of hydrogen atoms become H^+ ions and their corresponding electrons combine with oxygen, following their transport down the respiratory chain.

Isotopic Tests of the Tricarboxylic Acid Cycle

That the Krebs cycle actually takes place in intact cells and can account quantitatively for the oxidation of carbohydrate, fatty acids, and amino acids has been verified by stringent tests with precursors and intermediates in which specific carbon atoms were isotopically labeled with either the ^{13}C or ^{14}C isotopes. However, one of the earliest isotopic experiments produced an unexpected result, which aroused considerable controversy about the pathway and mechanism of the cycle reactions. Acetate labeled with isotopic carbon in the carboxyl group ($CH_3\overset{*}{C}OOH$) was incubated with a tissue suspension while it was carrying out the oxidations of the cycle. Various intermediates of the cycle were then isolated from the suspension and degraded in order to establish whether the positions of the isotopic carbon in each intermediate were those predicted from the cycle. Condensation of oxaloacetate with carboxyl-labeled acetate would be expected to produce citrate labeled in one carboxyl group (Figure 16-13), but since citrate is a completely symmetrical molecule, one would expect the two terminal carboxyl groups to be chemically indistinguishable. Half the citrate molecules would then be acted upon in the subsequent steps to form α-ketoglutarate with the isotope in the α-carboxyl group, and half would react to form α-ketoglutarate with the isotope in the γ-carboxyl group. When the labeled α-ketoglutarate was isolated from the medium and degraded, the isotope originally introduced as the carboxyl carbon of acetate was found *only* in the γ-carboxyl group of the α-ketoglutarate and not in both groups. It was at first concluded that citric acid itself, or any other symmetrical molecule, could not be an intermediate in the path from acetate to α-ketoglutarate. As a consequence, an asymmetrical tricarboxylic acid, *cis*-aconitic acid, was postulated as the first condensation product formed from acetate and oxaloacetate, to account for formation of α-ketoglutarate with the observed labeling pattern. Then Ogston pointed out in 1948 that although citric acid is a symmetrical molecule, it may be able to react asymmetrically with the active site of aconitase. The simplest way of visualizing his argument is to assume that the citric acid combines with the active site of the enzyme through more than two points of attachment, e.g., by a three-point landing, in which three different functional groups of citrate interact specifically with three complementary groups on the active site (Figure 16-14). Since the citrate molecule can bind to these three complementary groups in only one way, it is readily possible to see (in this model at least) how the dehydration of citrate can occur from carbon atoms 2 and 3 but not from carbon atoms 3 and 4. As it turned out, Ogston's hypothesis is correct; citric acid *is* the true intermediate, but the two $—CH_2COOH$ ends of the citric acid molecule are not equivalent in the aconitase reaction. This has been unambigously proved by different types of isotope tracer experiments. In one, labeled citric acid formed from carboxyl-labeled acetate and unlabeled oxaloacetate in the citrate synthase reaction, which contained isotope only in one of the two terminal carboxyl groups, was isolated and then allowed to react with aconitase and isocitrate dehydrogenase. The α-ketoglutarate so formed contained isotope only in the γ-carboxyl carbon atom, proving that citric acid, a symmetrical molecule, must react asymmetrically in the aconitase reaction. Once this relationship was established, tests of the cycle with other labeled precursors, such as $\overset{*}{C}H_3COOH$, $\overset{*}{C}H_3COCOOH$, and $H\overset{*}{C}O_3^-$, were found to yield labeled cycle intermediates with the isotopes in positions consistent not only with the postulated pathway of the cycle reactions but also with the asymmetry of the reactions by which citrate is converted to α-ketoglutarate.

Succinate dehydrogenase shows no ability to discriminate between the two carboxyl groups of succinate, presumably because they are sterically completely equivalent. For this reason succinate labeled in one carboxyl

Figure 16-13
Fate of carboxyl carbon atom (starred) of acetate. Because it appears in only the γ-carboxyl group of α-ketoglutarate, the symmetrical intermediate citrate must be formed and must react asymmetrically.

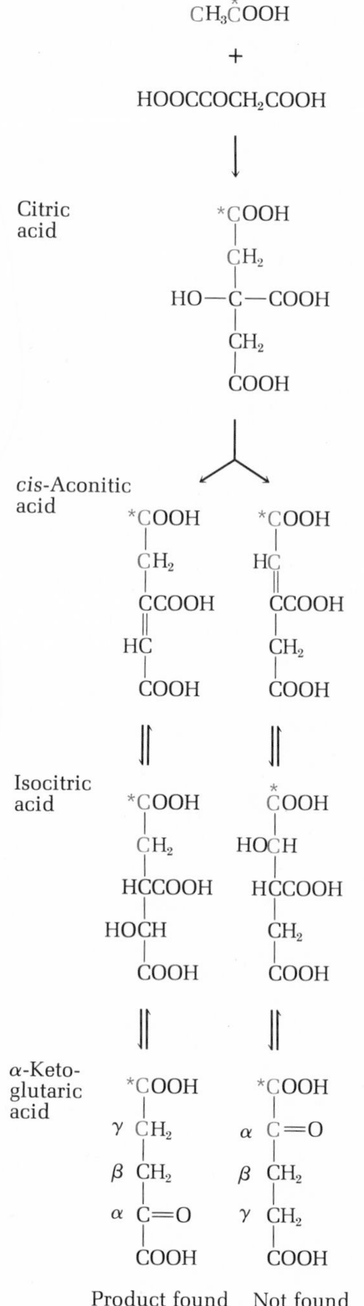

Figure 16-14
Asymmetric behavior of active site of aconitase. Three-point attachment of the substrate to three complementary points on the active site allows a symmetrical molecule to be acted upon asymmetrically; only one of the two C—Z bonds can be correctly positioned. Similarly, only one (C_2—C_3) of the two central bonds (C_2—C_3; C_3—C_4) of citric acid can be correctly positioned to be dehydrated.

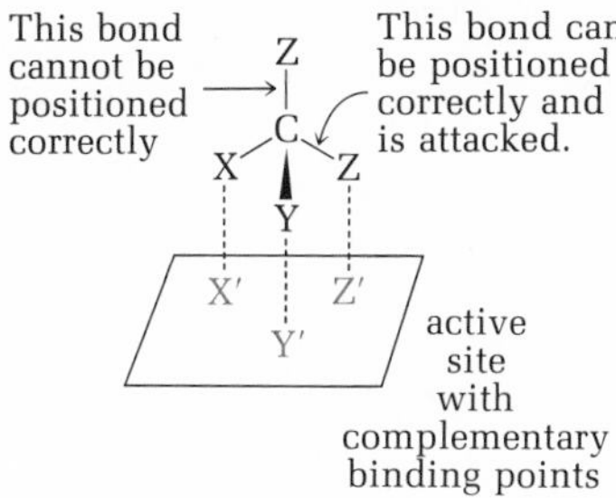
This bond cannot be positioned correctly
This bond can be positioned correctly and is attacked.
Z
C
X
Y
Z
X′
Y′
Z′
active site with complementary binding points

(4) (5)
CH_2COOH
(3)C — susceptible bond
HO — CH_2COOH (2) (1)
COOH

Citric acid

group leads to formation of malate and oxaloacetate containing isotope in both carboxyl carbon atoms.

It is clear from Figure 16-2 that when a molecule of acetic acid enters the cycle, the two molecules of carbon dioxide evolved during one revolution of the cycle are not the same two carbon atoms introduced as acetate; the latter actually remain in the four-carbon dicarboxylic acids.

Amphibolic Nature of the Cycle: Anaplerotic Reactions

We must now recall from Chapter 13 that the Krebs cycle is an amphibolic pathway and functions not only in catabolism but also to generate precursors for anabolic pathways. By means of several important auxiliary enzymatic reactions, specific intermediates of the Krebs cycle, such as α-ketoglutarate, succinate, and oxaloacetate, can be removed from the cycle to serve as precursors of amino acids (Chapter 24). Since many of these reactions are reversible, they also constitute pathways by which Krebs cycle intermediates can be formed from amino acids. Normally the reactions by which cycle intermediates are drained away and formed are in dynamic balance, so that their concentrations in the mitochondria remain constant.

The special enzymatic mechanisms by which tricarboxylic acid cycle intermediates can be replenished, are called *anaplerotic* ("filling up") reactions. The most important is the enzymatic carboxylation of pyruvate to form oxaloacetate, a reaction first discovered by Wood and Werkman. The pathway of this carboxylation and the identity of the enzymes involved proved to be exceptionally difficult problems which required many years of work to clarify. Ultimately, Utter and his colleagues showed that the basic reaction in the liver is that catalyzed by *pyruvate carboxylase*, which is located in the mitochondria of the liver in most species

$$\text{Pyruvate} + CO_2 + \text{ATP} \xrightleftharpoons{Mg^{2+}} \text{oxaloacetate} + \text{ADP} + P_i \qquad \Delta G^{\circ\prime} = -0.5 \text{ kcal}$$

When the tricarboxylic acid cycle is deficient in oxaloacetate or other intermediates, pyruvate is carboxylated to produce more oxaloacetate. Conversely, in time of oxaloacetate excess, the latter can be decarboxylated, with the formation of pyruvate and CO_2.

Pyruvate carboxylase has a molecular weight of about 650,000 and contains a large number of polypeptide-chain subunits. It is inactivated at 0°, at which it dissociates into subunits. The native enzyme contains four molecules of *biotin*, a water-soluble vitamin required by higher animals and by many microorganisms (Figure 16-15). Biotin is covalently attached to the enzyme protein through a peptide linkage with the ϵ-amino group of a lysine residue at the active site; the peptide of biotin and lysine is called *biocytin*. A ring nitrogen atom of biotin is the site at which CO_2 combines in an ATP-dependent reaction. In a subsequent reaction at the enzyme active site, the bound CO_2 is transferred to pyruvate to form oxaloacetate (Figure 16-15). The native enzyme has four catalytic subunits.

Pyruvate carboxylase is an allosteric enzyme. The rate of its forward reaction, leading to oxaloacetate formation, is very low unless acetyl CoA, its positive modulator, is present. Thus, whenever acetyl CoA, the fuel of the tricarboxylic acid cycle, is present in excess, it stimulates the pyruvate carboxylase reaction to produce more oxaloacetate and thus enables the cycle to oxidize more acetyl CoA. Although this is the most important anaplerotic reaction in the liver and kidney of higher animals, other reactions appear to perform this function in heart and muscle tissue. One such reaction is that catalyzed by *malic enzyme*

$$\text{L-Malate} + \text{NADP}^+ \rightleftharpoons \text{pyruvate} + CO_2 + \text{NADPH} + H^+$$

Another is that catalyzed by *phosphoenolpyruvate carboxykinase*

$$\text{Phosphoenolpyruvate} + CO_2 + \text{IDP} \rightleftharpoons \text{oxaloacetate} + \text{ITP}$$

These reactions, which are important links in the biosynthesis of glucose from pyruvate, will be discussed further in Chapter 22. Another type of anaplerotic reaction, the glyoxylate cycle, occurs in plants and many microorganisms where it plays a special role.

Figure 16-15
Forms of biotin. In pyruvate carboxylase the biotin carboxyl group forms a peptide linkage with the ε-amino group of lysine. During CO_2 transfer an N-carboxy derivative of biotin is formed.

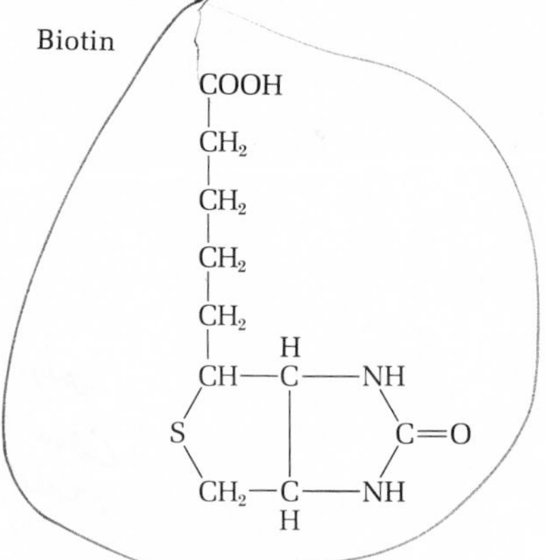

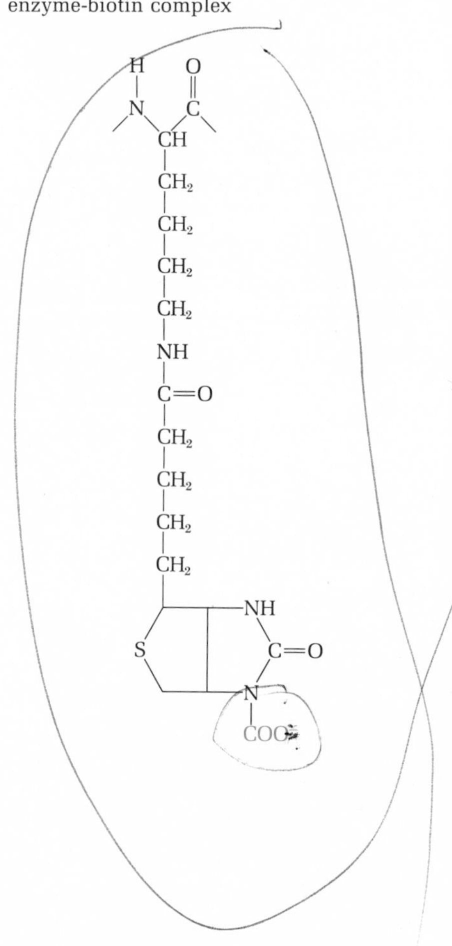

The Glyoxylate Cycle and Glyoxysomes

When acetate must serve both as a source of energy and as a source of various intermediates required to synthesize the carbon skeletons of all the major cellular components (which may occur in microorganisms such as *E. coli*, *Pseudomonas*, and algae, as well as in higher plants), the tricarboxylic acid cycle is modified to a form called the *glyoxylate cycle*. The overall plan of the glyoxylate cycle is shown in Figure 16-16. Acetyl CoA is the fuel; it condenses with oxaloacetate to form isocitrate ultimately. However, at this point the further breakdown of isocitrate occurs not via the usual NAD-linked isocitrate dehydrogenase but by way of an aldol cleavage catalyzed by the enzyme *isocitratase* to form succinate and glyoxylate (margin). The glyoxylate so formed condenses with another molecule of acetyl CoA to form malate, catalyzed by *malate synthase* (margin). The malate then is oxidized to oxaloacetate, which can condense with another molecule of acetyl CoA. In each turn of the glyoxylate cycle, two molecules of acetyl CoA enter; one molecule of succinate is formed, which is used for biosynthetic purposes, and a pair of hydrogen atoms pass from malate to oxygen via the respiratory chain and thus cause oxidative phosphorylation of ADP (Chapter 17). The glyoxylate cycle thus provides both energy and four-carbon intermediates for the biosynthetic pathways of the cell. This pathway does not occur in higher animals, which have no need for it, simply because they are never forced to survive on two-carbon fuel molecules alone. It is prominent, however, in the seeds of higher plants, which can convert acetyl residues derived from the fatty acids of storage triacylglycerols into carbohydrate via succinic acid (Chapter 22).

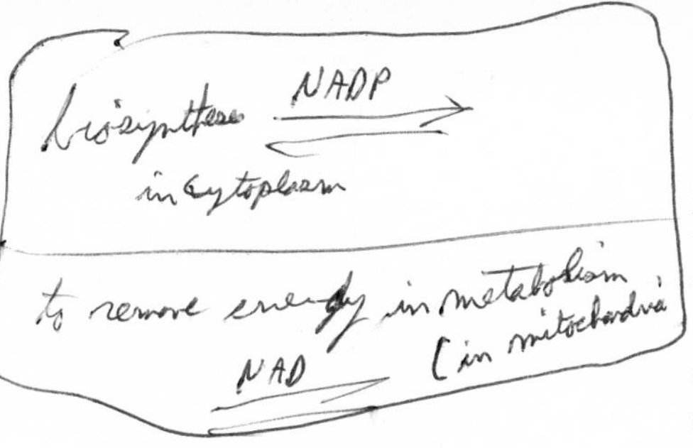

Figure 16-16
The glyoxylate cycle. The overall equation of the cycle is

2 Acetyl CoA ⟶ succinate + 2H

The reactions in color are those catalyzed by the auxiliary enzymes isocitratase and malate synthase; all others are reactions of the tricarboxylic acid cycle.

The isocitratase reaction.

The malate synthase reaction.

Although the mitochondria are the sites of the tricarboxylic acid cycle reactions in higher plants, the enzymes of the glyoxylate cycle, particularly isocitratase and malate synthase, are localized in another class of cytoplasmic organelles called *glyoxysomes*. These membrane-surrounded organelles lack many of the enzymes of the tricarboxylic acid cycle and possess no cytochrome system. They are found only in plant cells capable of converting fatty acids to sugar. Since they are rich in catalase, glyoxysomes may be related to or derived from the microbodies or peroxisomes (Chapter 20).

The Phosphogluconate Pathway

Many cells possess, in addition to the tricarboxylic acid cycle, another pathway of glucose degradation whose first reaction is the oxidation of glucose 6-phosphate to 6-phosphogluconate. The phosphogluconate pathway, also known as the *pentose phosphate pathway* or the *hexose monophosphate shunt*, is not a mainline pathway for the oxidation of glucose. Its primary purpose in most cells is to generate reducing power in the extramitochondrial cytoplasm in the form of NADPH. This function is especially prominent in tissues that actively carry out the reductive synthesis of fatty acids and steroids from small precursors, such as the liver, mammary gland, adipose or fat tissues and the adrenal cortex. Skeletal muscle, which is not active in synthesizing fatty acids, is virtually lacking in this pathway. A second function of the phosphogluconate pathway is to generate pentoses, particularly D-ribose, which is used in the synthesis of nucleic acids. Another major function is to participate in the formation of glucose from CO_2 in the dark reactions of photosynthesis (Chapter 22).

The various steps of the phosphogluconate pathway take place in the soluble portion of the extramitochondrial cytoplasm of animal cells. All the enzymes required in this sequence have been isolated in highly purified form. The first reaction of the phosphogluconate pathway is the enzymatic dehydrogenation of glucose 6-phosphate by *glucose 6-phosphate dehydrogenase,* also known as *Zwischenferment,* to form 6-phosphogluconate (margin)

$$\text{Glucose 6-phosphate} + \text{NADP}^+ \rightleftharpoons \text{6-phosphogluconate} + \text{NADPH} + \text{H}^+$$

This enzyme, which is not present in mitochondria, is specific for NADP as electron acceptor. It carries out dehydrogenation of carbon atom 1 of the pyranose form of glucose 6-phosphate to yield the corresponding 6-phosphoglucono-δ-lactone. Although the latter is unstable and undergoes spontaneous hydrolysis to the free acid, there is a specific *lactonase* capable of catalyzing this reaction (margin). The overall equilibrium lies far in the direction of formation of NADPH, which acts as electron donor in reductive biosynthesis (Chapter 23).

In the next step 6-phosphogluconate undergoes oxidative decarboxylation by *6-phosphogluconate dehydrogenase* to form the ketopentose *D-ribulose 5-phosphate* (margin) a reaction that generates a second molecule of NADPH. By the action of *phosphopentose epimerase,* D-ribulose 5-phosphate is reversibly transformed into D-xylulose 5-phosphate, its epimer at carbon atom 3. By the action of *phosphopentose isomerase,* D-ribulose 5-phosphate may also be converted reversibly into its aldo isomer, D-ribose 5-phosphate (margin), which can be used in the synthesis of the pentose-containing nucleotides and RNA. Under some circumstances, the phosphogluconate pathway ends at this point, and its overall equation is then written

$$\text{Glucose 6-phosphate} + 2\text{NADP}^+ + \text{H}_2\text{O} \rightleftharpoons \text{D-ribose 5-phosphate} + \text{CO}_2 + 2\text{NADPH} + 2\text{H}^+$$

The net result is the production of NADPH for reductive biosynthetic reactions in the extramitochondrial cytoplasm and the production of D-ribose as a precursor for nucleotide synthesis.

Under other circumstances, however, the phosphogluconate pathway continues further, since the isomeric pentose 5-phosphates can undergo other transformations made possible by two additional enzymes, *transketolase* and *transaldolase.* Transketolase, which contains tightly bound thiamine pyrophosphate as a coenzyme, as well as Mg^{2+}, carries out the transfer of a glycolaldehyde group from D-xylulose 5-phosphate to D-ribose 5-phosphate. In this process the glycolaldehyde group ($CH_2OH—CO—$) is first transferred from D-xylulose 5-phosphate to enzyme-bound thiamine pyrophosphate to form the α,β-dihydroxyethyl derivative of the latter, which is analogous to the acetaldehyde derivative of thiamine pyrophosphate formed during the action of pyruvate dehydrogenase described earlier. In the transketolase reaction, the thiamine

The phosphogluconate pathway

HCOH | HCOH | HOCH | HCOH | HC (ring O) | $CH_2OPO_3^{2-}$ — Glucose 6-phosphate

↓ $NADP^+$ → NADPH; glucose 6-phosphate dehydrogenase (reversible)

C=O | HCOH | HOCH | HCOH | HC (ring O) | $CH_2OPO_3^{2-}$ — 6-Phosphoglucono-δ-lactone

↓ $+H_2O$ / $-H_2O$; lactonase

COO^- | HCOH | HOCH | HCOH | HCOH | $CH_2OPO_3^{2-}$ — 6-Phosphogluconate

↓ $NADP^+$ → NADPH; 6-phosphogluconate dehydrogenase; → CO_2

CH_2OH | C=O | HCOH | HCOH | $CH_2OPO_3^{2-}$ — D-Ribulose 5-phosphate

↓ phosphopentose isomerase (reversible)

CHO | HCOH | HCOH | HCOH | $CH_2OPO_3^{2-}$ — D-Ribose 5-phosphate

The pentose epimerase reaction

CH_2OH
$C{=}O$
HCOH
HCOH
$CH_2OPO_3^{2-}$

D-Ribulose 5-phosphate

⇌

CH_2OH
$C{=}O$
HOCH
HCOH
$CH_2OPO_3^{2-}$

D-Xylulose 5-phosphate

pyrophosphate is an intermediate carrier of the glycolaldehyde group, which is then transferred to the acceptor molecule D-ribose 5-phosphate. The net result is the formation of a seven-carbon keto sugar *D-sedoheptulose 7-phosphate* and a three-carbon sugar, D-glyceraldehyde 3-phosphate (below). Although this is the most prominent reaction catalyzed by transketolase, the enzyme can actually catalyze the transfer of a glycolaldehyde group from a number of different 2-keto sugar phosphates having the L configuration at carbon atom 3 to carbon atom 1 of any of a number of different aldose phosphates. Free glycolaldehyde does not appear during such transformations; enzyme-bound thiamine pyrophosphate is the carrier of the dihydroxyethyl group in transketolase reactions. It will be noted that one of the products of the action of transketolase on the two isomeric pentose phosphates is D-glyceraldehyde 3-phosphate, an intermediate of the glycolytic sequence. Its formation provides a point of connection between the glycolytic and phosphogluconate pathways.

The second enzyme participating in further reactions of the phosphogluconate pathway is transaldolase, which acts on the products of the transketolase reaction, namely, D-sedoheptulose 7-phosphate and D-glyceraldehyde 3-phosphate.

It catalyzes the transfer of the dihydroxyacetone group (in color), corresponding to carbon atoms 1, 2, and 3 of sedoheptulose 7-phosphate, to D-glyceraldehyde 3-phosphate, to form a six-carbon sugar, D-fructose 6-phosphate, and to leave behind a four-carbon sugar, D-erythrose 4-phosphate (below). Although this reaction is very

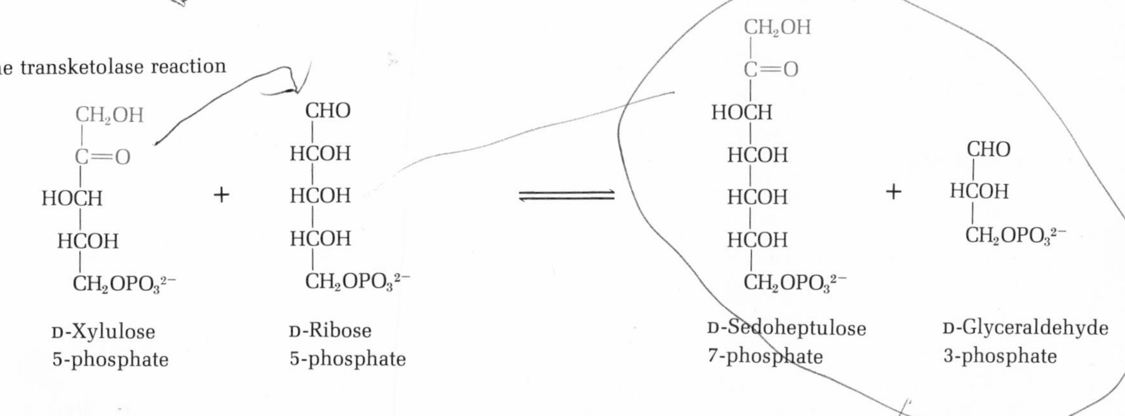

The transaldolase reaction

CH_2OH / $C{=}O$ / HOCH / HCOH / HCOH / HCOH / $CH_2OPO_3^{2-}$ (D-Sedoheptulose 7-phosphate) + CHO / HCOH / $CH_2OPO_3^{2-}$ (D-Glyceraldehyde 3-phosphate) ⇌ CH_2OH / $C{=}O$ / HOCH / HCOH / HCOH / $CH_2OPO_3^{2-}$ (D-Fructose 6-phosphate) + CHO / HCOH / HCOH / $CH_2OPO_3^{2-}$ (D-Erythrose 4-phosphate)

similar to that catalyzed by aldolase (Chapter 15), transaldolase cannot react with or form *free* dihydroxyacetone or its phosphate. Since one product of the transaldolase reaction is fructose 6-phosphate, an intermediate in glycolysis, we have a second point of interconnection between the glycolytic and phosphogluconate pathways.

An important consequence of the action of the enzymes of the phosphogluconate pathway is that they make possible, together with enzymes of the glycolytic sequence, the reversible interconversion of three-, four-, five-, six-, and seven-carbon sugars, by reversible transfer of either two-carbon (glycolaldehyde) or three-carbon (dihydroxyacetone) moieties. For example, another prominent reaction catalyzed by transketolase is

D-Xylulose 5-phosphate + D-erythrose 4-phosphate ⟶
D-fructose 6-phosphate + D-glyceraldehyde 3-phosphate

in which two intermediates of the phosphogluconate pathway can be converted into two intermediates of the glycolytic pathway.

D-Xylulose 5-phosphate		D-Erythrose 4-phosphate			D-Fructose 6-phosphate		D-Glyceraldehyde 3-phosphate
CH_2OH		CHO			CH_2OH		CHO
$C{=}O$		$HCOH$			$C{=}O$		$CHOH$
$HOCH$	+	$HCOH$	transketolase	⇌	$HOCH$	+	$CH_2OPO_3^{2-}$
$HCOH$		$CH_2OPO_3^{2-}$			$HCOH$		
$CH_2OPO_3^{2-}$					$HCOH$		
					$CH_2OPO_3^{-}$		

It is clear that a variety of different nonoxidative reactions may ensue through the action of pentose epimerase, pentose isomerase, transketolase, and transaldolase acting independently or in concert with enzymes of the glycolytic sequence. This latter part of the phosphogluconate pathway is therefore not a well-defined route leading to only one end product but a branching pathway with diffuse ends capable of great metabolic flexibility. On paper, at least, the enzymes of the phosphogluconate pathway can even carry out the complete oxidation of glucose 6-phosphate to CO_2 by a complex sequence of reactions (Figure 16-17) in which six molecules of glucose 6-phosphate are oxidized to six molecules each of ribulose 5-phosphate and CO_2; five molecules of glucose 6-phosphate are then regenerated from the six molecules of ribulose five-phosphate. The overall equation is

6 Glucose 6-phosphate + 12NADP$^+$ ⟶
5 glucose 6-phosphate + 6CO_2 + 12NADPH + 12H$^+$ + P_i

If we cancel out common terms, we get

Glucose 6-phosphate + 12NADP$^+$ ⟶
6CO_2 + 12NADPH + 12H$^+$ + P_i

Figure 16-17
Complete oxidation of one molecule of glucose 6-phosphate (G6P) to CO_2, with equivalent reduction of $NADP^+$. Full equation is given in the text. All products are in color. Other abbreviations are

6PG = *6-phosphogluconate*
Ru5P = *ribulose 5-phosphate*
R5P = *ribose 5-phosphate*
X5P = *xylulose 5-phosphate*
S7P = *sedoheptulose 7-phosphate*
G3P = *glyceraldehyde 3-phosphate*
E4P = *erythrose 4-phosphate*
DHAP = *dihydroxyacetone phosphate*
FDP = *fructose 1,6-diphosphate*
F6P = *fructose 6-phosphate*

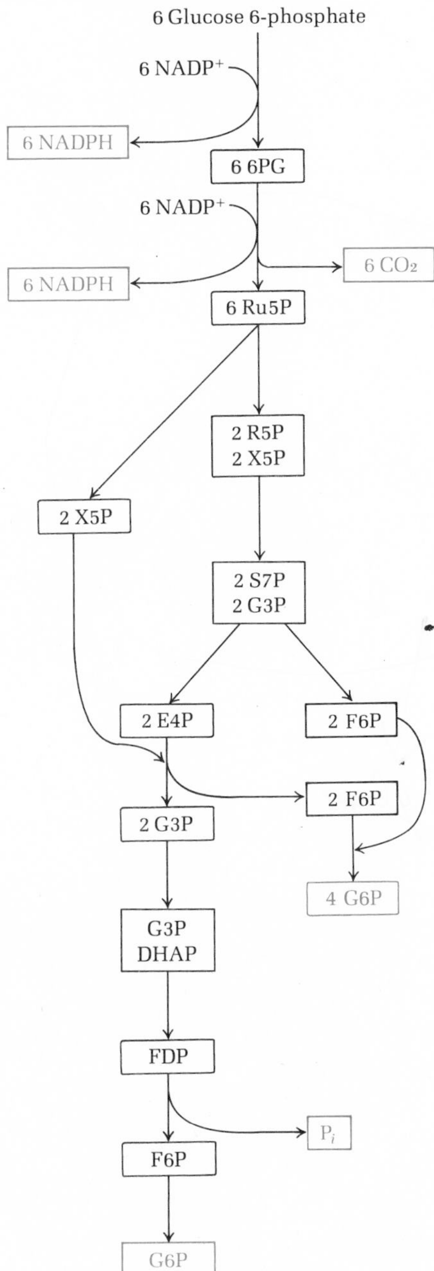

It is not altogether certain that the complete oxidation of glucose 6-phosphate according to the reactions of Figure 16-17 occurs in all cells. It appears more likely that the phosphogluconate pathway normally rejoins the glycolytic cycle by the transketolase-catalyzed reaction described above, in which D-xylulose 5-phosphate and D-erythrose 4-phosphate are converted into D-fructose 6-phosphate and D-glyceraldehyde 3-phosphate.

An isotopic approach can be used to assess what fraction of glucose oxidation in a given cell or tissue proceeds via the phosphogluconate pathway. The cells are divided into two batches, one being incubated with glucose 1-^{14}C and the other with glucose 6-^{14}C. A comparison is then made of the initial rates at which ^{14}C appears in the CO_2 formed by their oxidation. The combined action of the glycolytic sequence and the tricarboxylic acid cycle yields $^{14}CO_2$ from both types of labeled glucose at equal initial rates, whereas the phosphogluconate pathway initially yields $^{14}CO_2$ only from the 1-labeled glucose substrate. Such tests have been carried out on many tissues. In the liver of the rat, almost 30 percent of the $^{14}CO_2$ appears to come from the phosphogluconate pathway; an even larger fraction is formed in the mammary gland, where fatty acid synthesis is a major metabolic activity. However, in heart and skeletal muscle, relatively little oxidation occurs via the phosphogluconate pathway.

Summary

Respiration occurs in three stages: (1) the oxidative formation of acetyl CoA from pyruvate, fatty acids, and amino acids, (2) the degradation of acetyl residues by the Krebs tricarboxylic acid cycle to yield CO_2 and H atoms, and (3) the transport of electrons equivalent to these hydrogen atoms to molecular oxygen, a process which is accompanied by coupled phosphorylation of ADP. The tricarboxylic acid cycle, which takes place in the mitochondria, consists of a cyclic series of reactions in which acetyl residues are condensed with the four-carbon oxaloacetic acid to form the six-carbon citric acid. Two carbon atoms of the latter are lost as CO_2 during a sequence of reactions which regenerate a molecule of oxaloacetate. Pyruvic acid, the end product of glycolysis under aerobic conditions, first undergoes oxidation by the pyruvate dehydrogenase system, which requires five different coenzymes, to yield acetyl CoA and CO_2. The cycle then begins when citrate synthase catalyzes the condensation of acetyl CoA with oxaloacetic acid to form citric acid. Aconitase then catalyzes the reversible formation of isocitrate from citrate in a reaction in which the substrates are attached at three different points to the catalytic site to yield an asymmetric enzyme-substrate complex. Isocitrate is then oxidized to α-ketoglutarate plus CO_2 by NAD-linked isocitrate dehydrogenase, an allosteric enzyme which is activated by ADP; it is often the rate-limiting step of the cycle. The α-ketoglutarate undergoes oxidation to succinyl CoA in a sequence of reactions similar to the oxidation of pyruvate to acetyl CoA. The succinyl CoA is deacylated by GDP and phosphate to form free succinate and GTP, which transfers its terminal phosphate group to ADP. The succinate is then oxidized to fumarate by succinate dehydrogenase, a flavin enzyme. Fumarate is hydrated by fumarase to L-malate, which is oxidized by NAD-linked

L-malate dehydrogenase to regenerate a molecule of oxaloacetate. The latter can then combine with another molecule of acetyl CoA and start another revolution of the cycle. Isotopic tracer tests with carbon-labeled fuel molecules or intermediates have established that the tricarboxylic acid cycle is the major mechanism of oxidation in intact cells. The overall rate of the cycle in the liver is controlled by the citrate synthase reaction, which is inhibited by the negative modulators ATP and NADH. Other control points exist.

The tricarboxylic acid cycle also can furnish intermediates for biosynthesis. The cycle intermediates are then replenished by anaplerotic reactions, the most important of which is the reversible carboxylation of pyruvate to oxaloacetate at the expense of ATP. In organisms living on acetate as sole carbon source, a variation of the Krebs cycle, the glyoxylate cycle, comes into play and makes possible the net formation of succinate (and other cycle intermediates) from acetate for biosynthesis.

Glucose 6-phosphate can also be oxidized via 6-phosphogluconate to pentose phosphates, particularly D-ribose 5-phosphate, by a sequence of enzymes in the soluble cytoplasm. The electron acceptor for these reactions is NADP; the NADPH so formed is a major reductant in the synthesis of hydrogen-rich biomolecules such as fatty acids and cholesterol. The phosphogluconate pathway may rejoin the glycolytic pathway or it may bring about more complete oxidation of glucose 6-phosphate.

References

Books

BOYER, P. D., H. LARDY, and K. MYRBÄCK (eds.), *The Enzymes*, 2d ed., vols. 1–5, Academic Press Inc., 1961, particularly vol. 5, pp. 495–510, "Aconitase"; pp. 531–544, "Fumarase"; vol. 3, pp. 3–103, "Coenzyme A." Detailed accounts of the properties of these enzymes and coenzymes.

GOODWIN, T. W. (ed.), *The Metabolic Roles of Citrate*, Academic Press Inc., New York, 1968. A Biochemical Society Symposium in honor of Sir Hans Krebs. An important collection of informative articles.

KREBS, H. A., and H. L. KORNBERG, *Energy Transformations in Living Matter*, Springer-Verlag OHG, Berlin, 1957.

LOWENSTEIN, J. M. (ed.), *The Citric Acid Cycle*, vol. 13 of *Methods in Enzymology*, Academic Press Inc., New York, 1969. Comprehensive up-to-date collection of authoritative articles on experimental methods.

LOWENSTEIN, J. M. ed. *Citric Acid Cycle: Control and Compartmentation*, Marcel Dekker, Inc. New York, 1969.

Reviews and Articles

AXELROD, B., "Other Pathways of Carbohydrate Metabolism," in D. M. Greenberg (ed.), *Metabolic Pathways*, 3d ed., vol. I, pp. 272–308, Academic Press Inc., New York, 1967. The phosphogluconate pathway, as well as minor pathways of carbohydrate metabolism.

GLUSKER, J. P., "Mechanism of Aconitase Action Deduced from Crystallographic Studies of its Substrates," *J. Mol. Biology*, **38**:149–162 (1968).

GREVILLE, G. D., "Pyruvate Oxidation and the Citrate Cycle," in E. Dickens, P. J. Randle, and W. J. Whelan (eds.), *Carbohydrate Metabolism and Its Disorders*, vol. 1, pp. 297–334, Academic Press Inc., New York, 1967.

KORNBERG, H. L., "Anaplerotic Sequences and Their Role in Metabolism," in P. N. Campbell and G. D. Greville (eds.), *Essays in Biochemistry*, vol. 2, Academic Press Inc., New York, 1966. The amphibolic nature of the Krebs cycle and the replenishment of cycle intermediates.

LOWENSTEIN, J. M., "The Tricarboxylic Acid Cycle," in D. M. Greenberg (ed.), *Metabolic Pathways*, 3d ed., vol. 1, pp. 146–270, Academic Press Inc., New York, 1967. An excellent review of the present knowledge of the cycle, with special reference to stereochemical relationships; the glyoxylate cycle is also reviewed.

MÜLLER, F., J. F. HOGG, and C. DE DUVE, "Distribution of Tricarboxylic Acid Cycle Enzymes and Glyoxylate Cycle Enzymes between Mitochondria and Peroxisomes in *Tetrahymena Pyriformis*" J. Biol. Chem., 243, 5385–5395 (1968). An important investigation into the role of peroxisomes in metabolism.

REED, L. J., "Chemistry and Function of Lipoic Acid," in M. Florkin and E. H. Stotz (eds.), *Comprehensive Biochemistry*, vol. 14, pp. 99–126, New York, 1967. The role of lipoic acid in α-keto acid dehydrogenase systems.

REED, L. J., "Pyruvate Dehydrogenase Complex," in *Current Topics in Cellular Regulation*, Academic Press, New York, 1969, Vol I, (In press). A short review of the structure, function, and regulation of this important multienzyme complex.

ROSE, I. A., and E. L. O'CONNELL, "The Mechanism of Aconitase Action," *J. Biol. Chem.*, **242**:1870–1879 (1967).

Problems

1. Isotopically labeled substrates were incubated with respiring muscle suspensions poisoned with malonate, and the tricarbolylic acid cycle intermediates listed were isolated. In each case, predict the position(s) of the isotopes in the intermediate listed.

Substrate added		*Product isolated*
$\overset{*}{C}H_3COOH$	$\longrightarrow$	citric acid
$H\overset{*}{C}O_3^-$	$\longrightarrow$	malic acid
3-^{14}C-glyceraldehyde 3-phosphate	$\longrightarrow$	α-ketoglutaric acid
5-^{14}C-fructose 6-phosphate	$\longrightarrow$	succinic acid

2. The substrates indicated below were added to suspensions of minced rat liver amply supplied with oxygen but in which succinate dehydrogenase was completely inhibited by malonate. The reactions were allowed to take place until no further oxygen uptake took place. The tissue contains glycogen, and CO_2 is available. Write balanced equations for the oxidation of (a) citrate, (b) pyruvate, and (c) fumarate, under the conditions described.

3. Using the relative concentrations of citrate, *cis*-aconitate, and isocitrate found in the aconitase equilibrium (text), calculate

the equilibrium constant and the standard free-energy change for the reaction

$$\text{Citrate} \rightleftharpoons \text{isocitrate}$$

4. From data in the text calculate the equilibrium constant and standard free-energy change for the conversion of malate to citrate according to the equation

$$\text{Malate} + \text{NAD}^+ + \text{acetyl—S—CoA} + \text{H}_2\text{O} \longrightarrow \text{citrate} + \text{CoA—SH} + \text{NADH} + \text{H}^+$$

5. Write a balanced equation for the complete oxidation of fructose 6-phosphate via the glycolytic and tricarboxylic acid cycle pathways.

6. Write equations for the conversion of acetate into succinate by *E. coli* cells: (*a*) when acetate is the sole source of carbon and (*b*) when glucose is available. If the acetate is labeled with ^{14}C in the carboxyl group, in what atoms of succinic acid will it be found in (*a*) and (*b*)?

7. Write a balanced equation for the conversion of 3-^{14}C-D-glucose into D-ribose 5-phosphate in the liver. What carbon atoms of the product will be labeled?

8. Write a balanced equation for the conversion of D-ribose 5-phosphate into D-glucose 6-phosphate in the liver. If the former is labeled with ^{14}C in carbon atom 1, which carbon atom(s) in D-glucose will become labeled?

9. Write a balanced equation for the conversion of D-glucose into pyruvic acid by a pathway that does not require phosphofructokinase as an essential enzyme.

CHAPTER 17 ELECTRON TRANSPORT AND OXIDATIVE PHOSPHORYLATION

In this chapter we shall see how pairs of electrons derived from the intermediates of the tricarboxylic acid cycle flow down a multimembered chain of electron-carrier enzymes of successively lower energy level until they reduce molecular oxygen, the ultimate electron acceptor in respiration. During this process much of the free energy of these electrons is conserved in the form of the phosphate-bond energy of ATP, in the process called *oxidative phosphorylation*. Electron transport and oxidative phosphorylation take place in nearly all aerobic cells. In eucaryotic cells the enzymes catalyzing these reactions are located in the inner membrane of the mitochondria; in procaryotic cells, they are found in the cell membrane.

The enzyme systems catalyzing electron transport and oxidative phosphorylation are exceedingly complex and difficult to approach experimentally, since they are bound to the membrane structure in the form of organized complexes, or assemblies. Very little is known of the ultimate molecular mechanism by which the energy of electron flow is conserved as phosphate-bond energy, but it seems certain that the membrane itself is a vital element in the energy-coupling process.

Oxidation-Reduction Reactions

Although several oxidation-reduction reactions have already been described, they will now be treated in a more systematic manner so that their mechanisms, equilibria, and energetic relationships can be analyzed. Oxidation-reduction reactions (also called oxidoreductions or redox reactions) are those in which there is transfer of electrons from an electron donor (the reducing agent or reductant) to an electron acceptor (the oxidizing agent or oxidant). In some oxidation-reduction reactions the transfer of electrons is made via the transfer of hydrogen atoms; thus, dehydrogenation is equivalent to oxidation. In others both an electron and a hydrogen atom may be transferred. Often the neutral terms *reducing equivalents* or *electron equivalents* are used to refer to electrons or hydrogen atoms participating in oxidoreductions.

Oxidizing and reducing agents function as conjugate redox pairs or couples, just as Brönsted acids and bases function as conjugate acid-base pairs:

Acid-base reactions:

$$\text{Proton donor} \rightleftharpoons H^+ + \text{proton acceptor}$$

Oxidation-reduction reactions:

$$\text{Electron donor} \rightleftharpoons e^- + \text{electron acceptor}$$

Just as an equilibrium constant may be used to express the tendency of an acid to dissociate a proton (Chapter 2), it may also be used to express the tendency of a reducing agent to lose electrons. Customarily, however, this tendency is expressed by the *standard reduction potential,* defined as the electromotive force (emf) in volts given by a half-cell in which the reductant and oxidant species are both present at 1.0 *M* concentration, 25°, and pH 7.0, in equilibrium with an electrode which can reversibly accept electrons from the reductant species (Figure 17-1), according to the equation

$$\text{Reductant} \rightleftharpoons \text{oxidant} + ne^-$$

where *n* is the number of electrons transferred. The standard reduction potential is a measure of the electron pressure a given reductant-oxidant pair generates at equilibrium under the specified conditions. The ultimate standard of reference is the reduction potential of the reaction

$$H_2 \rightleftharpoons 2H^+ + 2e^-$$

which is by convention set at 0.0 volts under conditions in which the pressure of H_2 gas is 1.0 atm, $[H^+]$ is 1.0 *M*, that is pH = 0.0, and the temperature is 25°. When this value is corrected to pH 7.0 ($[H^+] = 1 \times 10^{-7}$ *M*), the reference pH assumed in all biochemical calculations, the standard reduction potential of the hydrogen–hydrogen-ion system becomes −0.42 volt.

The standard reduction potentials of a number of biologically important redox couples are given in Table 17-1. Systems having a more negative standard reduction potential than the H_2–$2H^+$ couple have a greater tendency to lose electrons than hydrogen; those with a more positive potential have a lesser tendency to lose them. Note that the water-oxygen couple, the electrode equation of which is

$$H_2O \rightleftharpoons \tfrac{1}{2}O_2 + 2H^+ + 2e^-$$

has a strongly positive standard reduction potential, +0.815 volt. Water therefore has very little tendency to lose electrons and form molecular oxygen. Put in another way, molecular oxygen has a very high affinity for electrons, much higher than such biological electron acceptors as NAD^+, flavoproteins, and the cytochromes (Table 17-1).

Just as the Henderson-Hasselbalch equation (Chapter 2) expresses the quantitative relationship between the dissociation constant of an acid, its pH, and the concentration of its proton donor and acceptor species, a formally

Figure 17-1
Measurement of the standard reduction potential.

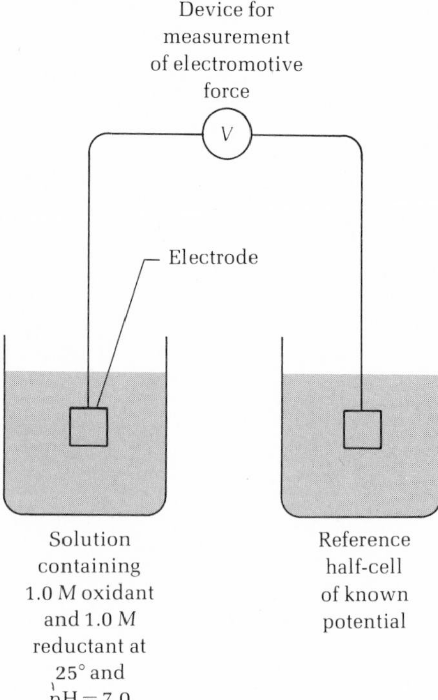

Table 17-1 Standard reduction potentials of some conjugate redox couples†

Reductant	*Oxidant*	E_0', *volts*
Acetaldehyde	Acetate	−0.60
H_2	$2H^+$	−0.42
Isocitrate	α-Ketoglutarate + CO_2	−0.38
NADH + H^+	NAD^+	−0.32
NADPH + H^+	$NADP^+$	−0.32
Lactate	Pyruvate	−0.19
NADH dehydrogenase (reduced)	(oxidized)	−0.11
Cytochrome *b* [Fe(II)]	[Fe(III)]	0.00
Cytochrome *c* [Fe(II)]	[Fe(III)]	+0.26
H_2O	$\tfrac{1}{2}O_2$	+0.82

† The data are calculated on the basis of two-electron transfers at pH ≅ 7.0 and *T* = 25 to 37°C.

similar relationship, the Nernst equation, expresses the relationship between the standard reduction potential of a given redox couple, its observed potential, and the concentration ratio of its electron donor and acceptor species. The Nernst equation is

$$E_h = E_0' + \frac{2.303\ RT}{n\mathscr{F}} \log \frac{[\text{electron acceptor}]}{[\text{electron donor}]} \tag{1}$$

in which E_0' is the standard reduction potential (pH = 7.0, T = 25°C, all concentrations at 1.0 M), E_h the observed electrode potential, R the gas constant (8.31 joules degree^{-1} mole^{-1}), T the absolute temperature, n the number of electrons being transferred, and $\mathscr{F}$ the faraday (96,406 joules volt^{-1}). At 25° the term $2.303RT/n\mathscr{F}$ has the value 0.059 when $n = 1$ and 0.03 when $n = 2$. Since it is customary to calculate equilibria of biological redox couples in terms of two-electron transfers, the Nernst equation simplifies to

$$E_h = E_0' + 0.03 \log \frac{[\text{electron acceptor}]}{[\text{electron donor}]} \tag{2}$$

The Nernst equation expresses mathematically the shape of a titration curve of a reductant by some oxidant, just as the Henderson-Hasselbalch equation does the same for titration of an acid with a base (Figure 17-2). At 100 percent reductant, the observed E_h is maximally negative. As the titration with an oxidizing agent proceeds, an

Figure 17-2
Oxidation-reduction titration curves of three reducing agents, showing midpoint potential E_0' values.

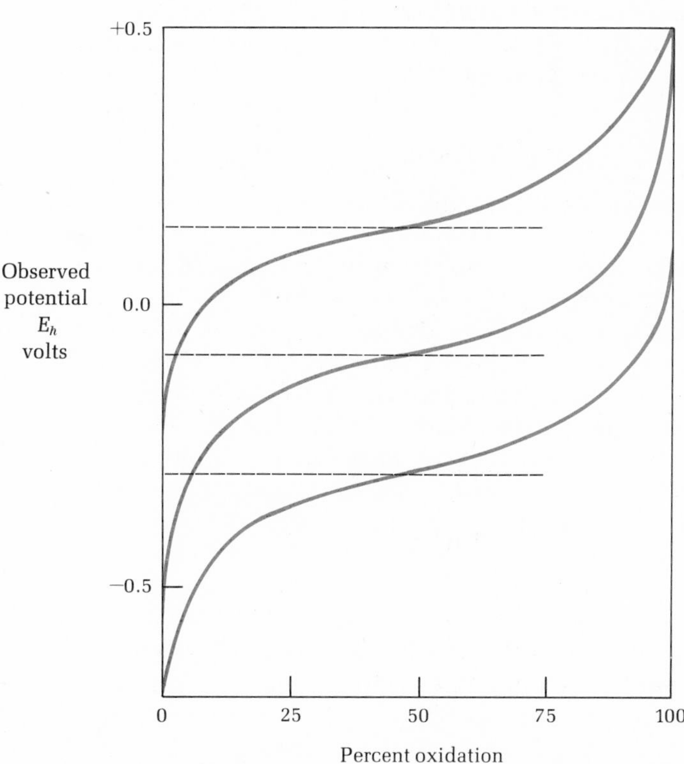

increasing fraction of the reductant being titrated is present in its oxidized form, resulting in an increase in the ratio [electron acceptor]/[electron donor] until a midpoint is reached at which [electron acceptor] = [electron donor]. At this point it is clear that the term 0.03 log ([electron acceptor]/[electron donor]) is zero, and the Nernst equation simplifies to

$$E_h = E_0'$$

The standard reduction potential is therefore the emf in volts at the precise midpoint of the titration curve of a given reductant at pH 7.0, 25°, and 1.0 atm, just as the pK′ of an acid equals the pH at the midpoint. E_0' is often called the *midpoint potential*.

Experimental determination of a standard reduction potential is not so simple a matter as determining the pK′ of a weak acid. Since oxidation-reduction reactions do not usually proceed as rapidly as ionic acid-base reactions, catalysts must often be added to bring them to equilibrium and to equilibrate with the metallic electrode, usually platinum, used to sense the electron pressure at any given ratio of reductant to oxidant species. The potential generated by such an electrode is measured by comparing it with that of another half-cell of known potential, the *reference half-cell* (Figure 17-1).

The standard reduction potentials of various biological oxidation-reduction systems allow us to predict the direction of flow of electrons from one redox couple to another under standard conditions, just as the phosphate-group transfer potential allows us to predict the direction in which phosphate groups will be enzymatically transferred (Chapter 14). Furthermore, as in the case of phosphate-group transfer reactions, we can calculate the final equilibrium resulting when electrons flow from one redox system of known standard potential to another of known potential, as well as the free-energy changes occurring during such reactions (below).

Classes of Oxidation-Reduction Enzymes

Three major classes of oxidation-reduction enzymes participate in the mainstream of electron transport from organic substrates to molecular oxygen. In the order of their participation they are (1) the *pyridine-linked dehydrogenases*, which require either NAD or NADP as coenzyme, (2) *flavin-linked dehydrogenases*, which contain flavin adenine dinucleotide (FAD) or flavin mononucleotide (FMN) as prosthetic group, and (3) the *cytochromes*, which contain an iron-porphyrin ring system.

Pyridine-Linked Dehydrogenases

Since members of this class of dehydrogenases require either NAD or NADP, which contain *nicotinamide*, a derivative of pyridine, they are generically termed *pyridine-linked dehydrogenases*. Over 150 are known, some of which are listed in Table 17-2. They catalyze the

Table 17-2 Properties of pyridine-linked dehydrogenase systems

System	*E_0' of substrate couple*	*Type*
NAD-linked:		
Isocitrate	−0.38	
D-β-Hydroxybutyrate	−0.32	
Glyceraldehyde 3-phosphate	−0.29	B
Dihydrolipoyl	−0.29	A or B
L-β-Hydroxyacyl CoA	−0.24	B
Ethanol	−0.20	A
Lactate	−0.19	A
Glycerol 3-phosphate	−0.19	B
L-Malate	−0.17	A
NADP-linked:		
Isocitrate	−0.38	
Glucose 6-phosphate	−0.32	
NAD or NADP:		
L-Glutamate	−0.14	B

Structure of NAD

Space-filling model of extended form of NAD

following general reactions:

$$\text{Reduced substrate} + \text{NAD}^+ \rightleftharpoons \text{oxidized substrate} + \text{NADH} + \text{H}^+$$

$$\text{Reduced substrate} + \text{NADP}^+ \rightleftharpoons \text{oxidized substrate} + \text{NADPH} + \text{H}^+ \quad (3)$$

The pyridine-linked dehydrogenases transfer reversibly two reducing equivalents from the substrate to the oxidized form of the pyridine nucleotide; one of these appears in the reduced pyridine nucleotide as a hydrogen atom, the other as an electron. The other hydrogen atom removed from the substrate appears as a free H^+ in the medium (Chapter 15).

NAD and NADP (Chapters 12, 15, and 16) were first isolated and identified in the period 1933–1936 by Warburg and by von Euler. Shortly later, one of their components, *nicotinic acid*, was recognized as being essential in the nutrition of mammals. NAD and NADP are found in all types of cells; NAD usually is present in much greater amounts than NADP. In liver cells, about 60 percent of the total NAD is present in the mitochondria and the rest in the extramitochondrial cytoplasm. Conversely, relatively more NADP is found in the soluble cytoplasm than in the mitochondria. NAD-linked dehydrogenases serve primarily in respiration and participate in the transfer of electrons from substrates toward oxygen, whereas NADP-linked dehydrogenases are primarily concerned in the transfer of electrons from substrates generated in catabolism to the reductive reactions of biosynthesis (Chapters 18, 23, and 24). Many of the pyridine-linked dehydrogenases have been obtained in crystalline form, including glyceraldehyde 3-phosphate dehydrogenase, lactate dehydrogenase, and malate dehydrogenase.

Most of the pyridine-linked dehydrogenases are specific for either NAD or NADP, but a few, such as glutamate dehydrogenase, can react with either coenzyme (Table 17-2). NAD and NADP undergo reversible binding and dissociation with the dehydrogenase protein during the catalytic cycle. Thus the oxidized and reduced forms of NAD and NADP should be regarded more as substrates than as prosthetic groups. The only prominent exception is the energy-conserving glyceraldehyde 3-phosphate dehydrogenase, to which NAD is covalently bound (Chapter 15).

Many pyridine-linked dehydrogenases contain tightly bound divalent metal ions; alcohol dehydrogenase, for example, contains Zn^{2+}. It is believed that the metal serves to bind the NAD or NADP to the enzyme protein. Many dehydrogenases also contain thiol groups that are essential for catalytic activity. In addition, some dehydrogenases contain an essential tryptophan residue at the catalytic site. The structure of NAD is shown in the margin.

Measurement

The enzymatic reduction of NAD^+ and $NADP^+$ [equation (3)] is accompanied by three characteristic changes useful for measuring the course of the reaction. In their oxidized forms, these coenzymes show no absorption in the visible range but an intense peak at about 260 nm, contributed largely by the adenine ring. When NAD and NADP are reduced, a new absorption band at 340 nm appears, with some decrease in the light absorbed at 260 nm (Figure 17-3). Advantage is taken of this spectral change to follow the course of reactions catalyzed by pyridine-linked dehydrogenases. It reflects the reduction of the aromatic pyridine ring of nicotinamide, which proceeds via transfer of a hydride ion (:H^-) from the substrate to the 4 position of the pyridine ring and the loss of the other hydrogen atom of the substrate as a proton (Figure 15-6).

The second method of following pyridine-linked oxidoreductions is by measurement of changes in pH, since reduction of NAD^+ (or $NADP^+$) results in formation of a proton [equation (3)]. The third method is by measurement of fluorescence changes, since the oxidized forms of NAD and NADP fluoresce strongly at about 440 nm. Although the fluorescence method is extremely sensitive, it is subject to interference by a number of factors.

NAD^+ and $NADP^+$ can also be reduced nonenzymatically by chemical reducing agents such as sodium dithionite or sodium borohydride. NADH and NADPH can in turn be nonenzymatically reoxidized with ferricyanide, but they are not oxidized by molecular oxygen at pH 7.0.

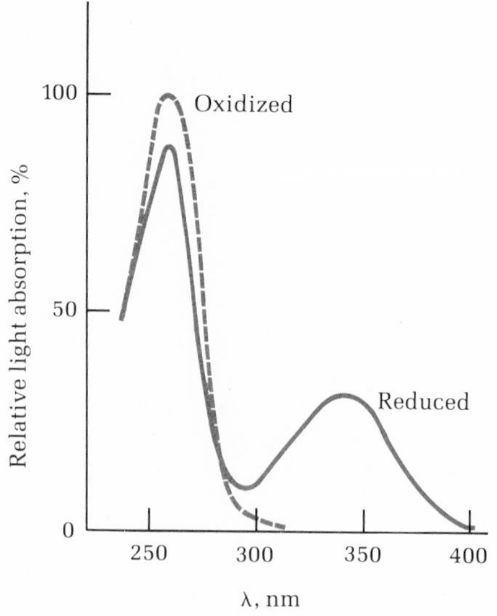

Figure 17-3
Absorption spectra of NAD^+ and NADH. Measurements of the reduction of NAD^+ to NADH are carried out at 340 nm.

Stereospecificity

We have seen that one hydrogen atom of the substrate of a pyridine-linked dehydrogenase becomes a proton and the other is transferred to NAD^+ or $NADP^+$. That this transfer is direct and does not proceed via a free H^+ ion has been proved by labeling the substrate hydrogen with deuterium or tritium.

When the pyridine ring of NAD^+ or $NADP^+$ is reduced by nonenzymatic means, a hydrogen atom from the reducing agent can attack carbon atom 4 of the pyridine ring from either side of the ring. However when the pyridine ring is reduced enzymatically, the hydrogen atom is transferred stereospecifically to only one side of the ring (margin), as has been shown in isotopic experiments. Table 17-2 shows that some dehydrogenases transfer hydrogen to the A side of the ring and some to the B side. Stereospecificity has been proved by use of substrates labeled with tritium or deuterium. Only one known dehydrogenase is not stereospecific, namely, dihydrolipoyl dehydrogenase (Chapter 16). Moreover, dehydrogenation of the substrate molecule by pyridine-linked dehydrogenases is also stereospecific; isotopic experiments have proved that only one specific hydrogen atom of the pair undergoing removal from a substrate, such as ethanol, is transferred to the pyridine ring, in this case its A side (margin). Evidently both the substrate and NAD^+ molecules must possess specific stereochemical orientation toward each other on the enzyme catalytic site.

Oxidized and reduced forms of NAD.

In the oxidized form of NAD the hydrogen atom at position 4 is in the plane of the pyridine ring. When it is reduced with a deuterium-labeled substrate, the deuterium may combine with the 4 carbon atom from either side, to yield one of two possible products, one with deuterium on the A side, the other with deuterium on the B side.

NAD^+, oxidized form

NADH, reduced form

A side B side

Kinetics

The kinetics of many pyridine-linked dehydrogenases has been examined in detail. These enzymes show characteristic Michaelis-Menten, or saturation, behavior with both the substrate and the pyridine nucleotide; the Michaelis constants for the oxidized and reduced substrates and for oxidized and reduced pyridine nucleotides have been established (Chapter 8). During their catalytic cycles, pyridine-linked dehydrogenases form two different binary complexes with the coenzyme, E—NAD^+ and E—NADH, as well as two ternary complexes, S_{ox}—E—NADH and S_{red}—E—NAD^+. The complexes E—S_{red} and E—S_{ox} do not form.

Equilibria

The direction of reaction and the equilibrium composition of pyridine-linked oxidoreduction systems can be predicted from the standard reduction potential of the NADH–NAD^+ (or NADPH–$NADP^+$) couple ($E_0' = -0.32$ volt) in relation to that of the reduced-substrate–oxidized-substrate couple with which the coenzyme interacts. Table 17-2 gives the standard oxidation-reduction potentials of some NAD- and NADP-linked substrate couples. Systems having a more negative standard reduction potential than NAD or NADP tend to lose electrons to the oxidized forms of these coenzymes; those having a more positive standard potential tend to accept electrons from NADH or NADPH, when tested under standard conditions of 1.0 *M* concentration of all reactants and products.

The equilibrium concentrations of all four components in a pyridine-linked oxidoreduction reaction can be calculated. Suppose we start with 0.01 *M* concentrations of both ethanol and acetaldehyde ($E_0' = -0.18$ volt) and 0.01 *M* concentrations of both NAD^+ and NADH ($E_0' = -0.32$ volt). Alcohol dehydrogenase is now added at pH 7.0 and the reaction allowed to proceed until it reaches equilibrium

$$\text{Ethanol} + NAD^+ \rightleftharpoons \text{acetaldehyde} + \text{NADH} + H^+$$

Since we started with equimolar concentrations of reductants and oxidants, the initial E_h for each couple was equal to its E_0'. Electrons flow from the more negative couple (NADH–NAD^+) to the more positive (ethanol-acetaldehyde) until an equilibrium is reached at which the E_h values of the two systems are identical, which will obviously be midway between their initial values of $E_0' = -0.32$ volt (NADH–NAD^+) and $E_0' = -0.18$ volt (ethanol-acetaldehyde), namely, $E_h = -0.25$ volt. We can then calculate the ratio $[NAD^+]/[NADH]$ as

$$E_h = E_0' + 0.03 \log \frac{[\text{electron acceptor}]}{[\text{electron donor}]}$$

$$-0.25 = -0.32 + 0.03 \log \frac{[NAD^+]}{[NADH]}$$

$$\log \frac{[NAD^+]}{[NADH]} = 2.3$$

$$\frac{[NAD^+]}{[NADH]} = 210$$

$$[NAD^+] = 210[NADH] \qquad (4)$$

Since the sum of $[NAD^+]$ and $[NADH] = 0.02$, $[NAD^+]$ is equal to $0.02 - [NADH]$. Substitution of this expression for $[NAD^+]$ into equation (4) yields

$$0.02 - [NADH] = 210[NADH]$$

Solving for [NADH], we get 9.5×10^{-5} *M* as the concentration of NADH. $[NAD^+]$ is then $0.02 - 9.5 \times 10^{-5}$, or 0.0199 *M*. Because one molecule of ethanol is formed with each molecule of NAD^+, the equilibrium concentration of ethanol is 0.0199 *M* and that of acetaldehyde is 9.5×10^{-5} *M*.

The NADH–NAD^+ system can transfer electrons from one substrate couple to another, by virtue of its capacity to act as a common intermediate shared by two pyridine-linked reactions, each catalyzed by a specific enzyme. For example, in the glycolytic sequence glyceraldehyde 3-phosphate is oxidized by pyruvate in the following reactions, which share NADH as common intermediate (Chapter 15):

$$\text{Glyceraldehyde 3-phosphate} + P_i + NAD^+ \rightleftharpoons \text{1,3-diphosphoglycerate} + NADH + H^+$$

$$NADH + H^+ + \text{pyruvate} \rightleftharpoons NAD^+ + \text{lactate}$$

$$\text{Sum: glyceraldehyde 3-phosphate} + \text{pyruvate} + P_i \rightleftharpoons \text{1,3-diphosphoglycerate} + \text{lactate}$$

If we start with equimolar concentrations of all components, the direction of flow of electrons is from the electronegative glyceraldehyde 3-phosphate couple ($E_0' = -0.29$ volt) to the more positive lactate-pyruvate couple ($E_0' = -0.19$ volt). The overall equilibrium is therefore far in the direction of lactate; the exact equilibrium ratios can be calculated (try this). Remember, however, that all such calculations assume that the pH is 7.0. Since a proton is always formed or utilized in NAD-linked reactions, their equilibria will change with pH. The standard reduction potential of the NADH-NAD^+ couple becomes 0.03 volt more negative for an increase in pH of 1.0 unit.

Many cells contain *transhydrogenases,* which catalyze reversible electron transfer between NADPH and NAD^+.

$$NADH + NADP^+ \rightleftharpoons NAD^+ + NADPH$$

Transhydrogenases are found in the mitochondria, where they play a regulatory role.

Flavin-Linked Dehydrogenases

These enzymes contain either *flavin adenine dinucleotide* (FAD) or *flavin mononucleotide* (FMN) (Chapters 12 and

Figure 17-4
Flavin mononucleotide. Reduction of the isoalloxazine ring takes place at the points shown in color.

```
FMN
        H           O
        C     N     C
CH3—C       C     C     NH
CH3—C       C     C     C=O
        C     N     N
        H     |
              CH2
              |
              CHOH
              |
              CHOH
              |
              CHOH
              |
              CH2OPO3 2−
              ↓
FMNH2
              H     O
        H     |     ‖
        C     N     C
CH3—C       C     C     NH
CH3—C       C     C     C=O
        C     N     N
        H     |     |
              R     H
```

Space filling model of FMN

16) as prosthetic groups. Both coenzymes were first isolated and their structures (Figures 12-5 and 17-4) determined in the middle 1930s by Warburg and by Kuhn, at a time when the vitamin riboflavin (vitamin B_2), a component of the flavin nucleotides, was first identified. In most flavin-linked dehydrogenases, the flavin nucleotide is very tightly bound and does not leave the enzyme during the catalytic cycle; an exception is D-amino acid oxidase, which has relatively low affinity for its FAD prosthetic group. The most important mainstream flavin-linked dehydrogenases are (1) *NADH dehydrogenase,* which catalyzes transfer of electrons from NADH to some unknown acceptor, possibly a nonheme-iron protein, in the respiratory chain, (2) *succinate dehydrogenase* (Chapter 16), (3) *dihydrolipoyl dehydrogenase* of the pyruvate and α-ketoglutarate dehydrogenase systems (Chapter 16), and (4) the flavoproteins that catalyze the first dehydrogenation step during fatty acid oxidation (Chapter 19). Many other flavin dehydrogenases are known, such as *D-amino acid oxidase* and *xanthine oxidase* (Table 17-3).

The active portion of FAD or FMN that participates in the oxidoreduction is the *isoalloxazine ring* of the riboflavin moiety, which may become reduced (Figure 17-4). The reaction is usually shown as a direct transfer of a pair of hydrogen atoms from the substrate to yield the reduced forms, designated $FADH_2$ and $FMNH_2$. Some flavin dehydrogenases contain more than one molecule of FAD or FMN. Some also contain metals. NADH dehydrogenase (below) contains or is associated with nonheme iron proteins.

Although the oxidation and reduction of the FAD or FMN prosthetic groups of the flavin dehydrogenases are usually written formally as reactions involving simultaneous transfers of two hydrogen atoms or two electrons,

Table 17-3 Properties of some flavin-linked dehydrogenases

	Molecular weight	*Prosthetic group*	*Metal*
"Mainstream" dehydrogenases:			
NADH dehydrogenase†	100,000–250,000	FMN	8 Fe‡
Succinate dehydrogenase	~300,000	FAD	8 Fe‡
α-Lipoyl dehydrogenase	~100,000	2FAD	
Acyl CoA dehydrogenases	~200,000	FAD	
Electron-transferring flavoproteins	70,000	FAD	
Others:			
Glycerol 3-phosphate dehydrogenase		FAD	Fe
D-Amino acid oxidase	~100,000	FAD	
Glucose oxidase	154,000	2FAD	
Xanthine oxidase	300,000	2FAD	8 Fe, 2 Mo
Dihydroorotate dehydrogenase	125,000	FAD	

† May consist of two flavoproteins or one protein with two flavin groups.
‡ Includes nonheme iron protein.

there is evidence that these reactions occur in two separate one-electron steps. Transfer of but one electron to FAD (or FMN) leads to formation of its *semiquinone*, or *free radical*, which contains an unpaired electron. The semiquinone may then accept a second electron to go into the fully reduced form. The semiquinone forms of some flavin dehydrogenases can be detected either by their characteristic absorption spectrum or by means of *electron spin resonance spectroscopy*, which can detect the occurrence of molecules with unpaired electron spins by their characteristic behavior in a magnetic field. FAD and FMN can also be reduced nonenzymatically with reducing agents such as dithionite.

In their oxidized form, flavin dehydrogenases are intensely colored and may be red, brown, or green in color; they usually have broad absorption peaks near 370 and 450 nm (Figure 17-5). When they are reduced, enzymatically or chemically, they undergo bleaching with loss of the 450-nm absorption. Characteristic changes in fluorescence also occur during the oxidation-reduction cycle. The reduced forms of most flavin-linked dehydrogenases are not readily reoxidized by molecular oxygen; an exception is D-amino acid oxidase. In the cell, the ultimate electron acceptor from flavin-linked dehydrogenases is the cytochrome system. However, reduced flavin dehydrogenases are readily oxidized by artificial electron acceptors such as ferricyanide or the reducible dyes methylene blue (Chapter 16), phenazine methosulfate, and 2,6-dichlorophenolindophenol (margin).

$$\underset{\text{Blue}}{\text{E—FADH}_2 + \text{methylene blue}_{ox}} \longrightarrow \underset{\text{Colorless}}{\text{E—FAD} + \text{methylene blue}_{red}}$$

These artificial acceptors are extremely useful for quantitative assay of flavin-linked dehydrogenases.

Figure 17-5
Absorption spectrum of the oxidized form of a flavin dehydrogenase. Reduction of the enzyme causes loss of the absorption peak near 450 nm.

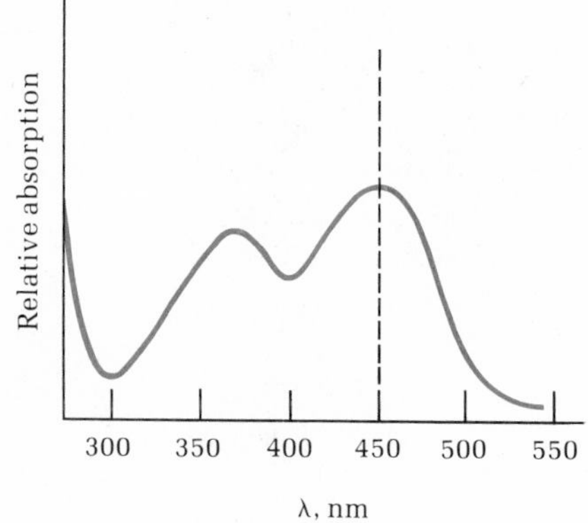

Artificial electron acceptors.

Phenazine methosulfate.

$\left[\text{N-methylphenazinium}\right]_2 \; SO_4^{2-}$ (structure: N, $\overset{+}{N}$—CH_3)

2,6-Dichlorophenolindophenol

(structure: O=, Cl, Cl, =N—, —N(CH_3)$_2$)

Nonheme Iron Proteins

Although the cytochrome system is the ultimate acceptor of electrons from the flavin-linked dehydrogenases, there is considerable evidence that both NADH dehydrogenase and succinate dehydrogenase either contain or are bound tightly to specific proteins called generically *nonheme iron proteins* because the iron they contain is present in some form other than heme groups. Several nonheme iron proteins have been isolated in highly purified, homogeneous form (Chapter 21). Characteristically they have very low molecular weights, ranging from about 6,000 to 12,000. It is not yet clear whether these are true electron carriers and function as independent molecular entities or whether they actually constitute subunits of the flavin-linked dehydrogenases. Nonheme iron proteins usually contain from two to eight iron atoms per molecule and an equivalent number of cysteine residues, to which the iron is attached in some specific linkage whose structure has not yet been established. Treatment of nonheme iron proteins with acid yields the sulfur as H_2S. The nonheme iron proteins can be either enzymatically or chemically reduced, but it is not certain which of their atoms undergo reduction. Reduction of nonheme iron proteins is a one-electron step and is accompanied by bleaching of the red or pink oxidized form, which has an absorption peak at 450 nm, and by appearance of a characteristic electron spin resonance signal.

Nonheme iron proteins also participate in photosynthesis (Chapter 21) and nitrogen fixation (Chapter 24).

Cytochromes

The cytochromes are a group of iron-containing electron-transferring proteins of aerobic cells that act sequentially to transfer electrons from flavoproteins to molecular oxygen. They all contain iron-porphyrin prosthetic groups, resembling hemoglobin and myoglobin in this respect. The cytochromes undergo reversible Fe(II)-Fe(III) valence changes during their catalytic cycle. The terminal cytochrome of the chain, which can react with oxygen, is called *cytochrome oxidase*. The reduced forms of the other cytochromes cannot be reoxidized by molecular oxygen. In the mitochondria of higher animal and plant cells, where the respiratory chain has been most thoroughly studied, at least five different cytochromes have been identified: cytochromes *b*, *c*, c_1, *a*, and a_3. Their molar ratios to each other appear to be constant. In addition to the cytochromes found in mitochondria, another type, *cytochrome* b_5, occurs in the endoplasmic reticulum. Vertebrate cells also contain other heme enzymes, such as *peroxidase* and *catalase*. Although catalase has been very intensively studied, its role in biological oxidations is not known with certainty. Since it is found in the microbodies in some cells, it is believed to catalyze decomposition of hydrogen peroxide produced in the latter structures (Chapter 20).

The porphyrin ring is present not only in the various heme enzymes and heme proteins but also in the chlorophylls of green plant cells. Porphyrins are derivatives of the parent *tetrapyrrole* compound *porphin* (Figure 17-6). The porphyrins are named and classified on the basis of their side-chain substituents, e.g., *etioporphyrins, mesoporphyrins, protoporphyrins*, and *coproporphyrins*. Of these, protoporphyrins are by far the most abundant. Protoporphyrin contains four methyl groups, two vinyl groups, and two propionic acid groups. Since protoporphyrins contain three different kinds of substituent groups, they may exist in fifteen isomeric forms depending on the sequence of substitution in the eight available side-chain positions. Of these many possible forms, one, protoporphyrin IX (Figure 17-6), is the most abundant. It is found in hemoglobin, myoglobin, and most of the cytochromes.

Protoporphyrin forms quadridentate (literally "four teeth") chelate complexes with metal ions such as iron, magnesium, zinc, nickel, cobalt, and copper. Such a chelate complex of protoporphyrin with Fe(II) is called

Figure 17-6
Structures of porphin, protoporphyrin, and hemes.

Porphin

Protoporphyrin IX

Hemochrome

Heme A
(prosthetic group of cytochromes of class A)

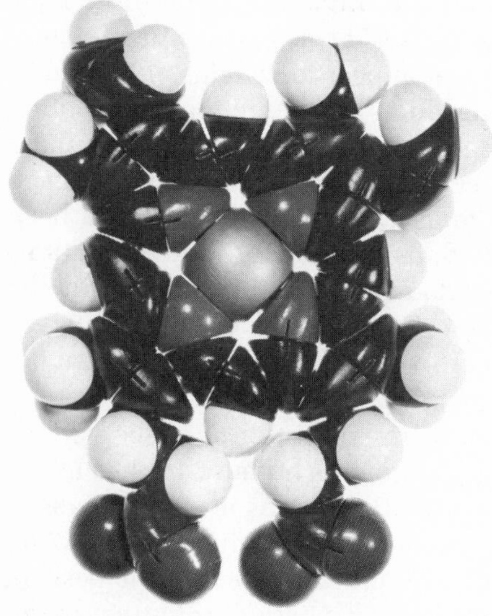

Space-filling model of protoheme.

protoheme, or more simply, heme; a similar complex with Fe(III) is called hemin or hematin. In heme, the four ligand groups of the porphyrin form a square-planar complex with the iron; the remaining fifth and sixth coordination positions of iron are perpendicular to the plane of the porphin ring. When the fifth and sixth positions of iron are occupied, the resulting structure is a hemochrome, or hemochromogen. In the heme proteins myoglobin and hemoglobin, the fifth position is occupied by an imidazole group of a histidine residue. In these hemes the sixth position is either unoccupied (deoxyhemoglobin and deoxymyoglobin) or occupied by oxygen (oxyhemoglobin and oxymyoglobin) or other ligands such as carbon monoxide, cyanide, etc. In nearly all the cytochromes, on the

Figure 17-7
The absorption spectrum of cytochrome c.

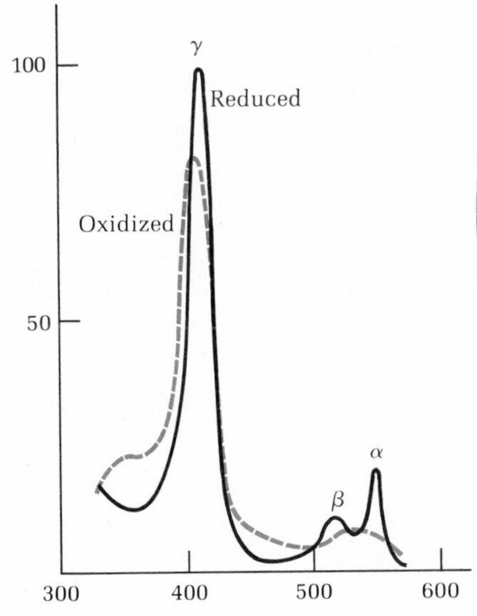

other hand, *both* the fifth and sixth positions of the iron are occupied by the R groups of specific amino acid residues of the proteins, and they are unavailable to bind with ligands such as oxygen, carbon monoxide, or cyanide.

In hemoglobin and myoglobin the iron atom does not undergo change in valence as oxygen is bound and lost; it remains in the Fe(II) state, but both hemoglobin and myoglobin can be oxidized to the Fe(III), or hemin form, by oxidizing agents such as ferricyanide, with a change in color from red to brown. The respective products are called *methemoglobin* and *metmyoglobin;* the latter do not function reversibly as oxygen carriers. In the cytochromes, however, the iron atom normally undergoes reversible changes between Fe(II) and Fe(III) forms; their real function is to serve as electron carriers, whereas hemoglobin and myoglobin act as ligand (oxygen) carriers.

The cytochromes were first discovered and called *histohematins* in 1866 by MacMunn, but their significance in biological oxidations did not become clear until 1925, when they were rediscovered by Keilin. With a spectroscope he observed that insect muscles contained substances resembling heme proteins, which evidently underwent oxidation and reduction during respiration. He renamed them cytochromes, postulated that they acted in a chain to carry electrons from fuel molecules to oxygen, and classified them into three major classes, *a*, *b*, and *c*, depending on the characteristic position of their absorption bands in the reduced state. Each type of cytochrome in its reduced state has three distinctive absorption bands in the visible range, the α bands, the β bands, and the γ, or *Soret*, bands (Figure 17-7).

Although many cytochromes have been highly purified, with one exception they are usually very tightly bound to the mitochondrial membrane and difficult to obtain in soluble and homogeneous form. The exception is cytochrome *c*, which is very easily extracted from mitochondria by strong salt solutions. The cytochrome *c* of many species has been obtained in crystalline form, and the amino acid sequences are known (Chapters 6 and 7). The iron protoporphyrin group of cytochrome *c* is covalently linked to the protein via thioether bridges between the porphyrin ring and two cysteine residues in the peptide chain, presumably formed by addition of the —SH group across the double bond of the 2- and 4-vinyl groups of the protoporphyrin. It is the only common heme protein in which there is such a covalent linkage. In hemoglobin and myoglobin, as in cytochromes *b* and *a*, the porphyrin ring is noncovalently associated with the protein and can be removed by extraction of the acidified protein with pyridine or other solvents. In cytochrome *c* the fifth and sixth coordination positions of iron are believed to be occupied by a histidine residue and a methionine residue, which prevent cytochrome *c* from reacting with oxygen or carbon monoxide at pH 7.0. The properties of various cytochromes are summarized in Table 17-4.

Cytochromes *a* and a_3, (together called cytochrome oxidase or the respiratory enzyme) deserve special attention. Instead of protoporphyrin they contain porphyrin A,

Table 17-4 Properties of mitochondrial cytochromes

Cytochrome	*Molecular weight*	E_0', *volts*	*Absorption maxima in reduced form, nm* α	β	γ
b	30,000	+0.050	563	532	429
c_1	370,000	+0.220	554	524	418
c	13,000	+0.254	550	521	415
a	240,000	+0.28	600		439
a_3			603.5		443

which differs from protoporphyrin in having a formyl group ($-\underset{\displaystyle \text{O}}{\overset{\|}{\text{CH}}}$) instead of a methyl group at position 8, no methyl group at position 5, and a long hydrophobic 15-carbon isoprenoid side-chain at position 2 instead of a vinyl group (Figure 17-6). Porphyrin A is structurally related to the porphyrin of chlorophyll (Chapter 21), which also has a long isoprenoid side-chain. The fifth coordination position of iron in cytochrome *a* is believed to be occupied by an amino group contributed by an amino-sugar moiety of the protein.

The oxidized, or Fe(III), form of cytochrome $a + a_3$ can accept electrons from reduced cytochrome *c* to become the Fe(II) form, which in turn is reoxidized by molecular oxygen to the Fe(III) form. There is evidence that the cytochrome $a + a_3$ system is a complex with a molecular weight of about 240,000 consisting of six possibly identical subunits, each containing a single heme A group and a copper atom. When these associate into a hexameric complex, two of the subunits show a different absorption spectrum from the rest; these are called cytochrome *a*; the remaining four subunits, which correspond to cytochrome a_3, can react directly with oxygen whereas cytochrome *a* cannot. Presumably electrons are received by cytochrome *a* subunits and are then transferred to the cytochrome a_3 subunits, which can pass them to oxygen. The copper atoms of the cytochromes a_3 units give characteristic electron spin resonance signals and undergo Cu(II) to Cu(I) transitions during electron transport to oxygen. Cytochrome a_3 and hemoglobin both combine with carbon monoxide, which competes with oxygen. Carbon monoxide inhibition of cytochrome *a* is reversed by illumination with visible light. Cyanide and hydrogen sulfide also inhibit the cytochrome $a + a_3$ complex. Much uncertainty still surrounds the structure and mechanism of action of this extremely important terminal enzyme of respiration.

The Pathway of Electron Transport: The Respiratory Chain

The concept of a chain of electron carriers capable of transferring electrons from substrate molecules to molecular oxygen represents the confluence of two lines of investigation. Early investigators of biological oxidations in the period 1900–1920, among them Thunberg, had discovered many dehydrogenases, which appeared to act by removal of hydrogen atoms from their substrates in the complete absence of oxygen. Wieland later postulated that dehydrogenation of substrates is the basic process involved in biological oxidations and that oxygen reacts directly with such activated hydrogen atoms. However, in 1913 Warburg discovered that cyanide in very small concentrations inhibited the oxygen consumption of respiring cells and tissues nearly completely. Since cyanide forms very stable complexes with iron, e.g., ferricyanide, Warburg postulated that an iron-containing enzyme capable of activating oxygen must be essential in biological oxidation. These views were brought together by Szent-Györgyi, who later postulated that flavoproteins play the role of intermediate electron carriers between the dehydrogenases and the cytochromes, and by Keilin, who demonstrated that the cytochromes act in series as electron carriers. Further experimental proof came from work of Warburg, Keilin, Green, Okunuki, and others, who carried out *in vitro* reconstructions of segments of the electron-transport chain starting from purified components.

The sequence of electron-transfer reactions in the respiratory chain shown in (Figure 17-8 and Table 17-5) is supported by several lines of evidence: (1) It is consistent with the standard reduction potentials of the different electron carriers, in that the potentials become more positive as electrons pass from substrate to oxygen. (2) *In vitro* reconstruction experiments with isolated electron carriers support the sequence; thus NADH can reduce NADH dehydrogenase but cannot directly reduce cytochromes b, c, or $a + a_3$. Similarly, reduced NADH dehydrogenase cannot interact directly with cytochrome $a + a_3$ but requires the presence of cytochromes b and c. (3) Complexes containing functionally linked carriers have been isolated, among them complexes of cytochromes b and c_1, of $a + a_3$, and of NADH dehydrogenase, nonheme iron, cytochrome b, and coenzyme Q (see below). (4) By means of sensitive spectrophotometric measurements perfected by Chance, it is possible to determine the sequence

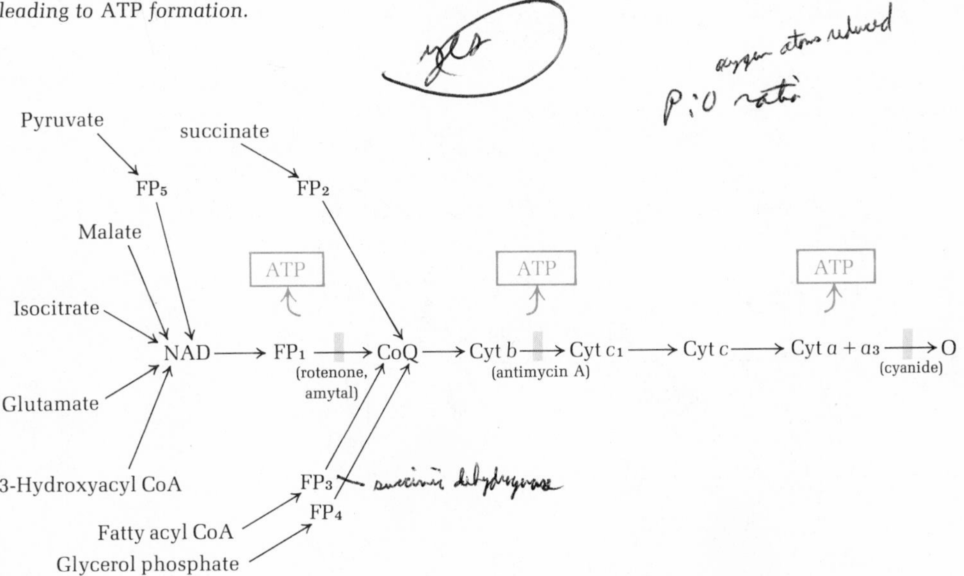

Figure 17-8
The respiratory chain and the points of entry of electrons from various substrates. Also shown are the sites of inhibition of electron transport and the probable sites of energy conservation leading to ATP formation.

Table 17-5 The sequential reactions of electron transport†

$NADH + H^+ + E_1\text{—FAD}$	$\rightleftharpoons$	$NAD^+ + E\text{—FADH}_2$
$E\text{—FADH}_2 + 2E_2\text{—Fe(III)}$	$\rightleftharpoons$	$E_1\text{—FAD} + 2E_2\text{—Fe(II)} + 2H^+$
$2E_2\text{—Fe(II)} + 2H^+ + CoQ$	$\rightleftharpoons$	$2E_2\text{—Fe(III)} + CoQH_2$
$CoQH_2 + 2\text{ cyt } b\text{(III)}$	$\rightleftharpoons$	$CoQ + 2H^+ + 2\text{ cyt } b\text{(II)}$
$2\text{ cyt } b\text{(II)} + 2\text{ cyt } c\text{(III)}$	$\rightleftharpoons$	$2\text{ cyt } b\text{(III)} + 2\text{ cyt } c\text{(II)}$
$2\text{ cyt } c\text{(II)} + 2\text{ cyt } a\text{(III)}$	$\rightleftharpoons$	$2\text{ cyt } c\text{(III)} + 2\text{ cyt } a\text{(II)}$
$2\text{ cyt } a\text{(II)} + 2\text{ cyt } a_3\text{(III)}$	$\rightleftharpoons$	$2\text{ cyt } a\text{(III)} + 2\text{ cyt } a_3\text{(II)}$
$2\text{ cyt } a_3\text{(II)} + \frac{1}{2}O_2 + 2H^+$	$\rightleftharpoons$	$2\text{ cyt } a_3\text{(III)} + H_2O$

† The following abbreviations are used: E_1—FAD (NADH dehydrogenase), E_2—Fe(III) (oxidized form of nonheme iron protein), cyt *b*(III) (oxidized form of cytochrome *b*), etc.

of reduction of the carriers. In the aerobic steady state during Krebs cycle oxidations by isolated mitochondria Chance and Williams found that the electron carrier nearest the reducing, or substrate end, of the chain, namely, NAD, is the most reduced member of the chain whereas the carriers at the oxygen end (cytochromes $a + a_3$) are almost entirely in the oxidized form. The intermediate carriers are present in successively more oxidized steady states going from substrate to oxygen. When the respiratory chain is blocked with a specific inhibitor, carriers at the reducing side of the block in the chain become more reduced and those at the oxygen side become more oxidized (Figure 17-9). A difference spectrum of the respiratory carriers of rat liver mitochondria is shown below.

The discovery of inhibitors specific for certain points in the chain has greatly helped the study of electron transport. The most important are rotenone, an extremely toxic

Figure 17-9 Hydraulic analogs of the state of reduction of the electron carriers in the aerobic steady state and following inhibition. The inhibition produces a "crossover point"; the carriers to the left of the crossover point become more reduced and those to the right become more oxidized.

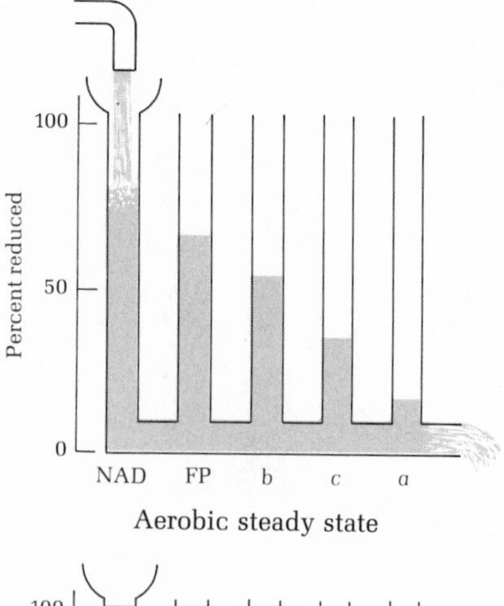

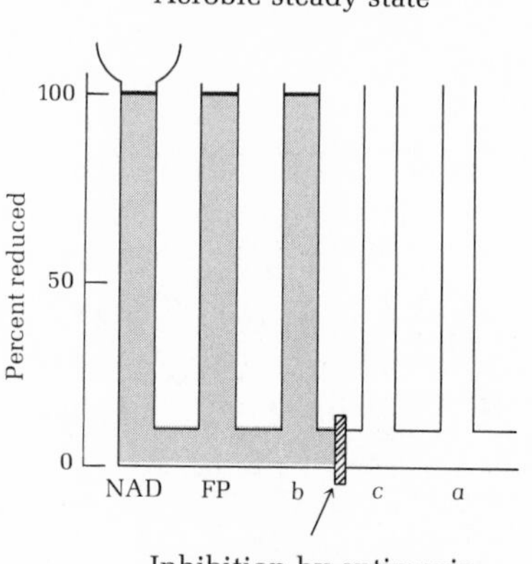

A difference spectrum of the respiratory carriers of rat liver mitochondria.

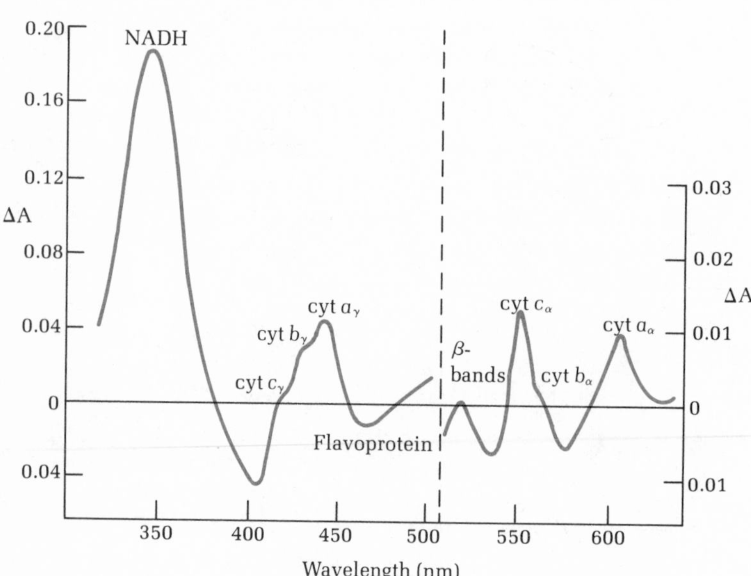

Figure 17-10
Coenzyme Q. The oxidized form absorbs strongly at 280 to 289 nm. CoQ_6 is present in some microorganisms and CoQ_{10} in mitochondria of most mammals.

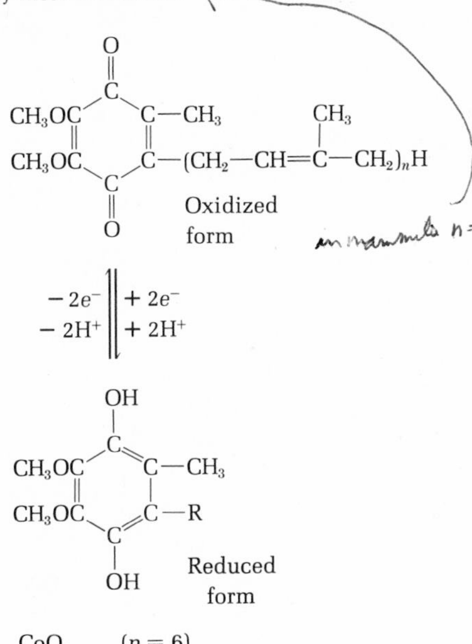

insecticide and fish poison and *sodium amytal*, a barbiturate drug, both of which block electron transfer from NAD to cytochrome *b*; the antibiotic *antimycin A*, isolated from a strain of *Streptomyces*, which blocks transfer of electrons from cytochrome *b* to *c*; and *cyanide*, which blocks the terminal cytochrome $a + a_3$ step (Figure 17-8).

There are still some uncertainties in connection with the identity and sequence of interaction of some of the electron carriers. Of special interest is the substance designated CoQ in Figure 17-8, first discovered by Morton in England and named *ubiquinone* because it is ubiquitous in cells. Later it was shown by Crane and Green to function as an electron carrier and called *coenzyme Q*. CoQ is a benzoquinone derivative with a long isoprenoid side chain (Figure 17-10), which in most mammalian tissues has 10 five-carbon isoprenoid units (and is thus designated CoQ_{10}) but in other organisms has only six or eight isoprene units (CoQ_6 and CoQ_8). The possible role of CoQ in the electron-transport chain has been the subject of much work and controversy. Some investigators have denied that it is an obligatory electron carrier in the chain, but important recent experiments of Klingenberg and others strongly suggest that CoQ is indeed a component carrier of the respiratory chain, possibly functioning as a fat-soluble molecule shuttling between the flavoproteins and the cytochrome system in the lipid phase of the mitochondrial membrane. This view is strongly supported by the observation that the antibiotic *piericidin*, which resembles CoQ in structure, is a potent inhibitor of electron transport between NADH dehydrogenase and cytochrome *b*.

There is increasing evidence that a nonheme iron protein participates in electron transfer from cytochrome *b* to cytochrome c_1.

Another property of electron transport currently receiving much attention is the formation and utilization of protons at several points in the respiratory chain (Table 17-5). In Chapter 18 it will be seen how these acid-base changes may be important in energy conservation during electron transport.

Although it is usually assumed that electron transport occurs in two-electron steps between NAD and CoQ and in one-electron steps from cytochrome *b* to oxygen, other arrangements are not excluded (see Figure 17-11). The reduction of one molecule of molecular oxygen to two OH^- ions requires a total of four electrons (Table 17-5). Whether these are furnished one at a time, two at a time, or in groups of four by the respiratory chain is not yet known.

Much evidence is available that the electron carrier molecules constituting the electron-transport chain are arranged into supramolecular clusters called *respiratory assemblies*, which contain a fixed number of molecules of each electron carrier and which are embedded in the structure of the inner mitochondrial membrane (Chapter 18). Presumably the adjacent carriers of the chain are oriented so that their prosthetic groups can make contact through limited vibrational or rotational movements.

Figure 17-11
Electron-transfer patterns. In (*a*) electron transfers are in two-electron steps up to FP and in one-electron steps thereafter. In (*b*) all transfers are in two-electron steps.

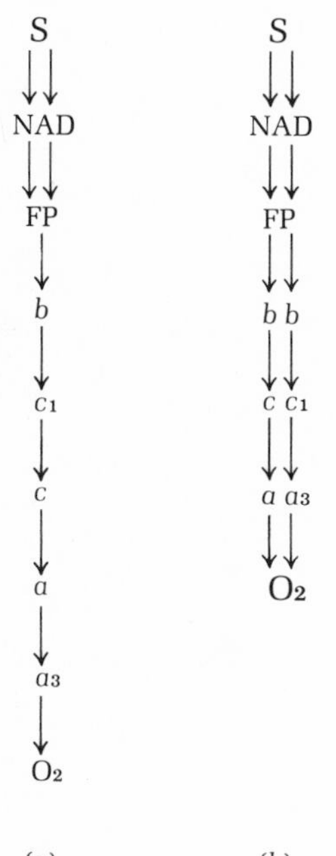

The Energetics of Electron Transport

We have seen that the standard free-energy change occurring during any chemical reaction is a function of its equilibrium constant (Chapter 14)

$$\Delta G^{\circ\prime} = -RT \ln K'_{eq}$$

A modified form of this expression can be used to calculate the standard free-energy change occurring when two oxidation-reduction couples of known standard reduction potentials react with each other

$$\Delta G^{\circ\prime} = -n\mathscr{F}\ \Delta E'_0$$

in which $\Delta G^{\circ\prime}$ is the standard free-energy change in calories, n is the number of electrons transferred, $\mathscr{F}$ is the caloric equivalent of the faraday (23,062 cal), and $\Delta E'_0$ is the difference between the standard reduction potential of the electron acceptor and that of the electron donor. All components are assumed to be at 1.0 M concentration at 25° and pH 7.0. With this relationship we can now calculate the standard free-energy change as a pair of electron equivalents goes from NADH ($E'_0 = -0.32$ volt) to molecular oxygen ($E'_0 = +0.82$ volt), i.e., the entire length of the respiratory chain

$$\begin{aligned}\Delta G^{\circ\prime} &= -2 \times 23{,}062 \times [0.82 - (-0.32)] = -52{,}700 \text{ cal}\\ &= -52.7 \text{ kcal}\end{aligned}$$

A very large free-energy change thus occurs during the process of electron transport from NADH to molecular oxygen via the respiratory chain. This value may be compared with the standard free energy of formation of ATP from ADP and phosphate

$$\text{ADP} + \text{phosphate} \rightleftharpoons \text{ATP} + \text{HOH} \qquad \Delta G^{\circ\prime} = +7.3 \text{ kcal}$$

It is seen that the passage of one pair of electrons from NADH to oxygen is accompanied by a sufficiently large decline in free energy to make possible the synthesis of several molecules of ATP from ADP and phosphate under standard conditions, providing a coupling mechanism is available.

Similar calculations give the free-energy change occurring at each of the major electron-transferring steps in the respiratory chain for which the standard reduction potentials are known (Tables 17-1 and 17-4). There are three spans in the chain in which there are relatively large standard free-energy changes, i.e., between NAD and the flavin group of NADH dehydrogenase, between cytochromes b and c, and between cytochrome a and oxygen. At each of these there is a sufficiently large decrease in free energy to cause the coupled formation of ATP from ADP and phosphate. At other points in the chain, there are only relatively small free-energy changes, perhaps insufficient to cause formation of a molecule of ATP (Figure 17-12). It must be emphasized that all such calculations assume thermodynamic equilibrium, which may

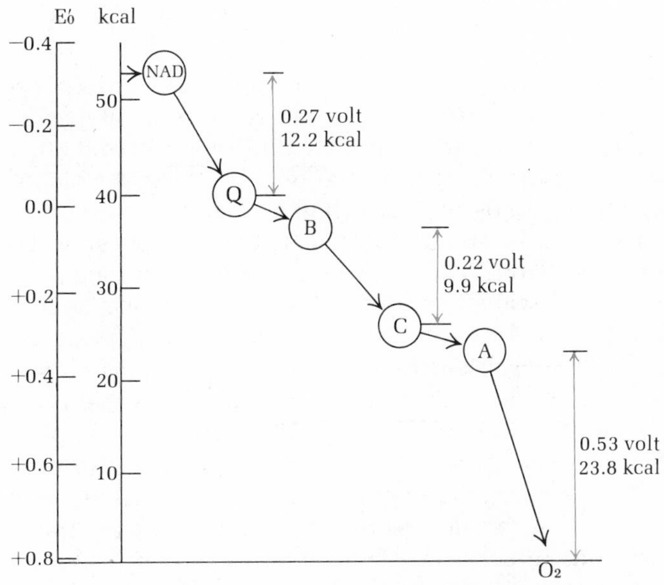

Figure 17-12
The decline in free energy as electron pairs flow down the respiratory chain to oxygen. Each of the three segments denoted in color yields sufficient energy to generate a molecule of ATP from ADP and phosphate.

not necessarily exist in any of these steps, and that all components are present in standard concentrations of 1.0 M.

Oxidative Phosphorylation

The coupling of ADP phosphorylation to aerobic respiration was first postulated by Engelhardt in the Soviet Union in the early 1930s, but it was not until after the tricarboxylic acid cycle was formulated in 1937 that more penetrating evidence appeared. Kalckar in Denmark and Belitser in the Soviet Union found that when various intermediates of the cycle were oxidized by suspensions of freshly minced liver, kidney, or muscle tissue, inorganic phosphate present in the medium disappeared and could be recovered in the form of various organic phosphates, e.g., ADP or ATP, glucose 6-phosphate and fructose 6-phosphate. Under anaerobic conditions or when respiration was poisoned with cyanide, such phosphorylations did not take place. Most important, it was proved with the use of inhibitors of glycolysis, such as fluoride (Chapter 15), that the aerobic phosphorylations were not the result of glycolysis, which could result in glycolytic or anaerobic phosphorylation of ADP. It was therefore concluded that phosphorylation of ADP is coupled to respiration and represents a mechanism for aerobic energy recovery.

A new aspect of the problem was uncovered when Belitser showed in 1940 that more than one molecule of ATP could be formed from ADP and phosphate during the passage of each pair of electrons from substrate to oxygen. He found that the P:O *ratio*, or moles of inorganic phosphate recovered in organic form per atom of oxygen taken up, was 2.0 or more. Later and more refined measurements of the P:O ratio gave values of about 3.0, on the average, for each of the five oxidative steps involved in complete oxidation of one molecule of pyruvate to CO_2 and H_2O via the tricarboxylic acid cycle (Table 17-6).

Table 17-6 P:O ratios of oxidative steps in the tricarboxylic acid cycle

Step	P:O
Pyruvate ⟶ acetyl CoA	3
Isocitrate ⟶ α-ketoglutarate	3
α-Ketoglutarate ⟶ succinate	4†
Succinate ⟶ fumarate	2
Malate ⟶ oxaloacetate	3

† One of these phosphorylations is substrate-level (Chapter 16).

Two other important properties of the oxidative phosphorylation process became evident in the period 1948–1950: (1) Loomis and Lipmann found that oxidative phosphorylation can be dissociated from respiration by specific chemical agents, particularly 2,4-dinitrophenol and other halo- and nitrophenols. In the presence of these agents, respiration of a tissue suspension may continue normally, or may even be stimulated, but no coupled phosphorylation of ADP to ATP takes place. For this reason such compounds are known as *uncoupling agents*. Many uncoupling agents are now known (Figure 17-13); most are lipid-soluble substances that contain an aromatic ring system and an ionizable acidic group. These agents do not uncouple glycolytic phosphorylation, nor do they affect cellular reactions other than oxidative phosphorylation. Uncoupling agents have since become very important diagnostic agents in the study of energy transformations in cells. (2) The second important discovery arose from the observation that oxidative phosphorylation is extremely labile and is most active in relatively fresh, unfractionated tissue suspensions; it does not take place in soluble extracts of tissues. Most important, it was found to be sensitive to the osmotic pressure of the medium, suggesting that it occurs in a membrane-surrounded-organelle. In 1948 Kennedy and Lehninger discovered that isolated mitochondria catalyze the process of oxidative phosphorylation coupled to oxidation of tricarboxylic acid cycle intermediates. Isolated mitochondria have since become the standard preparation for the study of oxidative phosphorylation. To this day, it has been a universal observation that reasonably intact structure of the mitochondrial inner membrane is required for the process of oxidative phosphorylation.

Figure 17-13
Some uncoupling agents.

2,4-Dinitrophenol

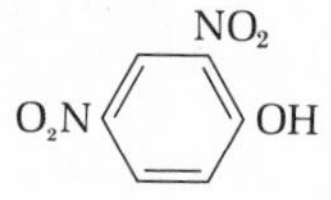

Dicumarol

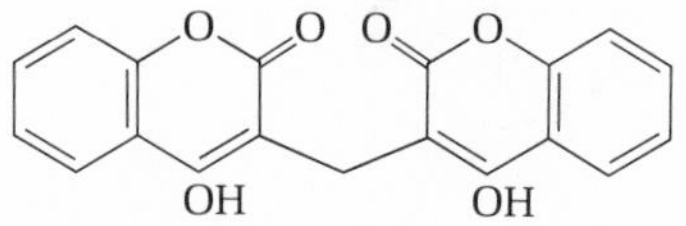

Carbonylcyanide *p*-trifluoromethoxyphenylhydrazone

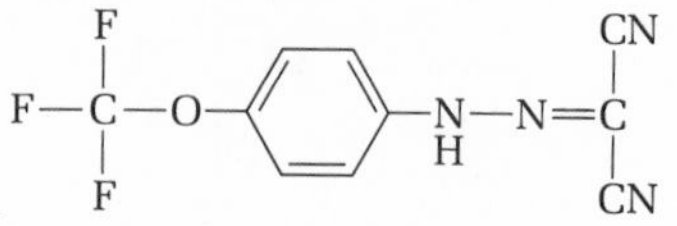

5-Chloro-3-*t*-butyl-2′-chloro-4′-nitrosalicylanilide

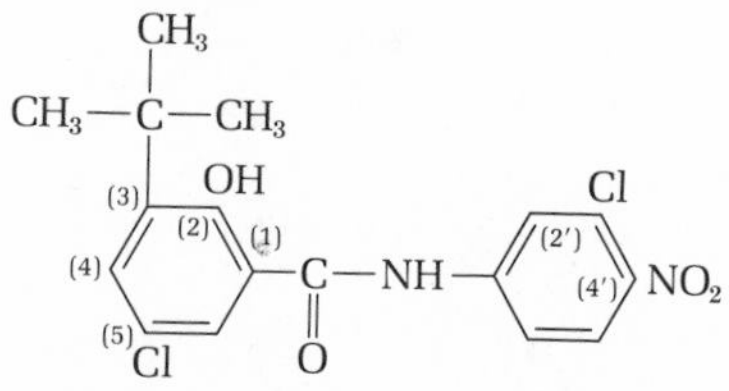

oligomycin stops both phosphorylation and electron transport

DNP inhibits oligomycin

Coupling of Oxidative Phosphorylation to Electron Transport

Although Belitser had postulated that oxidative phosphorylation is coupled to the transfer of an electron pair from NAD^+ to molecular oxygen along the respiratory chain, for a long time no success attended efforts to substantiate this hypothesis. However, in 1949–1951 Lehninger and his colleagues provided experimental proof. Pure NADH was incubated aerobically with water-treated mitochondria in the complete absence of tricarboxylic acid cycle intermediates or any other substrate. It was rapidly oxidized to NAD^+ at the expense of molecular oxygen via the respiratory chain. The electron transport was accompanied by the formation of two to three molecules of ATP from ADP and phosphate added to the suspending medium. This demonstration suggested that at three points in the chain of electron carriers from NADH to oxygen oxidation-reduction energy is transformed into phosphate-bond energy. For this reason, oxidative phosphorylation is more accurately called *respiratory-chain phosphorylation*. Water treatment of the mitochondria was required to make their membranes permeable to the added NADH, which normally cannot penetrate to the site of electron transport (Chapter 18).

The overall equation for the respiratory-chain phosphorylations could then be written as

$$NADH + H^+ + 3ADP + 3P_i + \tfrac{1}{2}O_2 \longrightarrow NAD^+ + 4H_2O + 3ATP$$

which can now be analyzed in terms of its exergonic component

$$NADH + H^+ + \tfrac{1}{2}O_2 \longrightarrow NAD^+ + H_2O \qquad \Delta G^{\circ\prime} = -52.7 \text{ kcal}$$

and its endergonic component

$$3ADP + 3P_i \longrightarrow 3ATP + 3H_2O \qquad \Delta G^{\circ\prime} = 3 \times 7.3 = 21.9 \text{ kcal}$$

Coupled phosphorylation of three molecules of ATP thus conserves 21.9/52.7 × 100, or about 40 percent of the total free energy decline during electron transport from NADH to oxygen, under standard conditions, assuming equilibrium. Under steady-state conditions in intact mitochondria, the efficiency is probably considerably higher.

From these considerations it is clear that the oxidation of all NAD-linked substrates by molecular oxygen in mitochondria is accompanied by formation of three molecules of ATP during electron transport between NADH and oxygen. Thus, each of the three NAD-linked oxidative steps of the tricarboxylic acid cycle, namely, the oxidation of isocitrate to α-ketoglutarate, of α-ketoglutarate to succinyl CoA, and of malate to oxalacetate, is accompanied by formation of three molecules of ATP in mitochondria.

The approximate locations of the three energy-conserving sites in the respiratory chain have also been worked out, in part from thermodynamic calculations (as in Figure 17-12) and in part from experimental observations made by Lehninger, Chance, and other investigators. The probable locations of these three mechanisms (Figure 17-8) are: (1) at one of the flavoproteins of the chain, (2) where a pair of electrons passes from cytochrome *b* to cytochrome *c*, and (3) where a pair of electrons passes from cytochrome *a* to oxygen.

The multimembered respiratory chain appears to be a device for breaking up the rather large decline in free energy occurring as a pair of electrons moves from the standard electrode potential of NADH ($E_0' = -0.32$ volt) to that of molecular oxygen ($E_0' = +0.815$ volt), namely, some 52.7 kcal, into a series of smaller energy drops, of which three are approximately the size of the energy currency of the cell, i.e., the 7.3 kcal "quantum" required to generate ATP from ADP and phosphate. The respiratory chain is therefore a kind of cascade delivering free energy in useful packets.

The Energy Balance Sheet

From the data in Table 17-6 we can now write the overall equation for the oxidation of pyruvate via the tricarboxylic acid cycle. For each molecule of pyruvate oxidized to completion, 14 molecules of ATP are formed during electron transport and 1 molecule of ATP by the substrate-level phosphorylation at the α-ketoglutarate step

$$\text{Pyruvate} + 2.5O_2 + 15P_i + 15ADP \longrightarrow 3CO_2 + 15ATP + 17H_2O$$

From this reaction we can write the equations for the exergonic and endergonic components as

Exergonic:

$$\text{Pyruvate} + 2.5O_2 \longrightarrow 3CO_2 + 2H_2O \qquad \Delta G^{\circ\prime} = -280 \text{ kcal}$$

Endergonic:

$$15P_i + 15ADP \longrightarrow 15ATP + 15H_2O \qquad \Delta G^{\circ\prime} = +110 \text{ kcal}$$

This yield of ATP represents conservation of 110/280 × 100 = 39 percent of the free energy of pyruvate oxidation.

We can now write a set of equations for the complete oxidation of glucose to CO_2 and water via the glycolytic sequence and the tricarboxylic acid cycle

$$\text{Glucose} + 2P_i + 2ADP + 2NAD^+ \longrightarrow 2\text{ pyruvate} + 2NADH + 2H^+ + 2ATP + 2H_2O$$

$$2\text{ Pyruvate} + 5O_2 + 30ADP + 30P_i \longrightarrow 6CO_2 + 30ATP + 34H_2O$$

to which we must add the equation for the oxidation by oxygen of the two molecules of extramitochondrial NADH formed in the aerobic conversion of glucose to pyruvate, a process which generates two molecules of ATP per pair of electrons (Chapter 18)

$$2NADH + 2H^+ + O_2 + 4P_i + 4ADP \longrightarrow 2NAD^+ + 4ATP + 6H_2O$$

The sum of these three equations is then

$$\text{Glucose} + 6O_2 + 36P_i + 36ADP \longrightarrow 6CO_2 + 36ATP + 42H_2O$$

Breaking up the overall equation into its components gives

Exergonic component:

$$\text{Glucose} + 6O_2 \longrightarrow 6CO_2 + 6H_2O \qquad \Delta G^{\circ\prime} = -680 \text{ kcal}$$

Endergonic component:

$$36P_i + 36ADP \longrightarrow 36ATP + 36H_2O \qquad \Delta G^{\circ\prime} = +263 \text{ kcal}$$

The overall efficiency of energy recovery is thus 263/680 × 100 = 39 percent.

The Partial Reactions of Oxidative Phosphorylation

Although the enzymatic mechanism of oxidative phosphorylation has been intensively investigated for many years, it has not yet been elucidated. However, a number of observations offer important leads to the nature of the process. Among these is the recognition that oxidative phosphorylation may be influenced not only by uncoupling agents such as 2,4-dinitrophenol, but by other classes of specific inhibitors. Table 17-7 lists some compounds, including a number of antibiotics, which affect

Table 17-7 Types of agents affecting oxidative phosphorylation

Uncoupling agents
2,4-Dinitrophenol
Dicumarol
Carbonyl cyanide phenylhydrazones
Salicylanilides
K^+-dependent uncoupling agents (also called ionophorous agents)
Valinomycin
Gramicidin
Nonactin
Inhibitors of ATP formation
Oligomycin
Rutamycin
Triethyltin
Aurovertin

phosphorylation in characteristically different ways. The uncoupling agents, we have seen, do not inhibit respiration, but prevent the associated phosphorylations. Another class of compounds, represented by the antibiotics gramicidin and valinomycin, also prevent phosphorylation without inhibiting respiration. They differ from 2,4-dinitrophenol in that they require a monovalent cation such as K^+ to exert their uncoupling effects. The action of these agents, also called *ionophorous* antibiotics, will be more fully discussed in Chapter 18. A third class of inhibitor includes the antibiotics oligomycin and rutamycin, which inhibit phosphorylation in such a way that electron transport is also inhibited. The inhibition of electron transport by oligomycin can be reversed by 2,4-dinitrophenol, which does not, however, restore phosphorylation. Oligomycin has been concluded to act primarily on the energy coupling mechanisms rather than on the electron carriers. These three classes of inhibitors have become important diagnostic tools.

Table 17-8 Partial reactions of oxidative phosphorylation

The isotopically labeled component is in color. AMP~P~P represents ATP and AMP~P, ADP.

1. ATPase activity

$$ATP + HOH \rightleftharpoons ADP + P_i$$

2. ATP-phosphate exchange

$$AMP{\sim}P{\sim}P + {}^{32}P_i \rightleftharpoons AMP{\sim}P{\sim}{}^{32}P + P_i$$

3. Phosphate-water oxygen exchange

$$HPO_4^{2-} + H_2{}^{18}O \rightleftharpoons HP^{18}O_4^{2-} + H_2O$$

4. ADP-ATP exchange

$${}^{14}C{-}AMP{\sim}P + AMP{\sim}P{\sim}P \rightleftharpoons {}^{14}C{-}AMP{\sim}P{\sim}P + AMP{\sim}P$$

Another set of observations deals with a group of four reactions catalyzed by mitochondria which are believed to represent individual steps or partial reactions in the ATP-forming process, since they are characteristically influenced by 2,4-dinitrophenol and oligomycin (Table 17-8). These reactions take place in the absence of net flow of electrons down the chain. The first of these reactions is the ATPase activity of mitochondria, which is normally very low but which is greatly stimulated by 2,4-dinitrophenol. The stimulated ATPase activity is blocked by oligomycin. The second partial reaction is an isotopic exchange reaction in which inorganic phosphate labeled with ^{32}P exchanges rapidly with the terminal phosphate group of ATP in the absence of electron transport. This reaction, called the P_i-ATP exchange, is completely inhibited by both 2,4-dinitrophenol and oligomycin. The third partial reaction is an isotopic exchange between oxygen atoms of the water of the medium and those of the inorganic phosphate; the phosphate-water exchange is also inhibited by 2,4-dinitrophenol and oligomycin. The fourth partial reaction is a rapid reversible transfer of the terminal phosphate group from ATP to ADP, called the ADP-ATP exchange reaction; it is also inhibited by 2,4-dinitrophenol and oligomycin. When mitochondrial structure is severely disrupted, the capacity to catalyze these four partial reactions is lost, parallel with the loss of oxidative phosphorylation.

The properties of these partial reactions strongly indicate that the reactions by which ATP is formed are reversible. Moreover, they have held out the hope that the enzymes catalyzing separate steps in ATP formation might be studied individually, since the partial reactions can be arranged into a hypothetical reaction scheme (below).

Oxidative Phosphorylation in Submitochondrial Systems: Coupling Factors

Early investigations showed that oxidative phosphorylation is a very labile process and occurs only in intact, freshly prepared mitochondria, leaving little hope that the enzymes responsible for this process would be sufficiently stable so that they could be extracted from mitochondrial structure and purified. However, beginning in 1955 several investigators succeeded in obtaining phosphorylating particles by treatment of mitochondria with membrane-dispersing agents such as digitonin or by sonic irradiation. These particles consisted of membrane fragments which evidently retained most of the enzymatic machinery required in electron transport and oxidative phosphorylation. More recently it has been found by electron microscopy that such membrane fragments actually are continuous closed vesicles formed by resealing of the edges of the membrane fragments after disruption of mitochondrial structure.

An important outcome of investigations on such submitochondrial preparations is the identification of protein factors that are necessary for oxidative phosphorylation. Mitochondria can be treated so that they lose their ability to generate ATP but still can carry out electron transport from substrate to oxygen. Such treatments lead to the loss from the mitochondria of specific proteins, called *coupling factors*, which have been recovered and purified. When they are returned to the pretreated inactive mitochondria, the ability to carry out oxidative phosphorylation is partially restored. Two proteins isolated by Racker are of special interest, an ATPase of large molecular weight (~ 280,000), called F_1, and another protein F_0, which confers oligomycin sensitivity. The F_1 factor has been highly purified and contains no electron carriers. It appears to be the enzyme that actually transfers phosphate to ADP; however, its mode of action is still obscure and no information is available as to the form in which this factor receives energy from the electron-transfer reactions. The F_1 factor will be discussed further in Chapter 18.

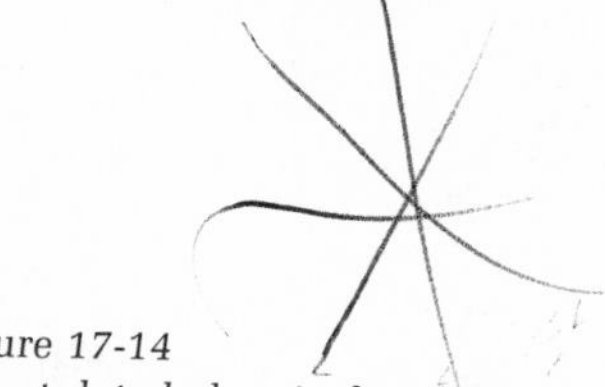

Figure 17-14
A postulated chemical coupling mechanism for respiratory-chain phosphorylation. A and B are two electron carriers, I is an auxiliary coupling factor and E is the ATP-forming enzyme.

$$A_{red} + I + B_{ox} \overset{DNP}{\rightleftharpoons} A_{ox} \sim I + B_{red} \quad (1)$$

$$A_{ox} \sim I + E \rightleftharpoons A_{ox} + E \sim I \quad (2)$$

$$E \sim I + P_i \overset{Oligo}{\rightleftharpoons} I + E \sim P \quad (3)$$

$$E \sim P + ADP \rightleftharpoons E + ATP \quad (4)$$

When A_{red}, a reduced carrier at one of the coupling sites in the chain, is oxidized by B_{ox}, the following carrier, a high-energy compound $A_{ox}\sim I$ is generated. I is presumably a protein. A_{ox} is then displaced by enzyme E to form $E\sim I$. Phosphate enters in the next step to form a phosphoenzyme $P\sim E$, which is the immediate phosphate donor to ADP. Oligomycin is believed to block the sequence at the point labeled, and 2,4-dinitrophenol (DNP) causes cleavage of $A_{ox}\sim I$, or $E\sim I$, to regenerate, respectively, A_{ox} and I, or E and I. ATPase activity is the sum of reactions (4), (3), and (2), followed by the action of 2,4-dinitrophenol. The P_i-ATP and ADP-ATP exchanges are probably catalyzed by reactions (2) to (4) and (3) and (4) respectively.

The Chemical Coupling Hypothesis

The properties of these partial reactions together with many other observations have led to a working hypothesis for the mechanism of oxidative phosphorylation called the *chemical-coupling hypothesis*. It uses as its model the enzymatic mechanism of the energy-conserving oxidoreduction catalyzed by glyceraldehyde 3-phosphate dehydrogenase during glycolysis (Chapter 15), and is based on the concept of energy transfer by a series of consecutive reactions having common chemical intermediates possessing high-energy bonds. Figures 17-14 and 17-15 show one form of the chemical-coupling hypothesis, which postulates that when a pair of electrons passes from an energy-conserving electron carrier A_{red} to B_{ox}, the next carrier in the chain, a high-energy linkage is generated with a third component I (not an electron carrier) to form A_{ox} I. The high-energy bond so formed becomes the precursor of the high-energy phosphate bond of ATP through a series of consecutive reactions. Figure 17-14 shows how this series of reactions could account for the partial reactions and the characteristic action of oligomycin and of 2,4-dinitrophenol.

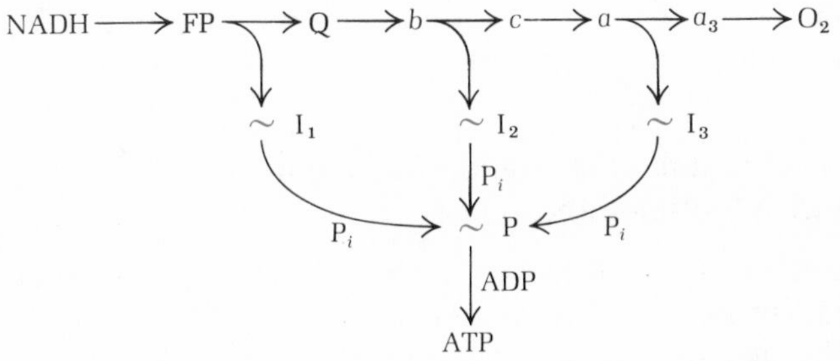

$$\begin{array}{c} \text{NADH} \longrightarrow \text{FP} \longrightarrow \text{Q} \longrightarrow b \longrightarrow c \longrightarrow a \longrightarrow a_3 \longrightarrow O_2 \\ \sim I_1 \qquad \sim I_2 \qquad \sim I_3 \\ P_i \rightarrow \sim P \leftarrow P_i \\ \downarrow \text{ADP} \\ \text{ATP} \end{array}$$

Figure 17-15
Schematic representation of electron transport and phosphorylation according to the chemical coupling hypothesis. High-energy intermediates are postulated to be generated at each energy-conserving site according to mechanisms such as those shown in Figure 17-14. An enzyme E is postulated to collect high-energy phosphate groups from the 3 sites and to donate them to ADP.

Although the chemical-coupling hypothesis can explain most of the known experimental observations on oxidative phosphorylation, two facts are not easily explained: (1) After over 15 years of research, it has not been possible to isolate or detect the existence of the postulated high-energy intermediates such as $A_{ox} \sim I$ (Figure 17-14), and (2) oxidative phosphorylation occurs only in preparations of mitochondria retaining reasonably intact membrane structure, suggesting that the membrane is an important part of the phosphorylation machinery. These two stumbling blocks have recently suggested other hypotheses, which will be discussed in Chapter 18.

Oxygenases, Hydroxylases, and Microsomal Electron Transport

The microsomes, i.e., endoplasmic reticulum of liver and other tissues contain electron transport systems capable of utilizing molecular oxygen to oxidize specific organic molecules, by direct insertion of one or both its oxygen atoms into the product. Those systems capable of inserting both oxygen atoms are called *oxygenases.* Most oxygenases function to cleave hydroxylated alicyclic or aromatic rings. For example, homogentisic acid oxygenase (Chapter 20) brings about cleavage of the benzene ring of homogentisic acid by direct incorporation of O_2 (margin). Those enzymes inserting but one of the two oxygen atoms of O_2 into the substrate are called *hydroxylases* or *mixed-function oxygenases.* The other oxygen atom is utilized to oxidize NADPH or NADH, usually the former. An example is the aromatic hydroxylase of liver microsomes (margin). Many different hydroxylases are known. The microsomes of the adrenal gland are particularly rich in hydroxylases, which carry out oxidation of various steroid hormone intermediates.

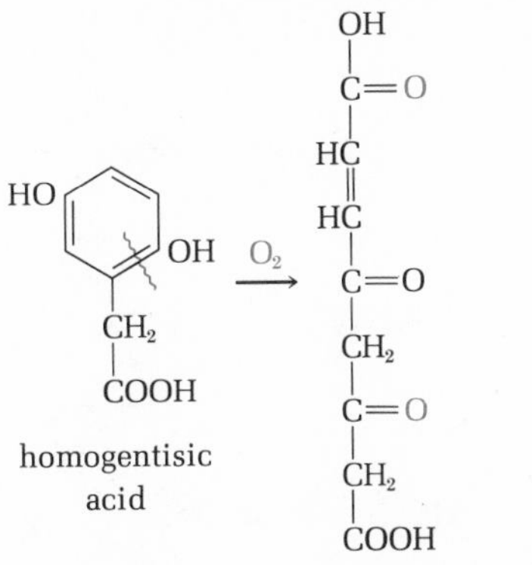

Attack of oxygen in the action of homogentisic acid oxygenase

homogentisic acid (HO, OH, CH_2, COOH) $\xrightarrow{O_2}$ maleylacetoacetic acid (OH–C=O–HC=HC–C=O–CH_2–C=O–CH_2–COOH)

Attack of oxygen in the action of microsomal aromatic hydroxylase

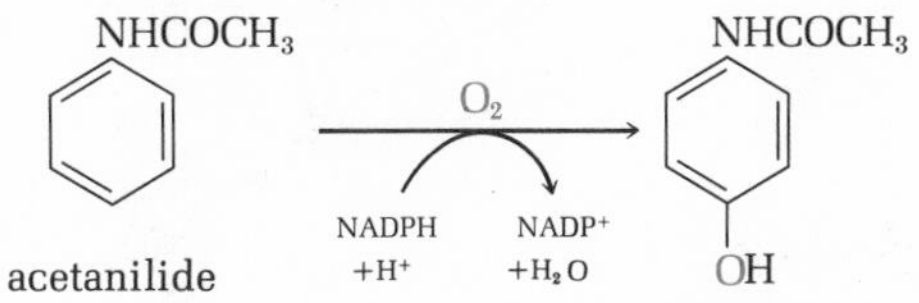

acetanilide ($NHCOCH_3$) $\xrightarrow{O_2}$ p-hydroxyacetanilide ($NHCOCH_3$, OH)
NADPH $+H^+$ → $NADP^+$ $+H_2O$

Oxygenases and hydroxylases of the endoplasmic reticulum function with flavoproteins and cytochromes differing from those in mitochondria. They are organized into short non-phosphorylating electron transport chains. The chain for hydroxylations is best understood. It contains cytochrome P_{450}, which forms a reduced CO-complex having an absorption band at 450 nm, as well as a specific flavoprotein containing FAD. A postulated form of the electron transport chain in adrenal gland endoplasmic reticulum is shown in Figure 17-16. The carrier designated Fe protein is *adrenodoxin,* a nonheme iron protein. Liver microsomes contain a similar chain, in which adrenodoxin is replaced by another carrier of unknown structure.

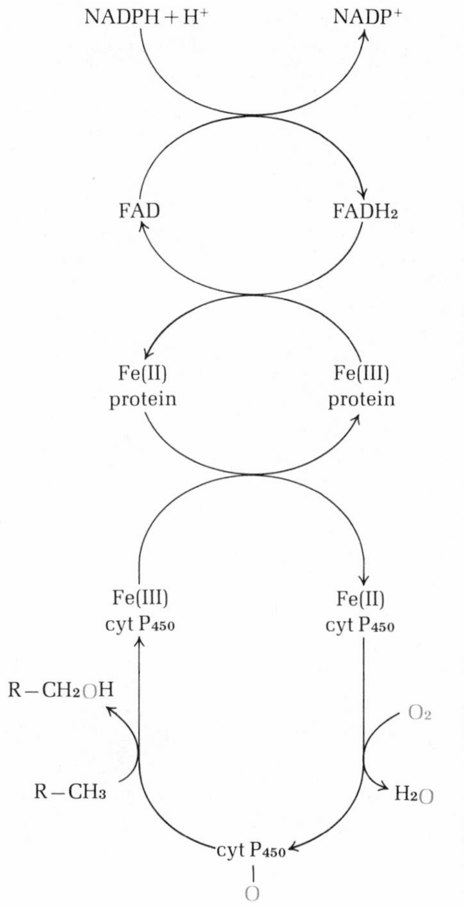

Transformation of Oxidation-Reduction Energy into Bioluminescence

Luminescent organisms include some bacteria, protozoa, fungi, worms, and crustaceans, and particularly, the firefly. In many, enzymatic oxidoreductions take place in which the free energy change is utilized to excite a molecule to a high-energy state. This is followed by the molecule's return to the *ground state*, accompanied by emission of visible light, a phenomenon called bioluminescence.

The molecular components and the mechanism of firefly luminescence have been investigated by McElroy and his associates. Two components—a heat-stable heterocyclic phenol, *luciferin* (Figure 17-17) and a heat-labile enzyme, *luciferase*—have been extracted from fireflies and crystallized. Luciferase (mol wt ~ 100,000) appears to have no prosthetic group. Luciferin exists in reduced (LH_2) and oxidized (L) forms. In the first step, reduced luciferin (LH_2) and ATP react to form *luciferyl adenylate*, which remains tightly bound on the catalytic site of luciferase

$$LH_2 + ATP + E \overset{Mg^{2+}}{\rightleftharpoons} LH_2\text{—}AMP\text{—}E + PP_i$$

When this form of the enzyme is exposed to molecular oxygen the enzyme-bound luciferyl adenylate is oxidized to yield products in an excited state (Chapter 21), which subsequently emit light

$$LH_2\text{—}AMP\text{—}E + O_2 \longrightarrow \text{bioluminescence} + \text{reaction products}$$

One quantum of light (Chapter 21) is emitted for each molecule of luciferin oxidized; no hydrogen peroxide is formed. The color of the light is determined by the enzyme

Figure 17-16
Microsomal electron transport chain for hydroxylation reactions. R—CH_3 represents the substrate undergoing hydroxylation.

Figure 17-17
Components in the luciferase reaction.

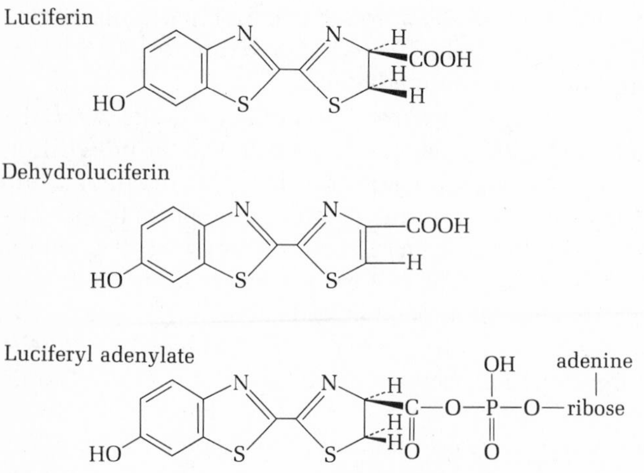

protein, since different species of firefly have the same luciferin but emit light of different colors. The chemical identities of the light-emitting compounds and the reaction products are not known. This unusual type of energy transformation apparently serves the firefly as a mating signal.

Summary

In oxidation-reduction reactions electrons are transferred from the reductant, or electron donor, to the oxidant, or electron acceptor. The tendency of any biological reductant to donate electrons is given by the standard reduction potential, the electromotive force given by 1.0 *M* reductant in the presence of 1.0 *M* oxidant species at an inert electrode at 25° and pH 7.0. The standard of reference in biochemical systems is the standard reaction potential E_0' given by the equilibrium $H_2 \rightleftharpoons 2H^+ + 2e^-$ at 1 atm H_2 gas, 25°C, and pH 7.0, namely, −0.420 volt. Reducing agents stronger than H_2 have a more negative E_0'; those weaker have a more positive value. The E_0' value of any given conjugate redox pair allows prediction of the direction of net electron flow in its reaction with another redox pair, as well as the calculation of the equilibrium concentrations of reactants and products.

There are three major classes of oxidation-reduction enzymes: (1) The pyridine-linked dehydrogenases catalyze a reversible transfer of electrons from substrates to the loosely bound coenzymes NAD^+ or $NADP^+$, to form NADH and NADPH, respectively. Such reactions can be followed by measurement of the light absorption at 340 nm given by NADH or NADPH. The enzymatic reduction of the pyridine ring of NAD^+ to form a quinoid structure is stereospecific. The direction of interaction and the final equilibrium of coupled oxidoreductions catalyzed by pairs of dehydrogenases can be calculated from the E_0' values of their substrate couples. (2) The flavin-linked dehydrogenases contain tightly bound FMN or FAD as prosthetic groups and usually a metal ion. In oxidized form they are intensely colored; on reduction they are colorless. The most important are succinate dehydrogenase and NADH dehydrogenase. (3) The cytochromes, acting in series, transfer electrons from flavoproteins to oxygen. They contain iron protoporphyrin prosthetic groups and undergo Fe(II) to Fe(III) transitions, which are easily followed spectrophotometrically.

The respiratory chain of mitochondria consists of the sequence NADH, flavoproteins, nonheme iron proteins, coenzyme Q, and cytochromes b, c_1, c, a, and a_3. Electron transport along this chain is characteristically inhibited at specific sites by amytal, rotenone, antimycin A, and cyanide. This sequence was established from standard reduction-potential data, action of inhibitors, reconstruction experiments, and spectroscopic observations. The large free-energy change on passage of a pair of electron equivalents from NADH to oxygen is broken up into three packets by the respiratory chain, each capable of causing the phosphorylation of ADP to ATP in a coupled reaction. Such oxidative phosphorylations, which recover some 40 percent of the energy released during electron transport, are uncoupled by 2,4-dinitrophenol and inhibited by oligomycin. A chemical coupling hypothesis for the mechanism of oxidative phosphorylation which invokes high-energy intermediates has been postulated, based in part on the characteristic effects of 2,4-dinitrophenol and oligomycin on partial reactions or steps in this process. Specific proteins called coupling factors are capable of restoring phosphorylation in submitochondrial particles. However, high energy intermediates have never been identified and all current information indicates intact membrane structure is required for oxidative phosphorylation to occur.

References

(See also references to Chapter 18)

Books

FLORKIN, M., and STOTZ, E. H. (eds.), *Biological Oxidations*, vol. 14 of *Comprehensive Biochemistry*, American Elsevier Publishing Company, New York, 1967.

KEILIN, D., *TheHistory of Cell Respiration and Cytochromes*, Cambridge University Press, New York, 1966.

LEHNINGER, A. L., *The Mitochondrion: Molecular Basis of Structure and Function*, W. A. Benjamin, Inc., New York, 1964.

OKUNUKI, K., M. D. KAMEN, and I. SEKUZU, *Structure and Function of Cytochromes*, Univ. of Tokyo Press, Tokyo, 1967. Proceedings of an international symposium (English).

RACKER, E., *Mechanisms in Bioenergetics*, Academic Press Inc., New York, 1965.

SINGER, T. P. (ed.), *Biological Oxidations*, John Wiley & Sons, Inc., New York, 1966.

SLATER, E, C., (ed.), *Flavins and Flavoproteins*, Elsevier Publishing Company, Amsterdam, 1966.

Articles

GREEN D. E., and D. H. MACLENNAN, "The Mitochondrial System of Enzymes," in D. M. Greenberg (ed.), *Metabolic Pathways*, 3rd ed., vol. 1, pp. 47–111, Academic Press Inc., New York, 1967.

HAYAISHI, O., and M. NOZAK, "Nature and Mechanisms of Oxygenases," *Science*, **164:**389–396 (1969).

KING, T. E., "Reconstitution of the Respiratory Chain," *Advan. Enzymol.*, **28:**155–236 (1966).

KRÖGER, A. and M. KLINGENBERG, "On the Role of Ubiquinone," in D. R. Sanadi (ed.), *Current Topics in Bioenergetics*, vol. II, pp. 152–190, Academic Press Inc., New York, 1967.

MALKIN, R., and J. C. RABINOWITZ, "Nonheme Iron Electron Transport Proteins," *Ann. Rev. Biochem.*, **36:**113–148 (1967).

LARDY, H. A. and S. M. FERGUSON, Oxidative phosphorylation in mitochondria, *Ann. Rev. Biochem.*, **38:**991–1034 (1969) An excellent review of recent progress.

Problems

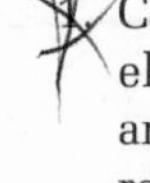

1. Calculate the electromotive force in volts registered by an electrode immersed in a solution containing 0.01 *M* Fe^{3+} and 0.001 *M* Fe^{2+} at pH = 7.0 and $T = 25°C$. The standard reduction potential of the Fe^{2+}–Fe^{3+} couple is +0.748 volt. Assume equilibrium exists.

2. Assuming a pH of 7.0 and $T = 25°C$ and that all reactants and products are maintained at 1.0 *M* concentration, calculate the standard free-energy change in kilocalories when a pair of electrons passes from: (*a*) isocitrate to NAD^+, (*b*) succinate to cytochrome *b*, (*c*) malate to NAD, and (*d*) NADH to cytochrome *c*.

3. Calculate the equilibrium concentrations of malate, oxaloacetate, NAD^+, and NADH in the reaction

$$\text{L-Malate} + NAD^+ \rightleftharpoons \text{oxaloacetate} + NADH + H^+$$

when the reaction is carried out at pH 7.0, the initial concentration of each component being 20 m*M*.

4. Unless the reaction of Problem 3 is carried out in a buffered system, the pH of the reaction mixture will change as the reaction proceeds.
   (*a*) Would the pH tend to rise or fall under the conditions described in Problem 3?
   (*b*) How many H^+ ions per liter would the buffer have to supply or absorb in order to maintain the pH constant at 7.0? Express the answer in milliequivalents.

5. Calculate the equilibrium concentrations of L-malate and oxaloacetate in the overall reaction

$$\text{D-}\beta\text{-Hydroxybutyrate} + \text{oxaloacetate} \rightleftharpoons \text{acetoacetate} + \text{L-malate}$$

catalyzed by NAD-linked D-β-hydroxybutyrate dehydrogenase and malate dehydrogenase in the presence of NAD. Assume the reaction takes place at 25° and pH 7.0, with all components at 10.0 m*M* initial concentration.

6. Calculate the percentage efficiency of energy conservation in ATP as succinate is oxidized to fumarate by molecular oxygen in intact mitochondria.

7. Predict the oxidation-reduction states of NAD, NADH dehydrogenase, cytochrome *b*, cytochrome *c*, and cytochrome *a* in liver mitochondria amply supplied with isocitrate as substrate, P_i, ADP, and oxygen, but inhibited by (*a*) rotenone, (*b*) antimycin A, and (*c*) cyanide.

8. How many ATP molecules are generated during the complete oxidative degradation of each of the following to CO_2 and H_2O: (*a*) phosphoenolpyruvate, (*b*) acetyl CoA, (*c*) glyceraldehyde 3-phosphate, and (*d*) glycerol?

9. Write the complete equation for the oxidation of one molecule of isocitrate in a mitochondrial suspension containing excess P_i and ADP in which succinate dehydrogenase has been completely blocked by malonate. Include all energy-conserving steps.

10. Write the overall equation for Problem 9 assuming the reaction to be carried out in the presence of 2,4-dinitrophenol.

CHAPTER 18 MITOCHONDRIAL COMPARTMENTATION AND THE INTEGRATION OF ENERGY-YIELDING REACTIONS

The mitochondria are perhaps the best understood of the cell organelles in terms of ultrastructure, molecular organization, and functional role in cell metabolism. Although it has been known for some 20 years that the mitochondria are the power plants of the cell, recent research on mitochondrial structure has opened many new challenges: the role of membrane structure in the mechanism of phosphorylation, the compartmentation of enzymatic reactions within mitochondria, the interplay between glycolysis and respiration, and the role of mitochondria in ion-transport processes. Furthermore, the ability of mitochondria to undergo self-replication and the presence in them of a specific form of DNA have raised important questions in the field of genetics and cell differentiation. The mitochondrion has in fact become a microcosm of some of the most important problems in cell biology today.

Cellular Distribution and Location

Mitochondria are present in the cytoplasm of all aerobic eucaryotic cells. Their number per cell appears to be relatively constant and characteristic for any given cell type but may change with the stage of development or with functional activity. Mitochondria divide by fission after cell division has taken place. A single rat liver cell contains more than 1,000 mitochondria. (See Figure 1-8.)

Mitochondria are often located near structures that require ATP, the product of their activity, or near a source of fuel, on which they are dependent. In intensely active muscle cells, such as the flight muscles of insects, the mitochondria are regularly arranged in rows along the myofibrils, coinciding with the cross striations (Chapter 26). The ATP formed by these mitochondria need diffuse only a short distance to the ATP-requiring contractile elements in the myofibrils. In epithelial cells, which carry out secretory work, i.e., the transport of ions, sugars, and amino acids against gradients, the mitochondria are often aligned in the direction of the secretory activity, for which ATP is required. Mitochondria are also frequently located adjacent to cytoplasmic fat droplets, which serve as a source of fatty acid fuel for oxidation. In some cells, as in the liver, the mitochondria are free and can move about in the cytoplasm, whereas in muscle cells they are more or less fixed. The mitochondria may make up a relatively large fraction of the cytoplasmic volume; in the liver cell, this is about 22 percent (Figure 1-8).

Size, Shape, and Ultrastructure

The size and shape of mitochondria vary greatly from one cell type to another: spherical, or nearly so, in yeast cells, football-shaped in liver cells, cylindrical in the kidney, and threadlike in fibroblasts. Slab-shaped and stellate structures are also seen. Mitochondria are not rigid but may undergo rapid and dramatic changes in shape and volume, depending on the metabolic state of the cell; they also often aggregate end to end to form long filamentous structures. The most intensively studied mitochondria are those of rat liver, which electron microscopy shows to be about 2 μ in length and somewhat less than 1 μ in width in the intact cell. They are thus about the same size as bacteria.

Mitochondria have two membranes (Figure 18-1) an outer surrounding membrane that is smooth and usually

Figure 18-1
Structure of mitochondria.

Electron micrograph of mitochondrion in thin section of a bat pancreas cell.

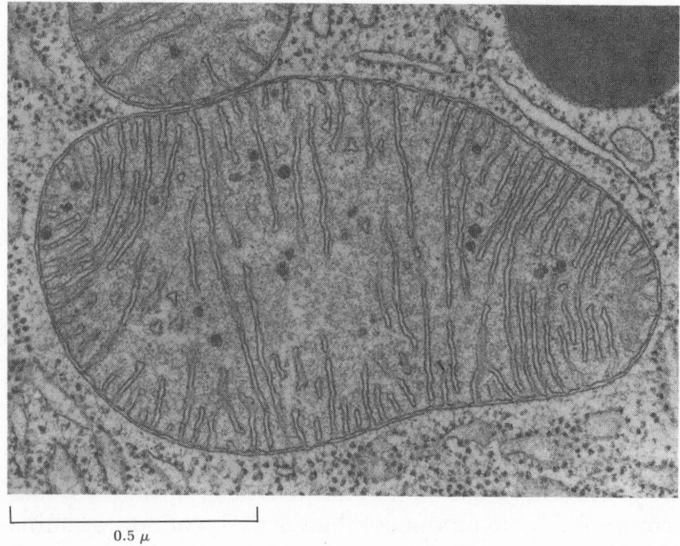

Drawing of heart mitochondrion showing three-dimensional arrangement of membranes.

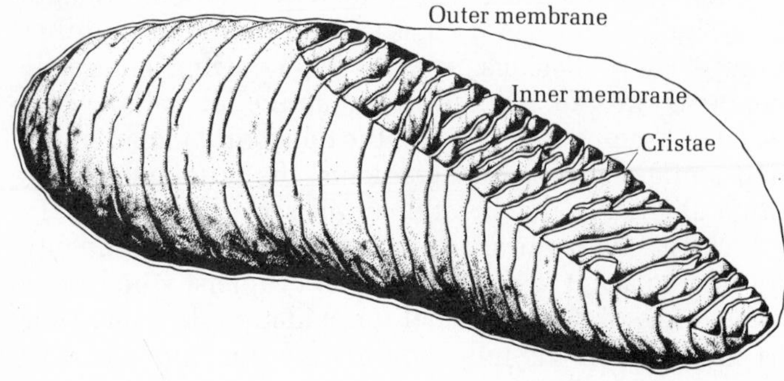

Figure 18-2
Variations in structure of the cristae in mitochondria from different types of cells.

Rat liver (plate-like).

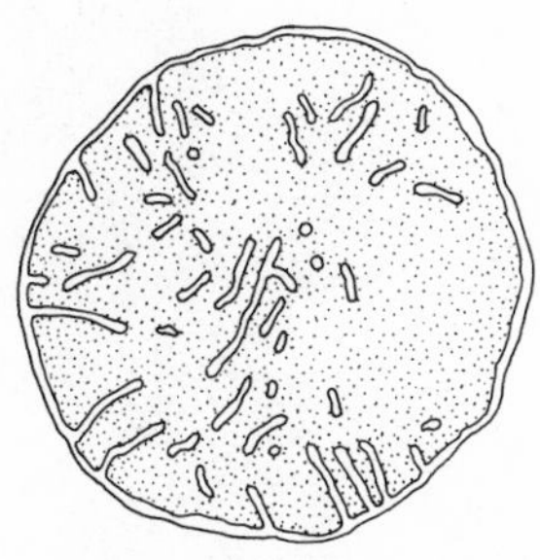

Rat brown fat (septa).

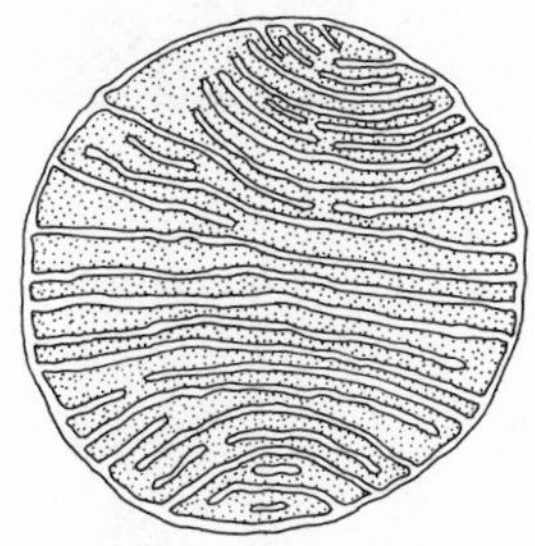

Paramecium (tubular).

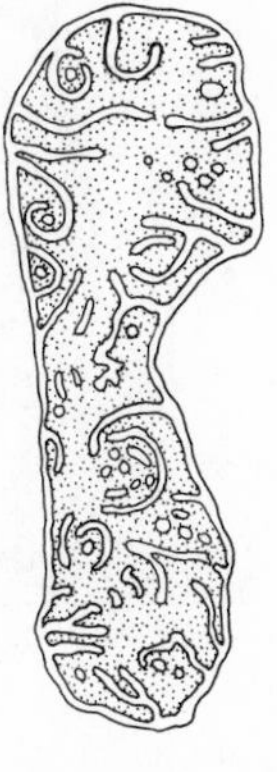

Blowfly flight muscle (perforated leaflets).

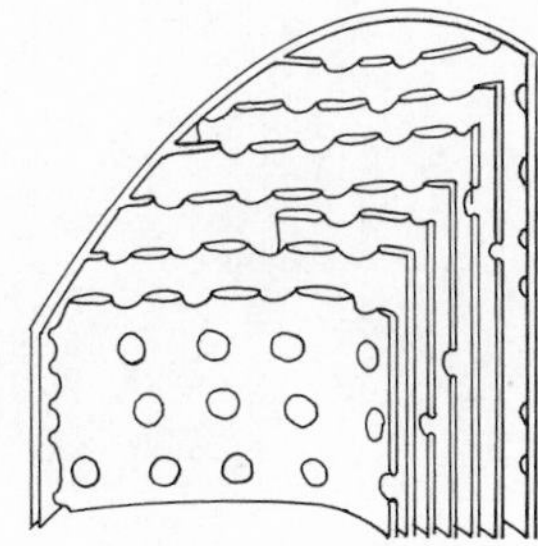

shows no folds and an inner membrane that usually has many inward folds called cristae. In liver mitochondria, the cristae are sparse and irregular, but in kidney or heart mitochondria they are numerous and nearly fill the entire lumen of the mitochondrion, giving the appearance of a stack of coins. In the mitochondria of some protozoa, the cristae are fingerlike, or viliform, and in still others, they form complex reticular networks (Figure 18-2). Such arrangements appear to be devices for increasing the surface area of the inner membrane, where the enzymes of electron transport and oxidative phosphorylation are found. We shall see later how the cristae undergo remarkable changes in shape depending on the respiratory state of the mitochondria.

Inside the inner compartment is the *matrix*, a gel-like semisolid phase with considerable fine structure and containing about 50 percent protein. The matrix also undergoes dramatic changes in organization during changes in respiratory activity. Mitochondria with many cristae have relatively little matrix and vice versa. The matrix also contains large *electron-dense granules*, of unknown function. Ribosomes have been found in some mitochondria, but they are not usually visible in electron micrographs.

High-resolution electron microscopy shows the outer and inner mitochondrial membranes to differ in ultrastructure. Most revealing is the technique of *negative-contrast staining*, in which the unfixed mitochondria are mixed with phosphotungstate solution, dried, and then examined directly. Because the phosphotungstate is electron-opaque and is not absorbed or bound, it surrounds the membrane structure, outlining its profile, particularly in edge-on views. By this method Fernández-Morán and others have shown that the inner surface of the inner membrane is covered with regularly spaced spherical particles (diameter 80 to 90 Å) connected to the membrane by a narrow stalk (Figure 18-3). These knoblike structures, or *elementary particles*, are not present on the outer surface of the inner membrane or on either surface of the outer membrane. Since they are not seen in mitochondria fixed or stained by other procedures, it now appears probable that the elementary particles are made to protrude from the membrane by exposure to the phosphotungstate staining procedure. This view is also supported by the observation that the inner membrane, following fixation with osmium tetroxide, shows no spheres and yields an exceedingly thin image of 50–55 Å, or much less than the diameter of the spheres. The outer membrane is about 70 Å thick.

The outer and inner membranes also have different permeabilities: sucrose and other simple sugars pass the outer membrane readily but do not penetrate the inner compartment. Other permeability characteristics of mitochondrial membranes are discussed below.

Separation of Outer and Inner Membranes

The outer membrane of liver mitochondria has been successfully removed and separated from the inner membrane and its enclosed matrix. After the mitochondria have been exposed to a detergent or to phosphate, the outer membrane peels off and can be recovered as empty folded envelopes by centrifugation in a density gradient of sucrose (Chapter 7). The inner membrane, still containing the matrix, can also be recovered in intact form (Figure 18-4). The outer membrane, the inner membrane, and the matrix have been directly analyzed for molecular composition and enzyme content (Table 18-1). The inner membrane contains cytochromes *b*, *c*, *a*, and a_3, the ATPase activity associated with the mechanism of oxidative phosphorylation, and the succinate and NADH dehydrogenase activities. The outer membrane contains none of the components of the respiratory chain but does have characteristic enzymes absent from the inner membrane, the most distinctive being *monoamine oxidase*, a flavoprotein which catalyzes the oxidation of various monoamines, such as *tryptamine*, a decarboxylation product of tryptophan. Monoamine oxidase is extremely useful as a marker enzyme to detect the presence of outer membrane; cytochrome oxidase is similarly used as a marker for the inner membrane. The matrix contains fumarase, aconitase, and glutamate and malate dehydrogenases; the latter are markers for the matrix contents.

The outer membrane has a higher content of total lipids and is richer in cholesterol and phosphatidyl inositol than the inner.

Figure 18-3
Electron micrographs of inner membrane spheres (elementary particles) on cristae.

Profile of cristae in heart mitochondria (low magnification).

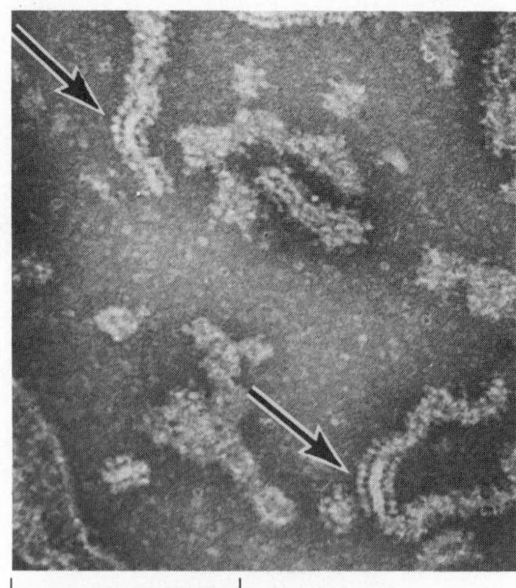

3,000 Å

Profile of cristae in blowfly flight muscle (high magnification).

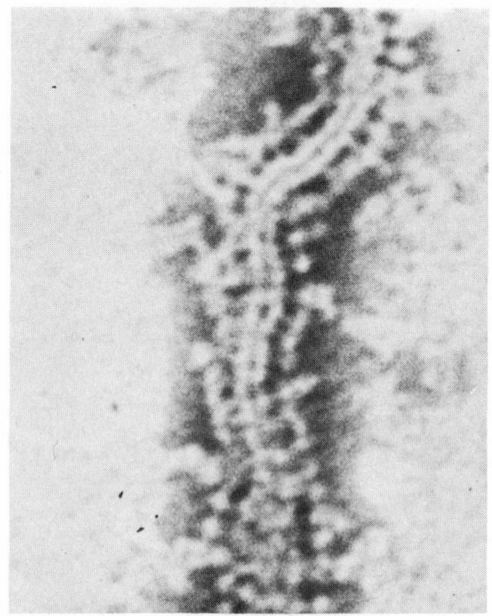

1,000 Å

Inner surface of inner membrane.

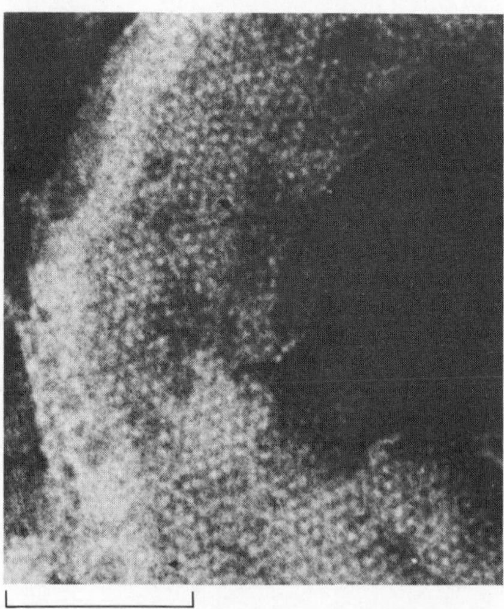

1,000 Å

The Molecular and Enzymatic Organization of the Inner Mitochondrial Membrane

About 20 to 25 percent of the total protein of the inner membrane consists of enzymatically active proteins functioning in electron transport and oxidative phosphorylation: the flavoproteins, the cytochromes, and the enzymes

Table 18-1 Location of some mitochondrial enzymes

Outer membrane:
Monoamine oxidase
Fatty acid thiokinases (Chapter 19)
Kynurenine hydroxylase
Rotenone-insensitive cytochrome *c* reductase
Space between the membranes:
Adenylate kinase
Nucleoside diphosphokinase
Inner membrane:
Respiratory chain enzymes
ATP-synthesizing enzymes
α-Keto acid dehydrogenases
Succinate dehydrogenase
D-β-Hydroxybutyrate dehydrogenase (Chapter 19)
Carnitine fatty acyl transferase (Chapter 19)
Matrix:
Citrate synthase
Isocitrate dehydrogenase
Fumarase
Malate dehydrogenase
Aconitase
Glutamate dehydrogenase
Fatty acid oxidation enzymes (Chapter 19)

Figure 18-4
Rat liver mitochondria after removal of the outer membrane. The protruding structures are presumably everted cristae.

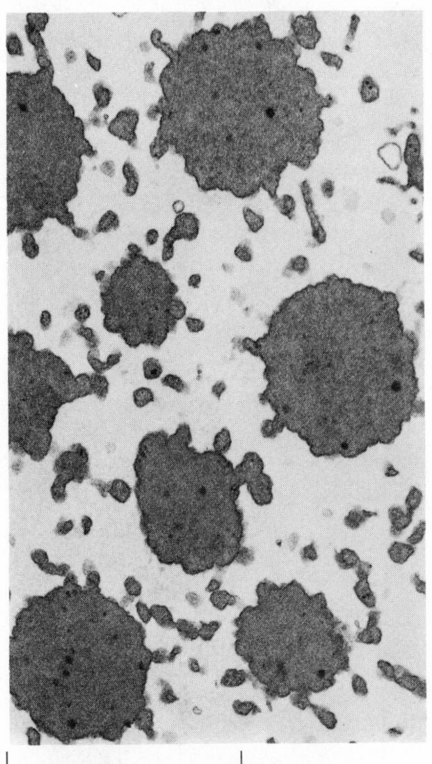

Table 18-2 Molar ratio of electron carriers in beef heart mitochondria†

Carrier	*Ratio*
Cytochrome $a + a_3$	1.0
Cytochrome $c + c_1$	1.5
Cytochrome b	1.0
Total flavins	~1.0
Nonheme Fe	6
Coenzyme Q	8
NAD	12
NADP	2

† Cytochrome $a + a_3 = 1.0$.

Schematic representation of surface of inner mitochondrial membrane.

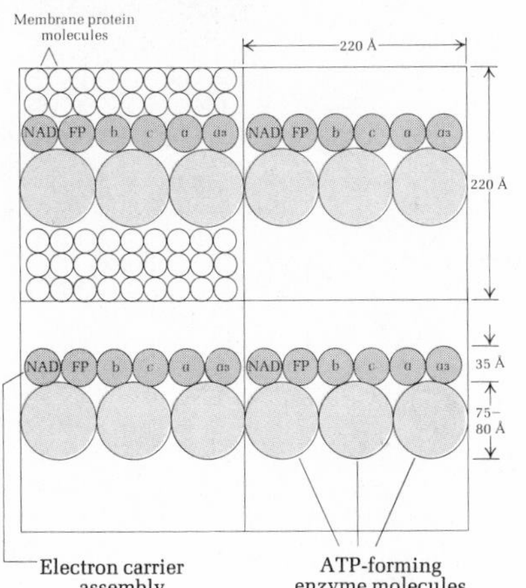

concerned in ATP formation. The remaining protein is enzymatically inactive and serves a structural function in association with the membrane lipids; it has been called structure protein.

There is much evidence that flavoproteins and cytochromes are arranged in clusters or complexes in the membrane, so that each cluster, or *respiratory assembly*, is a complete self-contained unit, comprising NADH dehydrogenase, succinate dehydrogenase, and cytochromes b, c_1, c, a, and a_3 in specific molar ratios (Table 18-2 and margin). It has been calculated from spectroscopic analysis of cytochrome content that each liver mitochondrion contains about 5,000 and each heart mitochondrion about 20,000 complete respiratory assemblies in their inner-membrane system. Furthermore, the assemblies appear to be uniformly distributed in the plane of the membrane with a center-to-center distance of about 200 Å between them, so that there is one complete respiratory assembly for each 40,000 to 50,000 $Å^2$ of inner-membrane surface. This type of structural arrangement appears to be constant in all mitochondria. Mitochondria from such tissues as flight muscle, heart, and kidney, which have high respiratory rates, have numerous cristae and therefore a relatively large inner-membrane surface area; correspondingly, they have a relatively large number of respiratory assemblies. Mitochondria from cells with low respiratory rates, such as the liver, have fewer cristae, a smaller surface area, and fewer respiratory assemblies. The inner membrane of rat liver mitochondria has been calculated to have a surface of about 40 square meters per gram of mitochondrial protein (equivalent to the number of mitochondria present in the liver of a large adult white rat); for heart mitochondria the figure is about 200 to 250 square meters per gram, and for blowfly flight muscle mitochondria, in excess of 400 square meters per gram.

When the knoblike elementary particles (better called *inner-membrane spheres*) of the inner surface of the inner mitochondrial membrane were first discovered, Green and his coworkers postulated that they were identical with the respiratory assemblies. This conclusion has not been sustained by more recent work, which indicates that the respiratory assemblies of flavoprotein and cytochromes are present within the plane of the membrane, possibly located at the base of the inner-membrane spheres, which are now known to be molecules of the F_1 coupling factor for oxidative phosphorylation (Chapter 17), a relatively large protein (mol wt = 280,000) with a diameter of ~80 Å. Racker and his colleagues have shown that when beef heart mitochondria are depleted of the F_1 protein so that they cannot carry out oxidative phosphorylation coupled to electron transport, they no longer contain the spheres; when the purified F_1 protein is returned to depleted mitochondria, the ability to phosphorylate ADP is restored and the spheres again show up in the electron micrograph, attached to the membrane.

Permeability of the Mitochondrial Membranes; Carrier Systems

Although the outer mitochondrial membrane is, relatively speaking, freely permeable to most low-molecular-weight solutes, the inner membrane is permeable only to water, various small neutral molecules such as urea and glycerol, and short-chain fatty acids. It is not permeable to the cations Na^+, K^+, or Mg^{2+}, or the anions Cl^-, Br^-, NO_3^-, sugars such as sucrose, or most amino acids. Since the inner membrane is also impermeable to NAD^+, $NADP^+$, NADH, and NADPH, nucleoside 5′-mono-, di-, and triphosphates, and to CoA and its esters, the inner compartment of mitochondria thus contains an internal pool of these coenzymes and nucleosides which is physically separate and functionally distinct from the extramitochondrial, or cytoplasmic, pool.

It has been discovered that the inner membrane contains several permeases, or carriers, which effect the transfer of specific metabolities across the membrane. Such carriers resemble enzymes in that they are specific for certain substances, they can be saturated as the substrate concentration is increased and they may also be inhibited specifically. In rat liver mitochondria carriers have been identified for ADP and ATP, for phosphate, and for certain intermediates of the Krebs tricarboxylic acid cycle (Table 18-3).

Table 18-3 Specific transport systems in the mitochondrial membrane

Substance transported	*Inhibitor*
ADP (ATP)	Atractyloside
Phosphate	Mersalyl
Succinate or malate	*n*-Butylmalonate
Isocitrate, citrate or *cis*-aconitate	*n*-Butylmalonate
Glutamate	4-Hydroxyglutamate

The most intensively studied inner-membrane carrier is that for ADP and ATP, which cannot pass the membrane by simple diffusion. The existence of such a carrier was deduced from study of the inhibitor *atractyloside,* a toxic glycoside from the Mediterranean plant *Atractylis gummifera,* which inhibits oxidative phosphorylation of externally added ADP in isolated mitochondria. Unlike other inhibitors of oxidative phosphorylation, such as oligomycin, atractyloside does not inhibit oxidative phosphorylation of intramitochondrial ADP. This and other observations have led to the conclusion that instead of inhibiting the oxidative phosphorylation process itself, atractyloside inhibits the transfer of ADP and ATP across the mitochondrial membrane by a specific carrier (Figure 18-5). Recent research has shown that this carrier allows a molecule of ADP to enter the mitochondria only if a molecule of ATP comes out. This molecule-for-molecule exchange is known as *exchange diffusion.* The ATP-ADP carrier has very high affinity for ADP and ATP, shows the phenomenon of saturation, and is extremely specific, since it does not promote the transfer of other XTPs or XDPs, such as GTP, GDP, CTP, CDP. It thus has many characteristics of an enzyme, but instead of catalyzing a homogeneous reaction it brings about two-way exchange across the membrane.

Figure 18-5
Exchange of ADP and ATP across the inner mitochondrial membrane by the ATP carrier. The carrier is inhibited by very low concentrations of atractyloside, which bears some resemblance to the ATP molecule.

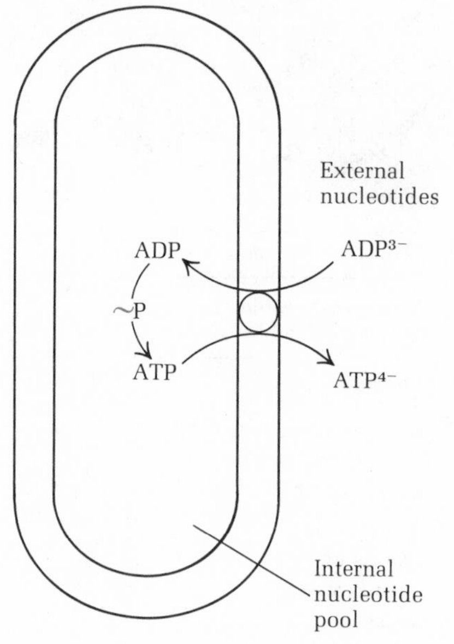

Another carrier system appears responsible for the exchange of phosphate and hydroxyl ions across the inner membrane; it is inhibited by the mercurial drug *mersalyl.* Recent research indicates that the phosphate carrier and the ADP carrier systems may be functionally linked.

Some of the dicarboxylic and tricarboxylic acid intermediates of the Krebs cycle are also transported by

Figure 18-6
Phosphorylation of ADP and accumulation of cations are alternative processes during electron transport.

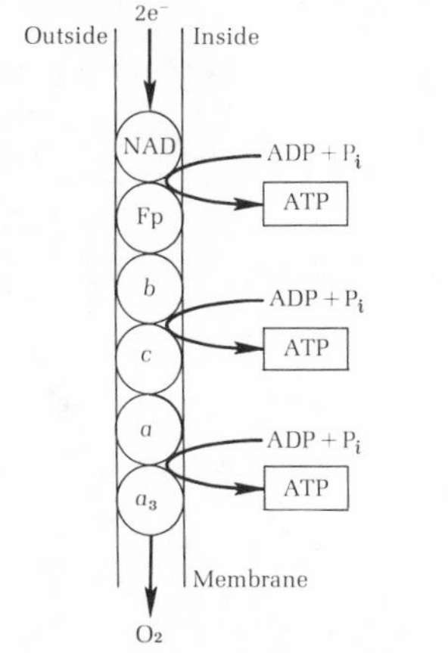

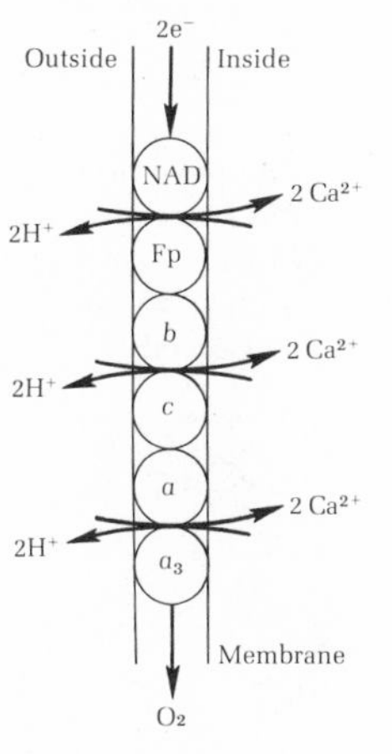

specific carriers. Two such carriers have been identified by Chappell. The succinate-malate carrier can transport succinate or malate, but not the other dicarboxylic acids (fumarate, oxaloacetate, or α-ketoglutarate), and is inhibited by *n*-butylmalonate. The tricarboxylic acid carrier can transport citrate, *cis*-aconitate, and isocitrate; it requires the presence of both phosphate and malate. The succinate-malate and the tricarboxylic acid carrier systems are present in mitochondria of liver and kidney but not in the mitochondria of blowfly flight muscle cells. The latter cannot oxidize external tricarboxylic acid cycle intermediates but carry out the cycle reactions internally at great velocity because they contain high internal concentrations of cycle intermediates, which cannot leave the inner compartment.

These and other observations have led to the general conclusion that fuel molecules, phosphate, and ADP must penetrate the inner compartment of mitochondria prior to oxidation, that the Krebs cycle reactions as well as electron transport and oxidative phosphorylation, take place in the inner compartment or on the inner surface of the inner membrane, and that the ATP so formed must eventually leave the inner compartment to reach the cytoplasm. The intramitochondrial pool of ATP and ADP is segregated from the cytoplasmic pool, but they communicate via the atractyloside-sensitive carrier. There is also an extremely complex interchange of tricarboxylic acid cycle intermediates and phosphate between the cytoplasm and the intramitochondrial compartment. As we shall see, compartmentation of intermediates is important in the control and integration of the glycolytic and respiratory pathways, as well as those anabolic pathways in which the tricarboxylic acid cycle participates (Chapter 22).

Respiration-Dependent Ion Transport by Mitochondria

Electron micrograph of rat liver mitochondria after respiration-coupled accumulation of Ca^{2+} and phosphate. The dark electron-dense spots correspond to granular deposits having the composition of hydroxyapatite.

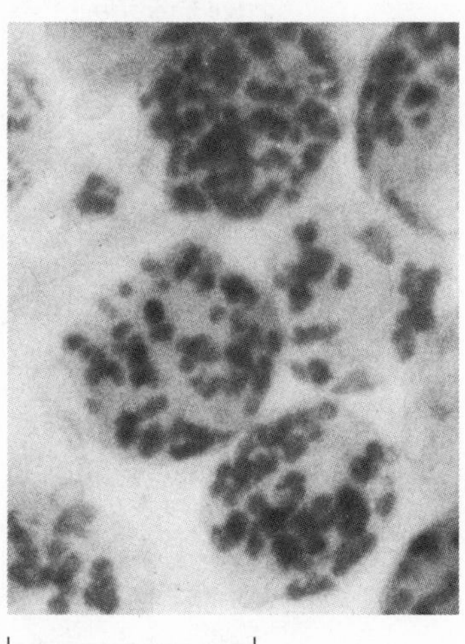

Isolated intact mitochondria have the ability to accumulate certain divalent cations from the suspending medium during respiration. If Ca^{2+} ions are added to isolated rat kidney mitochondria respiring in a medium containing phosphate, the Ca^{2+} is very rapidly accumulated from the medium. Since this process is prevented by 2,4-dinitrophenol or by respiratory inhibitors such as cyanide, it is evidently dependent on energy delivered by the respiratory chain. Rossi and Lehninger have shown that the accumulation of Ca^{2+} is stoichiometrically related to electron transport (Figure 18-6). For every pair of electrons passing from NADH to oxygen, five Ca^{2+} ions are accumulated from the medium, about 1.7 at each energy-conserving site. With the uptake of Ca^{2+} there is also stoichiometric uptake of one molecule of inorganic phosphate per site. Ca^{2+} and phosphate are taken up in the ratio in which they occur in *hydroxyapatite*, or bone mineral. When Ca^{2+} is accumulated in this fashion, no oxidative phosphorylation of ADP occurs. These are *alternative* processes: the energy of electron transport can be used to carry out either Ca^{2+} accumulation or ATP formation but not both simultaneously. Sr^{2+} and Mn^{2+} ions are also accumulated by isolated mitochondria and behave very much like Ca^{2+}, but Mg^{2+}, which cannot penetrate the mitochondrial membrane, is not accumulated. The capacity of mitochondria to accumulate and release Ca^{2+} and phosphate enables them to function in biological calcification and decalcification processes, as well as in the sequestration of Ca^{2+} during relaxation of red muscles (Chapter 26).

Electron transport generates pH gradient across inner membrane of mitochondrion.

Monovalent cations such as K^+, the major cation in the extramitochondrial cytoplasm, are not normally accumulated by intact respiring mitochondria, since mitochondrial membranes are not penetrated by K^+, Na^+, and other monovalent cations. However, Pressman has found that several specific compounds known to inhibit or uncouple oxidative phosphorylation, particularly the uncoupling antibiotics *valinomycin* and *gramicidin* (Figure 18-7), can cause isolated mitochondria to accumulate K^+. These antibiotics can form complexes with K^+ which, because of their hydrophobic nature, can pass through the membrane. Valinomycin can carry K^+ (but not Na^+) through, whereas gramicidin carries either K^+ or Na^+. When K^+ is pumped into mitochondria by respiration in the presence of these substances, the mitochondria no longer can phosphorylate ADP. The action of these "ionophorous" antibiotics will be discussed further in Chapter 27.

The pH gradient is the energy-rich state in which electron transport energy is conserved.

The respiration-dependent accumulation of the divalent cations Ca^{2+}, Mn^{2+} and Sr^{2+} and the monovalent cations K^+ and Na^+ (in the presence of valinomycin or gramicidin) share a significant property: as these cations are accumulated, an equivalent number of H^+ ions are ejected from the mitochondria into the medium. Careful balance studies have shown that for each pair of electrons passing down the respiratory chain, two H^+ ions are pumped out of mitochondria at each energy-conserving site, making a total of six for the entire chain. These observations, together with other considerations, have prompted the

The pH gradient is the driving force for the phosphorylation of ADP. The high internal OH^- "pulls" H^+ from the active site of the ATPase and the high external H^+ pulls away OH^- from the active site.

Figure 18-7
Structure of valinomycin. Many of the ionophorous antibiotics that induce passage of K^+ across the mitochondrial membrane are circular or annular molecules with a central opening which can bind K^+.

A = L-Lactate
B = L-Valine
C = D-Hydroxyisovalerate
D = D-Valine

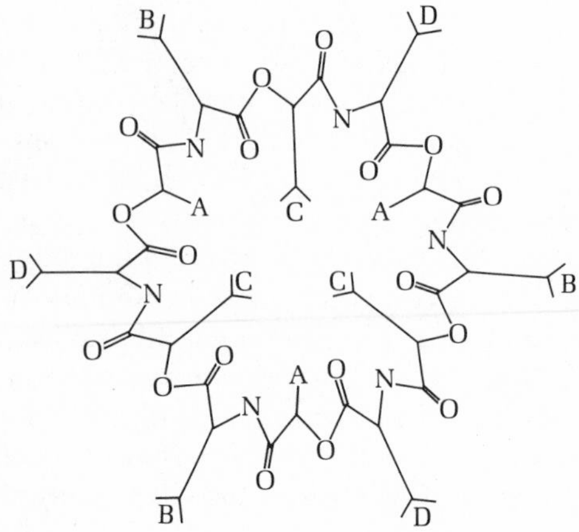

postulation of a mechanism of oxidative phosphorylation, the chemiosmotic hypothesis, which is alternative to the chemical coupling hypothesis (Chapter 17).

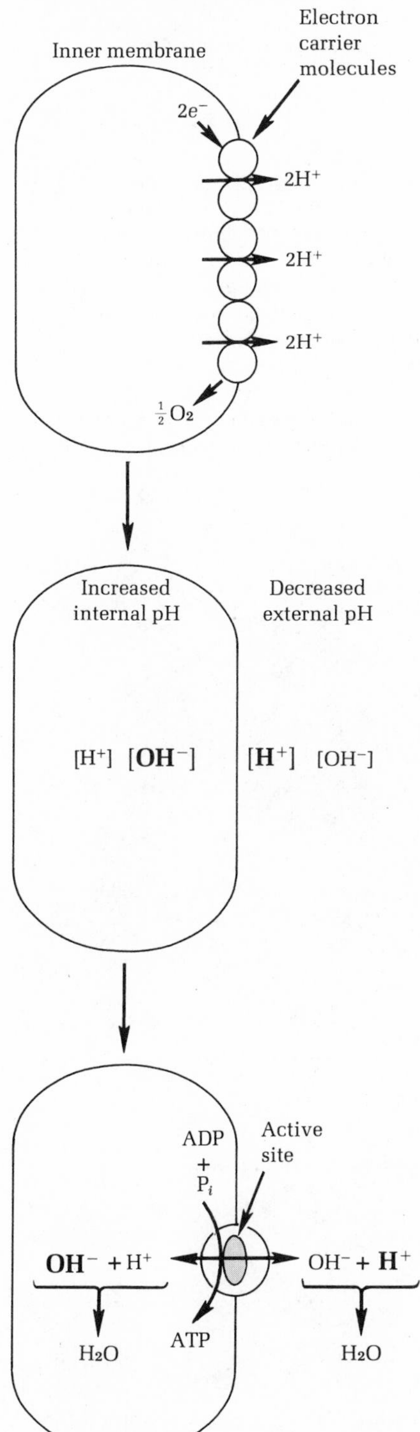

Figure 18-8
The chemiosmotic hypothesis. More recently it has been proposed that some of the H^+ gradient is replaced by an energetically equivalent electrical potential difference.

The Chemiosmotic Hypothesis

Although the chemiosmotic hypothesis had earlier origins, Mitchell, a British biochemist, is largely responsible for formulating it precisely and has been its strongest exponent. He points out that the chemical coupling hypothesis fails to explain why no high-energy intermediates have ever been isolated or proved to exist or why the mitochondrial membrane must be reasonably intact in order for oxidative phosphorylation to occur (see Chapter 17). Assuming that the mitochondrial membrane is an essential element in the mechanism of oxidative phosphorylation and that it is impermeable to H^+ ions, Mitchell further suggests that transport of electrons along the carriers of the respiratory chain, which are located in the membrane, generates a gradient of H^+ ions across the membrane. He postulates that this gradient is formed by extraction of H^+ ions from the intramitochondrial compartment and their ejection into the surrounding medium. The free-energy decline occurring in electron transport is thus conserved in the form of a gradient of H^+ ions across the membrane, which can exist only if the membrane is impermeable to H^+ ions (Figure 18-8). It is postulated that this energy-rich H^+ ion gradient arises because the reactions of electron transport that involve uptake or production of H^+ ions (Table 17-5) are catalyzed by enzymes whose active sites are located in the plane of the mitochondrial membrane in such a way that H^+ ions can be extracted only from the inside compartment and H^+ ions formed can be lost only to the outside of the membrane. As each pair of electrons goes down the chain from NAD to oxygen, three pairs of H^+ ions are extracted from the internal matrix and through enzymatic transfers are ejected into the outside medium (Figure 18-8). These amounts are in obvious agreement with those observed during active cation accumulation by mitochondria.

The energy-rich H^+ gradient generated by electron transport is postulated to cause the formation of ATP from ADP and phosphate, which is formally a dehydration or condensation reaction

$$\mathrm{ADP} + \mathrm{P}_i \rightleftharpoons \mathrm{ATP} + \mathrm{HOH}$$

by promoting the removal of HOH as H^+ and OH^- ions. Because the standard free energy of this reaction is $\Delta G^{\circ\prime} = +7.3$ kcal, it can proceed to the right at a high rate only if the water formed can be quickly and completely removed, as may be predicted from the law of mass action. Mitchell postulates that an ATPase capable of removing water from ADP and phosphate [presumably the F_1 coupling enzyme (Chapter 17)] is oriented in the plane of the mitochondrial membrane in such a way that H_2O is removed from the ADP and phosphate as H^+ and OH^- ions, the former entering the inner compartment, where the pH is postulated to be relatively high, and the latter entering the outer compartment, where the pH is relatively low. Since the ion product of water is very small ($K_w = [H^+][OH^-] = 1 \times 10^{-14}$), the H^+ ions extracted from ADP and phosphate are effectively trapped by the excess OH^- ions in the inner compartment, with formation of water, and the OH^- ions leaving the outer surface are trapped by the excess H^+ ions in the surrounding medium. The postulated gradient of H^+ ions across the membrane is never large since the system is in a steady state, in which the rate of formation of the gradient is counterbalanced by the rate of its discharge as ATP is formed. A characteristic feature of the chemiosmotic hypothesis is the absence of a common high-energy chemical intermediate shared by both the electron-transport mechanism and the ATP-forming mechanism.

Mitchell has also postulated that 2,4-dinitrophenol and similar agents uncouple oxidative phosphorylation because they are weak aromatic acids, which are lipid-soluble and can be absorbed in the lipid phase of the membrane to act as proton carriers, thus equalizing the concentration of H^+ on both sides of the membrane and discharging the pH gradient required for ATP formation.

A number of observations support or are consistent with this hypothesis, for example, the "sidedness" and stoichiometry of H^+ ejection during Ca^{2+} accumulation linked to electron transport. Moreover, recent research on the action of uncoupling agents on mitochondrial and synthetic phospholipid membranes also supports the conclusion that uncoupling agents promote H^+ leakage across the membrane. However, we are still left with a dilemma since nearly all available evidence on the properties of the oxidative phosphorylation process can be explained equally well by the chemical-coupling or chemiosmotic hypothesis.

Recently Mitchell has modified his hypothesis by providing evidence that the energy gradient generated across the mitochondrial membrane by electron transport need not involve H^+ ions alone. Some of the H^+ gradient may be replaced by an energetically equivalent gradient of electrical potential across the membrane, the total gradient generated by electron transport thus being the sum of the H^+ gradient and the transmembrane electrical potential. (See Chapter 27.)

Energy-Linked Conformation Changes of Mitochondrial Membranes

For some years it has been known that isolated mitochondria swell in the presence of certain agents, such as phosphate, and contract again, with extrusion of water, in the presence of ATP. These volume changes depend on electron transport and are characteristically inhibited by 2,4-dinitrophenol or oligomycin. They are easily measured optically as changes in light scattering. Mitochondria in intact cells also undergo energy-dependent volume changes. From such observations, it was postulated that the energy of electron transport in mitochondria is conserved by the coupling enzymes in such a way that it can

Figure 18-9
Electron micrographs showing conformational changes in mouse liver mitochondria during transition from resting to active respiration. In resting respiration, in which there is little or no ADP, the conformation is that usually seen in thin sections of intact tissue and is thus called orthodox. When ADP is present in excess and the rate of respiration is maximal, the condensed conformation results.

Orthodox conformation

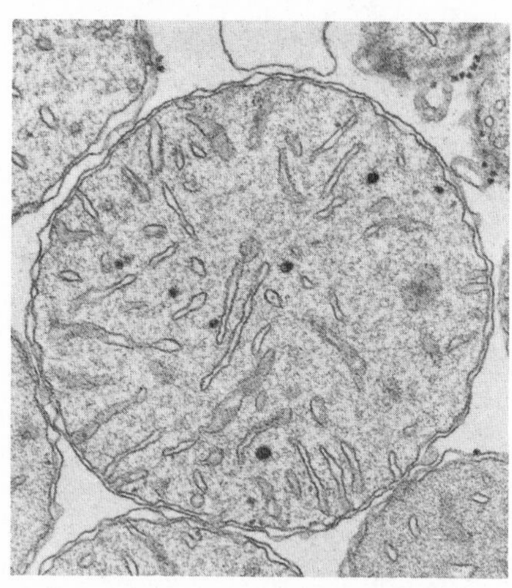

1.0 μ

Condensed conformation

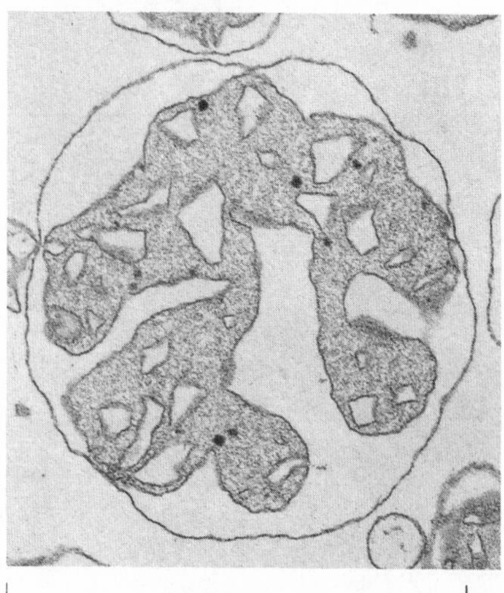

1.0 μ

do three different kinds of work: (1) the chemical work of oxidative phosphorylation, (2) the osmotic work required for accumulation of ions, and (3) the mechanical work of conformational changes in the mitochondrial membranes. The question now is: Which of these energy transformations is primary to the others? Recent investigations indicate that the conformational changes generated by electron transport must be given serious consideration. We therefore have 3 hypotheses of energy-coupling: chemical-coupling, chemiosmotic coupling and mechano-chemical or conformational coupling.

Hackenbrock has found by electron microscopy that mitochondria exist in two different ultrastructural states, depending on whether they are respiring without ADP (see below) or actively phosphorylating (Figure 18-9). In the absence of ADP, the mitochondria show the usually observed, or orthodox, conformation, as seen in sections of intact tissues; in the actively phosphorylating state, in the presence of excess ADP, the mitochondria have a highly condensed inner compartment, apparently caused by puckering of the inner membrane. These observations, confirmed by Green and others, are supported by sensitive optical measurements indicating that conformational changes in mitochondria may be extremely rapid. From this evidence it has been suggested by these investigators that electron-transport energy is directly converted into an energy-rich conformational state of the inner membrane, a state postulated to be the immediate driving force for ATP formation in oxidative phosphorylation, conformational energy being converted into chemical or osmotic energy. The existence of three major hypotheses (Figure 18-10) for the mechanism of energy conservation during electron transport has created lively and interesting controversy. Whatever the outcome, the mechanism of oxidative phosphorylation and its counterpart, photosynthetic phosphorylation (Chapter 21), represents one of the most interesting theoretical and experimental challenges in modern biochemistry.

Figure 18-10
The three hypotheses for the mechanism of energy conservation during electron transport. They differ in the primary form in which oxidoreduction energy is conserved.

Chemical coupling

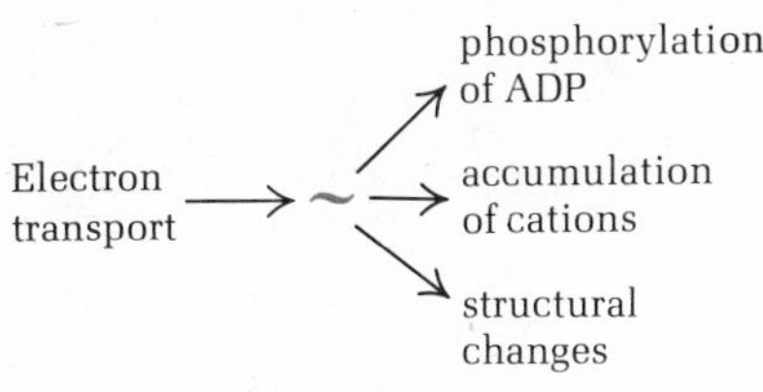

Chemiosmotic coupling

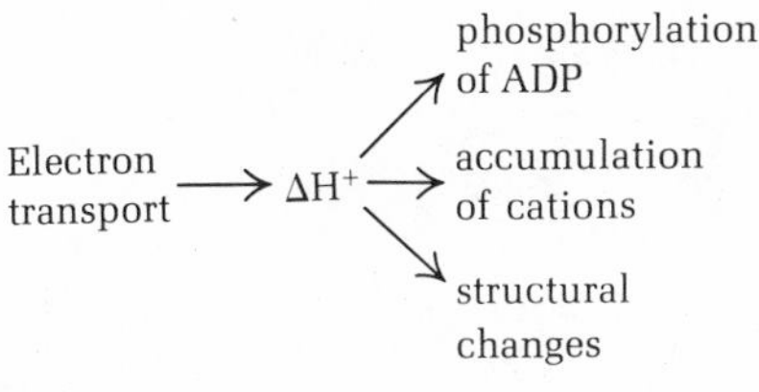

Conformational coupling

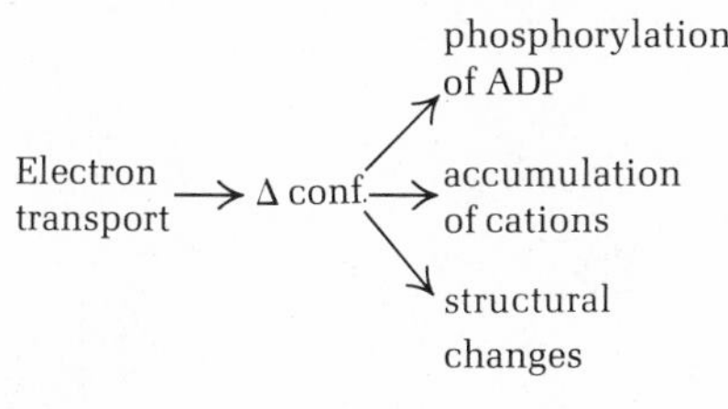

~ = high-energy chemical bond
ΔH^+ = pH gradient
Δ conf. = conformational change

Role of Mitochondria in Metabolic Regulation; Acceptor Control of Respiration

In respiring mitochondria the rate of electron transport, and thus the rate of ATP production, is determined primarily by the relative concentrations of ADP, ATP, and phosphate in the external medium and not by the concentration of respiratory substrates such as pyruvate. When the supply of respiratory substrate is ample, the maximal rate of oxygen consumption occurs when the ADP and phosphate concentration in the medium are high and the concentration of ATP low. On the other hand, when the concentration of ATP is high and that of ADP or phosphate essentially zero, mitochondria show only a very low respiratory rate, as little as 5 to 10 percent of the maximal rate. Of the three components, the ADP concentration is the most critical in setting the respiratory rate because of the extraordinarily high affinity of the mitochondria for ADP. Maximal rates of respiration occur at concentrations of ADP as low as 0.02 m*M*. Figure 18-11 illustrates the dramatic effect of ADP concentration on the respiratory rate of mitochondria supplied with excess substrate and phosphate. Addition of even small amounts of ADP evokes a maximal rate of respiration, which continues until nearly all the ADP is phosphorylated to ATP, at which point oxygen consumption abruptly returns to the low resting level. The dependence of respiratory rate on ADP concentration is called *respiratory control* or, more specifically, *acceptor control*.

The dependence of respiratory rate on ADP concentration is also seen in intact cells. A muscle at rest and using no ADP has very low respiratory rate. Under these conditions the ATP concentration is high and the ADP concentration low. If the muscle is stimulated to a series of contractions, its cytoplasmic ATP is rapidly broken down to ADP and phosphate (Chapter 26). The onset of the contractions is accompanied by an abrupt and dramatic increase in rate of oxygen consumption, which may increase in excess of 100-fold in some muscles. The signal for this increase in rate of respiration is the sudden increase in ADP concentration accompanying contraction, which immediately stimulates respiration and the accompanying phosphorylation of ADP. The respiration continues at a high rate as long as ADP is generated by the ATP-requiring contractile system. When the contractions cease, ADP formation ceases and the rate of respiration is automatically and quickly throttled down to the resting rate.

Figure 18-11
Acceptor control of respiration. When substrate is present in excess, addition of ADP causes a jump in oxygen uptake, followed by return to the resting rate of respiration when the ADP is all phosphorylated to ATP. The ratio of moles ADP added to atoms extra oxygen consumed is equal to the P:O ratio. Acceptor control was first observed by Lardy and Wellman and studied in detail by Chance and Williams.

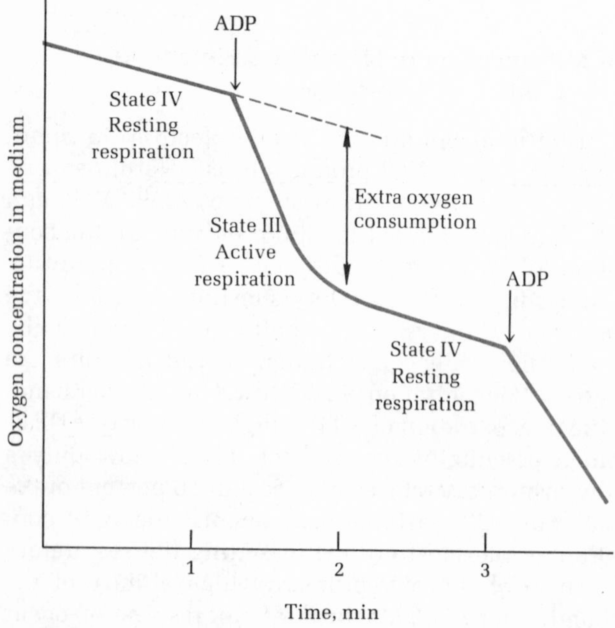

Entry of Electrons from Cytoplasmic NADH: The Glycerol Phosphate Shuttle

When pure NADH is added to suspensions of isolated intact mitochondria from liver, kidney, muscle, and a number of other tissues, it is not oxidized, even though the mitochondria readily oxidize added NAD-linked substrates, e.g., malate, via the intramitochondrial NAD^+. This and other observations have shown that the mitochondrial membrane in these tissues is impermeable to NADH, NADPH, and their oxidized forms NAD^+ and $NADP^+$. This permeability barrier effectively segregates the cytoplasmic and the intramitochondrial pools of NADH. An important question now arises. Many NAD^+-linked dehydrogenases in the cytoplasm can reduce cytoplasmic NAD^+, e.g., lactate dehydrogenase, malate dehydrogenase, and glyceraldehyde phosphate dehydrogenase. Can cytoplasmic NADH formed by action of these extramitochondrial dehydrogenases be oxidized to NAD^+ by the electron-transport chain of mitochondria? We shall see later that this question is extremely important because the conversion of glucose to pyruvate via the glycolytic sequence under aerobic conditions causes constant reduction of cytoplasmic NAD^+, through the action of glyceraldehyde phosphate dehydrogenase.

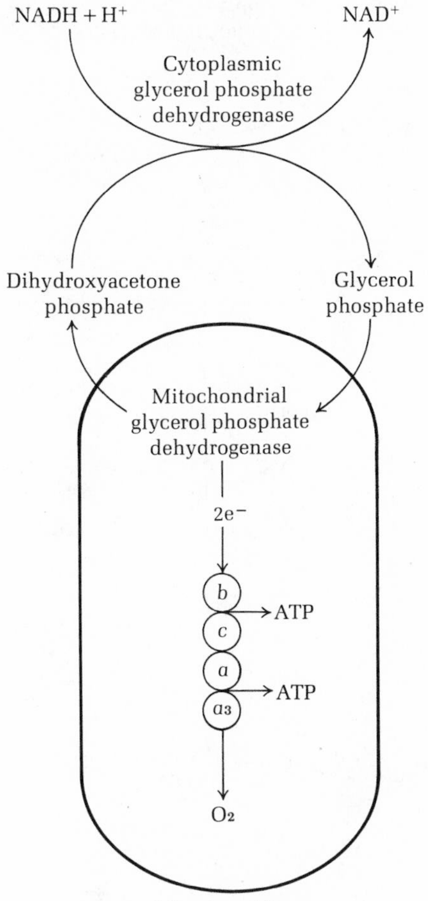

Figure 18-12
The glycerol phosphate shuttle for transfer of reducing equivalents from cytoplasmic NADH *to the mitochondrial electron-transport chain.*

Although extramitochondrial NADH itself cannot penetrate the mitochondrial membrane, electrons derived from it can enter the mitochondrial electron-transport chain by indirect routes called *shuttles*. The best known is the *glycerol phosphate shuttle* (Figure 18-12), in which the cytoplasmic NADH first reacts with cytoplasmic dihydroxyacetone phosphate, one of the intermediates of glycolysis, to form L-glycerol 3-phosphate in a reaction catalyzed by the cytoplasmic NAD-linked *glycerol phosphate dehydrogenase*

$$\text{Dihydroxyacetone phosphate} + \text{NADH} + \text{H}^+ \rightleftharpoons \text{L-glycerol 3-phosphate} + \text{NAD}^+$$

The glycerol 3-phosphate so formed readily penetrates through the mitochondrial membrane. Within the mitochondria, another glycerol 3-phosphate dehydrogenase (which is not an NAD-linked enzyme but a flavin dehydrogenase) oxidizes glycerol 3-phosphate back to dihydroxyacetone phosphate, and its flavin prosthetic group becomes reduced

$$\text{Glycerol 3-phosphate} + \text{FP} \longrightarrow \text{dihydroxyacetone phosphate} + \text{FPH}_2$$

The reduced flavoprotein now donates its reducing equivalents to the electron-transport chain at the level of CoQ; they ultimately pass to oxygen. The dihydroxyacetone phosphate formed in this reaction now diffuses out of the mitochondria into the cytoplasm, where it can accept electrons from another molecule of extramitochondrial

NADH. The glycerol phosphate–dihydroxyacetone phosphate couple thus acts as a shuttle of reducing equivalents from extramitochondrial NADH to the intramitochondrial respiratory chain. The pair of electrons that enters the respiratory chain via the shuttle causes the oxidative phosphorylation of only two molecules of ADP as it passes to oxygen, since the electrons from L-glycerol 3-phosphate enter *after* the first energy-conservation site.

The glycerol phosphate shuttle is unidirectional; it transports reducing equivalents *into* mitochondria, particularly in the liver and in insect flight muscle. In other tissues, as well as the liver, the malate shuttle appears to operate. Extramitochondrial NADH is oxidized by oxaloacetate by the action of cytoplasmic malate dehydrogenase, to yield malate, which enters the mitochondrion via the malate-succinate carrier and is oxidized to oxaloacetate by the action of intramitochondrial malate dehydrogenase (Figure 18-13). As we shall see, the malate shuttle is reversible and can function in either direction.

Figure 18-13
The malate shuttle. The oxaloacetate (OAA) formed inside the mitochondrion is converted to aspartate by transamination. The aspartate passes through the membrane via a specific carrier. A similar transaminase is found in the cytoplasm, thus allowing the malate shuttle to function reversibly.

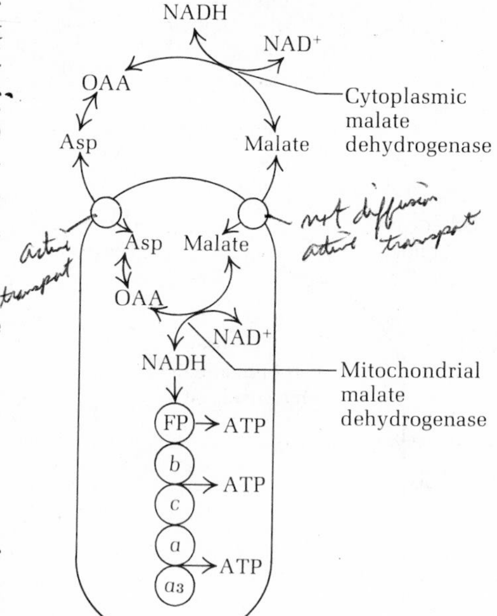

The Pasteur Effect: Integration of Glycolysis and Respiration

It has long been known that when a facultative cell utilizes glucose under anaerobic conditions, with formation of lactate, the rate of breakdown of glucose is manyfold greater than it is in the same cell under aerobic conditions. Since anaerobic glycolysis delivers a net of only 2 molecules of ATP per molecule of glucose whereas complete aerobic oxidation of 1 molecule of glucose delivers 36 molecules of ATP, the anaerobic cell requires 36/2 or 18 times as much glucose per unit weight per unit time to generate ATP at the same rate as an aerobic cell. Facultative cells living anaerobically thus consume relatively enormous amounts of glucose. If oxygen is admitted to a suspension of anaerobic cells utilizing glucose by glycolysis, the onset of oxygen consumption is immediate and the rate of glucose consumption declines dramatically to a small fraction of its anaerobic rate. At the same time, the accumulation of lactate, which is quantitative under anaerobic conditions according to the equation

$$\text{Glucose} \longrightarrow 2\ \text{lactate}$$

is reduced to zero in the presence of oxygen, since respiration leads to quantitative formation of CO_2 and H_2O from glucose, with no lactate accumulation

$$\text{Glucose} + 6O_2 \longrightarrow 6CO_2 + 6H_2O$$

This phenomenon, the inhibition of glucose consumption and the cessation of lactate accumulation with the onset of respiration, is called the *Pasteur effect*. Pasteur discovered it during his important investigations of fermentation processes in wine making, but it is a general property of all facultative cells, including those of higher animals. It is a spectacular instance of control and integration of two enzyme systems, and its mechanism has been under study for many years.

The first major question posed by the Pasteur effect is: Why does no lactate accumulate during aerobic respiration? We have seen that in anaerobic glycolysis lactate is formed from pyruvate at the expense of NADH generated at the triose oxidation step. Unless NAD^+ is regenerated by this reaction, glycolysis cannot occur past the triose stage. Under aerobic conditions, however, the cytoplasmic NADH formed by triose oxidation is reoxidized, not by pyruvate, but by the shuttle system and the respiratory chain, which, because they have a much higher affinity for NADH than lactate dehydrogenase, win in the competition for cytoplasmic NADH. For this reason pyruvate is not normally reduced to lactate during respiration but is oxidized directly to acetyl CoA and CO_2. Proof that the glycerol phosphate shuttle is responsible for preventing aerobic formation of lactate comes from studies of glycolysis and respiration in cancer cells. The glycolytic enzymes and mitochondrial systems in cancer cells appear to be completely identical to those in normal cells, but the manner in which glycolysis and respiration are integrated appears to differ. During respiration most cancer cells accumulate significantly large amounts of lactate, even when they are amply supplied with oxygen and their respiratory rate is high. Such cells have been found to be deficient in their ability to operate the glycerol phosphate shuttle; they lack cytoplasmic glycerol phosphate dehydrogenase. Because they cannot oxidize NADH via the mitochondrial pathway, cancer cells reoxidize NADH with pyruvate via lactate dehydrogenase, thus causing lactate to accumulate aerobically, even though the tricarboxylic acid cycle and electron transport are proceeding at normal aerobic rates.

The Role of Phosphofructokinase in Regulation of Glycolysis

The second question raised by the Pasteur effect is: how does the occurrence of respiration slow the rate of glycolysis? An early clue to the mechanism came with the observation that 2,4-dinitrophenol, which uncouples oxidative phosphorylation, also blocks the Pasteur effect and promotes formation of lactic acid, even when the tissue is respiring. We have seen above that mitochondria have an extremely high affinity for ADP and will continue phosphorylating ADP until high [ATP]/[ADP] ratios are achieved. We have also seen (Chapter 15) that phosphofructokinase, which is a regulatory enzyme, catalyzes the rate-limiting reaction in the glycolytic sequence, namely, the phosphorylation of fructose 6-phosphate to fructose 1,6-diphosphate. Phosphofructokinase is a multivalent regulatory enzyme; its activity is stimulated by ADP and phosphate, and it is inhibited by ATP and by citrate. When the [ATP]/[ADP] ratio is high, the enzyme is severely inhibited, and when this ratio is low, it increases in activity. The high [ATP]/[ADP] ratio that occurs during phosphorylating respiration as a result of the high affinity of mitochondria for ADP therefore causes phosphofructokinase to "turn off" and thus slow down the rate of glycolysis. This explanation has been strongly supported by direct analysis of the concentrations of glucose, glucose 6-phosphate, fructose 6-phosphate, and other glycolytic intermediates in intact cells before and after the transition from anaerobic glycolysis to aerobic respiration As oxygen is supplied to anaerobic cells, glucose consumption decreases and lactate is no longer formed; simultaneously the concentrations of glucose 6-phosphate and fructose 6-phosphate in the cell increase, but the concentration of fructose 1,6-diphosphate becomes very low. These observations show that phosphofructokinase is the inhibited reaction in glycolysis, since intermediates preceding this reaction pile up and those after it decrease in concentration. The intracellular concentrations of fructose 6-phosphate and ATP are in the range where the rate of the phosphofructokinase reaction is extremely sensitive to ATP inhibition.

Although phosphofructokinase is the major pacemaker enzyme for glycolysis, it is now clear that glycolysis, like many other multienzyme sequences, contains a number of secondary control points. In fact, a whole network of controls is operative in the integration of the rates of glycolysis and respiration. For example, citrate is known to be a specific negative modulator of phosphofructokinase. Citrate produced by the tricarboxylic acid cycle can leave the mitochondria and enter the cytoplasm via the citrate carrier system of the mitochondrial membrane. Whenever citrate is overproduced, it acts as an inhibitor of phosphofructokinase and slows down the rate of glycolysis and thus the supply of acetyl CoA fuel. The hexokinase reaction is also a secondary control point in the glycolytic cycle, since it is strongly inhibited by glucose 6-phosphate, its own product, which acts as a negative modulator.

Another mechanism by which respiration can inhibit glycolysis is through competition for ADP between mitochondria and those enzymes of the glycolytic sequence which require ADP, namely, phosphoglycerate kinase and pyruvate kinase. Since mitochondria have a higher affinity for ADP than the glycolytic enzymes, their ability to phosphorylate ADP at very low concentrations may cause glycolysis to slow down for lack of phosphate acceptor. The important mechanisms for regulation of glycolysis and respiration are summarized in Figure 18-14.

Figure 18-14
Summary of the important control mechanisms in glycolysis and respiration. The dotted colored arrows show the origin of feedback inhibitors (ATP, NADH, citrate, glucose 6-phosphate) and the colored bars indicate the sites of feedback inhibition. The points of action of positive or stimulatory modulators (AMP, ADP, acetyl CoA, NAD⁺) are shown by colored arrows parallel to the black reaction arrows. There is significant variation among species as to the identity of the modulators for a given allosteric enzyme, as well as the identity of the controlled reaction. The citrate synthase reaction is the primary control point of the tricarboxylic acid cycle in the liver of vertebrates; in some muscles the isocitrate dehydrogenase reaction apparently serves as the controlling reaction.

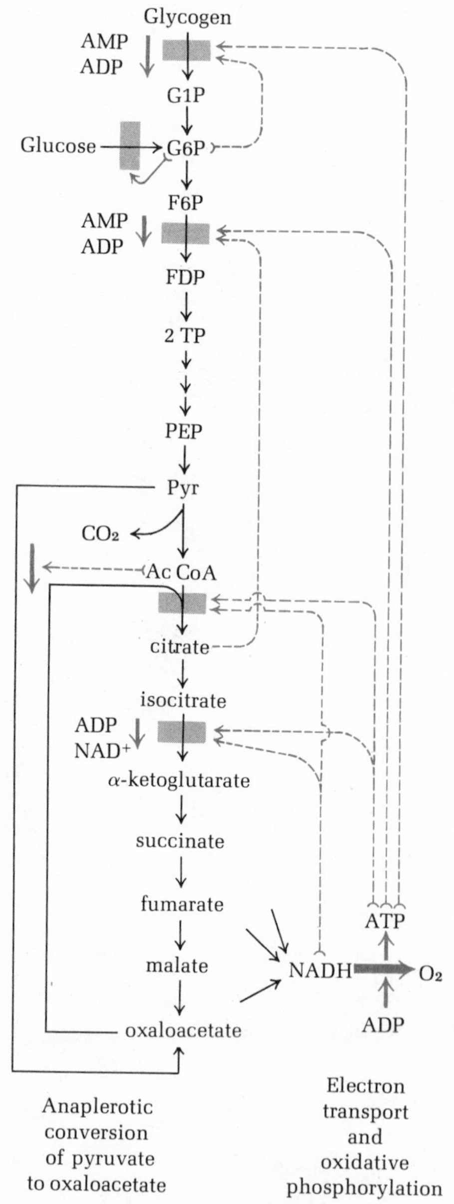

The Energy Charge of the ATP System and the Regulation of Energy-Requiring and Energy-Generating Systems

In discussing the regulation of glycolysis and respiration, we have seen that the relative concentrations of ADP and ATP in the cell are the most important controlling elements. We can broaden this concept to apply to the integration of all processes capable of generating or utilizing phosphate-bond energy. When ATP is utilized in many biosynthetic reactions, it undergoes pyrophosphate cleavage to yield AMP (Chapters 14 and 19 and Part III), whereas in muscular contraction, ADP is the primary product of ATP utilization. At any given moment, a living cell contains not only ATP and ADP but also AMP (Table 18-4).

Table 18-4 The adenine nucleotide content of some tissues†

Tissue	*ATP*	*ADP*	*AMP*
Rat liver	4.7	1.5	0.6
Rat heart	13.3	2.6	0.43
Blowfly muscle	14.0	3	0.25

† Data in micromoles per gram wet weight.

Recall that AMP can be phosphorylated to ATP only after the action of adenylate kinase

$$ATP + AMP \rightleftharpoons 2ADP$$

Atkinson has pointed out that the energy status of the cell is best expressed in terms of the extent to which the ATP-ADP-AMP system is "filled" with high-energy phosphate bonds. If all the adenine nucleotide in the cell is ATP, the system is completely filled and is considered to have an *energy charge* of 1.0. At the other extreme, if all the adenine nucleotide is present as AMP, the system is empty of high-energy bonds and has an energy charge of 0.0. If all the adenine nucleotide is present as ADP or as an equimolar mixture of ATP and AMP, it is only half-full of high-energy bonds and has an energy charge of 0.5. The energy charge of the ATP-ADP-AMP system can easily be calculated for any given set of concentrations of ATP, ADP, and AMP by the equation

$$\text{Energy charge} = \frac{1}{2}\left(\frac{[ADP] + 2[ATP]}{[AMP] + [ADP] + [ATP]}\right)$$

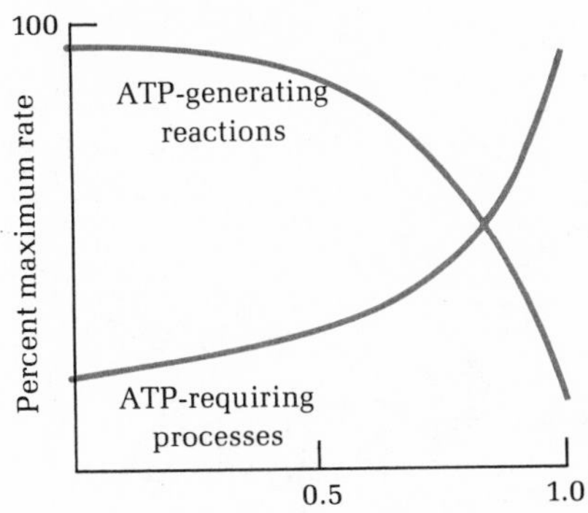

Figure 18-15
Response of ATP-generating and ATP-utilizing reactions to the energy charge of the ATP system.

Because many regulatory enzymes in both catabolic and anabolic pathways are responsive to AMP, ADP, or ATP as modulators, Atkinson has suggested that the regulation of pathways that produce and utilize high-energy phosphate bonds is a function of the energy charge of the ATP-ADP-AMP system. He has shown that the regulation of these pathways can be best represented by the curves in Figure 18-15, showing how ATP-generating metabolic sequences and ATP-utilizing sequences respond to the energy charge of the ATP-ADP-AMP system. The metabolic steady state in which ATP production is equal to ATP utilization is given by the intersection of the two curves. If the energy charge decreases below this point, the ATP-generating sequences are accelerated through the response of their regulatory enzymes to the concentration of ATP, ADP, and AMP; similarly the ATP-utilizing sequences are inhibited. If the energy charge increases above the normal level, a reversal takes place. The ATP-ADP-AMP system is thus poised to run optimally in a steady state and strongly resists any deviations from it.

Control of Glycolysis by Lactate Dehydrogenase Isozymes

We have seen (Chapter 9) that lactate dehydrogenase isozymes are constituted of two types of polypeptide chains (M and H) in five possible combinations: M_4, M_3H, M_2H_2, MH_3, H_4. The M_4 and M_3H isozymes are found to predominate in tissues highly dependent on glycolysis for energy, e.g., white skeletal muscle and embryonic tissues. The MH_3 and H_4 isozymes predominate in tissues with a purely aerobic or respiratory metabolism. Close study of the kinetic properties of the different lactate dehydrogenase isozymes has revealed that those from rapidly glycolyzing tissues have a very high affinity for pyruvate as electron acceptor and those from actively respiring tissues have a relatively low affinity. The lactate dehydrogenase isozymes present in the glycolytic type of muscle are thus very effective in reoxidizing NADH with pyruvate to produce lactate, whereas the isozymes in aerobic muscles are less reactive with pyruvate and allow NADH to be more readily reoxidized aerobically by the mitochondria. The synthesis of the different lactate dehydrogenase isozymes is genetically programmed so that the regulation of energy-yielding reactions is correlated with the stage of development or with cell differentiation.

Movement of Intramitochondrial Reducing Power to the Cytoplasm

As will be seen in Chapter 22, the biosynthesis of glucose from pyruvate requires cytoplasmic NADH to reduce 1,3-diphosphoglycerate to glyceraldehyde 3-phosphate. Mitochondria continuously generate internal NADH from the oxidation of substrates, but internal NADH cannot leave the mitochondria and enter the cytoplasm directly. However, Krebs has shown that electrons from intramitochondrial NADH can pass to the cytoplasm via a shuttle that operates in principle like the glycerol phosphate shuttle for bringing reducing equivalents from external NADH into the mitochondria. The outward-directed NADH shuttle employs the malate-oxaloacetate couple. Intramitochondrial malate dehydrogenase catalyzes transfer of electrons from intramitochondrial NADH to intramitochondrial oxaloacetate, reducing it to malate. Malate can freely pass through the mitochondrial membrane via its specific carrier and gain access to the cytoplasmic compartment. Here it can reduce cytoplasmic NAD^+ to form NADH by action of cytoplasmic malate dehydrogenase, thus making intramitochondrial reducing equivalents of NADH available for extramitochondrial use. The oxaloacetate formed in the cytoplasm can pass back into the mitochondria again, either directly or following decarboxylation to pyruvate or transamination from glutamate (Chapter 20). The malate shuttle is shown in Figure 18-13.

Similarly, intramitochondrial reducing power can be used to form extramitochondrial NADPH. Intramitochondrial isocitrate may leave mitochondria via the citrate carrier to the cytoplasm, where it donates electrons to $NADP^+$ through the action of cytoplasmic isocitrate dehydrogenase, which is NADP-linked (Chapter 16), thus generating cytoplasmic NADPH. By operation of these shuttle systems very effective regulation and control over the ratio of the intra- and extramitochondrial NADH–NAD^+ and NADPH–$NADP^+$ couples are maintained.

From these considerations, we may conclude that the mitochondria are not only the power plants of the cell but also play a key role in the distribution of ATP for performance of cellular work, in the division of electron flow to oxygen and to reductive biosynthetic reactions, and in the integration of metabolic pathways. Like a computerized automobile factory programmed to build many different models with many different colors and sets of accessories in response to the orders of distant dealers, the mitochondrion is a self-adjusting power plant and distributing center, which is exquisitely sensitive to the metabolic needs of all parts of the cell.

The Control of Oxidative Metabolism by Thyroid Hormones

The thyroid hormones

Thyroxine 3,5,3′-triiodothyronine

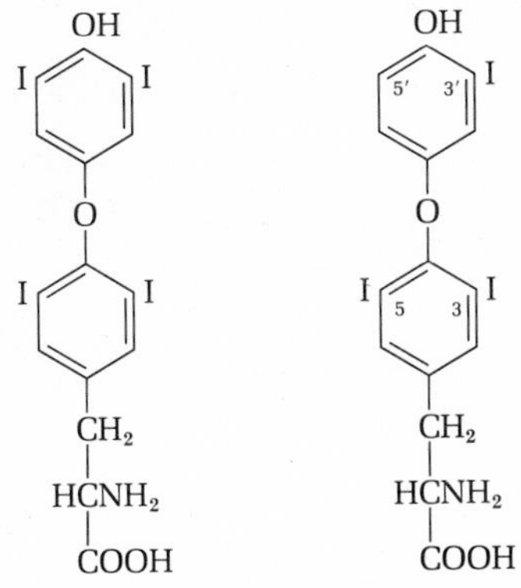

When the thyroid gland of mammals fails to produce normal amounts of its hormones, *thyroxine* and *triiodothyronine* (margin), the basal rate of oxygen consumption and the overall rate of metabolic processes decreases. Conversely, when excessive amounts of these hormones are administered, the basal metabolic rate increases above normal levels. Many investigations have been carried out with the goal of identifying some specific enzyme-catalyzed reaction in oxidative metabolism that is controlled by the thyroid hormones. In early investigations it was found that thyroxine stimulates respiration and uncouples oxidative phosphorylation when added to isolated mitochondria. Moreover, thyroxine also promotes the respiration-dependent swelling of mitochondria. However, such effects require excessively high concentrations of thyroxine and it is now doubtful whether they represent true endocrine effects of the hormone. More significant perhaps is the discovery that thyroxine administration causes a greatly increased synthesis of the flavoprotein mitochondrial glycerol phosphate dehydrogenase, which participates in the glycerol phosphate shuttle system (above). Although this effect could be responsible for the increased basal respiratory rate in hyperthyroid animals, it must be pointed out that the synthesis of many enzymes is now known to be increased by thyroxine administration. The molecular basis for the mode of action of thyroxine is still a challenging puzzle. One hypothesis is that it increases the rate of translation of the messenger RNA for certain specific enzymes (Chapter 30).

Summary

Mitochondria are frequently located near fuel sources or ATP-requiring structures. They vary in shape but are about the same size as bacteria. Mitochondria have two membranes, which can be separated. The outer membrane contains monoamine oxidase and fatty acid–activating enzymes; it is freely permeable to most low-molecular-weight solutes. The inner membrane has a much greater area, provided by infoldings called cristae. It is not permeable to Na^+, Mg^{2+}, Cl^-, or sucrose. It contains clusters of the electron-transport enzymes, called respiratory assemblies, spaced about 200 Å apart on the membrane surface; it also contains ATP-synthesizing enzyme molecules in the form of elementary particles, attached to its inner surface. The internal matrix of mitochondria contains much protein, including a number of enzymes of the tricarboxylic acid cycle, and pools of ADP, ATP, NAD, NADP, and CoA, which are segregated by the impermeability of the inner membrane from the extramitochondrial, or cytoplasmic, pools of these factors. Oxidative phosphorylation takes place within the inner compartment. ADP enters and ATP leaves the latter by equimolar exchange across the inner membrane, catalyzed by an ADP-ATP carrier that is inhibited by atractyloside. Similar specific carriers effect exchange of phosphate, succinate, isocitrate, malate, and glutamate across the inner membrane.

Mitochondria can accumulate Ca^{2+} and other cations at the expense of electron-transport energy in a process that is alternative to oxidative phosphorylation. During cation accumulation, two H^+ are ejected per pair of electrons per energy-conserving site. The chemiosmotic hypothesis for oxidative phosphorylation postulates that electron transport provides the energy to create across the inner membrane a pH or electrical potential gradient, which is suggested as the immediate energy source for oxidative phosphorylation. Mitochondria undergo changes in the shape of the cristae when respiration is stimulated by ADP. Conformational changes induced by respiration have also been postulated as the immediate energy source for formation of ATP.

Reducing equivalents of extramitochondrial NADH can enter the inner mitochondrial compartment indirectly by the glycerolphosphate or malate shuttles, which make it possible for electrons generated during the oxidation step of glycolysis in the cytoplasm to pass to the electron-transport chain of mitochondria, with the result that pyruvate is the end product of the glycolytic sequence under aerobic conditions. The electron-transport rate in mitochondria is controlled by the external ADP concentration. The glucose breakdown rate in the glycolytic sequence is inhibited by respiration; this is called the Pasteur effect. It is caused by the inhibition of phosphofructokinase, an allosteric glycolytic enzyme, by ATP or citrate, which are products of aerobic oxidation in the mitochondria. The regulation of the ATP-generating and ATP-utilizing metabolic sequences is best correlated with the energy charge of the ATP-ADP-AMP system, which is constant in the cellular steady state. Reducing equivalents generated within mitochondria may reach the cytoplasm via outward-directed shuttle systems.

References

(See also references to Chapter 17)

Books

CHANCE, B., R. W. ESTABROOK, and J. R. WILLIAMSON (eds.), *Control of Energy Metabolism*, Academic Press Inc., New York, 1965. Proceedings of a symposium.

LOWENSTEIN, J. M. (ed.), *Citric Acid Cycle: Control and Compartmentation*, Marcel Dekker, Inc., New York, 1969. An extremely valuable collection of articles.

QUAGLIARIELLO, E., S. PAPA, E. C. SLATER, and J. M. TAGER (eds.), *Mitochondrial Structure and Compartmentation*, Adriatica Editrice, Bari, Italy, 1967. Proceedings of a symposium.

PAPA, S., J. M. TAGER, E. QUAGLIARIELLO, and E. C. SLATER, (eds.), *The Energy Level and Metabolic Control in Mitochondria*, Adriatica Editrice, Bari, Italy, 1969.

Articles

ATKINSON, D. E., "The Energy Charge of the Adenylate Pool as a Regulatory Parameter. Interaction with Feedback Modifiers," *Biochem.* **7**:4030–4034 (1968).

CHAPPELL, J. B., "Systems for the Transport of Substances into Mitochondria," *Brit. Med. Bull.* **24**:150 (1968).

HACKENBROCK, C. R., "Ultrastructural Bases for Metabolically Linked Mechanical Activity in Mitochondria, I, II," *J. Cell*

Biol., **30**:269–297 (1967), **37**:345–369 (1968). Electron microscopy of mitochondria in different states of respiration; the conformational hypothesis of energy coupling.

HARRIS, R. A., J. T. PENNISTON, J. ASAI, and D. E. GREEN, "The Conformational Basis of Energy Transformations in Membrane Systems II Correlation between Conformational Change and Functional States," *Proc. Natl. Acad. Sci. U.S.*, **59**:830 (1968). Statement of the conformational hypothesis.

LEHNINGER, A. L., E. CARAFOLI, and C. S. ROSSI, "Energy-linked Ion Movements in Mitochondrial Systems," *Advan. Enzymol.*, **29**:259 (1967). A review of research on mitochondrial ion transport.

MITCHELL, P., "Chemiosmotic Coupling in Oxidative and Photosynthetic Phosphorylation," *Biol. Rev.*, **41**:445 (1965). Detailed exposition of the chemiosmotic hypothesis.

MITCHELL, P., and J. MOYLE, "Estimation of Membrane Potential and pH difference across the Cristae Membrane of Rat Liver Mitochondria," *Eur. J. Biochem.*, **7**:471–484 (1969). Theoretical and experimental aspects of chemiosmotic hypothesis.

PRESSMAN, B. C., "Induced Active Transport of Ions in Mitochondria," *Proc. Natl. Acad. Sci.*, **53**:1076–1083 (1965). The action of valinomycin and gramicidin.

RACKER, E., (ed.), *Structure and Function of Membranes of Mitochondria and Chloroplasts*, Reinhold, New York, 1969. A collection of valuable articles on the structure, function, and dynamic role of membranes.

SCHNAITMAN, C., and J. W. GREENAWALT, "Enzymatic Properties of the Inner and Outer Membranes of Rat Liver Mitochondria," *J. Cell. Biol.*, **38**:158–175 (1968). Use of marker enzymes to identify inner and outer membranes.

Problems

1. Calculate how many ADP molecules must enter each mitochondrion per min in a liver cell containing 1000 mitochondria, if the rate of oxygen consumption is 35 μl of oxygen (STP) per hour per mg wet weight of liver. Assume that mitochondria make up 20 per cent of the mass of a liver cell, that each cell is a sphere of density 1.05 and a diameter of 20 μ, and that all the respiration of the liver cell takes place in the mitochondria. Also assume an overall P:O ratio of 3.0.

   If there are 5000 ADP-ATP carrier molecules per mitochondrion, calculate the turnover number of each carrier i.e. the number of molecules of ADP transferred per molecule of carrier per min.

2. If there are 1,500 mitochondria in a spherical rat liver cell of diameter 16 μ, compare the total area of the inner membranes of all the mitochondria with the area of the cell membrane. Assume that liver mitochondria have a surface area of 40 square meters per gram of mitochondrial protein.

3. Calculate the number of H^+ ions in the inner compartment of a single rat liver mitochondrion, assuming it is a cylinder 1.8 μ long and 1.0 μ in diameter at (*a*) pH 6.0, (*b*) 7.0, and (*c*) pH 9.0.

4. Write the overall equation for the oxidation of extramitochondrial NADH to NAD^+ by oxygen via the respiratory

chain, assuming that the glycerol phosphate shuttle is operating.

5. Write a similar equation for oxidation of extramitochondrial NADH assuming the malate-oxaloacetate shuttle is operating.

6. Calculate the energy charge of the ATP system in rat liver and in blowfly flight muscle from the data in Table 18-4.

CHAPTER 19 **OXIDATION OF FATTY ACIDS**

Although carbohydrates, because of their abundance, are the major fuel for most organisms, fatty acids also play an extremely important role as energy source. Fatty acid oxidation is prominent in higher animals and plants, which can store large amounts of neutral fat as fuel reserve. Neutral fat has a high caloric value (~9 kcal $gram^{-1}$) and can be stored in nearly anhydrous form in intracellular fat droplets, whereas glycogen or starch (caloric value ~4 kcal $gram^{-1}$) are too hydrated to be stored in such concentrated form. In vertebrates, it is estimated that fatty acid oxidation normally provides at least half of the oxidative energy in the liver, kidneys, heart muscle, and resting skeletal muscle. In fasting, or in hibernating animals or migrating birds, fat is virtually the sole source of energy. On the other hand, little or no fatty acid oxidation occurs in the brain, which depends solely on glucose as energy source.

Intracellular Hydrolysis of Lipids

Fatty acids undergoing oxidation in tissues of higher animals come either from extracellular fluid or from endogenous intracellular lipids. Vertebrate blood contains considerable amounts of triacylglycerols and phosphoglycerides and very small amounts of free fatty acids noncovalently bound to the protein serum albumin, which serves to transport fatty acids. The latter are directly oxidized in such tissues as heart and muscle. The major endogenous source of fatty acids for fuel is storage fat, in the form of fat droplets in the cytoplasm, which consist largely of triacylglycerols. Since fatty acids must be in free form, i.e., non-esterified, before they can undergo activation and oxidation, the triacylglycerols must first undergo hydrolysis by intracellular lipases to yield free fatty acids and glycerol (Chapter 10). Another source of fatty acids are the membrane phosphoglycerides (Chapter 10). Although they are relatively constant in composition and amount, because of their structural role, they undergo continuous metabolic turnover in higher animal cells (Chapter 13) and yield free fatty acids following action of phospholipases (Chapter 10).

Relatively little is known about the sequence and details of intracellular lipid hydrolysis. However, normally there is no significant accumulation of free fatty acids or other hydrolysis products, such as lysophosphatides, which are extremely toxic and injurious to membrane structure. Evidently the rate and pathway of the hydrolysis of intracellular lipids is adjusted to the rate of utilization of fatty acids.

The Fatty Acid Oxidation Cycle

It was long suspected that fatty acids are synthesized and degraded in the cell by addition or subtraction of two-carbon fragments because most natural fatty acids have an even number of carbon atoms. This idea was also supported by the observation that in fasting mammals or in the disease diabetes mellitus fatty acids are incompletely oxidized, leading to the accumulation of the β-oxidized four-carbon acids *acetoacetic acid* and *D-β-hydroxybutyric acid* (margin) in the blood and urine. Another line of evidence came from classical experiments by the German biochemist Knoop in 1904, who observed that rabbits fed an even-carbon fatty acid labeled with a phenyl group at the terminal, or ω-carbon, atom excreted urinary *phenylacetic acid* (Figure 19-1), regardless of the length of the carbon chain of the acid. On the other hand, when ω-phenyl derivatives of odd-carbon fatty acids were fed, *benzoic acid* was excreted. (Phenylacetic and benzoic acid appear in the urine in conjugated form, esterified with D-glucuronic acid.)

Acetoacetic acid

CH_3CCH_2COOH (with =O on the second carbon)

D-β-Hydroxybutyric acid

CH_3CHCH_2COOH (with OH on the third carbon)

These results suggested that ω-phenyl fatty acids are degraded by removal of successive two-carbon fragments starting from the carboxyl end. In the even-carbon acids, the last two-carbon fragment is not oxidized further but is excreted as phenylacetic acid. Successive removal of two-carbon fragments from odd-carbon acids would yield the phenyl-substituted terminal carbon atom, which is excreted as benzoic acid. From these experiments (perhaps the first metabolic tracer experiments reported) Knoop postulated that fatty acids are oxidized by *β oxidation*, i.e., oxidation at the β carbon to yield a β-keto acid, which was assumed to undergo cleavage to form acetic acid and a fatty acid shorter by two carbon atoms.

Figure 19-1
Knoop's experiments on oxidation of phenyl fatty acids. Even-carbon acids always yield phenylacetic acid; odd-carbon acids always yield benzoic acid.

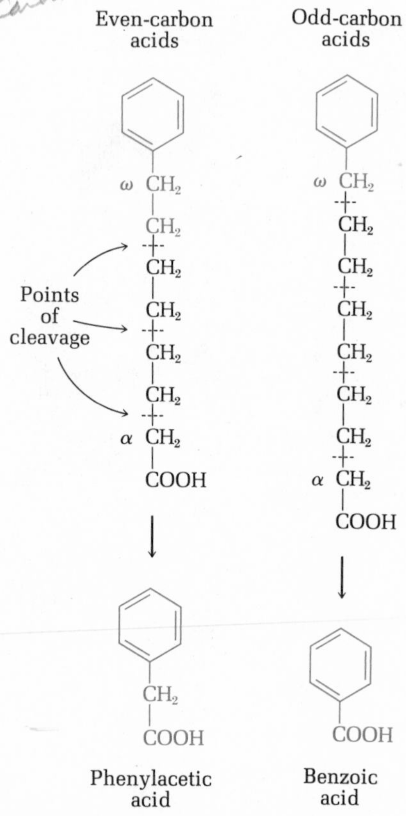

For many years, however, no success attended efforts to demonstrate fatty acid oxidation in cell-free extracts of animal tissues known to be active in this process. The enzymes involved in oxidation of fatty acids were believed to require intact cell structure. Furthermore, no evidence could be found of the occurrence of the medium-length β-keto fatty acid intermediates predicted by the β-oxidation hypothesis. Not until 1943 was oxidation of fatty acids by molecular oxygen in a cell-free system first demonstrated, by Leloir in Argentina, who found the system to be extremely labile. Shortly later, Lehninger showed that when ATP was added to homogenates of rat liver, the ability to oxidize fatty acids was restored, and he postulated that ATP was required to activate the fatty acid enzymatically. He also found that fatty acids are degraded into two-carbon units that can enter the Krebs

Figure 19-2
The fatty acid oxidation spiral. One acetyl CoA is removed during each pass through the sequence. One molecule of palmitic acid (C_{16}), after activation to palmitoyl CoA, yields eight molecules of acetyl CoA.

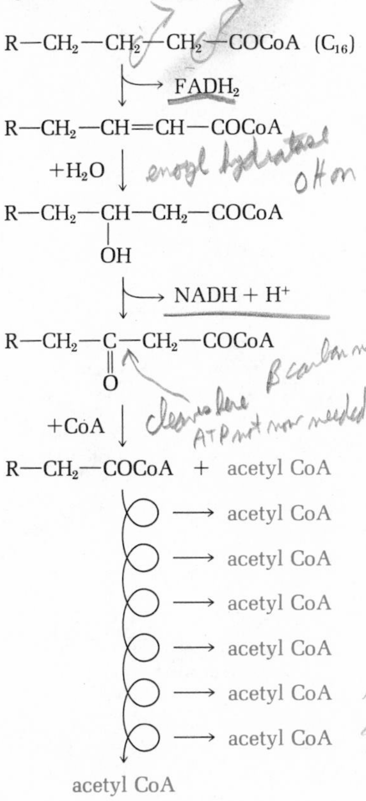

$$R—CH_2—CH_2—CH_2—COCoA \quad (C_{16})$$
$$\downarrow \rightarrow FADH_2$$
$$R—CH_2—CH=CH—COCoA$$
$$+H_2O \downarrow$$
$$R—CH_2—CH(OH)—CH_2—COCoA$$
$$\downarrow \rightarrow NADH + H^+$$
$$R—CH_2—C(=O)—CH_2—COCoA$$
$$+CoA \downarrow$$
$$R—CH_2—COCoA + \text{acetyl CoA}$$

→ acetyl CoA
→ acetyl CoA
→ acetyl CoA
→ acetyl CoA
→ acetyl CoA
→ acetyl CoA
acetyl CoA

tricarboxylic acid cycle. In 1948–1949, Kennedy and Lehninger showed that the oxidation of fatty acids occurs exclusively in the mitochondria.

The next important clue, which quickly led to recognition of the nature of the enzymatic steps of fatty acid oxidation, came from work of Lynen and his colleagues in Germany. They found that the ATP-dependent activation of fatty acids involves their esterification with the thiol group of CoA and that all the subsequent enzymatic steps in fatty acid oxidation take place in the form of their CoA esters. This observation explained why intermediate-length free fatty acids or β-keto acids are not found in most cells and tissues during oxidation of long-chain fatty acids. The various enzymes catalyzing the successive steps in fatty acid oxidation have since been isolated in highly purified form by Lynen, Green, Ochoa, and other investigators. The overall pathway of fatty acid oxidation is shown in Figure 19-2. Long-chain fatty acids are first activated by an energy-requiring step in which the fatty acid ester of CoA is formed enzymatically at the expense of ATP. This step is analogous to the priming step of glycolysis, in which glucose is phosphorylated by ATP. The fatty acids then enter the mitochondria as esters of the compound *carnitine* and are converted back into CoA esters. In the first step of the oxidative cycle, the fatty acyl CoA is dehydrogenated by removal of a pair of hydrogen atoms from the α and β carbon atoms to yield the α,β-unsaturated acyl CoA. The latter is then enzymatically hydrated to form a β-hydroxyacyl CoA ester, which in turn is dehydrogenated in an NAD-linked reaction to form the β-ketoacyl CoA ester. The latter then undergoes enzymatic cleavage by attack of the thiol group of a second molecule of CoA, to form acetyl CoA, derived from the α and the carboxyl carbon atoms of the original fatty acid chain. The other product, a long-chain saturated fatty acyl CoA ester having two fewer carbon atoms than the starting fatty acid, now becomes the substrate for another round of reactions, beginning with the first dehydrogenation step, until a second two-carbon fragment is removed as acetyl CoA. At each passage through this spiral process, the fatty acid chain loses a two-carbon fragment as acetyl CoA and two pairs of hydrogen atoms to specific acceptors. The 16-carbon palmitic acid thus undergoes a total of seven such cycles, to yield altogether eight molecules of acetyl CoA and 14 pairs of hydrogen atoms. The palmitic acid must be primed or activated only once, since at the end of each round the shortened fatty acid appears as its CoA ester.

The acetyl CoA formed as product of the fatty acid oxidation system then may enter the tricarboxylic acid cycle. The 14 pairs of hydrogen atoms removed during dehydrogenation of palmitic acid enter the respiratory chain, 7 pairs in the form of the reduced flavin coenzyme of fatty acyl CoA dehydrogenase and 7 pairs in the form of NADH. The passage of electrons from $FADH_2$ to oxygen and from NADH to oxygen in each case leads to the expected number of oxidative phosphorylations of ADP.

During fatty acid oxidation, there is no significant accumulation of the various intermediate CoA esters. The total amount of CoA in mitochondria is in fact very small, and fatty acid oxidation cannot continue without regeneration of free CoA, which occurs when acetyl CoA combines with oxaloacetate on entering the tricarboxylic acid cycle. The separate enzymatic steps in fatty acid oxidation will now be examined in detail.

Activation and Entry of Fatty Acids into Mitochondria

Recent research shows that there are three stages in the entry of fatty acids into mitochondria from the extramitochondrial cytoplasm. (1) The enzymatic esterification of the free fatty acid with extramitochondrial CoA, at the expense of ATP, which occurs in the outer membrane (2) the transfer of the fatty acyl group from CoA to the carrier molecule carnitine, which carries it across the inner membrane and (3) the transfer of the fatty acyl group from carnitine to intramitochondrial CoA.

Activation of Fatty Acids

At least three different enzymes catalyze formation of fatty acyl CoA esters, each being specific for a given range of fatty acid chain length. They are called activating enzymes or, better, *fatty acid thiokinases* [International designation *fatty acid:*CoA *ligase* (AMP)]. *Acetate thiokinase* activates acetic, propionic, and acrylic acids, *medium-chain fatty acid thiokinase* activates fatty acids with 4 to 12 carbon atoms, and *long-chain fatty acid thiokinase* activates fatty acids with 12 to 22 or more carbon atoms. The last two thiokinases activate both saturated and unsaturated fatty acids and α- and β-hydroxy acids. Otherwise the properties and mechanisms of all three thiokinases, which have been isolated in highly purified form, are nearly identical. The overall reaction catalyzed by the ATP-linked thiokinases is

$$\mathrm{RCOOH + ATP + CoASH \rightleftharpoons R{-}\underset{\underset{\displaystyle O}{\|}}{C}{-}SCoA + AMP + PP_{\mathit{i}}}$$

As the thioester linkage is formed between the fatty acid carboxyl group and the thiol group of CoA, the ATP undergoes pyrophosphate cleavage (Chapter 14) to yield AMP and inorganic pyrophosphate. The equilibrium constant for fatty acid activation, regardless of chain length, is about 1.0. The standard free energy of hydrolysis of the thioester group of the fatty acyl CoA formed is about the same as that of acetyl CoA ($\Delta G^{\circ\prime} = -7.50$ kcal). The pyrophosphate formed in the activation reaction is hydrolyzed by inorganic pyrophosphatase

$$\mathrm{PP}_i + \mathrm{H_2O} \longrightarrow 2\mathrm{P}_i$$

The net effect of this hydrolysis is the utilization of two high-energy phosphate bonds to pull the overall equilibrium of the preceding activation step far in the direction of the formation of fatty acyl CoA. Because fluoride, an inhibitor of inorganic pyrophosphatase, inhibits oxidation of free fatty acids, the hydrolysis of pyrophosphate appears to be essential in the overall activation process.

A fatty acyl adenylate

$$\mathrm{R{-}\underset{\underset{O}{\|}}{C}{-}O{-}\overset{\overset{O^-}{|}}{\underset{\underset{O}{\|}}{P}}{-}O{-}CH_2{-}}\text{ribose(2',3'-OH)}\text{–Adenine}$$

An enzyme-bound intermediate has been identified in the action of fatty acid thiokinases. It is a mixed anhydride of the fatty acid and the phosphate group of AMP, a *fatty acyl adenylate.* It is formed on the active site, with discharge of pyrophosphate to the medium (margin). In the presence of free CoA—SH, the fatty acyl adenylate reacts to yield fatty acyl CoA and free AMP as products.

The fatty acid thiokinases are found in the outer mitochondrial membrane; they are also present in microsomes derived from endoplasmic reticulum.

Transfer to Carnitine

Fatty acyl CoA: carnitine fatty acid transferase reaction

$$\mathrm{(CH_3)_3\overset{+}{N}{-}CH_2{-}\underset{\underset{OH}{|}}{CH}{-}CH_2{-}COOH}\ \text{(Carnitine)} + \mathrm{R{-}\underset{\underset{O}{\|}}{C}{-}S{-}CoA}\ \text{(Fatty acyl CoA)}$$
$$\rightleftharpoons$$
$$\mathrm{(CH_3)_3\overset{+}{N}{-}CH_2{-}\underset{\underset{O{-}C(=O){-}R}{|}}{CH}{-}CH_2{-}COOH}\ \text{(Fatty acyl carnitine)} + \mathrm{CoA{-}SH}$$

Higher fatty acids have only a limited ability to cross the inner membrane as CoA esters, but their entry is greatly stimulated by *carnitine,* a substance long known to be present in animal tissues but whose function went unrecognized until it was found to be an essential growth factor for the mealworm, *Tenebrio molitor,* the first suggestion that it may be required for some vital cellular function. Later, Fritz and other investigators showed that carnitine has a stimulating effect on the oxidation of fatty acids by mitochondria. It is now known that this effect is due to the action of an enzyme, *fatty acyl CoA:carnitine fatty acid transferase,* which catalyzes transfer of the fatty acyl group from its thioester linkage with CoA to an oxygen-ester linkage with the hydroxyl group of carnitine (margin). Since the standard free-energy change of this reaction is quite small, the acyl carnitine linkage evidently represents a high-energy bond.

The O-fatty acyl carnitine so formed readily passes through the inner membrane; whether this occurs by simple diffusion or through some membrane carrier mechanism (Chapter 27) is not known.

Transfer to Intramitochondrial CoA

In the last stage of the entry process, the fatty acyl group is transferred from carnitine to intramitochondrial CoA by the action of intramitochondrial carnitine fatty acid transferase

$$\text{Fatty acyl carnitine} + \text{CoA} \rightleftharpoons \text{fatty acyl CoA} + \text{carnitine}$$

Space-filling model of carnitine

This entry mechanism has the effect of keeping extramitochondrial and intramitochondrial CoA separate. The fatty acyl CoA now is used as substrate by the fatty acid oxidation cycle, which occurs in the inner matrix compartment.

Mitochondria contain another type of acyl thiokinase participating in fatty acid activation. Since this enzyme requires GTP instead of ATP and causes an *orthophosphate* cleavage of the GTP, it is systematically named *fatty acid:CoA ligase* (GDP). The overall reaction catalyzed is

$$\mathrm{GTP + RCOOH + CoASH \rightleftharpoons R{-}\underset{\underset{O}{\|}}{C}{-}SCoA + GDP + P_i}$$

Its equilibrium constant is also approximately 1.0. Presumably the function of this enzyme, which is located in the matrix, is to make possible direct utilization of the GTP generated in mitochondria during the substrate-level phosphorylation associated with oxidation of α-ketoglutarate (Chapter 16). Since carnitine is not necessary for its action, it is probably concerned with the activation of free fatty acids formed internally in mitochondria.

In some microorganisms which ferment fatty acids, e.g., the strict anaerobe *Clostridium kluyveri*, the formation of acyl CoA esters occurs by an indirect route. In the first step a high-energy acyl phosphate of acetate or fatty acid is formed by direct phosphorylation of the carboxyl group by ATP

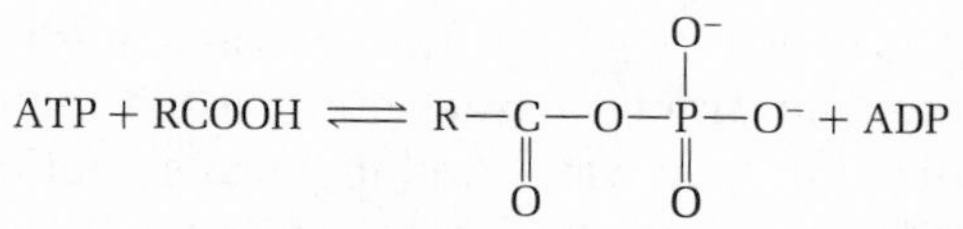

$$\mathrm{ATP + RCOOH \rightleftharpoons R{-}\underset{\underset{O}{\|}}{C}{-}O{-}\overset{\overset{O^-}{|}}{\underset{\underset{O}{\|}}{P}}{-}O^- + ADP}$$

The acyl phosphate so formed, a mixed anhydride of a carboxylic acid and phosphoric acid, is analogous to the 1,3-diphosphoglycerate formed during glycolysis (Chapters 14 and 15). The reaction written above is endergonic, but it is pulled to the right because the acyl phosphate undergoes a rapid reaction with CoA—SH catalyzed by a second enzyme, *phosphotransacetylase*, to form acyl CoA

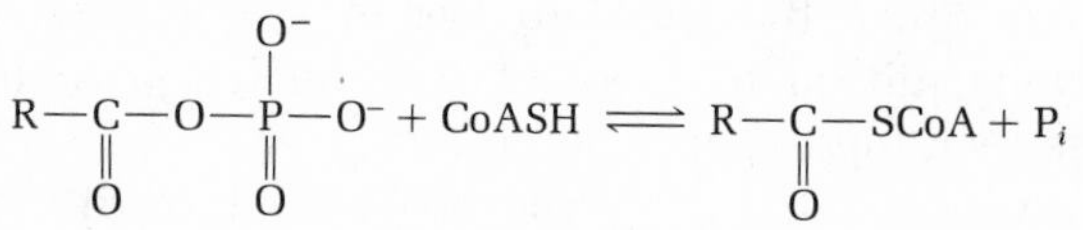

$$\mathrm{R{-}\underset{\underset{O}{\|}}{C}{-}O{-}\overset{\overset{O^-}{|}}{\underset{\underset{O}{\|}}{P}}{-}O^- + CoASH \rightleftharpoons R{-}\underset{\underset{O}{\|}}{C}{-}SCoA + P_i}$$

The First Dehydrogenation Step of Fatty Acid Oxidation

Following the activation step, the reactions of the fatty acid oxidation cycle take place in the inner compartment of mitochondria. The fatty acyl CoA ester first undergoes enzymatic dehydrogenation at the α and β carbon atoms, i.e., atoms 2 and 3, to form an unsaturated fatty acyl CoA as product; the position of the double bond is designated by the symbol $\Delta^{2,3}$. There are four different FAD-containing *fatty acyl CoA dehydrogenases*, each specific for a given range of fatty acid chain length. The reaction catalyzed is shown in the margin.

The tightly bound FAD of the enzyme becomes reduced, a process that probably occurs through distinct one-electron steps (Chapter 17). The $\Delta^{2,3}$-unsaturated bond formed in this reaction is the *trans* geometrical isomer. In contrast, the double bonds of the unsaturated fatty acids of natural fats are nearly always in the *cis* configuration (Chapter 10). We shall come back to this interesting point later.

The reduced form of the fatty acyl CoA dehydrogenase cannot react directly with oxygen. It donates its electrons to the respiratory chain via a second flavoprotein, *electron-transferring flavoprotein*, which in turn reduces some electron carrier of the respiratory chain that has not yet been identified with certainty, but is probably Coenzyme Q (margin).

The fatty acyl CoA dehydrogenase reaction.

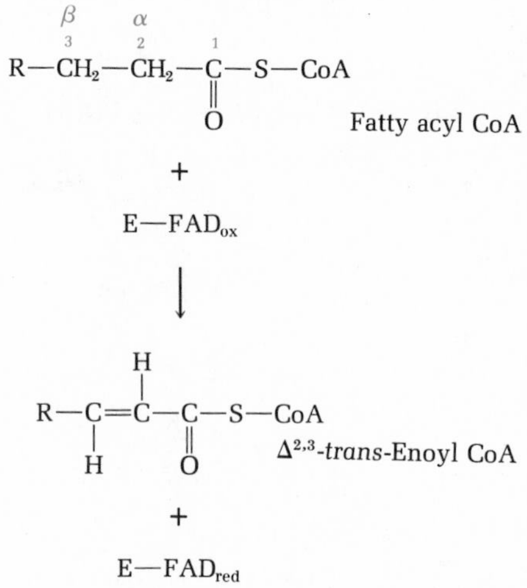

$$\mathrm{R{-}\overset{\beta\ 3}{CH_2}{-}\overset{\alpha\ 2}{CH_2}{-}\overset{1}{\underset{\underset{O}{\|}}{C}}{-}S{-}CoA}$$ Fatty acyl CoA

+

$\mathrm{E{-}FAD_{ox}}$

↓

$$\mathrm{R{-}\underset{\underset{H}{|}}{C}{=}\overset{\overset{H}{|}}{C}{-}\underset{\underset{O}{\|}}{C}{-}S{-}CoA}$$ $\Delta^{2,3}$-*trans*-Enoyl CoA

+

$\mathrm{E{-}FAD_{red}}$

Electron transport from fatty acyl CoA to cytochrome *b*.

Fatty acyl CoA

↓

fatty acyl CoA dehydrogenase

↓

electron-transferring flavoprotein

↓

CoQ

↓

cytochrome *b*

The enoylhydratase reactions

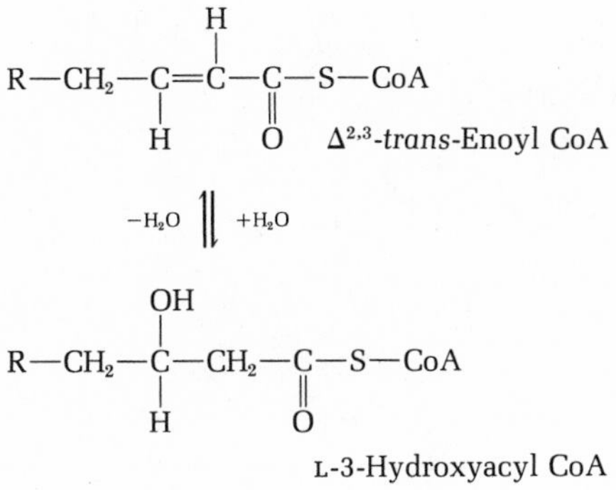

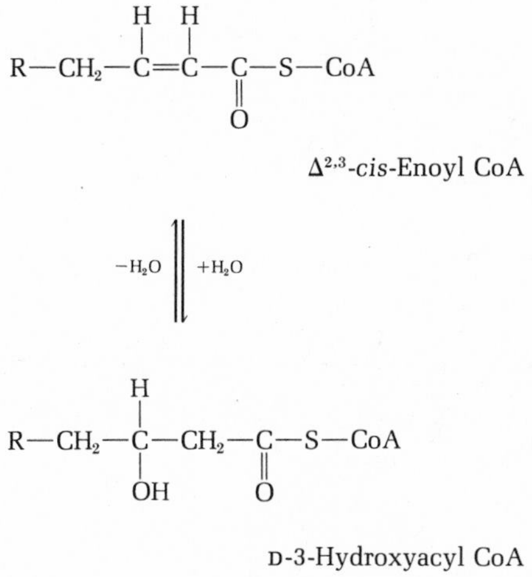

$$R{-}CH_2{-}\underset{H}{\overset{}{C}}{=}\overset{H}{C}{-}\underset{O}{\underset{\|}{C}}{-}S{-}CoA$$

$\Delta^{2,3}$-*trans*-Enoyl CoA

$$-H_2O \rightleftharpoons +H_2O$$

$$R{-}CH_2{-}\overset{OH}{\underset{H}{C}}{-}CH_2{-}\underset{O}{\underset{\|}{C}}{-}S{-}CoA$$

L-3-Hydroxyacyl CoA

$$R{-}CH_2{-}\overset{H}{C}{=}\overset{H}{C}{-}\underset{O}{\underset{\|}{C}}{-}S{-}CoA$$

$\Delta^{2,3}$-*cis*-Enoyl CoA

$$-H_2O \rightleftharpoons +H_2O$$

$$R{-}CH_2{-}\overset{H}{\underset{OH}{C}}{-}CH_2{-}\underset{O}{\underset{\|}{C}}{-}S{-}CoA$$

D-3-Hydroxyacyl CoA

The Hydration Step

The reversible hydration of the double bond of $\Delta^{2,3}$-enoyl CoA esters to form β-hydroxy (or 3-hydroxy) acyl CoA is catalyzed by the enzyme *enoylhydratase* (systematic name, *3-hydroxyacyl* CoA *hydrolyase*), which has been obtained in crystalline form. The reaction catalyzed is shown in the margin. The addition of water across the $\Delta^{2,3}$-*trans* double bond is stereospecific and results in the formation of the L stereoisomer of the 3-hydroxyacyl CoA ester. Enoylhydratase cannot hydrate $\Delta^{3,4}$-unsaturated fatty acyl CoA esters, but it can hydrate $\Delta^{2,3}$-*cis*-unsaturated fatty acyl CoA esters to yield the corresponding D stereoisomer of 3-hydroxy fatty acyl CoA esters (margin). This may appear puzzling, since the next enzyme in the fatty acid oxidation cycle is specific for the L stereoisomer of 3-hydroxy fatty acyl CoA. We shall see later, however, that the D- and L- stereoisomers of 3-hydroxy fatty acyl CoA differ in origin and function.

The Second Dehydrogenation Step

In the next step of the fatty acid cycle, the L-3-hydroxy fatty acyl CoA is dehydrogenated to form 3-keto fatty acyl CoA by *L-3-hydroxy fatty acyl CoA dehydrogenase;* NAD^+ is the specific electron acceptor. The reaction is

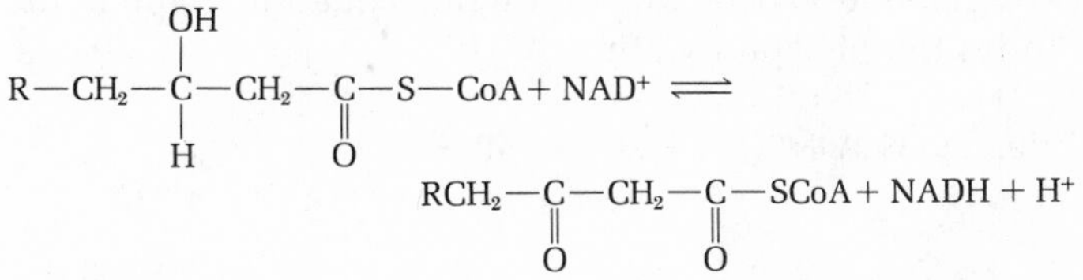

$$R{-}CH_2{-}\overset{OH}{\underset{H}{C}}{-}CH_2{-}\underset{O}{\underset{\|}{C}}{-}S{-}CoA + NAD^+ \rightleftharpoons$$
$$RCH_2{-}\underset{O}{\underset{\|}{C}}{-}CH_2{-}\underset{O}{\underset{\|}{C}}{-}SCoA + NADH + H^+$$

This enzyme is relatively nonspecific for fatty acid chain length but absolutely specific for the L stereoisomer. The NADH formed in the reaction donates its electron equivalents to the NADH dehydrogenase of the respiratory chain.

The Thiolytic Cleavage Step

In the last step of the fatty acid oxidation sequence, which is catalyzed by *β-ketothiolase* (more simply, *thiolase*), the 3-keto fatty acyl CoA undergoes cleavage by interaction with a molecule of free CoA, to yield the carboxyl-terminal two-carbon fragment as free acetyl CoA and the CoA ester of a fatty acid shortened by two carbon atoms

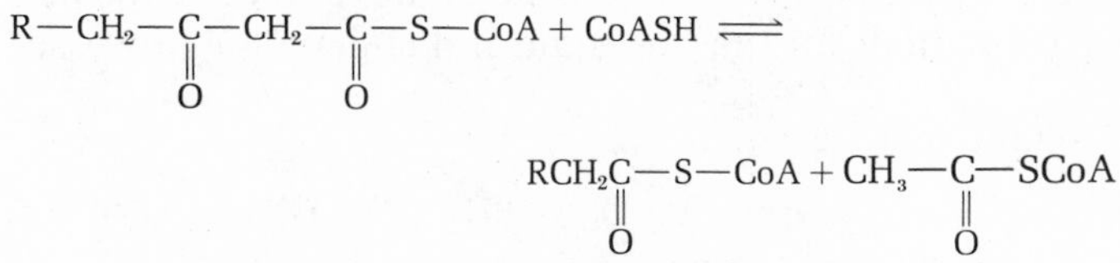

$$R{-}CH_2{-}\underset{O}{\underset{\|}{C}}{-}CH_2{-}\underset{O}{\underset{\|}{C}}{-}S{-}CoA + CoASH \rightleftharpoons$$
$$RCH_2\underset{O}{\underset{\|}{C}}{-}S{-}CoA + CH_3{-}\underset{O}{\underset{\|}{C}}{-}SCoA$$

This cleavage reaction, also called a *thiolysis* or a *thiolytic cleavage*, is analogous to a hydrolysis. The reaction is highly exergonic and thus the equilibrium favors cleavage. There appear to be two or three forms of the enzyme, each specific for different chain lengths.

The Balance Sheet

With the thiolysis reaction we have completed one round of the fatty acid oxidation sequence, in which one molecule of acetyl CoA and two pairs of hydrogen atoms have been removed from a long-chain fatty acyl CoA. The overall equation for one turn of the fatty acid oxidation sequence acting on palmitoyl CoA is

$$\text{Palmitoyl CoA} + \text{CoA} + \text{FAD} + \text{NAD}^+ + \text{H}_2\text{O} \longrightarrow \text{myristoyl CoA} + \text{acetyl CoA} + \text{FADH}_2 + \text{NADH} + \text{H}^+$$

We can now write the equation for the seven turns of the spiral required to convert one molecule of palmitoyl CoA to eight molecules of acetyl CoA

$$\text{Palmitoyl CoA} + 7\text{CoA} + 7\text{FAD} + 7\text{NAD}^+ + 7\text{H}_2\text{O} \longrightarrow 8\text{ acetyl CoA} + 7\text{FADH}_2 + 7\text{NADH} + 7\text{H}^+$$

Each molecule of reduced fatty acyl CoA dehydrogenase (FADH_2) donates a pair of electron equivalents to the respiratory chain at the level of CoQ or cytochrome *b*, and two molecules of ATP are generated during the ensuing electron transport (Chapter 17). Similarly, oxidation of each molecule of NADH results in formation of three molecules of ATP. Hence, a total of five molecules of ATP is formed per molecule of acetyl CoA cleaved. We can therefore write the following equation, which includes the phosphorylations:

$$\text{Palmitoyl CoA} + 7\text{CoA} + 7\text{O}_2 + 35\text{P}_i + 35\text{ADP} \longrightarrow 8\text{ acetyl CoA} + 35\text{ATP} + 42\text{H}_2\text{O} \quad (1)$$

The eight molecules of acetyl CoA formed in the fatty acid cycle may now enter the Krebs cycle. The following equation represents the balance sheet for their oxidation and the coupled phosphorylations:

$$8\text{ acetyl CoA} + 16\text{O}_2 + 96\text{P}_i + 96\text{ADP} \longrightarrow 8\text{CoA} + 96\text{ATP} + 104\text{H}_2\text{O} + 16\text{CO}_2 \quad (2)$$

Combining equations (1) and (2), we get the overall equation

$$\text{Palmitoyl CoA} + 23\text{O}_2 + 131\text{P}_i + 131\text{ADP} \longrightarrow \text{CoA} + 16\text{CO}_2 + 146\text{H}_2\text{O} + 131\text{ATP}$$

Since one molecule of ATP (or GTP) was required to activate the free palmitic acid to begin with, we may assume the net yield of ATP to be 130 molecules and write the partial equations for the exergonic and endergonic processes

$$\text{Palmitic acid} + 23\text{O}_2 \longrightarrow 16\text{CO}_2 + 16\text{H}_2\text{O} \qquad \Delta G^{\circ\prime} = -2{,}340\text{ kcal}$$

$$130\text{ADP} + 130\text{P}_i \longrightarrow 130\text{ATP} + 130\text{H}_2\text{O} \qquad \Delta G^{\circ\prime} = 130 \times 7.30 = +949\text{ kcal}$$

Thus some $949/2{,}340 \times 100 = 40$ percent of the standard free energy of oxidation of palmitic acid is recovered as phosphate-bond energy.

Oxidative removal of 3 acetyl CoA units from oleic acid

Oleyl CoA $\longrightarrow$ $\Delta^{3,4}$-*cis* enoyl CoA + 3 acetyl CoA

Oxidation of Unsaturated Fatty Acids

Unsaturated fatty acids, such as oleic acid, are oxidized by the same general pathways as saturated fatty acids, but two special problems arise. The double bonds of naturally occurring unsaturated fatty acids are in the *cis* geometrical configuration, whereas the $\Delta^{2,3}$-unsaturated acyl CoA esters functioning as intermediates in the oxidation of saturated fatty acids are *trans*. Moreover, the double bonds of most unsaturated fatty acids occur at such positions in the carbon chain that successive removal of two-carbon fragments from the carboxyl end up to the point of the first double bond yields a $\Delta^{3,4}$-unsaturated fatty acyl CoA rather than the $\Delta^{2,3}$-fatty acyl CoA serving as an intermediate in the fatty acid cycle (shown in margin for oleic acid). However, it will be recalled that enoylhydratase cannot hydrate $\Delta^{3,4}$-unsaturated fatty acyl CoA esters.

This anomaly has recently been resolved with the discovery of an auxiliary enzyme, *$\Delta^{3,4}$cis-$\Delta^{2,3}$-trans-enoyl CoA isomerase*, which catalyzes the reversible shift of the double bond from the $\Delta^{3,4}$-*cis* to the $\Delta^{2,3}$-*trans* configuration. The equilibrium constant of this reaction (margin) is about 7.0. The resulting $\Delta^{2,3}$-*trans*-unsaturated fatty acyl CoA is the normal substrate for the next enzyme of the fatty acid oxidation sequence, *enoyl hydratase*, which hydrates it to form L-3-hydroxy fatty acyl CoA (see above). The complete oxidation of oleyl CoA to nine acetyl CoA units by the fatty acid oxidation cycle thus requires an extra enzymatic step catalyzed by the $\Delta^{3,4}$-*cis*-$\Delta^{2,3}$-*trans* isomerase, in addition to the enzymes required in saturated fatty acid oxidation.

$\Delta^{3,4}$ *cis*-$\Delta^{2,3}$ *trans*-enoyl CoA isomerase reaction

$\Delta^{3,4}$-*cis*-enoyl CoA $\rightleftharpoons$ $\Delta^{2,3}$ *trans*-enoyl CoA

Polyunsaturated fatty acids, such as linoleic acid (Chapter 10), require a second auxiliary enzyme to complete their oxidation, since they contain two or more *cis* double bonds. When three successive acetyl CoA units are removed from linoleyl CoA, a $\Delta^{3,4}$-*cis* double bond is reached, as in the case of oleyl CoA. This is transformed by the $\Delta^{3,4}$-*cis*-$\Delta^{2,3}$-*trans* isomerase to the $\Delta^{2,3}$-*trans* isomer, which is then hydrated to the corresponding L-3-hydroxy fatty acyl CoA, dehydrogenated, and cleaved by thiolase to yield acetyl CoA and an eight-carbon $\Delta^{2,3}$-unsaturated acid (Figure 19-3); however, the double bond of the latter is in the *cis* configuration. Although the $\Delta^{2,3}$-*cis* double bond can be hydrated by enoyl hydratase, as mentioned above, the product is the D stereoisomer of a 3-hydroxy fatty acyl CoA, not the L stereoisomer formed during oxidation of saturated fatty acids. The utilization of the D-stereoisomeric 3-hydroxyacyl CoA ester generated from linoleic acid requires a second auxiliary enzyme, *3-hydroxy fatty acyl CoA epimerase*, which catalyzes the epimerization of carbon atom 3 (below). The product of

Conversion of $\Delta^{2,3}$ *cis*-enoyl CoA to L-3-hydroxy acyl CoA.

$$\underset{\Delta^{2,3}\text{-}cis\text{-Enoyl CoA}}{R{-}CH_2{-}CH{=}CH{-}CO{-}S{-}CoA} \underset{-H_2O}{\overset{+H_2O}{\rightleftharpoons}} \underset{\text{D-3-Hydroxyacyl CoA}}{R{-}CH_2{-}C(H)(OH){-}CH_2{-}CO{-}S{-}CoA} \overset{\text{epimerase}}{\rightleftharpoons} \underset{\text{L-3-Hydroxyacyl CoA}}{R{-}CH_2{-}C(OH)(H){-}CH_2{-}CO{-}S{-}CoA}$$

Figure 19-3
Pathway of oxidation of linoleic acid, showing action of auxiliary enzymes.

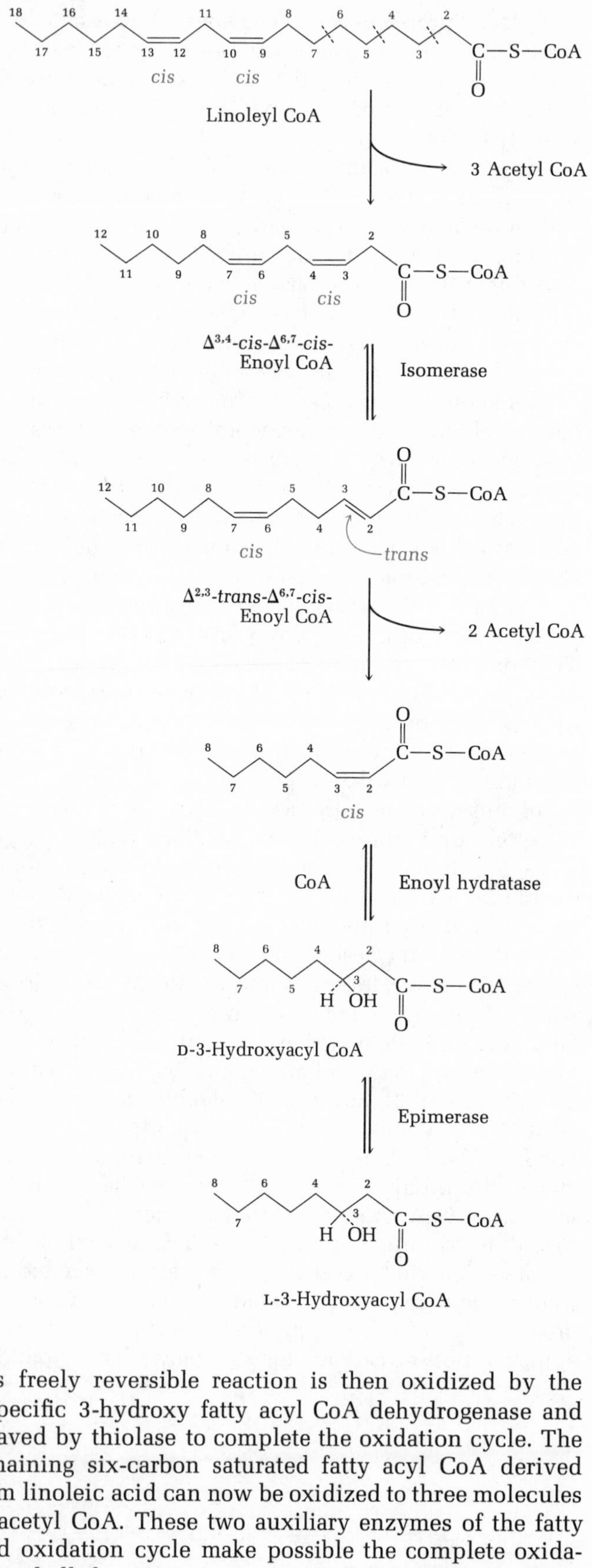

Linoleyl CoA

3 Acetyl CoA

$\Delta^{3,4}$-*cis*-$\Delta^{6,7}$-*cis*-Enoyl CoA

Isomerase

$\Delta^{2,3}$-*trans*-$\Delta^{6,7}$-*cis*-Enoyl CoA

2 Acetyl CoA

CoA

Enoyl hydratase

D-3-Hydroxyacyl CoA

Epimerase

L-3-Hydroxyacyl CoA

this freely reversible reaction is then oxidized by the L-specific 3-hydroxy fatty acyl CoA dehydrogenase and cleaved by thiolase to complete the oxidation cycle. The remaining six-carbon saturated fatty acyl CoA derived from linoleic acid can now be oxidized to three molecules of acetyl CoA. These two auxiliary enzymes of the fatty acid oxidation cycle make possible the complete oxidation of all the common unsaturated fatty acids found in naturally occurring lipids.

Ketone Bodies and Their Oxidation

In many vertebrates the liver has the enzymatic capacity to divert some of the acetyl CoA derived from fatty acid or pyruvate oxidation, presumably during periods of excess formation, into free acetoacetate and D-β-hydroxybutyrate, which are transported via the blood to the peripheral tissues, where they may be oxidized via the tricarboxylic acid cycle. These compounds are called the *ketone bodies*. Acetoacetate is formed in two ways. Some arises as the CoA ester from the last four carbon atoms of a long-chain fatty acid following prior removal of successive acetyl CoA residues during fatty acid oxidation, but most arises from the condensation of two molecules of acetyl CoA, catalyzed by thiolase

$$\text{Acetyl CoA} + \text{acetyl CoA} \rightleftharpoons \text{acetoacetyl CoA} + \text{CoA}$$

β-Hydroxy-β-methylglutaryl CoA

```
      COOH
       |
      CH2
       |
  HO—C—CH3
       |
      CH2
       |
      C—S—CoA
      ||
      O
```

The acetoacetyl CoA formed in these reactions then undergoes loss of CoA to become acetoacetate, a process known as *deacylation*. The major pathway for deacylation is the formation and enzymatic cleavage of *β-hydroxy-β-methylglutaryl CoA* (margin), which also serves as a precursor of sterols (Chapter 23)

$$\text{Acetoacetyl CoA} + \text{acetyl CoA} \rightleftharpoons \beta\text{-hydroxy-}\beta\text{-methylglutaryl CoA} + \text{CoA}$$

$$\beta\text{-Hydroxy-}\beta\text{-methylglutaryl CoA} \longrightarrow \text{acetoacetate} + \text{acetyl CoA}$$

The sum of these two reactions is

$$\text{Acetoacetyl CoA} \longrightarrow \text{acetoacetate} + \text{CoA}$$

The free acetoacetate so produced is enzymatically reduced to D-β-hydroxybutyrate by the NAD-linked *D-β-hydroxybutyrate dehydrogenase*. This enzyme is specific for the D stereoisomer; it does not act on CoA esters

$$\text{Acetoacetate} + \text{NADH} + \text{H}^+ \rightleftharpoons \text{D-}\beta\text{-hydroxybutyrate} + \text{NAD}^+$$

The mixture of free acetoacetate and β-hydroxybutyrate resulting from this reaction then may diffuse out of the liver cells into the blood stream to the peripheral tissues. Normally the concentration of ketone bodies in the blood is very low, but in fasting or in the disease diabetes mellitus, it may reach extremely high levels. This condition, known as *ketosis*, arises when the rate of formation of the ketone bodies exceeds the capacity of the peripheral tissues to utilize them.

In the peripheral tissues the D-β-hydroxybutyrate is oxidized to acetoacetate, which is then activated to form its CoA ester. Two enzymatic mechanisms for activation of acetoacetate are known. In the first, ATP is utilized in a reaction similar to the activation of fatty acid

$$\text{ATP} + \text{acetoacetate} + \text{CoA} \rightleftharpoons \text{acetoacetyl CoA} + \text{AMP} + \text{PP}_i$$

In the second, CoA is enzymatically transferred from succinyl CoA (Chapter 16) to acetoacetate, with little change in free energy. The acetoacetyl CoA formed in these reactions then undergoes thiolytic cleavage to two molecules of acetyl CoA, which then may enter the tricarboxylic acid cycle.

Oxidation of Odd-Carbon Fatty Acids

Odd-carbon fatty acids, which rarely occur in nature but arise during the oxidative degradation of valine and isoleucine (Chapter 20), can also be oxidized in the fatty acid oxidation cycle. Successive acetyl CoA residues are removed until the terminal three-carbon atom residue is reached; it becomes propionyl CoA.

Propionyl CoA undergoes enzymatic carboxylation to form *methylmalonyl* CoA (margin), catalyzed by *propionyl carboxylase*. This enzyme contains biotin as coenzyme (Chapter 16). In the following reaction step, catalyzed by *methylmalonylmutase*, methylmalonyl CoA is isomerized to succinyl CoA (margin) which may undergo deacylation in the succinyl thiokinase reaction to yield free succinate, which may enter the tricarboxylic acid cycle.

Although the metabolism of propionyl CoA in animal tissues appears to be a relatively minor pathway, quantitatively speaking, the methylmalonylmutase step involves a coenzyme of extraordinary chemical and biological properties. It is 5′-deoxyadenosylcobalamin, a derivative of *vitamin* B_{12}, which is necessary in the nutrition of man and probably most animal and plant species. The history of vitamin B_{12} is of interest since its discovery, isolation, structure determination, and mode of action have been exceedingly challenging problems. In 1926 Minot and Murphy discovered that eating liver cures patients suffering from pernicious anemia. Despite many attempts over the years to isolate the liver factor, little progress was made, since human pernicious anemia patients had to be used to assay the potency of liver-factor concentrates. In 1948, the liver factor, called vitamin B_{12}, was finally isolated in crystalline form. Despite a wide distribution in nature, the vitamin is present in only the minutest quantities in most organisms. Blood, for example, contains only 2×10^{-4} μg ml^{-1}. The richest sources of vitamin B_{12} are sewage, manure, soil, and mud, which contain anaerobic bacteria rich in the vitamin.

Pernicious anemia is not simply a deficiency of vitamin B_{12} but results from the failure to absorb vitamin B_{12} from ingested food, due to a lack of a mucoprotein in gastric juice called the *intrinsic factor*. Vitamin B_{12} promotes the development of normal erythrocytes. However, its mode of action was obscure until 1958, when Barker discovered that the 5′-deoxyadenosyl derivative of vitamin B_{12} is an essential coenzyme in the conversion of glutamic acid into β-methylaspartic acid (margin) in an anaerobic bacterium, *Clostridium tetanomorphum*. It was subsequently discovered that this coenzyme is also required for the action of methylmalonylmutase, which converts the car-

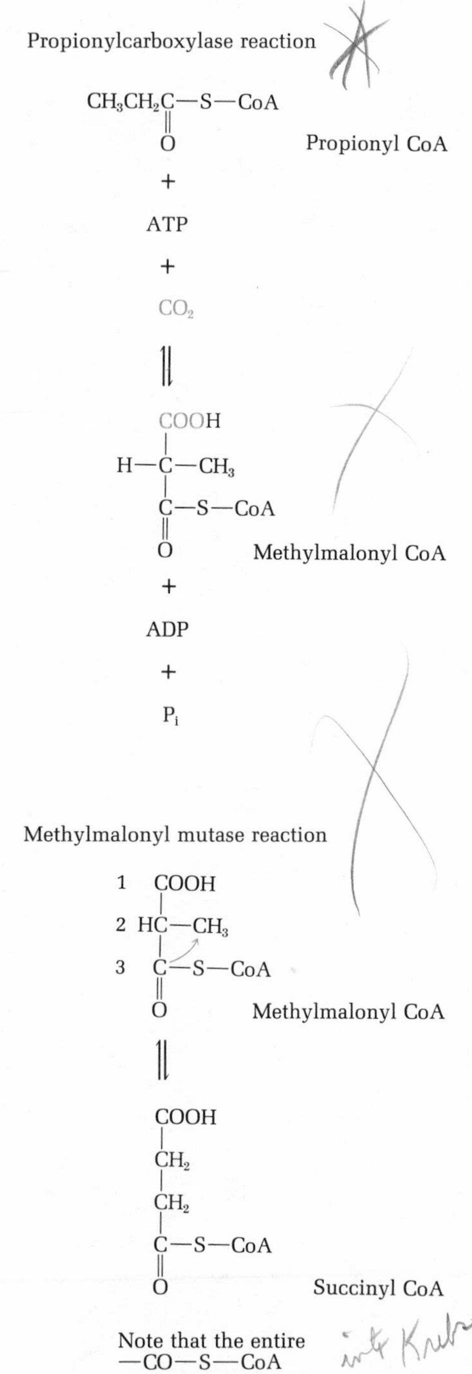

Formation of β-methylaspartic acid

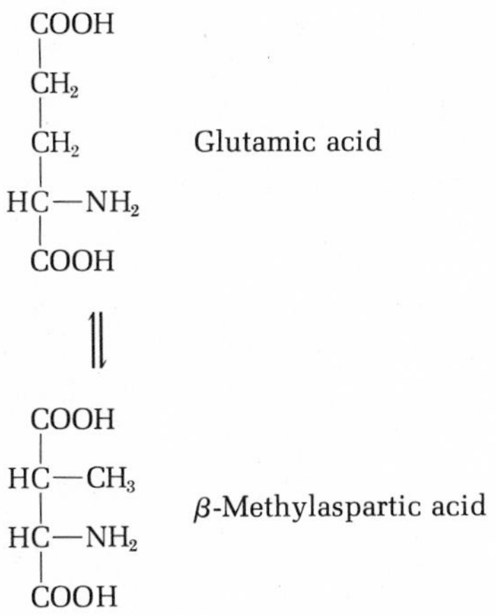

$$\begin{array}{l} COOH \\ | \\ CH_2 \\ | \\ CH_2 \\ | \\ HC{-}NH_2 \\ | \\ COOH \end{array} \quad \text{Glutamic acid}$$

$$\rightleftharpoons$$

$$\begin{array}{l} COOH \\ | \\ HC{-}CH_3 \\ | \\ HC{-}NH_2 \\ | \\ COOH \end{array} \quad \beta\text{-Methylaspartic acid}$$

boxylation product of propionyl CoA, namely, methylmalonyl CoA, into succinyl CoA.

Elucidating the structure of vitamin B_{12} (Figure 19-4) proved to be an extraordinarily difficult problem, which was solved by a combination of chemical and x-ray crystallography approaches in 1957. Vitamin B_{12} has two characteristic components. The first is a nucleotidelike structure, which is exceptional in containing as base *5,6-dimethylbenzimidazole* in α-glycosidic linkage with D-ribose rather than the β linkage present in most nucleotides; it also contains a phosphate group at the 3′ position. The second and most characteristic part of the molecule is the *corrin* ring system, which resembles porphyrins (Chapter 17) in containing four pyrrole rings but in which two of the pyrroles are joined directly rather than through methene bridges (Figure 19-4). Coordinated to the four inner nitrogen atoms of the corrin ring is an atom of cobalt, long known as an essential trace metal for growth. Vitamin B_{12} is also known as *cobalamin*. As usually isolated, the sixth coordination position of the Co(II) atom is filled by cyanide, an artifact of isolation; this derivative is called *cyanocobalamin.*

Vitamin B_{12} has no coenzyme activity itself, but its 5-deoxyadenosyl derivative is the active coenzyme form. The 5-deoxyadenosyl group is attached to the cobalt of vitamin B_{12} only through its methylene group; it replaces the cyanide of cyanocobalamin.

The methylmalonyl CoA mutase reaction has given a clue to the function of its coenzyme. Study of this intramolecular reaction with isotope tracers has re-

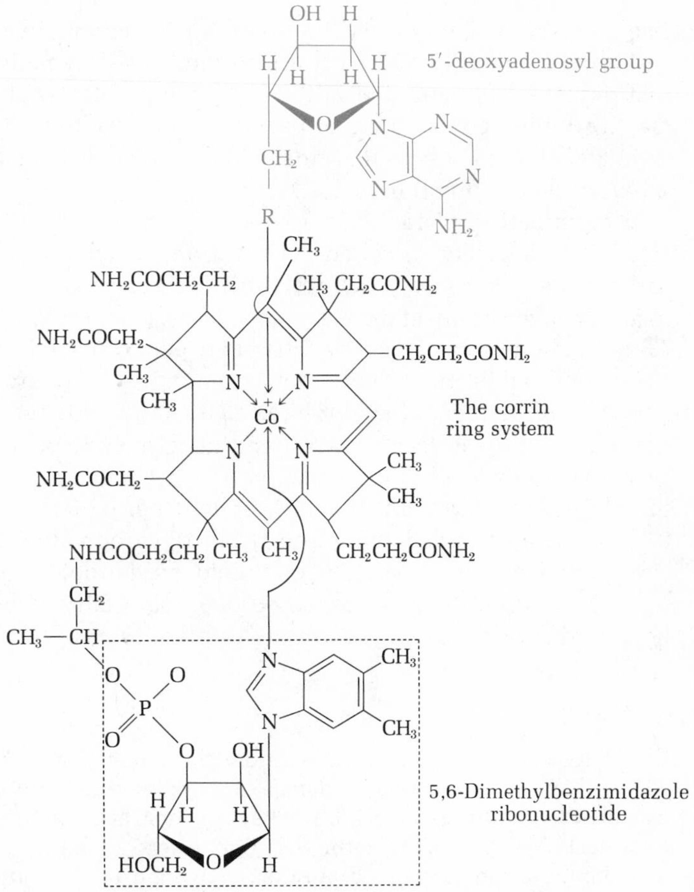

Figure 19-4
Vitamin B_{12} (cobalamin) and its derivatives. In cyanocobalamin R = cyanide; in chlorocobalamin R = chloride. Cobalamin forms similarly named complexes with sulfate, hydroxyl, and nitrite ions. In the coenzyme R is the 5′-deoxyadenosyl group (in color above). The name of the coenzyme is often abbreviated as DAcobalamin.

vealed that it takes place by the migration of the entire thioester group (—CO—S—CoA) from carbon atom 2 of methylmalonyl CoA to the methyl carbon atom, in exchange for an H atom. In each of the few known enzymatic reactions in which DAcobalamin is the required coenzyme, the reaction catalyzed is the exchange of a hydrogen atom on one carbon atom with a substituent group on a vicinal carbon atom, without exchange of the hydrogen atom with protons of the medium (margin). The mechanism of this process is not yet understood, but one hypothesis suggests that Co(II) undergoes reduction to Co(I), an extremely strong nucleophile, which can serve as a carrier of alkyl groups from one atom to another. This hypothesis is supported by the fact that this coenzyme is required for the formation of methane gas from methylated compounds in certain anaerobic bacteria and for the transfer of methyl groups in animal tissues (Chapter 24). In fact, an active methyl derivative of vitamin B_{12} has been identified; the methyl group, which replaces the deoxyadenosyl group, is covalently bonded to the cobalt atom. Alkylcobalamins are probably the only organometallic compounds found in nature.

It is noteworthy that people suffering from pernicious anemia, who are deficient in vitamin B_{12} because of the lack of intrinsic factor, excrete large amounts of methylmalonic acid and propionic acid in the urine, proving that the methylmalonylmutase reaction is defective in such patients. The function of the vitamin in transmethylations will be discussed further in Chapters 24 and 25.

Alkyl group shifts catalyzed by cobamide enzymes

$$
\begin{array}{c}
R_1 \\
| \\
-\text{C}-\text{H} \\
| \\
-\text{C}-\text{X} \\
| \\
R_2
\end{array}
\rightleftharpoons
\begin{array}{c}
R_1 \\
| \\
-\text{C}-\text{X} \\
| \\
-\text{C}-\text{H} \\
| \\
R_2
\end{array}
$$

Minor Pathways of Fatty Acid Oxidation

The α-hydroxy fatty acids found in some cerebrosides and gangliosides (Chapter 10) are formed by enzymatic hydroxylation of saturated fatty acids. Some fatty acids may also undergo oxidation at the ω carbon atom to form ultimately α,ω-dicarboxylic acids. This pathway is called *ω oxidation*; its function is not known.

In germinating plant seeds a special pathway of fatty acid oxidation occurs, called *α oxidation*, in which the carboxyl carbon is lost as CO_2 and the α carbon is oxidized to an aldehyde group at the expense of hydrogen peroxide. This reaction is catalyzed by *fatty acid peroxidase*. The H_2O_2 required is furnished from other oxidations, presumably of reduced flavoproteins. The fatty aldehyde formed is oxidized to the corresponding carboxylic acid. This two-enzyme reaction sequence is then repeated on the shortened fatty acid. Since fatty acid peroxidase attacks only fatty acids having from 13 to 18 carbon atoms, this pathway cannot lead to complete oxidation. It is believed to function as a source of long-chain fatty alcohols, which occur in large amounts in plant waxes.

The α-oxidation pathway

$$RCH_2CH_2COOH$$

$$\downarrow \text{Fatty acid peroxidase}, H_2O_2$$

$$RCH_2\underset{\underset{O}{\|}}{C}H + CO_2$$

$$\downarrow NAD^+ \rightarrow NADH + H^+$$

$$RCH_2COOH$$

Summary

Free fatty acids are derived either from the bloodstream, in which they are transported bound to serum albumin, or from hydrolysis of intracellular lipids. They are first activated by esterification with CoA to form acyl CoA esters at the outer mitochondrial membrane and are then converted into O-fatty acyl carnitine esters, which can cross the inner mitochondrial membrane into the matrix, where fatty acyl CoA esters are re-formed. All subsequent steps in the oxidation of fatty acids take place upon their CoA esters within the mitochondrial matrix. The successive oxidative removal of acetyl CoA units from long-chain saturated fatty acyl CoA is called β oxidation. Four reaction steps are required to remove each acetyl CoA residue: (1) The dehydrogenation of carbon atoms 2 and 3 by FAD-linked fatty acyl CoA dehydrogenases, (2) hydration of the resulting 2,3-*trans* double bond by enoylhydratase, (3) dehydrogenation of the resulting L-β-hydroxy fatty acyl CoA by an NAD^+-linked dehydrogenase, and (4) a CoA-requiring cleavage (thiolysis) of the resulting β-keto fatty acyl CoA, to form acetyl CoA and the CoA ester of a fatty acid shortened by two carbons. The shortened fatty acid CoA ester can then reenter the sequence. For complete oxidation of the 16-carbon palmitic acid, seven cycles through the system are required, yielding eight molecules of acetyl CoA. Electrons removed in the two dehydrogenation steps flow to oxygen via the respiratory chain, accompanied by oxidative phosphorylation of ADP. The acetyl CoA formed during fatty acid oxidation is then oxidized to CO_2 and H_2O via the tricarboxylic acid cycle. The overall equation for oxidation of palmitoyl CoA is

$$\text{Palmitoyl CoA} + 23O_2 + 131P_i + 131\text{ADP} \longrightarrow 16CO_2 + 146H_2O + 131\text{ATP}$$

This process recovers about 40 percent of the standard free energy of oxidation of palmitic acid as phosphate-bond energy.

Unsaturated fatty acids require additional enzymatic steps in order to shift their double bonds into the proper position for the hydration step and to yield the L-stereoisomer of the β-hydroxy intermediate. The ketone bodies acetoacetate and β-hydroxybutyrate are formed in the liver following deacylation of acetoacetyl CoA. They are carried to other tissues, where they are oxidized via acetyl CoA and the tricarboxylic acid cycle. Odd-carbon fatty acids are oxidized to acetyl CoA and propionyl CoA. Carboxylation of propionyl CoA yields methylmalonyl CoA, which undergoes isomerization to succinyl CoA. The latter reactions require 5′-deoxyadenosylcobalamin, a coenzyme form of vitamin B_{12}, which participates in a number of enzymatic reactions as an alkyl group carrier. α and ω oxidation represent minor pathways of fatty acid catabolism.

References

Books

DAWSON, R. M. C., and D. N. RHODES (eds.), *Metabolism and Physiological Significance of Lipids*, John Wiley & Sons, Inc., New York, 1964.

FLORKIN, M., and E. H. STOTZ (eds.), *Lipid Metabolism*, vol. 18 of *Comprehensive Biochemistry*, American Elsevier Publishing Company, New York, 1967.

GRAN, F. C. (ed.), *Cellular Compartmentation and Control of Fatty Acid Metabolism*, Proceedings, Federation of European Biochemical Societies, Academic Press Inc., New York, 1967.

HOFMANN, K., *Fatty Acid Metabolism in Microorganisms*, John Wiley & Sons, Inc., New York, 1963. The occurrence and metabolism of branched and cyclic acids.

TAGER, J. M., S. PAPA, E. QUAGLIARIELLO, and E. C. SLATER (eds.), *Regulation of Metabolic Processes in Mitochondria*, Bari

Symposium, Dutch Elsevier Publishing Company, Amsterdam, 1965.

Reviews and Articles

FRITZ, I. B., "Carnitine and Its Role in Fatty Acid Metabolism," *Advan. Lipid Res.*, **1**:285–334 (1963).

GARLAND, P. B., "Control of Citrate Synthesis in Mitochondria," in T. W. Goodwin (ed.), *Metabolic Roles of Citrate*, Academic Press Inc., New York, 1968. Short review of relationships between fatty acid oxidation and the tricarboxylic acid cycle.

GARLAND, P. B., B. CHANCE, L. ERNSTER, C. LEE, and D. WONG, "Flavoproteins of Mitochondrial Fatty Acid Oxidation," *Proc. Natl. Acad. Sci. U.S.*, **58**:1698–1702 (1967). Evidence for two or more flavoproteins.

GREVILLE, G. D., and P. K. TUBBS, "The Catabolism of Long-Chain Fatty Acids in Mammalian Tissues," in *Essays in Biochemistry*, vol. IV, Academic Press Inc., New York, 1968. Excellent and readable review.

HOGENKAMP, H. P. C., "Enzymatic Reactions Involving Corrinoids," *Ann. Review Biochem.*, **37**:225–248 (1968).

KLENK, E., "The Metabolism of Polyenoic Fatty Acids," *Advan. Lipid Res.*, **3**:2–23 (1965).

KREBS, H. A., "The Regulation of Release of Ketone Bodies by the Liver," *Advan. Enzyme Regulation*, **4**:339–354 (1966).

KUSUNOSE, M., E. KUSUNOSE, and M. J. COON, "Enzymatic ω-Oxidation of Fatty Acids," *J. Biol. Chem.*, **239**:1374–1380 (1964).

ROSSI, C. R., A. ALEXANDRE, and L. SARTORELLI, "Organization of Fatty Acid Oxidation in Rat Kidney Mitochondria," *Eur. J. Biochem.*, **4**:31–34 (1968).

STUMPF, P. K., "Metabolism of Fatty Acids," *Ann. Rev. Biochem.*, **38**:159–212 (1969). Comprehensive review of recent advances.

Problems

1. Write balanced equations for the following metabolic processes, including all required activation steps and all oxidative phosphorylations. Assume that the reactions are taking place in the liver, kidney, or heart.
   (*a*) Oxidation of myristic acid to acetyl CoA.
   (*b*) Oxidation of arachidonic acid to CO_2 and H_2O.
   (*c*) Oxidation of *n*-butyric acid in the presence of malonate. Assume oxaloacetate is readily available.
   (*d*) Oxidation of palmitic acid to acetoacetic acid.
   (*e*) Oxidation of monooleyldipalmitoylglycerol to CO_2 and H_2O.
   (*f*) Oxidation of D-β-hydroxybutyric acid to CO_2 and H_2O.
   (*g*) Oxidation of propionic acid to CO_2 and H_2O.
   (*h*) Oxidation of *n*-nonanoic acid to CO_2 and H_2O.

2. If *n*-nonanoic acid labeled with ^{14}C in carbon atom 7 is oxidized under conditions in which the tricarboxylic acid cycle is operating, which carbon atoms of the following intermediates will become labeled: (*a*) succinate, (*b*) oxaloacetate, (*c*) α-ketoglutarate?

3. Pyruvate labeled with ^{14}C in carbon atom 2 is incubated with liver tissue. Which carbon atoms of β-hydroxy-β-methylglutaryl CoA will become labeled rapidly?

CHAPTER 20 OXIDATIVE DEGRADATION OF AMINO ACIDS

Although amino acids function primarily as precursors of proteins and other biomolecules, they are often used as a source of energy. Higher animals actively oxidize both exogenous amino acids, arising from ingested protein, and endogenous amino acids, arising from the metabolic turnover of body proteins. For example, it has been estimated from isotopic tracer experiments that in a 70-kg man on an average diet about 400 grams of protein undergoes turnover each day. Up to one-fourth of this amount, some 100 grams of amino acids, undergoes oxidative degradation and is replaced daily from the exogenous intake; the remainder represents recycling of endogenous amino acids. Even when no protein is being ingested, human beings may excrete 5 grams of nitrogen per day, corresponding to net oxidation of about 30 grams of endogenous protein. The tricarboxylic acid cycle is the ultimate pathway for oxidation of the carbon skeletons of amino acids.

Higher plants have an extremely complex amino acid metabolism, since they contain and actively metabolize many amino acids besides the 20 commonly found in proteins. Since most plants grow continuously, the net direction of amino acid metabolism is toward synthesis rather than oxidation. Nevertheless, some oxidative catabolism of amino acids does take place in plants. Many microorganisms also have the genetic ability to utilize amino acids as sources of carbon and energy.

This chapter describes the oxidative degradation of the amino acids normally found as building blocks of proteins, which thus constitutes the mainstream of amino acid catabolism. Although the basic enzymatic reactions involved in amino acid catabolism are for the most part similar in most organisms, the actual rate of utilization and the proportion of the different amino acids utilized in a given organism depends on many factors, including (1) the genetic ability to catabolize amino acids, (2) the availability of amino acids from the environment, (3) the nutritional dependence of the organism on essential amino acids, (4) the availability of other caloric fuels, (5) the needs of the organism for amino acids in protein synthesis, and (6) the need for specific amino acids as precursors of other important biomolecules such as purines, pyrimidines, cell-wall components, hormones, and other specialized molecules.

Proteolysis

Before proteins can enter the catabolic pathways, they must undergo complete enzymatic hydrolysis to amino acids, since intact protein molecules and most peptides cannot pass through the cell membrane, whereas free amino acids are readily absorbed (Chapter 27). Extracellular peptides and proteins are often hydrolyzed by the action of enzymes secreted into the environment; e.g., many microorganisms form and secrete peptidases and proteolytic enzymes. However, extracellular proteolysis has been studied in greatest detail in the digestive tract of vertebrates.

In mammals, this process begins in the gastric juice, which has a pH of 1.0 to 1.5, by the action of pepsin, which is secreted by the chief cells of the gastric mucosa in the form of an inactive precursor or *zymogen*. This precursor, pepsinogen (mol wt 40,400), is converted to pepsin (mol wt 32,700) by free pepsin acting in the presence of gastric HCl. The activation of pepsinogen is therefore autocatalytic. In this process, 42 amino acid residues are removed from the NH_2-terminal end of pepsinogen as a mixture of peptides. The latter contain most of the 16 basic amino acid residues of pepsinogen, which accounts for the fact that pepsinogen is most stable at nearly neutral pH and has a high isoelectric point (pH 3.8), whereas pepsin is stable only at acid pH regions and has an isoelectric pH and an optimum pH of about 1.0 to 1.5. Pepsin initiates hydrolysis of native proteins in the stomach by cleaving peptide linkages in which the amino function is contributed by aromatic and acidic amino acids. Another proteolytic enzyme, called *gastricsin*, has also been isolated from gastric juice.

In the small intestine, which has a pH of about 7 to 8, polypeptides formed in the stomach are exposed to the action of several proteolytic enzymes. Some of these are secreted by the pancreas and enter the intestine via the pancreatic duct as inactive zymogens, namely, *trypsinogen, chymotrypsinogen, procarboxypeptidases*, and *proelastase*. These zymogens are converted into their enzymatically active forms in the intestine. Trypsinogen, which has been crystallized, consists of a single chain of 249 amino acids of known sequence. It is converted to active trypsin by *enterokinase*, a proteolytic enzyme secreted by the intestine, or by trypsin itself. This conversion involves simply the removal of a hexapeptide from the NH_2-terminal end of trypsinogen. Trypsin is maximally active at pH 7.0 and is rather specific (Chapter 5) for cleaving all peptide linkages in the substrate protein whose carbonyl groups are contributed by arginine and lysine, wherever they occur in the chain. Trypsin is thus an *endopeptidase*.

Chymotrypsinogen also consists of a single peptide chain, but it is cross-linked by five disulfide bridges. It is converted to α-chymotrypsin, the active form, by the action of trypsin, a conversion requiring three major steps:

(1) trypsin first cleaves the chymotrypsinogen chain between residues 15 and 16 to yield *π-chymotrypsin*, which is proteolytically active but not stable; (2) trypsin cleaves off residues 14 and 15 in one piece (Ser-Arg) to give *δ-chymotrypsin;* and (3) residues 148 and 149 are then "clipped" out (as Thr-Asn) to yield *α-chymotrypsin*, which contains three peptide chains held together by five disulfide bridges. In the small intestine, chymotrypsin, which is also an endopeptidase, hydrolyzes those peptide bonds whose carbonyl functions are contributed by tryptophan, phenylalanine, or tyrosine and, to a lesser extent, by leucine and methionine. Chymotrypsin and trypsin thus supplement each other in their substrate specificity.

The procarboxypeptidases are activated to *carboxypeptidase A* and *B*, respectively. The carboxypeptidases are exopeptidases and hydrolyze only terminal peptide bonds. Carboxypeptidase A contains Zn^{2+} and hydrolyzes all COOH-terminal peptide linkages except when the COOH-terminal amino acid is lysine or arginine or the penultimate residue is proline. Carboxypeptidase B attacks only COOH-terminal lysine or arginine residues. Proelastase, which is secreted by the pancreas and is converted to *elastase* by the action of trypsin, acts on peptide bonds involving neutral amino acids but is particularly active on elastin.

The secretion of the small intestine contributes *leucine aminopeptidase*, an exopeptidase which hydrolyzes NH_2-terminal peptide bonds. Despite its name, this enzyme is rather nonspecific and hydrolyzes most NH_2-terminal amino acids of peptides. By the combined action of the proteolytic enzymes secreted by the stomach, pancreas, and small intestine, ingested proteins are ultimately completely hydrolyzed to amino acids, which are absorbed by epithelial cells lining the small intestine in an active-transport process that requires energy (Chapter 27). Amino acids are then circulated to all tissues via the blood. On gaining entrance to individual cells, again by an energy-requiring transport process, they enter the metabolic channels.

Very little is known about the mechanism of intracellular proteolysis, which in some tissues, particularly the liver, takes place at a high rate.

The Flow Sheet of Amino Acid Oxidation

There are 20 different multienzyme sequences for the oxidation of the 20 different amino acids. They ultimately converge into a few terminal pathways leading to the tricarboxylic acid cycle (Figure 20-1). The carbon skeletons of 10 of the amino acids ultimately are converted into acetyl CoA via either pyruvate or acetoacetyl CoA, five are converted into α-ketoglutarate, three to succinyl CoA, and two to oxaloacetate. Two amino acids, namely, phenylalanine and tyrosine, are so degraded that one portion of the carbon skeleton enters as acetyl CoA and the other as fumarate. However, not all the carbon atoms of each of the 20 amino acids enter the tricarboxylic acid cycle, since some are lost en route by decarboxylation reactions. The catabolic pathways taken by the amino acids are not

Figure 20-1
Pathways of entry of the carbon skeletons of amino acids into Krebs tricarboxylic acid cycle.

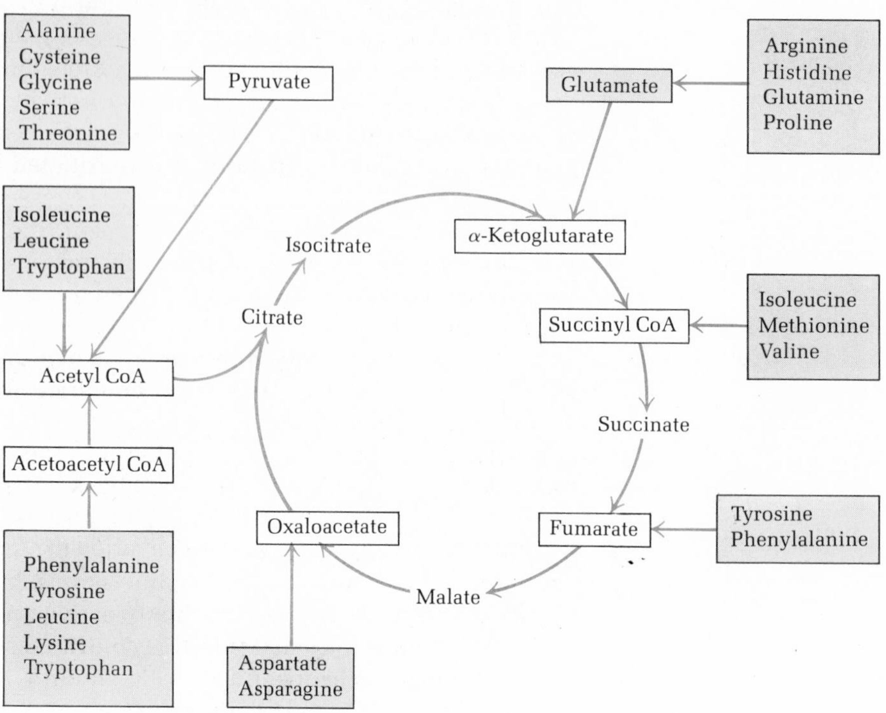

necessarily identical with those taken in their biosynthesis, but there are often common steps in the two routes, as will be seen in the discussion of amino acid biosynthesis (Chapter 25).

The catabolic pathways of amino acids are often long and complex, with many intermediates; it may indeed appear that they are unnecessarily long for the end achieved. However, many of the intermediates of amino acid oxidation have other functions in the cell, particularly as essential precursors of other cell components. The catabolic amino acid pathways are thus multifunctional, and from them lead many branches and collateral routes.

In mammals amino acid catabolism takes place largely in the liver. Although the kidney is also active, skeletal muscle is relatively inactive.

The α-amino groups share a common terminal fate, at least in vertebrates, which excrete amino nitrogen as urea, ammonia, or uric acid, depending on the species. The enzymatic mechanisms by which the α-amino groups are removed from various amino acids and collected for their ultimate conversion to one of these three end products are quite similar. Since removal of the α-amino group generally constitutes the first stage in amino acid catabolism, we shall now examine the two major processes involved, namely *transamination* and *oxidative deamination*.

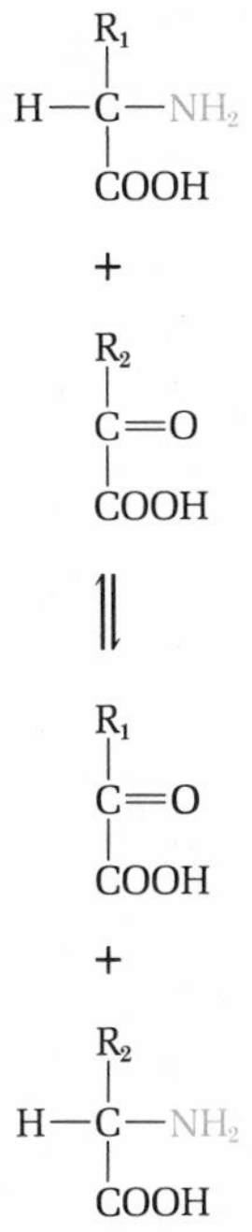

Figure 20-2
The transaminase reaction. The amino group is transferred reversibly from an α-amino acid to an α-keto acid.

$$\mathrm{H{-}C(R_1)(NH_2){-}COOH} + \mathrm{R_2{-}C({=}O){-}COOH} \rightleftharpoons \mathrm{R_1{-}C({=}O){-}COOH} + \mathrm{H{-}C(R_2)(NH_2){-}COOH}$$

Transamination and the Function of Pyridoxal Phosphate

At some stage in the catabolism of at least 11 of the amino acids (alanine, arginine, asparagine, aspartic acid, cysteine, isoleucine, lysine, phenylalanine, tryptophan, tyrosine, and valine) the α-amino group is enzymatically removed by transamination. In such reactions the α-amino group is transferred to the α-carbon atom of one of three different α-keto acids—pyruvate, α-ketoglutarate, or oxaloacetate—leaving behind the corresponding α-keto acid analog of the amino acid and causing the amination of the α-keto acid acceptor to the analogous α-amino acid (Figure 20-2). Two important transaminases are *alanine transaminase*

$$\alpha\text{-Amino acid} + \text{pyruvic acid} \rightleftharpoons \alpha\text{-keto acid} + \text{alanine}$$

and *glutamate transaminase*

$$\alpha\text{-Amino acid} + \alpha\text{-ketoglutaric acid} \rightleftharpoons \alpha\text{-keto acid} + \text{glutamic acid}$$

The reactions catalyzed by transaminases are freely reversible and have an equilibrium constant of about 1.0. It will be noted that there is no *net* deamination in such reactions, since the α-keto acid acceptor becomes aminated as the α-amino acid is deaminated. However, the whole point of transamination reactions is to *collect* the amino groups of various amino acids in the form of only one α-amino acid, usually glutamic acid, although aspartic acid and alanine also share in the collection process, depending on the organism. Alanine transaminase is specific for pyruvate-alanine as one substrate pair but is nonspecific for the other substrate pair. It therefore can bring about collection of amino groups in the form of alanine from many other amino acids so long as it is supplied with pyruvate. Glutamate transaminase also serves to collect amino groups and has an analogous specificity for glutamate–α-ketoglutarate as one of its substrate pairs. In organisms where alanine transaminase is dominant in the collection of α-amino groups from other amino acids, the amino groups are later transferred to α-ketoglutarate from alanine via the substrate-specific *glutamate-pyruvate transaminase*

$$\text{Alanine} + \alpha\text{-ketoglutaric acid} \rightleftharpoons \text{pyruvic acid} + \text{glutamic acid}$$

Whatever the pathway of transamination, α-ketoglutarate is the final acceptor of amino groups from most of the other amino acids; it channels amino groups into a final sequence of reactions by which the nitrogenous end products are formed.

Transaminases are found both in the mitochondria and and in the soluble portion of the cytoplasm of eucaryotic cells, the mitochondrial and extramitochondrial forms differing in physicochemical properties. There is evidence for a close metabolic interplay between mitochondria and the surrounding cytoplasm during deamination of amino acids. In particular, it now appears likely that collection of amino groups takes place in the extramitochondrial cytoplasm, with ultimate formation of glutamate. The glutamate then enters the mitochondria via a specific membrane carrier system. In the mitochondrial matrix there is a specific aspartate-glutamate transaminase. The transaminases thus play a role in amino group metabolism analogous to that of the phosphate-transferring enzymes in the energy cycle of the cell.

All the transaminases appear to have the same coenzyme and to share a common reaction mechanism. The coenzyme is *pyridoxal phosphate*, a derivative of vitamin B_6, which is required as an essential growth factor in the diet by many microorganisms and animals. The structures of vitamin B_6 (also called *pyridoxine* or *pyridoxol*), its aldehyde and amine forms, *pyridoxal* and *pyridoxamine*, and pyridoxal phosphate are shown in Figure 20-3. Pyridoxal phosphate is the prosthetic group not only of the transaminases but also of a number of other enzymes catalyzing reactions involving α-amino acids. In principle, pyridoxal phosphate functions as a carrier of amino groups or, in some cases, amino acids. The key to its action is its aldehyde group, which can reversibly form a Schiff's base, or *ketimine*, with ammonia or various amines. During its catalytic cycle in transaminases the coenzyme undergoes reversible transitions between its free aldehyde form, pyridoxal phosphate, and its aminated form, *pyridoxamine phosphate*. This cycle occurs in two stages (Figure 20-4): (1) The pyridoxal phosphate-enzyme complex accepts an amino group from the amino group donor, with formation of the pyridoxamine phosphate–enzyme complex; this occurs via two intermediate Schiff's bases. (2) The pyridoxamine phosphate–enzyme complex forms a Schiff's base with the incoming amino group acceptor, the α-keto acid, to which the amino group is then donated (Figure 20-4). By oscillation between the aldehyde and amino forms, the coenzyme thus acts as a carrier of amino groups from an amino acid to a keto acid. There is now strong experimental evidence that the aldehyde group of the pyridoxal phosphate forms a Schiff's base with the ϵ-amino group of a specific lysine residue of the enzyme protein whenever it is not occupied by an amino group arising from a substrate. The incoming amino group from the substrate displaces the enzyme ϵ-amino group to form the enzyme-substrate complex. Pyridoxal phosphate has a characteristic light-absorption spectrum which is useful in following the course of the formation and disappearance of the enzyme-substrate complexes.

The formulation in Figure 20-5 suggests a mechanistic basis for the fact that pyridoxal phosphate is a coenzyme not only for transmination reactions but also for enzymatic decarboxylation of α-amino acids, dehydration of serine, and removal of sulfur from cysteine, among others. The formation of an intermediate complex between the amino acid and the coenzyme, together with some electron-withdrawing structure M^+ contributed by the enzyme, may make possible labilization of bonds *a*, *b*, and *c* (Figure 20-5), rendering the amino acid molecule susceptible to several types of transformation.

Figure 20-3
Derivatives of vitamin B_6.

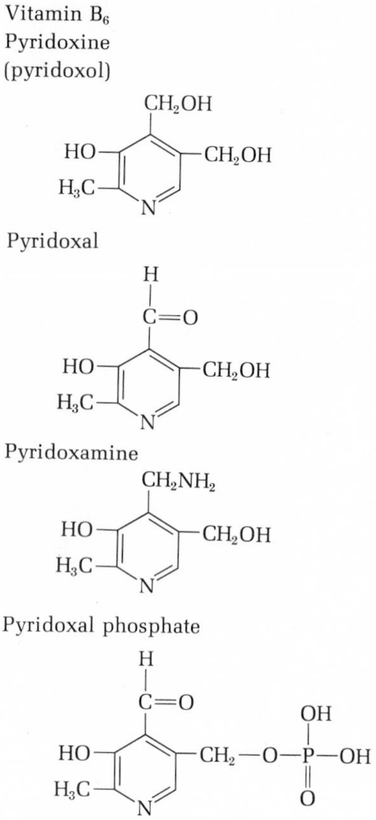

Vitamin B_6
Pyridoxine
(pyridoxol)

CH_2OH, HO, CH_2OH, H_3C, N

Pyridoxal

H, C=O, HO, CH_2OH, H_3C, N

Pyridoxamine

CH_2NH_2, HO, CH_2OH, H_3C, N

Pyridoxal phosphate

H, C=O, HO, $CH_2—O—P(OH)(=O)—OH$, H_3C, N

Figure 20-4
Intermediate steps in the transaminase reaction. Ⓔ—C(=O)—H *represents the transaminase-pyridoxal phosphate complex.*

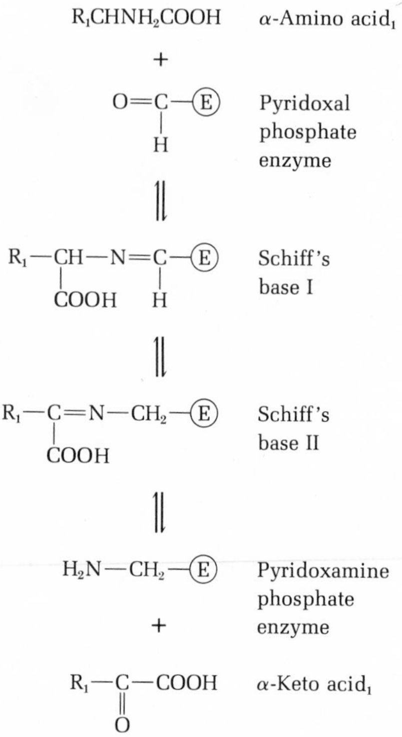

R_1CHNH_2COOH	α-Amino acid$_1$
+	
O=C(H)—Ⓔ	Pyridoxal phosphate enzyme
⇅	
R_1—CH(COOH)—N=C(H)—Ⓔ	Schiff's base I
⇅	
R_1—C(COOH)=N—CH_2—Ⓔ	Schiff's base II
⇅	
$H_2N—CH_2$—Ⓔ	Pyridoxamine phosphate enzyme
+	
R_1—C(=O)—COOH	α-Keto acid$_1$

Figure 20-5
Postulated intermediate at catalytic site of pyridoxal enzymes. The amino acid portion of the structure is in color.

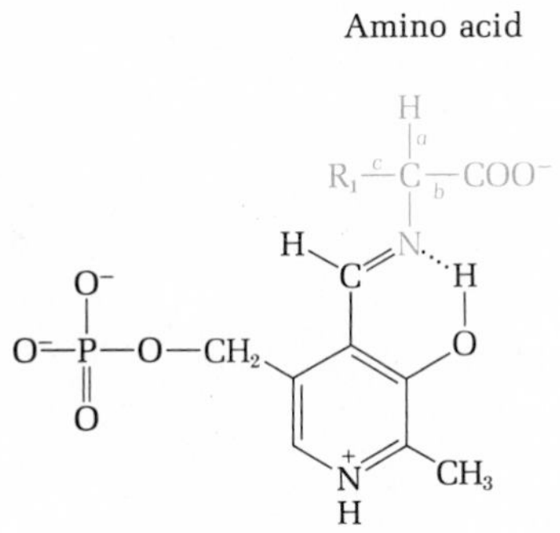

Amino acid

Schiff's base of pyridoxal phosphate and an amino acid

$R_2—C(=O)—COOH$ α-Keto acid$_2$

+

$H_2N—CH_2—(E)$ Pyridoxamine phosphate enzyme

$\rightleftharpoons$

$R_2—C(COOH)=N—CH_2—(E)$ Schiff's base III

$\rightleftharpoons$

$R_2—CH(COOH)—N=CH—(E)$ Schiff's base IV

$\rightleftharpoons$

$O=CH—(E)$ Pyridoxal phosphate enzyme

+

R_2CHNH_2COOH α-Amino acid$_2$

Oxidative Deamination

The amino groups collected from the various amino acids by the action of transaminases ultimately appear as the α-amino group of L-glutamate. In some cells, particularly bacteria, glutamate undergoes rapid oxidative deamination catalyzed by the pyridine-linked glutamate dehydrogenase

$$\text{L-Glutamate} + NAD^+ \rightleftharpoons \alpha\text{-ketoglutarate} + NH_4^+ + NADH + H^+$$

thus unloading as NH_4^+ ions the amino groups collected from the other amino acids. L-Glutamate dehydrogenase can also use $NADP^+$ as electron acceptor, the NADPH so formed acting as a reducing agent in biosynthetic reactions. L-Glutamate dehydrogenase thus plays a central role in amino acid deamination in many organisms, particularly those which excrete ammonia, because it is the only amino acid that has such a specific and active dehydrogenase. Glutamate dehydrogenase, probably because of its central role in the transfer of amino groups, is an allosteric enzyme. The beef liver enzyme has a molecular weight of 280,000 and contains a number of apparently identical subunits. The enzyme associates into larger aggregates of particle weight 2.2 million which are rod-shaped. The equilibrium between the monomeric and polymeric forms is shifted in one direction or the other by various effectors. The enzyme is inhibited by the effectors ATP, GTP, NADH and is activated by ADP and certain amino acids. It is also influenced by the presence of the thyroid hormone *thyroxine* and certain steroid hormones.

In many organisms two other types of dehydrogenases, both flavoproteins, can carry out oxidative deamination, but they are not considered part of the mainstream of amino group metabolism. One is specific for L-amino acids and is called *L-amino acid oxidase*

$$\text{L-}R—CH(NH_2)—COOH + E—FMN \longrightarrow R—C(=O)—COOH + NH_3 + E—FMNH_2$$

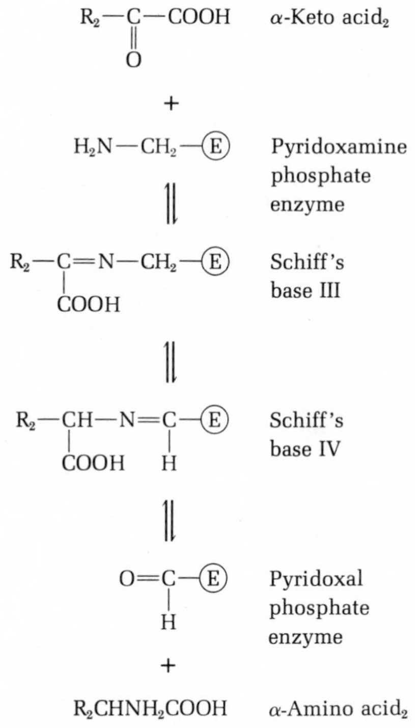

This enzyme, which contains FMN as prosthetic group, is present in the endoplasmic reticulum of the liver. It is only weakly active and is not considered to play a major role in amino acid deamination in most animal cells, except for lysine (see below). The other flavoprotein is *D-amino acid oxidase*, which catalyzes the reaction

$$\text{D-}R—CH(NH_2)—COOH + E—FAD \longrightarrow R—C(=O)—COOH + NH_3 + E—FADH_2$$

D-Amino acid oxidase contains FAD as prosthetic group and is localized in the microbodies of the liver cell (Chapter 2). Its function in animal cells is not known, since D-amino acids have only limited biological occurrence.

The reduced flavin nucleotides of both enzymes can react directly with molecular oxygen to form hydrogen peroxide

$$E{-}FMNH_2 + O_2 \longrightarrow E{-}FMN + H_2O_2$$

$$E{-}FADH_2 + O_2 \longrightarrow E{-}FAD + H_2O_2$$

which is decomposed to water and oxygen by catalase

$$H_2O_2 \longrightarrow H_2O + \tfrac{1}{2}O_2$$

In eucaryotic cells both the amino acid oxidases, as well as urate oxidase, are localized in the microbodies, which may be regarded as specialized oxidative vesicles or organelles. They also contain catalase, which catalyzes the decomposition of the hydrogen peroxide generated by these oxidases. For this reason microbodies are also called *peroxisomes*. An electron micrograph of a liver microbody is shown in the margin.

Microbody in a rat liver cell. Note the single surrounding membrane. The regular lattice-like structure in the center of the microbody consists of crystalline urate oxidase.

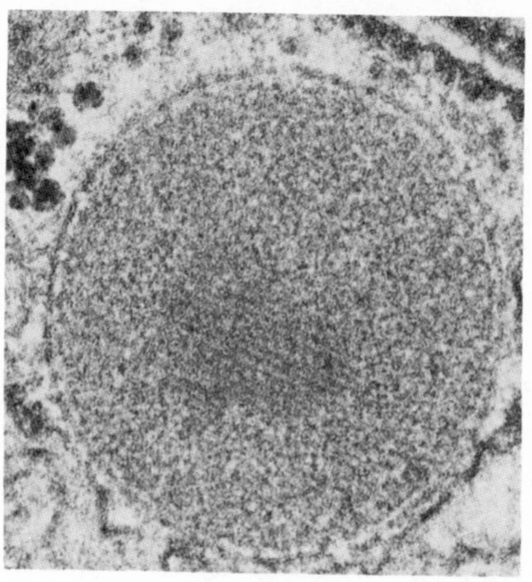

With this survey of the important deamination processes as background, we can now consider in detail the degradation of the 20 amino acids to yield deaminated products which may enter the tricarboxylic acid cycle.

Pathways Leading to Acetyl CoA

Figure 20-1 shows the portals through which the carbon skeletons of the different amino acids gain entry into the tricarboxylic acid cycle. The detailed pathways for the 20 amino acids are separated according to point of entry and are given as a series of metabolic maps (Figures 20-6 to 20-18). Not all the enzymes and intermediates will be described in detail, but reactions particularly noteworthy for their mechanisms or biological properties will be considered separately.

The major point of entry into the cycle is via acetyl CoA and ten amino acids enter by this route. Of these, five are degraded to acetyl CoA via pyruvate (Figure 20-6) and the remainder via acetoacetyl CoA (see below).

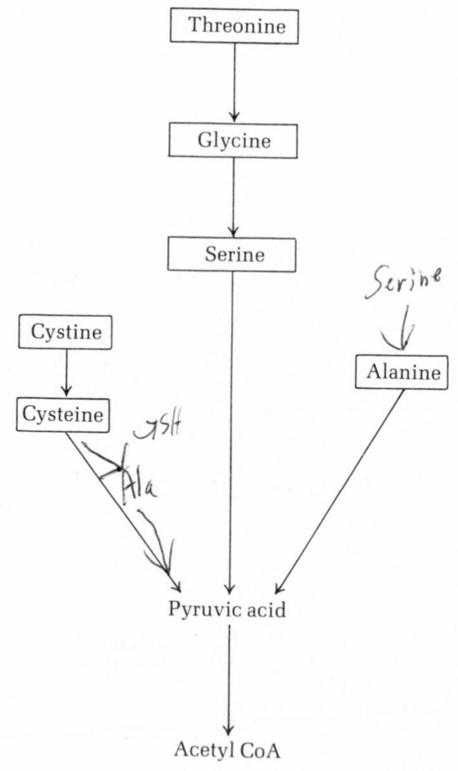

Figure 20-6
Pathways to acetyl CoA via pyruvic acid.

Via Pyruvate

The five amino acids entering via pyruvate are alanine, cysteine, glycine, serine, and threonine. Alanine yields pyruvate directly on transamination with α-ketoglutarate.

Serine is dehydrated and deaminated by *serine dehydratase*, a pyridoxal phosphate enzyme, presumably via an imino acid intermediate, to yield pyruvate.

Threonine (four carbon atoms) has two possible pathways: (1) It may be cleaved into two two-carbon compounds, glycine and acetaldehyde, by the action of *threonine aldolase*, a pyridoxal phosphate enzyme (Figure 20-7). The acetaldehyde ultimately becomes acetic acid and acetyl CoA. The glycine is converted to serine, a three-carbon compound, by enzymatic addition of a hydroxymethyl group donated by the coenzyme N^{10}-hydroxymethyltetrahydrofolate. Tetrahydrofolate serves as a coenzyme in many reactions involving the transfer of one-carbon groups, such as methyl, formyl, formimino, and hydroxymethyl groups (Chapter 24). Serine in turn is converted into pyruvate. (2) *Threonine dehydrase* converts threonine into α-ketobutyric acid, which undergoes oxidative decarboxylation to propionyl CoA, a precursor of succinyl CoA (Figure 20-16 and Chapter 19).

The conversion of cystine and cysteine to pyruvate (Figure 20-8) via cysteine sulfinic acid is also catalyzed by an enzyme containing pyridoxal phosphate. Cysteine degradation may proceed by at least three different pathways, as shown in Figure 20-8, depending on the nature of the sulfur-containing end product. These pathways will not be discussed in detail. Pyruvate formed as the end product of the degradation of this group of amino acids undergoes oxidative decarboxylation to acetyl CoA, which then enters the tricarboxylic acid cycle.

Via Acetoacetyl CoA

This pathway is taken by the amino acids phenylalanine, tyrosine, lysine, tryptophan, and leucine (Figure 20-9)

Figure 20-7
Conversion of threonine, glycine, and serine to acetyl CoA.

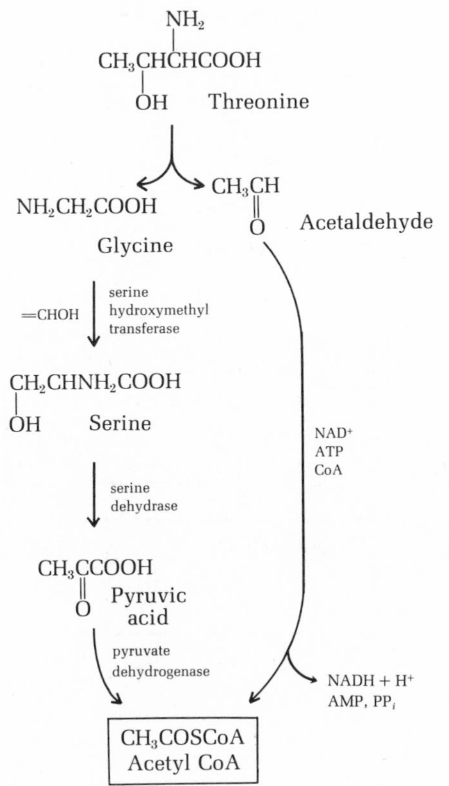

Figure 20-8
Conversion of cystine and cysteine to pyruvic acid.

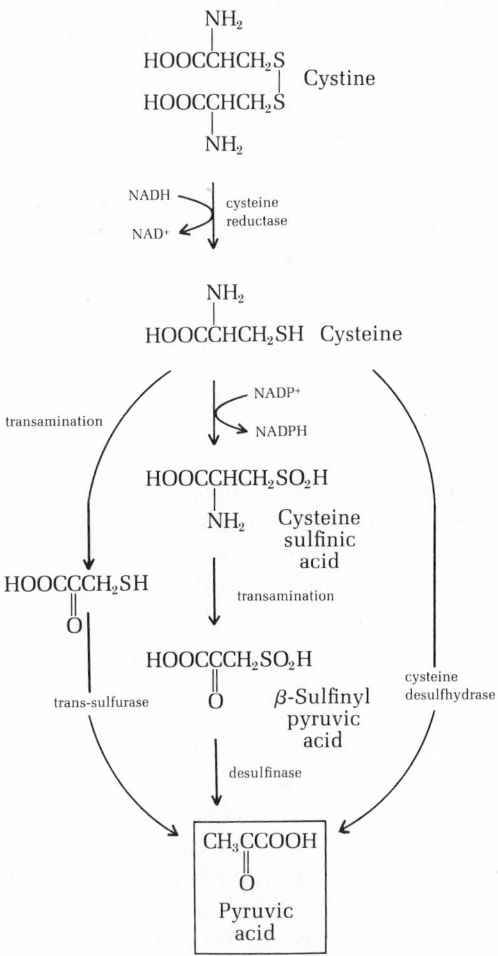

Figure 20-9
Pathways to acetyl CoA via acetoacetyl CoA.

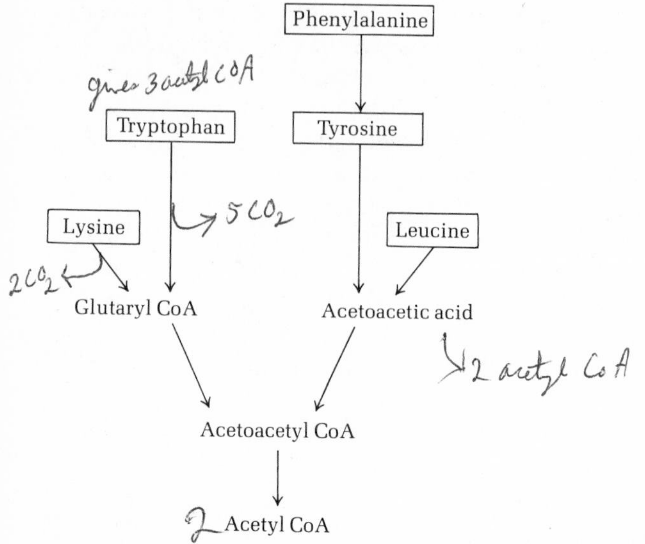

Figure 20-10
Conversion of phenylalanine and tyrosine to acetoacetic and fumaric acids.

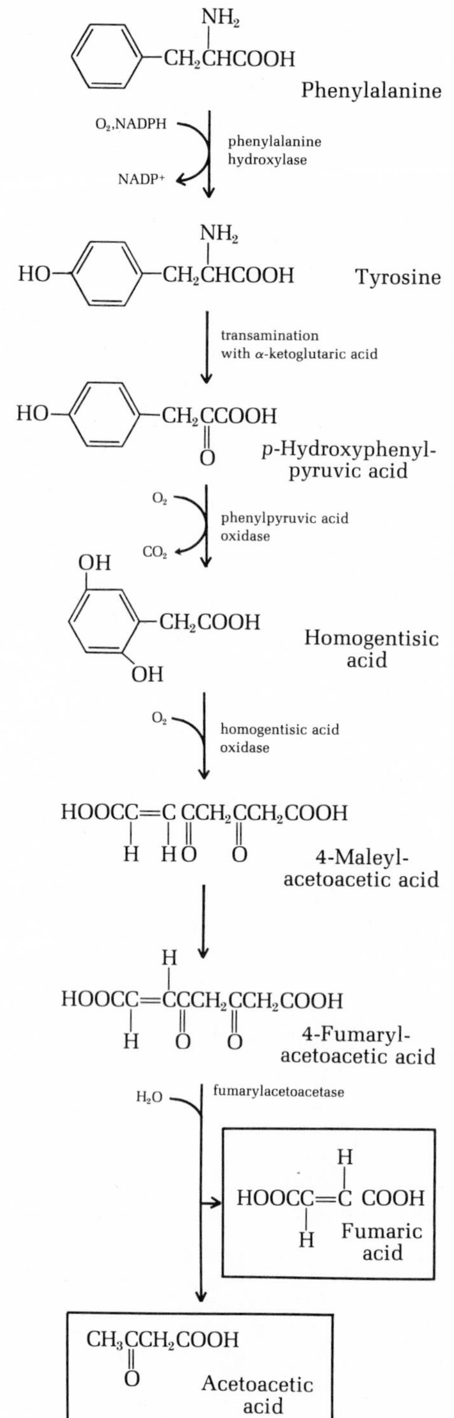

The steps in the degradation of phenylalanine and tyrosine are shown in Figure 20-10. Both yield free acetoacetate, which then is activated at the expense of ATP and CoA to form acetoacetyl CoA (Chapter 19). One of the five remaining carbon atoms of these two amino acids appears as CO_2, following oxidative decarboxylation of the intermediate *p-hydroxyphenylpyruvic acid*. The other four carbon atoms of tyrosine and phenylalanine are recovered as fumaric acid, an intermediate of the tricarboxylic acid cycle. Eight of the nine carbon atoms of these two amino acids thus may enter the tricarboxylic acid cycle.

Several enzymes in the phenylalanine-tyrosine pathway deserve special mention. *Phenylalanine hydroxylase* is representative of the mixed function oxygenases (Chapter 17). It incorporates one oxygen atom from molecular oxygen into the hydroxyl group generated on the benzene ring; the other oxygen atom is reduced to water at the expense of electrons donated by NADPH (below).

$$C_6H_5CH_2CHNH_2COOH + NADPH + H^+ + O{=}O \longrightarrow HO{-}C_6H_4CH_2CHNH_2COOH + NADP^+ + H_2O$$

Recently it has been found that phenylalanine hydroxylase requires another coenzyme, *dihydrobiopterin*, which accepts reducing equivalents from NADPH and transfers them to phenylalanine. In these reactions the 4-keto group of dihydrobiopterin undergoes reduction to the 4-hydroxyl analog, *tetrahydrobiopterin* (Figure 20-11).

Phenylalanine hydroxylase is absent in about 1 in every 10,000 human beings, owing to a recessive gene. In the absence of this gene, a secondary pathway of phenylalanine metabolism that is normally little used comes into play. In this minor pathway, phenylalanine undergoes transamination to yield phenylpyruvic acid, which accumulates in the blood and is excreted in the urine. The excess phenylpyruvate (or one of its products) in the blood

Figure 20-11
Structure of dihydro- and tetrahydrobiopterin.

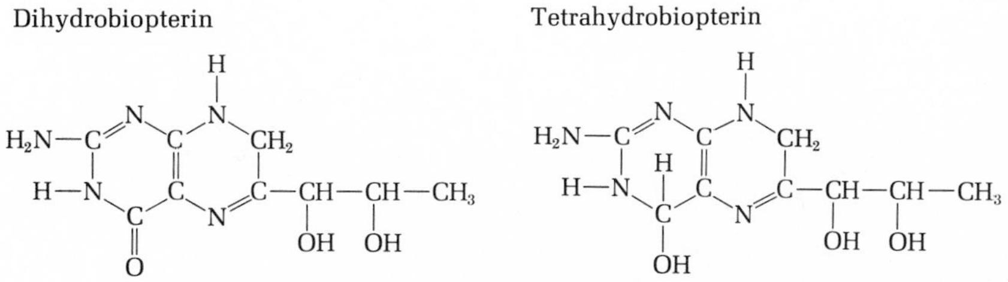

Dihydrobiopterin

Tetrahydrobiopterin

Figure 20-12
Conversion of leucine to acetyl CoA *and acetoacetic acid.*

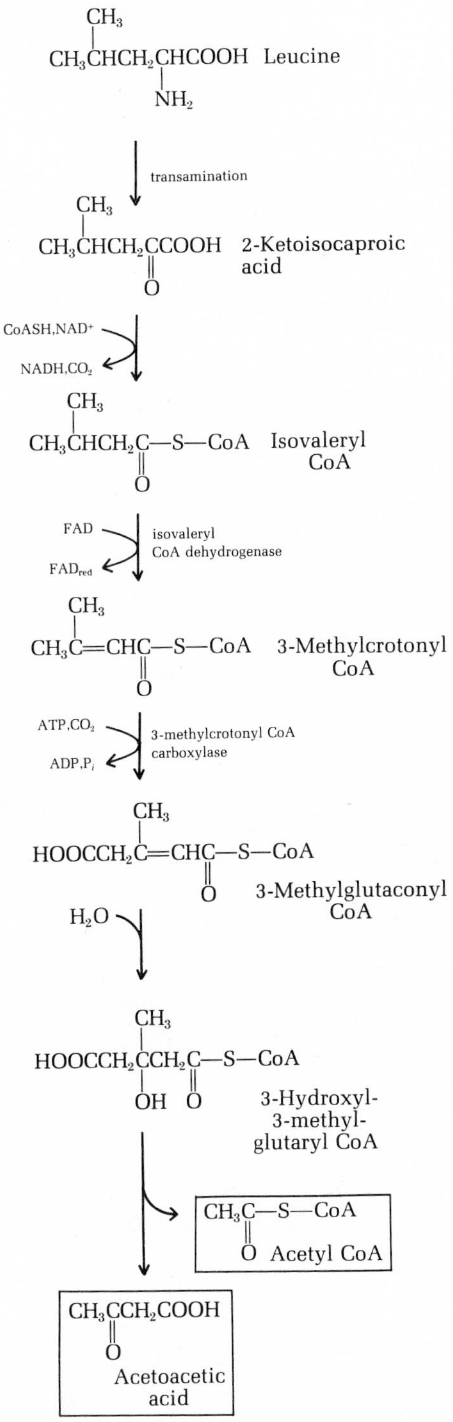

$CH_3CH(CH_3)CH_2CH(NH_2)COOH$ Leucine

↓ transamination

$CH_3CH(CH_3)CH_2C(=O)COOH$ 2-Ketoisocaproic acid

↓ CoASH, NAD^+ → NADH, CO_2

$CH_3CH(CH_3)CH_2C(=O)—S—CoA$ Isovaleryl CoA

↓ FAD → FAD_{red} (isovaleryl CoA dehydrogenase)

$CH_3C(CH_3)=CHC(=O)—S—CoA$ 3-Methylcrotonyl CoA

↓ ATP, CO_2 → ADP, P_i (3-methylcrotonyl CoA carboxylase)

$HOOCCH_2C(CH_3)=CHC(=O)—S—CoA$ 3-Methylglutaconyl CoA

↓ H_2O

$HOOCCH_2C(CH_3)(OH)CH_2C(=O)—S—CoA$ 3-Hydroxyl-3-methyl-glutaryl CoA

↓ → $CH_3C(=O)—S—CoA$ Acetyl CoA

$CH_3C(=O)CH_2COOH$ Acetoacetic acid

in childhood impairs normal development of the brain, causing severe mental retardation. This condition, *phenylketonuria,* was among the first genetic defects of metabolism recognized in man. Restriction of phenylalanine in the diet during childhood prevents the mental retardation. Many genetic defects in amino acid metabolism have been found in human beings (Table 20-1).

Hydroxyphenylpyruvic acid oxidase, which catalyzes oxidation of *p*-hydroxyphenylpyruvic acid to homogentisic acid (Figure 20-10), is a copper-containing hydroxylase. This oxidation step is very complex and involves hydroxylation of the phenyl ring, oxidation, decarboxylation, and migration of the side-chain. *Homogentisic acid oxygenase* is an Fe(II) enzyme; its reaction mechanism is also complex. Both reactions require vitamin C or ascorbic acid (Chapter 11) for maximum activity. Dietary deficiency of this vitamin in man and guinea pigs causes them to excrete phenylpyruvic and homogentisic acids in the urine.

Human beings genetically defective in homogentisic acid oxidase excrete homogentisic acid in the urine, which when made alkaline and exposed to oxygen turns dark, because the homogentisic acid is oxidized to a black melanin pigment. This condition is known as *alkaptonuria.*

Figure 20-12 shows the pathway by which all six carbon atoms of leucine can be ultimately converted into acetyl CoA. Following transaminative removal of the α-amino group of leucine and oxidative decarboxylation of the resulting α-keto acid, isovaleryl CoA is formed. After its dehydration and addition of a carboxyl group, the resulting six-carbon *β-hydroxy-β-methylglutaryl* CoA (Chapter 19) is cleaved to one molecule of acetyl CoA and one of

Table 20-1 Some genetic disorders in man affecting amino acid metabolism

Name	*Defective enzyme or process*
Albinism	Tyrosinase
Alkaptonuria	Homogentisic acid oxidase
Argininosuccinic acidemia	Argininosuccinase
Cystinosis	Cystine utilization
Cystinuria	Increased excretion of cystine, lysine, arginine
Fanconi's syndrome	Increased excretion of amino acids
Hartnup's disease	Tryptophan pyrrolase
Histidinemia	Histidase
Homocystinuria	Cystathionine synthetase
Isovaleric acidemia	Isovaleryl CoA dehydrogenase
Maple syrup urine disease	Amino acid decarboxylase
Phenylketonuria	Phenylalanine hydroxylase

acetoacetyl CoA. The latter is further cleaved to two molecules of acetyl CoA. The intermediate β-hydroxy-β-methylglutaryl CoA formed during leucine degradation is also an important precursor in the biosynthesis of cholesterol (Chapter 23).

Figure 20-13 shows the rather complex pathway by which four of the six carbon atoms of lysine are converted to acetyl CoA; the other two are lost in decarboxylation reactions. Lysine does not undergo simple transamination but is apparently oxidized by L-amino acid oxidase to the corresponding α-keto acid. The pipecolic acid and other oxidation products formed in lysine catabolism are precursors in the biosynthesis of certain plant alkaloids, nitrogenous substances which are often intensely toxic.

Figure 20-14 shows the important steps in the pathway by which 6 of the 11 carbon atoms of tryptophan are converted into acetyl CoA; the remainder appear as CO_2. The first step, catalyzed by *tryptophan pyrrolase,* employs molecular oxygen to oxidize tryptophan to *N-formylkynurenine*. This oxygenase is a heme protein which is sometimes genetically defective in man, giving rise to mental

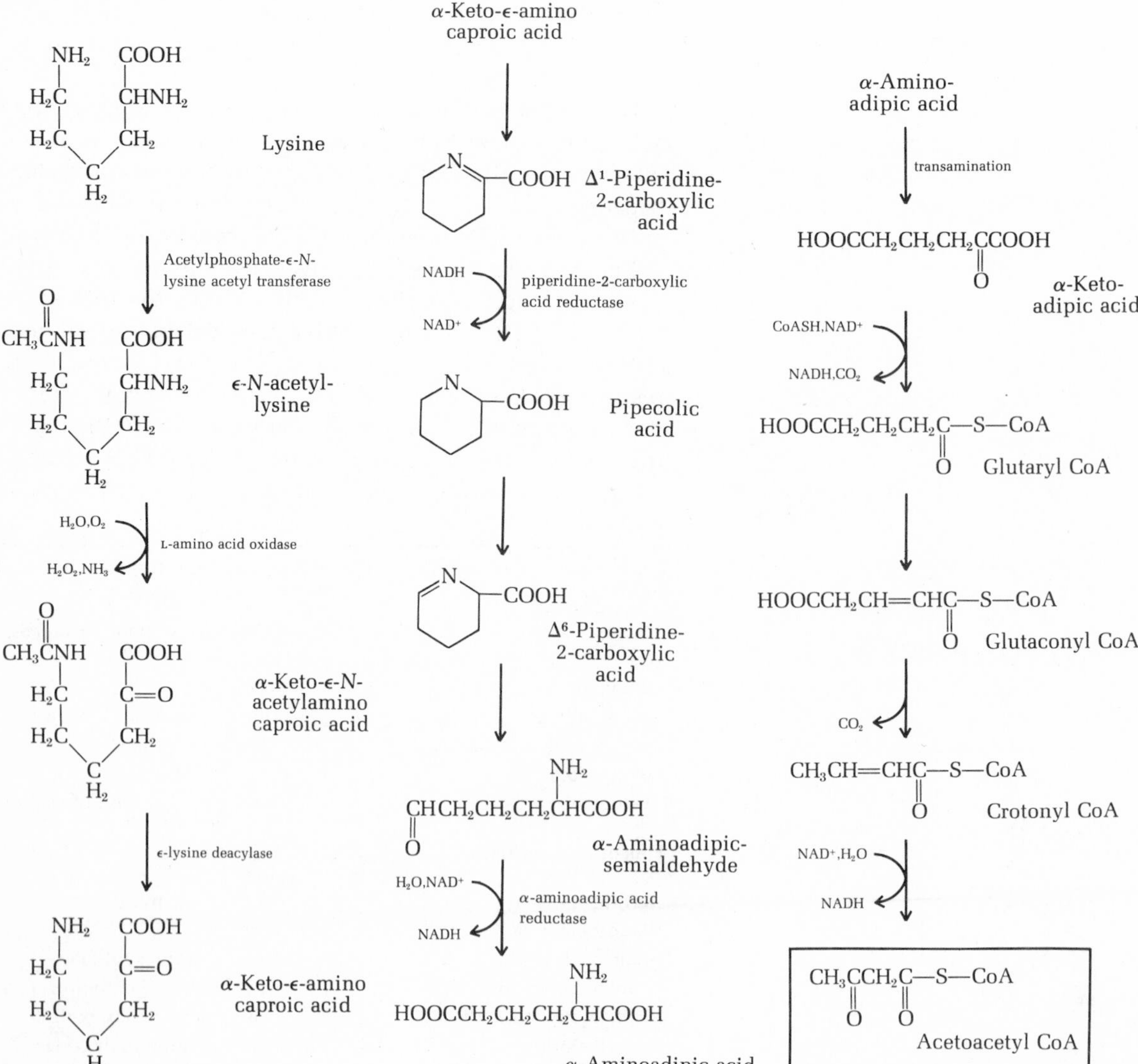

Figure 20-13
Conversion of lysine to acetoacetyl CoA.

Figure 20-14
Conversion of tryptophan to acetyl CoA and acetoacetyl CoA.

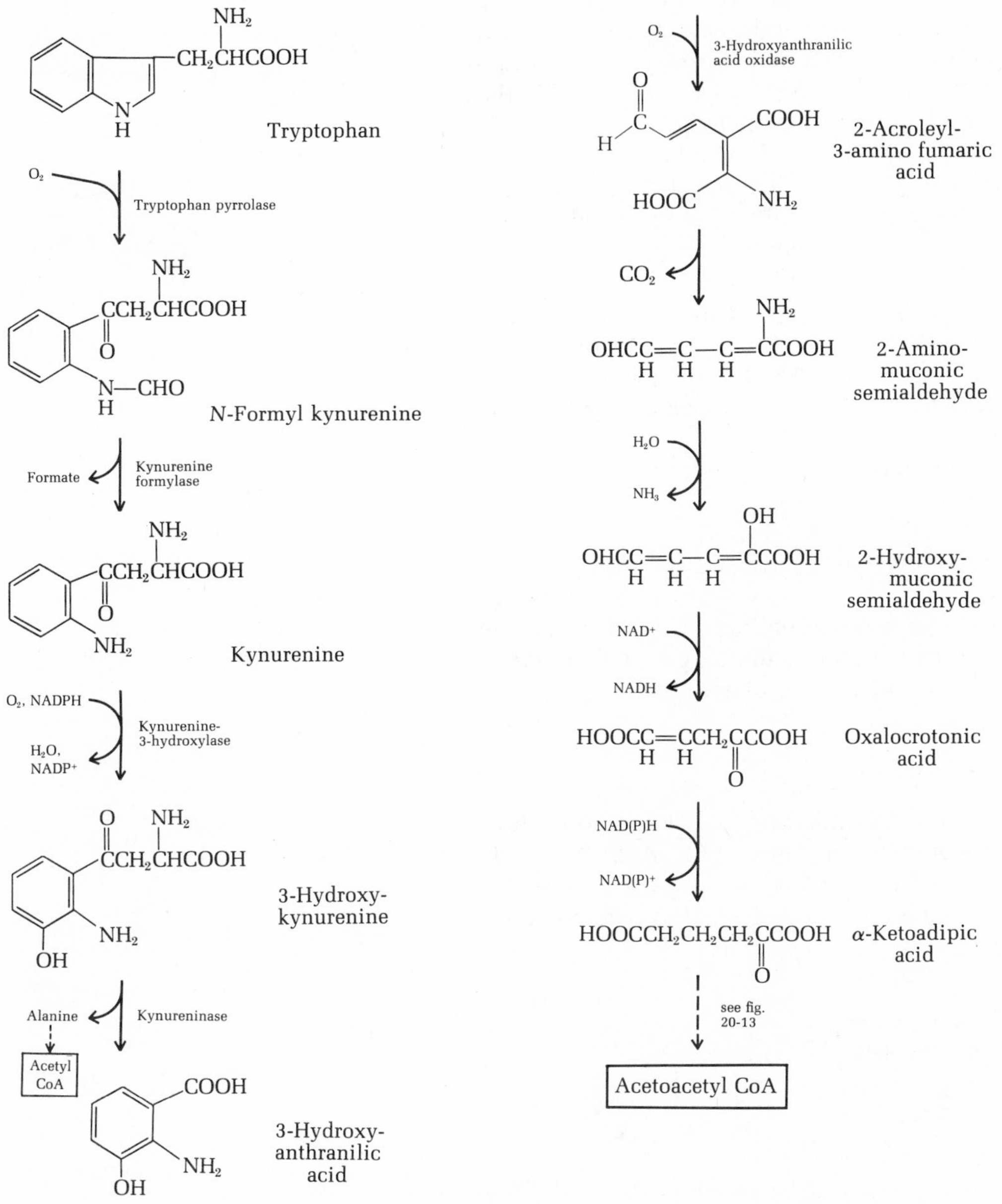

Tryptophan

O_2 → Tryptophan pyrrolase

N-Formyl kynurenine

Formate ← Kynurenine formylase

Kynurenine

O_2, NADPH → Kynurenine-3-hydroxylase → H_2O, $NADP^+$

3-Hydroxykynurenine

Alanine ← Kynureninase (Alanine → Acetyl CoA)

3-Hydroxyanthranilic acid

3-Hydroxyanthranilic acid

O_2 → 3-Hydroxyanthranilic acid oxidase

2-Acroleyl-3-amino fumaric acid

CO_2 ←

$OHCC{=}C{-}C{=}CCOOH$ (NH_2) 2-Amino-muconic semialdehyde

H_2O → NH_3 ←

$OHCC{=}C{-}C{=}CCOOH$ (OH) 2-Hydroxy-muconic semialdehyde

NAD^+ → NADH ←

$HOOCC{=}CCH_2CCOOH$ Oxalocrotonic acid

NAD(P)H → $NAD(P)^+$ ←

$HOOCCH_2CH_2CH_2CCOOH$ α-Ketoadipic acid

see fig. 20-13

Acetoacetyl CoA

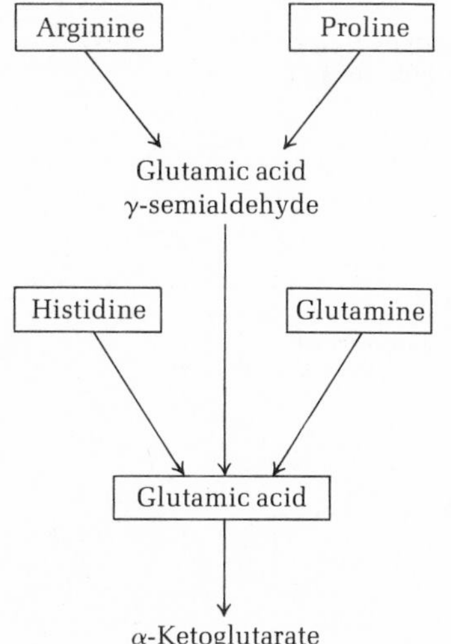

Figure 20-15
Pathways to α-ketoglutarate.

retardation. The intermediate 3-hydroxykynurenine is utilized by some insects as a precursor of the *ommochromes*, pigments of the eye. The enzyme *kynureninase* is also a pyridoxal phosphate enzyme. In deficiency of vitamin B_6 in mammals, large amounts of kynurenine are excreted in the urine. The intermediate 3-hydroxyanthranilic acid also serves as a precursor in the biosynthesis of the vitamin nicotinic acid. Intermediates in tryptophan catabolism are important precursors for biosynthesis of many other important substances, including the plant hormone indole acetic acid (Chapter 24).

The α-Ketoglutarate Pathway

The carbon skeletons of five amino acids (arginine, histidine, glutamic acid, glutamine and proline) enter the tricarboxylic acid cycle via α-ketoglutarate, whose immediate precursor is glutamic acid. Figure 20-15 shows the pathways leading from arginine, histidine, glutamine, and proline to glutamate. The pathway for arginine (Figure 20-16) is the one occurring in the liver of many mammals; an alternative path leads from arginine to glutamic acid in some microorganisms. Ornithine is formed from arginine by the action of arginase; this step is also employed in the synthesis of urea via the urea cycle (below). Ornithine is then converted into glutamic acid semialdehyde, which is also an intermediate in the oxidation of proline (Figure 20-17). Glutamic acid semialdehyde is oxidized to glutamic acid, NAD^+ serving as electron acceptor.

The pathway for oxidation of histidine to glutamic acid (Figure 20-18) is noteworthy because the imidazole ring is opened to yield *N-formimino glutamic acid* from which the formimino group (HN═CH—) is removed by an enzyme which employs tetrahydrofolate as acceptor of the formimino group.

Glutamine is hydrolyzed to glutamic acid by the enzyme glutaminase

$$\text{Glutamine} + H_2O \longrightarrow \text{glutamic acid} + NH_3$$

It may also undergo transamination with α-ketoglutaric acid to yield α-ketoglutaramic acid (margin) which in turn undergoes hydrolysis to α-ketoglutarate and ammonia.

α-Ketoglutaramic acid

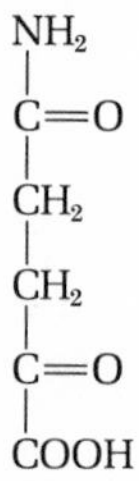

NH_2 | C═O | CH_2 | CH_2 | C═O | COOH

The Succinate Pathway

The carbon skeletons of methionine, isoleucine, and valine are ultimately degraded via propionyl CoA and methylmalonyl CoA to succinyl CoA which undergoes deacylation to yield succinate, an intermediate of the tricarboxylic

Figure 20-16
Major mammalian pathway for the conversion of arginine to glutamic acid.

NH_2—C(═NH)NH$CH_2CH_2CH_2$CH(NH_2)COOH Arginine

↓ arginase (→ urea)

$NH_2CH_2CH_2CH_2$CH(NH_2)COOH Ornithine

↓ transamination with α-ketoglutaric acid

HC(═O)CH_2CH_2CH(NH_2)COOH Glutamic acid γ-semialdehyde

↓ H_2O,NAD^+ → NADH

HOOCCH_2CH_2CH(NH_2)COOH Glutamic acid

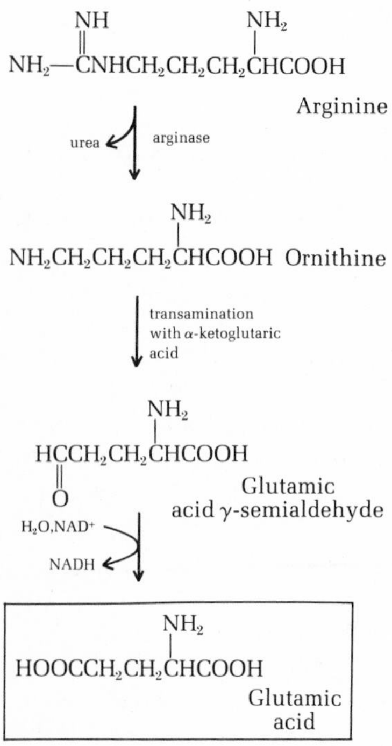

Figure 20-17
Conversion of proline to glutamic acid.

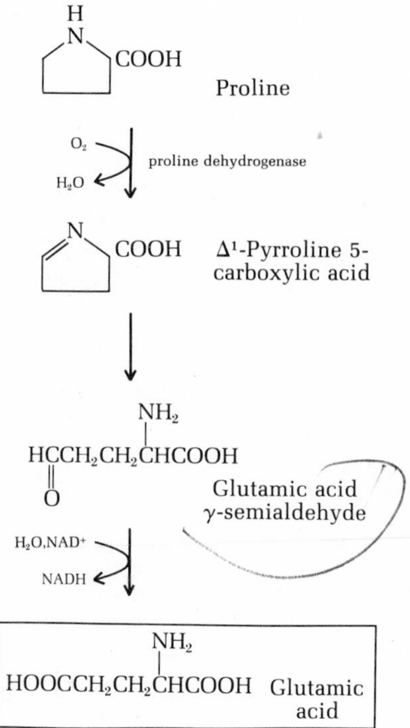

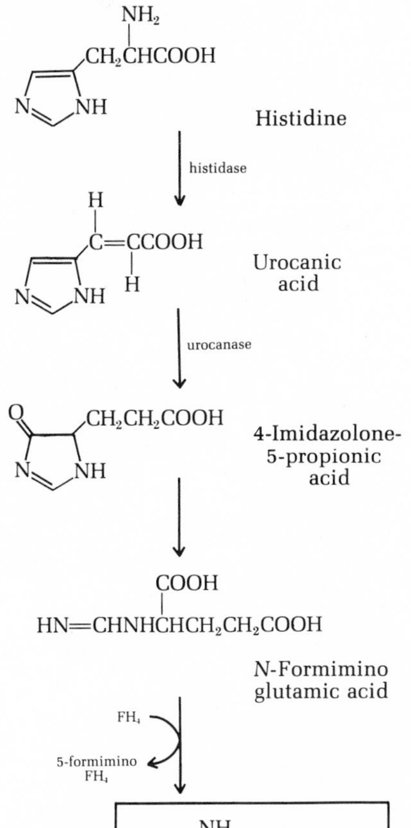

Figure 20-18
The major mammalian pathway for the conversion of histidine to glutamic acid. FH_4 symbolizes tetrahydrofolate, which serves as acceptor for the formimino group.

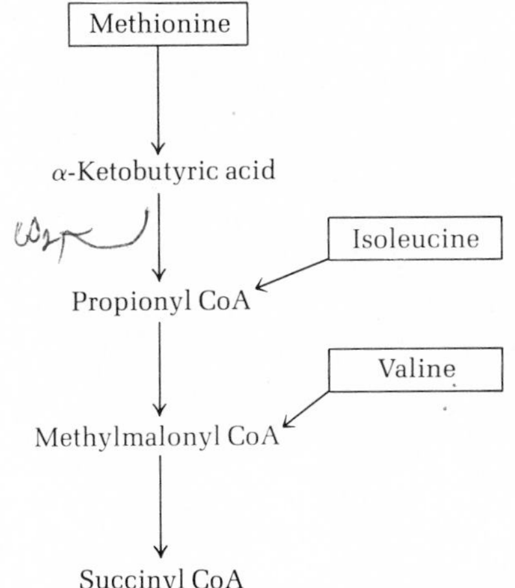

Figure 20-19
Pathways from methionine, isoleucine, and valine to succinyl CoA.

acid cycle (Figure 20-19). Methionine loses its methyl group and its sulfur atom (Figure 20-20) in two important reactions to be described in Chapter 24. The resulting homoserine loses its amino group to become α-ketobutyrate, which then undergoes oxidative decarboxylation to propionyl CoA. The latter is then carboxylated to succinyl CoA by known pathways (Chapter 19). Three of the five carbon atoms of methionine are thus converted into succinate.

Isoleucine and valine have rather similar patterns of degradation (Figures 20-21 and 20-22). Both undergo transamination followed by oxidative decarboxylation of the resulting α-keto acids. The branched chains are then degraded in a parallel manner. Methylmalonyl CoA is formed from both valine and isoleucine, then is converted to succinyl CoA by the cobamide enzyme methylmalonylmutase (Chapter 19). Four of the five carbon atoms of valine are converted to succinate, as are three of the six carbon atoms of isoleucine.

It is noteworthy that the oxidative decarboxylation of α-ketoisovalerate, α-keto-β-methylvalerate, and α-ketoisocaproate, the deamination products of valine, isoleucine, and leucine, respectively, is catalyzed by the same enzyme, which appears to be specific for only these α-keto acids. This enzyme is genetically defective in some people, leading to the excretion of these α-keto acids in the urine. This rare condition, which causes severe mental retardation in infants, is called *maple syrup urine disease*, because of the characteristic odor imparted to the urine by these keto acids. It is remarkable that several of the heritable genetic defects involving amino acid metabolism in man lead to mental retardation, which appears in some cases to be caused by failure of certain nerve bundles to become myelinated.

The Fumarate Pathway

This pathway is taken by four carbon atoms of phenylalanine and tyrosine. As was pointed out above, four carbon atoms of these amino acids enter the tricarboxylic acid cycle via acetoacetyl CoA and acetyl CoA. Four of the remaining 5 carbon atoms are converted to fumarate by the pathway shown in Figure 20-10.

The Oxaloacetate Pathway

Asparagine and aspartic acid ultimately enter the tricarboxylic acid cycle in the form of oxaloacetate. Asparagine is first hydrolyzed to aspartic acid and ammonia by *asparaginase*

$$\text{Asparagine} + H_2O \longrightarrow \text{aspartic acid} + NH_3$$

The aspartate so formed undergoes transamination with α-ketoglutaric acid to form oxaloacetic acid

$$\text{Aspartic acid} + \alpha\text{-ketoglutaric acid} \rightleftharpoons \text{oxaloacetic acid} + \text{glutamic acid}$$

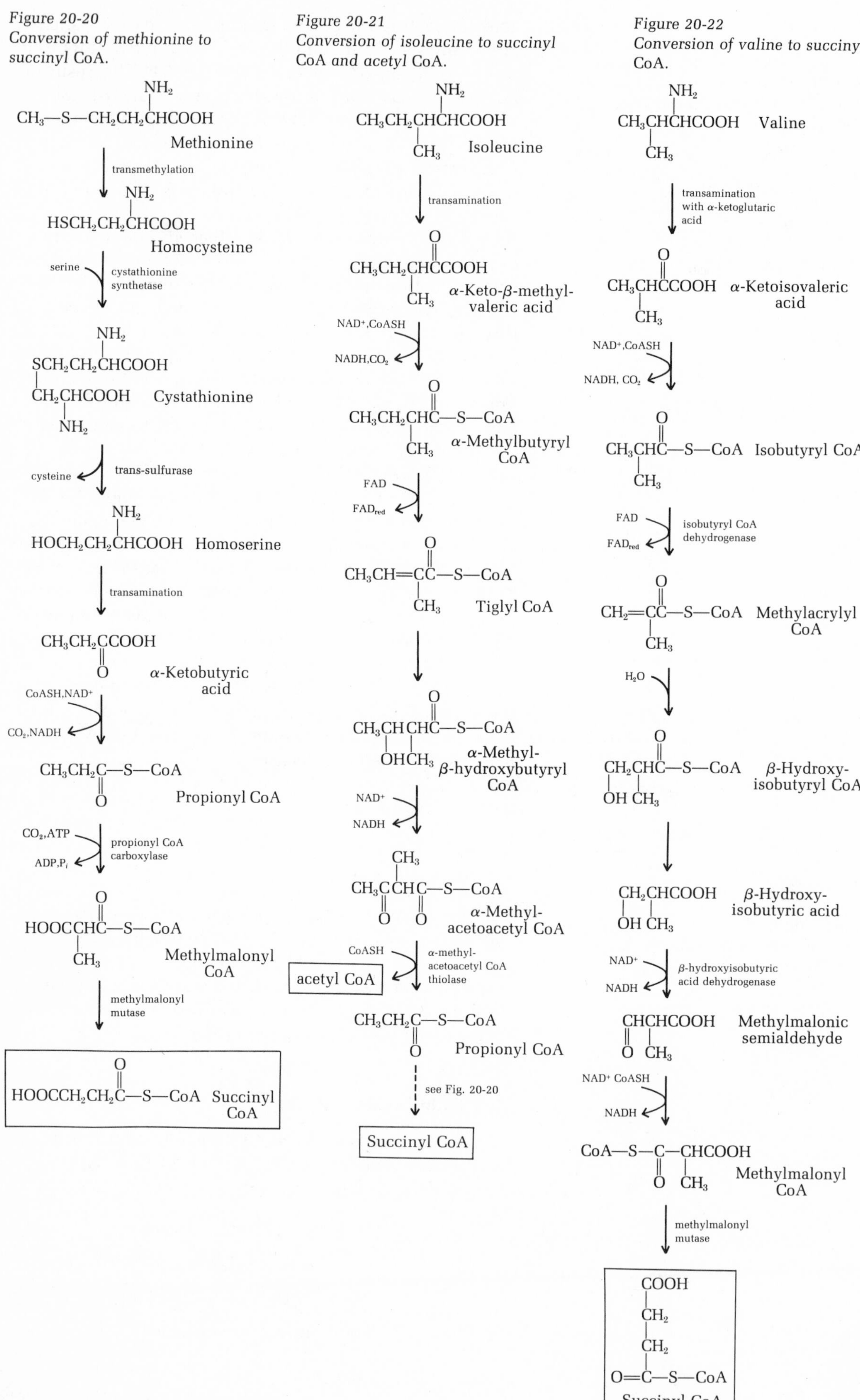

Figure 20-20
Conversion of methionine to succinyl CoA.

Figure 20-21
Conversion of isoleucine to succinyl CoA and acetyl CoA.

Figure 20-22
Conversion of valine to succinyl CoA.

In this way all four carbon atoms of these amino acids can enter the tricarboxylic acid cycle. In plants and some microorganisms aspartic acid undergoes direct elimination of NH_3 to yield fumarate, catalyzed by the enzyme *aspartase*, which is not present in animal tissues

$$\text{Aspartic acid} \longrightarrow \text{fumaric acid} + NH_3$$

Formation of Nitrogenous Excretion Products

Most organisms tend to re-use ammonia derived from the catabolism of amino acids and salvage it via the glutamate dehydrogenase reaction

$$\alpha\text{-Ketoglutarate} + NH_3 + NADH + H^+ \longrightarrow \text{glutamate} + NAD^+$$

However, a certain fraction of the ammonia formed is ultimately excreted by most invertebrates and vertebrates in one of three forms: as urea, ammonia, or uric acid. Amino nitrogen is excreted by most terrestrial vertebrates as urea; such organisms are termed *ureotelic*. Many aquatic animals, such as the teleost fishes, excrete amino nitrogen as ammonia; they are termed *ammonotelic*. Birds and land-dwelling reptiles, whose water intake is limited, excrete amino nitrogen in a semisolid form as suspensions of solid uric acid; these organisms are termed *uricotelic*. The amphibia occupy a midposition. The tadpole, which is aquatic in habits, excretes ammonia. After metamorphosis, during which the liver acquires the necessary enzymes, the adult frog excretes urea.

The Urea Cycle

Urea formation, which takes place almost entirely in the liver of ureotelic organisms, is catalyzed by a cyclic mechanism first postulated by Krebs and Henseleit in 1932, called the *urea cycle* (Figure 20-23). In this cycle two amino groups, originally derived from α-amino acids by deamination, enter the cycle, together with a molecule of carbon dioxide, to form arginine from ornithine, a diamino acid homologous to lysine. This part of the urea cycle occurs in nearly all organisms capable of arginine biosynthesis, but only ureotelic animals possess large amounts of the enzyme *arginase*, which catalyzes the irreversible

Figure 20-23
Flow of amino groups into the urea cycle in ureotelic organisms.

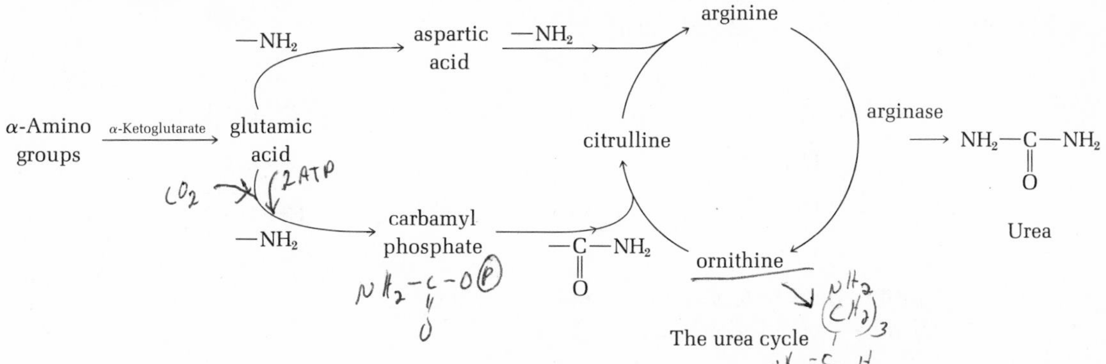

α-Amino groups
α-Ketoglutarate
glutamic acid
—NH₂
aspartic acid
—NH₂
arginine
citrulline
arginase
$NH_2-\overset{\overset{O}{\|}}{C}-NH_2$
Urea
—NH₂
carbamyl phosphate
$-\overset{\overset{O}{\|}}{C}-NH_2$
ornithine
The urea cycle

hydrolysis of arginine to form urea and regenerates ornithine. Urea, a neutral water-soluble molecule, is excreted in the urine.

It is presently believed that the first amino group to enter the urea cycle arises as free ammonia following NAD^+-linked oxidative deamination of glutamate in the mitochondria

$$\text{Glutamic acid} + NAD^+ \rightleftharpoons \alpha\text{-ketoglutaric acid} + NH_3 + NADH + H^+$$

The free ammonia is then utilized, together with carbon dioxide, to form carbamyl phosphate in a complex reaction catalyzed by *carbamyl phosphate synthetase*

$$CO_2 + NH_3 + 2ATP + H_2O \longrightarrow NH_2\text{—}\underset{\underset{\displaystyle O}{\|}}{C}\text{—}O\text{—}\overset{\overset{\displaystyle O^-}{|}}{\underset{\underset{\displaystyle O}{\|}}{P}}\text{—}O^- + 2ADP + P_i$$

Carbamyl phosphate

Two molecules of ATP are required to form each molecule of carbamyl phosphate in this reaction, which is essentially irreversible. Carbamyl phosphate is a high-energy compound. This complex reaction, which occurs in at least two steps on the catalytic site, requires *N-acetylglutamate* for activity; it is believed to be an allosteric activator (margin).

N-Acetylglutamate

$$\begin{array}{l} O \\ \| \\ C\text{—}O^- \\ | \\ CH_2 \\ | \\ CH_2 \\ | \\ HC\text{—}\underset{\underset{\displaystyle H}{|}}{N}\text{—}\underset{\underset{\displaystyle O}{\|}}{C}\text{—}CH_3 \\ | \\ C\text{—}O^- \\ \| \\ O \end{array}$$

The carbamyl phosphate generated in this reaction now donates its carbamyl group to ornithine to form *citrulline* and phosphate; the reaction is catalyzed by *ornithine transcarbamylase.*

$$\underset{\text{Carbamyl phosphate}}{NH_2\text{—}\underset{\underset{\displaystyle O}{\|}}{C}\text{—}O\text{—}\overset{\overset{\displaystyle O^-}{|}}{\underset{\underset{\displaystyle O}{\|}}{P}}\text{—}O^-} + \underset{\text{ornithine}}{NH_2CH_2CH_2CH_2\underset{\underset{\displaystyle NH_2}{|}}{C}HCOOH} \longrightarrow \underset{\text{citrulline}}{NH_2\text{—}\underset{\underset{\displaystyle O}{\|}}{C}\text{—}NHCH_2CH_2CH_2\underset{\underset{\displaystyle NH_2}{|}}{C}HCOOH} + H_3PO_4$$

The second amino group now enters the urea cycle, arriving in the form of aspartate, which in turn acquired it from glutamate by the action of aspartate-glutamate transaminase

$$\text{Glutamic acid} + \text{oxaloacetic acid} \rightleftharpoons \alpha\text{-ketoglutaric acid} + \text{aspartic acid}$$

The amino group of aspartate now condenses with the carbonyl carbon atom of citrulline in the presence of ATP to form *argininosuccinate;* this reaction is catalyzed by *argininosuccinate synthetase.*

$$\underset{\text{Citrulline}}{NH_2\text{—}\underset{\underset{\displaystyle O}{\|}}{C}\text{—}NHCH_2CH_2CH_2\underset{\underset{\displaystyle NH_2}{|}}{C}HCOOH} + \underset{\text{aspartic acid}}{HOOCCH_2\underset{\underset{\displaystyle NH_2}{|}}{C}HCOOH} + ATP \longrightarrow \underset{\text{argininosuccinic acid}}{HN\text{=}\underset{\underset{\underset{\underset{\underset{\displaystyle CH_2COOH}{|}}{H\text{—}C\text{—}COOH}}{|}}{NH}}{|}}{C}\text{—}NHCH_2CH_2CH_2\underset{\underset{\displaystyle NH_2}{|}}{C}HCOOH} + AMP + PP_i$$

Argininosuccinate is then reversibly cleaved by argininosuccinase to form free arginine and free fumarate

$$\text{Argininosuccinic acid} \longrightarrow \underset{\text{arginine}}{NH_2{-}\underset{\underset{NH}{\|}}{C}{-}NHCH_2CH_2CH_2\underset{\underset{NH_2}{|}}{C}HCOOH} + \underset{\text{fumaric acid}}{HOOC\overset{H}{C}{=}\underset{H}{C}COOH}$$

The fumarate so formed returns to the pool of tricarboxylic acid cycle intermediates. Up to this point the reaction sequence is that employed by most cells in the biosynthesis of arginine. Ureotelic animals, however, possess arginase, which cleaves urea from arginine and regenerates ornithine

$$\text{Arginine} + H_2O \longrightarrow \underset{\text{urea}}{NH_2{-}\underset{\underset{O}{\|}}{C}{-}NH_2} + \text{Ornithine}$$

The overall equation of the urea cycle is

$$2NH_3 + CO_2 + 3ATP + 2H_2O \longrightarrow \text{urea} + 2ADP + 2P_i + AMP + PP_i$$

Since the pyrophosphate formed is hydrolyzed to phosphate, the formation of one molecule of urea ultimately requires four high-energy phosphate bonds.

Many of the enzymes catalyzing reactions that feed amino groups into the urea cycle, e.g., glutamate transaminase, glutamate-aspartate transaminase, carbamyl phosphate synthetase, as well as the enzymes catalyzing the four major reactions of the urea cycle, are localized in the mitochondria of the liver cell. Recent evidence suggests a complex compartmentation of the reactions of amino acid catabolism and urea synthesis between cytoplasm and mitochondria. This separation appears to be necessary to prevent accumulation in the blood of free ammonia, which is exceedingly toxic in ureotelic vertebrates, particularly to the central nervous system. Ammonia is toxic because it leads to the reductive amination of α-ketoglutarate in mitochondria, catalyzed by glutamate dehydrogenase

$$NH_4^+ + \alpha\text{-ketoglutarate} + NADH \rightleftharpoons \text{glutamate} + NAD^+$$

Since the equilibrium of this reaction is far to the right (Chapter 17), ammonia effectively removes α-ketoglutarate from the tricarboxylic acid cycle and causes both severe inhibition of respiration and excess ketone body formation from acetyl CoA in the liver. The concentration of free ammonia is thus carefully regulated in the liver.

Glutamine synthetase reaction.

COOH—CH₂—CH₂—CHNH₂—COOH (Glutamic acid)

$$\begin{array}{ll} COOH & \\ | & \\ CH_2 & \\ | & \\ CH_2 & \text{Glutamic acid} \\ | & \\ CHNH_2 & \\ | & \\ COOH & \\ + & \\ NH_3 & \\ + & \\ ATP & \\ \downarrow Mg^{2+} & \\ NH_2 & \\ | & \\ C{=}O & \\ | & \\ CH_2 & \\ | & \text{Glutamine} \\ CH_2 & \\ | & \\ CHNH_2 & \\ | & \\ COOH & \\ + & \\ ADP & \\ + & \\ P_i & \end{array}$$

Ammonia Excretion

In ammonotelic animals, the amino groups derived from various α-amino acids are believed to be transaminated to form glutamate, which then undergoes oxidative deamination via glutamate dehydrogenase. The ammonia so formed is then converted to the amide nitrogen of *glutamine*, the transport form of ammonia in most organisms. Glutamine is formed by *glutamine synthetase* from glutamic acid. This reaction is shown in the margin on page 451. Glutamine synthetase is a very complex enzyme, which in some bacteria is subject to genetic repression and which also has allosteric properties. Its properties are more fully discussed in Chapters 24 and 25. The formation of glutamine takes place via the intermediate formation of *γ-glutamyl phosphate* (margin), which remains bound to the catalytic site. Glutamine gives up free ammonia into the kidney tubules of most vertebrates, but this reaction is most prominent in ammonotelic animals. The reaction catalyzed is

$$\text{Glutamine} + H_2O \longrightarrow \text{glutamate} + NH_4^+$$

The NH_4^+ so formed enters the urine directly. Since glutamine is nontoxic, it is an effective transport form of ammonia.

γ-Glutamyl phosphate

$$O{=}C(-O-PO_3^{2-})-CH_2-CH_2-CHNH_2-COOH$$

Formation of Uric Acid

In uricotelic organisms (terrestrial reptiles, birds, insects) uric acid is the chief form in which the amino groups of α-amino acids are excreted. Uric acid also happens to be the chief end product of purine metabolism in primates, birds, and terrestrial reptiles. The pathway of formation of uric acid is complex, since the purine ring must first be formed from smaller precursors; it will be discussed in detail in Chapter 25. The origin of uric acid is briefly summarized in Figure 20-24.

Urea, ammonia, and uric acid are not the only forms in which different species excrete nitrogen arising from amino acid catabolism. Spiders excrete nitrogen as guanine (Chapter 12) instead of uric acid, and many fishes excrete nitrogen as trimethylamine oxide (margin). In higher plants, the pathways for storing nitrogen involve the formation of the amides glutamine and asparagine, as well as the guanido group of arginine.

Figure 20-24
Major steps in conversion of amino groups into N atoms of uric acid in uricotelic organisms.

α-Amino acids

($-NH_2$)

The purine ring

Xanthine

O_2

Xanthine Oxidase

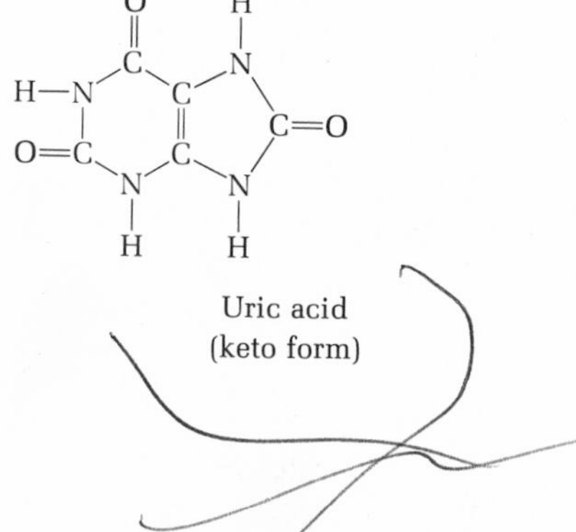

Summary

Extracellular proteins and peptides cannot pass the cell membrane and must first be hydrolyzed to amino acids, which can be transported into the cell. In the digestive tract of vertebrates, the proteolytic enzymes pepsin, trypsin, chymotrypsin, carboxypeptidase, and leucine aminopeptidase combine to carry out complete hydrolysis of ingested protein.

The carbon skeletons of amino acids undergo oxidative degradation to compounds that may enter the tricarboxylic acid cycle for oxidation. The amino groups of most amino acids are removed by transamination to pyruvate, oxaloacetate, or α-ketoglutarate. Ultimately all amino groups are collected by transamination to α-ketoglutarate, yielding glutamate. The amino groups of other amino acids may be removed by oxidative deamination. There are five pathways by which carbon atoms of amino acids enter the tricarboxylic acid cycle, namely, via: (1) acetyl CoA (2) α-ketoglutarate (3) succinate (4) fumarate and (5) oxaloacetate. The amino acids entering via acetyl CoA are divided into two groups. The first, which includes alanine,

Trimethylamine oxide

$$(CH_3)_3N{=}O$$

cysteine, glycine, serine, and threonine, yields acetyl CoA via pyruvate, and the second (leucine, lysine, phenylalanine, tyrosine, and tryptophan) yields acetyl CoA via acetoacetyl CoA. The amino acids proline, histidine, arginine, glutamine and glutamic acid enter via α-ketoglutarate; methionine, isoleucine and valine enter via succinate, four carbon atoms of phenylalanine and tyrosine enter via fumarate, and asparagine and aspartic acid enter via oxaloacetate. In man, a number of genetic defects in amino acid catabolic pathways occur. The pathways of amino acid catabolism are complex and have many intermediates which often serve as precursors of other important cell components.

In ureotelic animals (terrestrial mammals and amphibia), urea is the final excretion product of amino nitrogen. It is formed in a process called the urea cycle. Urea results from the action of arginase on arginine, the other cleavage product being ornithine. Arginine is resynthesized from ornithine by carbamylation of the latter to citrulline at the expense of carbamyl phosphate, followed by addition of an imino group to citrulline at the expense of aspartic acid. The urea cycle takes place in the liver. Ammonotelic animals (most fishes) excrete amino nitrogen as ammonia, which derives from the hydrolysis of glutamine in the kidney. Glutamine is formed by the action of glutamine synthetase from glutamic acid and ammonia derived from α-amino groups. Uricotelic animals (birds, terrestrial reptiles) excrete amino nitrogen as uric acid, a derivative of purine.

References

Books

MEISTER, A., *Biochemistry of the Amino Acids*, 2d ed., vols. I and II, Academic Press Inc., New York, 1965. Comprehensive and detailed treatise.

NYHAN, W. L. (ed.), *Amino Acid Metabolism and Genetic Variation*, McGraw-Hill Book Company, New York, 1967. Collection of articles on genetic alterations in amino acid metabolism.

STANBURY, J. O., J. B. WYNGAARDEN, and D. S. FREDRICKSON (eds.), *The Metabolic Basis of Inherited Disease*, 2d ed., McGraw-Hill Book Company, New York, 1966. Excellent text on human genetic defects affecting metabolism.

Articles and Reviews

COHEN, P. P., and G. W. BROWN, JR., "Ammonia Metabolism and Urea Biosynthesis," in M. Florkin and H. S. Mason (eds.), *Comparative Biochemistry*, vol. 11, pp. 161–294, Academic Press Inc., New York, 1961. Comparative and developmental aspects of urea excretion.

CUNNINGHAM, L., "The Structure and Mechanism of Action of Proteolytic Enzymes," in M. Florkin and E. H. Stotz (eds.), *Comprehensive Biochemistry*, vol. 16, pp. 85–188, Academic Press Inc., New York, 1965. Review of proteolytic reactions.

GUIRARD, B. M., and E. E. SNELL, "Vitamin B_6 Function in Transamination and Decarboxylation Reactions," in M. Florkin and E. H. Stotz (eds.), *Comprehensive Biochemistry*, vol. 15, chap. 5, Elsevier Publishing Co., Amsterdam, 1964. A review of the important role of pyridoxal phosphate in enzymatic reactions involving amino acids.

Problems

1. Write a complete balanced equation for the oxidation of phenylalanine, including all activation steps and energy-conserving steps for the process as it occurs in (*a*) an ammonotelic and (*b*) a ureotelic animal.

2. Calculate the number of ATP molecules generated during the oxidation of (*a*) valine to CO_2, H_2O, and NH_3 and (*b*) threonine to CO_2, H_2O, and urea.

3. During catabolism of histidine, in what positions of glutamic acid will the following numbered atoms appear?

$$\underset{\substack{|\\ {}_5N\underset{4}{\diagdown}\overset{}{C}H\diagup \underset{6}{NH}}}{HC{=}\overset{3}{C}}{-}\overset{2}{CH_2}{-}\underset{\substack{|\\ NH_2}}{CH}{-}\overset{1}{COOH}$$

4. Write the overall equation for the conversion of alanine to acetoacetate plus urea.

5. Which carbon atoms of α-ketoglutaric acid will become labeled after oxidation of the following labeled compounds in animal tissues?

   a. $CH_3\overset{*}{C}HNH_2COOH$

   b. C_6H_5–$CH_2\overset{*}{C}HNH_2COOH$ (benzene ring)

   c. $^*C_6H_5$–CH_2CHNH_2COOH (* on benzene ring)

6. On a given diet yielding 3000 kcal per day, a 70-kg man excretes 27.0 grams of urea daily. What percentage of his daily energy requirement is met by protein? Assume that 1.0 gram of protein yields 4.0 kcal and 0.16 gram of nitrogen as urea.

CHAPTER 21 PHOTOSYNTHETIC ELECTRON TRANSPORT AND PHOSPHORYLATION

We now turn to the molecular mechanisms by which solar energy is captured and converted into chemical energy by photosynthetic cells. Because solar energy is the source of nearly all biological energy, it might appear more logical to have considered photosynthesis first, before examining biological oxidations in heterotrophs, but in fact photosynthesis is best approached after the study of respiration, since the conversion of light into chemical energy involves electron transport and coupled phosphorylation processes that are very similar to those in respiration but not as well known.

Photosynthesis and respiration show other common features. In higher organisms, both processes take place in membranous organelles, the chloroplasts and mitochondria, respectively, which in turn have several common denominators of ultrastructure and molecular organization. In addition, both types of organelle also contain a distinctive form of DNA and both have self-replicating properties which are to some extent independent of nuclear chromosomes.

But most relevant at this point is the probability that the mechanisms of energy conservation in photosynthetic and respiratory electron transport are identical in principle.

Biological Occurrence of Photosynthesis

The capacity to carry out photosynthesis is found in a wide spectrum of organisms, including both procaryotes and eucaryotes. The photosynthetic eucaryotes include not only the higher green plants but also lower forms such as the multicellular green, brown, and red algae and unicellular organisms such as euglenoids, dinoflagellates, and diatoms.

The photosynthetic procaryotes include the blue-green algae, the green bacteria, and the purple bacteria. The green bacteria are strict anaerobes which live in ponds and lakes rich in sulfur-containing organic matter. The green color of some mountain lakes is due to the green bacterium *Chlorobium*. The purple bacteria are of two classes, sulfur and nonsulfur. The purple sulfur bacteria, e.g., *Chromatium*, are strict anaerobes which require hydrogen sulfide, sulfur, or thiosulfate; they are found in ponds and sulfur springs. The nonsulfur purple bacteria, e.g., *Rhodospirillum rubrum*, require organic molecules such as ethanol, acetate, β-hydroxybutyrate, or isopropanol. The procaryotic blue-green algae, which may live as single cells or in colonies, are very abundant in soil, fresh water, and the oceans. They can live on carbon dioxide as sole carbon source. Some of the blue-green algae also can fix atmospheric nitrogen and are thus quite self-sufficient.

It is a common misconception that photosynthesis in microorganisms is of minor importance, compared to photosynthesis in the familiar higher plants. Actually, however, it is believed that more than half of all the photosynthesis on the surface of the earth is carried out by unicellular organisms, particularly the algae, diatoms, and dinoflagellates.

The Equation of Photosynthesis

All photosynthetic organisms except bacteria use water as electron or hydrogen donor to reduce carbon dioxide or other electron acceptors; as a consequence they evolve molecular oxygen. The overall equation for this group of photosynthetic organisms, which includes higher plants, may be given for the present as

$$nH_2O + nCO_2 \xrightarrow{\text{light}} (CH_2O)_n + nO_2 \qquad (1)$$

in which n is often assigned the value 6 to correspond with formation of hexose ($C_6H_{12}O_6$) as end product of photosynthesis.

However, the photosynthetic bacteria neither produce nor use molecular oxygen; in fact, most of them are strict anaerobes and are poisoned by oxygen. Instead of water, they use as electron donors either inorganic compounds, e.g., hydrogen sulfide, thiosulfate, or hydrogen gas, or organic compounds, e.g., lactic acid or isopropanol. For example, the green sulfur bacteria use hydrogen sulfide according to the equation

$$2H_2S + CO_2 \xrightarrow{\text{light}} (CH_2O) + H_2O + 2S$$

The sulfur so formed accumulates in the form of globules, which are extruded from the cell. Some nonsulfur purple bacteria use an organic hydrogen donor, such as isopropanol, which is oxidized to acetone

$$2CH_3CHOHCH_3 + CO_2 \xrightarrow{\text{light}} (CH_2O) + 2CH_3\underset{\underset{\displaystyle O}{\|}}{C}CH_3 + H_2O$$

Van Niel, a pioneer in the study of the comparative aspects of metabolism, particularly of photosynthesis, postulated that plant and bacterial photosynthesis are fundamentally similar processes. The similarity is evident if the equation of photosynthesis is written in a more general form

$$2H_2D + CO_2 \xrightarrow{\text{light}} (CH_2O) + H_2O + 2D$$

in which H_2D symbolizes a hydrogen donor and D its oxidized form. H_2D may thus be water, hydrogen sulfide, isopropanol, or any one of a number of different hydrogen donors; the nature of the hydrogen donor is characteristic for each species of photosynthetic cell. Van Niel also predicted that the molecular oxygen formed during plant photosynthesis must be derived exclusively from the oxygen atoms of water and not from the carbon dioxide. Isotopic experiments with the use of ^{18}O-labeled water and carbon dioxide are consistent with this prediction. For this reason equation (1) for plant photosynthesis may be rewritten to show that oxygen derives from water instead of carbon dioxide:

$$2H_2O + CO_2 \xrightarrow{\text{light}} (CH_2O) + H_2O + O_2$$

Study of the comparative aspects of photosynthesis has similarly revealed that CO_2 is not the universal electron or hydrogen acceptor in photosynthetic cells. Carbon dioxide is of course the *major* electron acceptor in all photosynthetic autotrophs, such as higher plants, which must manufacture all their organic biomolecules from carbon dioxide. However, most higher plants can also use nitrate as electron acceptor instead of carbon dioxide. In nitrogen-fixing photosynthetic organisms, molecular nitrogen as well as carbon dioxide may be used as electron acceptors during photosynthesis; the nitrogen is reduced to ammonia. Moreover, many photosynthetic organisms can use hydrogen ions as electron acceptor, from which they can form molecular hydrogen. Typical equations for photosynthesis with different electron acceptors follow:

Electron donor		*Electron acceptor*		
$2H_2D$	+	CO_2	$\longrightarrow$	$(CH_2O) + H_2O + 2D$
$9H_2D$	+	$2NO_3^-$	$\longrightarrow$	$2NH_3 + 6H_2O + 9D$
$3H_2D$	+	N_2	$\longrightarrow$	$2NH_3 + 3D$
H_2D	+	$2H^+$	$\longrightarrow$	$2H_2 + D$

From these considerations, it is clear that photosynthesis may involve different electron donors and different electron acceptors, depending on the species. We may therefore write a completely general equation for photosynthesis

$$H_2D + A \xrightarrow{\text{light}} H_2A + D$$

in which H_2D is the electron or hydrogen donor and A is the electron or hydrogen acceptor.

We now come to a highly important characteristic of the process of photosynthesis. In all photosynthetic organisms, regardless of the electron donor and electron acceptor, the light-induced flow of electrons from electron donor to electron acceptor is *against* the normal gradient of the standard reduction potentials of the electron donor and acceptor systems; i.e., the net flow of electrons is in the direction of the system having the more electronegative standard potential. Light energy, therefore, is a powerful force that can cause electrons to flow in reverse, in the direction of a more negative or more energy-rich state, opposite to the direction of flow of electrons in respiration.

The Light and Dark Reactions

It was postulated many years ago that photosynthesis consists of two types of process, the *light reactions,* which are directly dependent on light energy, and the *dark reactions,* which can occur in the absence of light. One piece of evidence supporting this view is that the rate of photosynthesis is proportional to the intensity of the light only at relatively low light intensities; at high intensities, the rate of photosynthesis remains constant as light intensity is increased. This observation indicates that some light-independent, or dark, process is saturated or rate-limiting under these conditions. Another piece of evidence comes from the response of photosynthetic organisms to intermittent illumination. The length and temperature of the dark intervals is critical in determining the rate of photosynthesis in the light periods.

However, biochemical evidence for the existence of light and dark phases did not come until 1937, when Hill succeeded in demonstrating for the first time that light-dependent oxygen evolution can take place in cell-free preparations obtained from photosynthetic organisms. Illumination of these preparations, which contained chloroplasts, in the presence of artificial electron acceptors, such as ferricyanide or reducible dyes, caused evolution of oxygen and simultaneous reduction of the electron acceptor, according to the general equation

$$2H_2O + 2A \xrightarrow{\text{light}} 2AH_2 + O_2 \tag{2}$$

in which A is the hydrogen (electron) acceptor and AH_2 its reduced form. No electron donor other than water was required. Most important, Hill found that carbon dioxide was not required for this reaction nor was it reduced to a stable form that accumulated, demonstrating that oxygen evolution and carbon dioxide reduction can be dissociated from each other. Independently, both Warburg and Gaffron made observations that similarly demonstrated the dissociation of oxygen evolution and carbon dioxide reduction.

The reaction summarized in equation (2) is universally known as the *Hill reaction* and the acceptor A as a *Hill reagent.* The Hill reagent thus acts as an artificial acceptor for electrons arising from water, just as methylene blue may act as an acceptor for electrons removed from a substrate by dehydrogenase action (Chapter 17).

After discovery of the Hill reaction, the question arose: What is the identity of the intermediate electron acceptors in the plant cell from which electrons are tapped by the Hill reagent? In 1950 Ochoa and Vishniac showed that $NADP^+$ could replace artificial Hill reagents as an electron acceptor. In the presence of illuminated chloroplasts, $NADP^+$ became reduced to NADPH, and oxygen was evolved

$$2H_2O + 2NADP^+ \xrightarrow{\text{light}} 2NADPH + 2H^+ + O_2$$

Since NADPH was then already recognized to be an electron donor for biosynthetic reactions in the cell, this observation supported the view that a reducing agent is one of the end products of the light reactions, which can then be used in the dark phase to carry out reduction of electron acceptors, such as carbon dioxide.

Further evidence supporting the separation of photosynthesis into light and dark phases was implicit in the discovery of the process of *photosynthetic phosphorylation*. In 1954 Arnon and his colleagues found that illumination of isolated spinach chloroplasts in the presence of ADP and phosphate caused formation of ATP. Shortly later Frenkel made similar observations on membrane preparations from photosynthetic bacteria. Such light-dependent formation of ATP (described in more detail below) did not require or consume CO_2. From such observations the view gradually developed that light energy is used in the first phase of photosynthesis not only to reduce $NADP^+$ but also to phosphorylate ADP and that the products NADPH and ATP are then utilized in dark reactions to cause reduction of CO_2 and other electron acceptors. The remainder of this chapter deals only with the first phase of photosynthesis, the generation of NADPH and of ATP at the expense of light energy. The reduction of CO_2 to hexoses and other products is described in Chapter 22.

Before we turn to the molecular details of photosynthesis, we must sketch the intracellular organization of photosynthetic processes, since this aspect has become of central importance in the experimental approaches to the biochemical mechanisms.

Figure 21-1
Electron micrograph of a photosynthetic procaryote, the blue-green alga Oscillatoria rubescens. *The cell membrane infolds to form the photosynthetic lamellae or thylakoid membranes, arranged in stacks. Note that the entire algal cell strongly resembles the chloroplast of a eucaryotic photosynthetic cell (Figure 21-2).*

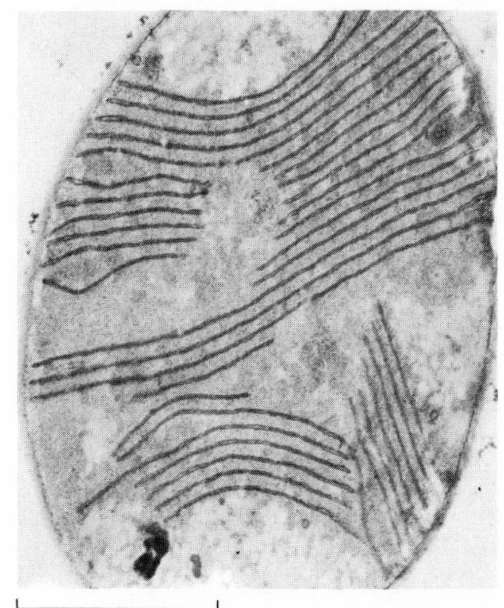

Intracellular Organization of Photosynthetic Systems

Photosynthetic bacteria lack chloroplasts. The molecular components of their photosystems are located in the cell membrane, which may be infolded to form specialized mesosomes. Sonic disruption of the photosynthetic bacteria yields chlorophyll-containing fragments of the membrane, which reseal to form vesicular or lamellar structures called *chromatophores*. Such preparations contain the photosensitive pigments and most of the enzymes necessary for light-induced electron transport and coupled phosphorylation. They are extremely useful preparations for study of these processes. Figure 21-1 shows the structure of a photosynthetic procaryote, the blue-green alga *Oscillatoria rubescens*.

In eucaryotic cells the photosynthetic apparatus is localized in the chloroplasts, one of several different kinds of *plastids*, membrane-surrounded organelles peculiar to higher plant cells. Plastids possess self-replicating properties; like mitochondria, they contain DNA different from that in the cell nucleus (Chapter 28). An electron micrograph of a photosynthetic eucaryotic cell was shown in Chapter 1 (Figure 1-9).

Chloroplasts are usually much larger than mitochondria, but they have a wide range of size, from 1 to 10 μ in diameter. They are usually globular or discoid in shape but sometimes assume exotic forms as in *Spirogyra*, in which they are ribbon-shaped and helical. In some eucaryotic algae, such as *Chlorella*, there is only one chloroplast per cell; however, higher plant cells may contain as many as 40 chloroplasts. Green plant cells usually contain both chloroplasts and mitochondria. Some respiration may occur when plants are under illumination, but at night, green plant cells become pure heterotrophs and depend on mitochondrial respiration for energy.

Chloroplasts are easily isolated from some algae and plants by differential centrifugation; spinach leaves are the most frequently used source. The leaves are gently homogenized in a blender in a medium of 0.35 *M* NaCl or 0.3 to 0.4 *M* sucrose, buffered at pH 8.0. The leaf suspension is filtered through muslin and centrifuged lightly to remove cell debris. The chloroplasts are then sedimented by centrifugation for some minutes at 1,000g. They are washed one or more times by resuspending them in 0.35 *M* NaCl. When isolated in this way, chloroplasts remain relatively intact in structure and retain the capacity to carry out light-induced electron transport and phosphorylation. When very carefully isolated to minimize damage, spinach chloroplasts also can carry out all the dark reactions involved in reduction of carbon dioxide (Chapter 22).

Chloroplasts are comparable in structure to mitochondria (Figure 21-2). They are surrounded by a single continuous outer membrane, which is rather fragile. The inner-membrane system, which is continuous but folded in a highly complex manner, encloses a matrix compartment. The inner membrane is arranged in the form of many flattened vesicles called *thylakoid disks*, which are usually stacked transversely across the chloroplast. These stacks are called grana (Figure 21-2). In most cells there are many grana per chloroplast, but in eucaryotic algae,

Figure 21-2
Electron micrograph of a chloroplast of Nitella.

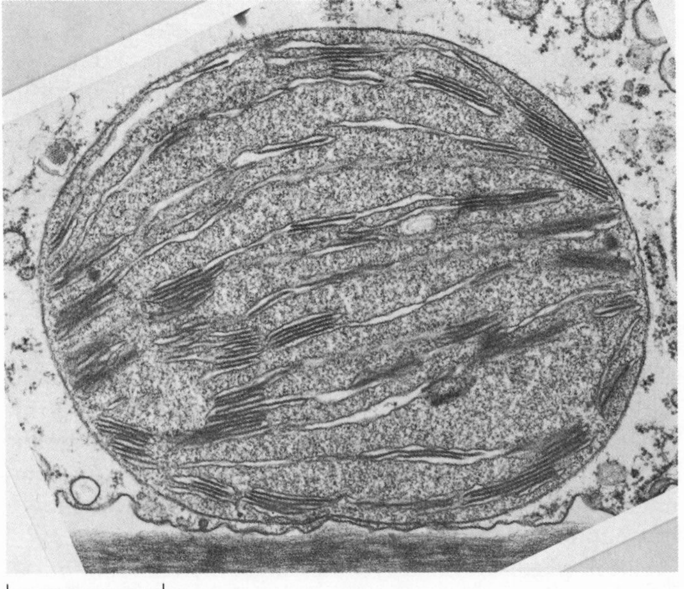

Schematic drawing showing arrangement of the membranes in the thylakoid discs. Studies of developing chloroplasts indicate that the thylakoid vesicles are derived from the inner membrane.

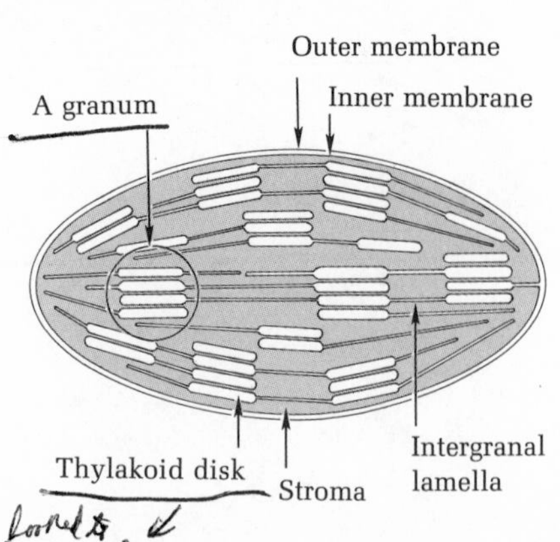

which have small chloroplasts, there is but one granum. The grana contain essentially all the photosynthetic pigments of the chloroplast and also the enzymes required for the primary light-dependent reactions. The paired thylakoid membranes are the sites of the light-trapping systems in the chloroplast structure; they are thus functionally comparable to the cristae of mitochondria. The inner membrane system of chloroplasts may be fragmented and washed free of stroma to yield a spectrum of particles from single thylakoid disks to complete grana, which may be recovered by differential centrifugation. When suitably supplemented with electron acceptors, such preparations carry out both the Hill reaction and photophosphorylation. They are widely used in study of photosynthesis.

Figure 21-3
Energy equivalent of the einstein at different wavelengths.

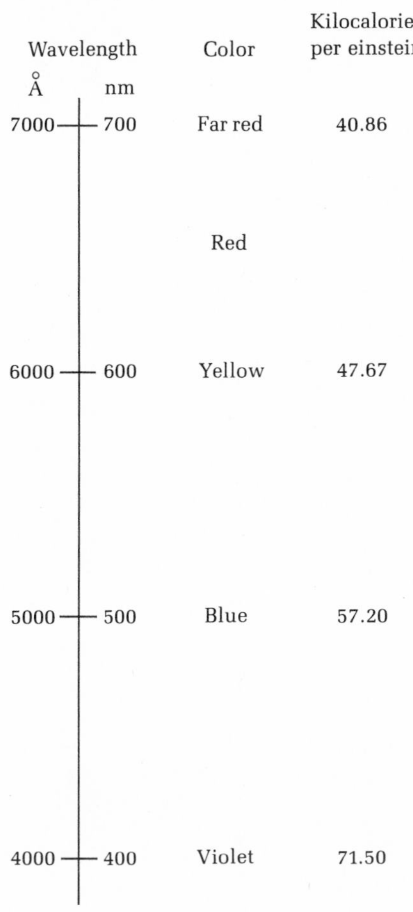

Excitation of Molecules by Light

Visible light is a form of electromagnetic radiation of wavelength 4000 to 7000 Å (Figure 21-3). It arises from the nuclear fusion of hydrogen atoms to form helium atoms and electrons in the sun, the temperature of which is some 20,000,000°K. The overall reaction is

$$4\,{}^{1}_{1}\mathrm{H} \longrightarrow {}^{4}\mathrm{He} + 2e^{-} + h\nu$$

The symbol $h\nu$ represents a quantum of energy, h is Planck's constant (6.62×10^{-27} erg-sec, or 1.58×10^{-34} cal sec), and ν is the frequency of the radiation, which is largely in the form of γ rays. A complex series of reactions ensues, in which the γ radiation is absorbed by the electrons and its energy emitted in the form of *photons*, or *quanta*, of visible light. The total amount of solar energy falling on the profile of the earth is immense; it is estimated to be about 10^{24} cal year^{-1}.

The energy of photons is inversely proportional to their wavelength (Figure 21-3). Thus, photons of short wavelength, at the violet end of the spectrum, have the greatest energy. The energy of photons is given by

$$E = Nh\nu = Nh\frac{c}{\lambda} = \frac{286{,}000}{\lambda}\ \text{kcal}$$

where E is the energy in kilocalories of 1 "mole" (or einstein) of photons; N is 6.023×10^{23}, Avogadro's number; ν the frequency in vibrations per second; h is Planck's constant (1.58×10^{-34} cal sec); c the velocity of light (186,000 miles sec^{-1} or 3×10^{10} cm sec^{-1}); and λ the wavelength in angstroms.

The ability of a substance to absorb light depends on its atomic structure, particularly on the arrangement of electrons surrounding the nucleus. It is in fact the electrons that absorb light, some electron orbitals being much more effective in absorbing light than others. The absorption spectrum of a compound indicates its capacity to absorb light as a function of wavelength. When a photon strikes an atom or molecule capable of absorbing light at a given wavelength, energy is absorbed by some of the electrons and the atom or molecule goes into an energy-rich *excited state*. Only photons of certain wavelengths can excite a given atom or molecule because the excitation of molecules is not continuous but quantized; i.e., light energy is absorbed only in discrete packets on an all-or-none basis, leading to the term *quantum*. Excitation of a molecule by light is very rapid, taking less than 10^{-15} sec. Excited molecules are usually quite unstable; their mean lifetime is only about 10^{-9}–10^{-8} sec. When the incident light is turned off, the excited molecule returns to its original low-energy state, called the *ground state*. The return is accompanied by loss of the energy originally absorbed during excitation, either as heat or as light. The light so emitted is called *fluorescence*. Fluorescent decay of excited molecules usually occurs at a longer wavelength than the exciting wavelength. It is very rapid and occurs at rates comparable to the rate of excitation.

Only absorbed light can excite molecules. We shall therefore examine the characteristic light-absorbing pigments of photosynthetic cells.

The Photosynthetic Pigments

All photosynthetic cells contain one or more types of the class of green pigments known as *chlorophylls*, but not all photosynthetic cells are green; photosynthetic algae and bacteria may be brown, red, or purple. This variety of colors results because, besides chlorophyll, most photosynthetic cells contain members of two other classes of light-trapping pigments, the yellow *carotenoids* (Chapter 10) and the blue or red *phycobilins*, often called *accessory pigments*.

Chlorophylls

Chlorophylls can be extracted free of protein from leaves with alcohol or acetone and purified by chromatography. Higher plants contain two forms, chlorophyll *a* and *b*. The structure of chlorophyll *a* was established from degradation studies by Willstätter and Hans Fischer in Germany and unequivocally proved by the total synthesis carried out by Woodward in 1960. Chlorophyll *a* (Figure 21-4) contains four substituted pyrrole rings, one of which (ring IV) is reduced. The pyrrole rings are arranged in a macrocyclic structure, in which the four central nitrogen atoms are coordinated with a Mg^{2+} ion to form an extremely stable, essentially planar complex. Chlorophyll has a long, hydrophobic terpenoid side-chain, consisting of the alcohol *phytol* (Chapter 10), esterified to a propionic acid substituent in ring IV (Figure 21-4). When the phytol is removed from chlorophyll *a* by hydrolysis, the remaining structure is called *chlorophyllide a*, which is an intermediate in the biosynthesis of chlorophyll.

Chlorophyll *a* in pure form dissolved in acetone has an absorption maximum at 663 nm. In the intact cell, however, chlorophyll *a* may show two or more different absorption maxima, for example, 672 and 683 nm. Moreover, the exact position of the absorption peak of chlorophyll *a* differs from one species of plant to another. The differences are not due to the existence of different molecular forms but apparently reflect the relative proximity of

Figure 21-4
The structure of chlorophylls. In chlorophyll a, X = —CH_3; in chlorophyll b, X = —CHO. Note that there is a fused cyclopentanone ring (V) in addition to the four pyrrole rings. In bacteriochlorophyll, pyrrole ring II is reduced. When the ester linkage with phytol is hydrolyzed, a chlorophyllide results.

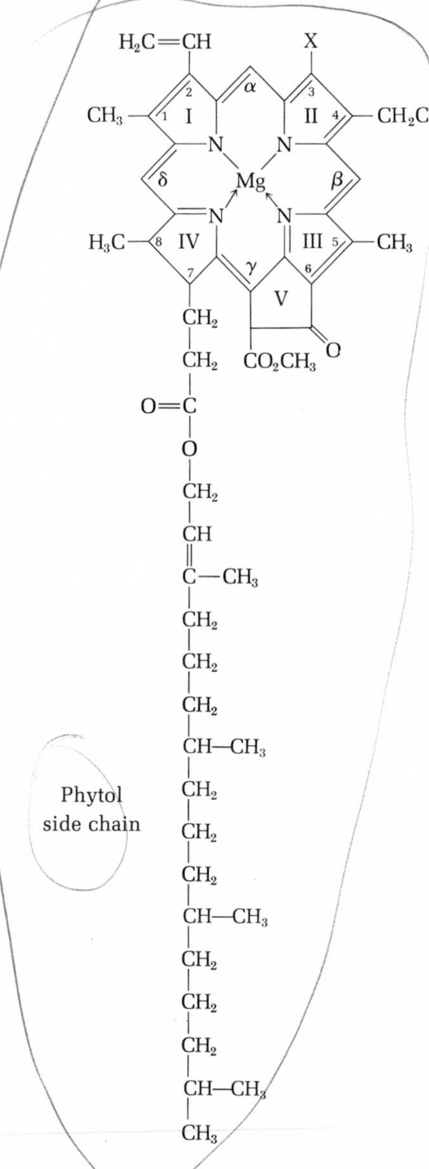

chlorophyll *a* molecules to other pigment molecules in the thylakoid membranes. Unlike the cytochromes, chlorophylls are not conjugated to proteins in the intact cell.

Most oxygen-producing photosynthetic cells contain two kinds of chlorophyll, of which one is always chlorophyll *a*. The other may be chlorophyll *b* (green plants), chlorophyll *c* (brown algae, diatoms, and dinoflagellates), or chlorophyll *d* (red algae). Photosynthetic cells that produce no oxygen do not contain chlorophyll *a*. They may contain only a single type of chlorophyll, either *bacteriochlorophyll*, which differs from the chlorophyll *a* of oxygen producers in that pyrrole ring II is reduced, or *Chlorobium chlorophyll*, or both.

All the chlorophylls absorb visible light efficiently because of their many conjugated double bonds. Moreover, the light energy of the photons absorbed by chlorophyll may become delocalized and spread throughout the characteristic electronic structure of the chlorophyll molecule.

That chlorophyll must be the primary light-trapping molecule in green cells has been established by means of a *photochemical action spectrum*, a plot of the efficiency of different wavelengths of visible light in supporting oxygen evolution. Figure 21-5 shows the action spectrum of photosynthesis in green algae and the light absorption spectrum of the cells, which is largely a function of their chlorophyll content. Since the action spectrum corresponds closely with the absorption spectrum, it has been concluded that chlorophyll is quantitatively the predominant light-trapping molecule in green algae.

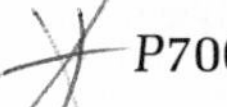

P700

Refined spectroscopic methods have revealed that photosynthetic cells contain a very small amount of a pigment with a light absorption maximum at 700 nm, which undergoes bleaching when the cell is illuminated. Since this

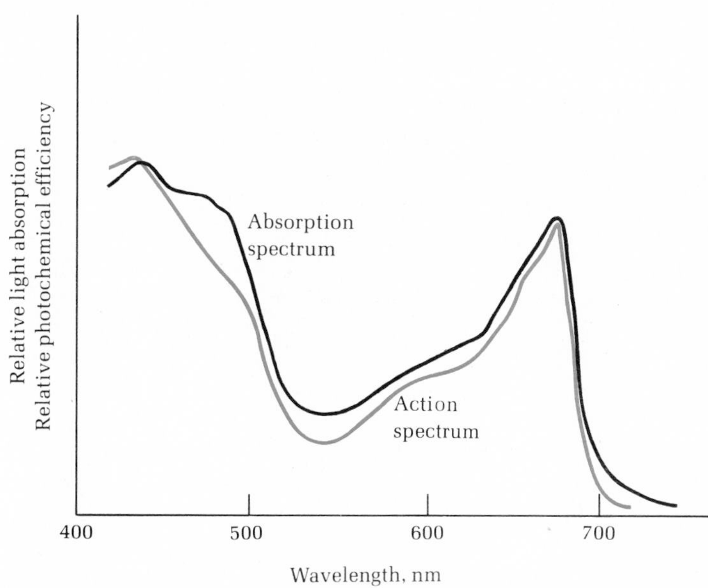

Figure 21-5
Correspondence between the light absorption spectrum and the photochemical action spectrum of the green alga Ulva taeniata.

change can also be produced by the oxidizing agent ferricyanide, the bleaching is believed to correspond to loss of an electron from this pigment, designated *P700*. It is thought to be a specialized chlorophyll molecule making up only $\frac{1}{400}$ of the total chlorophyll in the cell. Evidence suggests that P700 is a trap for collecting *excitons*, quanta of excitation energy, from the bulk chlorophyll molecules. When an exciton is trapped, it results in the loss of an electron from P700.

Carotenoids and Phycobilins

In addition to chlorophyll, two other classes of pigments can serve as light receptors, the yellow carotenoids and the red or blue phycobilins. For example, red algae contain not only chlorophyll but also yellow carotenoids and *phycoerythrobilin*, a red phycobilin. The photochemical action spectrum of red algae approximately coincides with their absorption spectrum, which is a composite of the spectra of chlorophyll and the yellow and red pigments. It has been postulated that these accessory pigments, which have absorption maxima at wavelengths other than those of the chlorophylls, serve as supplementary light receptors for portions of the visible spectrum not completely covered by chlorophyll. Carotenoids also function to protect chlorophyll from degradative attack by molecular oxygen.

The carotenoids (Chapter 10) are long polyisoprenoid molecules having conjugated double bonds; each end of the molecule consists of an unsaturated substituted cyclohexene ring. Among the carotenoids found in photosynthetic cells (Figure 21-6) are *β-carotene, spirilloxanthin,* and *lutein*.

Figure 21-6
Important carotenoid pigments in photosynthetic cells.

β-Carotene

Lutein

Spirilloxanthin

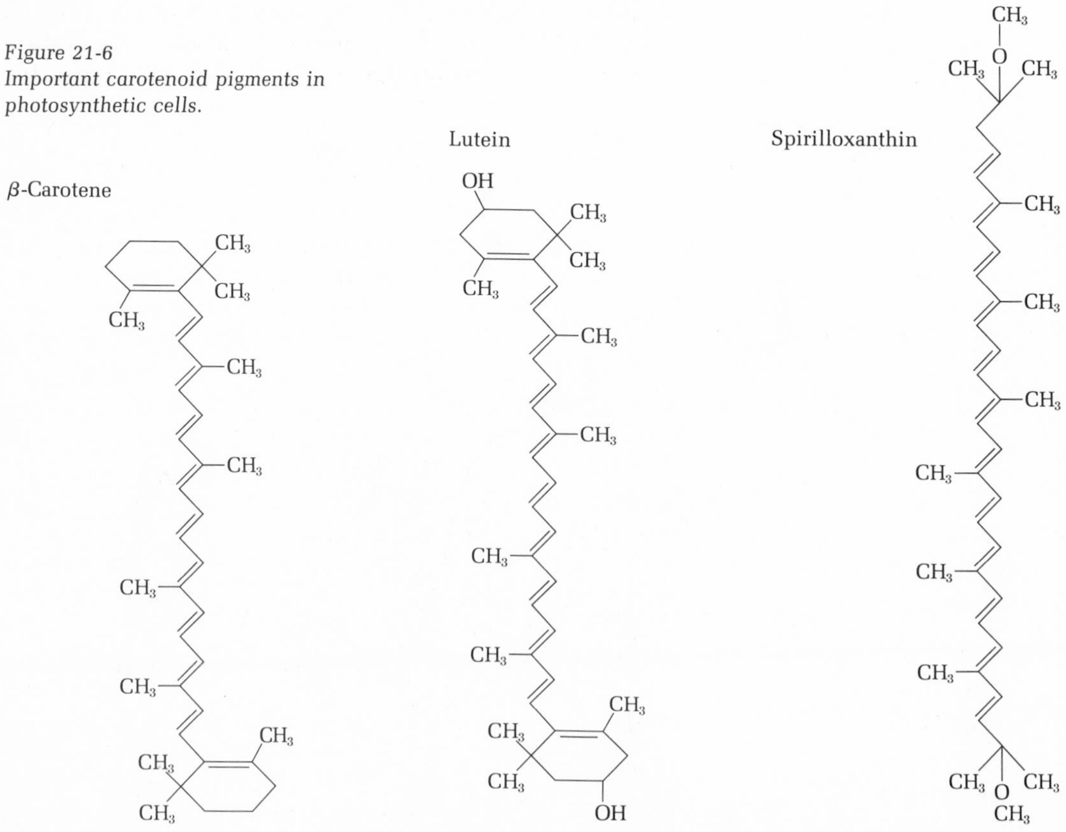

Figure 21-7
Phycoerythrobilin (red). In phycocyanobilin (blue) the $CH_2{=}CH$ group on the fourth pyrrole ring is replaced by CH_3CH_2.

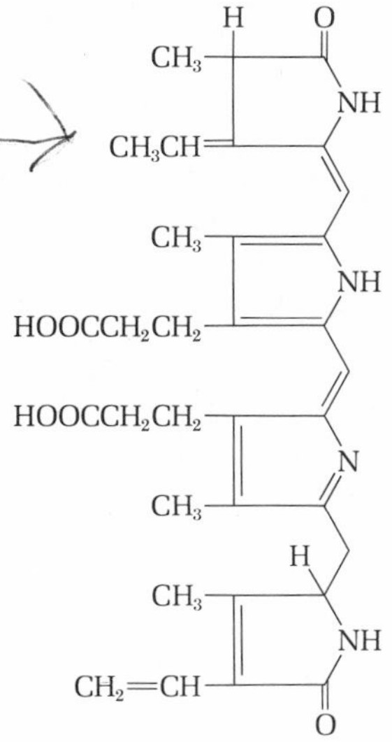

The phycobilin pigments occur only in red and blue-green algae. Phycobilins are open-chain tetrapyrroles (Figure 21-7), in contrast to chlorophyll, a cyclic tetrapyrrole. Phycobilins lack Mg^{2+} and unlike chlorophylls and carotenoids, they are conjugated to specific proteins. The protein conjugate of phycoerythrobilin is *phycoerythrin*, the major red pigment of red algae. The blue *phycocyanin* is the analogous conjugate found in the blue-green algae.

The photosynthetic pigments in the chloroplasts of plants are organized into two functional sets, or assemblies, which in turn are connected with characteristic electron-transport chains. These functional units, called photosystems I and II, will be described later.

Photoreduction and Light-Induced Electron Transport

We have seen earlier that absorption of light energy by photosynthetic cells causes electrons to flow from an electron donor to an electron acceptor in a direction opposite to that predicted from the standard oxidation-reduction potentials of the interacting oxidation-reduction systems. On illumination, green plant cells cause electrons to flow from water to $NADP^+$. This is obviously not a spontaneous process, since the standard reduction potential of the H_2O–$\frac{1}{2}O_2$ couple is +0.82 volt and that of the NADPH–$NADP^+$ couple is −0.32 volt at pH 7.0. If these two systems interacted in the presence of appropriate catalysts but in the *absence* of light or other sources of energy, electrons would flow from the more electronegative system to the more electropositive, that is, from NADPH to oxygen.

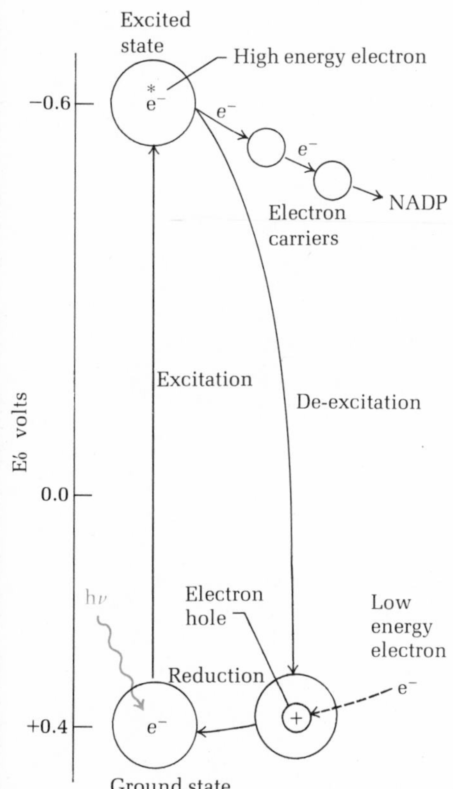

Figure 21-8
Boosting the energy level of transferrable electrons of the pigment assembly. The high-energy electrons leaving the excited pigment are used to reduce electronegative acceptors such as $NADP^+$. Low-energy electrons coming from a more electropositive donor can fill the electron holes.

How absorbed light energy can reverse the normal direction of electron flow can most easily be visualized on the basis of the standard reduction potentials of the excited and ground-state forms of P700, the photoreactive center of a chlorophyll assembly (Figure 21-8). In its ground state, P700 has a relatively positive standard reduction potential, believed to be about +0.40 volt. It therefore has little tendency to lose an electron. When it is excited and absorbs light energy, P700 loses an electron much more readily, and in this state it is believed to have a potential of about −0.60 volt. Absorption of an exciton by P700 thus serves to boost a transferable electron to an energy-rich condition so that it has a very negative potential. Electrons from an excited P700 molecule can thus easily reduce $NADP^+$ ($E'_0 = -0.32$ volt).

When an electron is lost from P700 and reduces some electronegative electron acceptor, such as $NADP^+$, the electron hole left behind in the deexcited, or ground-state, P700 must be refilled. Because of its rather positive potential, ground-state P700 readily accepts electrons from relatively electropositive donors.

In photosynthetic cells, the photoreactive center of the light-absorbing chlorophyll assembly is functionally (and probably physically) connected with a chain of electron carriers. This chain serves to lead electrons of very negative potential away from the excited photoreactive center in an energetically downhill direction toward $NADP^+$, causing its reduction. Similarly, a chain of electron carriers leads into the ground-state photoreactive center and provides electrons to refill the holes left when the system is excited. The light-induced flow of electrons via such a chain or chains is known as *photosynthetic electron transport*, the reduction of an electron acceptor by such a chain being *photoreduction*. It is generally agreed that there is only one true light reaction, or photoact, namely, the absorption of an exciton by a reactive center, such as P700, and the consequent displacement of an electron. All ensuing events, such as the passage of this electron from the first carrier leading away from the chlorophyll assembly to the final electron acceptor, are actually dark reactions.

Cyclic and Noncyclic Electron Flows

The light-induced electron flow taking place in the Hill reaction is called noncyclic electron flow, since electrons pass from H_2O (or some other electron donor) via chlorophyll to $NADP^+$ or some other electron acceptor, e.g., a dye or ferricyanide, whose reduced form then accumulates. There is another type of light-induced electron flow, namely, cyclic electron flow, which cannot be detected by the methods used for measuring noncyclic electron flow. It can be recognized only by an effect produced by the flow, namely, the phosphorylation of ADP to ATP. We have seen above that isolated chloroplasts can cause phosphorylation of ADP to ATP when illuminated in the absence of any added electron donor or electron acceptor and without accumulation of a reduced substance. It was therefore concluded that the energy required for the phosphorylation of ADP comes from light and that the phosphorylation must be coupled to the flow of electrons from excited chlorophyll along a chain of electron carriers in such a way that the electrons return to the electron holes left in the deexcited, or ground-state, chlorophyll, in a cyclic manner. Although it is not possible to measure the volume of cyclic electron flow directly, since the electrons do not accumulate in any product, it is possible to measure the ATP produced in this process, called *cyclic photophosphorylation*. By this means, cyclic electron flow has been found to be greatly stimulated by various oxidation-reduction carriers, such as the dye pyocyanine, by flavin nucleotides, and by ferredoxin. On the other hand, it is not stimulated by $NADP^+$ alone. It may also be inhibited by poisons acting primarily on the electron carriers, such as antimycin A.

In 1957 Arnon and his colleagues found that phosphorylation of ADP takes place not only during cyclic electron flow but also during the noncyclic electron flow occurring in the Hill reaction, with ferricyanide as artificial electron acceptor. Thus both cyclic and noncyclic light-induced electron flows are accompanied by phosphorylation of ADP.

The discovery of these two types of electron flows in plant photosynthesis suggested the occurrence of two types of photosystems in plants.

The Two Light Reactions in Plant Photosynthesis

There is much evidence that there are two light reactions in oxygen-evolving plant photosynthesis. Plant chloroplasts contain two distinct types of chlorophyll, whereas the photosynthetic bacteria, which do not evolve oxygen, usually contain only one. More evidence comes from studies of the quantum efficiency of photosynthesis in plant cells as a function of wavelength. Although the efficiency of photosynthesis is uniform over most of the spectrum, it declines significantly in the red, i.e., at wavelengths of 680 nm and above. This phenomenon is called *red drop*. However, it was shown by Emerson that if light at 680 nm is supplemented with light of a shorter wavelength (<600 nm), the quantum efficiency of photosynthesis in the red can be restored to normal. These findings suggested that two different light reactions are required for maximum photochemical efficiency. Duysens has postulated that the long-wavelength reaction, which he attributes to photosystem I, is associated with chlorophyll *a* and is not accompanied by oxygen evolution. Photosystem II, which is activated by shorter wavelengths, is postulated to be required for oxygen evolution; it involves not only chlorophyll *a* but also a second type of chlorophyll (*b*, *c*, or *d*) as well as the accessory phycobilin pigments. All oxygen-evolving photosynthetic cells contain both photosystems I and II, whereas the photosynthetic bacteria, which do not evolve oxygen, contain only photosystem I. It is also postulated that photosystem I arose first during biological evolution; the capacity of plants to use water as reductant and thus to cause oxygen evolution, which is conferred by photosystem II, arose later.

Each photosystem has its own characteristic assembly of light-absorbing pigments. The light-trapping unit of photosystem I contains about 200 chlorophyll *a* molecules and about 50 carotenoid molecules. Although these pigment molecules are capable of absorbing light energy as photons, only one pigment molecule of the entire assembly, namely, P700, can trap the absorbed excitons and undergo loss of electrons. P700 thus serves as an electron lead from the assembly. Pigment system II contains about 200 molecules of chlorophyll *a* and some 200 molecules of chlorophyll *b*, *c*, or *d*, depending on the species. Xanthophylls or phycobilins may also be present. There is evidence that the light-trapping unit of photosystem II also contains a reactive energy-trapping center comparable to P700 that serves as the electron lead. It has been postulated that the complete set of pigments and electron carriers constituting photosystems I and II and their associated lipids are clustered together into a single structural and functional unit called a *quantasome*. Such a particle would have a molecular weight of 2×10^6 and would be about 175 Å long. There is some electron microscopic evidence (see below) that such clusters are present in the thylakoid membranes.

Photosystems I and II have been successfully separated from each other by treating chloroplasts with digitonin and other detergents, followed by density-gradient centrifugation.

Interrelationships between Photosystem I and Photosystem II

Now some important questions arise. How are photosystems I and II related? Do they function independently, or are they connected? Is there only one photophosphorylation process that is shared by both cyclic and noncyclic phosphorylation, or does each photosystem have its own mechanism of phosphorylation? What is the identity and sequence of the electron carriers in the electron-transferring chains? These questions have dominated the course of recent research on photosynthesis and have generated a lively turnover of hypotheses and interpretations.

The available experimental evidence is best explained by the concept that the two photosystems operate in a connected sequential fashion, i.e., in series, as is shown in Figure 21-9. This formulation, which is accepted by most investigators, postulates that when P700 in photosystem I is excited, it loses electrons which are passed along a chain of carriers to $NADP^+$, causing its reduction. The electron hole left in the deexcited P700 of photosystem I must of course be refilled. It is postulated that the electrons required ultimately come from water via a chain of electron carriers extending from photosystem II to photosystem I. When photosystem II is illuminated, an electron from its reactive photocenter is boosted to an acceptor Q and then flows downhill via the central electron-transferring chain to the electron hole in P700 of photosystem I, restoring the latter to its reduced state. During this process of electron flow from photosystem II to photosystem I, one or, more likely, two molecules of ATP are generated per pair of electrons, in a coupled process similar to respiratory-chain phosphorylation. The restoration of the active center of photosystem II to its reduced state is in turn postulated to result from downhill transfer of electrons from water ($E_0' = +0.82$) to the active center, the standard potential of which is not known with certainty but which is presumably more positive than that of the water-oxygen system. Accompanying this process is oxygen evolution.

In this series hypothesis, cyclic electron flow is visualized to occur by a shunt or bypass (Figure 21-9). In cyclic electron flow electrons ejected from P700 of photosystem I thus return via the electron-transport chain back to the hole in P700 without oxygen evolution or net reduction of $NADP^+$; one phosphorylation occurs during cyclic electron flow.

Electron Transport from Photosystem I to $NADP^+$

We shall now examine the electron-transfer chain leading from P700 of photosystem I of plant chloroplasts to $NADP^+$, the normal acceptor of electrons in the first phase of photosynthesis. In 1958 San Pietro and Lang discovered that the reduction of $NADP^+$ and the evolution of oxygen by illuminated spinach-chloroplast suspensions could be greatly accelerated by addition of a soluble protein isolated from spinach. They showed this factor to be

Figure 21-9
Series arrangement of photosystems I and II. The two systems are connected by an electron-transport chain between acceptor Q of photosystem II and P700 of photosystem I. Non-cyclic electron flow employs both systems, starting from water and ending in NADPH. Cyclic electron flow requires only photosystem I; electrons boosted to Z in photosystem I can return to ground state P700 via a shunt provided by cytochrome b_6 or by an artificial electron carrier such as PMS (phenazine methosulfate). The point of entry of the shunt is not known but is such as to allow one phosphorylation.
The locations of the phosphorylation sites are not known with certainty.

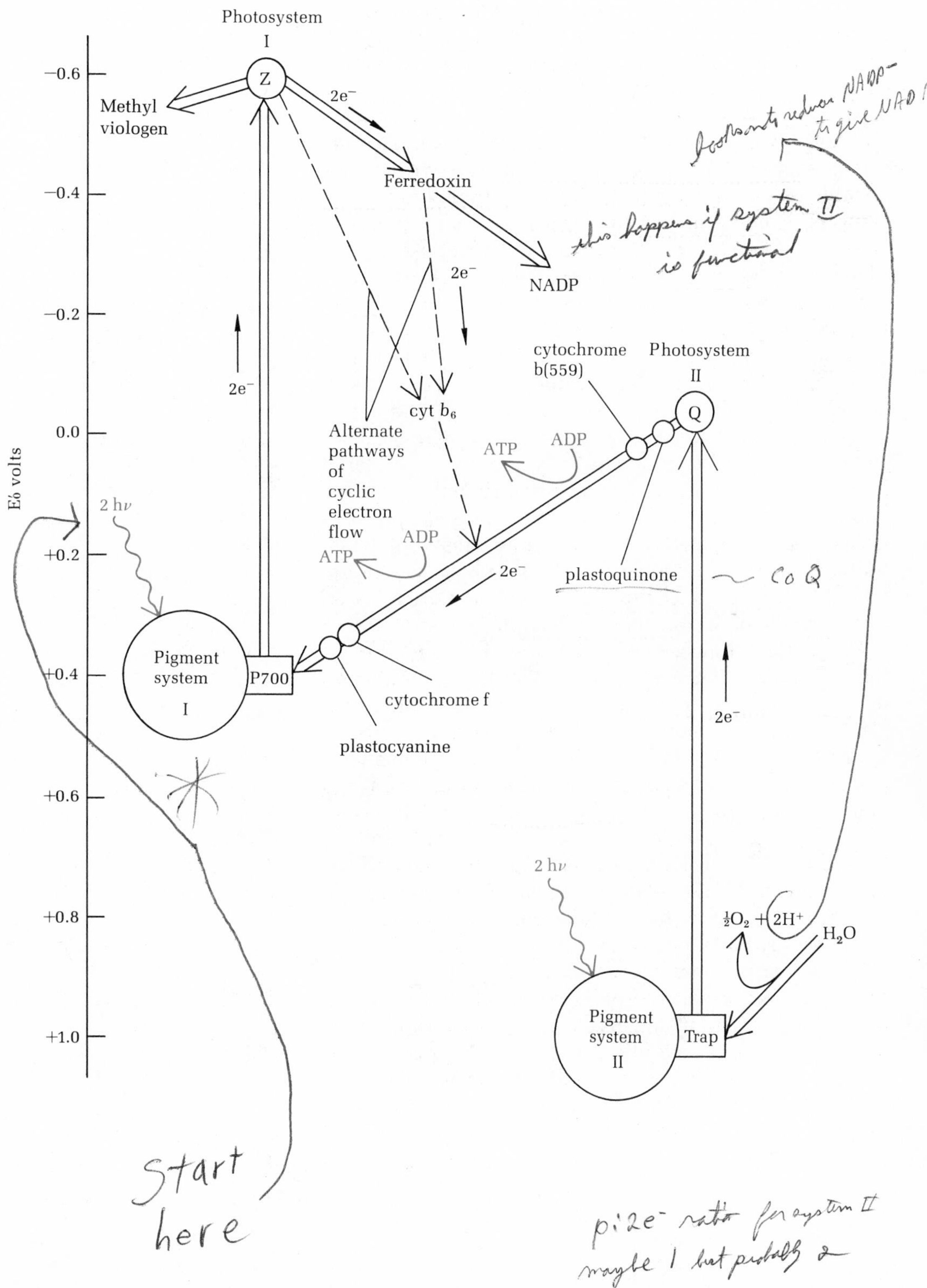

an enzyme which promotes the transfer of electrons from chlorophyll to $NADP^+$ and called it *photosynthetic pyridine nucleotide reductase*. Highly purified preparations of the enzyme revealed the presence of iron and sulfur in a labile form.

An important clue to the identity of this enzyme came from an unexpected quarter. Another group of investigators, headed by Carnahan, had found that certain nonphotosynthetic bacteria utilizing molecular hydrogen anaerobically contain a specific protein capable of accepting electrons from hydrogen. This protein, which they named *ferredoxin*, was isolated in pure crystalline form and also found to contain iron and labile sulfur but no porphyrin group. Arnon and his colleagues tested crystalline ferredoxin from the nonphotosynthetic anaerobic *Clostridium pasteurianum* and found that it was highly active in catalyzing photoreduction of $NADP^+$ in spinach chloroplasts depleted of their normal pyridine nucleotide reductase. Since the spinach photosynthetic pyridine nucleotide reductase resembled bacterial ferredoxin in many respects, Arnon renamed the former *spinach ferredoxin*.

Nonheme-iron proteins are widely distributed in both photosynthetic and nonphotosynthetic organisms and participate in at least four important types of oxidoreduction reactions: (1) in the hydrogenase system of many anaerobic bacteria, (2) in reduction of nitrogen in nitrogen-fixing bacteria, (3) in photosynthesis, and (4) in mitochondrial electron transport. (see Chapters 17 and 24).

Spinach ferredoxin has a molecular weight of about 11,600. The entire amino acid sequence of bacterial ferredoxin and most of that of spinach ferredoxin are known; they show some interesting homologies. Curiously, both lack histidine, methionine, and tryptophan. Spinach ferredoxin contains two iron atoms, which are bound to two specific sulfur atoms; the latter are released from ferredoxin as H_2S on acidification. The structure of the iron-sulfur linkages is not known with certainty, but the iron atoms are normally in the Fe(III) state. Although ferredoxin can be reduced and reoxidized via the one-electron steps, it is not certain that this necessarily occurs via Fe(III) to Fe(II) transitions. Spinach ferredoxin shows two strong absorption bands in its visible spectrum, at 463 and 420 nm, which decrease on reduction. It has a standard reduction potential of -0.432 volt at pH 7.0 and is thus about 0.1 volt more negative than the standard potential of the $NADPH$–$NADP^+$ couple (see Chapter 17).

Ferredoxin in its reduced state cannot pass its electrons directly to $NADP^+$, but an enzyme capable of catalyzing this reaction in the dark, *ferredoxin-NADP oxidoreductase*, has been isolated from spinach chloroplasts and crystallized by Arnon and his colleagues and others. It is a flavoprotein which can utilize either NAD^+ or $NADP^+$ as electron acceptor; however, its affinity for $NADP^+$ is 400 times greater than for NAD^+. The equation for this reaction is

$$2Fd_{red} + NAD_{ox} \longrightarrow 2Fd_{ox} + NAD_{red}$$

in which Fd designates ferredoxin. Although Arnon originally postulated that ferredoxin is the first electron acceptor from excited P700, the bulk of experimental evidence suggests that there is an as yet unidentified electron carrier, designated Z (Figure 21-9), between P700 and ferredoxin. It is believed to have a more negative potential than ferredoxin since photosystem I has been found capable of reducing dyes having a much more negative standard potential. For example, methyl viologen, (standard reduction potential −0.55 v) is readily reduced by spinach chloroplasts, indicating that the standard reduction potential of the carrier Z is at least as negative as −0.55 volt.

Electron Transport from Photosystem II to Photosystem I

In addition to ferredoxin, chloroplasts contain other types of electron carriers, some of which are believed to function in the transfer of electrons from photosystem II to photosystem I. Hill and Davenport have discovered two distinctive types of cytochromes in chloroplasts different from those participating in mitochondrial electron transport. The first, found in 1940, is cytochrome *f* (Latin, *frons*, leaf); it is bound to chloroplast structure and can be released only by use of alkaline nonpolar solvents. It has a molecular weight of about 100,000 and contains two hemes per molecule. The α band of its reduced form is at 555 nm, or very similar to that of cytochrome *c*. In fact, cytochrome *f* is a cytochrome of the *c* class (its alternative designation is cytochrome C555). Its standard oxidation-reduction potential is +0.365 volt, compared to the value of +0.265 volt for mitochondrial cytochrome *c*. Cytochrome b_6, or b_{563}, found in 1952, is less well understood, since it has not been obtained in water-soluble form, being very tightly bound to the chloroplast membrane structure. Its α band is at 563 nm, and its standard reduction potential is −0.060 volt. More recently, another *b* cytochrome, namely, cytochrome b_3 or b_{559} has been identified. Chloroplasts also contain a blue copper-protein called *plastocyanin*, which has a standard reduction potential of +0.400 volt. Also present are two quinones, vitamin K_1 and *plastoquinone* (margin), the latter an analog of CoQ of mitochondria. Very likely other carriers occur which remain to be identified.

Plastoquinone

$$\text{2,3-(CH}_3)_2\text{-1,4-benzoquinone, 5-H, 6-}(CH_2{-}CH{=}C(CH_3){-}CH_2)_nH$$

Elucidation of the carrier sequence in the photosynthetic electron-transport chain between photosystems II and I has been approached by many of the same methods used in analysis of mitochondrial electron transport. By piecing together information on the standard reduction potentials of the carriers, their behavior as observed spectroscopically, and the action of inhibitors and of artificial electron carriers, it has been possible to construct the sequence shown in Figure 21-9. The chain leading from photosystem II to P700 begins with an unidentified carrier Q. The next carrier is believed to be plastoquinone ($E_0' =$ 0.00). Since cytochrome *f* and plastocyanin have potentials near that of P700, there is thus a fairly large gap in our knowledge of the chain between photosystem II and photosystem I.

One of the most powerful experimental approaches to the identification of the sequence of carriers in this chain is through the use of genetic mutants of algae, such as *Chlamydomonas* and *Scenedesmus*, which are defective in one or another of the electron carriers or in P700. Studies of Levine and others on such mutants are yielding important and conclusive information which strongly supports the formulation shown in Figure 21-9.

Figure 21-10
The various pathways of electron flow in plant photosynthesis.

Normal noncyclic electron flow from water to $NADP^+$

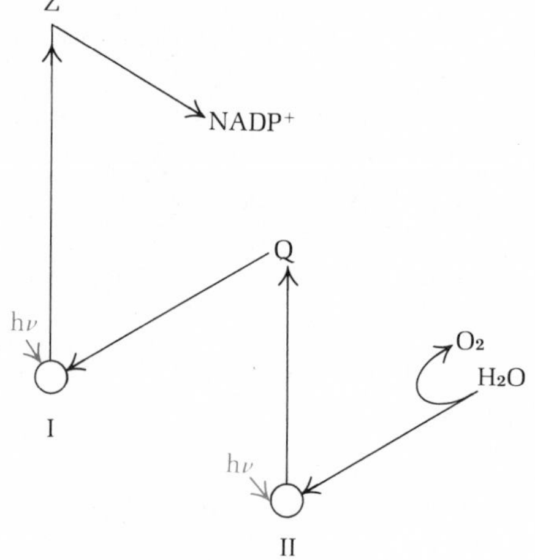

Cyclic electron flow

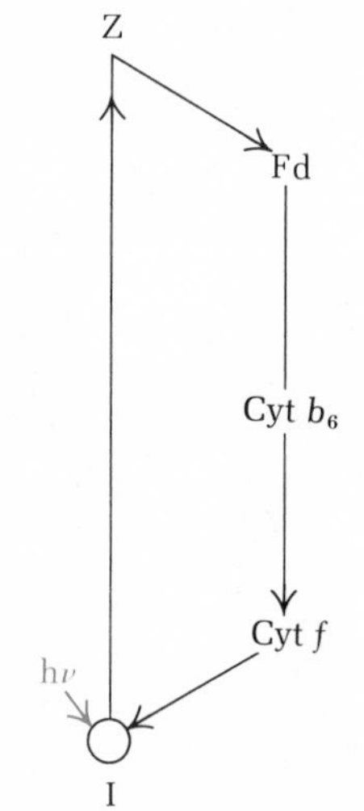

Hill reactions with methyl viologen (MV) or ferricyanide (FeCN) as acceptors.

Other Electron-Transfer Processes

The electron-transport chain from water to the pigments of photosystem II is obscure, but it is known that this step requires Mn^{2+} for activity.

The nature of the shunt mechanism which makes possible cyclic electron flow in photosystem I is also not entirely clear. Dyes such as phenazine methosulfate catalyze cyclic electron flow with phosphorylation, suggesting the possibility that the shunt may involve a specific cytochrome carrier, as shown in Figure 21-9, or that the shunt joins the central chain at some earlier point. Figure 21-10 summarizes the pathways taken by electrons during normal noncyclic electron flow, during cyclic electron flow, and during Hill reactions with different electron acceptors.

The Stoichiometry of Photophosphorylation and the Energetics of Photosynthesis

A major unresolved question is how many phosphorylations occur during the combined action of photosystems I and II in oxygen-evolving plant photosynthesis. Several technical difficulties stand in the way of solving this problem. For one thing, it is not possible to determine the P:2*e* ratio during cyclic electron flow, since there is no way to measure the number of electrons flowing around the closed chain. Measurements of the P:2*e* ratio are usually made on noncyclic electron flow, with ferredoxin, $NADP^+$, or ferricyanide as electron acceptor. Measurement of the amount of ferricyanide reduced and the amount of ATP formed yields a P:2*e* ratio of about 1.0. However, photophosphorylation is depressed by certain buffers and other ionic components used in such experiments and it has been suggested that the true P:2*e* ratio of noncyclic phosphorylation is perhaps 2.0, which would require two energy-coupling sites in the photosynthetic electron-transport chain(s). At least one and probably both of these phosphorylations occur between plastoquinone and P700 of photosystem I. The phosphorylation occurring during cyclic electron flow may be associated with the shunt via cytochromes *b* and *f*. It is possible that the shunt may enter the central chain at some point closer to photosystem II, so that the phosphorylation site in the central chain is shared by cyclic and noncyclic electron flows.

The maximum thermodynamic efficiency, i.e., the quantum efficiency, of photosynthesis has been one of the most hotly debated problems in biochemistry. In principle, the problem reduces to the experimental determination of the value of *n*, the number of light quanta required in the overall equation of photosynthesis

$$CO_2 + 2H_2O + n(h\nu) \longrightarrow (CH_2O) + H_2O + O_2 \qquad (3)$$

The standard free-energy change for the synthesis of hexose from CO_2 and H_2O is $\Delta G^{\circ\prime} = +686$ kcal. If we divide this value by 6, we obtain the energy input required to reduce one molecule of CO_2 to (CH_2O), as called for in equation (3), namely, +114 kcal. Since the caloric value of a light quantum depends on its wavelength and may range from 70 kcal einstein^{-1} at 400 nm to about 42 kcal at 700 nm (Figure 21-3), we shall use the lower of these values for the ensuing calculations. Actually, excited chlorophyll emits light quanta of about 40 kcal regardless of the wavelength of the absorbed light. The theoretical quantum requirement *n* for equation (3) would then be 114/42 = 2.7 quanta at 700 nm, but since light quanta are indivisible, we must assume that the theoretical minimum is three quanta per molecule of carbon dioxide reduced.

The actual quantum requirement of photosynthesis in the intact cell is determined by experimental measurement of the amount of light absorbed by a suspension of photosynthesizing cells in relation to the amount of carbon dioxide reduced or oxygen evolved. There are many experimental difficulties in such measurements. Since intact cells are open systems, the changes occurring on turning the light on and off are transitions between steady states. Moreover, as was shown by Warburg, a pioneer in this field, the measured quantum requirement depends on the metabolic state and the past history of the algae used for such experiments. The lowest value he observed was $n = 5$; because of known errors which he believed overestimated the quantum requirement, he argued that the true value of *n* is 4.0. Most other investigators of the problem, particularly Emerson and his followers, have not been able to observe such low values and suggest that the true value is 8 or higher. Warburg's value $n = 4$, compared to the theoretical requirement of 3, implies that photosynthesis is 75 percent efficient. The quantum requirement of 8 favored by other investigators represents a thermodynamic efficiency of some 38 percent at 700 nm, or nearly the same as that of the overall process of glucose combustion and oxidative phosphorylation (Chapter 17).

We may now anticipate a point developed more fully in Chapter 22 and give the overall equation for the reduction of CO_2 to (CH_2O) during the second, or dark, phase of photosynthesis

$$CO_2 + 2NADPH + 2H^+ + 3ATP + 2H_2O \longrightarrow (CH_2O) + 2NADP^+ + 3ADP + 3P_i$$

This equation demands three molecules of ATP and two of NADPH to reduce one molecule of CO_2. To provide these in terms of the series hypothesis of Figure 21-9, four electrons must be ejected by photosystem I, to form two NADPH, and four electrons must be ejected in photosystem II, to yield one molecule of O_2. Since one light quantum is required to eject each electron, we require eight light quanta altogether by the series formulation. If only one photophosphorylation per pair of electrons occurs during the overall process, only two molecules of ATP will be generated by the two pairs of electrons flowing from photosystem II to I, according to the equation

$$8h\nu + 2NADP^+ + 2ADP + 2P_i \longrightarrow O_2 + 2NADPH + 2H^+ + 2ATP$$

This is an insufficient amount of ATP to complete the overall equation of CO_2 reduction, since three molecules of ATP are required. If two phosphorylations take place during light-induced electron transport, as most investigators postulate, then four ATPs will be formed, which is more than enough:

$$8h\nu + 2NADP^+ + 4ADP + 4P_i \longrightarrow O_2 + 2NADPH + 2H^+ + 4ATP + 2H_2O$$

It also appears likely that under some conditions cyclic electron flow may occur in the intact plant, which would yield ATP but no NADPH.

The efficiency of photosynthesis in nature is much lower than the figures calculated for the basic molecular process. It has been calculated from the output of fixed carbon by a field of corn in one growing season that only about 1 to 2 percent of the solar energy falling on the field is recovered. Sugar cane is much more efficient; it can recover up to 8 percent of the captured light in the form of organic products. As will be seen below, the process of *photorespiration*, tends to lower the net efficiency of photosynthesis in nature.

The Mechanism of Photosynthetic Phosphorylation

The phosphorylation of ADP accompanying light-induced electron transport strongly resembles the analogous process of oxidative phosphorylation coupled to mitochondrial electron transport. Light-induced noncyclic electron transport can be stimulated by addition of ADP and phosphate and thus shows acceptor control, similar to the requirement of ADP for maximal electron-transport rates in mitochondria. Photosynthetic phosphorylation can also be uncoupled. Actually, some agents capable of uncoupling mitochondrial phosphorylation also uncouple photophosphorylations, such as 2,4-dinitrophenol and carbonyl cyanide phenylhydrazones (Chapter 17). *Desaspidin*, a toxic substance found in some ferns, also uncouples both photosynthetic and oxidative phosphorylation. It is of interest that photosynthetic phosphorylation is uncoupled by NH_4^+ ions, which do not uncouple oxidative phosphorylation in mitochondria.

Photophosphorylation can also be inhibited by phloridzin and a synthetic compound called Dio-9; their action resembles that of oligomycin on mitochondrial phosphorylation.

Chloroplasts normally show no ATPase activity, but on treatment with sulfhydryl compounds such as dithiothreitol in the light, a Mg^{2+}-dependent ATPase activity is evoked, similar to that observed in mitochondria treated with 2,4-dinitrophenol.

It is also possible to extract chloroplasts so that a protein factor required for photophosphorylation is removed. These extracted chloroplasts are unable to phosphorylate ADP, but they still allow photoreductions. Addition of the factor restores the phosphorylating activity. This protein factor lacks ATPase activity when freshly isolated, but when exposed to heat, trypsin action, or certain sulfhydryl compounds, it acquires the ability to hydrolyze ATP in the presence of Ca^{2+}. Because the ATPase activity of the coupling protein is inhibited by phloridzin, which inhibits photosynthetic phosphorylation in intact chloroplasts, it appears likely that the ATPase activity of the isolated coupling factor is functionally related to the energy-coupling process in which ATP is formed. The ATPase activity of this coupling factor is thus analogous to that of the F_1 coupling factor for oxidative phosphorylation, which also shows ATPase activity (Chapter 17). High-resolution electron micrographs of the surface of thylakoid membranes show the presence of 100-Å knob-like particles which are believed to be molecules of the ATPase or coupling factor (Figure 21-11).

From such developments, it seems very likely that the mechanism of photosynthetic phosphorylation may prove to be identical in principle to that of oxidative phosphorylation.

Figure 21-11
Ultrastructure of thylakoids. Electron micrograph of the membrane surfaces of a thylakoid disk of a spinach chloroplast, following freeze-fracturing. In this technique the sample is frozen and then fractured with a knife edge to yield cleavage surfaces, which are replicated by metal-casting. The image is that of the metal replica.

Ion Movements During Light-Induced Electron Transport

We have seen that there are currently three hypotheses for the mechanism of oxidative phosphorylation (Chapters 17 and 18), namely, chemical coupling, chemiosmotic

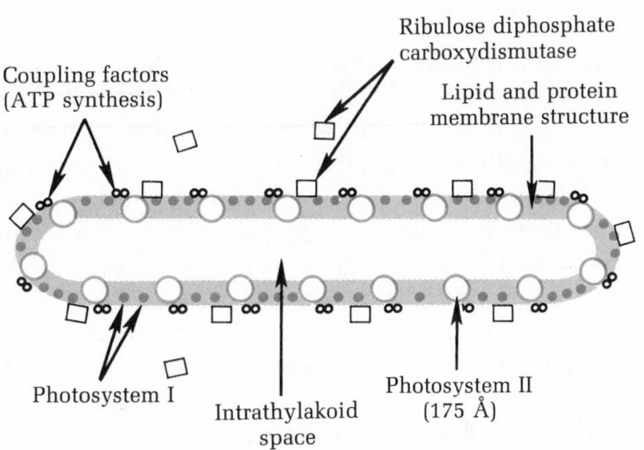

A schematic representation of ultrastructure of the thylakoid. The coupling-factor molecules appear to be constructed of four major subunits. They may be visualized by negative contrast. The quantasomes, which contain a complete set of pigments, a number of lipids, as well as electron carriers, are believed to protrude from the inner surface of the membrane, according to freeze-etching observations. Quantasomes have a particle weight of 2×10^6 and a diameter of 175 Å.

coupling, and conformational, or mechanochemical, coupling. These three hypotheses also apply to the mechanism of photophosphorylation.

When chloroplasts are illuminated under conditions in which they exhibit cyclic electron flow, H^+ ions are absorbed from the suspending medium, which becomes more alkaline, and K^+ and Mg^{2+} are ejected into the medium. When the light is turned off, H^+ returns to the medium and K^+ and Mg^{2+} are reabsorbed by the chloroplasts. These ion movements are remarkably similar to those occurring during electron transport in isolated mitochondria, with one important difference. In mitochondria, H^+ is *ejected* during electron transport, whereas in chloroplasts H^+ is *absorbed*. The sidedness of the chloroplast membrane thus is the reverse of that of mitochondria. These characteristic H^+ movements during light-induced electron transport in chloroplasts have been taken to support the Mitchell chemiosmotic coupling hypothesis.

Jagendorf has made the important discovery that a pH gradient artificially imposed across the chloroplast membrane can drive the phosphorylation of ADP (Figure 21-12). He has found that the internal pH of chloroplasts can be artificially lowered by placing them in an acid bath, a solution buffered at pH 4.0 with succinate or some other organic acid buffer. After some minutes, an alkaline buffer containing phosphate and ADP is added to the acid suspension in the dark, to bring it rapidly to pH 8.0. As a result of this rapid transition, a large amount of ATP is formed, apparently at the expense of the transitory pH gradient produced across the membrane after neutralization of the acid. These observations are consistent with the Mitchell chemiosmotic hypothesis for the mechanism of oxidative and photosynthetic phosphorylation, but at the same time they are not inconsistent with the chemical-coupling hypothesis, for a high-energy intermediate generated by a chemical coupling mechanism could be postulated to drive a proton pump in the membrane. However, critical kinetic tests of the rate of the acid-base changes taking place on illumination of chloroplasts recently carried out in other laboratories, have given very strong support to the chemiosmotic hypothesis.

Figure 21-12
Light-independent phosphorylation of ADP at the expense of an artificial pH gradient induced in chloroplasts in the dark.

Spinach chloroplasts are exposed to "acid-bath"

Internal pH equilibrates with external pH on incubation

ADP and P_i are added in the dark, together with sufficient alkali to bring external pH to 8.5, thus creating momentary pH gradient across membrane

ATP is formed from ADP and P_i in the dark at expense of pH gradient

Conformational Changes in Chloroplast Membranes

The inner chloroplast membranes undergo striking changes in conformation which are dependent on light-induced electron transport. Chloroplasts kept in the dark swell and undergo separation of their paired membranes. If they are then illuminated, the membranes pair together again in close juxtaposition and regain their normal conformation. When the light is turned off, the paired membranes relax and separate again. It has been postulated that these conformational changes of the chloroplast membranes, which are very similar to those occurring in the inner mitochondrial membrane (Chapter 18), may represent the means by which the free-energy decline associated with light-induced electron transport is harnessed to drive ATP synthesis and energy-linked movement of ions.

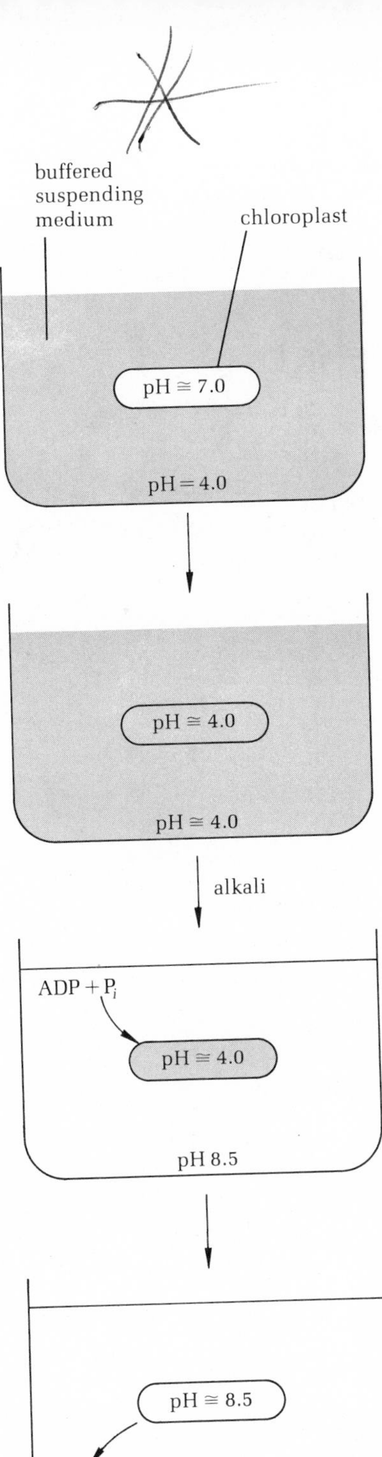

We are left then with three major hypotheses for the mechanism of phosphorylation coupled to electron transport. Today, 40 years after the discovery of ATP and almost 30 years after Lipmann proposed his theory of the central role of ATP in cellular energy transfers, we are still far from understanding how ATP is regenerated from ADP during electron transport, either in the mitochondrion or in the chloroplast.

Photorespiration

Green plant cells contain mitochondria in addition to chloroplasts, and it has been established that such cells exhibit mitochondrial respiration and oxidative phosphorylation in the dark, at the expense of substrates generated by photosynthesis in earlier light periods. The question arises as to whether green plant cells also respire in the light, during active photosynthesis, or whether respiration is turned off. From careful measurements of the rates of oxygen and carbon dioxide exchanges in illuminated plants, particularly with the use of isotopic oxygen, it has been found that most plants do respire in the light while they are carrying out photosynthesis. However, the type of respiration that occurs in illuminated green plants is not mitochondrial respiration, since it is not sensitive to characteristic inhibitors of mitochondrial respiration. Such "light" respiration, which is called *photorespiration*, consumes reducing power generated by photosynthesis and uses it to reduce molecular oxygen. Photorespiration thus "short-circuits" photosynthesis since it diverts the normal flow of light-induced reducing power from the reduction of carbon dioxide into the reduction of oxygen. Moreover, photorespiration is not accompanied by oxidative phosphorylation of ADP and thus appears to be wasteful of energy-rich reducing power generated by photosynthesis.

In some plants the rate of photorespiration is very high and utilizes 50 per cent or more of the reducing power generated by photosynthesis; however, some tropical plants show no photorespiration, which is a genetically determined capability. The function of photorespiration is not entirely clear, but it may participate as a safety valve in regulating the steady state level of reducing power in the light. A regulatory role is also implied by the observation that photorespiration is especially prominent when the light intensity is high and when the partial pressure of oxygen in the cell is high. It has been deduced, however, that photorespiration may waste a substantial fraction of reducing power under natural conditions. Indeed, it has been estimated that the productivity of certain crop plants might well be doubled if it were possible to prevent this waste by selective inhibition of photorespiration.

The mechanism of photorespiration and the enzymes involved are not yet clear, but they are under very active investigation. It appears probable that the major substrate for photorespiration is *glycolic acid* which is the form in which light-generated reducing power is enzymatically oxidized. Green leaves contain glycolic acid oxidase, a flavoprotein of wide distribution and high activity. This enzyme, which oxidizes glycolic acid to glyoxylic acid (below) at the expense of oxygen, is not present in either chloroplasts or mitochondria; it is localized in the microbodies or peroxisomes. The oxidation of glycolic acid to glyoxylic acid at the expense of oxygen yields hydrogen peroxide, which is decomposed by the catalase present in the peroxisomes.

The mechanism by which light-generated reducing power is incorporated into glycolic acid has been under active investigation. Ultimately, this reducing power originates as NADPH, but there is no known reaction by which NADPH can reduce glyoxylic acid directly to glycolic acid. Recent research indicates that glycolic acid arises from one of the intermediates of the cycle of dark reactions in which CO_2 is fixed and ultimately yields glucose. Photorespiration thus drains off an important reduced intermediate generated in photosynthesis, and prevents it from being utilized for glucose formation.

Oxidation of glycolic acid during photorespiration

CH_2OH — $COOH$ Glycolic acid

↓ O_2 → H_2O_2

CHO — $COOH$ Glyoxylic acid

Summary

Water is used as electron donor, and from it oxygen is evolved in all photosynthetic organisms except the photosynthetic bacteria, which employ H_2S, H_2, or organic compounds as electron donors. Although CO_2 is the major electron acceptor in most photosynthetic organisms, nitrate, nitrogen, and hydrogen ions may also serve. The direction of net electron flow in photosynthesis is always against the normal gradient of the standard reduction potential, toward the more electronegative system. The energy for such reverse electron flow is provided by light. The first stage of photosynthesis is the light-dependent reduction of $NADP^+$ and phosphorylation of ADP; in the second stage, NADPH and ATP are used to reduce CO_2 to hexose. In eucaryotic cells photosynthesis takes place in the thylakoids, flattened vesicles within chloroplasts, which are stacked to form the grana. Photosynthetic cells contain three types of light-capturing pigments, chlorophylls, carotenoids, and phycobilins. In the primary photoact, light energy, which varies with wavelength, is absorbed by the pigment assembly, raising its energy level to the excited state. The excitation energy is trapped by one specialized pigment molecule, from which an electron is tapped away and used ultimately to reduce $NADP^+$. There are two photosystems in oxygen-evolving cells. Photosystem I contains chlorophyll *a* and β-carotene, as well as a single molecule of P700, the energy-trapping molecule; it is activated largely by longer wavelengths of light. Photosystem II has its own set of pigments; it is activated by shorter wavelengths and is responsible for oxygen evolution. Organisms that do not evolve O_2 lack photosystem II. Photosystems I and II are linked in series. Boosting an electron to a highly reducing potential by excitation of photosystem I leads to reduction of $NADP^+$ via a chain of carriers, including ferredoxin and ferredoxin-NADP oxidoreductase. The electrons required to fill the electron holes left in pigment system I come from excited photosystem II via a central electron-transport chain, which includes a plastoquinone, cytochrome b_6, cytochrome f, and plastocyanin. The electrons required to fill the electron holes in photosystem II come from H_2O, which is dehydrogenated by unknown mechanisms.

Phosphorylation of ADP is coupled to one or more of these electron-transport chains. Photosynthetic phosphorylation appears to have many of the same properties as oxidative phosphorylation; it may be uncoupled or inhibited by specific agents. A coupling factor for photosynthetic phosphorylation has been isolated; it has Ca^{2+}-induced ATPase activity. Chloroplasts absorb H^+ and eject K^+ during illumination; their grana also undergo characteristic conformational changes during light-induced electron transport. Chemical-coupling, chemiosmotic-coupling, and conformational-coupling mechanisms have been proposed for photophosphorylation.

Apparently eight light quanta at 700 nm are required to evolve each molecule of oxygen and to reduce one molecule of CO_2, for which two NADPH and three ATP are necessary intermediates.

References

Books

Brookhaven Symposia in Biology, vol. 19, *Energy Conversion by the Photosynthetic Apparatus*, 1965. A valuable collection of symposium articles on all aspects of photosynthesis.

KIRK, J. T. O. and R. A. E. TILNEY-BASSETT, *The Plastids*, W. H. Freeman and Co., San Francisco, 1967. The chemistry, structure, growth, and inheritance of chloroplasts and other plastids.

SAN PIETRO, A. G. (ed.), *Non heme Iron Proteins: Their Role in Energy Conversion*. Antioch Press, Yellow Springs, Ohio, 1965.

VERNON, L. P., and G. R. SEELY (eds.), *The Chlorophylls*, Academic Press Inc., New York, 1966.

Articles and Reviews

ARNON, D. I., "Photosynthetic Activity of Isolated Chloroplasts," *Physiol. Rev.*, **47**:317–358 (1967). The role of ferredoxin and the "parallel" hypothesis for photosystems I and II.

AVRON, M., "Mechanism of Photoinduced Electron Transport in Chloroplasts," in D. R. Sanadi (ed.), *Current Topics in Bioenergetics*, vol. 2, pp. 1–20, Academic Press Inc., New York, 1967. A brief, succinct review of the main features.

BOARDMAN, N. K., "The Photochemical System of Photosynthesis," *Advan. Enzymol.*, **30**:1–80 (1968). A more comprehensive review: up to date and impartial.

BRANTON, D., and R. B. PARK, "Subunits in Chloroplast Lamellae," *J. Ultrastructure Res.*, **19**:283–303 (1967). Use of freeze-fracturing method to delinate structure of thylakoid membranes with the electron microscope.

GOODWIN, T. W., and O. LINDBERG (eds.), "Structure and Function of Chloroplasts and Chromatophores, in *Biological Structure and Function*, pp. 271–461, Academic Press Inc., New York, 1961.

GROSS, E. L., and L. PACKER, "Ion Transport and Conformational Changes in Spinach Chloroplast Grana, I, II," *Arch. Biochem. Biophys.*, **121**:779–789 (1967), **122**:237–245 (1967).

HILL, R., "The Biochemists' Green Mansions: The Photosynthetic Electron Transport Chain in Plants," in P. N. Campbell and G. D. Greville (eds.), *Essays in Biochemistry*, vol. 1, pp. 121–152, Academic Press Inc., New York, 1965. An interesting account written by a pioneer.

JAGENDORF, A. T., "Acid-Base Transitions and Phosphorylation by Chloroplasts," *Fed. Proc.*, **26**:1361–1369 (1967). The formation of ATP at the expense of pH gradients across the chloroplast membrane.

LEVINE, R. P., "Genetic Dissection of Photosynthesis," *Science*, **162**:768–771 (1968). Use of mutants defective in specific electron carriers to analyze photosynthetic electron transport.

MOUDRIANAKIS, E., "Structural and Functional Aspects of Photosynthetic Lamellae," *Fed. Proc.*, **27**:1180–1185 (1968). Correlated biochemical and electron microscopic study.

PACKER, L., and A. R. CROFTS, "The Energized Movement of Ions and Water by Chloroplasts," in D. R. Sanadi (ed.), *Current Topics in Bioenergetics*, vol. 12, pp. 24–64, Academic Press Inc., New York, 1967. Conformational changes in chloroplasts.

Problems

1. Calculate the maximum number of ATP molecules that could be formed from ADP and P_i under standard conditions by absorption of a quantum of light at 400, 550, and 700 nm, providing an appropriate mechanism exists.

2. Calculate the standard free-energy change on passage of a pair of electrons from the first acceptor Z of photosystem I ($E_0' = -0.60$ volt) to ferredoxin. Then calculate the standard free-energy change on passage of a pair of electrons from ferredoxin to $NADP^+$.

3. If the P:2*e* ratio of the phosphorylation of ADP coupled to cyclic electron flow in photosystem I is 1.0, calculate the thermodynamic efficiency of the conversion of light energy (540 nm) into phosphate-bond energy. Assuming that $E_0'^\circ$ of P700 is +0.40 volt and of Z is −0.60 volt, calculate the efficiency of the coupling of phosphorylation to electron flow from Z to P700.

4. Calculate the number of phosphorylations of ADP that may take place on passage of a pair of electrons from photosystem II to photosystem I under conditions in which the intrachloroplast concentration of ATP is 3.0 m*M*, that of ADP is 3.0 m*M* and that of phosphate is 3.0 m*M*. Assume that E_0' of Q is 0.0 volts and that of P700 is +0.4 volt.

PART 3 BIOSYNTHESIS AND THE UTILIZATION OF PHOSPHATE-BOND ENERGY

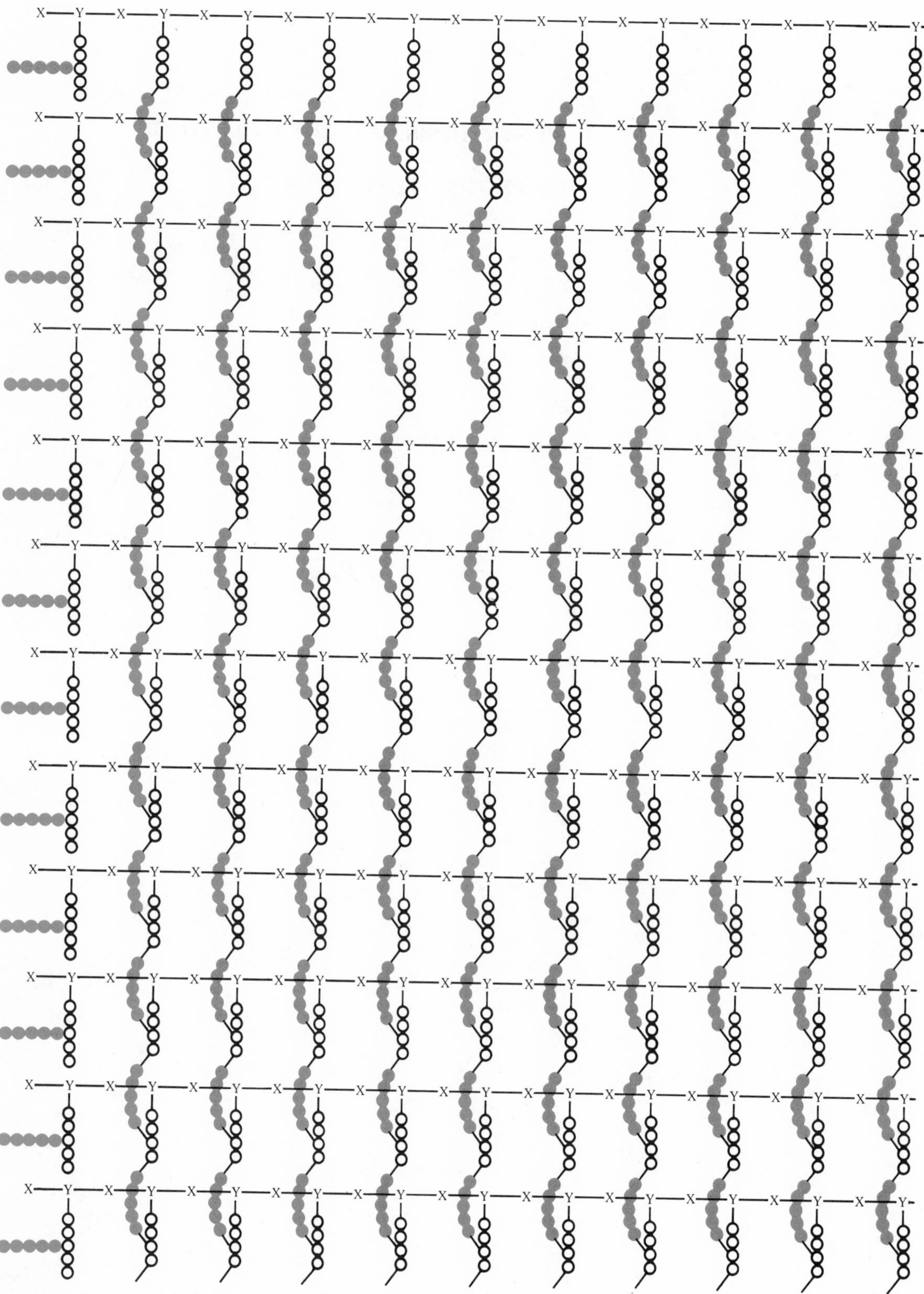

Schematic representation of the peptidoglycan backbone of the cell wall of Staphylococcus aureus. *Its enzymatic assembly outside the cell membrane from precursors made in the cytoplasm is among the more complex biosynthetic activities known.*

X = N-*acetylglucosamine residues*

Y = N-*acetylmuramic acid residues*

OOOO *Side-chains of* L-*alanyl*-D-*isoglutamyl*-L-*lysyl*-D-*alanine*

●●●●● *Cross-bridges of pentaglycine*

PART 3 BIOSYNTHESIS AND THE UTILIZATION OF PHOSPHATE-BOND ENERGY

The cellular processes that require free energy are (1) biosynthesis, in which chemical work is carried out, (2) contraction and motility, which are forms of mechanical work, and (3) active transport, which is a reflection of osmotic or concentration work. The required free energy is furnished by the phosphate-bond energy of ATP and by the reducing power of NADPH and other reduced coenzymes.

Foremost in complexity among the energy-requiring processes is the biosynthesis of cell constituents from simple precursors, the principal process involved in the creation and maintenance of the intricate orderliness of living cells at the expense of their environment. In this part of the book we shall limit our discussion of biosynthesis to noninformational biomolecules, namely, carbohydrates, lipids, amino acids, and mononucleotides, but in Part 4 we shall continue our discussion of biosynthesis to include the incorporation of genetic information into the covalent structures of the nucleic acids and proteins.

As we now turn from the biochemistry of catabolism to the biochemistry of anabolism, some of the organizing principles of biosynthetic pathways require reiteration and emphasis. The first principle, mentioned in Chapter 13, is that the chemical pathway taken in the biosynthesis of a biomolecule is not usually identical to the pathway taken in its degradation. The two pathways may contain one or even several identical steps, but there is always at least one enzymatic step that is dissimilar in the anabolic and catabolic pathways leading to and from a given biomolecule. Thus, the mechanisms of biosynthesis and degradation of cell components are not simply the reverse of each other. This fact has profound biological significance: If the reactions of catabolism and anabolism were catalyzed by the same set of enzymes acting reversibly, no stable biological structure of any complexity could exist, since equilibria between precursors and products mediated by freely reversible reaction systems would, through mass-action effects, undergo fluctuation whenever the concentration of precursors changes.

The second organizing principle underlying biosynthetic reactions also concerns the independence of catabolic and anabolic routes. We have seen that ATP serves as a common intermediate between those chemical processes in the cell that yield free energy (namely, glycolysis, respiration, and the light reactions of photosynthesis) and those cellular processes that consume free energy, such as the biosynthetic pathways. The conservation of the free energy of an oxidative reaction in the form of ATP is made possible because the overall coupled oxidation reaction is exergonic and proceeds in the direction of oxidation and ATP formation. We shall now see that, in a similar way, energy-requiring biosynthetic processes are obligatorily coupled to the energy-yielding breakdown of ATP, in such a way that the overall coupled reaction is also exergonic and thus essentially irreversible in the direction of biosynthesis. Thus, the total amount of phosphate bond energy released from ATP usually greatly exceeds the amount of free energy required to bring about the biosynthesis. The overall equation for an energy-coupled biosynthetic reaction always has a negative standard free energy change in the direction of synthesis.

One way in which a large driving force in the direction of biosynthesis is achieved is through pyrophosphate cleavage of ATP (Chapters 14 and 16), i.e., the release of pyrophosphate rather than orthophosphate during a coupled biosynthetic reaction. Since free pyrophosphate undergoes enzymatic hydrolysis to orthophosphate, often two high-energy phosphate bonds are expended to create only one new covalent linkage in the biosynthetic product. Moreover, biosynthetic reactions often take place in different intracellular compartments from the corresponding degradation pathways. Such compartmentation assures independence of the pathways and a favorable energetic milieu for each.

The third important principle is that biosynthetic reactions are regulated independently of the mechanisms by which catabolic reactions are regulated. Such independent control is made possible by the fact that the catabolic and anabolic pathways are not identical; usually the regulatory or allosteric enzyme controlling the rate of the catabolic pathway does not participate in the anabolic pathway. Conversely, the regulatory enzyme controlling the biosynthetic pathway is not shared by the catabolic pathway.

Most catabolic pathways are regulated by the "energy charge" of the ATP system (Chapters 14 and 18); AMP or ADP usually serve as stimulating modulators and ATP as an inhibitory modulator. The accumulation of certain catabolic products such as citrate also serves to inhibit catabolic pathways through their negative modulatory activity. Biosynthetic pathways, on the other hand, are primarily regulated by the concentration of the end product of the biosynthetic process, in such a way that the cell synthesizes only as much of a given biomolecule as it immediately needs. In biosynthetic pathways the regulatory enzyme that is under allosteric control by the biosynthetic end product is almost always the first enzyme in the sequence, starting from some key precursor or from a branch point in a metabolic chain. This arrangement has a biological advantage, in that allosteric inhibition of the first step in a biosynthetic sequence avoids wasting precursors to make unneeded intermediates. Moreover, the first reaction in a biosynthetic sequence is usually irreversible in the direction of synthesis. This first reaction is often spoken of as the "committed" step, since once it occurs, the remainder of the biosynthetic process nearly always proceeds to completion.

One final point needs to be made. The question can be simply framed: Does catabolism, which produces ATP, "drive" anabolism, which requires ATP? Or does anabolism "drive" catabolism? The answer is neither. The correct statement is that biosynthesis and all other ATP-requiring activities of the cell *pull* the process of ATP-yielding catabolism. In general, the rate of utilization of the phosphate-bond energy of ATP determines the rate at which ATP is regenerated from ADP at the expense of energy from the environment. This relationship is but another aspect of the principle of maximum economy in the molecular logic of living cells.

CHAPTER 22 THE BIOSYNTHESIS OF CARBOHYDRATES

From the standpoint of sheer mass, the biosynthesis of glucose and other carbohydrates from simpler precursors is the most prominent biosynthetic process carried out in the biosphere. In the domain of photosynthetic organisms, enormous amounts of hexoses are generated from carbon dioxide and water, and the hexoses in turn are converted into starch, cellulose, and other polysaccharides. In the domain of heterotrophic cells, the conversion of pyruvate, lactate, amino acids, and other simple precursors into glucose and glycogen is also a central process in cell metabolism.

Major Pathways in Carbohydrate Synthesis

We have seen that the conversion of glucose to pyruvate, catalyzed by the glycolytic enzymes, is the central pathway of carbohydrate catabolism in most cells, under either aerobic or anaerobic conditions. In a comparable manner, the reverse process, the conversion of pyruvate to glucose, is the most important common pathway in the biosynthesis of monosaccharides and polysaccharides (Figure 22-1). Converging into this central biosynthetic pathway are two main "feeder" pathways leading from two different sets of noncarbohydrate precursors. One consists of the various reactions by which intermediates of the tricarboxylic acid cycle are transformed into pyruvate. This process occurs in all organisms and is called *gluconeogenesis* (i.e., the formation of new sugar). The other major feeder pathway consists of the reactions bringing about the net reduction of CO_2 to form glucose; this pathway does not occur in heterotrophs but is an identifying characteristic of autotrophs, particularly of photosynthetic cells. Starting from the glucose 6-phosphate formed in the central biosynthetic pathway, several diverging auxiliary pathways (Figure 22-1) lead to formation of (1) free glucose, (2) the storage polymers starch and glycogen, (3) other monosaccharides and their derivatives, (4) disaccharides and oligosaccharides, and (5) cell wall and coat components such as cellulose, xylans, mureins, and the acid mucopolysaccharides.

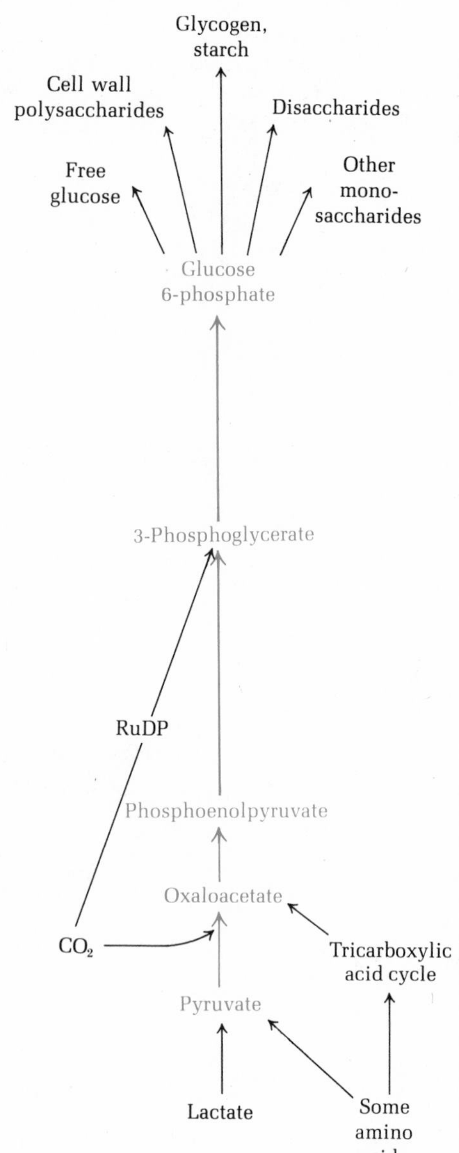

Figure 22-1
The central pathway in biosynthesis of carbohydrates from simpler precursors (color). RuDP = *Ribulose* 1,5-*diphosphate.*

Although all cells, including both heterotrophs and autotrophs, employ the central biosynthetic pathway leading from pyruvate to glucose 6-phosphate, different types of cells utilize the auxiliary pathways to different degrees. For example, only photosynthetic and chemosynthetic autotrophs cause the *net* reduction of CO_2 to form new glucose. On the other hand, all organisms can convert amino acids into certain tricarboxylic acid cycle intermediates and thus into glucose; however, the amount so transformed may vary considerably depending on the needs of the organism for amino acids for protein synthesis and the availability of other fuels. The net synthesis of glucose from blood lactate, which occurs largely in the liver, is a particularly active process in higher animals during recovery from intense muscular activity.

In a similar way, the pathways leading from glucose 6-phosphate to other products also differ widely among different organisms. The capacity to form free glucose is relatively limited; it is present in some plants and in the liver, kidney, and small intestine of vertebrates. On the other hand, the pathways to starch and glycogen appear to be nearly universal in occurrence, but are used to widely varying degrees, depending on metabolic demands and nutritional supply. Finally, the pathways leading to the extracellular polymers are highly specific and differentiated.

We shall now examine in detail the central pathway leading from pyruvate to glucose.

The Formation of Phosphoenolpyruvate from Pyruvate

Most of the reaction steps in the heavily traveled biosynthetic pathway from pyruvate to glucose are catalyzed by enzymes of the glycolytic cycle and thus proceed by reversal of steps employed in glycolysis. However, there are

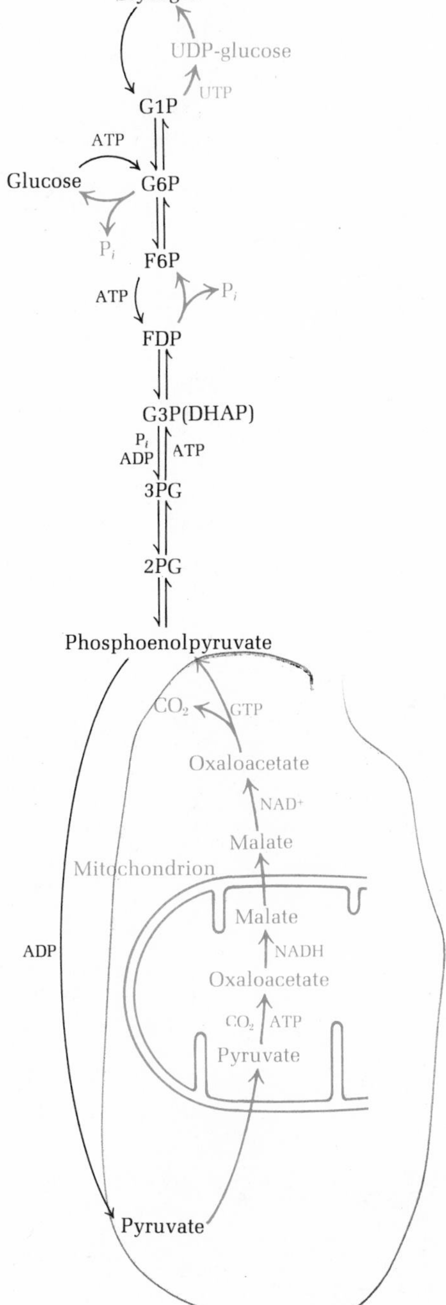

Figure 22-2
By-pass reactions (in color) in the synthesis of glucose and glycogen from pyruvate.

three irreversible steps in the normal "downhill" glycolytic pathway (Chapter 15) which cannot be utilized in the "uphill" conversion of pyruvate to glucose. In the biosynthetic direction these steps are bypassed by alternative reactions (Figure 22-2), which are thermodynamically favorable in the direction of synthesis. The first of these is the conversion of pyruvate to phosphoenolpyruvate, which obviously cannot occur by direct reversal of the pyruvate kinase reaction because of its large positive standard free energy change ($\Delta G°' = +7.5$ kcal).

$$\text{Pyruvate} + \text{ATP} \rightarrow \text{phosphoenolpyruvate} + \text{ADP}$$

The phosphorylation of pyruvate is achieved by a somewhat roundabout sequence of reactions, which requires the cooperation of enzymes in both the cytoplasm and the mitochondria (Figure 22–2). At one time this sequence represented a rather puzzling challenge, and some years of research were required to identify the enzymes involved. The first step is catalyzed by the pyruvate carboxylase of mitochondria, which we have earlier seen (Chapter 16) catalyzes the major anaplerotic reaction by which tricarboxylic acid cycle intermediates are generated from pyruvate

$$\text{Pyruvate} + CO_2 + \text{ATP} \xrightarrow{\text{Acetyl CoA}} \text{oxaloacetate} + \text{ADP} + P_i \qquad \Delta G°' = -0.5 \text{ kcal}$$

Pyruvate carboxylase is a regulatory enzyme which is completely inactive in the absence of its positive modulator acetyl CoA. The oxaloacetate formed in this reaction is then reduced to malate in the mitochondria at the expense of NADH:

$$\text{NADH} + H^+ + \text{oxaloacetate} \rightleftharpoons NAD^+ + \text{malate} \qquad \Delta G°' = -6.7 \text{ kcal}$$

The malate then diffuses out of the mitochondria into the surrounding cytoplasm, where it is reoxidized by the cytoplasmic form of NAD-linked malate dehydrogenase (Chapter 16) to form extramitochondrial oxaloacetate:

$$\text{Malate} + NAD^+ \rightleftharpoons \text{oxaloacetate} + \text{NADH} + H^+ \qquad \Delta G°' = +6.7 \text{ kcal}$$

Although this reaction is strongly endergonic as written, it proceeds to the right because the end products are quickly removed. The oxaloacetate is acted upon by *phosphoenolpyruvate carboxykinase* to yield phosphoenolpyruvate, a reaction in which GTP (or ITP) serves as the phosphate donor:

$$\text{Oxaloacetate} + \text{GTP} \xrightarrow{Mg^{2+}} \text{phosphoenolpyruvate} + CO_2 + \text{GDP} \qquad \Delta G°' = +0.7 \text{ kcal}$$

This enzyme is found in the cytoplasm of the liver in the rat and mouse, in the mitochondria in the rabbit and chicken, and in both cytoplasm and mitochondria in the guinea pig.

We may now write the overall equation of this bypass pathway for the formation of phosphoenolpyruvate, together with a summation of the free-energy changes:

$$\text{Pyruvate} + \text{ATP} + \text{GTP} \rightleftharpoons \text{phosphoenolpyruvate} + \text{ADP} + \text{GDP} + \text{P}_i \qquad \Delta G^{\circ\prime} = +0.2 \text{ kcal}$$

It is clear that the overall reaction is reversible because of its very small standard free energy change. It will therefore tend to go to the right whenever the [ATP]/[ADP] ratio is high and excess pyruvate is present.

We may now dissect this equation into its endergonic and exergonic components. The endergonic or energy-requiring process is

$$\text{Pyruvate} + \text{GTP} \rightarrow \text{phosphoenolpyruvate} + \text{GDP} \qquad \Delta G^{\circ\prime} = +7.5 \text{ kcal}$$

The energy-yielding process is

$$\text{ATP} + \text{H}_2\text{O} \rightarrow \text{ADP} + \text{P}_i \qquad \Delta G^{\circ\prime} = -7.3 \text{ kcal}$$

It is clear that two high-energy phosphate bonds, one from ATP and one from GTP, each equivalent to −7.3 kcal, are ultimately expended to phosphorylate one molecule of pyruvate. We shall see many other instances in which two or more high-energy phosphate bonds of ATP are ultimately consumed to bring about the formation of but a single covalent bond during biosynthetic reactions. The bypass pathway to phosphoenolpyruvate capitalizes on the fact that the NADH:NAD^+ ratio is relatively high in the mitochondria, a fact which would cause intramitochondrial oxaloacetate to be readily reduced to malate; whereas the NADH:NAD^+ ratio is extremely low in the cytoplasm (Chapter 18), which would favor the reoxidation of extramitochondrial malate to oxaloacetate. Malate, which readily passes through the mitochondrial membrane, serves as the carrier of reducing equivalents between the two compartments.

Conversion of Phosphoenolpyruvate to Glucose

Phosphoenolpyruvate generated from pyruvate by these reactions is now easily converted to fructose 1,6-diphosphate by reversal of the glycolytic reactions, beginning with enolase and ending with aldolase:

$$\text{Phosphoenolpyruvate} + \text{H}_2\text{O} \xrightarrow{\text{Enolase}} \text{2-phosphoglycerate}$$

$$\text{2-Phosphoglycerate} \rightarrow \text{3-phosphoglycerate}$$

$$\text{ATP} + \text{3-phosphoglycerate} \rightarrow \text{ADP} + \text{1,3-diphosphoglycerate}$$

$$\text{1,3-Diphosphoglycerate} + \text{NADH} + \text{H}^+ \rightarrow \text{glyceraldehyde 3-phosphate} + \text{NAD}^+ + \text{P}_i$$

Glyceraldehyde 3-phosphate → dihydroxyacetone phosphate

Glyceraldehyde 3-phosphate + dihydroxyacetone phosphate → fructose 1,6-diphosphate

Parenthetically, it may be mentioned that free glycerol, which may be derived from hydrolysis of triacylglycerols, as well as glycerol 3-phosphate, are also precursors of glucose; they enter the pyruvate → glucose pathway following conversion to dihydroxyacetone phosphate.

We now come to the second reaction of the downhill glycolytic sequence which does not occur in the direction of synthesis, namely, that catalyzed by phosphofructokinase:

Fructose 1,6-diphosphate + ADP → fructose 6-phosphate + ATP
$\Delta G^{\circ\prime} = +3.4$ kcal

During glucose synthesis this endergonic reaction is bypassed (Figure 22-2) by the enzyme *diphosphofructose phosphatase,* also known as *fructose diphosphatase,* which carries out the essentially irreversible hydrolysis of the 1-phosphate group

Fructose 1,6-diphosphate + H_2O → fructose 6-phosphate + P_i
$\Delta G^{\circ\prime} = -4.0$ kcal

The properties of this phosphatase were long obscure, but have been clarified by the discovery that it is a regulatory enzyme which is strongly inhibited by the negative modulator AMP. The enzyme has three or more binding sites for AMP, which are distinct from the substrate binding site(s). The enzyme is maximally active and favors biosynthesis of glucose when the AMP concentration is low and the ATP concentration high. It contains four or more subunits and, like many regulatory enzymes, has an anomalous temperature dependence of its activity.

In the next step in the pathway to glucose, fructose 6-phosphate is reversibly converted into glucose 6-phosphate by phosphohexoisomerase:

Fructose 6-phosphate ⇌ glucose 6-phosphate

In most cells glucose 6-phosphate formed during gluconeogenesis is employed as a precursor in the formation of storage polymers, monosaccharides other than glucose, disaccharides, and structural polymers. However, in some cells, such as the liver, kidney, and intestinal epithelial cells in vertebrates, glucose 6-phosphate may be dephosphorylated to form free glucose. The liver is the most prominent source of blood glucose. The cleavage of glucose 6-phosphate cannot occur by reversal of the hexokinase reaction, because of the large positive standard free energy change in the direction of formation of free glucose:

Glucose 6-phosphate + ADP → glucose + ATP
$\Delta G^{\circ\prime} = +4.0$ kcal

However, the formation of free glucose is brought about by *glucose 6-phosphatase,* which catalyzes the exergonic hydrolytic reaction

$$\text{Glucose 6-phosphate} + H_2O \rightarrow \text{glucose} + P_i \qquad \Delta G^{\circ\prime} = -3.3 \text{ kcal}$$

This enzyme is characteristically found in the endoplasmic reticulum of the liver and kidney of vertebrates. Its activity is dependent on lipids and on the structure of the membrane. Glucose 6-phosphatase is a rather complex enzyme which has been found to catalyze two additional reactions whose function is still unknown. It can act as a hydrolytic pyrophosphatase

$$\text{Pyrophosphate} + H_2O \rightarrow 2P_i$$

and also catalyzes an unusual reaction, the phosphorylation of glucose at the expense of pyrophosphate

$$PP_i + \text{glucose} \rightarrow \text{glucose 6-phosphate} + P_i$$

Glucose 6-phosphatase is not present in muscles or in the brain, which thus have no capacity to donate free glucose to the blood.

We may now sum up the reactions leading from pyruvate to free glucose in the following equation:

$$2CH_3COCOOH + 4ATP + 2GTP + 2NADH + 2H^+ + 6H_2O \rightarrow \text{glucose} + 2NAD^+ + 4ADP + 2GDP + 6P_i$$

For each molecule of glucose formed, six high-energy phosphate bonds are consumed and two molecules of NADH are required as reductant; the overall reaction is exergonic. This equation is clearly very different from that for the conversion of glucose into pyruvate, which is also exergonic:

$$\text{Glucose} + 2ADP + 2P_i + 2NAD^+ \rightarrow 2CH_3COCOOH + 2ATP + 2NADH + 2H^+ + 2H_2O$$

Regulation of the Pathway from Pyruvate to Glucose

Figure 22-3 summarizes the control points in the pathway leading from pyruvate to glucose. As in most biosynthetic pathways, the first step is catalyzed by a regulatory enzyme, and it represents the primary control point. This reaction, which is catalyzed by pyruvate carboxylase, is promoted by the positive modulator acetyl CoA. As a consequence, glucose synthesis is promoted whenever excess mitochondrial acetyl CoA builds up beyond the immediate need of the cell for fuel. The secondary control point of this pathway, the reaction catalyzed by diphosphofructose phosphatase, is inhibited by AMP but stimulated by ATP. Thus control is exerted over the pathway leading from pyruvate to glucose both by the level of respiratory fuel (acetyl CoA) and by the energy charge of the ATP system.

Figure 22-3
Control points in the pathway between pyruvate and glucose 6-phosphate. Positive modulation of regulatory enzymes is designated by parallel arrows in color; negative modulation by ■

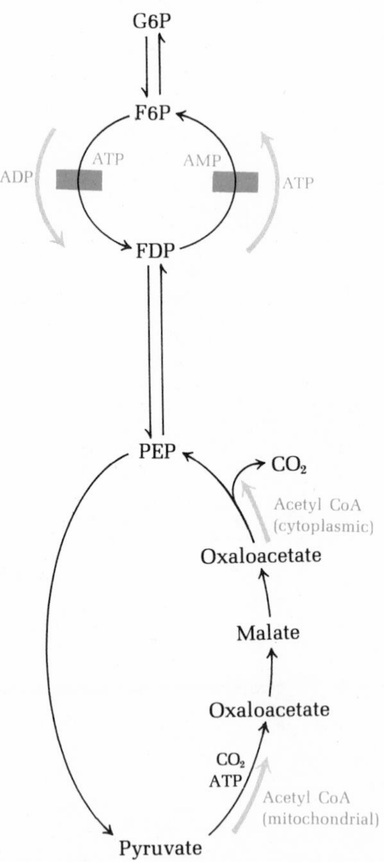

Gluconeogenesis from Tricarboxylic Acid Cycle Intermediates

The pathway from pyruvate to glucose described above also allows the net synthesis of glucose from various precursors of pyruvate or phosphopyruvate. Chief among them are the tricarboxylic acid cycle intermediates, which may undergo oxidation to malate. Malate then may leave the mitochondria and undergo oxidation to oxaloacetate in the extramitochondrial cytoplasm, where the formation of phosphoenolpyruvate takes place by the action of cytoplasmic phosphoenolpyruvate carboxykinase.

In animal tissues there is an alternative pathway for the generation of phosphoenolpyruvate from α-ketoglutarate and the preceding six-carbon acids of the tricarboxylic acid cycle. The enzymatic steps in this second pathway, which is entirely mitochondrial, are not yet known. Presumably intramitochondrial GTP generated during the oxidation of α-ketoglutarate (Chapter 16) is employed as phosphate donor in the phosphorylation of oxaloacetate to yield phosphoenolpyruvate. It is possible that phosphoenolpyruvate carboxykinase also participates in this pathway.

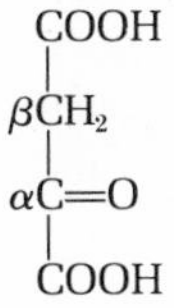

By either mechanism, three carbon atoms of the various tricarboxylic acid cycle intermediates are ultimately convertible into the three carbon atoms of phosphopyruvate. These carbon atoms arise from the α-carboxyl, α (carbonyl), and β-carbon atoms of oxaloacetate (margin). This pathway has been amply verified by many isotopic tracer experiments carried out on intact animals, as well as on tissue slices or extracts. For example, the isotopic carbon of carboxyl-labeled pyruvate or succinate fed to rats can be recovered as carbon atoms 3 and 4 of the glucose residues isolated from liver glycogen.

Oxaloacetic acid

COOH
|
βCH_2
|
$\alpha C{=}O$
|
COOH

It has also been established by various experimental approaches that the tricarboxylic acid cycle intermediates give rise to *net* synthesis of new glucose in vertebrates. In one type of experiment, rats are fasted for 24 hr or longer, a treatment which reduces the glycogen level in the liver from about 7 percent of the wet weight to 1 percent or less. Feeding of succinate and other cycle intermediates to such fasted rats causes a *net* increase in the total amount of glycogen in the animal, largely because of an increase in the liver glycogen. Such a net conversion of tricarboxylic cycle intermediates into glucose is also observed in animals treated with the toxic glycoside *phloridzin* (margin). This poison blocks reabsorption of glucose from the kidney tubule and thus causes blood glucose to be excreted nearly quantitatively into the urine (Chapter 27). Feeding of succinate or other cycle intermediates to phloridzin-poisoned animals causes excretion of an amount of glucose nearly equivalent to three of the carbon atoms of the intermediate fed.

Phloridzin

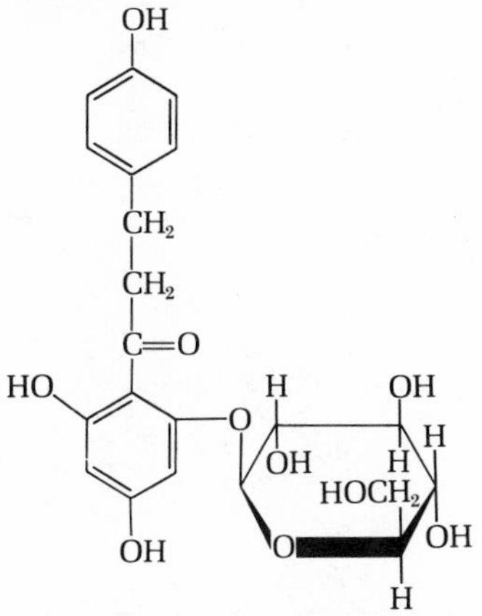

Gluconeogenesis from Acetyl CoA

It is most important to distinguish between *net* synthesis of glucose, on one hand, and mere incorporation of an isotopic carbon atom from a labeled precursor into glucose, on the other. For example, when methyl-labeled acetic acid is fed to an animal, the isotopic carbon atom will be incorporated into the glucose residues of liver glycogen, specifically into carbon atoms, 1, 2, 5, and 6 as some pencil-and-paper work will show (see Chapter 19). However, in higher animal tissues there is no *net* formation of new glucose from the two carbon atoms of the acetyl group of acetyl CoA. For one thing, citrate, the six-carbon condensation product of acetyl CoA and oxaloacetate, ultimately undergoes loss of three carbon atoms as CO_2 during its oxidation to phosphoenolpyruvate; thus it can form no more glucose than oxaloacetate can. Moreover, acetyl CoA cannot be directly converted into either pyruvate or succinate in animal tissues. In higher animals there is *no* metabolic pathway by which the carbon atoms of fatty acids can be used to form *new* glucose.

On the other hand, plants and many microorganisms are able to carry out the net synthesis of carbohydrate from fatty acids by way of acetyl CoA, a process made possible by the reactions of the glyoxylate cycle (Chapter 16). This cycle permits the *net* conversion of acetyl CoA to succinate according to the overall reaction

$$\text{2 acetyl CoA} + \text{NAD}^+ + 2\text{H}_2\text{O} \rightarrow \text{succinate} + 2\text{CoA} + \text{NADH} + \text{H}^+$$

Two specific enzymes are required for this pathway, *isocitrate lyase* and *malate synthetase* (Chapter 16); they are completely lacking in higher animals. The succinate formed in the glyoxylate pathway yields oxaloacetate, which in turn is the precursor of phosphoenolpyruvate. By this pathway stored fat is converted into glucose by germinating seeds.

Gluconeogenesis from Amino Acids

As has been shown in Chapter 20, some or all of the carbon atoms of the various amino acids derived from proteins are ultimately convertible either into acetyl CoA or into intermediates of the tricarboxylic acid cycle. Those amino acids which can serve as precursors of phosphoenolpyruvate, and thus of glucose, are *glycogenic* amino acids. Examples are glutamic and aspartic acids, which are directly convertible to α-ketoglutarate and oxaloacetate, respectively. Table 22-1 lists the amino acids that are glycogenic in mammals. There is one amino acid, leucine, which cannot yield net formation of glucose in vertebrates, since all of its carbon atoms are converted into either acetyl CoA or CO_2. However, the carbon atoms of leucine can enter the glucose molecule without net synthesis of the latter. Leucine and other amino acids that yield acetyl CoA on degradation are also capable of forming acetoacetate, particularly in fasting animals. They are thus called *ketogenic* amino acids. Phenylalanine and tyrosine are examples of amino acids that are *both* glycogenic and ketogenic, since on degradation (Chapter 20) they are cleaved to form fumaric acid,

Table 22-1 Fate of Amino Acids

Glycogenic		
	Ala	His
	Arg	Met
	Asp	Pro
	Asn	Ser
	Cys	Thr
	Glu	Trp
	Gln	Val
	Gly	
Ketogenic		
	Leu	
Glycogenic and ketogenic		
	Ile	
	Lys	
	Phe	
	Tyr	

which is glycogenic, and acetyl CoA, which is ketogenic.

In plants and many microorganisms no distinction can be made between glycogenic and nonglycogenic amino acids, because all the amino acids may ultimately contribute to the net formation of glucose through the reactions of the tricarboxylic acid and glyoxylate cycles (see above).

Photosynthetic Formation of Hexose by Reduction of Carbon Dioxide

The enzymatic reactions by which light energy is conserved as the phosphate-bond energy of ATP and as reducing power in the form of NADPH in photosynthesizing cells were described in Chapter 21. The ATP and NADPH so generated are then utilized to bring about the reduction of carbon dioxide to form glucose and other reduced products in the dark phase of photosynthesis. Parenthetically, it must be pointed out that the major end products of photosynthesis are hexose residues of cellulose, starch, and other polysaccharides; free glucose *per se* is not present in significant quantities in most higher plants. We shall use the general term "hexose" to designate all free and combined six-carbon sugar residues formed in photosynthesis.

Although the tissues of higher animals possess the capacity of fixing carbon dioxide as the carboxyl carbon of oxaloacetate and other compounds, the carbon dioxide fixed in such reactions cannot be employed to cause net synthesis of new glucose. For example, when carbon dioxide is fixed in the β-carboxyl group of oxaloacetate by the action of pyruvate carboxylase

$$\text{Pyruvic acid} + CO_2 + \text{ATP} \rightarrow \text{oxaloacetic acid} + \text{ADP} + P_i$$

it is ultimately lost again as CO_2 in the subsequent reactions by which three carbon atoms of the oxaloacetate are converted to phosphoenolpyruvate and then to glucose, as already outlined. Furthermore, the oxidative decarboxylations of pyruvate to acetyl CoA and of α-ketoglutarate to succinyl CoA are irreversible in animal tissues and thus cannot lead to net formation of glucose from CO_2 (Chapter 16). From these considerations it is clear that the biosynthetic pathways in green plant cells that lead to *net* hexose formation from CO_2 must be qualitatively different from the carboxylation reactions taking place in animal tissues.

An important clue to the nature of the pathway from CO_2 to hexose in photosynthesis came from the work of Calvin and his associates. They illuminated green algae in the presence of radioactive carbon dioxide ($^{14}CO_2$) for very short intervals (only a few seconds) and then quickly "killed" the cells, extracted them, and with the aid of chromatographic methods, searched for the earliest radioactive products in which the labeled carbon could be found. One of the compounds which became labeled earliest was 3-phosphoglyceric acid, a known intermediate of glycolysis; the isotope was found predominantly in its carboxyl carbon atom. This carbon atom, which corresponds to the carboxyl carbon atom of pyruvate, does not become labeled in animal tissues in the presence of radioactive CO_2. These findings strongly suggested that the labeled 3-phosphoglycerate is an early intermediate in photosynthesis in algae, a view supported by the fact that 3-phosphoglycerate is readily converted into glucose by reversal of the steps of glycolysis. However, no reactions capable of incorporating CO_2 into the carboxyl group of 3-phosphoglycerate were then known. After an intensive search, an enzyme that catalyzes incorporation of $^{14}CO_2$ into the carboxyl carbon of 3-phosphoglycerate was found in large amounts in extracts from spinach leaves. This enzyme, called *diphosphoribulose carboxylase* or *ribulose diphosphate carboxydismutase*, catalyzes the carboxylation and hydrolytic cleavage of ribulose 1,5-diphosphate to form two molecules of 3-phosphoglycerate, one of which bears the isotopic carbon introduced as $^{14}CO_2$ (Figure 22-4). The enzyme has a molecular weight of 550,000 and is extremely abundant in the cell, making up about 15 percent of the total protein of the chloroplast. Electron microscopic observations on spinach chloroplasts have suggested that individual molecules of the enzyme, which have a diameter of about 200 Å, are located on the surface of the thylakoids. Although the enzyme has a rather low turnover number, its very high concentration presumably accounts for the physiological rate of CO_2 uptake. The immediate chemical form in which carbon dioxide is fixed by the enzyme is free CO_2 rather than the HCO_3^- ion.

The 3-phosphoglycerate formed by the enzyme can be converted into glucose 6-phosphate by reversal of the glycolytic reactions and the diphosphofructose phosphatase bypass reaction described above. It is noteworthy that the glyceraldehyde 3-phosphate dehydrogenase of green plants, which is required to reduce 3-phosphoglycerate to glyceraldehyde 3-phosphate, is NADP-linked rather than NAD-linked.

This set of reactions does not by itself account for the fact that all six carbon atoms of hexose are ultimately formed from CO_2 during photosynthesis. To provide such a pathway, a cyclic mechanism for hexose synthesis was proposed by Calvin in which one molecule of ribulose 1,5-diphosphate is regenerated for each molecule of CO_2 reduced. Figure 22-5 shows the schematic outline of this pathway in its most recent form. It employs seven of the enzymes of the synthetic glycolytic pathway, three enzymes of the phosphogluconate pathway (Chapter 16), diphosphoribulose carboxylase (described above), and phosphoribulokinase (see below). One way of writing the equation of this complex cycle is as follows:

$$\begin{aligned}&6\ \text{ribulose 1,5-diphosphate} + 6CO_2 + 18ATP \\ &\qquad + 12NADPH + 12H^+ \rightarrow \\ &\qquad\qquad 6\ \text{ribulose 1,5-diphosphate} + \text{hexose} \\ &\qquad\qquad\qquad + 18P_i + 18ADP + 12NADP^+\end{aligned}$$

Ribulose 1,5-diphosphate is written on both sides of the equation only to show that it is a necessary component which is regenerated at the end of the cycle. The net

Figure 22-4
Fixation of CO_2 by diphosphoribulose carboxylase. The carbon atom of the entering CO_2 is in color.

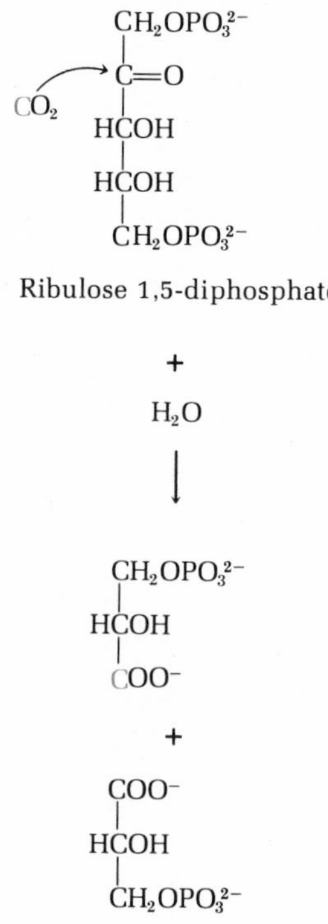

$CH_2OPO_3^{2-}$
$CO_2 \rightarrow C{=}O$
HCOH
HCOH
$CH_2OPO_3^{2-}$

Ribulose 1,5-diphosphate

\+

H_2O

↓

$CH_2OPO_3^{2-}$
HCOH
COO^-

\+

COO^-
HCOH
$CH_2OPO_3^{2-}$

3-Phosphoglycerate

Figure 22-5
The photosynthetic formation of glucose from CO_2 via the Calvin cycle in spinach leaves. The inputs are shaded in gray and the products in color. Abbreviations are 3PG = 3-phosphoglyceric acid; G3P = glyceraldehyde 3-phosphate; DHAP = dihydroxyacetone phosphate, FDP = fructose 1,6-diphosphate, F6P = fructose 6-phosphate, G6P = glucose 6-phosphate, E4P = erythrose 4-phosphate, X5P = xylulose 5-phosphate; SDP = sedoheptulose 1,7-diphosphate; S7P = sedoheptulose 7-phosphate; R5P = ribose 5-phosphate; Ru5P = ribulose 5-phosphate; RuDP = ribulose 1,5-diphosphate.

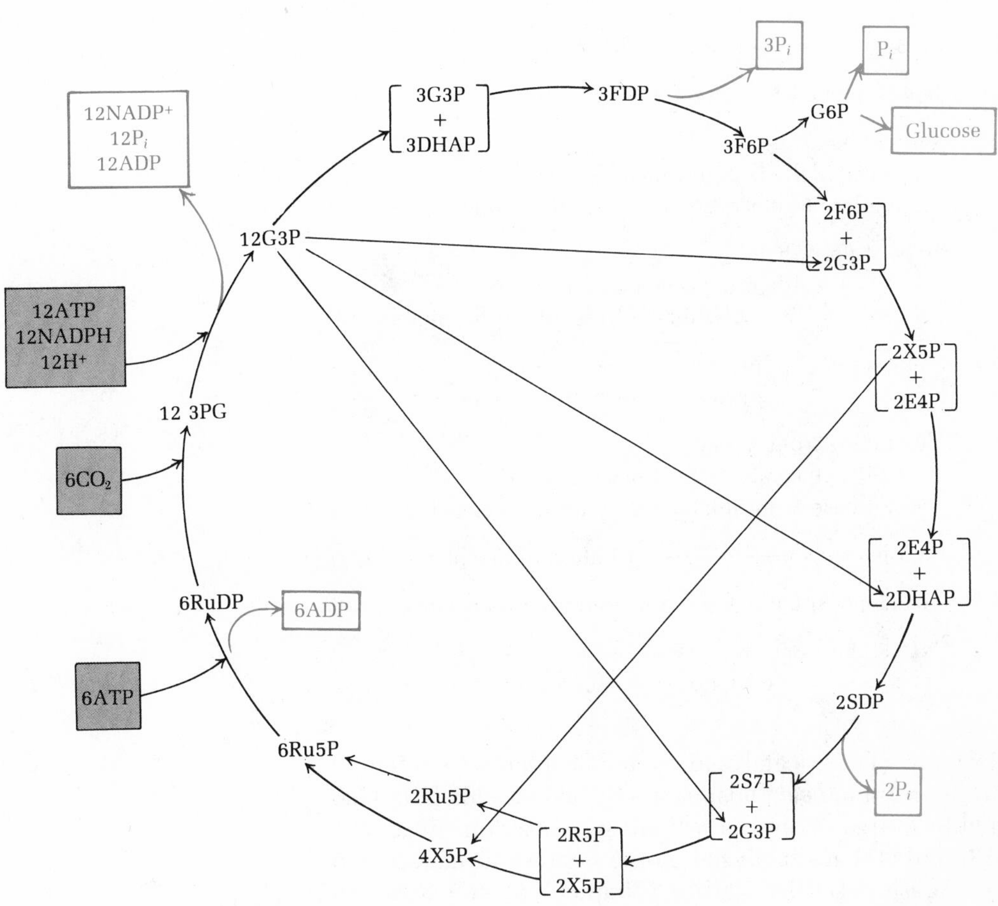

reaction, after canceling out the ribulose 1,5-diphosphate, is

$$6CO_2 + 18ATP + 12NADPH + 12H^+ \rightarrow \text{hexose} + 18P_i + 18ADP + 12NADP^+$$

The separate reactions contributing to this overall equation may now be given in sequence. Reactions (1) to (8) are reactions already given for the formation of glucose from CO_2 and ribulose 1,5-diphosphate; reactions (9) to (15) are concerned with the regeneration of ribulose 1,5-diphosphate. The glucose formed as end product (Reaction (8)) is shown in a box.

$$6CO_2 + 6 \text{ ribulose 1,5-diphosphate} \rightarrow 12 \text{ 3-phosphoglycerate} \quad (1)$$

12 3-phosphoglycerate + 12ATP →
12 1,3-diphosphoglycerate (2)

12 1,3-diphosphoglycerate + 12NADPH + 12H⁺ →
12 glyceraldehyde 3-phosphate + 12NADP⁺ (3)

5 glyceraldehyde 3-phosphate →
5-dihydroxyacetone phosphate (4)

3 glyceraldehyde 3-phosphate
+ 3 dihydroxyacetone phosphate →
3 fructose 1,6-diphosphate (5)

3 fructose 1,6-diphosphate →
3 fructose 6-phosphate + 3P_i (6)

fructose 6-phosphate → glucose 6-phosphate (7)

glucose 6-phosphate → **glucose** + P_i (8)

2 fructose 6-phosphate
+ 2 glyceraldehyde 3-phosphate $\xrightarrow{\text{Transketolase}}$
xylulose 5-phosphate + 2 erythrose 4-phosphate (9)

2 erythrose 4-phosphate
+ 2 dihydroxyacetone phosphate $\xrightarrow{\text{Aldolase}}$
2 sedoheptulose 1,7-diphosphate (10)

2 sedoheptulose 1,7-diphosphate $\xrightarrow{\text{Phosphatase}}$
2 sedoheptulose 7-phosphate + 2P_i (11)

2 sedoheptulose 7-phosphate
+ 2 glyceraldehyde 3-phosphate $\xrightarrow{\text{Transketolase}}$
2 ribose 5-phosphate + 2 xylulose 5-phosphate (12)

2 ribose 5-phosphate $\xrightarrow{\text{Isomerase}}$ 2 ribulose 5-phosphate (13)

4 xylulose 5-phosphate $\xrightarrow{\text{Epimerase}}$ 4 ribulose 5-phosphate (14)

6 ribulose 5-phosphate + 6ATP $\xrightarrow{\text{Phosphoribulokinase}}$
6 ribulose 1,5-diphosphate + 6ADP (15)

Reaction (11) is catalyzed by a phosphatase similar to diphosphofructose phosphatase (Chapter 15); it is also highly exergonic and is a "pulling" reaction. Reactions (13) and (14) are catalyzed by the pentose isomerase and epimerase described earlier (Chapter 16) and Reaction (15) by phosphoribulokinase, an enzyme similar in many respects to phosphofructokinase. The latter reaction is also strongly exergonic. The intermediate *sedoheptulose 1,7-diphosphate* (margin) is similar in its chemical and biochemical properties to its six-carbon analog fructose 1,6-diphosphate. This complex but thermodynamically feasible pathway accounts for many of the experimental observations on the formation of hexose from CO_2 during plant photosynthesis; it is now believed to represent the major pathway for this process.

Sedoheptulose
1,7-diphosphate

$CH_2OPO_3^{2-}$
|
C=O
|
HOCH
|
HCOH
|
HCOH
|
HCOH
|
$CH_2OPO_3^{2-}$

Other Possible Pathways of Hexose Formation

It appears very likely that pathways other than the Calvin cycle may exist for the reduction of CO_2 during photosynthesis. In photosynthetic bacteria the oxidative decarboxylations of pyruvate to acetyl CoA and of α-ketoglutarate to succinyl CoA, which are irreversible in

Figure 22-6
Postulated reversal of tricarboxylic acid cycle for photosynthetic reduction of CO_2 to glucose. Z_{red} designates an electronegative reductant generated in the light reactions. For each revolution there is net reduction of 3 molecules of CO_2.

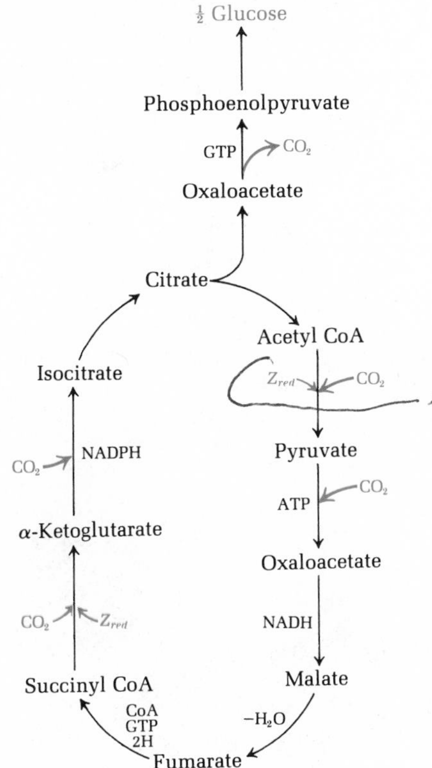

animal cells, can be reversed, so that CO_2 is incorporated into the α-carboxyl groups of pyruvate and of α-ketoglutarate. In animal tissues the decarboxylations of these α-keto acids are irreversible largely because NAD^+, the normal electron acceptor, has a much more positive standard reduction potential (−0.32 volt) than the redox couples pyruvate-acetyl CoA + CO_2 and α-ketoglutarate-succinyl CoA + CO_2. However, the photoreduction process in photosystem I generates a much more electronegative reductant than NADH (Chapter 21), which is proposed to reverse the decarboxylation of the α-keto acids:

$$Z_{red} + 2H^+ + CO_2 + \text{acetyl CoA} \rightarrow Z_{ox} + \text{pyruvate} + \text{CoA}$$

In photosynthetic bacteria, the entire tricarboxylic acid cycle may thus operate in reverse to cause the synthesis of phosphoenolpyruvate from three molecules of CO_2 (Figure 22–6).

Some tropical grasses have a very high affinity for CO_2 and show no photorespiration; they apparently do not employ the ribulose diphosphate carboxydismutase pathway, which has a low affinity for CO_2. Hatch and Slack have proposed an alternative cycle in which phosphoenolpyruvate is carboxylated to form oxaloacetate, whose carboxyl group is transferred to become the carboxyl group of 3-phosphoglycerate. Phosphoenolpyruvate carboxylase has a very high affinity for CO_2.

Synthesis of Glycogen and Starch and the Role of Nucleoside Diphosphate Sugars

A very heavily traveled biosynthetic pathway starting from glucose 6-phosphate is that leading to formation of the storage polymers glycogen and starch. This path begins with the conversion of glucose 6-phosphate to glucose 1-phosphate, catalyzed by phosphoglucomutase (Chapter 15):

$$\text{Glucose 6-phosphate} \rightleftharpoons \text{glucose 1-phosphate} \qquad \Delta G^{\circ\prime} = +1.74 \text{ kcal}$$

It was once thought that glycogen phosphorylase (Chapter 15) catalyzes both the synthesis and degradation of glycogen, since the glycogen phosphorylase reaction can be reversed experimentally in the test tube. However, it is now certain that under intracellular conditions it catalyzes only the breakdown of glycogen. A different pathway has been found for the conversion of glucose 1-phosphate to glycogen, one which involves a reaction principle widely utilized in the biosynthesis of disaccharides, oligosaccharides, and polysaccharides. Through the work of Leloir and his colleagues it is now recognized that the glycosyl donor in most such biosynthetic reactions is a nucleoside diphosphate sugar derivative, which is formed from a nucleoside 5′-triphosphate and the sugar

1-phosphate by the action of enzymes known generically as *pyrophosphorylases*

$$\text{NTP} + \text{sugar 1-phosphate} \rightleftharpoons \text{NDP-sugar} + \text{PP}_i$$

Although there is only a very small standard free energy change in the reaction, the subsequent hydrolysis of the pyrophosphate by inorganic pyrophosphatase has the effect of making it irreversible in the direction of formation of the NDP-sugar, with an overall $\Delta G^{\circ\prime}$ of about -7.0 kcal. The nucleoside diphosphate so formed now serves as a glycosyl group carrier. Uridine diphosphate usually serves as the glycosyl carrier in higher animals, whereas ADP, CDP, and GDP carry out this function in plants and microorganisms.

The first step in glycogen synthesis in animals is catalyzed by *UDP-glucose pyrophosphorylase*

$$\alpha\text{-D-Glucose 1-phosphate} + \text{UTP} \rightleftharpoons \text{UDP-glucose} + \text{PP}_i$$

UDP-Glucose

The structure of UDP-glucose is given in the margin.

In the second step leading to glycogen formation, the glucosyl group of UDP-glucose is transferred to the terminal glucose residue at the nonreducing end of an amylose chain, to form an α $(1 \rightarrow 4)$ glycosidic linkage between carbon atom 1 of the added glucosyl residue and the 4-hydroxyl of the terminal glucose residue of the chain. This reaction is catalyzed by *glycogen synthetase:*

$$\text{UDP-glucose} + (\text{glucose})_n \rightarrow \text{UDP} + (\text{glucose})_{n+1}$$

Space-filling model of UDP-Glucose

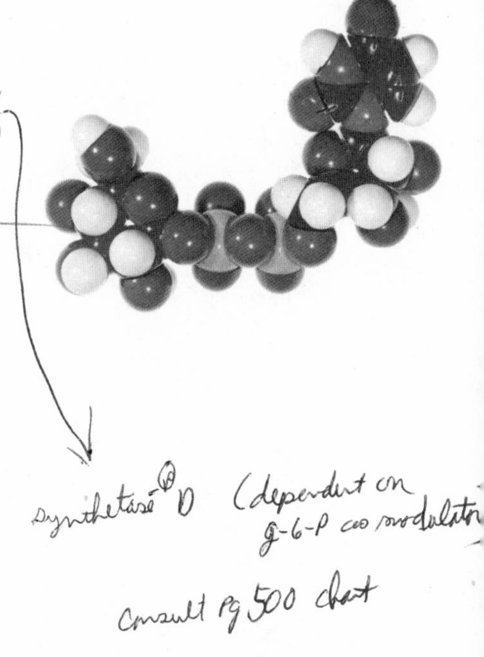

The $\Delta G^{\circ\prime}$ of this reaction is about -3.2 kcal. The overall $\Delta G^{\circ\prime}$ for insertion of one glucosyl residue, starting from glucose 1-phosphate and assuming that inorganic pyrophosphate is completely hydrolyzed, is approximately -10 kcal. The overall equilibrium thus greatly favors synthesis of glycogen. Glycogen synthetase requires as a primer an α $(1 \rightarrow 4)$ polyglucose chain having at least four glucose residues, to which it adds successive glucosyl groups. However, it is most active with long-chain glucose polymers as primers. In higher animal tissues UDP-glucose is the most active glucosyl donor; ADP-glucose is only about 50 percent as active. In lower organisms, however, ADP-glucose is the preferred substrate for glycogen synthetase.

Glycogen synthetase cannot make the α $(1 \rightarrow 6)$ bonds found in the branch points of glycogen (Chapter 11). However, a glycogen branching enzyme, *amylo* $(1,4 \rightarrow 1,6)$ *transglycosylase*, which is present in many animal tissues, catalyzes transfer of a terminal oligosaccharide fragment of six or seven glucosyl residues from the end of the main glycogen chain to the 6-hydroxyl group of a glucose residue of the same or another glycogen chain, in such a manner as to form an α $(1 \rightarrow 6)$ linkage and thus create a branch point (Figure 22-7). The standard free energy change in this reaction is very small.

In plant tissues starch synthesis occurs by an analogous pathway catalyzed by *amylose synthetase.* However,

Figure 22-7
Action of amylo (1,4 → 1,6) trans-glycosylase (branching enzyme) on a branch of glycogen.

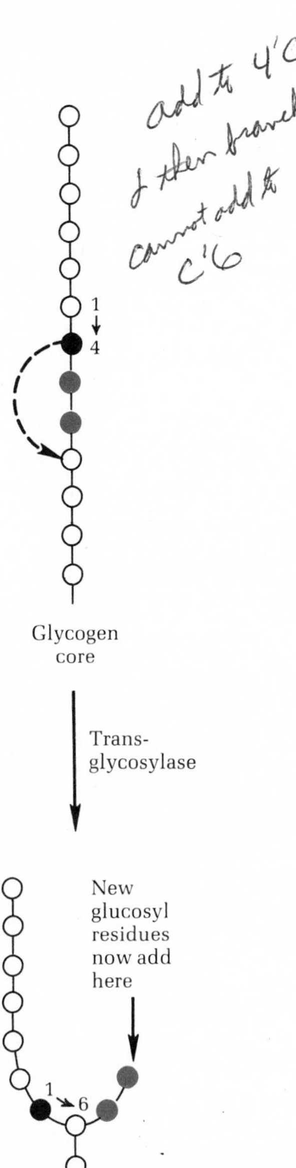

ADP-glucose (ADPG) rather than UDPG is the active glucose donor in most plants:

$$\text{ATP} + \alpha\text{-D-glucose 1-phosphate} \rightleftharpoons \text{ADP-glucose} + \text{PP}_i$$

$$\text{ADP-glucose} + (\text{glucose})_n \rightarrow \text{ADP} + (\text{glucose})_{n+1}$$

The first of these reactions is catalyzed by *ADP-glucose pyrophosphorylase,* an allosteric enzyme which is stimulated by 3-phosphoglycerate and fructose 1,6-diphosphate, early products of the photosynthetic reduction of CO_2 (see below). In some plants, ADPG and UDPG are equally active as glucose donors.

The Control of Glycogen Synthesis in Mammals

In animal tissues the factors regulating the rate of glycogen synthesis and breakdown have been studied in great detail, particularly since these processes have long been known to be under endocrine control and to be modified in various endocrine disturbances. Characteristic changes in carbohydrate metabolism are produced in mammals by removal of certain endocrine glands or by administration of their respective secretions, namely, the growth hormone of the anterior pituitary, insulin and glucagon of the pancreas, the steroids secreted by the adrenal cortex, and epinephrine, which is secreted by the adrenal medulla. These hormones act at different points in the pathways of glucose metabolism. However, two of them, namely, epinephrine and glucagon, appear to exert their characteristic effects on the enzymatic steps between glucose 1-phosphate and glycogen. The synthesis and breakdown of glycogen are not only catalyzed by different enzymes but also independently controlled. When either glucagon or epinephrine is administered to mammals, there is a prompt decline in the glycogen content of the liver and a rise in blood glucose. This change results from stimulation of glycogen phosphorylase activity and depression of glycogen synthetase activity. The molecular basis of these changes has been studied in some detail and may now be outlined (Figure 22-8).

Earlier (Chapter 15) we saw that glycogen phosphorylase exists in a phosphorylated active form (phosphorylase *a*) and a dephosphorylated inactive form (phosphorylase *b*). Glycogen synthetase also exists in phosphorylated and dephosphorylated forms. The phosphorylated form is a regulatory enzyme which has little or no activity by itself, but is greatly stimulated by its positive modulator glucose 6-phosphate, which increases V_{max} of the enzyme. This form of glycogen synthetase is called the D or *dependent form* since it is dependent on glucose 6-phosphate for maximal activity. The stimulation produced by glucose 6-phosphate is prevented by the negative modulator UDP. On the other hand, the dephosphorylated form of glycogen synthetase (also called the I or *independent form*) is active in the absence of glucose 6-phosphate. The D form is dephosphorylated to the I form by the action of the enzyme *glycogen synthetase phosphatase:*

Figure 22-8
Important factors in the regulation of the activity of glycogen synthetase and glycogen phosphorylase in muscle and liver.

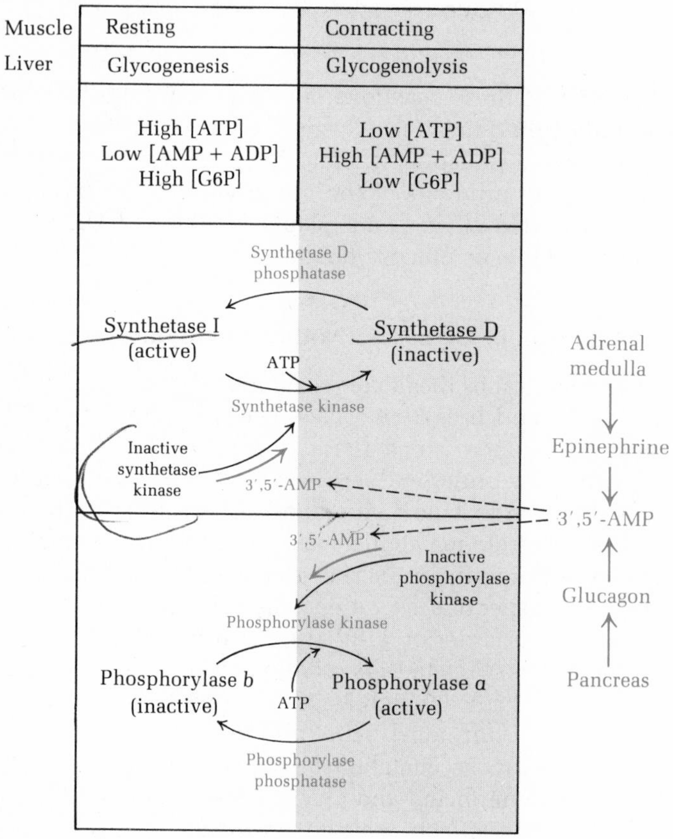

Muscle	Resting	Contracting
Liver	Glycogenesis	Glycogenolysis
	High [ATP] Low [AMP + ADP] High [G6P]	Low [ATP] High [AMP + ADP] Low [G6P]

Synthetase D phosphatase
Synthetase I (active)
Synthetase D (inactive)
ATP
Synthetase kinase
Inactive synthetase kinase
3',5'-AMP
3',5'-AMP
Inactive phosphorylase kinase
Phosphorylase kinase
Phosphorylase *b* (inactive)
ATP
Phosphorylase *a* (active)
Phosphorylase phosphatase
Adrenal medulla
Epinephrine
3',5'-AMP
Glucagon
Pancreas

$$\underset{\text{(D form)}}{\text{Phosphosynthetase}} + H_2O \xrightarrow{\text{Phosphatase}} \underset{\text{(I form)}}{\text{synthetase}} + P_i$$

The dephosphorylated or I form can be rephosphorylated to the D form by *glycogen synthetase kinase*

$$\text{ATP} + \underset{\text{(I form)}}{\text{synthetase}} \xrightarrow{\text{Kinase}} \text{ADP} + \underset{\text{(D form)}}{\text{phosphosynthetase}}$$

This kinase in turn is a regulatory enzyme, which exists in two forms, one active and the other inactive. The inactive form is activated by the positive modulator cyclic adenylic acid (3',5'-AMP), whose structure is in the margin (Chapter 12). Cyclic AMP is formed from ATP by *adenyl cyclase*, which catalyzes the reaction

$$\text{ATP} \rightarrow \text{cyclic AMP} + PP_i$$

Adenyl cyclase is present in the plasma membrane of many cells, particularly in the liver. The formation of cyclic AMP by membrane preparations containing the cyclase is greatly stimulated by *epinephrine* (margin), a catecholamine hormone secreted into the blood stream by the adrenal medulla during physiological stress. Just

3',5'-Cyclic adenylic acid

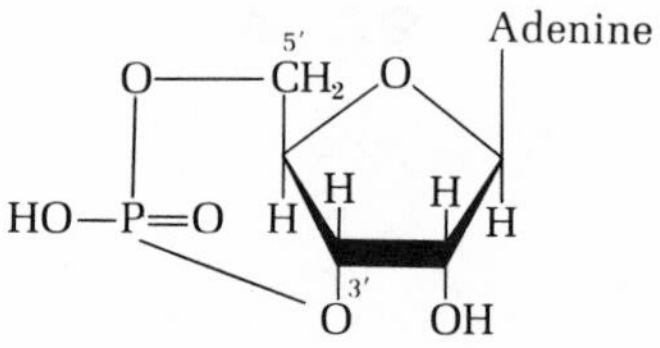

Epinephrine

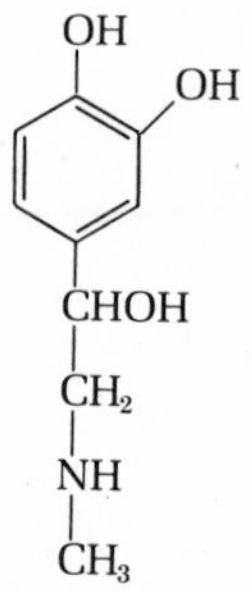

as epinephrine is an extracellular chemical messenger between the adrenal medulla and target cells, such as those of the liver, so is cyclic AMP an intracellular chemical messenger between the cell membrane and certain target enzyme systems inside the cell. Since cyclic AMP appears to function as a positive modulator for glycogen synthetase kinase, which in turn generates the D form of glycogen synthetase, the effects of very small quantities of epinephrine are greatly amplified by the intermediate action of adenyl cyclase and cyclic AMP. The overall effect of epinephrine, which favors the synthesis of the D form of glycogen synthetase, is to turn off the synthesis of glycogen, since the D enzyme is not maximally active in the absence of relatively high concentrations of glucose 6-phosphate.

Figure 22-9
The amino acid sequence of bovine glucagon.

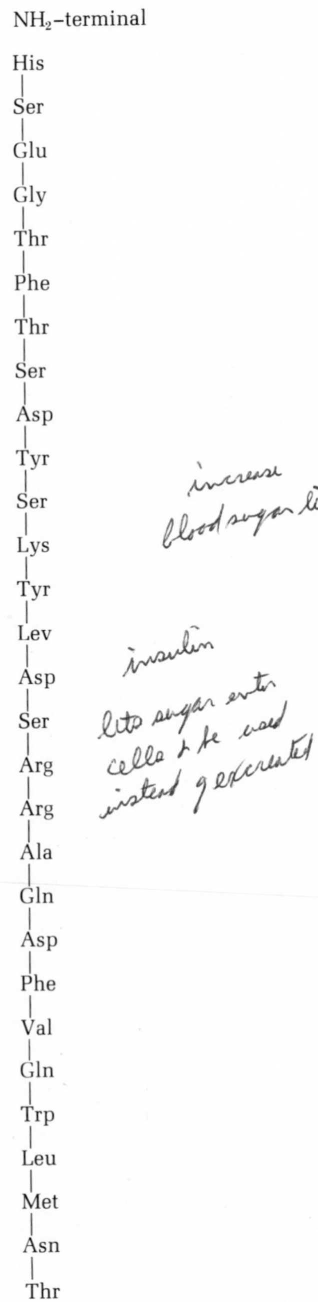

The glycogen phosphorylase reaction in the liver is differently affected by epinephrine (Figure 22-8). Cyclic AMP generated by adenyl cyclase activates phosphorylase kinase kinase (Chapter 15), which in turn activates phosphorylase kinase, which in turn causes the phosphorylation of the inactive glycogen phosphorylase *b* to yield the phosphorylated or active *a* form of glycogen phosphorylase, which in turn promotes the breakdown of glycogen to glucose 1-phosphate. Thus epinephrine has a dual action: it promotes the breakdown of glycogen and inhibits its synthesis from UDP-glucose. The net effect is to promote the conversion of liver glycogen to blood sugar. Similar epinephrine-induced changes occur in muscles, but since muscle cannot form blood glucose, the end effect of epinephrine is to promote glycolysis and respiration.

Glucagon, a polypeptide hormone secreted by the α cells of the pancreas (Figure 22-9), also increases the level of blood sugar and causes depletion of liver glycogen; it has no effect on muscle. It functions by stimulating adenyl cyclase of the liver, thus promoting breakdown of glycogen to glucose and inhibiting the synthesis of glycogen from UDP-glucose. However, epinephrine and glucagon are quite different in other respects, since glucagon does not cause increases in blood pressure or other changes characteristic of epinephrine.

The rates of the synthesis and breakdown of muscle glycogen are influenced not only by endocrine factors but also by the Ca^{2+} concentration, by electrical stimulation, and by other factors. In resting muscle, the active or I form of glycogen synthetase and the relatively inactive or *b* form of glycogen phosphorylase predominate, whereas in actively contracting muscle, the relatively inactive or D form of glycogen synthetase and the active or *a* form of phosphorylase predominate (Figure 22-8). The liver enzymes are genetically and structurally different from those in muscle and their responses to various effectors are quantitatively different.

In humans several hereditary disorders of glycogen metabolism have been recognized in which abnormally large amounts of glycogen are accumulated, particularly in the liver. The genetically defective enzymes in such patients have been detected by assay of small samples of tissue obtained by surgical biopsy. In one of these disorders, von Gierke's disease, glucose 6-phosphatase activity is defective. In Andersen's disease the branching enzyme is defective and the glycogen has abnormally long, unbranched chains. In McArdle's disease the muscle glycogen phosphorylase is defective, leading to excessive glycogen deposition in the muscle.

Regulation of Glucose Metabolism by Insulin

The hormone insulin (Chapter 6) is secreted by the β cells of the islets of Langerhans in the pancreas in the form of an inactive precursor, *proinsulin*. The latter, a single chain of 81 to 84 residues, is cleaved at two points to yield an inactive middle fragment of 30 to 33 residues and the A and B chains of insulin, which arise from the ends (Chapter 6). Insulin exerts profound effects on the metabolism of glucose and other nutrients, which have been studied not only in humans suffering from diabetes mellitus, but also in animals rendered deficient in insulin by removal of the pancreas or by treatment with the pyrimidine derivative *alloxan* (margin), which destroys the capacity of the β-cells to produce insulin.

The most conspicuous effect of insulin deficiency is an extremely high level of blood glucose (*hyperglycemia*), excessive excretion of glucose in the urine (*glycosuria*), and a decreased glycogen level in the liver. Although some tissues in such animals, such as the brain, can still utilize glucose from the blood, there is a deficiency of glucose utilization in the muscles and liver, which literally "starve in the midst of plenty." When insulin is administered to insulin-deficient animals, these metabolic deficiencies are corrected. When it is administered to normal animals, the uptake of glucose by the muscles and liver is promoted and the blood glucose level becomes very low, to yield the condition known as *hypoglycemia*.

Alloxan

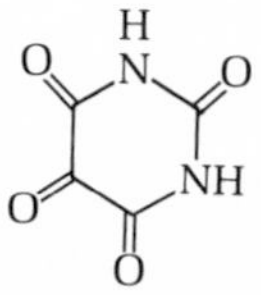

H, O, N, O, NH, O, O

Insulin deficiency has many other metabolic consequences. The biosynthesis of fatty acids from glucose and acetate and the biosynthesis of body protein are greatly depressed. There is an increased synthesis of those enzymes participating in gluconeogenesis from amino acids, such as pyruvate carboxylase, phosphoenolpyruvate carboxykinase, and fructose 1,6-diphosphatase. The major defect in insulin deficiency appears to be a greatly decreased affinity of the muscles and liver for glucose, so that much higher concentrations of blood glucose are required in order to enable glucose to penetrate into them and to enter the metabolic channels. Most of the metabolic effects of insulin deficiency appear to be compensatory responses that allow the animal to maximize its blood glucose concentration and thus to overcome the defect in glucose utilization. Thus, the decreased conversion of glucose into fatty acids, decreased protein synthesis, and increased gluconeogenesis from amino acids are responses which lead to excess glucose production.

The mode of action of insulin is not yet known in molecular terms. Early research favored the concept that it controls the activity of an enzyme concerned in glucose utilization, i.e., hexokinase or glucokinase. However, it now appears more likely that it is concerned in the regulation of the synthesis of membrane-linked transport systems for glucose and other metabolites, by enhancing the rate of translation of specific messenger RNA species at the ribosomes (Chapter 30).

Conversion of Glucose to Other Monosaccharides

Pathways for the conversion of glucose 6-phosphate into D-fructose 6-phosphate and then into D-mannose 6-phosphate have been described in Chapter 15. Other hexose interconversions proceed via nucleoside diphosphate hexoses formed by the action of pyrophosphorylases. One of the most important is the conversion of D-glucosyl into D-galactosyl residues, which proceeds by enzymatic epimerization of UDP-glucose at carbon atom 4 of the glucose residue, to form uridine diphosphate galactose

$$\text{UDP-glucose} \rightleftharpoons \text{UDP-galactose}$$

Since the enzyme catalyzing this reaction, *uridine diphosphate glucose epimerase*, has an absolute requirement for NAD, it is believed that epimerization occurs in two separate steps:

UDP-4-Ketoglucose

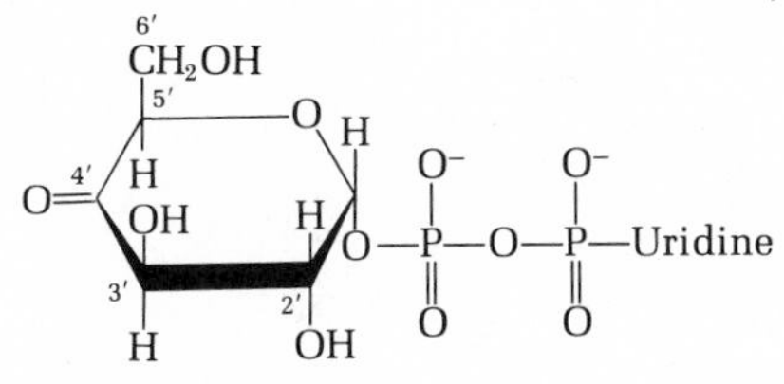

$$\text{UDP-glucose} + NAD^+ \rightleftharpoons \text{UDP-4-ketoglucose} + NADH + H^+$$

$$\text{UDP-4-ketoglucose} + NADH + H^+ \rightleftharpoons \text{UDP-galactose} + NAD^+$$

The postulated 4-ketoglucose intermediate (margin), which can accept a pair of hydrogens at the keto group to form either epimer, remains tightly bound to the enzyme active site during the catalytic cycle. UDP-galactose formed in this reaction is a required precursor in the synthesis of the disaccharide lactose in the mammary gland.

Free D-galactose, formed by the enzymatic hydrolysis of lactose in the intestinal tract, is ultimately converted into D-glucose in animal tissues by a series of reactions which has attracted much attention because a genetic defect in one of the steps results in *galactosemia*, a rare hereditary disorder in human infants. In the liver, D-galactose is first phosphorylated at carbon atom 1 by *galactokinase*, to yield D-galactose 1-phosphate:

$$\text{ATP} + \text{D-galactose} \rightarrow \text{ADP} + \text{D-galactose 1-phosphate}$$

The resulting galactose 1-phosphate can be converted into UDP-galactose by one of two possible reactions. The first is catalyzed by *phosphogalactose uridyl transferase*

$$\text{UDP-glucose} + \text{galactose 1-phosphate} \rightleftharpoons \text{UDP-galactose} + \text{glucose 1-phosphate}$$

This enzyme is normally present in high amounts in the liver of infants, but is genetically defective in galactosemic infants. The second enzyme capable of utilizing galactose 1-phosphate is *uridine diphosphate galactose pyrophosphorylase*, which catalyzes the reaction

$$\text{UTP} + \text{galactose 1-phosphate} \rightleftharpoons \text{UDP-galactose} + \text{PP}_i$$

The latter enzyme is present only in traces in fetal and infant liver, but is much more active in adult liver. The hereditary lack of the first of these two enzymes, the phosphogalactose uridyl transferase, causes infants to lack the capacity to metabolize D-galactose derived from the lactose of milk, since they also lack the second enzyme. Such infants have an excessively high concentration of D-galactose in the blood and suffer from cataract (opacity) of the lens of the eye as well as mental disorders. This condition can be successfully treated by withholding milk and other sources of galactose from the diet during childhood. The adult galactosemic metabolizes galactose in a normal manner, via uridine diphosphate galactose pyrophosphorylase.

UDP-glucose may undergo oxidation to UDP-D-glucuronic acid (margin)

$$\text{UDP-glucose} + 2\text{NAD}^+ \rightleftharpoons \text{UDP-glucuronic acid} + 2\text{NADH} + 2\text{H}^+$$

In this reaction, two oxidation steps occur, one oxidizing the hydroxyl group at carbon atom 6 to the aldehyde and the second oxidizing the aldehyde to a carboxyl group. UDP-glucuronic acid is a precursor of *glucosiduronides* (see below).

Free D-glucuronic acid, which is formed from UDP-glucuronic acid by enzymatic hydrolysis, is a precursor in the biosynthesis of L-ascorbic acid or vitamin C. This process occurs in the liver of most animals with the exception of man, monkeys, the guinea pig, and the Indian fruit bat. The D-glucuronic acid is first reduced to L-gulonic acid, which lactonizes in the presence of a lactonase to L-gulonolactone, which then is oxidized to L-ascorbic acid, presumably via 3-keto-L-gulonolactone (margin).

Uridine diphosphate D-glucuronic acid

Enzymatic synthesis of L-ascorbic acid

UDP-D-glucuronic acid → (H_2O) → D-Glucuronic acid → ($NADPH + H^+$) → L-Gulonic acid → ($-H_2O$) → L-Gulonolactone → ($-2H$) → L-Ascorbic acid

Synthesis of Disaccharides and Other Glycosides

Nucleoside diphosphate sugars also function as precursors in the biosynthesis of various disaccharides. In plants, sucrose is formed from glucose and fructose by the following series of reactions:

$$\text{ATP} + \text{glucose} \rightarrow \text{glucose 6-phosphate} + \text{ADP}$$

$$\text{Glucose 6-phosphate} \rightleftharpoons \text{glucose 1-phosphate}$$

$$\text{UTP} + \text{glucose 1-phosphate} \rightarrow \text{UDP-glucose} + \text{PP}_i$$

UDP glucose pyrophosphorylase

$$\text{ATP} + \text{fructose} \rightarrow \text{fructose 6-phosphate} + \text{ADP}$$

$$\text{UDP-glucose} + \text{fructose 6-phosphate} \rightarrow \text{UDP} + \text{sucrose 6}'\text{-phosphate}$$

$$\text{Sucrose 6}'\text{-phosphate} + \text{H}_2\text{O} \rightarrow \text{sucrose} + \text{P}_i$$

Sum: $$2\text{ATP} + \text{UTP} + \text{glucose} + \text{fructose} \rightarrow \text{sucrose} + 2\text{ADP} + \text{UDP} + \text{PP}_i + \text{P}_i$$

If the pyrophosphate formed is hydrolyzed to P_i, then the overall reaction is

$$2ATP + UTP + glucose + fructose \rightarrow sucrose + 2ADP + UDP + 3P_i$$

Three high-energy phosphate bonds ($\Delta G^{\circ\prime} = -21.9$ kcal) are thus required to form the single glycosidic bond of sucrose ($\Delta G^{\circ\prime}$ for hydrolysis is -6.6 kcal). The overall reaction of sucrose synthesis from glucose and fructose is therefore quite irreversible. Presumably the strongly exergonic nature of this set of biosynthetic reactions enables the sugar cane to form a juice containing an extremely high concentration of sucrose from very dilute precursors. In some plants, sucrose is formed by an alternative reaction employing fructose rather than fructose 6-phosphate:

$$\text{UDP-glucose} + \text{fructose} \rightarrow \text{UDP} + \text{sucrose}$$

Some bacteria contain the enzyme *sucrose phosphorylase,* which catalyzes the reversible reaction

$$\text{Sucrose} + P_i \rightleftharpoons \text{glucose 1-phosphate} + \text{fructose}$$

Although this reaction can be made to form sucrose if the P_i is rapidly removed, under intracellular conditions it normally catalyzes the breakdown of sucrose.

The disaccharide lactose is formed in the mammary gland from D-glucose and UDP-galactose by the action of two enzyme proteins, which together constitute the *lactose synthetase* system. The first, *protein A,* which is found not only in the mammary gland but also in the liver and small intestine, catalyzes the reaction

$$\text{UDP-galactose} + N\text{-acetyl-D-glucosamine} \rightarrow \text{UDP} + N\text{-acetyllactosamine}$$

The second, *protein B,* is a protein long known as the *α-lactalbumin* of milk; it has no catalytic activity of its own. This protein has quite recently been found to alter the specificity of protein A, regardless of its source, so that it will utilize D-glucose instead of N-acetyl-D-glucosamine as galactose acceptor, causing the A protein to make lactose instead of N-acetyllactosamine:

$$\text{UDP-galactose} + \text{D-glucose} \rightarrow \text{UDP} + \text{lactose}$$

The α-lactalbumin protein is remarkable in another respect: it has a striking homology in its amino acid sequence to the enzyme lysozyme (Chapters 5 and 6).

Glucosiduronides (see above) are glycosidic excretory products formed by vertebrates from foreign aromatic or alicyclic alcohols and amines by the action of enzymes in the endoplasmic reticulum of the liver. The general reaction catalyzed is

$$\text{UDP-glucuronic acid} + \text{ROH} \rightarrow \text{R-O-glucosiduronide} + \text{UDP}$$

where ROH is the foreign alcohol. Phenol is excreted by some animals as *phenol glucosiduronide* (margin).

Phenol glucosiduronide

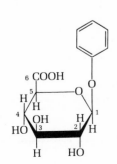

6 COOH
5 H H O O 1
4 OH H
HO 3 2 H
H HO

Nucleoside diphosphate sugars also may undergo rather complex reduction reactions to form nucleoside diphosphate derivatives of deoxy sugars, such as L-fucose and L-rhamnose (Chapter 11), which are important components of lipopolysaccharides of bacterial cell walls. One such reaction is

$$\text{GDP-D-Mannose} + \text{NADPH} + H^+ \rightarrow \text{GDP-L-fucose} + \text{NADP}^+ + H_2O$$

Structural Polysaccharides of Cell Walls and Coats

Nucleoside diphosphate sugars also function as the glycosyl group donors in the biosynthesis of the structural polysaccharides of cell walls and coats. In most cases the glycosyl unit is added to one end of a pre-existing polysaccharide molecule, to lengthen it by one unit, with liberation of the free nucleoside diphosphate.

Plants and Insects

Cellulose, the major structural polysaccharide in plant cell walls, is a β (1 → 4) glucan (Chapter 11). It is synthesized in some plants from GDP-glucose and in others from UDP-glucose by the following general type of reaction:

$$\text{NDP-glucose} + \underset{\text{Pre-existing chain}}{(\text{glucose})_n} \rightarrow \text{NDP} + \underset{\text{Lengthened cellulose chain}}{(\text{glucose})_{n+1}}$$

In similar reactions, plant xylans, which contain α (1 → 4) linkages between D-xylose residues, are formed from UDP-D-xylose. Chitin, a β (1 → 4) homopolymer of N-acetyl-glucosamine found in insect exoskeletons, is formed in a similar reaction from UDP-N-acetylglucosamine.

Animals

Hyaluronic acid, which consists of alternating D-glucuronic acid and N-acetylglucosamine residues (Chapter 11), is formed by successive alternating reactions of UDP-glucuronic acid and UDP-N-acetylglucosamine with the growing end of the chain, in a manner similar to the formation of homopolysaccharides.

The sialic acids, or N-acylneuraminic acids, which serve as the terminal residues in the oligosaccharide and polysaccharide chains of gangliosides and glycoproteins of animal cell coats, are derived from glucosamine. The following sequence of reactions shows the formation of N-acetylneuraminic acid:

$$\text{N-Acetylglucosamine} \xrightarrow{\text{Epimerization}} \text{N-acetylmannosamine}$$

$$\text{N-Acetylmannosamine} \xrightarrow{\text{ATP}} \text{N-acetylmannosamine 6-phosphate}$$

Figure 22-10
Steps in the biosynthesis of the murein (peptidoglycan) of a bacterial cell wall.

Stage I
Formation of UDP-N-acetylmuramyl-pentapeptide. This stage takes place within the cell.

Stage II
Formation of recurring disaccharide unit linked to undecaprenyl phosphate and transfer to the end of murein chain

Stage III
Construction of cross-linking pentaglycine chain

Stage IV
Completion of cross-linkage

N-Acetylmannosamine 6-phosphate
+ phosphoenolpyruvate → N-acetylneuraminic acid 9-phosphate + P_i

N-Acetylneuraminic acid 9-phosphate →
N-acetylneuraminic acid + P_i

N-Acetylneuraminic acid (usually abbreviated NANA) is prepared for reaction with oligosaccharides and polysaccharides by formation of a CMP derivative, analogous to the UDP derivatives of glucose already described:

CTP + N-acetylneuraminic acid →
CMP-N-acetylneuraminic acid + PP_i

The product of this reaction, which is abbreviated CMP-NANA, then becomes the donor of NANA to the terminal sugar residue of a ganglioside or glycoprotein by the action of *sialyl transferase*, releasing free CMP

CMP-NANA + —X-X-X-galactose →
Oligosaccharide
CMP + —X-X-X-galactose-NANA
Sialyloligosaccharide

The nature of the linkage between the N-acetylneuraminic acid residue and the sugar residues in gangliosides was shown in Chapter 10.

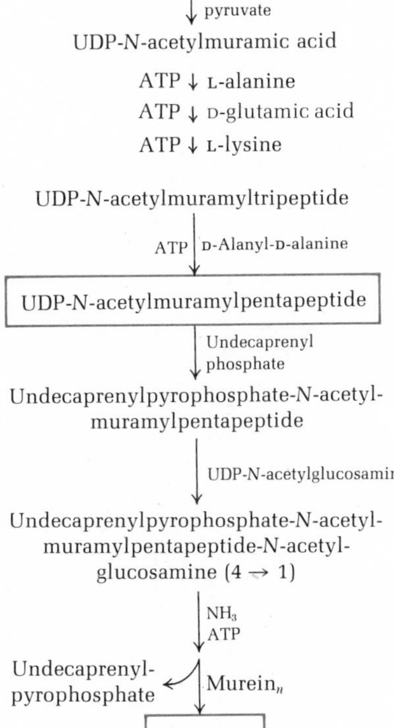

Bacterial Cell Walls

The mechanism of biosynthesis of the cell wall polymers of bacteria has attracted many investigators, not only because of the extraordinary complexity of their structure, but also because of the fact that they are assembled outside the cell by the action of enzymes attached to the membrane. Such a location suggests that the spatial relationships and topography of the membrane and its attached enzymes must be highly specific to carry out this remarkable feat in biosynthetic construction. Moreover, the enzymatic synthesis of the cell walls of some bacteria has been found to be inhibited by penicillin and other antibiotics. An important early clue to the nature of the reactions by which the cell wall polymer is synthesized, as well as to the mode of action of penicillin, came from the early discovery of Park that uridine nucleotide derivatives accumulate in cultures of bacteria whose growth is inhibited by penicillin.

The cell wall peptidoglycan or murein of Gram-positive bacteria, whose structure was discussed in Chapter 11, is synthesized in four major stages, as revealed by work of Strominger and other investigators (Figure 22-10). In the first stage N-acetylmuramylpentapeptide, a recurring unit of the backbone structure, is synthesized in the form of its UDP derivative (Figure 22-11) from its precursors N-acetylglucosamine, phosphoenolpyruvate, and the amino acids L-alanine, D-alanine, D-glutamic acid, and L-lysine (or diaminopimelic acid in some species). The pentapeptide side-chain is built by successive additions of

Figure 22-11
UDP-N-acetylmuramylpentapeptide.

L-Alanine D-Isoglutamic acid L-Lysine D-Alanine D-Alanine

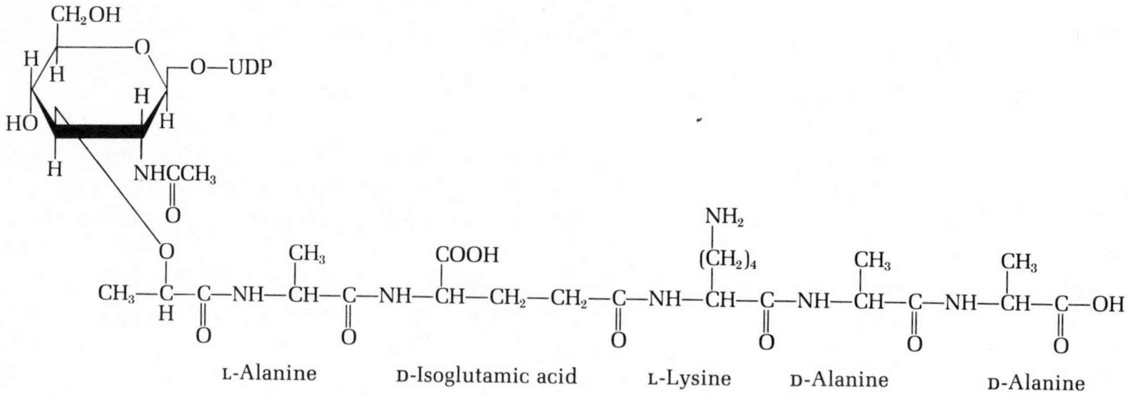

L-alanine, D-glutamic acid, and L-lysine to the carboxyl group of the pyruvic acid moiety to form *N*-acetylmuramyltripeptide; a molecule of ATP is cleaved to ADP and phosphate for each amino acid residue added. To the end of the tripeptide side-chain is then attached the dipeptide D-alanyl-D-alanine, which is formed separately by the reaction

$$2\ \text{D-alanine} + \text{ATP} \rightarrow \text{D-alanyl-D-alanine} + \text{ADP} + \text{P}_i$$

The latter reaction is inhibited by the antibiotic cycloserine (margin).

Up to this point, all the reactions have taken place within the cell. In the second stage, the completed *N*-acetylmuramylpentapeptide is now transferred enzymatically from UDP to a membrane-bound "lipid intermediate," undecaprenyl phosphate, a linear 55-carbon terpenoid molecule made up of 11 isoprene units whose terminal hydroxyl group is esterified with inorganic phosphate (Figure 22-12). The nonpolar end of its hydrocarbon chain is anchored to the cell membrane, whereas the polar end carries the monosaccharide unit. The undecaprenyl phosphate thus serves as an arm to accept and deliver sugar groups to the appropriate points as the wall is built on the outer surface of the cell. To the *N*-acetylmuramylpentapeptide attached to this arm is now added the other monosaccharide unit, *N*-acetylglucosamine, which is donated by UDP-*N*-acetylglucosamine. To complete the second stage of murein synthesis, the entire disaccharide unit is enzymatically transferred from the undecaprenyl carrier to the growing end of the peptidoglycan polymer.

In the third stage, short cross-linking peptide chains are built by successive additions of amino acid residues to the lysine residue of the pentapeptide side-chain of *N*-acetylmuramylpentapeptide. The length of the cross-linking peptide and its amino acid components vary with the species; in *M. lysodeikticus* it is pentaglycine.

In the last stage of murein synthesis, the cross-linkage is established through a transpeptidation reaction in

Cycloserine

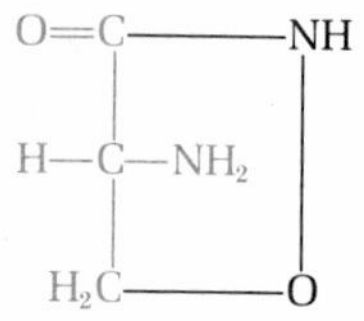

D-Alanine

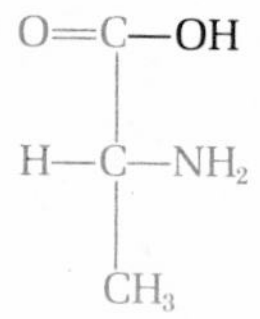

The similar structures in the antibiotic and D-alanine are in color

Figure 22-12
Undecaprenyl phosphate.

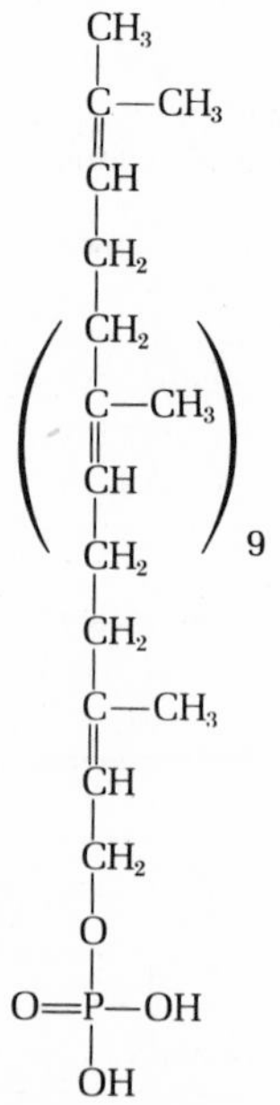

which the NH_2-terminal glycine residue of the cross-linking chain displaces the COOH-terminal D-alanine from the end of the pentapeptide side-chain of a *N*-acetylmuramylpentapeptide residue in an adjacent murein polymer (Figure 22-13). It is this reaction that is inhibited by *penicillin* (margin). Penicillin thus prevents completion of the synthesis of the cell wall at its last stage, after the bacterial cell has already made a heavy biosynthetic investment.

Benzylpenicillin (penicillin G)

Many different penicillins are known. They differ in the structure of the R group. Penicillin G is the most widely used in medicine

In Gram-positive bacteria the rigid murein framework is covered with a layer of teichoic acid (Chapter 11), whose backbone structure is synthesized from CDP-ribitol or CDP-glycerol precursors by the action of polymerases. Sugar side-chains are introduced into teichoic acids from UDP derivatives.

In Gram-negative organisms, such as *E. coli*, the murein framework is surrounded by a soft, rubbery coat consisting of a polymeric lipopolysaccharide (Chapter 11). Although the details of the biosynthesis of this very complex polymer cannot be given here, the major pathways are now understood from recent research in a number of laboratories.

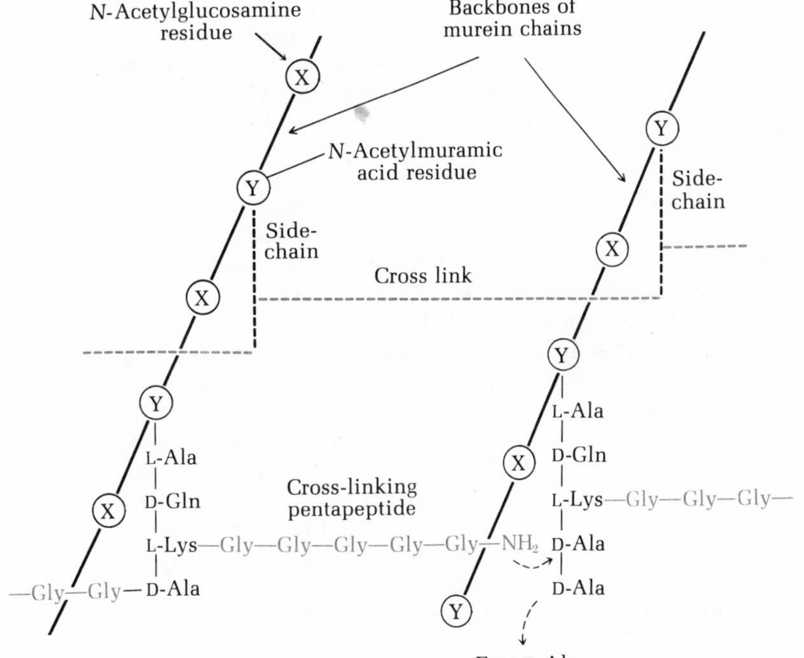

Figure 22-13
Completion of a cross link between two adjacent murein chains in bacterial cell wall. This reaction is blocked by penicillin.

Summary

The central common pathway in the biosynthesis of all carbohydrates from noncarbohydrate precursors is the route from pyruvate to glucose 6-phosphate, which occurs by reversal of most of the reactions of the glycolytic cycle. However, three reactions of glycolysis are replaced by "bypass" reactions that are energetically favorable for synthesis. In the first, pyruvate is converted to phosphoenolpyruvate by the mitochondrial sequence pyruvate $\xrightarrow{CO_2}$ oxaloacetate → malate followed by the cytoplasmic sequence malate → oxaloacetate $\xrightarrow{GTP}$ phosphoenolpyruvate. The second bypass is the hydrolysis of fructose 1,6-diphosphate to fructose 6-phosphate, and the third is the hydrolysis of glucose 6-phosphate to yield free glucose. The overall pathway, which is exergonic, is regulated by the first reaction of the sequence (pyruvate carboxylase) and secondarily by diphosphofructose phosphatase.

Three carbon atoms of each of the tricarboxylic acid cycle intermediates can undergo net conversion into glucose, since each can form oxaloacetate. Similarly, those amino acids capable of yielding oxaloacetate ultimately will also yield glucose and thus are glycogenic. Neither acetyl CoA nor CO_2 can undergo net conversion into glucose in animal tissues. However in plants and microorganisms, acetyl CoA can be converted into glucose by operation of the glyoxylate cycle.

In plant photosynthesis, CO_2 gains entry into the carbon backbone of glucose by a dark reaction with ribulose 1,5-diphosphate to yield 3-phosphoglycerate. At the expense of ATP and NADPH generated in the light reactions, six molecules of CO_2 can ultimately be converted into glucose by cyclic operation of the Calvin cycle, which consists of reactions of the phosphogluconate and glycolytic pathways. Alternate pathways for glucose formation from CO_2 exist.

The pathway from glucose 6-phosphate to formation of starch and glycogen is not the reverse of the degradative pathway catalyzed by phosphorylases, but proceeds by a sequence involving glycogen synthetase and uridine diphosphate glucose as intermediate glucose carrier. Glycogen synthetase occurs in two forms. The phosphorylated or D form requires glucose 6-phosphate for activity; the dephosphorylated or I form does not. The phosphate group is removed by a specific phosphatase and is reattached by a specific kinase. Glycogen synthetase kinase in turn exists in an inactive form, whose conversion to the active form is promoted by the modulator 3′,5′-AMP, whose formation from ATP is stimulated by epinephrine or glucagon. Glycogen phosphorylase and glycogen synthetase activities are independently controlled in muscle activity and in formation of liver glycogen and blood glucose.

Nucleoside diphosphate sugars are precursors of other monosaccharides such as D-galactose, of disaccharides such as sucrose and lactose, and of extracellular structural polysaccharides such as cellulose, xylan, hyaluronic acid, and the mureins or peptidoglycans of the cell walls of bacteria. The biosynthetic pathways leading to formation of the bacterial cell walls are noteworthy because of their complexity, the fact that the entire synthesis takes place outside the cell by the action of enzymes attached to the membrane, and the fact that specific enzymatic steps in wall formation are inhibited by antibiotics such as cycloserine and penicillin.

References

(see also Chapters 11, 16)

Books

GREENBERG, D. M. (ed.): *Metabolic Pathways*, vols. I and II, 3d ed., Academic Press, Inc., New York, 1967. A series of articles and reviews; especially good on biosynthetic role of the tricarboxylic acid cycle.

HOLLMAN, S., and O. TOUSTER: *Nonglycolytic Pathways of Metabolism of Glucose*, Academic Press, Inc., New York, 1964. A number of alternate pathways are reviewed in detail.

STANBURY, J. B., J. B. WYNGAARDEN, and D. S. FREDRICKSON: *The Metabolic Basis of Inherited Disease,* McGraw-Hill Book Company, 2d ed., New York, 1966. Correlation of basic biochemical aspects with clinical aspects of genetic diseases.

Articles

GINSBURG, V.: "Sugar Nucleotides and The Synthesis of Carbohydrates," *Advances in Enzymol.,* **26:**35–88 (1964).

HALES, C. N.: "Actions of Hormones in The Regulation of Glucose Metabolism," in P. N. Campbell and G. D. Greville (eds.), *Essays in Biochemistry,* vol. 3, pp. 73–104, Academic Press, Inc., New York, 1967. Excellent, readable review.

HASSID, W. Z.: "Biosynthesis of complex saccharides," in D. M. Greenberg (ed.) *Metabolic Pathways,* vol. I, 3d ed., Academic Press, Inc., New York, 1967. Plant polysaccharides are given special attention.

______: "Biosynthesis of Oligosaccharides and Polysaccharides in Plants," *Science,* **165:** 137–144 (1969).

NIKAIDO, H.: "Biosynthesis of Cell Wall Lipopolysaccharide in Gram-negative Enteric Bacteria," *Advances in Enzymol.,* **31:**77 (1968).

PREISS, J.: "The Regulation of The Biosynthesis of α $(1 \rightarrow 4)$ glucans in Bacteria and Plants," in B. Horecker and E. Stadtman (eds.), *Current Topics in Cellular Regulation,* vol. I, Academic Press, Inc., New York, *in press.* A valuable review of comparative aspects.

ROBISON, G. A., R. W. BUTCHER, and E. W. SUTHERLAND: "Cyclic AMP," *Ann. Rev. Biochem.,* **37:**149–174 (1968). Review of current knowledge of this important intracellular "messenger."

SCRUTTON, M. C., and M. F. UTTER: "The Regulation of Glycolysis and Gluconeogenesis in Animal Tissues," *Ann. Rev. Biochem.,* **37:**249–302 (1968). A comprehensive and authoritative review.

Problems

1. Write a balanced equation for the net formation of D-glucose from citric acid in the liver of the rat.
2. Write a balanced equation for the net formation of D-glucose from phenylalanine in the liver of the rat.
3. Write a balanced equation for the net conversion of palmitic acid into D-glucose in the seeds of a higher plant.
4. Write a balanced equation for the net conversion of L-leucine into D-glucose in a higher plant.
5. In what carbon atoms of D-glucose residues in liver glycogen and palmitic acid in liver phosphatidyl choline will the isotopic carbon atom in L-leucine-3-^{14}C be found?
6. Write a balanced equation for the synthesis of one D-glucosyl residue of glycogen starting from pyruvic acid. How many high-energy phosphate bonds are required?
7. Write a balanced equation for the biosynthesis of L-ascorbic acid from pyruvic acid.

8. If a green leaf is illuminated in the presence of radioactive CO_2 for a short period and then extracted, in which positions of the following compounds found in the extract would you expect to find isotopic carbon? (*a*) D-Glucose 6-phosphate, (*b*) sedoheptulose 7-phosphate, and (*c*) ribose 5-phosphate.

9. L-Xylulose is excreted in the urine of humans having the genetic disease pentosuria. If 1-^{14}C-D-glucose is fed to such individuals, 5-^{14}C-L-xylulose is found in the urine. In normal individuals, labeled D-xylose is formed. Suggest a pathway for the synthesis of D-xylose from D-glucose.

CHAPTER 23 THE BIOSYNTHESIS OF LIPIDS

The biosynthetic pathway leading from glucose to the fatty acids is a prominent metabolic route in most organisms. Because the capacity of higher animals to store polysaccharides is rather limited, glucose ingested in excess of immediate caloric needs and storage capacity is converted into fatty acids and they in turn into triacylglycerols, which may be stored in large amounts in adipose or fat tissues. Triacylglycerols are also stored in large amounts in seeds of higher plants. The biosynthesis of the complex polar lipids of membranes is also a prominent process, since they undergo a relatively high rate of metabolic turnover in most cells.

This chapter also considers the biosynthesis of cholesterol and other sterols. Although it is only a minor metabolic pathway from the quantitative point of view, the large number of different biologically active steroids that derive from cholesterol endow this route with considerable importance.

Biosynthesis of the Saturated Fatty Acids

After the discovery of the pathway of fatty acid oxidation in mitochondria and the role of CoA in this process (Chapter 19), it was widely expected that the biosynthesis of fatty acids would be found to occur by reversal of the same enzymatic steps employed for their oxidation. However, a number of puzzling observations were soon made that were inconsistent with this view. First, isolated mitochondria possess only feeble capacity to incorporate labeled acetic acid into their long-chain fatty acids, whereas incorporation occurs at a high rate in the cytoplasmic supernatant fraction of the liver remaining after centrifugal removal of the mitochondria. Secondly, citrate is necessary for maximal rates of incorporation of labeled acetic acid into fatty acids in the cytoplasm fraction, although citrate is not necessarily incorporated into the product nor utilized as a reductant. The effect of citrate can not be reproduced by NADH or NADPH alone. Perhaps the most unusual and unexpected observation was that carbon dioxide or the bicarbonate ion is essential for fatty acid synthesis in liver extracts, although isotopic carbon dioxide is not itself incorporated into the newly synthesized fatty acids.

The puzzling requirement for CO_2 turned out to be an important clue to the mechanism of fatty acid biosynthesis. During study of the fate of isotopic CO_2 in liver extracts capable of synthesizing long-chain fatty acids from acetate, Wakil and other investigators observed that CO_2 is incorporated into one of the carboxyl carbon atoms of *malonyl CoA* (margin). This finding quickly led to the discovery that the immediate precursor of the two-carbon units entering into fatty acid synthesis is not acetyl CoA, but rather malonyl CoA. Although malonic acid occurs naturally, particularly in higher plants, a possible role of free malonic acid as a major metabolite had long seemed unlikely because it is a competitive inhibitor of succinate dehydrogenase (Chapter 9). Once malonyl CoA was identified as the precursor of fatty acids, the overall pathway and the enzymes catalyzing the separate steps were quickly revealed by work in several laboratories. These recent advances have also brought fuller understanding of the intracellular location of the enzymes responsible for synthesis of fatty acids. The complete *de novo* synthesis of long-chain saturated fatty acids takes place only in the soluble fraction of the cytoplasm of either procaryotes or eucaryotes. It is catalyzed by a complex of seven enzymes called the *fatty acid synthetase complex*. Neither the mitochondria nor the endoplasmic reticulum, as represented by the microsome fraction, is capable of *de novo* synthesis of palmitic acid. However, they do contain enzymes capable of elongating the chains of fatty acids that already possess 12 to 16 carbon atoms.

Malonyl CoA

COOH
|
CH_2
|
C—S—CoA
‖
O

The de novo Synthesis of Palmitic Acid

The fatty acid synthetase system of the soluble cytoplasm catalyzes the following overall reaction, in which one molecule of acetyl CoA and seven molecules of malonyl CoA are condensed to make a molecule of palmitic acid. The reducing power is furnished by NADPH:

$$\text{Acetyl CoA} + 7\text{ malonyl CoA} + 14\text{NADPH} + 14\text{H}^+ \rightarrow$$
$$\text{CH}_3(\text{CH}_2)_{14}\text{COOH} + 7\text{CO}_2 + 8\text{CoA} + 14\text{NADP}^+ + 6\text{H}_2\text{O}$$

The single molecule of acetyl CoA required in the process serves as a *primer* or starter; the methyl and carboxyl carbon atoms of its acetyl group become carbon atoms 16 and 15, respectively, of the palmitic acid formed. Chain growth during fatty acid synthesis thus starts at the carboxyl group of the acetyl CoA and proceeds by successive addition of acetyl residues at the carboxyl end of the growing chain. Each successive acetyl residue is derived from the two carbon atoms of malonyl CoA nearest the CoA group; the third carbon atom, i.e., that of the unesterified carboxyl group, is lost as CO_2. In principle, the free carboxyl group of each residue of malonyl CoA entering is displaced by the carboxyl carbon atom of the acyl CoA undergoing lengthening, with formation of CO_2 and a β-keto fatty acyl derivative. The latter product is then reduced at the expense of NADPH to form a β-hydroxy fatty acyl derivative, which undergoes dehydration to the α,β- or $\Delta^{2,3}$-unsaturated fatty acyl derivative, which is then reduced to a saturated fatty acyl residue by a second molecule of NADPH. This cycle is repeated six more times and ends with the formation of a molecule of palmitic acid.

A second distinctive feature of the mechanism of fatty acid synthesis is that the acyl intermediates in the process are not thioesters of CoA, as in fatty acid oxidation, but rather thioesters of a small-molecular-weight protein called *acyl carrier protein,* abbreviated *ACP.* This protein can form a complex or complexes with one or more of the six other enzyme proteins required for the complete synthesis of palmitic acid. In yeast cells, all seven proteins of the fatty acid synthetase complex are tightly associated in a cluster having a particle weight of 2.3×10^6 daltons. Although the yeast complex can be dissociated into individual peptide chains, such subunits are not enzymatically active when separated. On the other hand, the fatty acid synthetase complex of pigeon liver can be dissociated into two major components without loss of activity. Most illuminating, however, is more recent work on the fatty acid synthetase system of *E. coli,* which normally occurs in dissociated form; in this organism each of the seven protein components is active by itself and can be studied separately. We shall now examine the individual steps in fatty acid synthesis in more detail.

Formation of Malonyl CoA

The ultimate source of all the carbon atoms of palmitic acid synthesized by the cytoplasmic fatty acid synthetase complex is cytoplasmic acetyl CoA, which in turn derives from intramitochondrial acetyl CoA by an indirect route. In mitochondria, acetyl CoA is formed in two processes, the oxidative decarboxylation of pyruvate (Chapter 16) and the β oxidation of long-chain fatty acids (Chapter 19). However, acetyl CoA cannot pass through the mitochondrial membrane into the cytoplasm. Rather, the acetyl group of mitochondrial acetyl CoA is first transferred to oxaloacetate to yield citrate. As was pointed out earlier (Chapter 18), citrate may pass through the mitochondrial membrane to the cytoplasm via a carrier system. In the cytoplasm, citrate undergoes cleavage by the ATP-dependent citrate-cleaving enzyme, which catalyzes the reaction

$$\text{Citrate} + \text{ATP} + \text{CoA} \rightarrow \text{acetyl CoA} + \text{ADP} + \text{P}_i + \text{oxaloacetate}$$

Citrate thus serves to carry acetyl groups from the mitochondria to the extramitochondrial cytoplasm. Acetyl groups may also be carried by carnitine, but this does not appear to be a major pathway.

The malonyl CoA required as the immediate precursor of fourteen of the sixteen carbon atoms of palmitic acid is formed from cytoplasmic acetyl CoA and carbon dioxide by the action of *acetyl CoA carboxylase*, which catalyzes the reaction shown in the margin. The carbon atom of the CO_2 becomes the distal or free carboxyl carbon of malonyl CoA; there is no exchange of the position of the carboxyl carbon atoms of malonyl CoA, since at no point in the reaction is free malonic acid an intermediate. Acetyl CoA carboxylase contains biotin as its prosthetic group; the carboxyl group of biotin is bound in amide linkage to the ϵ-amino group of a specific lysine residue of the enzyme protein, i.e., biocytin (Chapter 16). The biotin serves as an intermediate carrier of a molecule of CO_2 in a two-step reaction cycle:

$$CO_2 + \text{ATP} + \text{biotin-enzyme} \rightleftharpoons \text{carboxybiotin-enzyme} + \text{ADP} + P_i$$

$$\text{Carboxybiotin-enzyme} + \text{acetyl CoA} \rightleftharpoons \text{malonyl CoA} + \text{biotin-enzyme}$$

Acetyl CoA carboxylase reaction.

$$\underset{\text{Acetyl CoA}}{CH_3-\underset{\substack{\| \\ O}}{C}-S-\text{CoA}} + CO_2 + \text{ATP} \xrightarrow{Mn^{2+}} \underset{\text{Malonyl CoA}}{\text{COOH}-CH_2-\underset{\substack{\| \\ O}}{C}-S-\text{CoA}} + \text{ADP} + P_i$$

Acetyl CoA carboxylase will also carboxylate propionyl CoA, but at a much lower rate, to form methylmalonyl CoA (see Chapter 16).

The reaction catalyzed by acetyl CoA carboxylase, a regulatory enzyme, is the rate-limiting step for the synthesis of fatty acids. The carboxylation of acetyl CoA by the liver enzyme is greatly accelerated by the positive allosteric modulators citrate and isocitrate, as well as by α-ketoglutarate. The allosteric stimulation by citrate accounts for the early observation that citrate was required for fatty acid synthesis without being a precursor of either carbon atoms or reducing power.

The structure of acetyl CoA carboxylase and the manner of its allosteric modulation have been studied by Lane and his colleagues. The chicken liver enzyme occurs in two forms, an inactive protomer and an active polymer. The inactive protomer, which has a particle weight of about 400,000 and a sedimentation coefficient of 20S, contains 4 smaller subunits of about 100,000 molecular weight. Each protomer has a binding site for the substrate acetyl CoA and for the positive modulator isocitrate. In the presence of isocitrate the protomers aggregate to form the enzymatically active polymer of particle weight 4,000,000. The active polymer is a long narrow filament (4000 Å × 100 Å), which appears to consist of a twisted chain of the plate-like protomer molecules (Figure 23-1). When the isocitrate concentration is very low, the filamentous polymer disaggregates into the inactive protomers.

Figure 23-1
Electron micrograph of the enzymatically active polymeric form of chicken liver acetyl CoA carboxylase. A schematic interpretation of the relationship of the monomeric units is shown at the right.

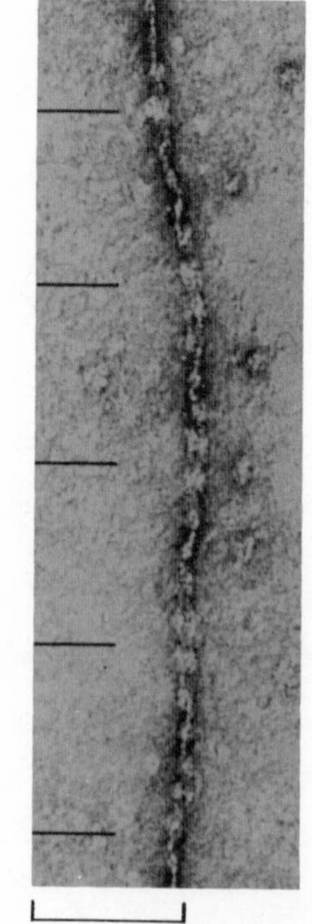

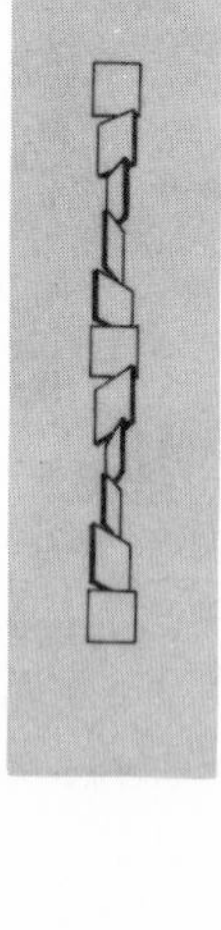

Acyl Carrier Protein (ACP) and the Transacylases

The acyl carrier protein of *E. coli*, which has been isolated in pure form by Vagelos and his colleagues, is a relatively small (mol wt 10,000) heat-stable protein. Its amino acid sequence has recently been established. The single sulfhydryl group, to which the acyl intermediates are esterified, is contributed by the prosthetic group of ACP,

Figure 23-2
Structure of the prosthetic group of acyl carrier protein (ACP). In the yeast fatty acid synthetase complex, which consists of ACP plus the 6 enzymes of the cycle, the 4′-phosphopantetheine moiety appears to serve as a swinging arm to rotate the fatty acyl group undergoing lengthening from one enzyme to the next.

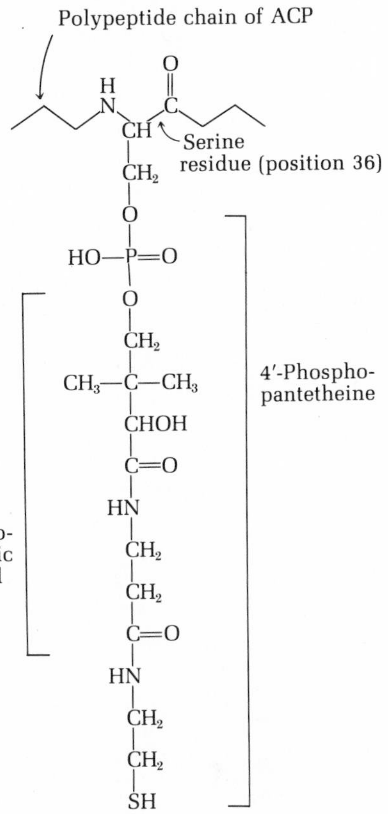

Polypeptide chain of ACP

H—N—CH—C(=O)
CH (Serine residue (position 36))
CH_2
O
HO—P=O
O
CH_2
CH_3—C—CH_3
CHOH
C=O
HN
CH_2
CH_2
C=O
HN
CH_2
CH_2
SH

Pantothenic acid

4′-Phosphopantetheine

namely, 4′-*phosphopantetheine*, which is covalently linked to the hydroxyl group of serine at residue 36 of the protein, as shown in Figure 23-2. The 4′-phosphopantetheine moiety is identical to that in CoA (Chapter 16). The function of ACP in fatty acid synthesis is analogous to that of CoA in fatty acid oxidation. It serves as an anchor to which the acyl intermediates are esterified during the reactions by which the aliphatic chain is built.

The acyl groups of both acetyl CoA and malonyl CoA are transferred to the thiol group of ACP by the action of the enzymes *acetyl transacylase* and *malonyl transacylase*, respectively. Both enzymes contain —SH groups essential for activity. The reactions are

$$\text{Acetyl-S-CoA} + \text{ACP-SH} \rightleftharpoons \text{acetyl-S-ACP} + \text{CoA-SH}$$

$$\text{Malonyl-S-CoA} + \text{ACP-SH} \rightleftharpoons \text{malonyl-S-ACP} + \text{CoA-SH}$$

The Steps in Fatty Acid Synthesis

Acetyl-S-ACP and malonyl-S-ACP now react in such a way that the acetyl group of the former becomes carbon atoms 3 and 4 of the acetoacetyl group of *acetoacetyl-S-ACP* (margin), with displacement of CO_2 from the free carboxyl group of malonyl-S-ACP:

$$\text{Acetyl-S-ACP} + \text{malonyl-S-ACP} \rightleftharpoons \text{acetoacetyl-S-ACP} + CO_2 + \text{ACP-SH}$$

The molecule of CO_2 so formed contains the same carbon atom that was introduced as CO_2 by the acetyl CoA carboxylase reaction. It is now clear why the carbon atom of $^{14}CO_2$ never appears in the fatty acid finally formed. In essence, CO_2 plays a catalytic role in fatty acid synthesis, since it is regenerated as each two-carbon unit is inserted. Study of the reaction equilibrium has also revealed the probable basis for the selection of malonyl CoA as the precursor of two-carbon residues for fatty acid synthesis. If acetoacetyl CoA were to be formed from acetyl CoA alone, by the action of thiolase:

$$\text{Acetyl-S-CoA} + \text{acetyl-S-CoA} \rightleftharpoons \text{acetoacetyl-S-CoA} + \text{CoA-SH}$$

the reaction would be strongly endergonic and its equilibrium would lie far to the left. On the other hand, the formation of acetoacetyl-S-ACP by the reaction

$$\text{Acetyl-S-ACP} + \text{malonyl-S-ACP} \rightarrow \text{acetoacetyl-S-ACP} + \text{ACP-SH} + CO_2$$

is strongly exergonic. Its equilibrium lies far to the right, in the direction of synthesis. Thus the decarboxylation of the malonyl residue provides a strong thermodynamic "pull" toward fatty acid synthesis.

The acetoacetyl-S-ACP next undergoes reduction with NADPH to form the D-stereoisomer of β-hydroxybutyryl-S-ACP, catalyzed by *β-ketoacyl-ACP-reductase:*

$$\text{Acetoacetyl-S-ACP} + \text{NADPH} + H^+ \rightleftharpoons \text{D-}\beta\text{-hydroxybutyryl-S-ACP} + \text{NADP}^+$$

The initiation of chain growth in fatty acid synthesis.

CH_3
ACP—S—C=O Acetyl-S-ACP
COOH
CH_2
ACP—S—C=O Malonyl-S-ACP
CO_2
ACP-SH
CH_3
C=O
CH_2
ACP—S—C=O Acetoacetyl-S-ACP

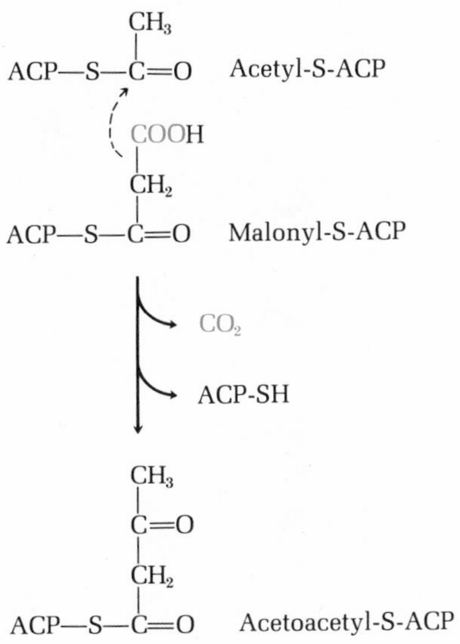

It is noteworthy that this is not the same stereoisomeric form as the β-hydroxyacyl intermediate in fatty acid oxidation, which is the L-stereoisomer (Chapter 19).

The D-β-hydroxybutyryl-S-ACP is then dehydrated to the *trans* α,β- or $\Delta^{2,3}$-unsaturated acyl-S-ACP (also called crotonyl-S-ACP) by *enoyl ACP dehydratase:*

$$\text{D-}\beta\text{-Hydroxybutyryl-S-ACP} \rightleftharpoons \text{crotonyl-S-ACP} + H_2O$$

Crotonyl-S-ACP is then reduced to butyryl-S-ACP by *crotonyl-ACP reductase;* the electron donor is NADPH in *E. coli* and in animal tissues:

$$\text{Crotonyl-S-ACP} + \text{NADPH} + H^+ \rightleftharpoons \text{butyryl-S-ACP} + \text{NADP}^+$$

Thus this reaction differs from the corresponding reverse reaction of fatty acid oxidation in mitochondria, namely, the oxidation of butyryl-S-CoA to crotonyl-S-CoA, in which a flavoprotein is the electron acceptor (Chapter 19). Since NADPH is a much more negative reducing agent than the flavoprotein, it favors reductive formation of the saturated fatty acid.

The formation of the butyryl-S-ACP completes the first of seven cycles, in each of which a molecule of malonyl-S-ACP enters at the carboxyl end of the growing fatty acyl chain, with displacement of the ACP molecule from the carboxyl group and loss of the distal carboxyl group of malonyl-S-ACP as CO_2. Palmityl-S-ACP is the final end product. It is remarkable that in some organisms fatty acid synthesis by the fatty acid synthetase system terminates in palmitic acid and does not make stearic acid, even though palmitic and stearic acid do not differ significantly in physical properties. At the end of the cycle free palmitic acid is discharged from ACP, by the action of a hydrolytic deacylase. The central function of the acyl carrier protein in the function of the yeast fatty acid synthetase complex is shown on the opposite page. Its 4′-phosphopantetheine moiety has been postulated by Lynen to serve as a long (20.2 Å) swinging arm which rotates from one enzyme of the complex to the next.

We may now write out the overall equation for fatty acid synthesis:

$$\begin{aligned} &8\ \text{acetyl CoA} + 14\text{NADPH} + 14H^+ + 7\text{ATP} \rightarrow \\ &\qquad \text{palmitic acid} + 8\text{CoA} + 14\text{NADP}^+ + 7\text{ADP} + 7P_i + 6H_2O \end{aligned}$$

The fourteen molecules of NADPH required for the reductive steps in a complete cycle arise largely from the NADP-dependent oxidation of cytoplasmic glucose 6-phosphate (Chapter 16). A total of seven molecules of glucose 6-phosphate must be oxidized to ribulose 5-phosphate + CO_2 to generate sufficient NADPH to form one molecule of palmitic acid. In liver and adipose tissue of vertebrates, in which the rate of fatty acid synthesis is rather high, the 6-phosphogluconate cycle is very active. The ribulose 5-phosphate produced with the NADPH is recovered or salvaged in the form of glycolytic cycle intermediates by the transketolase and transaldolase reactions (Chapter 16). Another source of NADPH for fatty acid

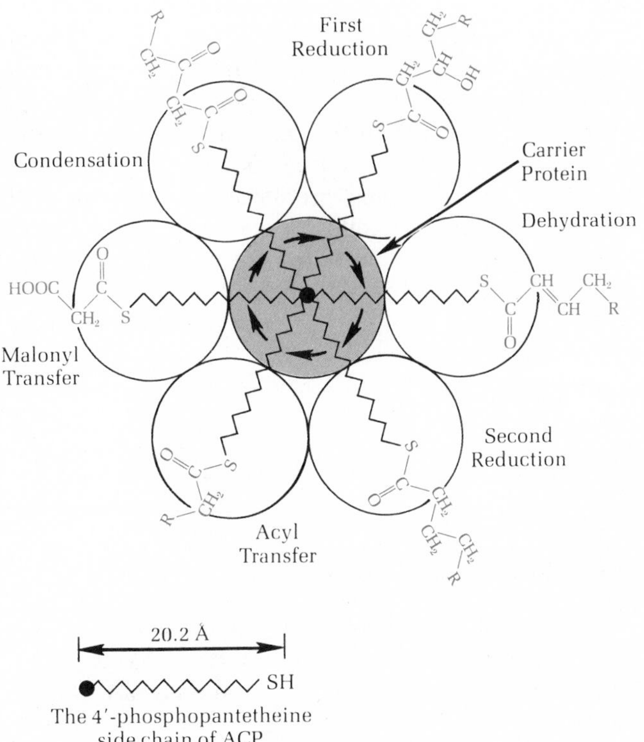

The yeast fatty acid synthetase complex.

synthesis in liver is the oxidation of malate to pyruvate + CO_2 by the "malic enzyme" (Chapter 16). In leaves of plants, the source of NADPH for fat synthesis is by photoreduction of $NADP^+$ (Chapter 21).

The enzymatic reactions leading to synthesis of palmitic acid differ from those involved in oxidation of palmitic acid in the following respects: (1) their intracellular location, (2) the molecular identity of the acyl carrier, (3) the form in which the two-carbon units are added or removed, (4) the pyridine nucleotide specificity of the β-ketoacyl-β-hydroxyacyl reaction, (5) the stereoisomeric configuration of the β-hydroxyacyl intermediate, and (6) the electron donor-acceptor system for the crotonyl-butyryl step. These differences illustrate how chemically incompatible, or opposing, metabolic processes may be segregated from each other in the cell.

The rate of biosynthesis of fatty acids appears to be integrated with and determined by the rate of formation of triacylglycerols and phosphoglycerides, because free fatty acids occur in only very small amounts in cells and do not normally accumulate.

Elongation of Saturated Fatty Acids in Mitochondria and Microsomes

Palmitic acid, the normal end product of the cytoplasmic fatty acid synthetase system, may now be lengthened by two different types of enzyme systems, one in the mitochondria and the other in the endoplasmic reticulum.

In mitochondria, saturated fatty acids having from 12 to 16 carbon atoms, in the form of CoA esters, are lengthened by successive additions of acetyl CoA; malonyl-S-ACP cannot replace acetyl CoA. The mitochondrial pathway appears to occur by direct reversal of the same enzymatic steps that are involved in oxidation, with the exception of the reduction of the α,β double bond to form the saturated fatty acid, which occurs at the expense of NADPH as reductant. The flavoprotein that normally carries out the reverse of this step evidently does not participate in the direction of reduction. The mitochondrial system will also elongate unsaturated fatty acids.

Both saturated and unsaturated fatty acyl CoA esters may also be lengthened in microsomal preparations, but in this case malonyl CoA, rather than acetyl CoA, serves as source of the acetyl groups. The microsomal system does not employ ACP as acyl carrier, but like both the mitochondrial and cytoplasmic systems, it employs NADPH as reductant in the reduction of the α,β double bond.

Formation of Monoenoic Acids

Palmitic and stearic acids serve as precursors of the two common *monoenoic* (monounsaturated) fatty acids of animal tissues, namely *palmitoleic* and *oleic acids*, both of which possess a *cis* double bond in the $\Delta^{9,10}$ position. These two fatty acids may be symbolized as 9-$C_{16:1}$ and 9-$C_{18:1}$, respectively; the prefixed number indicates the position of the double bond, the first subscript number the length of the chain, and the second the number of double bonds. Although most organisms have the capacity to form palmitoleic and oleic acid, the pathway and mechanism employed depends on whether the organism is anaerobic or aerobic. In mammals and most other aerobic organisms the double bonds are introduced by a specific *oxygenase* located in the microsome fraction, particularly in the liver and adipose tissue. Full details of the enzymatic mechanism are not known, but the reaction is unusual in that one molecule of molecular oxygen is used as the acceptor for two pairs of electrons, one pair derived from the fatty acyl CoA substrate and the other from NADPH, which is a required coreductant in the reaction:

$$\text{Palmitoyl CoA} + \text{NADPH} + \text{H}^+ + \text{O}_2 \rightarrow \text{palmitoleyl CoA} + \text{NADP}^+ + 2\text{H}_2\text{O}$$

This and other oxygenases which require a coreductant such as NADPH are called *mixed-function oxygenases*. Other and better understood examples of such enzymes will be considered elsewhere.

In certain bacteria an entirely different mechanism not employing molecular oxygen comes into play. In *E. coli* for example, the synthesis of palmitoleic acid starts with β-hydroxydecanoate. The enzyme *β-hydroxydecanoyl thioester dehydrase* dehydrates β-hydroxydecanoyl-S-ACP to yield the β,γ- or $\Delta^{3,4}$-enoyl-S-ACP, presumably in the *cis* form. Three more two-carbon units are then added to the carboxyl end of the twelve-carbon unsaturated acyl-S-ACP, in the form of malonyl CoA, to yield the ACP ester of palmitoleic acid.

Figure 23-3
Formation of polyenoic acids from palmitoleic and oleic acids.

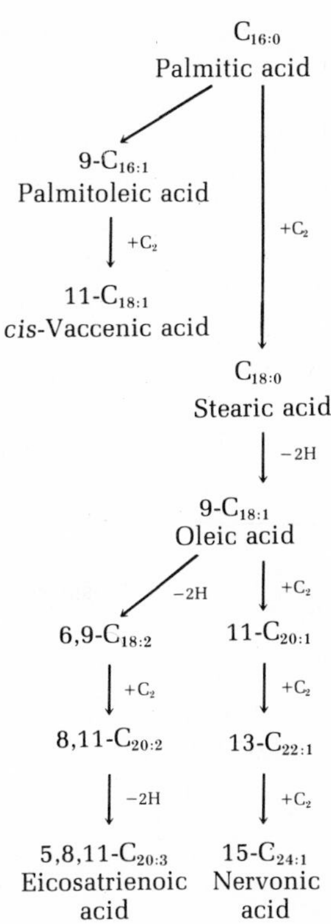

Formation of Polyenoic Acids

Bacteria do not contain polyenoic acids; however, they are common in both higher plants and animals. Mammals contain four distinct families of polyenoic acids, which differ in the length of the aliphatic chain between the terminal methyl group and the nearest double bond

1. Palmitoleic family $CH_3—(CH_2)_5—CH{=}CH—$
2. Oleic family $CH_3—(CH_2)_7—CH{=}CH—$
3. Linoleic family $CH_3—(CH_2)_4—CH{=}CH—$
4. Linolenic family $CH_3—CH_2—CH{=}CH—$

All polyenoic acids found in mammals are formed from these four precursors by further elongation and/or desaturation. However, linoleic and linolenic acids cannot be synthesized by mammals and must be obtained from plant sources; they are therefore called *essential fatty acids.*

The important animal polyenoic acids derived from palmitoleic and oleic acids are shown in Figure 23-3, which also outlines the pathway of their formation in the liver. The elongation of chains occurs by the mitochondrial or microsomal systems described above. The desaturation steps occur by the action of mixed-function oxygenases in the presence of NADPH; they are similar to the desaturation steps in the formation of palmitoleic and oleic acid described above.

Figure 23-4 shows some of the polyenoic acids derived from linoleic and linolenic acids. Arachidonic acid is the most abundant; the pathway of its formation is also shown. When young rats are placed on diets deficient in essential fatty acids, they grow slowly and develop a scaly dermatitis and thickening of the skin. This condition can be relieved by administration of not only linoleic or linolenic acid, but also arachidonic acid. However, mature mammals grown on a normal diet are not easily rendered deficient in essential fatty acids. The specific biological function of these fatty acids is not known; they may serve as essential precursors of arachidonic or other complex polyenoic acids or as precursors of the prostaglandins (Chapter 10).

In higher plants, linoleic and linolenic acids are synthesized from oleic acid, which undergoes aerobic desaturation reactions catalyzed by specific mixed-function oxygenases requiring NADPH as coreductant.

Figure 23-4
Pathways of polyenoic acid synthesis leading from the essential fatty acids.

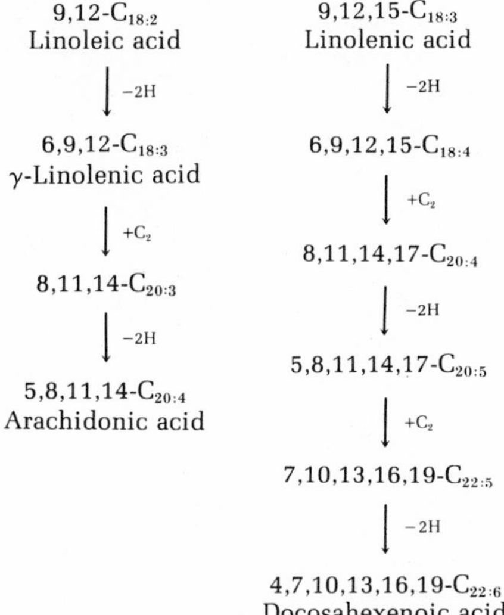

Biosynthesis of Triacylglycerols

The triacylglycerols, which function as *depot* or *storage lipids,* are actively synthesized in the liver and adipose cells of mammals, as well as in higher plants. Although most bacteria contain relatively small amounts of triacylglycerols, they also possess the capacity to synthesize this class of lipids.

In higher animals and plants, two major precursors are required for the synthesis of triacylglycerols: L-glycerol 3-phosphate and fatty acyl CoA. L-Glycerol phosphate is derived from two different sources. Its normal precursor is dihydroxyacetone phosphate, generated during glycolysis by action of the cytoplasmic NAD-linked glycerol phosphate dehydrogenase:

$$\text{Dihydroxyacetone phosphate} + \text{NADH} + \text{H}^+ \rightleftharpoons \text{L-glycerol 3-phosphate} + \text{NAD}^+$$

It may also be formed by action of *glycerol kinase*

$$\text{ATP} + \text{glycerol} \rightarrow \text{L-glycerol 3-phosphate} + \text{ADP}$$

In plants and animals, the first stage in triacylglycerol formation is the acylation of the free hydroxyl groups of glycerol phosphate by two molecules of fatty acyl CoA to yield an *L-phosphatidic acid* (margin). This reaction occurs preferentially with sixteen- and eighteen-carbon saturated and unsaturated acyl CoAs. In some microorganisms, such as *E. coli*, the fatty acyl group donor in the formation of phosphatidic acid is fatty acyl-ACP rather than fatty acyl CoA.

Phosphatidic acids occur in only trace amounts in cells, but they are important intermediates common to the biosynthesis of both triacylglycerols and the phosphoglycerides (see below). The partition of phosphatidic acids between these two pathways is crucial in the regulation of lipid synthesis.

To form the triacylglycerols, phosphatidic acids undergo hydrolysis by a specific phosphatase to form *diacylglycerols* (margin). The latter then react with a third molecule of a fatty acyl CoA to yield the triacylglycerol:

$$\text{L-Phosphatidic acid} + H_2O \rightarrow \text{diacylglycerol} + P_i$$

$$\text{R-CO-S-CoA} + \text{diacylglycerol} \rightarrow \text{triacylglycerol} + \text{CoA-SH}$$

In the intestinal mucosal cells of higher animals, which are very active in synthesizing triacylglycerols during absorption of fatty acids from the intestine, another type of acylation reaction comes into play. Monoacylglycerols formed during intestinal digestion may be acylated directly and need not pass through a phosphatidic acid stage:

$$\text{Monoacylglycerol} + \text{fatty acyl CoA} \rightleftharpoons \text{diacylglycerol} + \text{CoA}$$

The formation of a diacylglycerol.

2 R—C(=O)—S—CoA Fatty acyl CoA

+

CH_2OH—HCOH—CH_2—O—PO_3H_2

↓ 2 CoA-SH

H_2C—O—C(=O)—R
HC—O—C(=O)—R′
$H_2COPO_3H_2$

L-Phosphatidic acid

↓ phosphatase (P_i)

H_2C—O—C(=O)—R
HC—O—C(=O)—R′
CH_2OH

Diacylglycerol

Biosynthesis of Phosphoglycerides

The major phosphoglycerides, which serve as components of membranes and of transport lipoproteins, are formed by a branching biosynthetic pathway starting from phosphatidic acid (Figure 23-5). The central importance of phosphatidic acid and of cytidine nucleotides in these processes was first discovered by Kennedy. These reactions take place largely in the endoplasmic reticulum.

L-Phosphatidic acid is first converted by a reversible reaction with CTP into *cytidine diphosphate diacylglycerol,* which is the common precursor of all phosphoglycerides formed by this pathway:

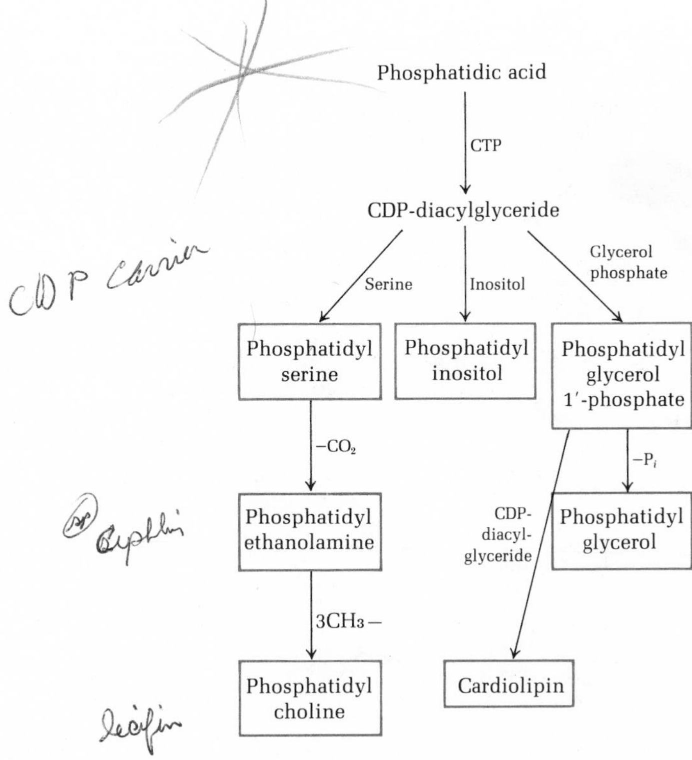

Figure 23-5
Pathways of biosynthesis of major phosphoglycerides.

$$\text{L-Phosphatidic acid} + \text{CTP} \rightleftharpoons \text{cytidine diphosphate diacylglycerol} + PP_i$$

Cytidine diphosphate diacylglycerol. The portion of the molecule arising from phosphatidic acid is in color.

The structure of CDP-diacylglycerol is shown in the margin. Its CMP moiety may be regarded as a carrier of phosphatidic acid. In ensuing reactions, each of which is catalyzed by a specific enzyme, the cytidine monophosphate moiety is displaced from CDP-diacylglycerol by one of the three alcohols, serine, inositol, or glycerol phosphate (Figure 23-5), to form phosphatidyl serine, phosphatidyl inositol, and 3-phosphatidyl glycerol 1′-phosphate, respectively.

$$\text{CDP-diacylglycerol} + \text{serine} \rightarrow \text{phosphatidyl serine} + \text{CMP}$$

$$\text{CDP-diacylglycerol} + \text{inositol} \rightarrow \text{phosphatidyl inositol} + \text{CMP}$$

$$\text{CDP-diacylglycerol} + \text{glycerol phosphate} \rightarrow \text{3-phosphatidyl glycerol 1}'\text{-phosphate} + \text{CMP}$$

Enzymatic decarboxylation of the serine residue of phosphatidyl serine leads to formation of phosphatidyl ethanolamine

$$\text{Phosphatidyl serine} \rightarrow \text{phosphatidyl ethanolamine} + CO_2$$

This reaction is catalyzed by an enzyme containing pyridoxal phosphate as prosthetic group; it is believed that a Schiff's base (Chapter 20) is formed between the α-amino group of the serine residue and the pyridoxal phosphate as an intermediate step.

Phosphatidyl ethanolamine then becomes the precursor of phosphatidyl choline, which is formed by consecutive transfer of three methyl groups from three molecules of the methyl donor *S-adenosylmethionine* (below) to the amino group of the ethanolamine residue. The methylated products are, consecutively, *phosphatidyl monomethylethanolamine, phosphatidyl dimethylethanolamine,* and *phosphatidyl choline.* The equation for the formation of the latter is

Phosphatidyldimethylethanolamine + S-adenosylmethionine →
phosphatidyl choline + S-adenosylhomocysteine

Further details on the synthesis and function of the methyl donor S-adenosylmethionine will be developed in Chapter 24.

Methylation of phosphatidyl ethanolamine.

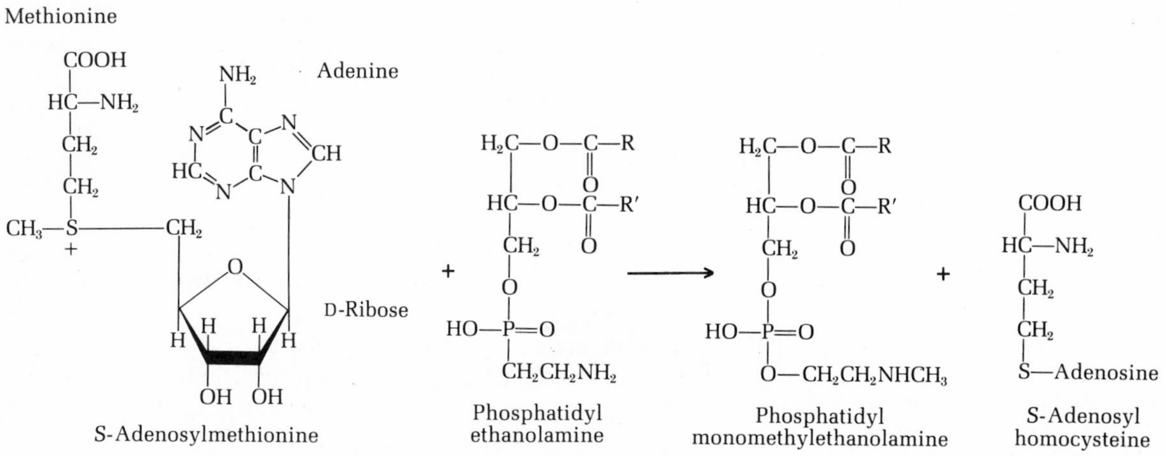

Methionine

Adenine

D-Ribose

S-Adenosylmethionine + Phosphatidyl ethanolamine → Phosphatidyl monomethylethanolamine + S-Adenosyl homocysteine

Phosphatidyl inositol is the precursor of two derivatives, *phosphatidyl inositol monophosphate* and *phosphatidyl inositol diphosphate* (also called *diphosphoinositide* and *triphosphoinositide*), which are formed by two successive phosphorylations by ATP of free hydroxyl groups in the inositol residue. These phosphorylated forms of phosphatidyl inositol are present in the mitochondrial membrane and in brain tissue; the rapid metabolic turnover of the phosphate groups in the inositol residue suggests that these lipids may be involved in membrane transport phenomena.

3-Phosphatidyl glycerol 1′-phosphate is the precursor of two interesting lipids which may also play a special role in the functional aspects of membranes. Dephosphorylation yields *phosphatidyl glycerol* (margin)

3-Phosphatidyl glycerol 1′-phosphate →
phosphatidyl glycerol + P_i

a major lipid component in the cell membrane of many bacteria. Reaction of 3-phosphatidyl glycerol 1′-phosphate with a second molecule of CDP-diacylglycerol yields *diphosphatidyl glycerol,* more commonly called *cardiolipin* (below), which characteristically makes up 10 per-

Phosphatidyl glycerol

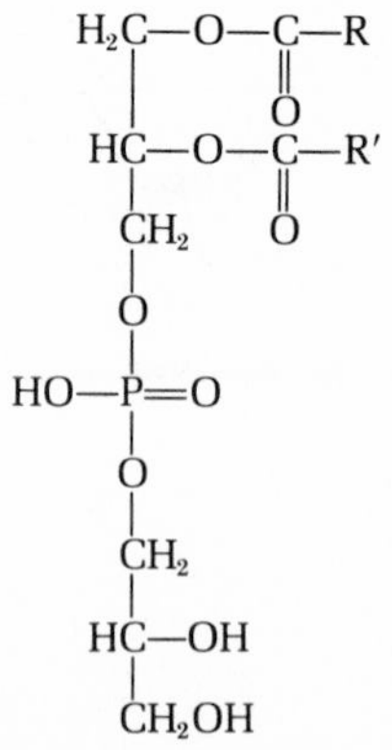

The formation of cardiolipin. The portions of the molecule arising from CDP-diacylglycerol are in color.

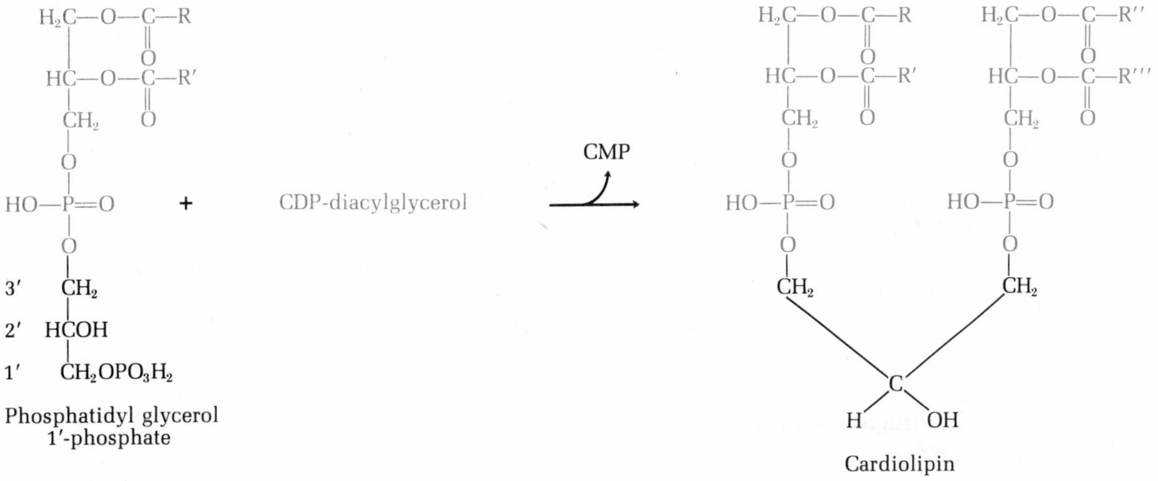

Phosphatidyl glycerol 1′-phosphate + CDP-diacylglycerol → (CMP released) Cardiolipin

cent or more of the lipids in the mitochondrial membrane. Cardiolipin is also a major component of the membrane lipids of many bacteria; it apparently plays some specific role in connection with electron transport and oxidative phosphorylation in mitochondria and bacteria.

The formation of cytidine diphosphate choline. The portion arising from phosphoryl choline is in color.

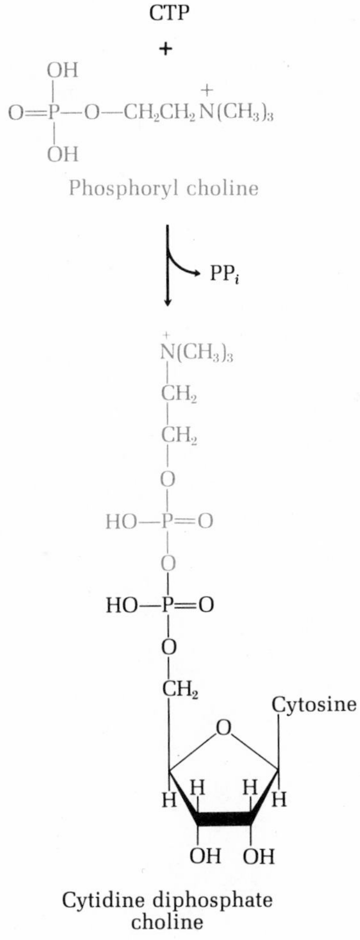

CTP + Phosphoryl choline → (PP_i released) Cytidine diphosphate choline

Other Routes to Phosphatidyl Ethanolamine and Phosphatidyl Choline

There is a second pathway leading to these common phosphoglycerides. It enables those organisms that cannot make choline (Chapter 24) to utilize exogenous choline directly. This direct route also serves as a "salvage" pathway for recovery of free choline resulting from breakdown of phosphatidyl choline, so that it may be reused for phosphoglyceride synthesis. The route also employs CMP as a carrier, but to transfer choline phosphate (margin) rather than phosphatidic acid. The salvage pathway is given by the following reactions:

Choline + ATP → phosphorylcholine + ADP

CTP + phosphorylcholine → cytidine diphosphate choline + PP_i

CDP-choline + 1,2-diacylglycerol → phosphatidyl choline + CMP

Phosphatidyl ethanolamine is formed by similar reactions:

Ethanolamine + ATP → phosphorylethanolamine + ADP

CTP + phosphorylethanolamine → cytidine diphosphate ethanolamine + PP_i

CDP-ethanolamine + 1,2-diacylglycerol → phosphatidyl ethanolamine + CMP

Phosphatidyl ethanolamine and serine are interconvertible by an auxiliary reaction:

Phosphatidyl ethanolamine + serine ⇌
phosphatidyl serine + ethanolamine

Formation of phosphatidal choline. The portion of the product arising from CDP-choline is shown in color.

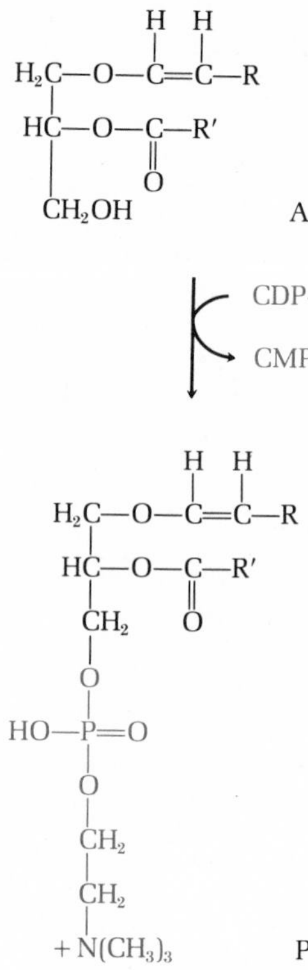

$$\begin{array}{l} \quad\quad\quad\quad H \;\; H \\ H_2C-O-C=C-R \\ HC-O-C(=O)-R' \\ CH_2OH \end{array}$$

Alkenyl glycerol ether

CDP-choline → CMP

$$\begin{array}{l} \quad\quad\quad\quad H \;\; H \\ H_2C-O-C=C-R \\ HC-O-C(=O)-R' \\ CH_2-O-P(=O)(OH)-O-CH_2-CH_2-\overset{+}{N}(CH_3)_3 \end{array}$$

Phosphatidal choline

Plasmalogens

The plasmalogens phosphatidal choline and phosphatidal ethanolamine (Chapter 10) are synthesized by the reaction of CDP-choline and CDP-ethanolamine, respectively, with the monoacyl derivative of an *alkenyl glycerol ether* (see margin), as in the example:

CDP-choline + alkenyl glycerol ether ⇌
phosphatidal choline + CMP

Biosynthesis of Sphingomyelin and Other Sphingolipids

The long-chain aliphatic amines sphingosine and dihydrosphingosine (Chapter 10), which are characteristic building blocks of sphingolipids, are formed from palmitoyl CoA by the following sequences of enzymatic reactions (structures are shown on the opposite page).

Palmitoyl CoA + serine $\xrightarrow[Mn^{2+}]{\text{Pyridoxal phosphate}}$
dihydrosphingosine + CO_2 + CoA

Dihydrosphingosine + flavoprotein →
sphingosine + reduced flavoprotein

In all sphingolipids the amino group of sphingosine is acylated by a long-chain fatty acid; *N*-acylsphingosines are called *ceramides*. They are formed as follows:

Sphingosine + fatty acyl CoA → ceramide + CoA

Sphingomyelin is formed by reaction of ceramide with CDP-choline:

Ceramide + CDP-choline → sphingomyelin + CMP

The formation of a ceramide and of sphingomyelin is shown on the opposite page. The class of sphingolipids known as *cerebrosides*, which are hexose derivatives of ceramides, are formed by a similar reaction of ceramide with UDP-glucose or UDP-galactose.

Ceramide + UDP-glucose → glucocerebroside + UDP

Ceramide + UDP-galactose → galactocerebroside + UDP

The formation of a glucocerebroside is shown on page 528.

The formation of dihydrosphingosine. The portion arising from serine is in color.

R—C(=O)—S—CoA

Palmitoyl CoA

\+

$HOCH_2$—CH(NH_2)—COOH Serine

→ CO_2 + CoA

CH_3—(CH_2)$_{14}$—CH(OH)—CH(NH_2)—CH_2OH

Dihydrosphingosine (Sphinganine)

The formation of a ceramide. The *N*-palmitoyl group arising from palmitoyl CoA is in color.

R—C(=O)—S—CoA

Palmitoyl CoA

\+

Sphingosine

→ CoA

CH_3—(CH_2)$_{12}$—CH=CH—CH(OH)—CH(NH—C(=O)—(CH_2)$_{14}$—CH_3)—CH_2OH

Ceramide (*N*-palmitylsphingosine)

The formation of sphingomyelin. The portion arising from CDP-choline is in color.

CDP-choline

\+

Ceramide

→ CMP

CH_3—(CH_2)$_{12}$—CH=CH—CH(OH)—CH(NH—C(=O)—(CH_2)$_{14}$—CH_3)—CH_2—O—P(=O)(OH)—O—$CH_2CH_2\overset{+}{N}(CH_3)_3$

Sphingomyelin

The cerebrosides may also be made by an alternative pathway, in which the order of substitution of the groups into sphingosine is different. In this pathway, the galactose-substituted sphingosine, called *psychosine*, is formed first; it is then acylated to form the cerebroside:

$$\text{Sphingosine + UDP-galactose} \rightleftharpoons \text{psychosine + UDP}$$

$$\text{Psychosine + palmitoyl CoA} \rightleftharpoons \text{galactocerebroside + CoA}$$

Gangliosides (Chapter 10), which are important lipids in the neuronal membrane, particularly at the synapses, are also formed from psychosine, through further addition of galactose and *N*-acetylneuraminic acid residues, donated in the form of UDP-galactose and cytidine monophosphate *N*-acetylneuraminic acid (Chapter 22). There are many different gangliosides which differ in length and degree of branching of their oligosaccharide polar head groups and the number of terminal *N*-acetylneuraminic acid residues.

The formation of a glucocerebroside. The portion arising from UDP-glucose is in color.

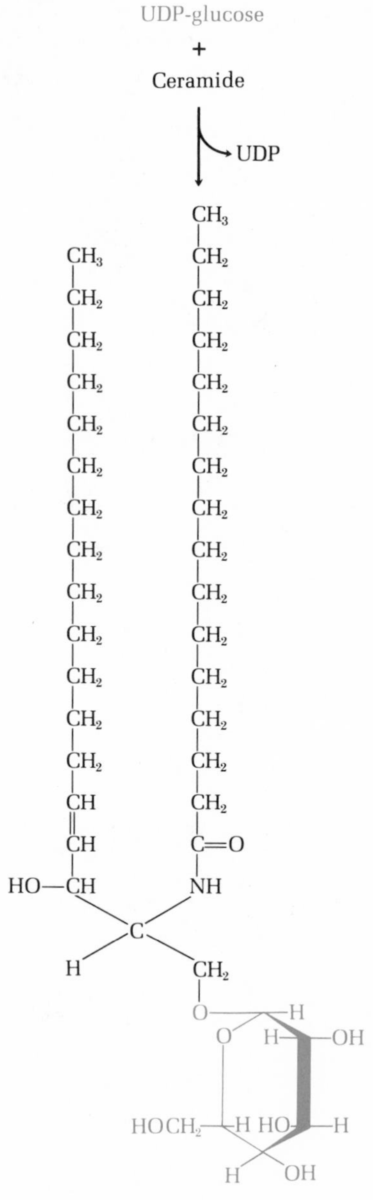

UDP-glucose + Ceramide → UDP

A glucocerebroside

The Pathway of Biosynthesis of Cholesterol

Most of the steps in the enzymatic synthesis of cholesterol are now known in some detail, as a result of the important work of Bloch in the United States, Lynen in Germany, and Popjak and Cornforth in Great Britain. Their interesting analyses of this complex process revealed a number of new metabolic intermediates and greatly illuminated the pattern of biosynthesis of many other complex natural products, particularly the terpenes. The story began in the 1940s when Bloch and his colleagues demonstrated that the carbon atoms of carbon-labeled acetate fed to rats are incorporated into the cholesterol of the liver. Both the steroid nucleus and the eight-carbon side-chain of cholesterol were found to be labeled. Comparison of the results with methyl-labeled and carboxyl-labeled acetate revealed that both carbon atoms of acetic acid are incorporated into cholesterol and in approximately equal amounts. In fact, all the carbon atoms of cholesterol were found to derive from acetate. Systematic degradation of biologically labeled cholesterol revealed the origin of each of its carbon atoms, as shown in Figure 23-6. This labeling pattern then became the guide for the elucidation of the pathway leading from acetate to cholesterol.

An important clue to the nature of this pathway came from the discovery that carbon-labeled acetate is incorporated into the open-chain isoprenoid hydrocarbon <u>squalene,</u> a dihydrotriterpene compound (margin). This hydrocarbon, first found in the liver of sharks, is present in small amounts in the livers of most higher animals. When isotopically labeled squalene (isolated

Figure 23-6
Formation of the carbon skeleton of cholesterol from the methyl (color) *and carboxyl* (black) *carbon atoms of acetic acid.*

Acetic acid → Cholesterol carbon skeleton

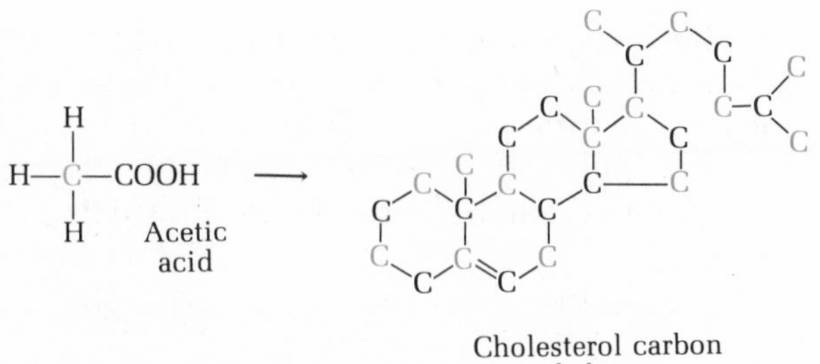

Squalene. The division of the molecule into 6 isoprene units is shown in color.

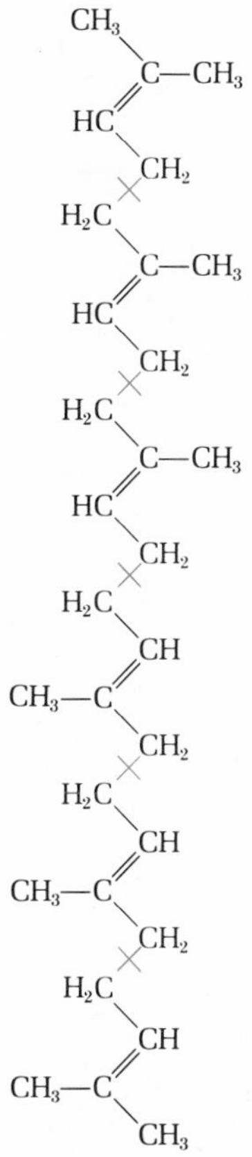

Figure 23-7
Postulated cyclization of squalene to yield cholesterol.

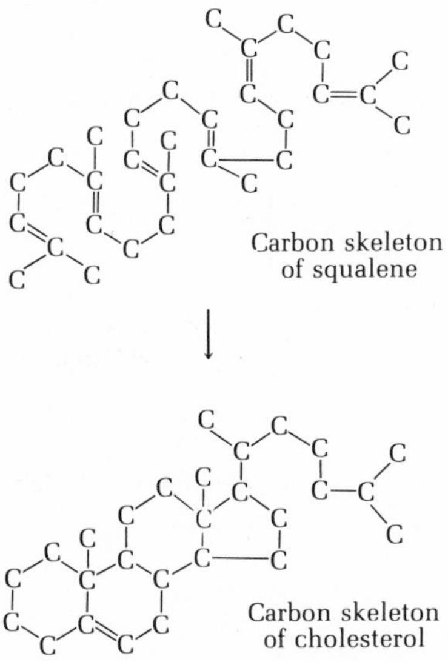

Carbon skeleton of squalene

Carbon skeleton of cholesterol

Mevalonic acid

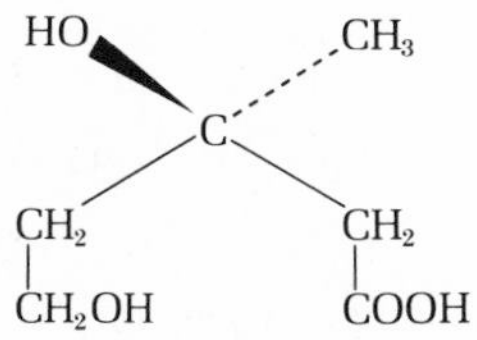

from animals fed radioactive acetate) was incubated with liver slices, much of the isotope was found to be incorporated into cholesterol. This incorporation occurred with such a high yield that it was concluded squalene is a rather direct precursor of cholesterol. These observations therefore strongly suggested that the steroid nucleus of cholesterol, which contains four condensed rings, is formed by cyclization of the open-chain hydrocarbon squalene, according to a scheme modified from that earlier proposed by Robinson and others (Figure 23-7). Moreover, since squalene and other terpenoid compounds (Chapter 10) are built from recurring five-carbon isoprene units, the entire structure of cholesterol can also be visualized as arising from isoprene units.

The mechanism by which isoprenoid units are formed from acetate remained a mystery, however, until the discovery of *mevalonic acid,* a metabolite formed from acetic acid. This compound is a direct precursor of squalene and other isoprenoid compounds and thus of cholesterol. Mevalonic acid was first discovered in an entirely different connection. Certain bacteria require acetate as a growth factor, presumably as a precursor of some essential molecular component of the cell. Detailed study of the nutritional requirements of such bacteria revealed that acetate could be replaced as a growth factor by an unidentified organic acid that was found to be present in many different natural sources, including the liver of mammals. The acetate-replacing growth factor was soon isolated and identified as *mevalonic acid* (margin). It was at once obvious that this six-carbon acid could theoretically give rise to a five-carbon isoprene unit by decarboxylation. Accordingly, isotopically labeled mevalonic acid was incubated with liver slices and found to be incorporated into squalene and also cholesterol with a very high yield. Furthermore, incubation of labeled acetate with liver slices showed that acetate carbon was an immediate precursor of mevalonic acid. These important experiments set the stage for more detailed research on the enzymatic mechanisms by which (1) acetate is converted to mevalonic acid, (2) mevalonic acid is converted into squalene, and (3) squalene is converted into cholesterol.

Enzymatic Steps in Cholesterol Biosynthesis

First we shall consider the steps in the conversion of acetate into mevalonic acid. Mevalonic acid has six carbon atoms; it is formed by condensation of three molecules of acetyl CoA. The key intermediate in this process is β-hydroxy-β-methylglutaryl CoA, which we have earlier (Chapter 19) seen to be an intermediate in the deacylation of acetoacetyl CoA:

$$\text{Acetyl CoA} + \text{acetoacetyl CoA} \rightleftharpoons \beta\text{-hydroxy-}\beta\text{-methylglutaryl CoA} + \text{CoA}$$

Although β-hydroxy-β-methylglutaryl CoA can undergo enzymatic cleavage to form acetoacetate plus acetyl CoA, as we have seen in Chapter 19, it also may undergo reduction of one of its carboxyl groups and loss of CoA by the action of *β-hydroxy-β-methylglutaryl CoA reductase* to yield mevalonic acid:

$$\beta\text{-Hydroxy-}\beta\text{-methylglutaryl CoA} + 2\text{NADPH} + 2\text{H}^+ \rightarrow \text{mevalonic acid} + 2\text{NADP}^+ + \text{CoA}$$

This complex reaction, which is irreversible and takes place in at least two steps, may be an important control point in cholesterol biosynthesis (see below).

There is a second route for formation of mevalonic acid, which is in principle identical to that shown above, but in which acetyl CoA reacts with acetoacetyl-S-ACP to form β-hydroxy-β-methylglutaryl-S-ACP, which is then reduced to mevalonic acid. This pathway takes place in the soluble portion of the cytoplasm.

In the next stage, mevalonic acid is converted into squalene. This sequence of reactions begins with the phosphorylation of mevalonic acid by ATP, first to the 5-monophosphate ester, and then to the 5-pyrophosphate (Figure 23-8). A third phosphorylation, at carbon atom 3, yields a very unstable intermediate which loses phosphoric acid and decarboxylates to form *3-isopentenyl pyrophosphate,* which isomerizes to *3,3′-dimethylallyl pyrophosphate.* These two isomeric isoprenyl pyrophosphates then undergo condensation with elimination of pyrophosphoric acid to form the monoterpene *trans-geranyl pyrophosphate.* A third isoprenyl pyrophosphate

Figure 23-8
The pathway from mevalonic acid to the isomeric isoprenyl pyrophosphates

Mevalonic acid

ATP → ADP

5-Phosphomevalonic acid

ATP → ADP

5-Pyrophosphomevalonic acid

ATP → ADP

3-Phospho-5-pyrophosphomevalonic acid

$-CO_2$, $-P_i$

3-Isopentenyl pyrophosphate

⇌

3,3′-Dimethylallyl pyrophosphate

pyrophospho-

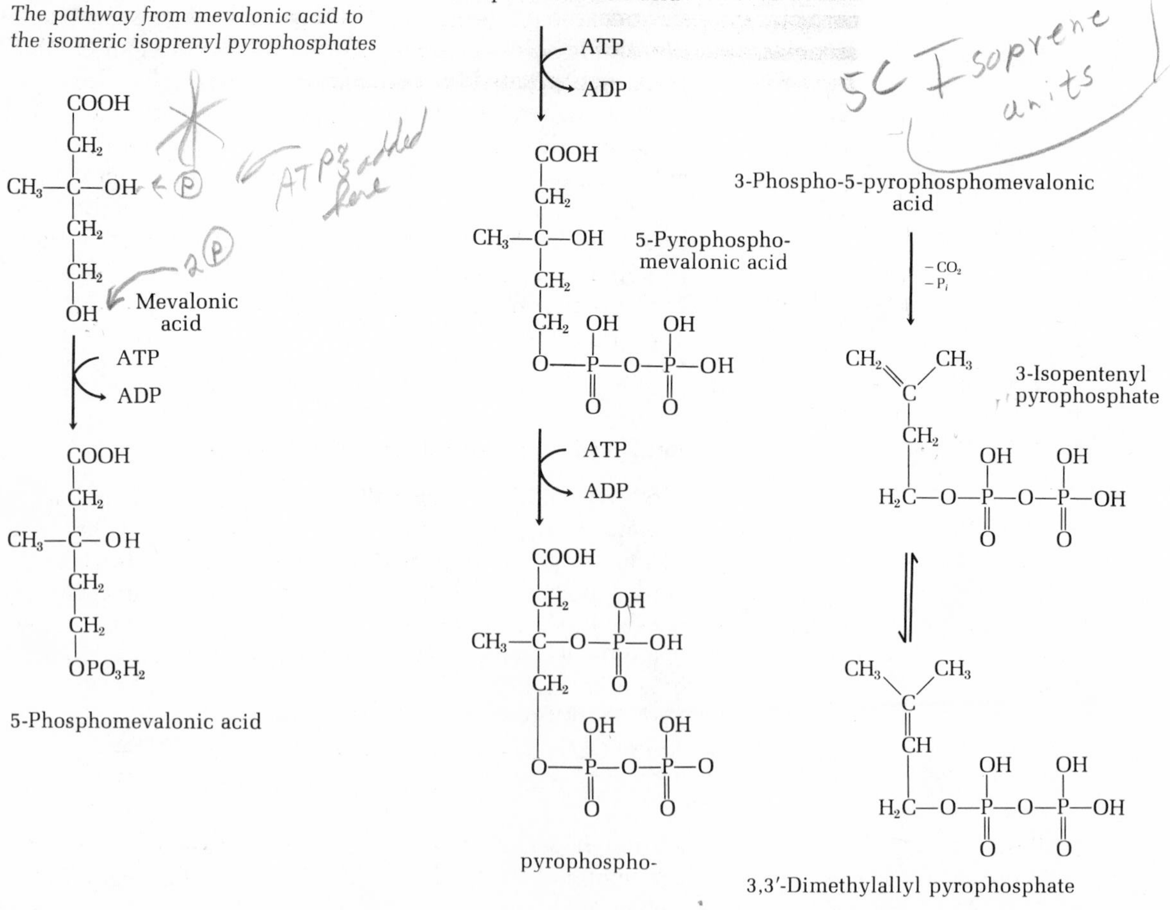

Figure 23-9
The pathway from isopentenyl pyrophosphate to squalene.

Isopentenyl pyrophosphate
+
Dimethylallyl pyrophosphate

↓ $-PP_i$

CH_3, CH_3
C
‖
CH
|
CH_2
|
CH_2 CH_3
C
‖
CH   O   O
| ‖   ‖
CH_2—O—P—O—P—OH
| |
OH   OH

trans-Geranyl pyrophosphate

↓ $-PP_i$ Isopentenyl pyrophosphate

CH_3, CH_3
C
‖
CH
|
CH_2
|
CH_2 CH_3
C
‖
CH
|
CH_2
|
CH_2 CH_3
C
‖
CH   O   O
| ‖   ‖
CH_2—O—P—O—P—OH
| |
OH   OH

trans-Farnesyl pyrophosphate

Farnesyl pyrophosphate
⇅
Nerolidol pyrophosphate

Farnesyl pyrophosphate
+
Nerolidol pyrophosphate
+
NADPH + H⁺
↓
Squalene

then reacts, again with elimination of pyrophosphoric acid, to yield the sesquiterpene derivative *trans-farnesyl pyrophosphate* (Figure 23-9). The latter compound is believed to undergo reductive condensation with its dimethylallyl isomer, namely, *nerolidol pyrophosphate*, to yield squalene (margin).

In the last major stage of cholesterol synthesis, squalene undergoes attack by molecular oxygen to form *squalene 2,3-epoxide*, a reaction catalyzed by a mixed-function oxidase. The squalene 2,3-epoxide then undergoes cyclization to *lanosterol* (Figure 23-10). In this extraordinary reaction, a series of electron shifts brings about closure of the four rings. The process is accompanied by concerted 1:2 methyl group and hydride ion shifts along the squalene chain; the methyl group shifts have been confirmed by appropriate isotopic experiments.

The conversion of lanosterol into cholesterol involves the removal of three methyl groups (at C_4 and C_{14}), saturation of the double bond in the side-chain, and shift of the double bond from the 8,9 to the 5,6 positions in ring B. The enzymatic mechanism of the conversion is not yet known in detail; probably more than one pathway exists.

The sterols of fungi and plants, such as ergosterol and stigmasterol, are synthesized by similar mechanisms which differ only in detail.

Regulation of Cholesterol Biosynthesis

Biosynthesis of cholesterol in the liver is severely depressed by dietary cholesterol, an effect which probably is caused by inhibition of the β-hydroxy-β-methylglutaryl-CoA reductase reaction, through which hydroxymethylglutaryl CoA is reduced to mevalonic acid. However, cholesterol itself appears not to be the inhibitor. It has been variously postulated that a cholesterol-containing lipoprotein, a bile acid, or a specific protein found in bile is the true inhibitor. Fasting also inhibits cholesterol biosynthesis, but high-fat diets accelerate the process.

The transport and deposition of cholesterol in mammals is subject to a number of control mechanisms which are still unknown in detail; defects in these control mechanisms in man lead to pathological abnormalities. Cholesterol is often deposited in the vascular system, a condition known as *atherosclerosis*. The concentration of cholesterol in the blood is abnormally high in the genetic disorders *familial hypercholesterolemia* and *xanthomatosis;* in the latter, lipid deposits rich in cholesterol also form in the skin.

Synthesis of Cholesterol Esters

Most of the cholesterol in the tissues of higher organisms is present in esterified form, in which long-chain fatty acids are in ester linkage with the 3-hydroxyl group. The liver contains an enzyme that forms cholesterol esters in the following reaction:

$$\text{Cholesterol} + \text{fatty acyl CoA} \rightarrow \text{cholesterol ester} + \text{CoA}$$

Figure 23-10
Cyclization of squalene. The migrating methyl groups are shown in color.

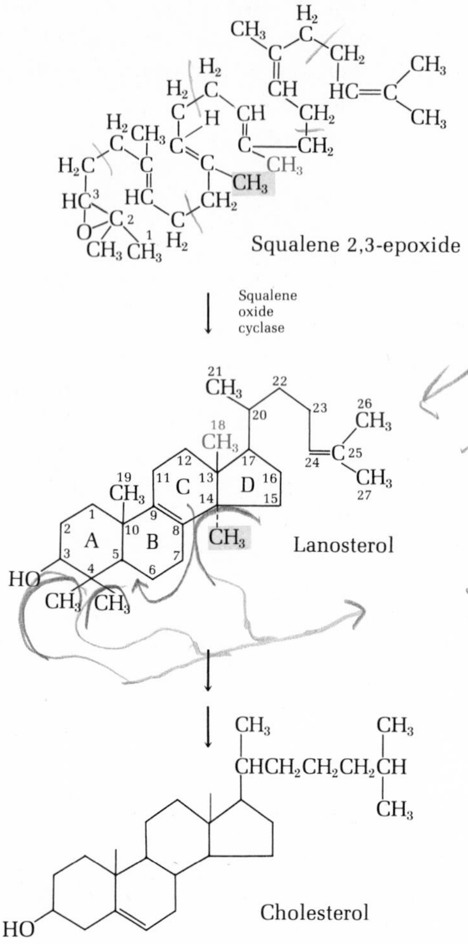

Squalene 2,3-epoxide

Squalene oxide cyclase

Lanosterol

Cholesterol

Another mechanism by which cholesterol esters are formed is by a transesterification between phosphatidyl choline and cholesterol:

Phosphatidyl choline + cholesterol ⇌
lysophosphatidyl choline + cholesterol ester

Formation of Other Steroids

Cholesterol is the precursor of a number of other types of steroids such as fecal sterols, bile acids, and steroid hormones. Cholesterol, coprostanol, and cholestanol (margin) are the major excretory forms of sterols in mammals; cholestanol and coprostanol, which are isomers, are formed from cholesterol by microbial action.

The major pathway of degradation of cholesterol in animals is conversion to the bile acids, a process that occurs in the liver. There are many different bile acids which vary characteristically with the species. They contain a shortened side-chain with a carboxyl group, which is often conjugated with glycine or taurine. These compounds are secreted into the small intestine and are largely reabsorbed during lipid absorption. The circulation of the bile acids, which promote absorption of the lipids, is called the *enterohepatic circulation.* The major

Coprostanol

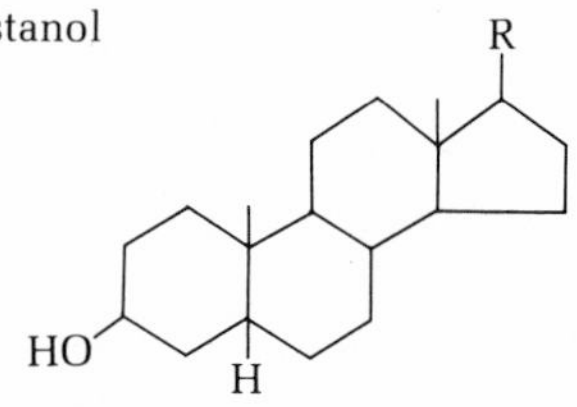

Cholestanol

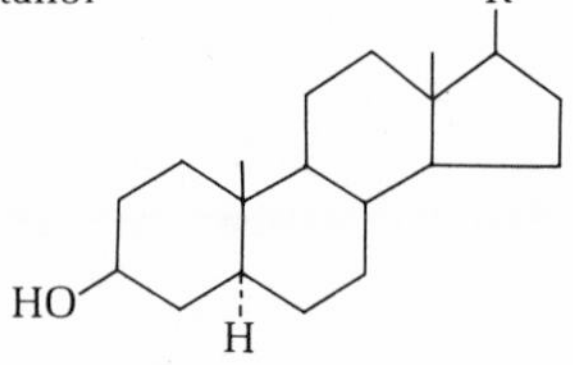

(R designates the normal side-chain of cholesterol)

Figure 23-11
Formation of bile acids.

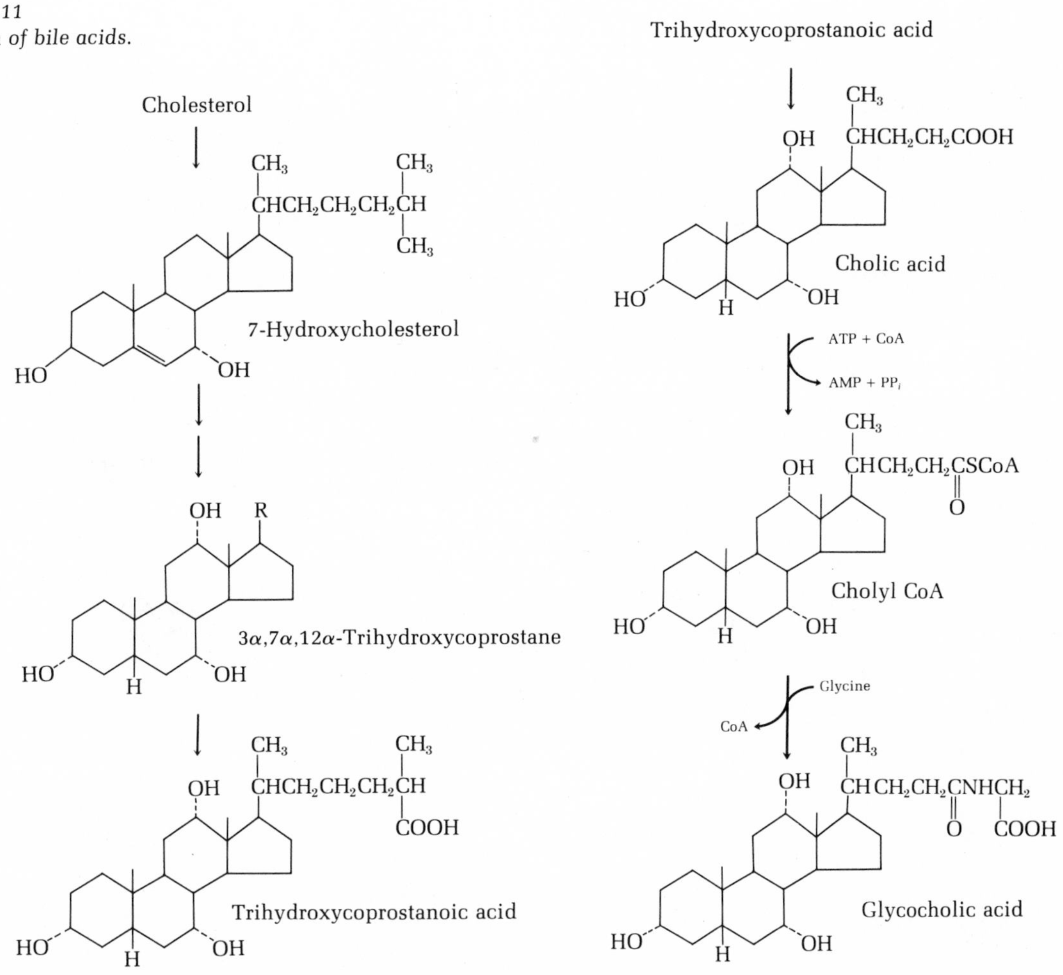

steps in the formation of cholic acid and its conjugation products glycocholic and taurocholic acids are shown in Figure 23-11.

The formation of steroid hormones from cholesterol occurs through intermediary formation of pregnenolone (below), which contains the cholesterol nucleus, but has only a two-carbon side-chain. Pregnenolone is the precursor of progesterone, the progestational hormone of

Formation of some steroid hormones

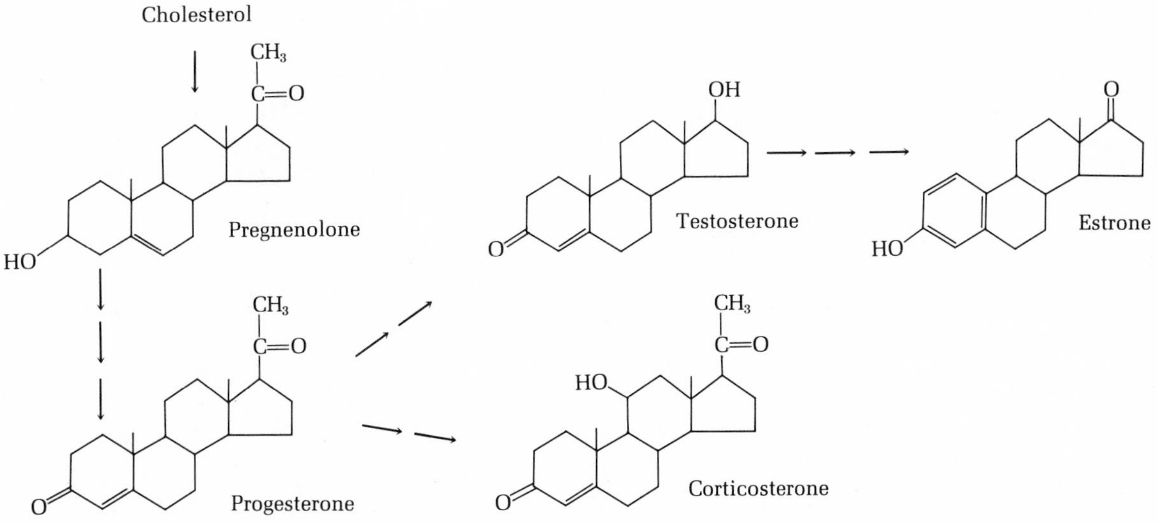

the placenta and corpus luteus, of androgens or male sex hormones such as *testosterone,* of the estrogens or female sex hormones such as *estrone,* and of the adrenal corticosteroids such as *corticosterone.*

The Central Role of Acetic Acid as a Biosynthetic Precursor

Acetic acid, in the form of acetyl CoA, is a precursor not only of fatty acids and steroids, but also of many other naturally occurring compounds, particularly the terpenes and acetogenins. *Terpenes* may be broadly defined as naturally occurring substances which are built of recurring isoprene units. They occur in two major classes, linear and cyclic, and also in subclasses, depending on the number of isoprene units. *Acetogenins* are broadly defined as substances built of recurring two-carbon units, in which one of the two carbon atoms, that corresponding to the carboxyl carbon of acetic acid, is frequently oxidized. Terpenes and acetogenins exist in large variety in the plant world. The important role of acetic acid in the biogenesis of terpenes and acetogenins is summarized in Figure 23-12. Examples of a terpene and an acetogenin are shown in the margin.

Limonene, a cyclic terpene containing two isoprene units connected by bonds with colored bars.

Formation of phloroacetophenone, a cyclic acetogenin

Figure 23-12
Acetyl CoA as precursor of terpenes and acetogenins.

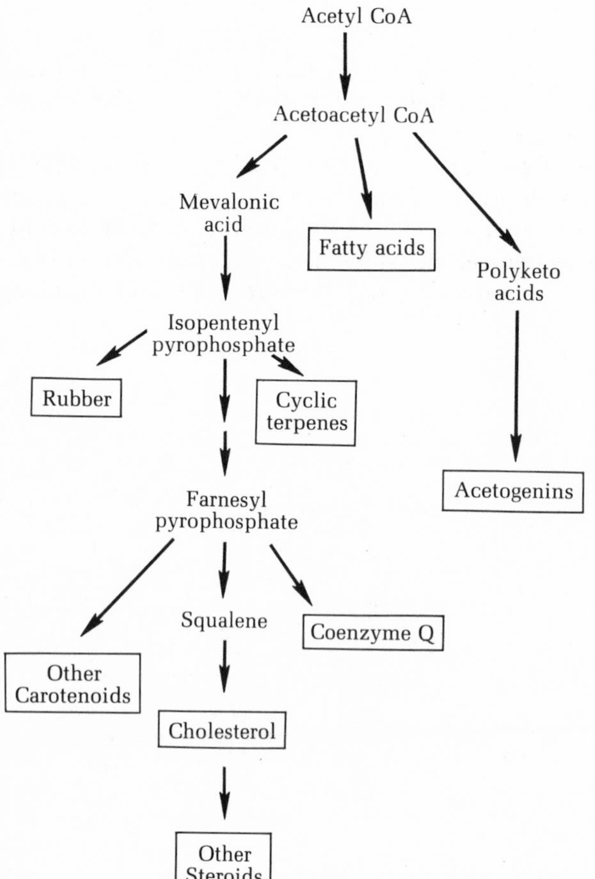

Integration of Lipid and Carbohydrate Metabolism in Mammals

We may now assemble some metabolic relationships discussed earlier (Chapters 16, 19, 20, and 22) into a more unified picture. Figure 23-13 shows the various pathways of formation and utilization of acetyl CoA. The major sources of acetyl CoA are carbohydrate, fatty acid and amino acid. The major pathways of utilization of acetyl CoA are (1) oxidation via the tricarboxylic acid cycle, (2) fatty acid synthesis via malonyl CoA, and (3) conversion to hydroxymethyl glutaryl CoA (HMG CoA), which in turn leads to the ketone bodies and to cholesterol.

In insulin deficiency or in fasting, utilization of acetyl CoA by the tricarboxylic acid cycle is depressed, as is the synthesis of fatty acids, the result of the tendency of the insulin-deficient animal to convert all its metabolically available resources into blood glucose (Chapter 22). Under these conditions, acetyl CoA tends to be shunted into the formation of HMG CoA, leading to increased formation of ketone bodies and cholesterol. However, the amount of acetyl CoA that can be shunted into cholesterol formation is very limited, so the great bulk of the HMG CoA is converted into the ketone bodies, acetoacetic and β-hydroxybutyric acids, whose concentration in the blood and urine may become very high in diabetes mellitus or depancreatized animals. Thus, insulin deficiency causes profound alterations in a complex network of metabolic interrelationships, in which acetyl CoA and hydroxymethyl glutaryl CoA constitute important switching-points.

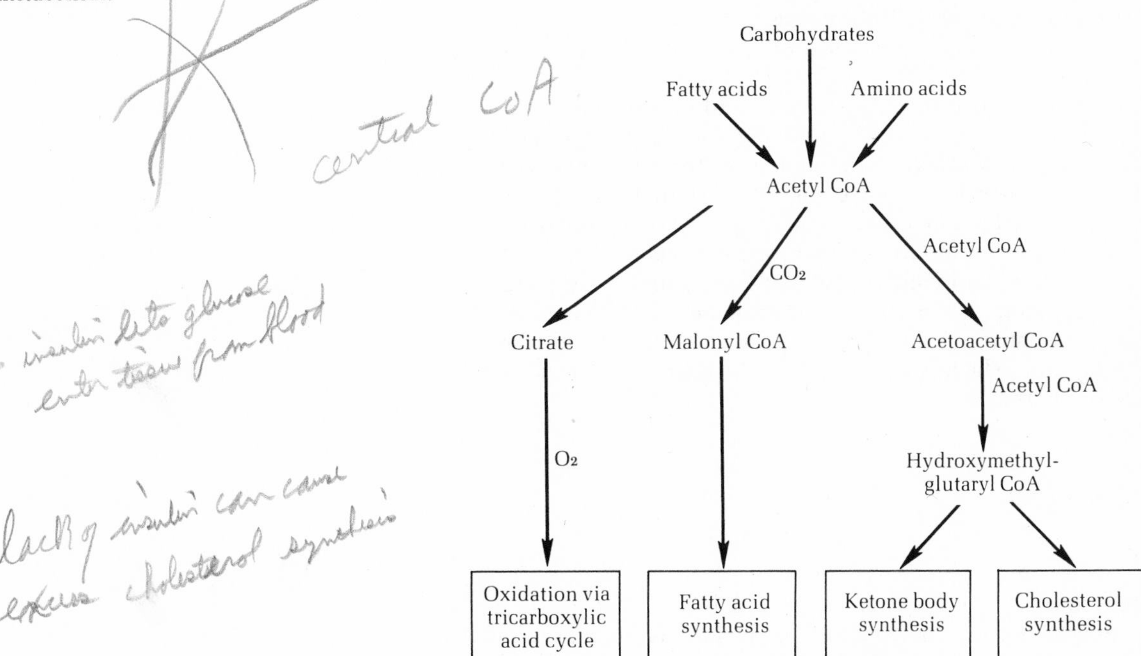

Figure 23-13
Importance of Acetyl CoA and hydroxymethylglutaryl CoA in the integration of metabolism.

Summary

Long-chain saturated fatty acids are synthesized by a cytoplasmic complex of enzymes which employs a specific –SH protein, acyl carrier protein (ACP), as an acyl group carrier, instead of CoA. Acetyl-S-ACP reacts with malonyl-S-ACP to yield acetoacetyl-S-ACP and free CO_2. Reduction to the β-hydroxy derivative and its dehydration to the $\Delta^{2,3}$-unsaturated compound is followed by reduction to butyryl-S-ACP at the expense of NADPH. Six more molecules of malonyl-S-ACP react successively at the carboxyl end of the growing chain to form palmityl-S-ACP, the usual end product. Palmitic acid may be elongated by reaction with acetyl CoA in mitochondria or with malonyl CoA in microsomes. Palmitoleic and oleic acids are formed from palmitic and oleic acids, respectively, by action of mixed-function oxygenases, which require NADPH as co-reductant. Polyenoic acids are formed from oleic and palmitoleic acids by further action of desaturating oxygenases. Linoleic and linolenic acids are readily formed by plants, but not by mammals, which require them in the diet. Other polyenoic acids can be formed from the essential fatty acids.

Triacylglycerols are formed in a sequence of reactions in which two molecules of fatty acyl CoA react with glycerol 3-phosphate to form phosphatidic acid, which is dephosphorylated and then acylated by a third molecule of fatty acyl CoA. Phosphatidic acid is also the major precursor of phosphoglycerides. It reacts with CTP to form cytidine diphosphate diacylglycerol. The latter reacts with serine, inositol, or glycerol phosphate to form, respectively, phosphatidyl serine, phosphatidyl inositol, and 3-phosphatidyl glycerol 1′-phosphate, which is the precursor of phosphatidyl glycerol and of cardiolipin. Phosphatidyl serine is decarboxylated to phosphatidyl ethanolamine, which is directly methylated to phosphatidyl choline at the expense of S-adenosylmethionine.

Sphingosine, the characteristic base of sphingolipids, is formed by reduction of palmitoyl CoA to palmitaldehyde and condensation of the latter with serine and oxidation by a flavoprotein. Sphingosine is acylated by long-chain fatty acyl CoA esters to yield ceramide, a direct precursor of sphingomyelin. Cerebrosides are also formed from ceramide by their reaction with UDP-glucose or UDP-galactose, or by an alternative pathway starting from a hexose-substituted sphingosine, namely, psychosine.

Cholesterol is formed from acetic acid in three major stages. In the first, mevalonic acid is formed via β-hydroxy β-methylglutaryl CoA. Mevalonic acid undergoes three phosphorylation steps, decarboxylation, and dephosphorylation to yield isomeric 3-isopentenyl pyrophosphate and dimethylallyl pyrophosphate, which condense to form geranyl pyrophosphate, which in turn leads to farnesyl pyrophosphate. The latter undergoes a similar condensation with its isomer to yield squalene. Squalene undergoes oxidative cyclization to yield lanosterol and finally cholesterol, which is a precursor of bile acids, fecal sterols, and steroid hormones.

References

Books

DAWSON, R. M. C., and D. W. RHODES (eds.): *Metabolism and Physiological Significance of Lipids*, John Wiley & Sons, Inc., New York, 1964. Authoritative and comprehensive monograph.

DORFMAN, R. I., and F. UNGAR: *Metabolism of Sex Hormones*, Academic Press, Inc., New York, 1965. Comprehensive treatise.

GREENBERG, D. M. (ed.): *Metabolic Pathways*, vol. II, Academic Press, Inc., New York, 1968. Contains a number of important up-to-date reviews of fatty acid and lipid synthesis.

HASLEWOOD, G. A. D.: *Bile Salts*, Methuen, London, 1967. The evolution and comparative biochemistry of bile salts, reviewed in brief, readable form.

MASORO, E. J.: *Physiological Chemistry of Lipids in Mammals*, Saunders, Philadelphia, 1968. A short textbook and review.

RICHARDS, J. H., and J. B. HENDRICKSON: *Biosynthesis of Steroids, Terpenes, and Acetogenins*, W. A. Benjamin, Inc., New York, 1964. The organic approach to problems of biosynthesis.

Articles

BLOCH, K.: "The Biological Synthesis of Cholesterol," *Science*, **150**:19–28 (1965). Nobel award address, which recapitulates the history and experimental narrative.

______: "Enzymatic Synthesis of Monounsaturated Fatty Acids," *Accounts of Chemical Research*, **2**:193–202 (1962).

GOLDFINE, H.: "Lipid Chemistry and Metabolism," *Ann. Rev. Biochem.*, **37**:303–330 (1968). Recent literature review.

KENNEDY, E. P.: "The Metabolism and Function of Complex Lipids," *Harvey Lectures*, **57**:143–171 (1962). Short review of early research.

LOWENSTEIN, J. M.: "Citrate and The Conversion of Carbohydrate into Fat," in T. W. Goodwin (ed.), *Metabolic Roles of Citrate*, p. 61, Academic Press, Inc., New York, 1968. An excellent and clearly organized review.

LYNEN, F.: "The Role of Biotin-dependent Carboxylations in Biosynthetic Reactions," *Biochem. J.*, **102**:381–400 (1967). Also includes discussion of the yeast fatty acid synthetase complex.

VAGELOS, P. R., P. W. MAJERUS, A. W. ALBERTS, A. R. LARRABEE, and G. P. AIHAUD: "Structure and Function of Acyl Carrier Protein," *Federation Proc.*, **25**:1485–1494 (1966). A review.

WILLETT, J. D., K. B. SHARPLESS, K. E. LORD, E. E. VANTAMELIN, and R. B. CLAYTON: "Squalene 2,3-oxide, An Intermediate in The Enzymatic Conversion of Squalene to Lanosterol and Cholesterol," *J. Biol. Chem.*, **242**:4182–4191 (1967). Experimental paper.

Problems

1. Write a balanced equation for the biosynthesis of stearic acid starting from acetyl CoA, NADPH, and ATP.
2. Write a balanced equation for the biosynthesis of palmitoleic acid starting from acetyl CoA, NADPH, and ATP.
3. Write a balanced equation for the biosynthesis of stearic acid starting from lauric acid and NADPH, as it occurs in microsomes.
4. Write a balanced equation for the biosynthesis of tripalmitin in an aerobic liver cell starting from glucose. Include changes in the ATP system.

5. How many high-energy phosphate bonds are required for the synthesis of a molecule of dipalmityl phosphatidyl serine starting from palmitic acid, glucose, and serine?

6. How many high-energy phosphate bonds are required in the biosynthesis of one molecule of dipalmityl phosphatidyl choline starting from palmitic acid, serine, glycerol, and methionine (see Chapter 24)?

7. Write a balanced equation for the synthesis of cholesterol from free acetic acid. How many high-energy phosphate bonds are required per molecule of cholesterol formed?

8. Contrast the number of high-energy phosphate bonds required per carbon atom for an albino rat to store the carbon of ingested D-glucose as glycogen and as the palmityl groups of tripalmitylglycerol, respectively.

CHAPTER 24 THE BIOSYNTHESIS OF AMINO ACIDS; NITROGEN FIXATION

The biosynthesis of amino acids from simpler precursors, although not as massive a process in the biosphere as the biosynthesis of carbohydrates, is vital for all forms of life, for amino acids are the precursors of proteins. However, living organisms differ considerably with respect to their ability to synthesize amino acids and with respect to the forms of nitrogen which they can utilize for this purpose. Higher vertebrates are not able to synthesize all the common amino acids; for example, the albino rat can make only ten of the twenty amino acids required as building blocks in protein synthesis. The remainder, which are called *essential amino acids,* must be obtained from exogenous sources. Higher animals may utilize ammonia as nitrogen source for the synthesis of the nonessential amino acids, but they are unable to use nitrite, nitrate, or N_2. Ruminants can utilize nitrite and nitrate, but only after reduction to ammonia by rumen bacteria.

Higher plants are more versatile; they can make all of the amino acids required for protein synthesis, starting from either ammonia or nitrate as the nitrogen source. They may use ammonia as such or after its oxidation to nitrate by soil bacteria. The leguminous plants, which harbor symbiotic bacteria in their root nodules, are able to fix molecular nitrogen from the atmosphere as ammonia, which is then used for amino acid synthesis.

Microorganisms differ widely in their capacity to synthesize amino acids. For example, *Leuconostoc mesenteroides* cannot grow unless it is supplied with a total of sixteen different amino acids. Such bacteria can survive only in environments rich in preformed amino acids from decaying biological matter. Other bacteria, such as *E. coli,* can manufacture all their amino acids starting from ammonia. Although most microorganisms require a reduced form of nitrogen, such as ammonia, numerous bacteria and fungi, like the higher plants, can utilize nitrite or nitrate.

The twenty different amino acids are synthesized by twenty different multienzyme sequences, some of which are exceedingly complex. As in the case of most biosynthetic routes, the pathways of amino acid synthesis are for the most part different from those employed in their degradation (Chapter 20). The great complexity of the interconnecting pathways of amino acid synthesis and degradation may at first be discouraging to contemplate; however, some exceedingly interesting biochemical relationships are involved in this area of intermediary metabolism. For one thing, the amino acids serve not only as building blocks in protein synthesis but also as precursors of many different biomolecules having a wide variety of specialized functions. Frequently the pathways of synthesis and degradation of amino acids include branches or extensions leading to the formation of such specialized products.

We have seen that biologically available forms of nitrogen are relatively scarce in the nonliving environment (Chapter 1), because fixation of molecular nitrogen of the atmosphere is a process limited to only a few organisms. For this reason, most living organisms tend to practice stringent economy in their metabolic use of reduced forms of nitrogen. We shall encounter instances in which amino groups or nitrogenous intermediates are "salvaged" and reutilized for amino acid synthesis. We shall also see that the biosynthesis of most of the amino acids is under constant regulation and feedback control, through the action of regulatory enzymes. Moreover, the synthesis of the enzymes catalyzing the formation of the amino acids is also under control; their synthesis may be repressed if the cell is amply supplied with amino acids from exogenous sources. Both forms of regulation are reflections of an intrinsic cellular economy in the synthesis and use of amino acids.

Biosynthesis of the Nonessential Amino Acids

For present purposes, the nonessential amino acids are defined as those which can be synthesized by the albino rat. It is convenient to consider this group of amino acids first because most organisms can bring about their synthesis. Moreover, this group of amino acids is distinctive in that they have relatively short biosynthetic pathways, with relatively little variation from species to species.

Glutamic acid, Glutamine, and Proline

The biosynthetic pathways for these closely related amino acids appear to be identical in all forms of life. All three are degraded by pathways leading to α-ketoglutarate and the same pathways are utilized in their synthesis. Glutamic acid is of course formed from ammonia and α-ketoglutaric acid by the action of L-glutamate dehydrogenase

$$NH_3 + \alpha\text{-ketoglutaric acid} + NADPH + H^+ \rightleftharpoons \text{L-glutamic acid} + NADP^+$$

This reaction is of fundamental importance in the biosynthesis of all amino acids in all species, since it is the primary if not the only significant pathway for the formation of α-amino groups directly from ammonia. Transamination of α-keto acids with glutamic acid as amino

γ-Glutamyl phosphoric acid

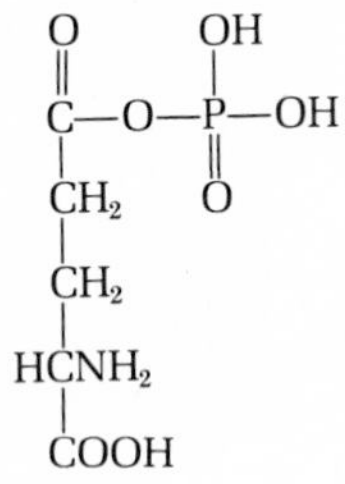

group donor (Chapter 20) represents the major pathway for the introduction of α-amino groups in the biosynthesis of most other amino acids.

Glutamine is formed from glutamic acid by the action of *glutamine synthetase,* which has been discussed earlier (Chapter 20):

$$NH_3 + \text{glutamic acid} + ATP \rightleftharpoons \text{glutamine} + ADP + P_i$$

This reaction is rather complex and involves two or more intermediate steps. It has been shown that *γ-glutamyl phosphate* (margin) functions as an enzyme-bound high-energy intermediate:

$$ATP + \text{glutamic acid} \rightleftharpoons ADP + [\gamma\text{-glutamyl phosphate}]$$

$$[\gamma\text{-Glutamyl phosphate}] + NH_3 \rightleftharpoons \text{glutamine} + P_i$$

The substrate specificity, kinetics, inhibition, and mechanism of action of glutamine synthetase have been studied in great detail. In particular, extensive substrate-specificity studies have permitted "mapping" of the active site of the enzyme, which has been shown to bind the extended conformation of the glutamic acid molecule at three sites, namely, at the two carboxyl groups and the amino group. This conclusion has been shown to account for the curious fact that the enzyme will accept either the D or the L stereoisomer of glutamic acid as substrate.

Glutamine synthetase is a structurally complex enzyme of mol wt 500,000 to 600,000, depending on the species. In some species, such as *E. coli*, glutamine synthetase is a regulatory enzyme of central importance, because glutamine is a major precursor in the synthesis of a number of important biomolecules. The allosteric regulation of glutamine synthetase activity will be considered below.

Proline is synthesized from glutamic acid by reversal of the pathway earlier described (Chapter 20) for the oxidation of proline; this pathway is shown in Figure 24-1. Hydroxyproline residues, which are found in collagen and a few other fibrous proteins, are formed from certain proline residues in these proteins by the action of *proline hydroxylase.* This mixed-function oxygenase (Chapter 23) utilizes α-ketoglutarate as coreductant and oxygen as electron acceptor. Fe^{3+} and ascorbic acid are required in the reaction as cofactors. Proline hydroxylase will not, however, convert free proline to hydroxyproline.

Figure 24-1
Biosynthesis of proline. All five carbon atoms arise from glutamic acid. The end product proline is an allosteric inhibitor at the point shown. In this and all other biosynthetic sequences shown in this chapter, the feed-back inhibitory mechanism is shown by colored arrows and the point of inhibition by a colored bar.

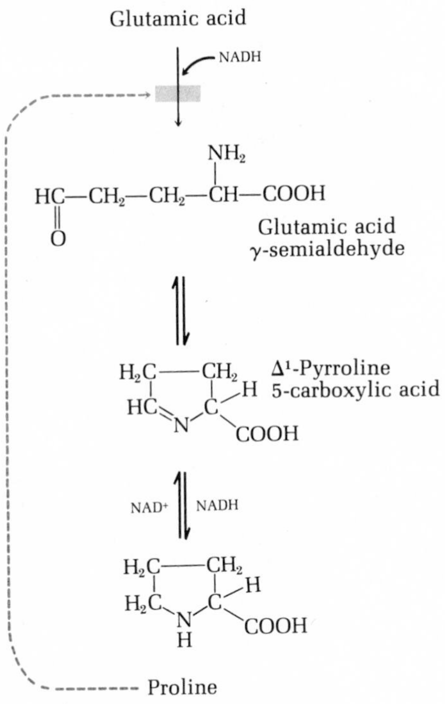

Glutamic acid

NADH

Glutamic acid γ-semialdehyde

Δ¹-Pyrroline 5-carboxylic acid

NAD⁺ NADH

Proline

Alanine, Aspartic Acid and Asparagine

In most organisms alanine and aspartic acid arise by transamination to pyruvic acid and oxaloacetic acid, respectively:

$$\text{Glutamic acid} + \text{pyruvic acid} \rightleftharpoons \alpha\text{-ketoglutaric acid} + \text{alanine}$$

$$\text{Glutamic acid} + \text{oxaloacetic acid} \rightleftharpoons \alpha\text{-ketoglutaric acid} + \text{aspartic acid}$$

In some plants, however, they are formed by reductive amination.

Aspartic acid is the direct precursor of asparagine. In most organisms asparagine is formed in a reaction similar to that catalyzed by glutamine synthetase:

$$NH_3 + \text{aspartic acid} + ATP \rightarrow \text{asparagine} + ADP + P_i$$

In other organisms an alternative pathway may occur, in which the amide amino group of glutamine is transferred to aspartic acid:

$$\text{Glutamine} + \text{aspartic acid} \rightleftharpoons \text{glutamic acid} + \text{asparagine}$$

Tyrosine

Although tyrosine is a nonessential amino acid, its synthesis requires the essential amino acid phenylalanine as precursor. Tyrosine is formed from phenylalanine by a hydroxylation reaction catalyzed by *phenylalanine hydroxylase,* which we have seen (Chapter 20) participates in the degradation of phenylalanine. This mixed-function oxygenase requires NADPH as coreductant and dihydrobiopterin (Chapter 20) as cofactor. The overall reaction is

$$\text{Phenylalanine} + NADPH + H^+ + O_2 \rightarrow \text{tyrosine} + NADP^+ + H_2O$$

The biosynthesis of phenylalanine will be considered later.

Cysteine

Cysteine is not an essential amino acid, but it arises in mammals from methionine, which is essential, and serine which is not. Three major stages are involved in its synthesis (Figure 24-2). In the first, methionine loses the methyl group from its sulfur atom to become homocysteine. This reaction, which takes place in three or more steps, requires ATP to convert methionine into an activated form, *S-adenosylmethionine* (Figure 24-2):

$$\text{L-Methionine} + ATP \rightarrow \text{S-adenosylmethionine} + PP_i + P_i$$

The methyl sulfonium linkage of S-adenosylmethionine has high-energy characteristics. Its methyl group is readily donated to a number of different methyl group acceptors in the presence of the appropriate enzyme, leaving *S-adenosylhomocysteine* as the demethylated product. We have seen, for example (Chapter 23), that S-adenosylmethionine is the methyl group donor in the conversion of phosphatidyl ethanolamine to phosphatidyl choline.

S-adenosylhomocysteine then undergoes hydrolysis to free *homocysteine:*

$$\text{S-Adenosylhomocysteine} \xrightarrow{H_2O} \text{homocysteine} + \text{adenosine}$$

In the second stage of cysteine synthesis, homocysteine reacts with serine in a reaction catalyzed by *cystathionine synthetase* to yield *cystathionine* (Figure 24-2).

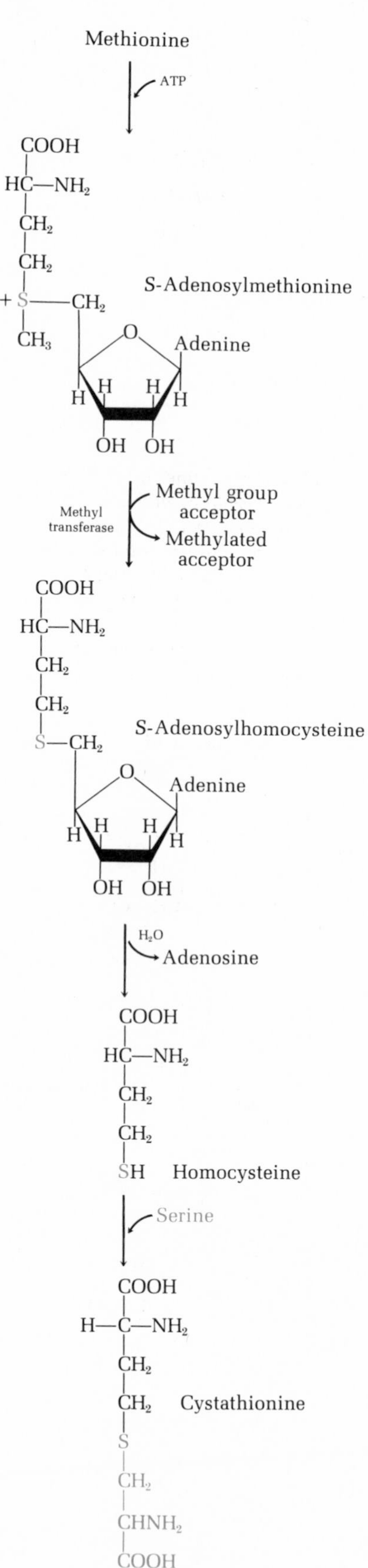

Figure 24-2
The pathway from methionine to cysteine.

Figure 24-2 (cont.)

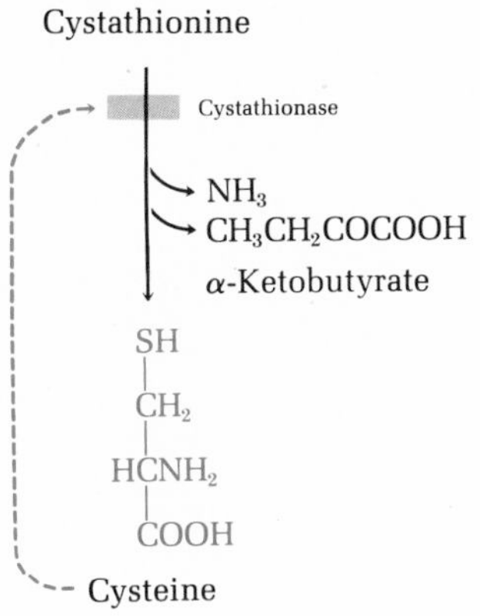

Cystathionine → (Cystathionase) → NH_3, $CH_3CH_2COCOOH$ (α-Ketobutyrate) → $HS{-}CH_2{-}CH(NH_2){-}COOH$ Cysteine

$$\text{Homocysteine} + \text{serine} \rightarrow \text{cystathionine} + H_2O$$

In the last step, *cystathionase,* a pyridoxal phosphate enzyme, catalyzes the cleavage of cystathionine to yield free cysteine

$$\text{Cystathionine} \rightarrow \alpha\text{-ketobutyrate} + NH_3 + \text{cysteine}$$

The overall equation of cysteine synthesis is thus

$$\text{L-Methionine} + \text{ATP} + \text{methyl acceptor} + H_2O + \text{serine} \rightarrow \text{methylated acceptor} + \text{adenosine} + \alpha\text{-ketobutyrate} + NH_3 + \text{cysteine} + PP_i + P_i$$

The final result of this reaction is to bring about replacement of the —OH group of serine with an —SH group. Note that the carbon chain of cysteine comes from serine, but the sulfur atom comes from methionine (Figure 24-2).

In some microorganisms a somewhat different pathway is taken:

$$\text{Serine} + \text{acetyl CoA} \rightarrow O\text{-acetylserine} + \text{CoA}$$

$$O\text{-Acetylserine} + H_2S \rightarrow \text{cysteine} + \text{acetic acid} + H_2O$$

Serine and Glycine

Figure 24-3
Biosynthesis of serine.

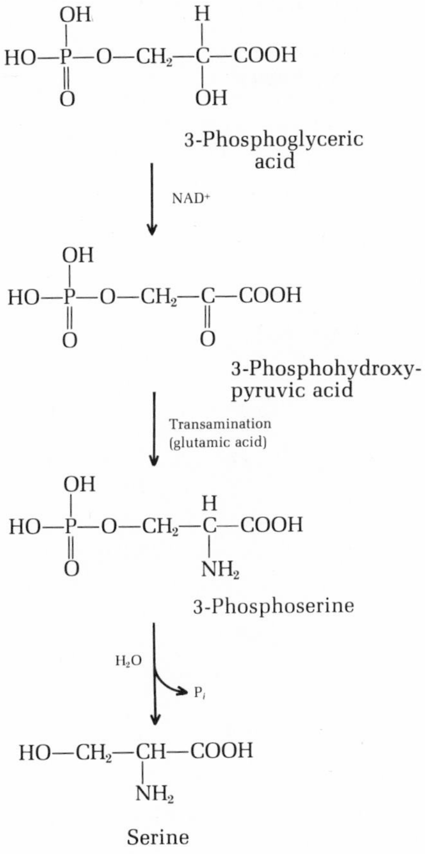

$HO{-}P(O)(OH){-}O{-}CH_2{-}CH(OH){-}COOH$ 3-Phosphoglyceric acid
↓ NAD^+
$HO{-}P(O)(OH){-}O{-}CH_2{-}C(O){-}COOH$ 3-Phosphohydroxypyruvic acid
↓ Transamination (glutamic acid)
$HO{-}P(O)(OH){-}O{-}CH_2{-}CH(NH_2){-}COOH$ 3-Phosphoserine
↓ H_2O → P_i
$HO{-}CH_2{-}CH(NH_2){-}COOH$ Serine

Since serine is the precursor of glycine, these two amino acids are considered together. The major pathway for the formation of serine in animal tissues, shown in Figure 24-3, begins with 3-phosphoglyceric acid, an intermediate of glycolysis. In the first step the α-hydroxyl group is oxidized by NAD^+ to yield *3-phosphohydroxypyruvic acid.* Transamination from glutamic acid yields *3-phosphoserine,* which undergoes hydrolysis by serine phosphatase to yield free serine.

The mechanism of synthesis of glycine was a puzzling problem for a long time. That serine is the precursor of glycine was first discovered in an experiment in which serine labeled with ^{15}N in the amino group and ^{13}C in the carboxyl group was administered to rats. The animals formed glycine having the same ^{15}N:^{13}C ratio as the administered serine, thus showing that the β-carbon atom must have been detached from the serine that was fed. However, the chemical identity of the one-carbon fragment so removed was not ascertained for some years. The problem was finally solved when the mode of action of the vitamin *folic acid* was elucidated.

Folic Acid and Its Role in 1-Carbon Transfer

Folic acid (Latin, *folium,* leaf) is a broadly distributed vitamin, first found in spinach leaves, whose deficiency in mammals results in failure to grow and in various forms of anemia. It contains three characteristic building blocks (1) a substituted pterin, (2) *p*-aminobenzoic acid, and (3) glutamic acid; it is also known as *pteroylglutamic acid* (Figure 24-4). The pterins are widely distributed in nature.

Figure 24-4
Structure of folic acid and tetrahydrofolic acid. The four hydrogen atoms added to form tetrahydrofolic acid are shown in color. The N^5 and N^{10} nitrogen atoms participate in the transfer of one-carbon groups.

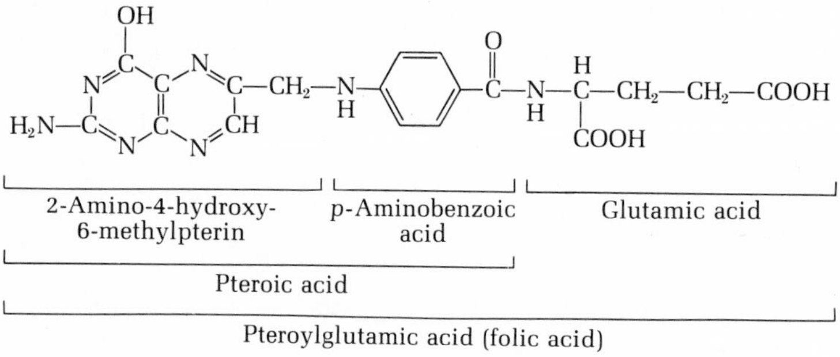

2-Amino-4-hydroxy-6-methylpterin | p-Aminobenzoic acid | Glutamic acid

Pteroic acid

Pteroylglutamic acid (folic acid)

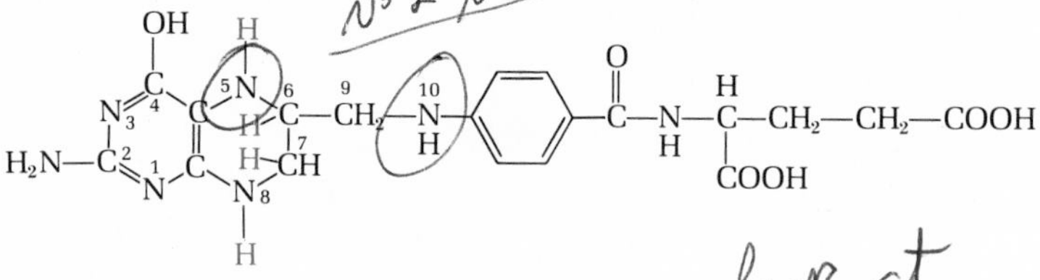

Tetrahydrofolic acid

Some, such as *xanthopterin* (margin), serve as eye and wing pigments in insects.

Some organisms do not require the entire folic acid molecule for growth, but only the *p*-aminobenzoic acid portion; they can synthesize folic acid if *p*-aminobenzoic acid is available. The most conspicuous biochemical symptom of folic acid deficiency is the inability to synthesize purines and the pyrimidine thymine. In some folic acid–requiring microorganisms, such as *S. faecalis*, the nutritional requirement for folic acid can be met by thymine and adenine. However, more detailed investigation has revealed that folic acid and its derivatives have a more generalized function which is concerned with the transfer of one-carbon compounds. Folic acid itself has no coenzyme activity, but it is converted by reduction into its active coenzyme form *tetrahydrofolic acid* (Figure 24-4). The terminal step in this process is the reduction of *dihydrofolic acid* (Figure 24-5), which is catalyzed by *dihydrofolic acid reductase*.

Xanthopterin

(2-amino-4,6-dihydroxy pteridine)

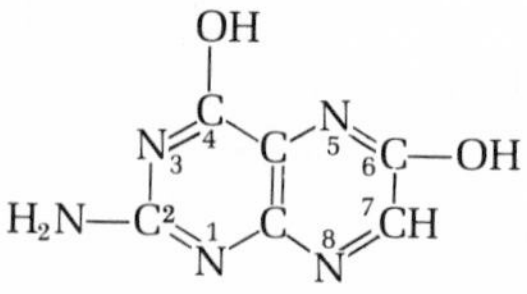

$$\text{NADPH} + \text{H}^+ + \text{dihydrofolic acid} \longrightarrow \text{NADP}^+ + \text{tetrahydrofolic acid}$$

This enzyme is particularly noteworthy in that it is very strongly and specifically inhibited, in a competitive manner, by certain structural analogs of its substrate, notably the synthetic compounds *aminopterin* and *amethopterin* (Figure 24-5). The affinity of the enzyme for these analogs is so high that they are not readily displaced by intracellular concentrations of the normal

Figure 24-5
Inhibitors (in color) of dihydrofolic acid reductase. Glu *symbolizes the glutamic acid residue.*

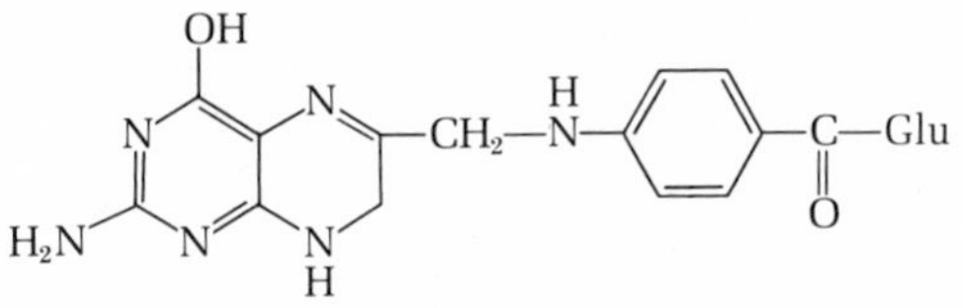

Dihydrofolic acid
(normal substrate)

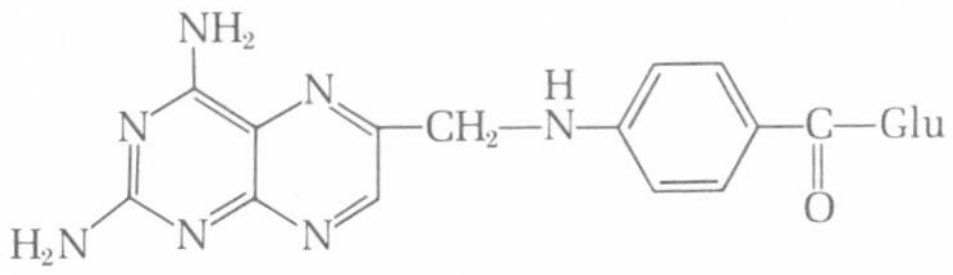

Aminopterin

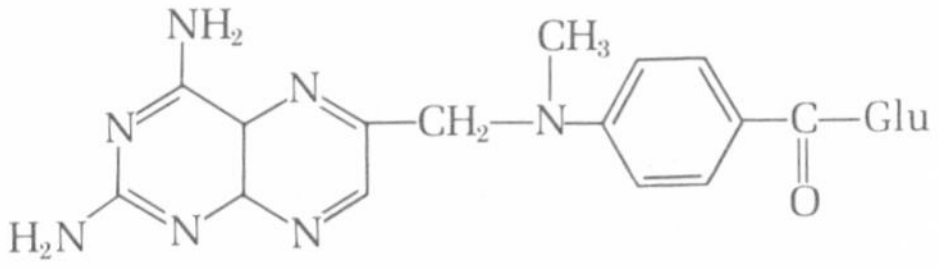

Amethopterin

Figure 24-6
Formation of glycine and N^5,N^{10}-*methylenetetrahydrofolate from serine.*

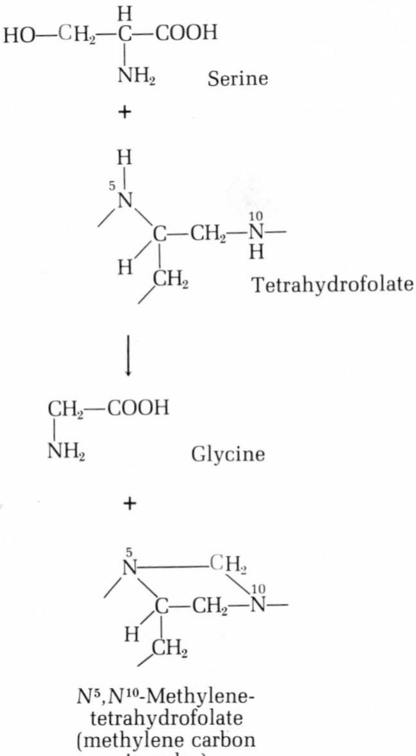

N^5,N^{10}-Methylene-tetrahydrofolate (methylene carbon in color)

substrate dihydrofolic acid. The analogs thus can prevent the normal synthesis of tetrahydrofolic acid coenzymes from dihydrofolate; they are therefore known as *anti-folic acid agents.* Aminopterin and amethopterin are clinically effective in halting the growth of certain fast-growing cancer cells, particularly in leukemias. Since the conversion of dihydrofolate into tetrahydrofolate is required in the biosynthesis of thymidylic acid and thus of nucleic acids, the growth of such cells is greatly retarded when dihydrofolate reductase is inhibited.

Tetrahydrofolate, which is often abbreviated as FH_4, serves as the acceptor of the β-carbon atom of serine when the latter is cleaved to yield glycine, a reaction which requires pyridoxal phosphate. The carbon atom so removed from serine forms a methylene bridge between nitrogen atoms 5 and 10 of tetrahydrofolate to yield *N^5,N^{10}-methylenetetrahydrofolate* (Figure 24-6). The overall reaction is

$$\text{Serine} + FH_4 \rightarrow \text{glycine} + N^5,N^{10}\text{-methylene } FH_4$$

Although this reaction completes the formation of glycine from serine, the further fate of the one-carbon fragment carried by tetrahydrofolate requires some consideration at this point, since it must be transferred to a one-carbon group acceptor to regenerate free tetrahydrofolate. N^5,N^{10}-methylenetetrahydrofolate is one member of the family of folic acid coenzymes, which are capable of carrying different kinds of one-carbon groups, such as methyl, hydroxymethyl, formyl, and formimino groups (Figure 24-7). N^5,N^{10}-methylenetetrahydrofolate may be oxidized at the expense of $NADP^+$ to form *N^5,N^{10}-methenyltetrahydrofolate*, which is not itself a coenzyme. However, its hydrolysis yields *N^{10}-formyltetrahydrofolic acid*, an active coenzyme which functions as a carrier of the formyl group in a number of enzymatic reactions. The formyl group can also be attached directly to tetrahydrofolate at the expense of ATP and formic acid (Figure 24-7). A second formylated species of tetrahydrofolate, namely *N^5-formyltetrahydrofolate*, may also be formed from the N^{10}-formyl derivative by an isomerase reaction, or by

Figure 24-7
The tetrahydrofolic acid coenzymes.

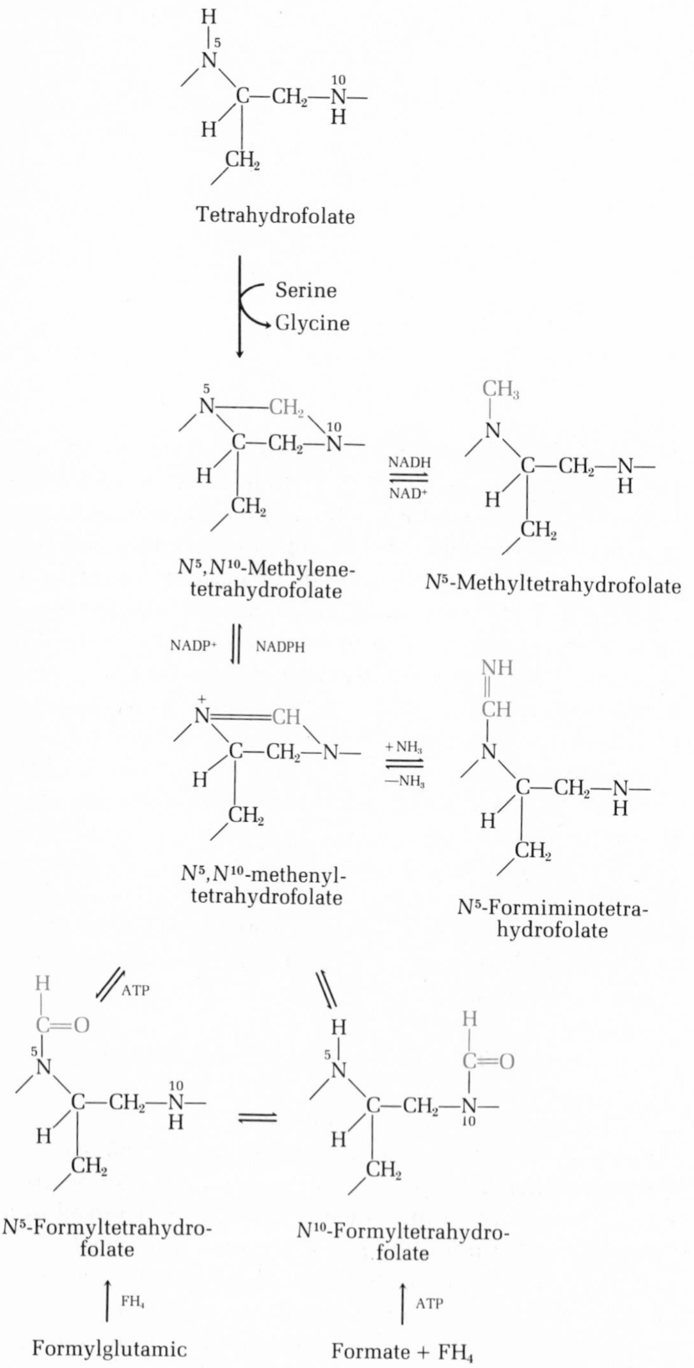

Figure 24-8
Conversion of aspartic acid to threonine. Allosteric inhibition is shown in color.

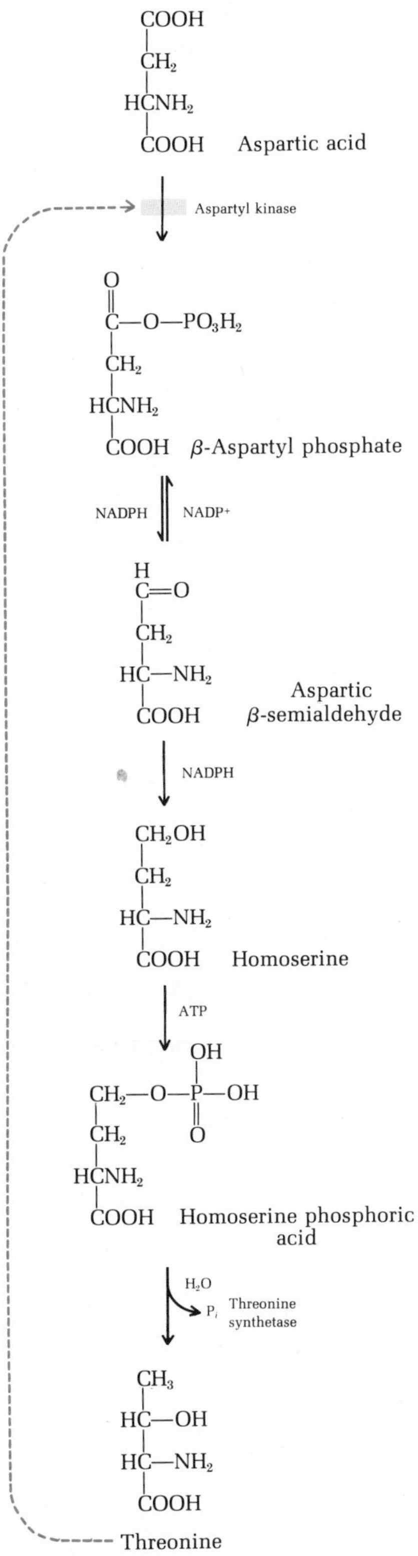

$HOOC{-}CH_2{-}CHNH_2{-}COOH$ Aspartic acid

↓ Aspartyl kinase

$H_2O_3P{-}O{-}C(=O){-}CH_2{-}CHNH_2{-}COOH$ β-Aspartyl phosphate

⇅ NADPH / $NADP^+$

$H{-}C(=O){-}CH_2{-}HC{-}NH_2{-}COOH$ Aspartic β-semialdehyde

↓ NADPH

$CH_2OH{-}CH_2{-}HC{-}NH_2{-}COOH$ Homoserine

↓ ATP

$(HO)_2P(=O){-}O{-}CH_2{-}CH_2{-}HCNH_2{-}COOH$ Homoserine phosphoric acid

↓ H_2O, P_i; Threonine synthetase

$CH_3{-}HC{-}OH{-}HC{-}NH_2{-}COOH$ Threonine

(Threonine ⇢ Aspartyl kinase: allosteric inhibition)

transfer of a formyl group from formylglutamic acid. The N^5 position is utilized to carry another species of one-carbon compound, namely, the formimino group, to yield formimino derivatives such as formiminoglycine, a precursor of purines (Chapter 25). Because of these interconversions, the tetrahydrofolate coenzymes participate in a wide variety of important one-carbon transfers, of which the transfer of methyl groups by way of methionine is quantitatively of greatest importance. The one-carbon unit derived from serine can thus be transferred in the form of a methyl group to various acceptors, such as phosphatidyl ethanolamine (Chapter 23).

Biosynthesis of the Essential Amino Acids

The pathways for the synthesis of the essential amino acids have been largely deduced from biochemical and genetic studies on bacteria. In general, the biosynthetic pathways for this group of amino acids are similar, if not identical, in most species of bacteria and higher plants. Sometimes, however, there are species differences in certain individual steps. The pathways leading to synthesis of the essential amino acids are longer (five to fifteen steps) than those leading to nonessential amino acids, most of which have fewer than five steps. They are also more complex, possibly because various intermediates in these pathways serve as precursors of many other kinds of biomolecules.

Methionine and Threonine

These two essential amino acids have a common denominator: their carbon skeletons arise from *homoserine*, a four-carbon analog of serine. The carbon chain of homoserine is in turn derived from the carbon skeleton of aspartic acid, in a series of reactions (Figure 24-8) which does not take place in mammals. The reaction pathway for the reduction of the β-carboxyl group of aspartic acid to the aldehyde resembles the reduction of 1,3-diphosphoglycerate to 3-glyceraldehyde phosphate in the reversal of the glycolytic path.

Homoserine formed in the first stage is then phosphorylated to homoserine phosphate, in an ATP-requiring reaction (Fig. 24-8). Homoserine phosphate is now converted to threonine by *threonine synthetase*, a pyridoxal phosphate enzyme (Figure 24-9). In this reaction, phosphoric acid is eliminated from carbon atoms 3 and 4 to yield a $\Delta^{3,4}$ double bond, which isomerizes to the $\Delta^{2,3}$ position and then hydrates to form threonine. The entire sequence is believed to take place with the α-amino group of the substrate linked as a Schiff's base to the aldehyde group of the pyridoxal phosphate of the enzyme; in this complex the α-hydrogen atom is labile. Threonine, the end product of the sequence, is an inhibitory modulator for the first enzyme in the system, the regulatory enzyme *aspartyl kinase* (Figure 24-8).

The conversion of homoserine to methionine (Figure 24-10) begins with the enzymatic formation of *O*-succinylhomoserine by transfer of the succinyl group of succinyl

Figure 24-9
Conversion of homoserine phosphate to threonine by threonine synthetase.

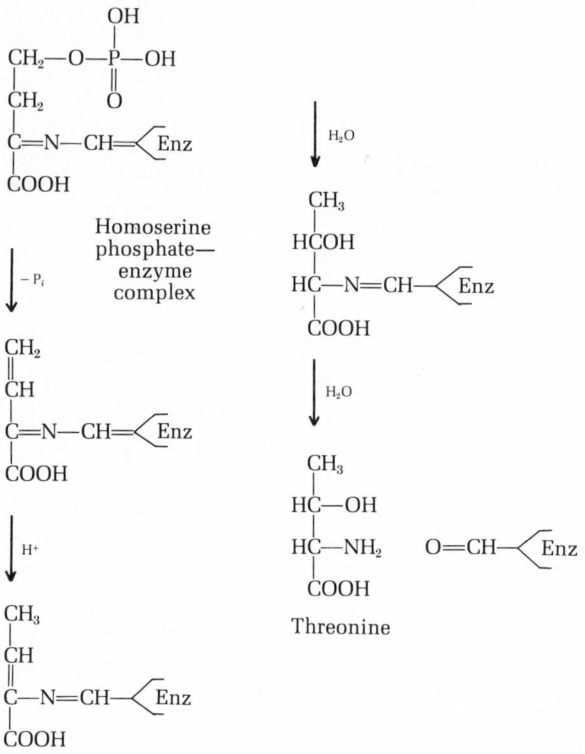

Homoserine phosphate—enzyme complex

Threonine

Figure 24-10
Conversion of homoserine to methionine. The sulfur atom of methionine arises from cysteine, and the carbon chain from homoserine.

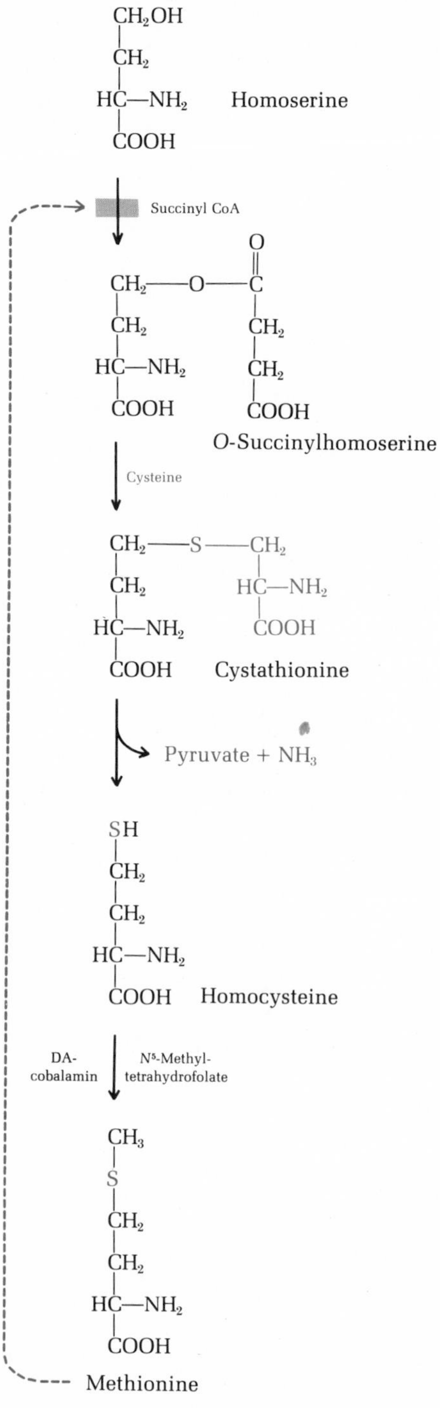

Homoserine

Succinyl CoA

O-Succinylhomoserine

Cysteine

Cystathionine

Pyruvate + NH_3

Homocysteine

DA-cobalamin

N^5-Methyltetrahydrofolate

Methionine

CoA. In the next reaction, cystathionine is formed from *O*-succinylhomoserine and cysteine, which in turn is cleaved to yield homocysteine, pyruvic acid, and NH_3. Cystathionine can undergo two types of cleavage, on either side of the sulfur atom; thus it can serve as an intermediate in the conversion of methionine to cysteine in mammals and of cysteine to methionine in plants and bacteria.

The methylation of homocysteine to methionine in *E. coli* takes place by transfer of the methyl group from N^5-methyltetrahydrofolate

$$N^5\text{-Methyltetrahydrofolate} + \text{homocysteine} \xrightarrow{\text{DA-cobalamin}} \text{tetrahydrofolate} + \text{methionine}$$

In this reaction deoxyadenosylcobalamin, a coenzyme containing vitamin B_{12}, is required; its action as a methyl group carrier has been described in Chapter 19. The methyl group of N^5-methyltetrahydrofolate may ultimately arise from a number of different methyl group donors, such as choline or S-adenosylmethionine (Table 24-1). In turn, homocysteine is one of a number of possible methyl group acceptors.

Table 24-1 Some methyl group donors and acceptors.

Donors	Acceptors
Methionine	Homocysteine
S-adenosylmethionine	S-adenosylhomocysteine
Choline	Guanidoacetic acid
Betaine	Phosphatidyl ethanolamine
N^5-methyltetrahydrofolate	Nicotinamide

Figure 24-11
Two pathways leading to lysine.

Lysine

There are two major routes of synthesis of lysine, one proceeding via *diaminopimelic acid*, which is the major route in bacteria and higher plants, and the other via *α-aminoadipic acid*, the route in most fungi (Figure 24-11).

The diaminopimelic route begins with aspartic semialdehyde (see left) and pyruvate, which undergo an aldol condensation and lose water to yield a cyclic inter-

The diaminopimelic pathway (bacteria).

Pyruvate
+
Aspartic semialdehyde

2,3-Dihydropicolinic acid

NADPH

Tetrahydropicolinic acid

succinyl CoA

$+NH_3$

N-Succinyl-L,L-α,ε-diaminopimelic acid

Succinate

L,L-α,ε-Diaminopimelic acid

meso-α,ε-Diaminopimelic acid

CO_2

L-Lysine

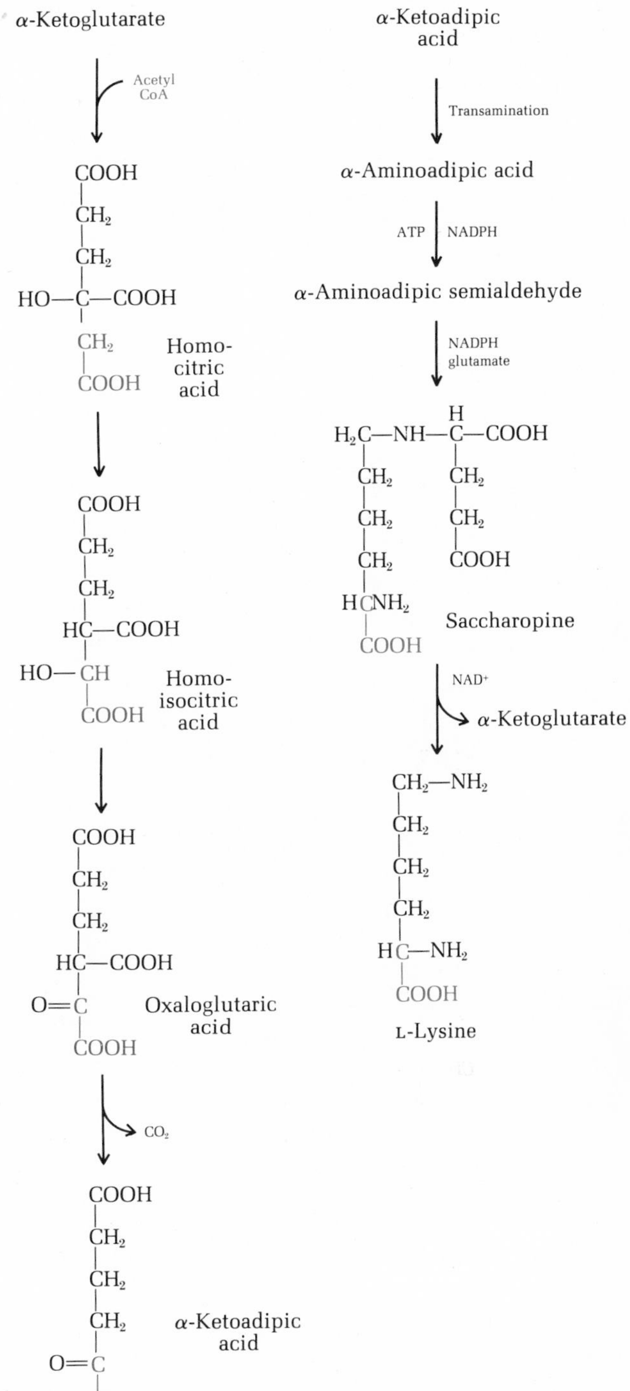

mediate, *2,3-dihydropicolinic acid*. At a later stage, L,L-*α,ε-diaminopimelic acid* is formed, which is converted to the meso form and then decarboxylated to yield L-lysine. The aminoadipic acid pathway begins with acetyl CoA and α-ketoglutarate and proceeds via *homoisocitric acid* to α-aminoadipic acid, which is then reduced to L-lysine.

Isoleucine, Valine, and Leucine

Pyruvate serves as a starting point for the synthesis of these three amino acids, which possess branched aliphatic R groups. Isoleucine and valine synthesis are very similar. Each begins with an active acetaldehyde group derived from pyruvate, attached to thiamine pyrophosphate. The active acetaldehyde is donated to an α-keto acid to yield the corresponding α-aceto-α-hydroxy acids (Figure 24-12). These undergo reduction with simultaneous migration of a methyl or ethyl group, a reaction formally

Figure 24-12
Pathways to valine and isoleucine.

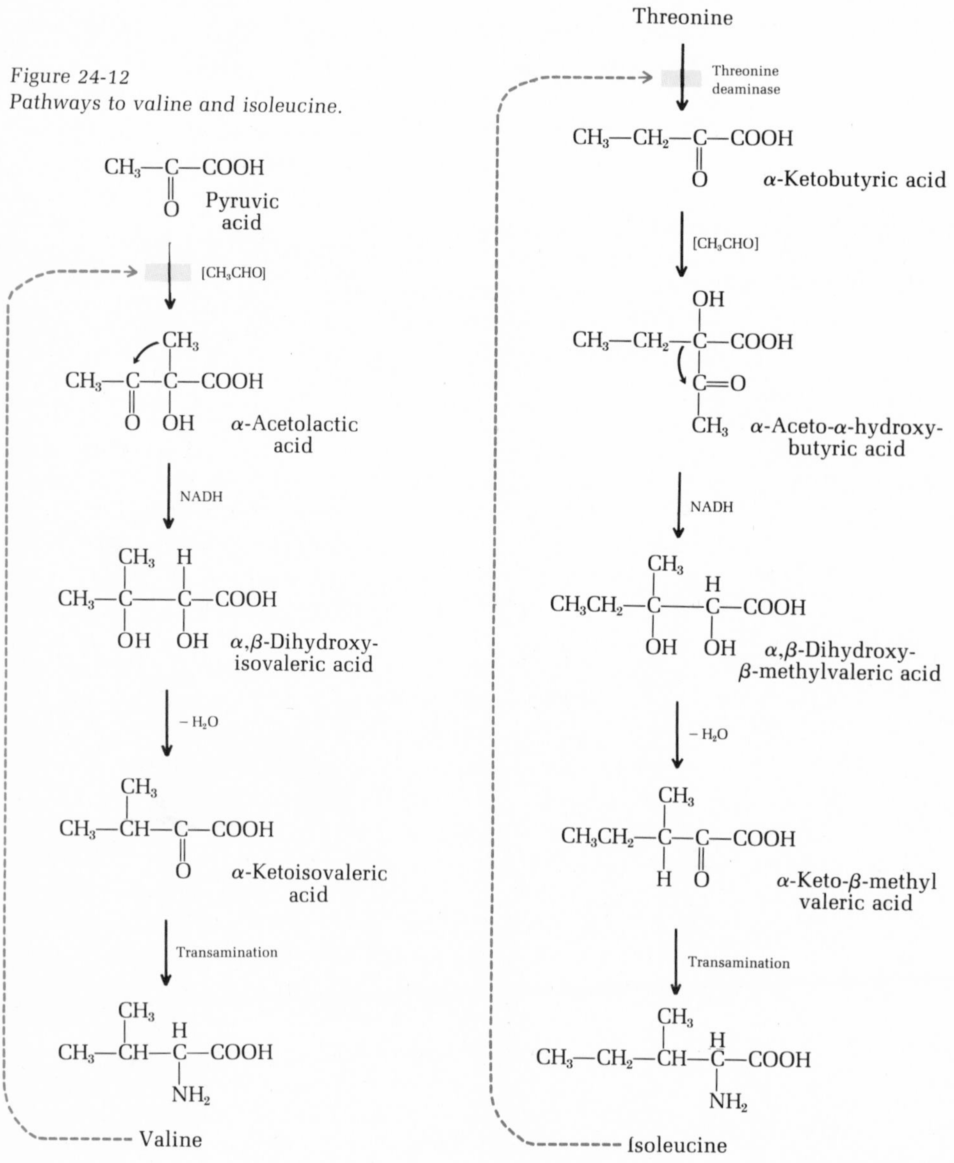

Figure 24-13
The pathway to leucine.

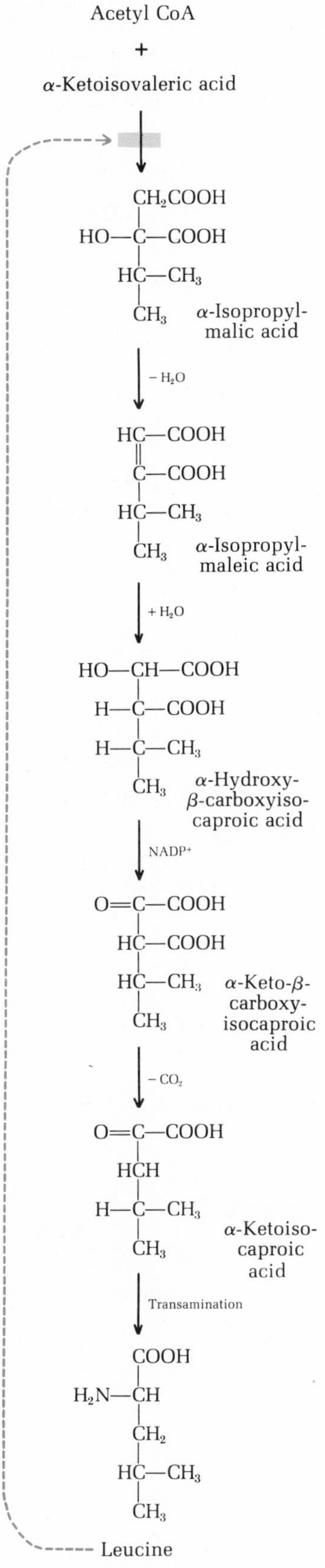

Acetyl CoA
+
α-Ketoisovaleric acid
↓
CH_2COOH / HO—C—COOH / HC—CH_3 / CH_3 α-Isopropylmalic acid
↓ $-H_2O$
HC—COOH / C—COOH / HC—CH_3 / CH_3 α-Isopropylmaleic acid
↓ $+H_2O$
HO—CH—COOH / H—C—COOH / H—C—CH_3 / CH_3 α-Hydroxy-β-carboxyisocaproic acid
↓ $NADP^+$
O=C—COOH / HC—COOH / HC—CH_3 / CH_3 α-Keto-β-carboxyisocaproic acid
↓ $-CO_2$
O=C—COOH / HCH / H—C—CH_3 / CH_3 α-Ketoisocaproic acid
↓ Transamination
COOH / H_2N—CH / CH_2 / HC—CH_3 / CH_3
Leucine

similar to the pinacol rearrangement. The products are then dehydrated to yield the α-keto analogs of isoleucine and valine, which are aminated by transaminases (Figure 24-12).

The formation of leucine (Figure 24-13) begins by condensation of α-ketoisovaleric acid (which is also the precursor of valine) with acetyl CoA, derived from pyruvate, to yield *α-isopropylmalic acid.* The subsequent steps are similar to those leading from citric acid to α-ketoglutaric acid in the tricarboxylic acid cycle.

Ornithine and Arginine

Although arginine can be made from ornithine by mammals during the operation of the Krebs-Henseleit urea cycle (Chapter 20), the net amount made is insignificant because of the rapid breakdown of arginine to form urea and the limited availability of ornithine, which is employed in only catalytic amounts in the urea cycle. Ornithine is formed in bacteria and plants from glutamic acid by two general routes; the major pathway is that shown in Figure 24-14. The final step in this route differs depending on the bacterial species. In *E. coli, N*-acetylornithine is hydrolyzed to yield ornithine and free acetic acid, whereas in other microorganisms and plants, *N*-acetylornithine donates its acetyl group to glutamic acid to yield free ornithine and *N*-acetylglutamic acid, which then serves as the precursor of *N*-acetylglutamic γ-semialdehyde. The *N*-acetyl group appears to prevent glutamic acid semialdehyde from spontaneous cyclization. This reaction sequence constitutes a cycle, sometimes called the *N-acetylornithine cycle.* The ornithine so formed is converted to arginine by reactions described in Chapter 20. Since arginase is lacking in many bacteria this pathway yields net synthesis of arginine.

Histidine

The pathway of biosynthesis of histidine has long been a challenging and difficult problem. It has been solved in an outstanding series of investigations by Ames and others, in which mutants of *Salmonella typhimurium* and *E. coli* were employed. The pathway of histidine formation is given in Figure 24-15; it contains a number of most unusual and complex reactions. The first step is particularly novel; 5-phosphoribosyl 1-pyrophosphate reacts with ATP in such a manner that its pyrophosphate group is lost and the 5-phosphoribosyl moiety forms an *N*-glycosidic linkage with nitrogen atom 1 of the purine ring of ATP. As can be seen by tracing through the reactions, the three-carbon side-chain and two carbon atoms of the imidazole ring of histidine arise from the 5-phosphoribosyl moiety. One of the —N=C— fragments of the imidazole ring arises from the adenine of the ATP, and the other nitrogen atom of the ring from the amide nitrogen of glutamine, after an unusual enzymatic fragmentation of the adenine ring of ATP. The remaining fragment of the adenine ring is in fact a precursor of purines, as we shall see in Chapter 25; evidently no byproducts are wasted during the formation of histidine.

In fact, the biosynthesis of histidine and of the purine ring are linked (see Chapter 25). Another noteworthy point is that the carboxyl group of histidine is formed by oxidation of the corresponding α-amino alcohol, whereas the carboxyl group of nearly all the other amino acids arises from the carboxyl group of a corresponding α-keto acid.

The first step in the reaction sequence leading to histidine is catalyzed by a regulatory enzyme, *phosphoribosyl pyrophosphate-ATP phosphorylase,* which is inhibited by histidine, the end product of the sequence. This enzyme system has been found to undergo coordinate repression; that is, the presence of excess histidine in the culture medium represses the synthesis of the entire sequence of histidine-forming enzymes. Genetic studies of the *his* operon, the segment of DNA coding this group of enzymes, have revealed extremely important information regarding the regulation of enzyme synthesis (Chapter 32; Figure 32-4).

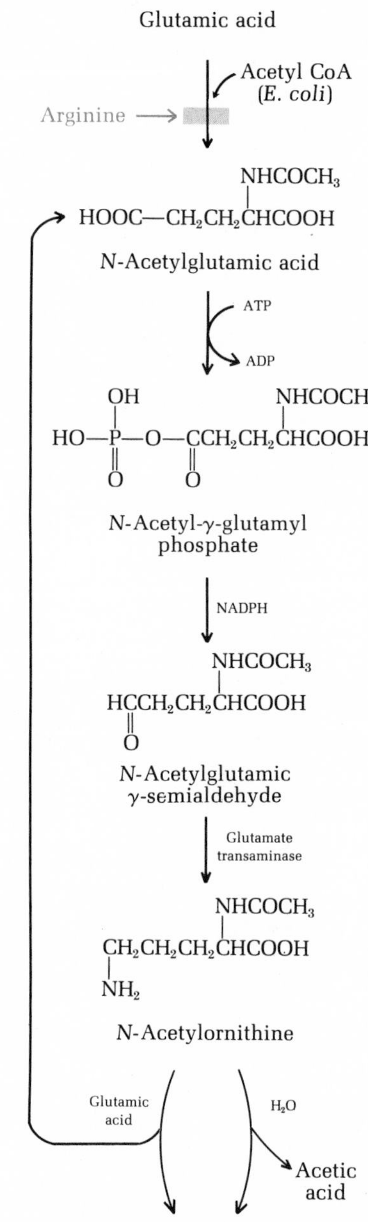

Figure 24-14
The pathway to ornithine. The conversion of N-acetylornithine to ornithine may occur by two different reactions. Displacement of the N-acetyl group with glutamic acid yields N-acetylglutamic acid and institutes the N-acetylornithine cycle.

Biosynthesis of the Aromatic Amino Acids Phenylalanine and Tryptophan

The most noteworthy aspect of the biosynthesis of these amino acids is the mechanism by which their aromatic rings are formed from purely aliphatic precursors. The pathway of these reactions (Figure 24-16) was deduced from experiments on auxotrophic mutants of *E. coli* and *A. aerogenes* which required phenylalanine, tyrosine, and tryptophan for growth. Davis made the important observation that the compound *shikimic acid* (Figure 24-16), a hydroaromatic acid abundant in some higher plants, can replace the aromatic amino acids in supporting growth of these mutants. Further study of compounds related to shikimic acid to determine their capacity to support the growth of these mutants, as well as isotopic experiments carried out by Sprinson, finally revealed the pathway of biosynthesis of the aromatic amino acids. The mechanism of aromatization employed in this pathway, in which shikimic acid is a key intermediate, is of the widest biological significance. For example, enormous quantities of *lignin,* a polymerized aromatic derivative making up a substantial portion of the woody portions of plant tissues, are synthesized in the plant kingdom via shikimic acid, as are many other aromatic biomolecules such as CoQ and plastoquinone.

In the pathway to shikimic acid, a four-carbon sugar phosphate, erythrose 4-phosphate, reacts with phosphoenolpyruvate to yield a phosphorylated seven-carbon keto sugar acid, which cyclizes to the six-carbon aliphatic ring of *5-dehydroquinic acid.* The latter is then converted to shikimic acid, which then leads via phosphorylated intermediates to *chorismic acid* (Greek, fork), at which there is an important metabolic branch point. One branch leads to *anthranilic acid* and thence to tryptophan, whereas the other leads to the quinonoid compound *prephenic acid,* the last nonaromatic compound in the sequence. Prephenic acid can be aromatized in two ways: (1) by dehydrogenation and simultaneous decarboxylation to yield

Figure 24-15
The biosynthetic pathway to histidine.

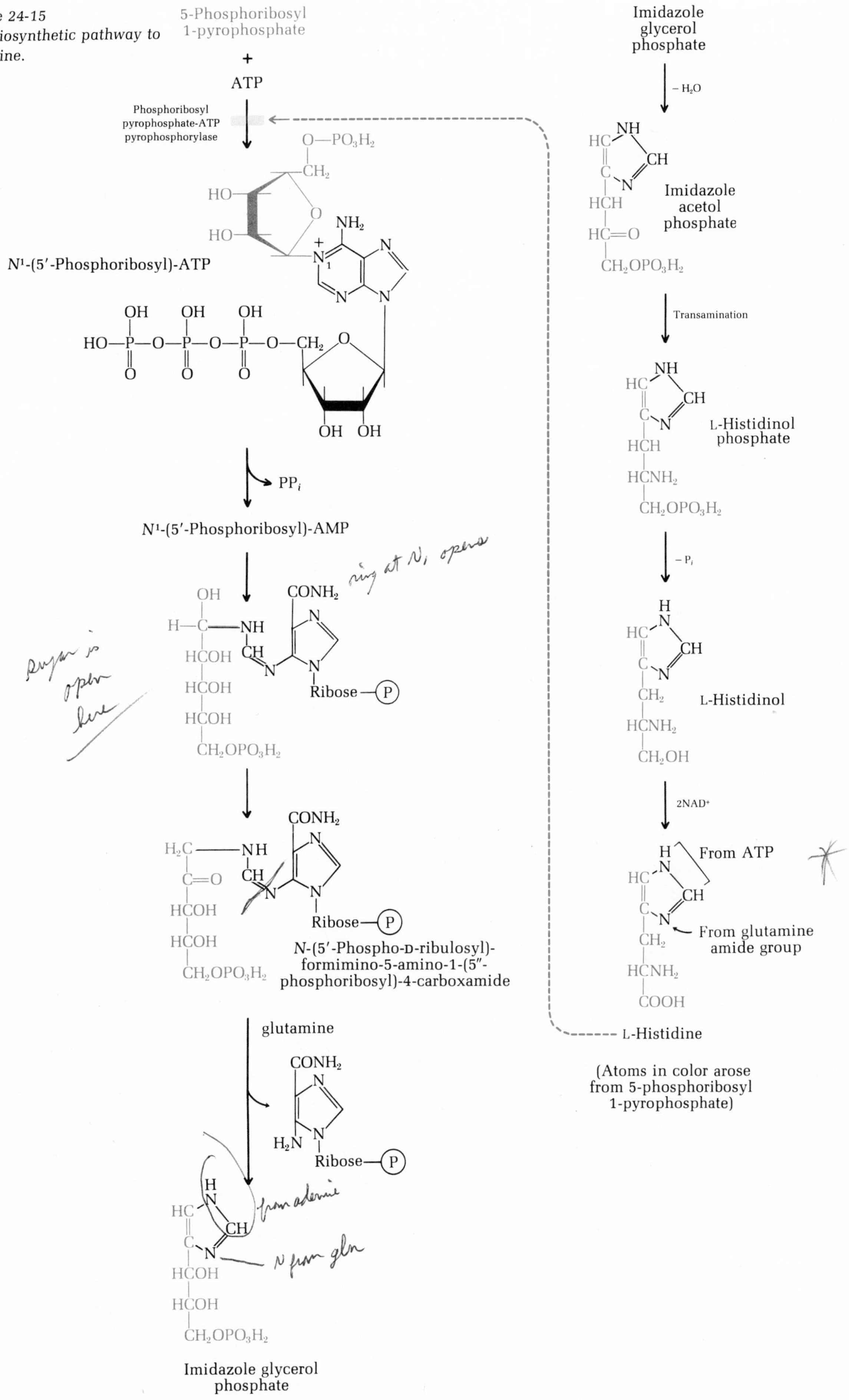

5-Phosphoribosyl 1-pyrophosphate

+

ATP

Phosphoribosyl pyrophosphate-ATP pyrophosphorylase

N^1-(5′-Phosphoribosyl)-ATP

PP_i

N^1-(5′-Phosphoribosyl)-AMP

N-(5′-Phospho-D-ribulosyl)-formimino-5-amino-1-(5″-phosphoribosyl)-4-carboxamide

glutamine

Imidazole glycerol phosphate

Imidazole glycerol phosphate

$-H_2O$

Imidazole acetol phosphate

Transamination

L-Histidinol phosphate

$-P_i$

L-Histidinol

$2NAD^+$

From ATP

From glutamine amide group

L-Histidine

(Atoms in color arose from 5-phosphoribosyl 1-pyrophosphate)

Figure 24-16
The biosynthetic pathway to tyrosine, phenylalanine and tryptophan.

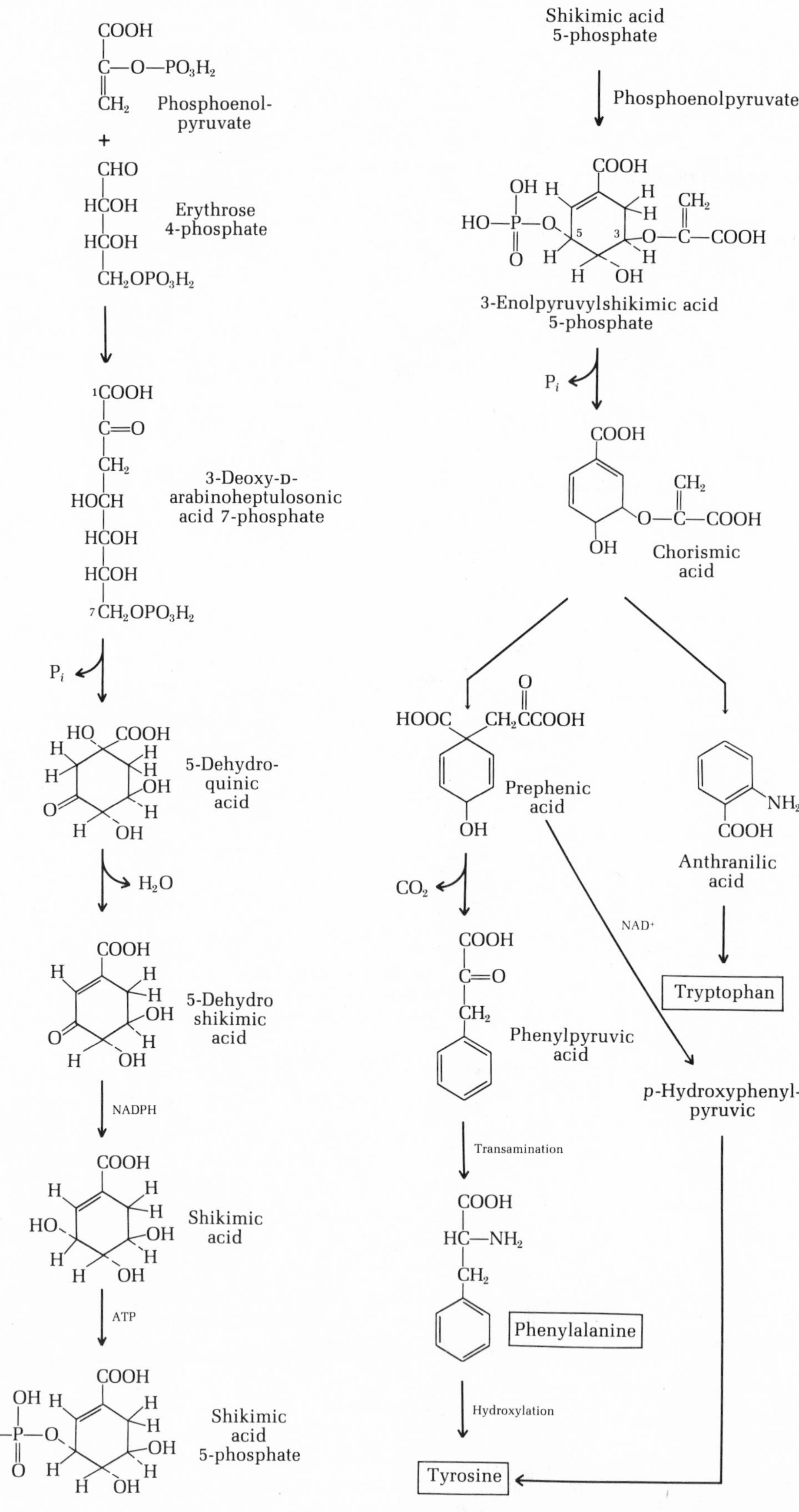

Figure 24-17
Details of the pathway from anthranilic acid to tryptophan. The portion of the molecule arising from phosphoribosyl pyrophosphate is shown in color.

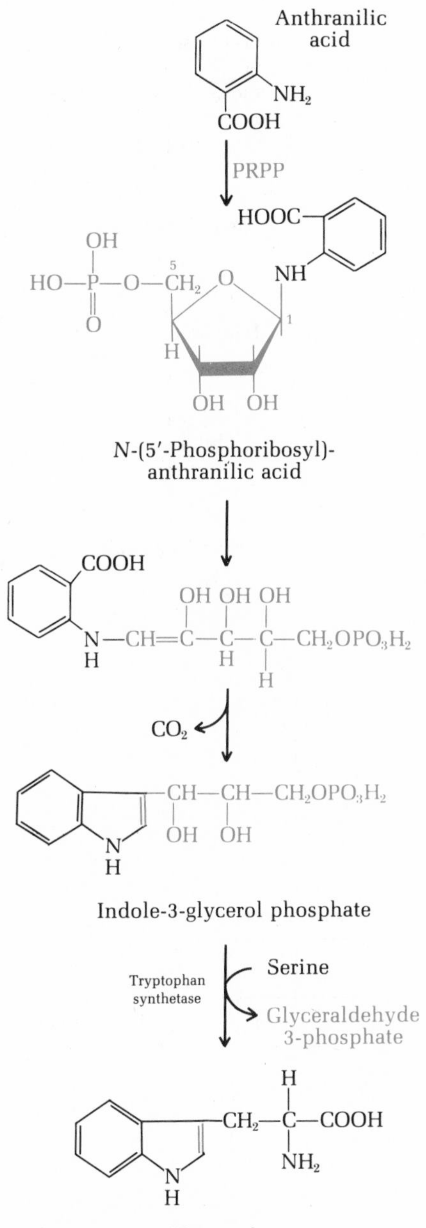

Anthranilic acid

PRPP

N-(5′-Phosphoribosyl)-anthranilic acid

CO_2

Indole-3-glycerol phosphate

Tryptophan synthetase

Serine

Glyceraldehyde 3-phosphate

Tryptophan

p-hydroxyphenylpyruvic acid, the precursor of tyrosine, and (2) by dehydration and decarboxylation to yield phenylpyruvic acid, the precursor of phenylalanine. Some of the enzymes catalyzing this sequence have not yet been well characterized.

Details of the formation of tryptophan from anthranilic acid are shown in Figure 24-17. The terminal step in this sequence is catalyzed by *tryptophan synthetase*, an enzyme that has received considerable attention, not only because it catalyzes an interesting reaction but especially because its enzymatically active subunits have been utilized as elements in the experimental proof by Yanofsky and his colleagues of one of the basic principles of molecular genetics, namely, the *colinearity* of the nucleotide triplet sequences in DNA and the amino acid sequence of its gene product (Chapter 31). Tryptophan synthetase is a pyridoxal phosphate enzyme having a molecular weight of about 135,000; it has been isolated in crystalline form. It catalyzes the overall reaction

$$\text{Indole-3-glycerol phosphate} + \text{serine} \rightarrow \text{tryptophan} + \text{glyceraldehyde 3-phosphate}$$

which takes place in two steps, with the intermediate indole remaining bound to the active site:

$$\text{Indole-3-glycerol phosphate} \rightarrow [\text{indole}] + \text{glyceraldehyde 3-phosphate} \quad (1)$$

$$[\text{Indole}] + \text{serine} \rightarrow \text{tryptophan} + H_2O \quad (2)$$

The enzyme contains four polypeptide chains, made up of two α chains and two β chains, which can be separated. The α subunit alone can catalyze Reaction (1), but at a low rate, and the β chains, associated as the dimer β_2, can catalyze Reaction (2), also at a low rate. When the α and β chains are mixed, the reaction rates of steps 1 and 2 are greatly increased. The amino acid sequence of both the α and β chains, as well as of several of their mutants, has been established.

Regulation of Amino Acid Biosynthesis

The most important mechanism by which amino acid synthesis is controlled is through *feedback inhibition* of the first reaction in the biosynthetic sequence by the end product of the sequence. The first reaction, which is usually irreversible, is catalyzed by an allosteric enzyme. Allosteric inhibition of enzyme activity yields what has been termed "fine" control over biosynthesis, since it is capable of second-by-second adjustment of the rate of biosynthesis of the amino acid to the steady-state level of the biosynthetic end product. Allosteric control is not limited to amino acid biosynthesis, but it is especially conspicuous in this area of metabolism, not only because of its many interconnecting pathways, but also because of the basic necessity of bacterial cells to conserve amino acids.

The second type of control mechanism is that given by genetic repression or derepression of enzyme synthesis, which is often spoken of as yielding "coarse" control. Such control is afforded by changes in the rate of transcription of DNA (Part IV). Repression of the synthesis of one or more enzymes of a biosynthetic pathway is produced when the product of the sequence is present in the cell (or the medium) in sufficiently high concentration to supply its metabolic needs, particularly for protein synthesis. However, although repression and derepression are dramatic processes in bacteria, they are relatively slow compared with feedback inhibition of regulatory enzymes. Indeed, it has been questioned whether repression of enzyme synthesis is in fact a device whose primary function is to regulate the rate of synthesis of a given product. It appears more likely that its primary purpose is to exert maximum economy in the use of amino acids and energy, by limiting the synthesis of unused enzymes. The "saving" in amino acids can be considerable, since in many biosynthetic pathways the entire multienzyme system may be repressed in coordinate fashion. Since each enzyme molecule contains hundreds of amino acid residues, it may be quite advantageous to bacterial cells to synthesize only those enzyme molecules it requires.

Most of the biosynthetic pathways leading to formation of amino acids have now been shown to be under allosteric regulation; the major control points have been designated in the appropriate Figures. The first example to be discovered, by Umbarger in 1957, was the feedback inhibition by isoleucine of *threonine deaminase*, the first enzyme in the sequence leading to the synthesis of isoleucine (see Chapter 9, Figure 9-7). When biosynthetic pathways involve branches leading to different amino acids, the feedback mechanisms become rather complex and may involve multivalent regulatory enzymes or parallel isozymes sensitive to different inhibitors. Figure 24-18 shows how divalent regulatory enzymes, which are independently inhibited by two different end products, in this case phenylalanine and tryptophan, can participate in regulating the biosynthesis of the aromatic amino acids. Sometimes a divalent regulatory enzyme is not inhibited by either of its effectors alone, but is inhibited when both are present; this is spoken of as *concerted divalent inhibition*.

Especially noteworthy is the remarkable set of multivalent allosteric controls exerted on the activity of glutamine synthetase of *E. coli*. Glutamine is a precursor or amino group donor of many metabolic products (Figure 24-19). Eight products of glutamine metabolism in *E. coli* are now known to serve as separate and independent negative feedback modulators of the activity of glutamine synthetase, which is perhaps the most complex regulatory enzyme now known. Work of Stadtman and his colleagues has shown that glutamine synthetase contains twelve identical subunits, each of molecular weight 50,000, arranged in two hexagonal layers (Figure 24-20). The enzyme molecule has been proved to contain twelve binding sites for the substrate ATP and twelve binding

Figure 24-18
Feedback controls in the biosynthesis of the aromatic amino acids. Regulatory enzymes inhibited (or activated) by more than one modulator are multivalent.

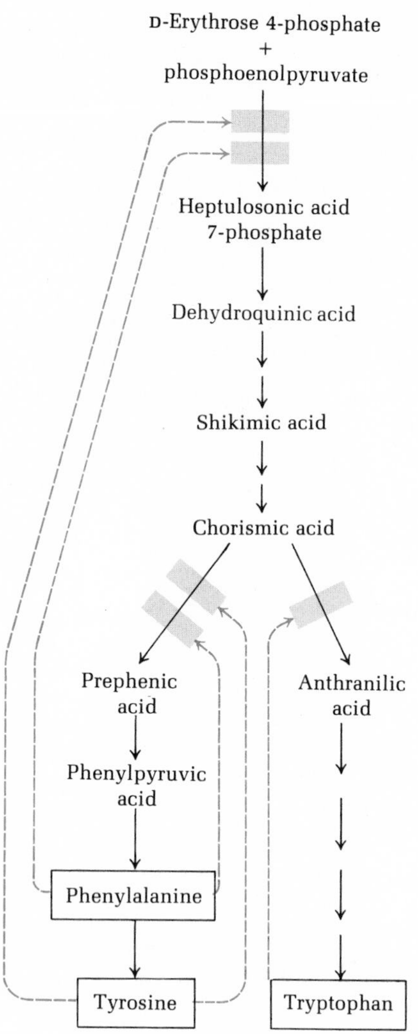

Figure 24-19
Multivalent allosteric inhibition of glutamine synthetase. Although glycine and alanine are not direct products of glutamine metabolism, they are very strong inhibitors, suggesting that the steady-state levels of glycine and alanine in the cell are critically related to glutamine synthesis and metabolism.

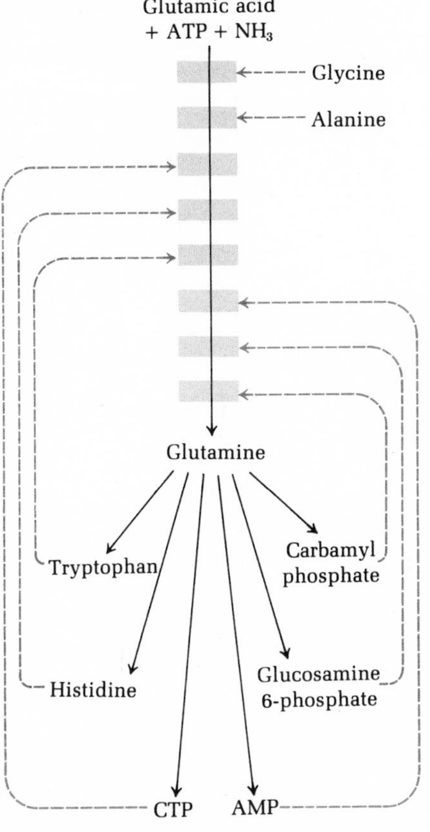

sites for each of the two feedback inhibitors AMP and tryptophan. Glutamine synthetase also may exist in two molecular species, one of which is adenylylated; the latter species contains twelve molecules of adenosine linked by 5′-pyrophosphate bridges to tyrosine hydroxyl groups on the enzyme subunits. The two enzyme forms differ in their sensitivity to certain feedback inhibitors.

Precursor Functions of Amino Acids: Biosynthesis of Porphyrins

The amino acids are precursors of many biomolecules (other than proteins) which serve important biological functions, such as hormones, vitamins, coenzymes, alkaloids, porphyrins, antibiotics, pigments, and neurotransmitter substances. Table 24-2 shows a few of the important biomolecules arising from some of the amino acids. It is especially noteworthy that the aromatic amino acids are major precursors of many alkaloids, among them morphine, codeine, and papaverine, as well as of many other substances having intense biological activity, such as the metabolic hormone thyroxine, the plant growth hormone indoleacetic acid, the powerful vasoconstrictor and neurohumor serotonin (5-hydroxytryptamine), and

Figure 24-20
Electron micrographs of glutamine synthetase molecules from E. coli, showing the arrangement of the 12 subunits.

Low magnification (negative contrast)

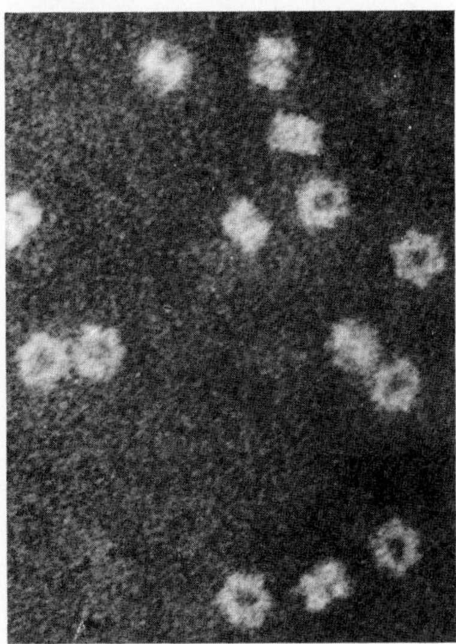

High magnification showing dimensions and arrangement of the subunits.

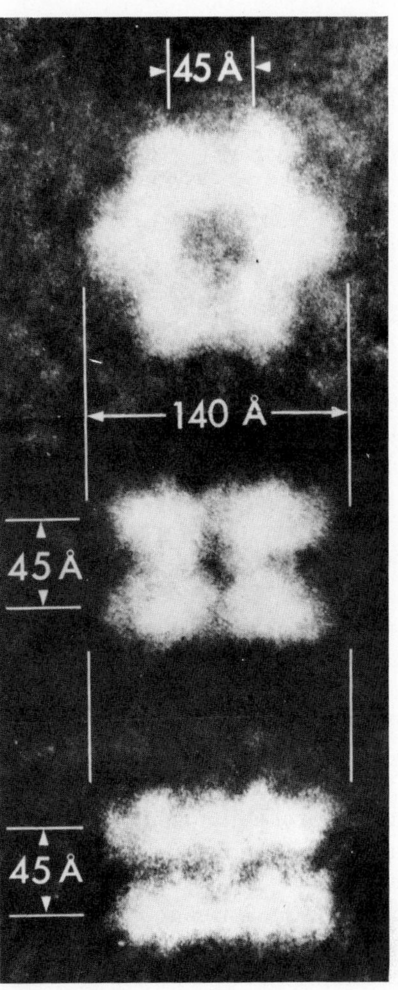

Table 24-2 Precursor functions of some amino acids

- Arginine
  - Spermine
  - Spermidine
  - Putrescine
- Aspartic acid
  - Pyrimidines
- Glutamic acid
  - Glutathione
- Glycine
  - Purines
  - Glutathione
  - Creatine
  - Phosphocreatine
  - Tetrapyrroles
- Histidine
  - Histamine
  - Ergothioneine
- Lysine
  - Cadaverine
  - Anabasine
  - Coniine
- Ornithine
  - Hyoscyamine
- Serine
  - Sphingosine
- Tyrosine
  - Epinephrine
  - Norepinephrine
  - Melanin
  - Thyroxine
  - Mescaline
  - Tyramine
  - Morphine
  - Codeine
  - Papaverine
- Tryptophan
  - Nicotinic acid
  - Serotonin
  - Kynurenic acid
  - Indole
  - Skatole
  - Indoleacetic acid
  - Ommochrome
- Valine
  - Pantothenic acid
  - Penicillin

Glutathione

$COOH$
$HCNH_2$
CH_2
CH_2
$C{=}O$
HN
$HS{-}CH_2{-}CH$
$C{=}O$
HN
CH_2
$COOH$

the catecholamine hormones *epinephrine* and *norepinephrine*. Amino acids are also precursors of small peptides, such as glutathione and of the peptide hormones, such as bradykinin, oxytocin, and vasopressin. The tripeptide glutathione (margin) is synthesized in the following reactions:

$$\text{Glutamic acid} + \text{cysteine} + \text{ATP} \xrightarrow{Mg^{++}} \gamma\text{-glutamylcysteine} + \text{ADP} + P_i$$

$$\gamma\text{-glutamylcysteine} + \text{glycine} + \text{ATP} \xrightarrow{Mg^{++}} \text{glutathione} + \text{ADP} + P_i$$

Space will not permit development of the many different biosynthetic pathways that start from the amino acids. However, the biosynthesis of porphyrins, for which glycine is a major precursor, does require special note because of the central importance of the porphyrin nucleus in the function of hemoglobin, of cytochromes, and of chlorophyll. The tetrapyrroles are constructed from four molecules of the monopyrrole derivative *porphobilinogen,* which is synthesized in the steps shown in Figure 24-21. This pathway was largely deduced from isotopic tracer and enzyme studies by Shemin and other investigators. In the first reaction, glycine reacts with succinyl CoA to yield enzyme-bound *α-amino-β-ketoadipic acid,* which then decarboxylates to yield *δ-aminolevulinic acid.* This reaction is catalyzed by *δ-aminolevulinic acid synthetase,* a pyridoxal phosphate enzyme which is found in the endoplasmic reticulum of liver cells. Two molecules of δ-aminolevulinic acid then condense to form porphobilinogen, through the action of *δ-aminolevulinic acid dehydrase.* The mechanism of this complex reaction is especially interesting, since it apparently involves the formation of a Schiff's base between the keto group of one molecule of δ-aminolevulinic acid and an ε-amino group of a lysine residue of the en-

Figure 24-21
Biosynthesis of porphobilinogen and the conversion of porphobilinogen into protoporphyrin IX. The carbon and nitrogen atoms originating from glycine are in color; the carbon atoms originating from the carboxyl carbon atoms of succinyl CoA are marked with •

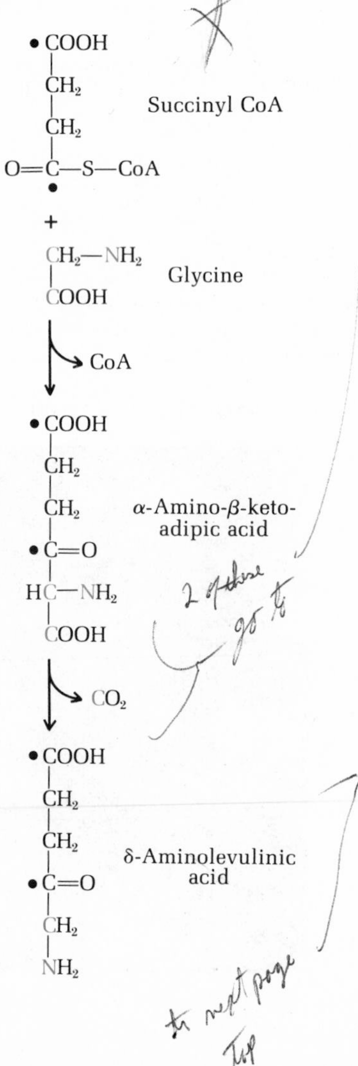

2 δ-Aminolevulinic acid

$2H_2O$

Porphobilinogen

Protoporphyrin IX

zyme. Both the synthetase and dehydrase are regulatory enzymes; they are inhibited by heme, hemoglobin, and other heme proteins, which are the ultimate end products of this biosynthetic pathway.

Four molecules of porphobilinogen now serve as the precursors of protoporphyrin, through a series of complex reactions, the first of which is catalyzed by *porphobilinogen deaminase.* Some of the steps in this series are still obscure. Iron is not incorporated until the protoporphyrin molecule is completed. The incorporation of iron requires an enzyme, *heme synthetase* or *ferrochelatase,* which is localized in the mitochondria. Figure 24-21 also shows the origin of the carbon and nitrogen atoms of protoporphyrin IX from glycine and succinyl CoA. Degradation of protoporphyrin IX leads to *bilirubin* and *biliverdin,* pigments secreted in the bile.

Nitrogen-Fixing Organisms

Some 13,000 species of leguminous plants have been described and most of them fix atmospheric N_2; in addition some 250 nonleguminous plants are also active in N_2 fixation. The fixation of nitrogen requires the cooperative action of the host plant and bacteria present in the root nodules; it is referred to as *symbiotic nitrogen fixation.* Representative N_2-fixing plants include peas, beans, clover, alfalfa, and soybeans, among the legumes, and alder, seabuckthorn, and wax myrtle, among nonlegumes. Enormous amounts of atmospheric nitrogen are fixed by crop legumes.

The microorganisms that invade the roots of leguminous plants are largely species of the bacterial genus *Rhizobium.* The infecting bacteria gain entrance into the cortical parenchyma of the root and give rise to a nodule, a highly organized structure with membranous sacs surrounding groups of the bacteria. The nodule is in direct connection with the vascular system of the plant. Curiously, such nodules contain considerable hemoglobin, which is otherwise absent in the plant kingdom. The hemoglobin appears to enhance N_2 fixation indirectly, by controlling the partial pressure of oxygen. The genetic information for hemoglobin synthesis comes from the plant, but hemoglobin is not formed in the absence of the bacteria.

Leguminous plants without bacteria and *Rhizobium* species grown outside the plant are incapable of N_2 fixation. However, it has recently been established that bacteria removed from the nodules of the host plant under proper conditions can fix N_2. This observation establishes that the N_2-fixing enzymes are located in the bacteria and that the plant apparently supplies some essential component that the bacterium lacks.

Nonsymbiotic nitrogen fixation occurs in a number of microorganisms, including the blue-green algae, the aerobic soil bacterium *Azotobacter,* and the facultative bacteria *Klebsiella* and *Achromobacter.* Among the anaerobes, species of *Clostridia* are especially active in nitrogen fixation. All the photosynthetic bacteria (Chapter 21) can fix nitrogen.

Bilirubin, a bile pigment

Enzymatic Mechanism of Nitrogen Fixation

The mechanism of nitrogen fixation has long been a challenging biochemical problem. Molecular nitrogen is an extremely stable molecule that is not easily reduced; it has also been difficult to imagine how this inert molecule can be tightly and specifically bound to the active site of the nitrogen-fixing enzyme. Moreover, until relatively recently biochemical studies of the nitrogen-fixation process were limited to intact nodules of leguminous plants or to intact cells of nitrogen-fixing microorganisms, since efforts to obtain cell-free extracts capable of nitrogen fixation had been unsuccessful.

Despite these limitations, a number of significant properties of the nitrogen-fixing mechanism were deduced from such studies. For one thing, it was established that the K_M for nitrogen in the fixation process in soybean nodules or blue-green algae is quite low, about 0.02 atm of nitrogen. Clearly, the nitrogen-fixing system is fully saturated at the normal partial pressure of nitrogen in the atmosphere. Another observation of importance is that the process is competitively inhibited by molecular hydrogen (H_2), nitrous oxide (N_2O), nitric oxide (NO), and carbon monoxide (CO). About 50 percent inhibition is given when the hydrogen partial pressure is ten times that of N_2. These observations suggested that the binding site for molecular nitrogen in the nitrogen-fixing enzyme is also capable of binding the competitive inhibitors.

Still another significant conclusion drawn from work with intact cells is that hydrogenase activity is usually associated with the capacity to fix N_2. Hydrogenase activity may be expressed by the equation

$$H_2 + \text{electron acceptor} \rightarrow 2H^+ + \text{reduced acceptor}$$

Since fixed nitrogen is usually recovered in a reduced form, such as NH_3 or an amino acid, it appeared possible that molecular nitrogen is the electron acceptor in the hydrogenase reaction, to yield ammonia as end product:

$$3H_2 + N_2 \rightarrow 2NH_3$$

In 1960, Mortenson and his colleagues finally succeeded in obtaining cell-free extracts from the anaerobic bacterium *Clostridium pasteurianum* that were consistently capable of fixing nitrogen when they were supplemented with an electron donor and ATP. The earliest stable end product of the fixation reaction is ammonia; the hydrogen required for its formation may come from H_2 and the hydrogenase reaction, or from the reducing agent sodium hydrosulfite ($Na_2S_2O_4$).

In 1964 Carnahan, Mortenson, and their colleagues discovered a protein (Chapter 17) in extracts of *Cl. pasteurianum* which they proved to be essential for N_2 fixation. Extracts of bacteria deficient in this factor were unable to fix nitrogen in the absence of added reducing agents; however, this capacity was restored by addition of the protein. The purified factor was found to have a molecular weight of 6,000, and to contain seven atoms of iron and seven atoms of acid-labile sulfur. No heme was present. This protein, which was called ferredoxin, was the first of a series of similar nonheme iron proteins to be isolated from various sources. As pointed out in Chapters 17 and 21, similar proteins participate in mitochondrial electron transport and in photoreduction in photosynthetic organisms. The ferredoxin of *Cl. pasteurianum* has a very negative standard reduction potential, −0.43 volt, and is thus capable in principle of reducing N_2, since a highly electronegative reductant is required in order to reduce the very stable N≡N triple bond. Although ferredoxin is the physiological electron donor in *Cl. pasteurianum*, it is not the obligatory electron donor; sodium hydrosulfite can function as reductant in the absence of ferredoxin.

ATP is an obligatory component of the N_2-fixing system, but the detailed nature of its function is not clear. Two molecules of ATP are required for each electron transported. The nitrogen-fixing enzyme exists as a complex of two proteins, neither of which has any demonstrable activity by itself. One is an iron-molybdenum protein (FeMo protein) with a molecular weight near 150,000 and the other is an iron protein (Fe protein) with a molecular weight near 45,000. The complex apparently carries these components in the ratio of 1 FeMo protein to 2 Fe proteins. The enzyme system is inactivated by oxygen; in addition, the Fe protein is cold-labile.

Figure 24-22 furnishes a working hypothesis for the mechanism of nitrogen fixation. Reduced ferredoxin (Fd) or $Na_2S_2O_4$ can serve as the electron donor. Four ATPs are required for the two electrons needed to reduce $\frac{1}{3}N_2$ to $\frac{2}{3}NH_3$. The overall equation is therefore

$$\tfrac{1}{3}N_2 + H_2 + 4ATP \rightarrow \tfrac{2}{3}NH_3 + 4ADP + 4P_i$$

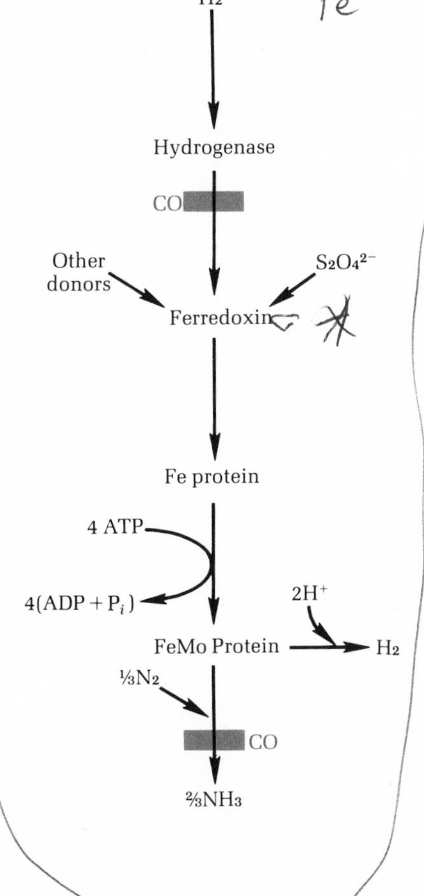

Figure 24-22
Postulated mechanism of nitrogen fixation.

An important clue to the process is given by the finding that when both nitrogen fixation and hydrogenase activity are poisoned by carbon monoxide, the enzyme system can cause reduction of $2H^+$ to H_2 by reduced ferredoxin, but ATP is then required. The N_2-fixing enzyme complex does not have a high specificity for N_2, but it can reduce nitrous oxide, acetylene, azide, and cyanide, as well as analogs of some of these compounds.

Although it has often been postulated that molecular nitrogen (N≡N) is reduced in two steps to *diimide* (NH═NH) and then to *hydrazine* (NH_2—NH_2), there is no evidence that these compounds are intermediates, nor can they be reduced by such enzyme preparations. It is possible that they may be formed, but remain tightly bound to the active site, in a form not exchangeable with added diimide or hydrazine.

Other Steps in the Nitrogen Cycle

Although reduced nitrogen in the form of ammonia or amino acids is the form utilized in most living organisms, there are some soil bacteria that derive their energy by oxidizing ammonia with the formation of nitrite and ultimately nitrate. Because these organisms are extremely abundant and active, nearly all ammonia reaching the soil ultimately becomes oxidized to nitrate, a process known as *nitrification.*

Nitrification occurs in two steps. In the first ammonia is oxidized to nitrite, almost exclusively by the aerobic chemolithotroph *Nitrosomonas.* In effect, ammonia plays the role of energy-yielding fuel, since it is the main electron donor in the respiration of *Nitrosomonas.* The electrons flow from the primary ammonia dehydrogenase system along a cytochrome-containing respiratory chain to oxygen; oxidative phosphorylation is coupled to this electron transport. Similarly, nitrite is then oxidized to nitrate by *Nitrobacter,* which also obtains nearly all its energy from the oxidation of the electron donor nitrite. *Nitrosomonas* and *Nitrobacter* obtain their carbon for growth from CO_2.

As a result of these nitrification reactions, nitrate is the principal form of nitrogen available to higher plants from the soil. Some nitrate is lost from the soil as molecular nitrogen by the action of bacteria that use nitrate as terminal electron acceptor; this process is called *denitrification.* Nitrate is readily absorbed from the soil by higher plants, in which its metabolic assimilation into the form of ammonia proceeds in two major steps: (1) reduction of nitrate to nitrite and (2) reduction of nitrite to ammonia.

The first reaction is catalyzed by *nitrate reductase,* which is widely distributed in plants and fungi; it has been most intensively studied in *Neurospora.* This enzyme, which is a molybdenum-containing flavoprotein, employs NADPH as electron donor. The overall process of electron flow to nitrate may be summarized in the following scheme:

$$\text{NADPH} \rightarrow \text{FAD} \rightarrow \text{Mo} \rightarrow NO_3^-$$

The molybdenum appears to undergo cyclic valence changes between Mo(V) and Mo(VI) during the reduction of nitrate.

The reduction of nitrite to ammonia by *nitrite reductase* of plants requires a highly electronegative reductant. In green plants ferredoxin reduced during the light reactions may serve as the ultimate reductant of nitrite in the following chain of reactions:

$$\text{Ferredoxin}_{\text{red}} \rightarrow \text{NADP} \rightarrow \text{FAD} \rightarrow NO_2^-$$

Free ammonia is formed as the end product, which is then utilized to aminate α-ketoglutarate and thus to provide amino groups by transamination.

Summary

The albino rat can synthesize ten of the twenty amino acids required as building blocks for protein synthesis; since the remainder of the amino acids are nutritionally essential, they must be obtained from other sources. Higher plants and many microorganisms can synthesize all the amino acids starting from ammonia as nitrogen source. In the dispensible or nonessential group, glutamic acid is formed by reductive amination of α-ketoglutarate and is the direct precursor of glutamine and proline. Alanine and aspartic acid are formed by transamination to pyruvic and oxaloacetic acids, respectively. Tyrosine is formed by hydroxylation of phenylalanine. Cysteine is formed from methionine by a more complex series of reactions in which S-adenosylmethionine, S-adenosylhomocysteine, and cystathionine are the most significant intermediates; the carbon chain of cysteine derives from serine and the sulfur atom from methionine. The carbon chain of serine is derived from 3-phosphoglycerate and the amino group from glutamic acid. Serine is the precursor of glycine; the β-carbon atom of serine is transferred to tetrahydrofolate and may then be transferred to one of several methyl group acceptors, such as phosphatidyl ethanolamine or creatine. Tetrahydrofolate is one of a group of related derivatives of the vitamin folic acid which serve as coenzyme carriers of one-carbon groups, such as methyl and formyl groups. Tetrahydrofolate is formed by enzymatic reduction of folic acid.

The pathways of synthesis of the essential amino acids have been established, largely in bacteria. The carbon skeletons of methionine and threonine arise from aspartic acid; the methyl group of methionine arises from N^5-methyltetrahydrofolate. Lysine is made by two routes, the aminoadipic and the aminopimelic pathways. Isoleucine, valine, and leucine synthesis begin with α-keto acids and involve unusual migrations of alkyl groups. Arginine is formed from ornithine, which in turn is derived from glutamic acid. The precursors of the aromatic amino acids are aliphatic compounds which are cyclized to shikimic acid, an essential precursor of many aromatic compounds. Shikimic acid yields phenylalanine and tyrosine via prephenic acid and yields tryptophan via anthranilic acid. The pathway to histidine is most complex and unusual and involves the carbon chain of a pentose and the fragmentation of the purine ring of ATP.

Most of the biosynthetic pathways leading to the amino acids are subject to allosteric or end-product inhibition; the regulatory enzyme is usually the first in the sequence. Some of the regulatory enzymes in the branched pathways are multivalent and thus respond to more than one modulator. Amino acids are precursors of many other important biomolecules; the porphyrin ring of heme protein is derived from glycine and succinyl CoA.

Formation of ammonia by fixation of molecular nitrogen in legume root nodules, nitrification of ammonia to form nitrate by soil organisms, and the denitrification of nitrate by higher plants complete the nitrogen cycle.

References

Books

MEISTER, A.: *Biochemistry of the Amino Acids*, vols. I and II, 2d ed., Academic Press, Inc., New York, 1965. Comprehensive review of amino acid biosynthesis and precursor functions, particularly in Vol. II.

GREENBERG, D. M. (ed.): *Metabolic Pathways*, vols. I, II, III, 3d ed., Academic Press, Inc., New York, 1967–1969. Excellent papers in review form.

SHAPIRO, S. K., and F. SCHLENK (eds.): *Transmethylation and Methionine Biosynthesis*, University of Chicago Press, Chicago, 1965.

STANBURY, J. B., J. B. WYNGAARDEN, and D. B. FREDRICKSON (eds): *The Metabolic Basis of Inherited Disease,* 2d ed., McGraw-Hill Book Company, New York, 1966. Comprehensive review of amino acid metabolism in man and its genetic defects.

Articles

DATTA, P.: "Regulation of Branched Biosynthetic Pathways in Bacteria," *Science,* **165:**556–562 (1969) Multiple feedback control patterns in amino acid biosynthesis.

GIBSON, F., and J. PITTARD: "Pathways of Biosynthesis of Aromatic Amino Acids and Vitamins and Their Control in Microorganisms," *Bacteriol. Rev.,* **32:**465 (1968).

HARDY, R. W. F., and R. C. BURNS: "Biological Nitrogen Fixation," *Ann. Rev. Biochem.,* **37:**331–358 (1968).

MEISTER, A.: "Specificity of Glutamine Synthetase," *Advances in Enzymol.,* **31:**183–218 (1968). An interesting review, illustrated with color stereophotographs of molecular models of substrates of the enzyme.

STADTMAN, E. R.: "Allosteric Regulation of Enzyme Activity," *Advances in Enzymol.,* **28:**41–154 (1966). An important survey of the regulation of metabolic pathways.

———, B. M. SHAPIRO, H. S. KINGDON, C. A. WOOLFOLK, and J. S. HUBBARD: *Advances in Enzyme Regulation,* **6:**257 (1968). A valuable account of the recently developed information on the structure and regulatory function of glutamine synthetase in *E. coli.*

Problems

1. Write a balanced equation for the synthesis of glycine starting from succinate as sole carbon source.
2. Write a balanced equation for the biosynthesis of threonine starting from isocitric acid as sole carbon source.
3. From isotopic tracer experiments on intact albino rats it was established that the labeled atoms of the metabolites shown were precursors of the specified atoms in the creatine molecule (margin). From these observations construct a possible pathway of biosynthesis of creatine.
4. How many high-energy phosphate bonds are required for the biosynthesis of one molecule of arginine from glutamate, ammonia, and carbon dioxide? Assume that Acetyl CoA is available.
5. Administration of serine labeled with ^{14}C in the α-carbon atom to rats was found to yield choline labeled in the 2-carbon atom (i.e. $(CH_3)_3N\text{-}^{14}CH_2CH_2OH$). In a parallel experiment, dimethylethanolamine deuterated in the methyl groups was found to give methyl-labeled choline when fed in the presence of methionine, but gave no labeled choline when fed in the presence of homocysteine. Suggest a mechanism for choline synthesis.
6. The dipeptide anserine (margin) is found in skeletal muscle. In which carbon atoms of anserine would you expect to find the label from 1-^{14}C-D-ribose? How would you determine the source of the methyl group of anserine?
7. Write a balanced equation for the formation of glutamate from nitrate, NADPH, NAD^+, ATP, and CO_2 in a photosynthetic cell of a higher plant.

Problem 3

```
     NH             NH2
     ||             |
  NH2CNHCH2CH2CH2CHCOOH
   \        Arginine
    \
     ↓
     NH2
     |
     C=NH        Creatine
     |
 CH3—N—CH2COOH
  ↑    ↖
  |      \
  |       NH2CH2COOH
  |        Glycine
  |
  CH3
  |
  S
  |
  CH2
  |
  CH2    Methionine
  |
  CHNH2
  |
  COOH
```

Problem 6

```
                 COOH
                 |
 CH═C—CH2CHNHC═O
 |   |            |
 N   N—CH3        CH2
  \ /             |
   C              CH2
   H              |
                  NH2
```

Anserine

β-alanyl-1-methyl-L-histidine

8. Write a balanced equation for the synthesis of proline from α-ketoglutarate. If the α-carbonyl carbon atom of α-ketoglutarate is labeled, where would the label appear in the proline?

9. In a bacterial mutant unable to synthesize pantothenic acid, the pantothenic acid requirement may be abolished by giving pantoic acid, α-ketopantoic acid, or α-ketoisovaleric acid in the presence of p-aminobenzoic acid. Labeled p-aminobenzoic acid does not give rise to labeled pantothenic acid in this mutant whereas 2-^{14}C-α-ketoisovaleric acid gives rise to pantothenic acid labeled as shown in the margin. In wild-type bacteria of the same species, α-^{14}C-aspartate was found to give rise to pantothenic acid labeled in the β-carbon atom of the β-alanine moiety. From these observations deduce the pathway for pantothenic acid synthesis.

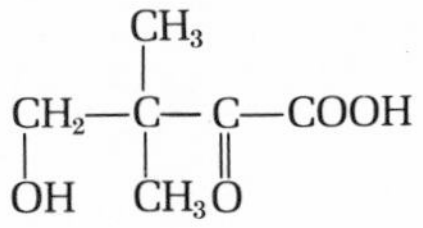

10. How many high-energy phosphate bonds are utilized in the conversion of serine and methionine to cysteine? If (a) 2-^{14}C-labeled methionine or (b) 2-^{14}C-labeled serine is utilized as the precursor, where will the label appear in the cysteine formed?

Problem 9

Pantoic acid

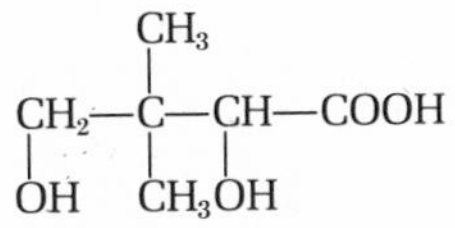

```
         CH3
         |
  CH2—C—CH—COOH
  |      |    |
  OH   CH3 OH
```

α-Ketopantoic acid

```
         CH3
         |
  CH2—C—C—COOH
  |      |   ||
  OH   CH3 O
```

α-Ketoisovaleric acid

```
         CH3
  4      |      2    1
  CH3—CH—C—COOH
         3      ||
                O
```

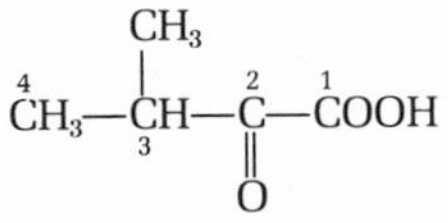

Labeled pantothenic acid

```
         CH2OH
         |
  CH3—C—CH3
         |
      14CHOH
         |
         C=O
         |
        HN
         |
         CH2
         |
         CH2
         |
         COOH
```

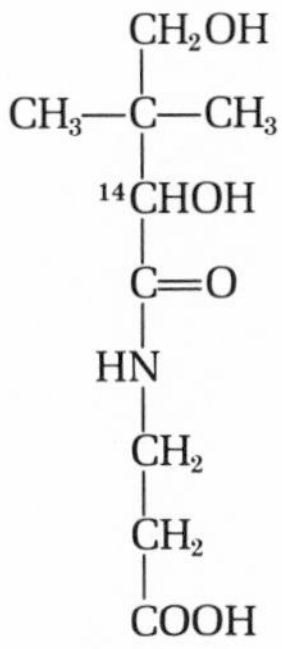

CHAPTER 25 THE BIOSYNTHESIS OF MONONUCLEOTIDES

The biosynthesis of the ribo- and deoxyribonucleotides is a vital process since they are direct precursors of RNA and DNA and of the nucleotide coenzymes. Central to the biosynthesis of the mononucleotides is the pathway of formation of their bases, the pyrimidines and purines. Nearly all living organisms, except for a few bacteria, appear to have the capacity to synthesize these bases from very simple precursors.

An important feature of the biosynthetic pathways leading to the mononucleotides is that they are under strict regulation by a number of allosteric control systems. Since the four major ribonucleotides and four major deoxyribonucleotides are inserted into RNA and DNA of the cell in fixed molar ratios, which differ depending on the species (Chapter 28), the regulatory mechanisms are apparently geared to yield the proper "mix" of mononucleotides appropriate for each type of cell. They also function to make the most economical use of nitrogenous precursors and intermediates, just as in amino acid biosynthesis. In fact, many cells also possess "salvage" mechanisms for recovery of free purines and pyrimidines resulting from the hydrolytic breakdown of nucleotides.

Biosynthesis of the Purine Nucleotides

Figure 25-1
Origin of the atoms of the purine ring.

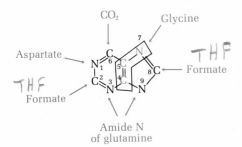

The first important clues as to the biosynthetic origin of the purine bases came from the experiments of Buchanan in which various isotopic precursors were fed to animals and the sites of incorporation of the labeled atoms into the purine ring determined. Such experiments were carried out in birds, which excrete nitrogen largely in the form of uric acid, a purine derivative (Chapter 20). As seen in Figure 25-1, two of the nitrogen atoms (N_3 and N_9) of the purine ring arise from the amide group of glutamine, another (N_1) arises from aspartate, and the last (N_7) from glycine. Carbon atoms 4 and 5 also arise from glycine, indicating that the glycine molecule contributes the three atoms shown in color. Carbon atoms 2 and 8 arise from formate and carbon 6 from CO_2. However, when these observations were first made, they were very puzzling because they did not conform to prevailing hypotheses for the mechanism of synthesis of purines. Some years of research were required to elucidate the various enzymatic steps involved, which are rather complex.

Contrary to the general expectation that the purine ring system is formed first, followed by attachment of D-ribose and phosphate, it has been found that an acyclic or open-chain ribonucleotide is formed first, followed by ring closure to yield the purine nucleotide. The pathway to adenylic and guanylic acids begins with D-ribose 5-phosphate, which undergoes enzymatic pyrophosphorylation at the expense of ATP to form *α-5-phosphoribosyl-1-pyrophosphate* (margin), an unusual reaction in which the pyrophosphate group of ATP is transferred intact. In the next step (Figure 25-2) this product reacts with glutamine in such a manner that the amino group from the amide portion of glutamine displaces the pyrophosphate group from the 1 position of the pentose to yield *β-5-phosphoribosyl-1-amine.* Free glutamic acid is formed, as well as inorganic pyrophosphate. In the third step, the carboxyl group of glycine reacts with the 1-amino group of 5-phosphoribosylamine, a reaction which requires ATP, to form an amide linkage between glycine and the amino sugar. An open-chain ribonucleotide, *glycinamide ribonucleotide,* is the product, together with ADP and phosphate. The glycosidic linkage joining D-ribose and glycine amide is the *β*-anomeric form.

Formation of *α*-5-phosphoribosyl-1-pyrophosphate (PRPP)

α-D-Ribose 5-phosphate

ATP → AMP

The purine ring is now built around the glycinamide moiety, which furnishes atoms 4, 5, 7, and 9 of the purine ring (Figure 25-1). This is accomplished by the addition of the one-carbon formyl group to yield carbon atom 8 of the purine ring (Figure 25-2). The formyl group, whose precursor is formic acid (Figure 25-1), is donated by *N^5,N^{10}-methenyltetrahydrofolate,* a formyl group carrier (Chapter 24); it is added to the free *α*-amino group of the glycinamide moiety, yielding *α-N-formylglycinamide ribonucleotide.*

In the next step, nitrogen atom 9, which is derived from the amide group of glutamine (Figure 25-1), is transferred to the formyl group of *α*-*N*-formylglycinamide ribonucleotide to yield *α-N-formylglycinamidine ribonucleotide.* The transfer of this amino group from glutamine requires ATP and proceeds with loss of its terminal high-energy phosphate bond. The product of this reaction is seen to possess in open-chain form the five atoms of the imidazole ring portion of purine. In the ensuing reaction the five-membered ring is closed by elimination of a molecule of water, to yield *5-aminoimidazole ribonucleotide.*

In the next step is added the carbon atom corresponding to carbon 6 of the purine ring, which ultimately arises from CO_2 (Figure 25-2). This carboxylation reaction proceeds directly, apparently without a coenzyme, to yield *5-aminoimidazole-4-carboxylic acid ribonucleotide.* The next step consists of a novel means of introducing a nitrogen atom into what will become position 1 of the purine ring (Figure 25-1). The entire aspartic acid mole-

Figure 25-2
Biosynthesis of inosinic acid. The ribose 5′-phosphate moiety is in color.

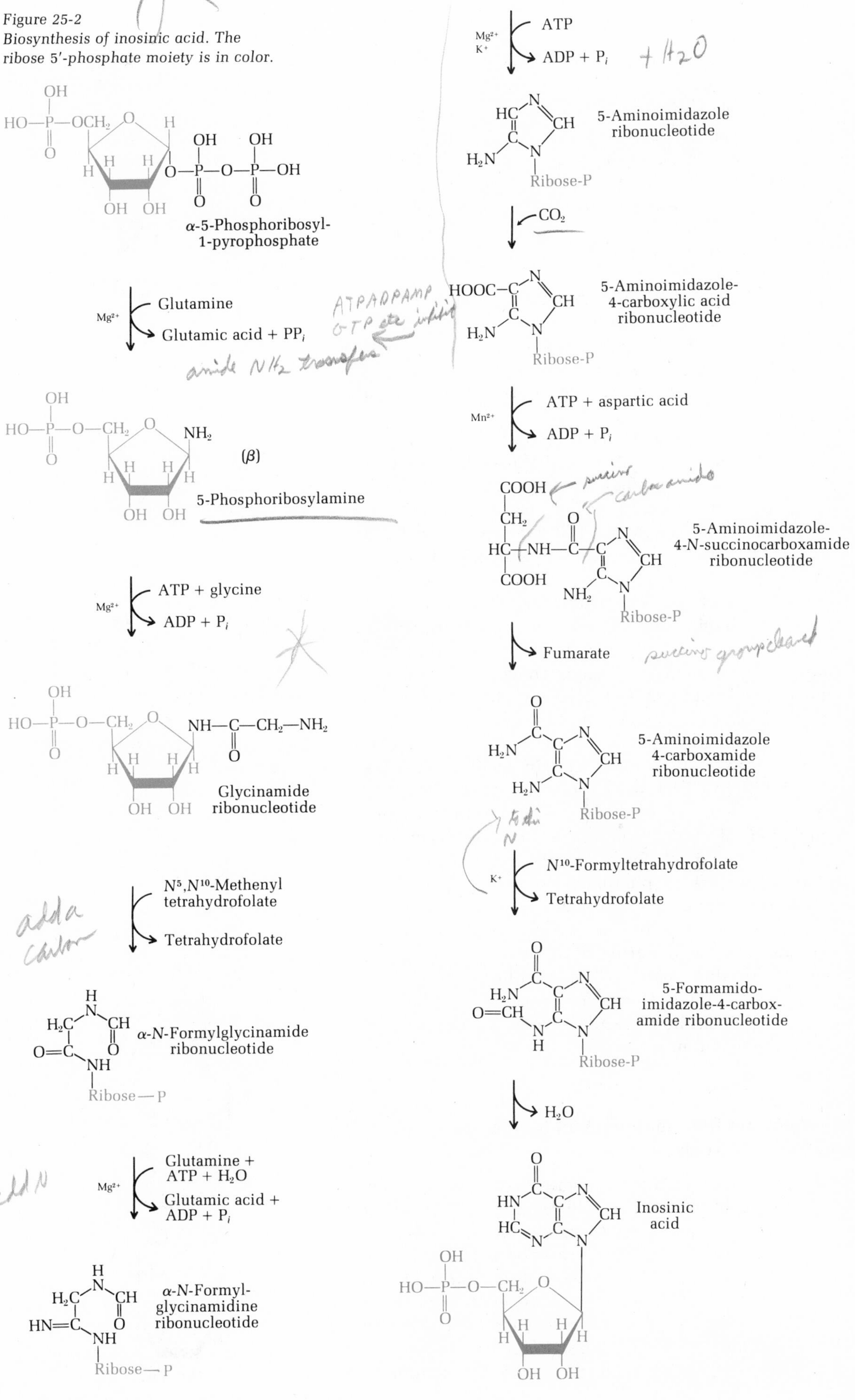

α-5-Phosphoribosyl-1-pyrophosphate

Mg^{2+} — Glutamine → Glutamic acid + PP_i

5-Phosphoribosylamine (β)

Mg^{2+} — ATP + glycine → ADP + P_i

Glycinamide ribonucleotide

N^5,N^{10}-Methenyl tetrahydrofolate → Tetrahydrofolate

α-*N*-Formylglycinamide ribonucleotide

Mg^{2+} — Glutamine + ATP + H_2O → Glutamic acid + ADP + P_i

α-*N*-Formylglycinamidine ribonucleotide

Mg^{2+}, K^+ — ATP → ADP + P_i

5-Aminoimidazole ribonucleotide

CO_2

5-Aminoimidazole-4-carboxylic acid ribonucleotide

Mn^{2+} — ATP + aspartic acid → ADP + P_i

5-Aminoimidazole-4-*N*-succinocarboxamide ribonucleotide

→ Fumarate

5-Aminoimidazole 4-carboxamide ribonucleotide

K^+ — N^{10}-Formyltetrahydrofolate → Tetrahydrofolate

5-Formamido-imidazole-4-carboxamide ribonucleotide

→ H_2O

Inosinic acid

cule is incorporated to yield *5-aminoimidazole 4-N-succinocarboxamide ribonucleotide,* from which free fumaric acid is subsequently eliminated, to yield *5-aminoimidazole-4-carboxamide ribonucleotide.*

The last carbon atom of the purine ring (number 2) is now introduced by transfer of the formyl group of N^{10}-formyltetrahydrofolate to the 5-amino group of the ribonucleotide. The pyrimidine portion of the purine ring system is now closed by elimination of water, to form the purine ribonucleotide *inosinic acid,* the first product in this biosynthetic pathway to possess a completed purine ring system.

It will be noted that six high-energy phosphate bonds are required for the formation of inosinic acid, starting from D-ribose 5-phosphate, if it is assumed that the pyrophosphate group displaced from 5-phosphoribosyl-1-pyrophosphate is ultimately hydrolyzed to orthophosphate by pyrophosphatase.

In the reaction sequence leading from D-ribose 5-phosphate to inosinic acid, there are three steps that are characteristically inhibited by specific antibacterial agents. The antibiotic *azaserine* (margin), which has been isolated from a species of *Streptomyces,* blocks the transfer of the amide amino group of glutamine to 5-phosphoribosyl-1-pyrophosphate, at the beginning of the reaction sequence. This antibiotic, which is a structural analog of glutamine and competes with it (margin), also inhibits a second step, namely, the transfer of the amino group of glutamine to α-*N*-formylglycinamide ribonucleotide. Azaserine apparently blocks essential —SH groups in the transferases catalyzing these reactions.

The antibacterial agents of the *sulfonamide* class (margin), which are widely used in medicine because they inhibit growth of many bacteria, prevent the formation of folic acid and hence block the step involving the formylation of *5-aminoimidazole-4-carboxamide ribonucleotide* in intact *E. coli* cells. Sulfonamides are structural analogs of *p-aminobenzoic acid* (margin), a precursor of folic acid (Chapter 24); through competitive inhibition they prevent the normal incorporation of *p*-aminobenzoic acid during the formation of folic acid from its building blocks. When sulfonamides block purine nucleotide synthesis in susceptible microorganisms, free 5-aminoimidazole-4-carboxamide accumulates in the medium.

Azaserine

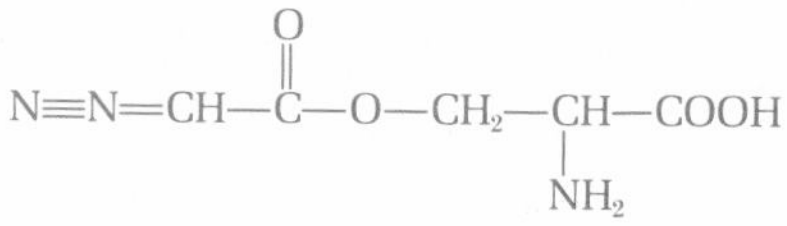

$$N{\equiv}N{=}CH{-}\overset{O}{\overset{\|}{C}}{-}O{-}CH_2{-}\underset{NH_2}{\underset{|}{CH}}{-}COOH$$

Glutamine

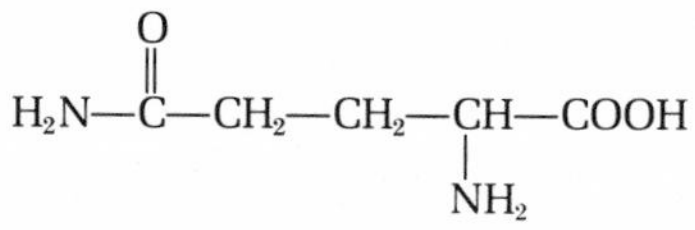

$$H_2N{-}\overset{O}{\overset{\|}{C}}{-}CH_2{-}CH_2{-}\underset{NH_2}{\underset{|}{CH}}{-}COOH$$

A sulfonamide

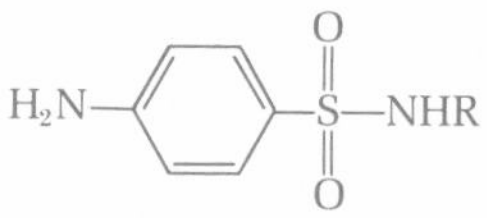

$$H_2N{-}C_6H_4{-}\overset{O}{\overset{\|}{\underset{O}{\underset{\|}{S}}}}{-}NHR$$

p-Aminobenzoic acid

$$H_2N{-}C_6H_4{-}COOH$$

Figure 25-3
Pathway from inosinic acid to adenylic acid.

Inosinic acid (Ribose-P)

GTP + Aspartic acid → GDP + P_i

Adenylosuccinic acid: HOOC—CH₂—CH—COOH, NH (Ribose-P)

→ Fumaric acid

Adenylic acid

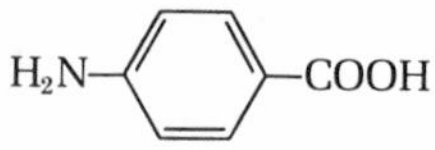

The Pathways from Inosinic Acid to Adenylic and Guanylic Acids

These pathways are shown in Figure 25-3. The conversion of inosinic acid to adenylic acid requires only the insertion of an amino group into position 6 of the purine ring of inosinic acid. However, this reaction is brought about in a circuitous fashion, by reaction of inosinic acid with aspartic acid, to yield *adenylosuccinic acid,* from which fumaric acid is then eliminated to yield adenylic acid. The reaction is catalyzed by the same enzyme responsible for causing elimination of fumaric acid from 5-aminoimi-

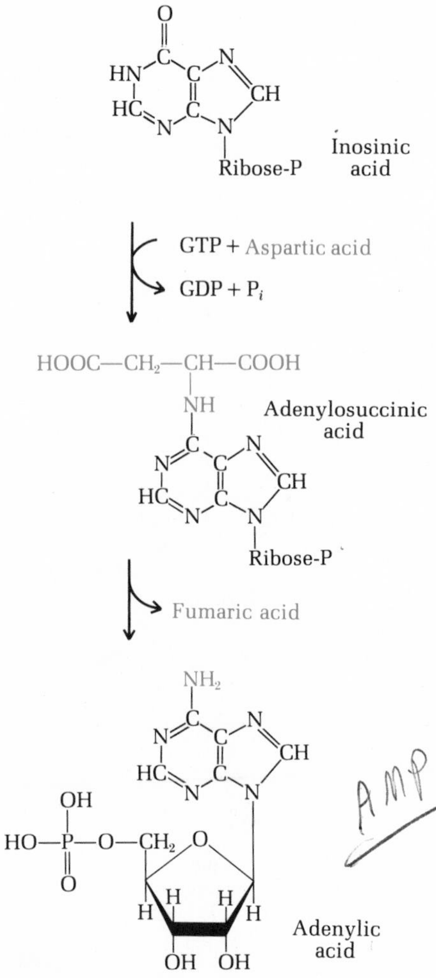

Figure 25-3 (cont.)
Pathway from inosinic acid to guanylic acid.

Inosinic acid

Xanthylic acid

ATP + glutamine

AMP + PP_i + glutamate

Guanylic acid

dazole-4-N-succinocarboxamide ribonucleotide (above). In this sequence, one high-energy phosphate bond, which is specifically donated by GTP, is required to make adenylic acid from inosinic acid. Thus, a total of seven high-energy phosphate bonds is required to make adenylic acid from D-ribose 5-phosphate.

In the formation of guanylic acid, inosinic acid is first oxidized to *xanthylic acid* by an oxygenase reaction (Chapter 17). Xanthylic acid is then aminated to form guanylic acid, a reaction that requires ATP. Since this step involves pyrophosphate cleavage and ultimate hydrolysis of pyrophosphate, two high-energy phosphate bonds are required to convert inosinic acid to guanylic acid; a total of eight is thus required to convert D-ribose 5-phosphate into guanylic acid.

The conversion of adenylic and guanylic acids to ATP and GTP, respectively, proceeds by two successive phosphokinase steps, catalyzed by nucleoside monophosphokinase and nucleoside diphosphokinase, respectively:

$$\text{GMP} + \text{ATP} \rightleftharpoons \text{GDP} + \text{ADP}$$

$$\text{GDP} + \text{ATP} \rightleftharpoons \text{GTP} + \text{ADP}$$

Figure 25-4
Control mechanisms in the biosynthesis of adenine and guanine nucleotides.

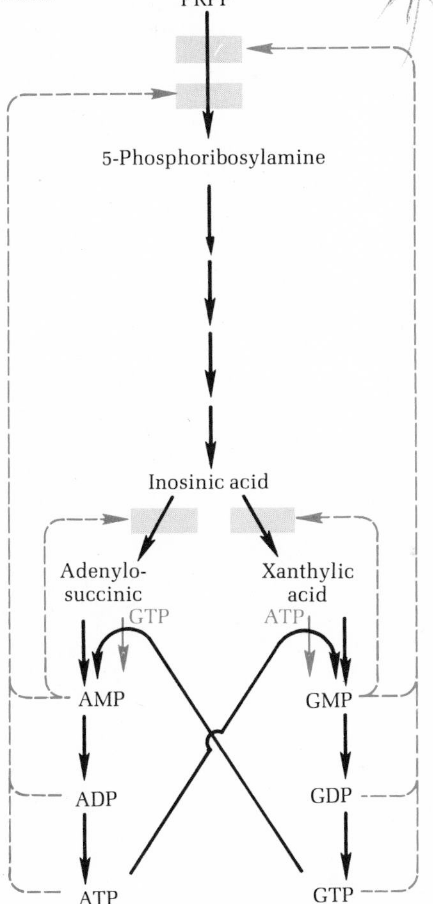

Regulation of Purine Nucleotide Biosynthesis

In *E. coli* cells, three major control mechanisms cooperate in regulating the overall rate of purine nucleotide synthesis and the relative rates of synthesis of the two end products adenylic acid and guanylic acid (Figure 25-4).

The first control is exerted on the early reaction step leading to the transfer of an amino group to 5-phosphoribosyl-1-pyrophosphate. The amidotransferase catalyzing this reaction is a multivalent regulatory enzyme; it is inhibited by ATP, ADP, or AMP, or by GTP, GDP, or GMP, each series of nucleotides apparently acting at a separate control site on the enzyme. Thus, whenever the purine mononucleotides accumulate, the first step in their synthesis undergoes feedback inhibition.

The second control mechanism is rather novel. It will be noted that the reaction pathway leading from inosinic to guanylic acid requires ATP as cofactor, whereas the pathway leading from inosinic acid to adenylic acid requires GTP. Thus, whenever there is an excess of ATP, the pathway leading to guanylic acid will be accelerated; similarly, whenever there is an excess of GTP, the synthesis of adenylic acid will be accelerated.

The third control mechanism is provided by the fact that an excess of GMP brings about allosteric inhibition of the conversion of inosinic acid to adenylosuccinic acid and thus inhibits synthesis of AMP.

Biosynthesis of Pyrimidine Nucleotides

The biosynthetic pathway to the pyrimidine nucleotides resembles that leading to the purine nucleotides in that the free bases are not intermediates. However, the pathway to the pyrimidine nucleotides is somewhat simpler.

Moreover, it differs in that the D-ribose moiety is attached *after* the pyrimidine ring has been formed from its open-chain precursors.

Although early isotopic experiments revealed that CO_2 and ammonia are precursors of the pyrimidine ring, the first important advance in our knowledge of pyrimidine biosynthesis came from studies of mutants of *Neurospora crassa* deficient in the ability to make pyrimidines and thus unable to grow unless cytosine or uracil is present in the medium. Such *pyrimidineless* mutants can, however, grow normally when presented with the pyrimidine derivative *orotic acid* (margin), which was first found in cow's milk. Tests with isotopic orotic acid showed that it is an immediate precursor in the biosynthesis of the pyrimidines in both *Neurospora* and a number of bacteria.

Orotic acid (6-carboxyuracil)

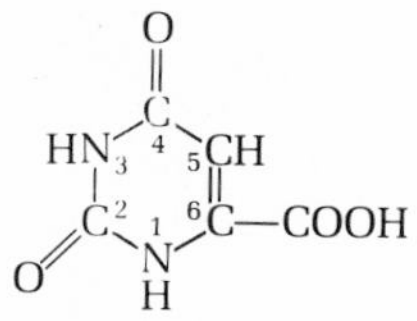

The first step in pyrimidine biosynthesis is the carbamylation of aspartic acid at the expense of carbamyl phosphate (Chapter 10) to yield *N*-carbamyl aspartic acid (Figure 25-5). This reaction is catalyzed by *aspartate transcarbamylase*, perhaps the most thoroughly studied allosteric or regulatory enzyme known. The regulatory aspects of this reaction will be discussed below.

By removal of water from *N*-carbamyl aspartic acid, which is catalyzed by *dihydroorotase*, the pyrimidine ring is closed with formation of the derivative L-*dihydroorotic acid*. This compound is now oxidized by the flavoprotein *dihydroorotate dehydrogenase* to yield *orotic acid*, a rather unusual reaction in which NAD^+ is the ultimate electron acceptor. Curiously, this dehydrogenase contains both FAD and FMN, as well as iron.

At this point, the D-ribose 5-phosphate side-chain, provided by 5-phosphoribosyl-1-pyrophosphate, is attached to orotic acid by the action of *orotidine 5′-phosphate pyrophosphorylase*, to yield *orotidine 5′-phosphate*, or *orotidylic acid*. Orotidylic acid is then decarboxylated to yield uridine 5′-phosphate (uridylic acid).

Although uridylic acid is a precursor of cytidine nucleotides, this conversion requires that uridylic acid (UMP) be first phosphorylated to UTP, which takes place by the reactions

$$\text{UMP} + \text{ATP} \rightleftharpoons \text{UDP} + \text{ADP}$$

$$\text{UDP} + \text{ATP} \rightleftharpoons \text{UTP} + \text{ADP}$$

UTP then undergoes an amination reaction on the 4 position of the pyrimidine ring, to yield cytidine 5′-triphosphate or CTP (Figure 25-6). ATP is required in this reaction; the amino group donor is free ammonia in *E. coli* or the amide group of glutamine in mammals.

Figure 25-5
Biosynthesis of uridylic acid.

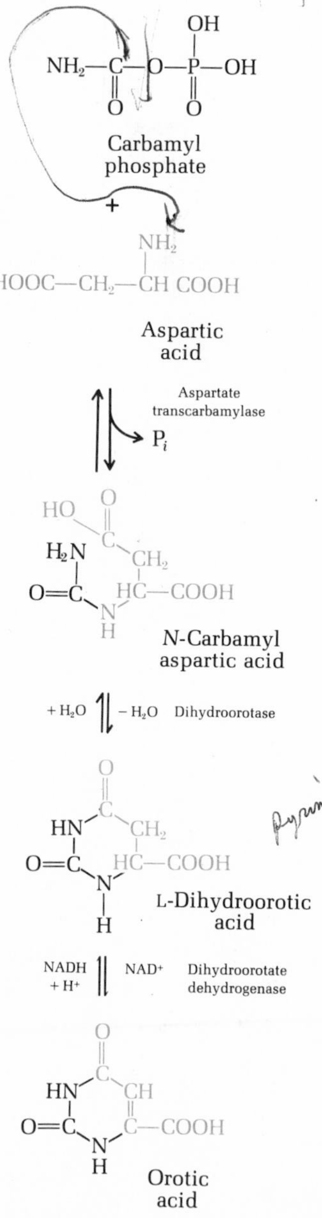

Carbamyl phosphate + Aspartic acid → (Aspartate transcarbamylase; P_i) → *N*-Carbamyl aspartic acid → (Dihydroorotase; $+H_2O$ / $-H_2O$) → L-Dihydroorotic acid → (Dihydroorotate dehydrogenase; NAD^+ / $NADH + H^+$) → Orotic acid

Regulation of Pyrimidine Nucleotide Biosynthesis

The regulation of the rate of pyrimidine nucleotide synthesis has been the subject of a number of penetrating investigations by Pardee and Gerhart. *Aspartate transcarbamylase* (often abbreviated *ATCase*), which catalyzes the first reaction in the sequence—the condensation of

Figure 25-6
Conversion of UTP to CTP (E. coli).
In mammals, the amide group of glutamine is the precursor of the 6-amino group, rather than ammonia.

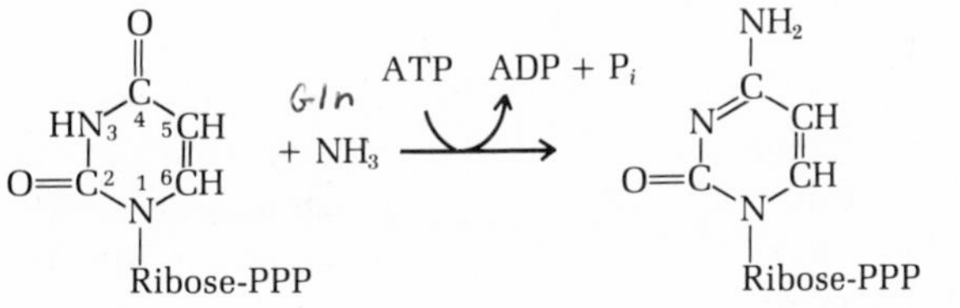

Uridine triphosphate (UTP) + NH_3 —(ATP → ADP + P_i)→ Cytidine triphosphate (CTP)

Figure 25-5 (cont.)

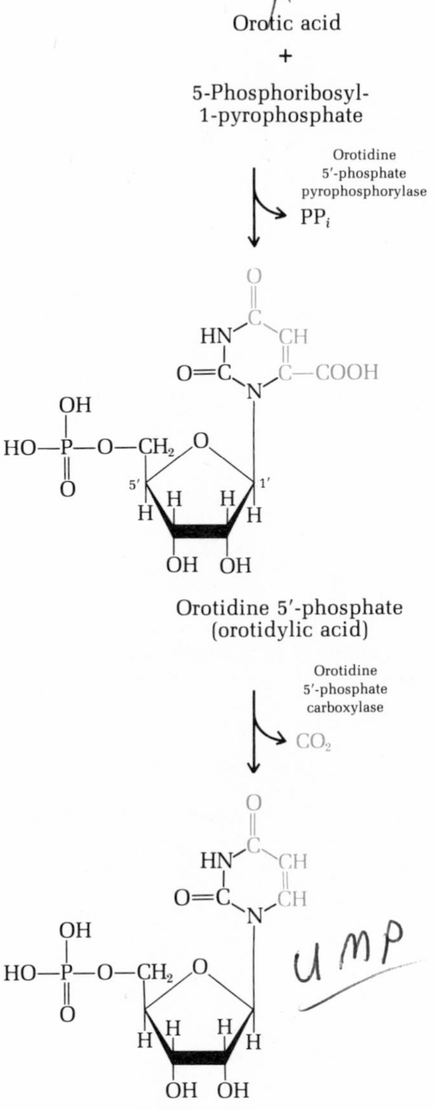

Orotic acid + 5-Phosphoribosyl-1-pyrophosphate —(Orotidine 5′-phosphate pyrophosphorylase; PP_i)→ Orotidine 5′-phosphate (orotidylic acid) —(Orotidine 5′-phosphate carboxylase; CO_2)→ Uridine 5′-phosphate (uridylic acid)

carbamylphosphate with aspartic acid to yield carbamylaspartic acid—was found to be inhibited by CTP, the end product of this sequence of reactions. When the steady-state level of CTP (and thus of UTP) is high, the formation of its precursor carbamylaspartic acid is inhibited (Figure 25-7). Gerhart and his colleagues have studied the kinetics and structure of ATCase in some detail. The highly purified enzyme from *E. coli*, like many allosteric enzymes, has a high molecular weight (300,000) and contains a number of subunits. A plot of aspartate concentration vs velocity of the reaction (Figure 25-8), with carbamyl phosphate concentration held constant, was sigmoid in shape (Chapter 9). When CTP was added in increasing concentrations, there was a decrease in the affinity of the enzyme for aspartate (i.e., an increase in K_M), but essentially no change in V_{max}. When ATP was also added, it overcame the effect of CTP in a competitive manner, indicating that ATP and CTP compete for the same site on the enzyme, which is evidently not the catalytic site, but rather an allosteric site. When the allosteric site is occupied by CTP, the binding of the substrate, and thus the catalyzed reaction, is inhibited. When this site is occupied by ATP, the reaction is stimulated. ATP is not intrinsically a positive modulator; it acts primarily by preventing the binding of CTP.

Addition of a mercurial, such as *p*-hydroxymercuribenzoate, causes the affinity for aspartate to increase and the sigmoid substrate-concentration curve to revert to the classical hyperbolic curve typical of ordinary, nonregulatory enzymes. The mercurial thus desensitizes the enzyme to its allosteric modulators and releases its full activity.

Physical-chemical analysis of the ATCase molecule has revealed that the mercurial causes its dissociation into two classes of subunits which can easily be separated. One type of subunit contains all the enzymatic activity but in this dissociated form, is not inhibited by CTP; it is called the *catalytic subunit*. It was found to bind succinate, a structural analog of aspartate. The other type of subunit has no catalytic activity but can bind CTP, the inhibitory modulator; it is therefore called the *regulatory subunit*. CTP can inhibit the enzymatic reaction only when the catalytic and regulatory subunits are combined and in contact, a view consistent with the fact that the mercurial, which desensitizes ATCase and releases it from inhibition by CTP, also causes dissociation of its subunits. There has been some uncertainty over the number of catalytic and regulatory subunits in ATCase; the most recent work suggests that there are six catalytic and six regulatory subunits. It is believed that each regulatory subunit can exist in two conformational states: one, a noninhibitory conformation, in which its binding site for CTP is unoccupied (or occupied by ATP), and the other, an inhibitory conformation, in which its binding site is filled with CTP. Similarly, the catalytic subunits are thought to exist in two conformational states, one fully active and one inhibited or inactive. In the intact ATCase molecule, the binding of a molecule of CTP by a regulatory subunit "locks" the latter in its inhibitory conformation; this conformational transition is then physically transmitted to an adjacent catalytic subunit, locking the latter into its catalytically inactive state.

The action of ATCase and other oligomeric regulatory enzymes has been explained by two different types of mechanism. One, the sequential hypothesis, which appears to account for most findings with ATCase, postulates that the interactions between regulatory and catalytic subunits are discrete and sequential, so that the regulatory enzyme molecule may exist in a number of conformational states, each having a characteristically different intrinsic catalytic activity, depending on the number of subunits that are "on" and the number that are "off." The other hypothesis postulates that any given regulatory enzyme molecule in a population may exist in only two states, with its subunits either all "on" or all "off," depending on the balance between substrate and modulator concentrations. It appears possible that some allosteric enzymes behave according to the sequential hypothesis and some according to the other.

Comparative studies of the behavior of aspartate transcarbamylase have revealed that its allosteric regulatory mechanisms are not identical in all types of cells, although the pattern may be similar. The picture developed above, in which the inhibitory modulator is CTP, appears to hold true for ATCase in *E. coli* and *Aerobacter aerogenes*. However, in the bacterium *P. fluorescens*, the major inhibitory modulator is UTP, and in some higher plants, it is UMP. Moreover, in some organisms, such as *B. subtilis*, aspartate transcarbamylase is not inhibited by any of these compounds, presumably because it lacks the regulatory subunits.

Biosynthesis of Deoxyribonucleotides

Since the deoxyribonucleotides differ from the ribonucleotides only in the presence of 2-deoxyribose instead of ribose, early efforts to establish the pathway of biosynthesis of the deoxyribonucleotides tacitly assumed that they would be formed by the same pathway described

Figure 25-7
Regulation of biosynthetic pathway to CTP by end-product inhibition of aspartate transcarbamylase. The inhibitory effect of CTP is prevented by ATP.

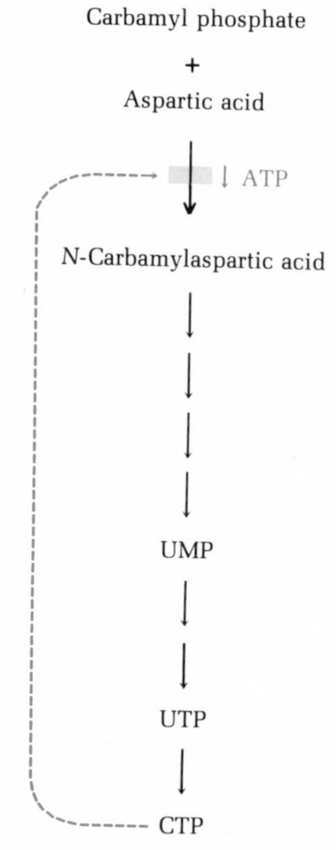

Figure 25-8
Effect of CTP, ATP and mercurials on the affinity of aspartate transcarbamylase for aspartate.

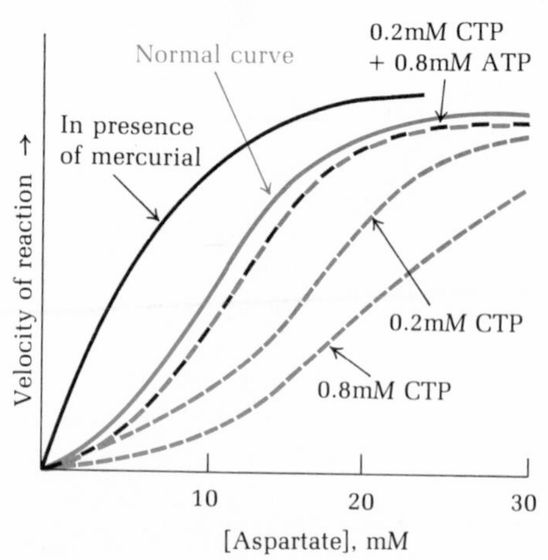

above for the ribonucleotides, with the phosphorylated ribose precursor replaced by an analogous 2-deoxyribose derivative. Much early research therefore centered on the mechanism of biosynthesis of free 2-deoxy-D-ribose and its phosphate derivatives. Even though a pathway for the synthesis of free 2-deoxyribose 5-phosphate from simpler precursors does exist in some cells, it is now quite clear from isotope tracer investigations that the deoxyribonucleotides are not normally synthesized starting from deoxyribose as a building block, but are formed by direct reduction of ribonucleotides at the 2′ carbon atom. When cytidine labeled with ^{14}C in both the pyrimidine ring and the ribose is presented to animals or bacterial cells, it is incorporated into the cytidylic acid residues of RNA and the deoxycytidylic acid residues of DNA without any change in the ratio of the isotopes in the pyrimidine and ribose (or deoxyribose) portions. This finding indicates that ribose was not detached from the cytosine of the labeled cytidine fed, prior to the formation of the labeled deoxyribonucleotide of DNA. Had ribose been detached, it would have become diluted by nonisotopic ribose (or deoxyribose). Moreover, more direct isotopic tests on cell-free bacterial extracts showed that labeled ribonucleotides are directly converted into the corresponding deoxyribonucleotides.

There appear to be two pathways for the direct reduction of ribonucleotides depending on the species. The pathway of deoxyribonucleotide synthesis in *E. coli* has been established in important research by Reichard. He and his colleagues have shown that all four ribonucleoside diphosphates, namely, ADP, GDP, UDP, and CDP, may be directly reduced to the corresponding deoxy analogs dADP, dGDP, dUDP, and dCDP, by an enzyme system which involves the action of four separate enzyme proteins. In the overall process the reduction of the ribose moiety to 2-deoxyribose requires a pair of hydrogen atoms, which are ultimately donated by NADPH and H^+. However, the immediate electron donor is not NADPH but the reduced form of a heat-stable protein called *thioredoxin*, which has two free —SH groups per 108 amino acid residues. Thioredoxin may be reversibly oxidized and reduced and oscillates between dithiol and disulfide forms. Its oxidized form is reduced by NADPH + H^+ in a reaction catalyzed by *thioredoxin reductase*, the second of the four enzyme proteins required in the complete process:

$$\text{Thioredoxin-S}_2 + \text{NADPH} + \text{H}^+ \xrightarrow[\text{Reductase}]{\text{Thioredoxin}} \text{thioredoxin-(SH)}_2 + \text{NADP}^+$$

Thioredoxin reductase is a flavoprotein of mol wt 68,000; it contains two molecules of bound FAD. The reducing equivalents of reduced thioredoxin so formed are now transferred to the ribonucleoside 5′-diphosphate acceptor, designated XDP.

$$\text{Thioredoxin-(SH)}_2 + \text{XDP} \xrightarrow[\text{Mg}^{2+}]{\text{Enzymes B}_1\text{ and B}_2} \text{thioredoxin-S}_2 + \text{dXDP}$$

This reaction is rather complex and requires two enzyme proteins B_1 and B_2, as well as Mg^{2+}. The complete system can reduce all four ribonucleoside 5′-diphosphates to yield the corresponding 2-deoxy-D-ribose analogs.

In some *Lactobacilli,* however, the corresponding enzyme system requires the ribonucleoside 5′-*tri*phosphates rather than the diphosphates; it requires deoxyadenosylcobalamin as coenzyme, and probably also requires thioredoxin. Since DAcobalamin is capable of acting as an intermediate carrier for the exchange of a hydrogen atom on one carbon atom for a substituent group on a vicinal carbon atom (Chapter 19), it is conceivable that the mechanism of reduction of ribose to 2-deoxyribose in *Lactobacilli* involves not only carbon atom 2 but also an adjacent carbon atom.

Because DNA contains thymine instead of the uracil present in RNA and in ribonucleotides, a pathway for deoxythymidylic acid (dTMP) synthesis is required. It is furnished by *thymidylate synthetase,* which catalyzes the methylation of dUMP to dTMP (margin). Note that the tetrahydrofolate coenzyme serves both as methyl donor and as hydrogen donor; the end product is dihydrofolate rather than tetrahydrofolate. Dihydrofolate may be reduced to tetrahydrofolate again by the action of dihydrofolate reductase (Chapter 24). A similar type of reaction is involved in the formation of 5-hydroxymethyldeoxycytidylic acid, which replaces deoxycytidylate in the DNA of certain bacteriophages.

Methylation of dUMP

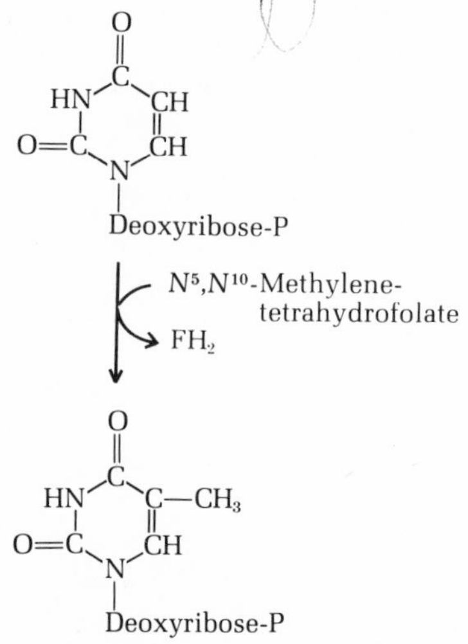

O, HN, C, CH, O=C, CH, N

Deoxyribose-P

N^5,N^{10}-Methylene-tetrahydrofolate

FH_2

O, HN, C, C—CH_3, O=C, CH, N

Deoxyribose-P

Thymidine 5′-phosphate thymidylic acid (dTMP)

To complete the synthesis of the deoxyribonucleoside 5′-triphosphates, which are direct precursors in DNA biosynthesis, the following types of phosphotransferase reactions occur

$$ATP + dADP \rightarrow ADP + dATP$$

$$ATP + dCDP \rightarrow ADP + dCTP$$

$$ATP + dTDP \rightarrow ADP + dTTP$$

$$ATP + dGDP \rightarrow ADP + dGTP$$

Regulation of Deoxyribonucleotide Biosynthesis

In *E. coli* cells, one set of control mechanisms for regulation of deoxyribonucleotide biosynthesis (Figure 25-9) involves the reaction between reduced thioredoxin and the NDPs, catalyzed by enzymes B_1 and B_2 described above. It has been found that the reduction of CDP to dCDP and of UDP to dUDP is strongly accelerated by ATP and that the reduction of ADP to dADP and of GDP to dGDP is stimulated by dGTP and dTTP. On the other hand, dATP acts as a feedback inhibitor, and inhibits the reduction of all the ribonucleoside 5′-diphosphates.

Degradation of Mononucleotides and "Salvage" of Bases

In higher animals, mononucleotides resulting from degradation of the nucleic acids by nuclease action usually

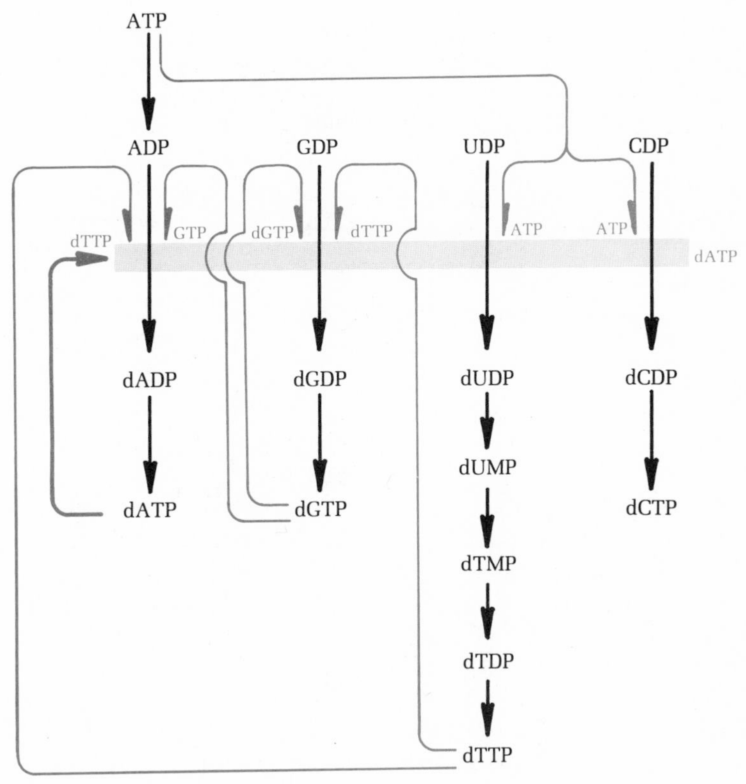

Figure 25-9
Allosteric control mechanisms in the biosynthesis of deoxyribonucleoside 5′-triphosphates. ATP and dTTP are important stimulatory modulators and dATP is a general inhibitor.

undergo enzymatic hydrolysis to yield, ultimately, the free purine and pyrimidine bases. The excreted product of purine degradation is uric acid in some vertebrates, including the primates, the Dalmatian coach hound, the birds, and some reptiles. However, in the remaining mammals and reptiles, and in mollusks, the end product is allantoin. In fishes, allantoin is broken down further to allantoic acid and urea, and in many invertebrates ammonia is the end product of purine catabolism. Curiously, guanine is a major excretory form of purines in the spider. The reactions shown in Figure 25-10 outline the major steps in the degradation of purines.

Free pyrimidines are finally degraded to urea and ammonia in most species. They may also be used as precursors in the synthesis of some β-amino acids, such as β-alanine and β-aminoisobutyric acid.

In many organisms, particularly bacteria, free bases formed on hydrolytic degradation of mononucleotides are often salvaged for reuse in nucleic acid synthesis. The free purines can be salvaged by at least two types of reactions. The first type is catalyzed by *purine phosphoribosyl transferases*

$$\text{Adenine} + \text{5-phosphoribosyl-1-pyrophosphate} \rightleftharpoons \text{AMP} + \text{PP}_i$$

$$\text{Guanine} + \text{5-phosphoribosyl-1-pyrophosphate} \rightleftharpoons \text{GMP} + \text{PP}_i$$

Figure 25-10
Degradation of purines to uric acid, allantoin, and urea.

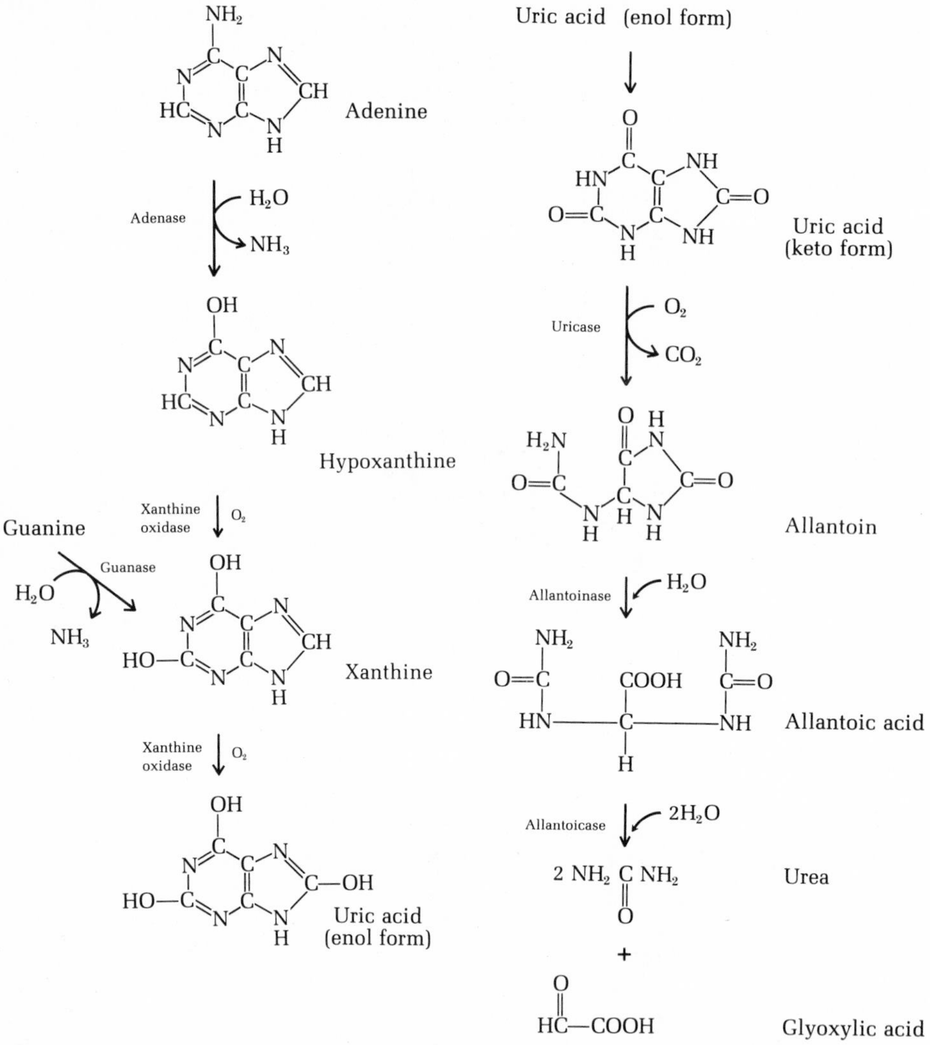

Adenine

Adenase (H_2O → NH_3)

Hypoxanthine

Guanine

Guanase (H_2O → NH_3)

Xanthine oxidase (O_2)

Xanthine

Xanthine oxidase (O_2)

Uric acid (enol form)

Uric acid (enol form)

Uric acid (keto form)

Uricase (O_2 → CO_2)

Allantoin

Allantoinase (H_2O)

Allantoic acid

Allantoicase ($2H_2O$)

2 NH_2CONH_2 Urea

+

$HC(=O)—COOH$ Glyoxylic acid

The second type is catalyzed by sequential action of *nucleoside phosphorylase* and *nucleoside kinase*, as in the following representative sequence:

$$\text{Guanine} + \text{ribose 1-phosphate} \rightleftharpoons \text{guanosine} + P_i$$

$$\text{Guanosine} + \text{ATP} \rightleftharpoons \text{GMP} + \text{ADP}$$

Biosynthesis of Nucleotide Coenzymes

The flavin nucleotides, pyridine nucleotides, and CoA are derivatives of adenylic acid and are synthesized from their component building blocks in enzymatic reactions that have some similarities to those employed in synthesis of the mononucleotides found in nucleic acids.

Flavin mononucleotide (FMN), which is not a true mononucleotide and is more accurately called riboflavin phosphate, is synthesized by the enzyme *flavokinase* from free riboflavin (vitamin B_2) and ATP in the reaction

$$\text{Riboflavin} + \text{ATP} \rightarrow \text{riboflavin 5}'\text{-phosphate} + \text{ADP}$$

FAD is then formed by the action of <u>flavin nucleotide phosphorylase:</u>

$$\text{Riboflavin 5'-phosphate} + \text{ATP} \rightarrow \text{flavin adenine dinucleotide} + PP_i$$

NAD is synthesized starting from free nicotinic acid (not nicotinamide) in the following series of reactions:

$$\text{Nicotinic acid} + \text{5-phosphoribosyl-1-pyrophosphate} \rightleftharpoons \text{nicotinic acid mononucleotide} + PP_i$$

$$\text{Nicotinic acid mononucleotide} + \text{ATP} \rightleftharpoons \text{desamido-NAD}^+ + PP_i$$

$$\text{Desamido-NAD}^+ + \text{glutamine} + \text{ATP} \rightleftharpoons NAD^+ + \text{glutamic acid} + ADP + P_i$$

It is noteworthy that the amide group of NAD is inserted *after* construction of the nicotinic acid analog of NAD, desamido-NAD. There are, however, some cells in which free nicotinamide or nicotinamide mononucleotide can be directly utilized instead of free nicotinic acid or nicotinic acid mononucleotide. $NADP^+$ is formed from NAD^+ by the reaction

$$NAD^+ + ATP \rightleftharpoons NADP^+ + ADP$$

Coenzyme A is assembled, starting from the free vitamin <u>pantothenic acid,</u> in the reaction sequence shown in Figure 25-11. In the last reaction, a phosphate group is introduced into the 3'-hydroxyl group of the adenosine portion of dephospho-CoA to yield the complete CoA molecule.

Figure 25-11
Biosynthesis of coenzyme A.

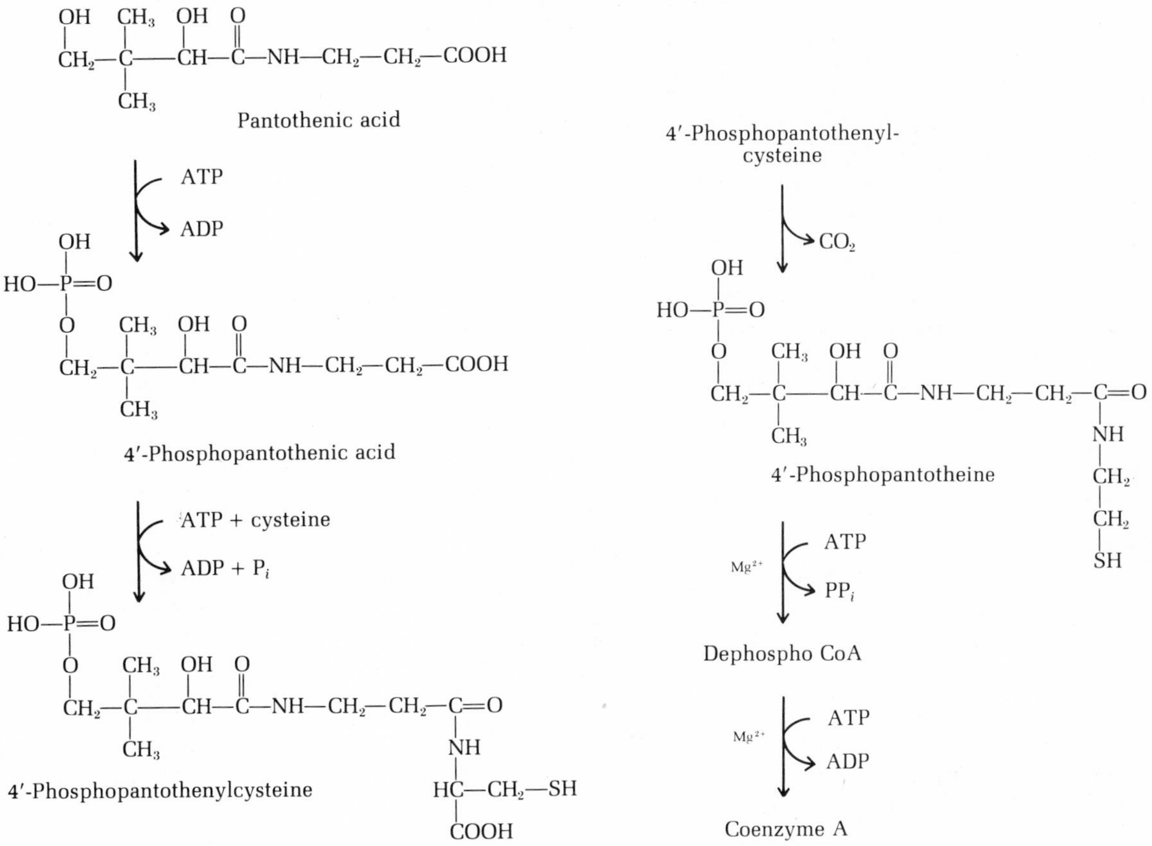

$HOCH_2—C(CH_3)_2—CH(OH)—C(=O)—NH—CH_2—CH_2—COOH$

Pantothenic acid

↓ ATP → ADP

$(HO)_2P(=O)—O—CH_2—C(CH_3)_2—CH(OH)—C(=O)—NH—CH_2—CH_2—COOH$

4'-Phosphopantothenic acid

↓ ATP + cysteine → ADP + P_i

$(HO)_2P(=O)—O—CH_2—C(CH_3)_2—CH(OH)—C(=O)—NH—CH_2—CH_2—C(=O)—NH—CH(COOH)—CH_2—SH$

4'-Phosphopantothenylcysteine

4'-Phosphopantothenyl-cysteine

↓ → CO_2

$(HO)_2P(=O)—O—CH_2—C(CH_3)_2—CH(OH)—C(=O)—NH—CH_2—CH_2—C(=O)—NH—CH_2—CH_2—SH$

4'-Phosphopantotheine

↓ Mg^{2+}; ATP → PP_i

Dephospho CoA

↓ Mg^{2+}; ATP → ADP

Coenzyme A

Summary

The purine ring of the purine ribonucleotides adenylic acid and guanylic acid is formed by closure of an open-chain ribonucleoside phosphate precursor. This biosynthetic sequence begins with the formation of glycinamide ribonucleotide; successive additions of a formyl group and an amino group to the glycinamide moiety are followed by closure of the imidazole ring. In subsequent reactions, the second ring of the purine nucleus is closed, yielding as the first purine-containing product the mononucleotide inosinic acid. Inosinic acid is the precursor of adenylic acid via adenylosuccinic acid and of guanylic acid via xanthylic acid. The biosynthesis of AMP and GMP is allosterically inhibited at the first step in the sequence by AMP, ADP, and ATP, and by GMP, GDP, and GTP; secondary control mechanisms also function.

Pyrimidine ribonucleotides are formed in a different pathway, in which the pyrimidine ring is synthesized first, in the form of orotic acid, before the attachment of ribose 5-phosphate. Uridylic acid is formed first and is then phosphorylated to UDP and UTP. UTP is the direct precursor of CTP. The first step in pyrimidine biosynthesis, which is catalyzed by the allosteric enzyme aspartate transcarbamylase, is inhibited by CTP and stimulated by ATP. This enzyme contains both catalytic and regulatory subunits, which interact with each other.

Ribonucleoside 5′-diphosphates are directly reduced to the corresponding 2-deoxy-ribonucleoside 5′-diphosphates. The ultimate electron donor is NADPH. In *E. coli*, electrons are transferred from NADPH + H^+ to the sulfur-containing protein thioredoxin, converting it into its dithiol form, which is the immediate reductant for conversion of the NDPs into the corresponding dNDPs. In some species, the 5′-triphosphates of ribonucleosides are reduced to the corresponding dNTPs in a reaction requiring cobamide. Biosynthesis of the deoxyribonucleoside triphosphates is subject to allosteric control; dTTP promotes synthesis of dATP and dGTP, whereas dATP inhibits synthesis of all the dNTPs. Deoxythymidylic acid is formed by methylation of deoxyuridylic acid; tetrahydrofolate is the intermediate methyl group and hydrogen donor.

Free purines and pyrimidines formed on degradation may be salvaged and reused for nucleic acid synthesis. They may also undergo further degradation. The purines are ultimately degraded by the sequence purines → uric acid → allantoin → allantoic acid → urea → ammonia. The nitrogenous end product excreted depends on the species.

The nucleotide coenzymes, FAD, NAD, NADP, and CoA, which are derivatives of adenylic acid, are synthesized from ATP and their vitamin precursors, namely, riboflavin, nicotinic acid, and pantothenic acid.

References

Books

HUTCHINSON, D. W.: *Nucleotides and Coenzymes,* John Wiley & Sons, Inc., New York, 1964.

REICHARD, P.: *The Biosynthesis of Deoxyribose,* John Wiley & Sons, Inc., New York, 1967. Excellent short account of the experimental background.

Articles

BLAKLEY, R. L., and E. VITOLS: "Control of Nucleotide Biosynthesis," *Ann. Rev. Biochem.,* **37**:201–224 (1968). A review of recent experimental progress.

KAPLAN, N. O. "Metabolic Pathways Involving Niacin and Its Derivatives," in D. M. Greenberg (ed.), *Metabolic Pathways*, Academic Press, New York, 3d ed., vol. II. pp. 627–672. (1961).

KOSHLAND, D. E., and K. E. NEET: "The Catalytic and Regulatory Properties of Enzymes," *Ann. Rev. Biochem.*, **37**:359–410 (1968). An important review including recent ideas on the structure and activity of regulatory enzymes.

LARSSON, A., and P. REICHARD: "The Enzymic Synthesis of Ribonucleotides," *Progress in Nucleic Acid Research and Molecular Biology*, **7**:303–347 (1967). Detailed review.

PLAUT, G. W. E.: "The Biosynthesis of Flavin Derivatives," in D. M. Greenberg (ed.), *Metabolic Pathways*, Academic Press, New York, 3d ed. vol. II, pp. 673–712. (1961).

SCHULMAN, M. P.: "Purines and Pyrimidines," in D. M. Greenberg (ed.), *Metabolic Pathways*, Academic Press, New York, 3d ed. vol. II, pp. 389–457. (1961).

STADTMAN, E.: "Allosteric Regulation of Enzyme Activity," *Advances in Enzymol.*, **28**:41–154 (1966). An excellent correlation of information.

WARREN, L.: "Nucleotides and Nucleosides," in D. M. Greenberg (ed.), *Metabolic Pathways*, Academic Press, New York, 3d ed. vol. II, pp. 459–524. (1961).

WEBER, K.: "New Structural Model of *E. coli* Aspartate Transcarbamylase and The Amino-acid Sequence of The Regulatory Polypeptide Chain," *Nature*, **218**:1116–1119 (1968).

Problems

1. In which atoms of adenylic acid isolated from the hydrolyzate of liver RNA would you expect to find (*a*) the carboxyl carbon of acetyl CoA, (*b*) carbon atom 3 of D-glucose, (*c*) the α-carbon atom of serine, (*d*) the amino nitrogen of aspartic acid, and (*e*) the amide nitrogen atom of glutamine?

2. In which atoms of cytidylic acid of rat liver RNA would you expect to find (*a*) the β-carboxyl carbon atom of oxaloacetic acid, (*b*) the nitrogen atom of ammonia, and (*c*) the nitrogen atom of glutamic acid?

3. Calculate the number of high-energy phosphate bonds "saved" by a cell if it salvages one molecule of free adenine and reuses it for nucleic acid synthesis.

4. Write a balanced equation for the formation of CTP from CO_2, NH_3, ATP, ribose 5-phosphate, and oxaloacetic acid in *E. coli*. How many high-energy bonds are required per CTP synthesized? How many D-glucose molecules must the cell oxidize to completion in order to obtain enough ATP to synthesize one molecule of CTP?

5. Write a balanced equation for the formation of NADP from nicotinic acid, ATP, ribose 5-phosphate and ammonia.

6. What labeled end products would be expected from the breakdown of adenine labeled in the following positions: (*a*) nitrogen atom 3, (*b*) carbon atom 5, and (*c*) the nitrogen atom of the 6-amino group in man? In an ammonotelic fish?

CHAPTER 26 CONTRACTILE AND MOTILE SYSTEMS

Among the most provocative and challenging problems in biochemistry is the molecular basis of the conversion of the chemical energy of ATP into the mechanical energy of contractile or motile processes. It is a difficult problem, because we lack simple models or prototypes for this type of energy conversion. In fact, there are no common man-made machines capable of converting chemical energy directly into mechanical energy.

The performance of mechanical work is most conspicuous in the contraction of muscle and in the propulsive activity of cilia and flagella. Actually, contractile filaments or microtubules are very widely distributed; they are present in most eucaryotic cells. They participate in the organization of the cell contents, in spindle formation and cell division, in movement and transport of cell materials, and in other cell activities involving mechanical stress, torsion, or translocation.

The mechanism of muscular contraction is more than a biochemical problem. Most of the recent advances in our knowledge have come from the integration of biochemical, biophysical, and electron microscopic approaches. We shall therefore examine muscular contraction from this broader point of view. Actually, muscles should be looked upon as highly efficient and versatile machines, with remarkable engineering and performance characteristics when compared to man-made machines (Figure 26-1).

Figure 26-1
A notice of a lecture presented to the Institution of Electrical Engineers in London on February 11, 1969.

Available *now*. LINEAR MOTOR. Rugged and dependable: design optimized by world-wide field testing over an extended period. All models offer the economy of "fuel-cell" type energy conversion and will run on a wide range of commonly available fuels. Low stand-by power, but can be switched within msecs to as much as 1 KW mech/Kg (peak, dry). Modular construction, and wide range of available subunits, permit tailor-made solutions to otherwise intractable mechanical problems.

Choice of two control systems:

(1) *Externally triggered mode.* Versatile, general-purpose units. Digitally controlled by picojoule pulses. Despite low input energy level, very high signal-to-noise ratio. Energy amplification 10^6 approx. Mechanical characteristics: (1 cm modules) max. speed; optional between 0·1 and 100 mm/sec. Stress generated; 2 to 5×10^{-5} newtons m^{-2}.

(2) *Autonomous mode with integral oscillators.* Especially suitable for pumping applications. Modules available with frequency and mechanical impedance appropriate for
   (*a*) Solids and slurries (0·01–1·0 Hz).
   (*b*) Liquids (0·5–5 Hz): lifetime $2{\cdot}6 \times 10^9$ operations (typ.) $3{\cdot}6 \times 10^9$ (max.)—independent of frequency.
   (*c*) Gases (50–1,000 Hz).

Many optional extras e.g. built-in servo (length and velocity) where fine control is required. Direct piping of oxygen. Thermal generation. Etc.

Good to eat.

The lecture is by Professor D. R. Wilkie. The subject is muscle.

Ultrastructural Organization of Skeletal Muscle

Both light and electron microscopy have given us vital information on the size, shape, and geometrical arrangement of the molecular components of the contractile elements in muscle. Skeletal muscle fibers are extremely long and multinucleated cells. Their plasma membrane is known as the *sarcolemma.* A large part of the volume of muscle cells is occupied by their contractile elements, the *myofibrils,* which are arranged in parallel bundles (Figure 26-2). The myofibrils in turn are surrounded and bathed by the *sarcoplasm,* the intracellular fluid of muscle, which contains glycogen, glycolytic enzymes, ATP, phosphocreatine, and inorganic electrolytes, as well as a number of amino acids and peptides. Mitochondria of the more active, aerobic muscles are very profuse and are regularly arranged along the myofibrils, with their positions relatively fixed. In less active muscles, the mitochondria are fewer in number and less regularly spaced. Muscle cells also contain a highly differentiated endoplasmic reticulum, usually referred to as the *sarcoplasmic reticulum;* its structure and function are described later.

Figure 26-2
Electron micrographs of skeletal muscle.

Longitudinal section of frog muscle in contracted state, showing the characteristic cross-striations in two parallel myofibrils.

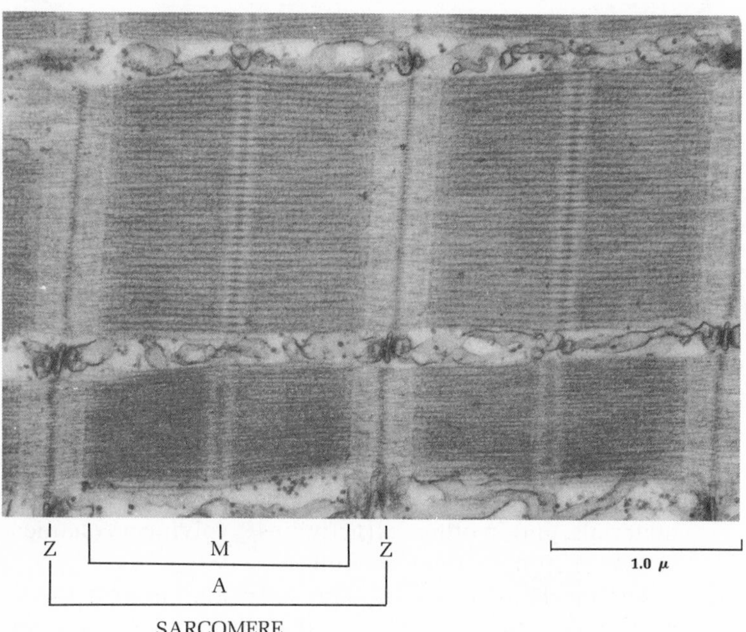

Transverse section of myofibril of blowfly flight muscle, showing hexagonal array of myofilaments.

The myofibrils of muscle fibers are long, thin structures, which possess along their length a structural pattern that repeats every 2.5 μ, more or less (Figures 26-2 and 26-3). In skeletal or striated muscle, the repeat units of many parallel myofibrils are in transverse register, yielding characteristic cross striations, which are the result of the alternation of optically dense and less-dense transverse bands. The light bands are called *isotropic* or *I bands;* the dark bands are called *anisotropic* or *A bands.* Isotropic structures possess uniform physical properties regardless of the direction in which they are measured, whereas in anisotropic structures the physical properties depend on the direction of measurement. For example, the A bands of muscle are optically anisotropic; that is, their index of refraction is not uniform in all directions, giving them the property of *double refraction* or *birefringence.* In general, birefringence is shown by those solids whose molecular components are asymmetric and oriented in one direction.

In resting muscle, the dark A bands are about 1.6 μ long and the I bands about 1.0 μ long. The I bands are bisected by a dense transverse line about 800 Å wide, the *Z line.*

Figure 26-3
Schematic representation of the structure of myofibrils.

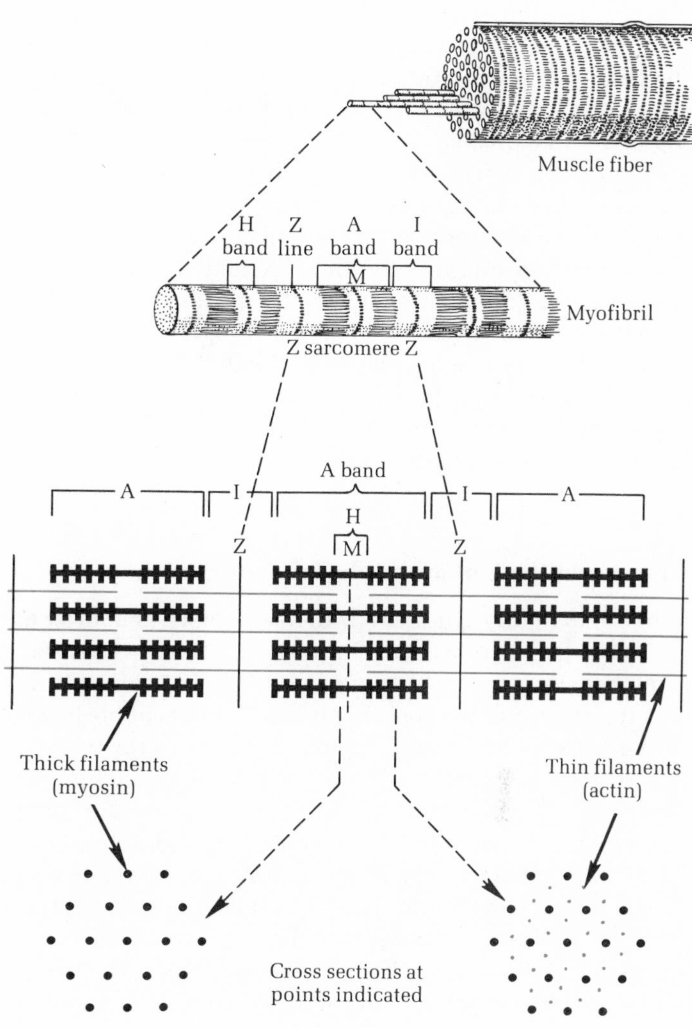

The central portion (~0.5 μ) of the A band, which is called the *H zone*, is less dense than the rest of the band; it is bisected by a transverse dense line, the *M line*. The complete longitudinal repeat unit, from Z line to Z line, is called a *sarcomere* (Figures 26-2 and 26-3).

More detailed examination with the electron microscope, particularly by H. E. Huxley and also J. Hanson, has revealed that each myofibril is composed of many parallel *myofilaments*, of which there are two types, thick and thin (Figure 26-3). In the I bands, only thin filaments are present; they are about 60 Å in diameter. The dense portions of the A bands contain not only the thin filaments found in the I band, but also a regular array of thick filaments (diameter 150 to 170 Å) which give the A bands their characteristic birefringence. Examination of cross sections has shown that the thick filaments are about 450 Å apart and are arranged in a hexagonal pattern; each thick filament is surrounded by six thin filaments, also in hexagonal array (Figure 26-3). The thick filaments extend continuously from one end of the A band to the other. The thin filaments, on the other hand, are not continuous through the entire A band. They begin at the Z line, are continuous through the I bands, and extend into the A bands. However, they terminate at the edge of the central H zone of the A bands. Since the thin filaments are also in lengthwise register, the edges of the H zone are distinctly demarcated.

Within the dense portions of the A bands, regularly disposed cross-bridges between the thick filaments and adjacent thin filaments have been observed by high-resolution electron microscopy; they are actually projections from the thick filaments. In skeletal muscle there are six cross-bridges in a period of about 430 Å. They are arranged in pairs, each pair being rotated by about 120° from the preceding pair (see below). The cross-bridges represent the only structural connection between the thick and thin filaments.

Changes in the Sarcomere during Contraction

When maximally contracted, the sarcomere is shortened by anywhere from 20–50 percent. When passively stretched, it may extend to about 120 percent of its normal length. By careful microscopic measurements of the length of the A bands and I bands in intact muscle in the relaxed, contracted, and stretched states, it has been conclusively demonstrated that the A bands, and thus the thick filaments, always remain constant in length. Similarly, the distance between the Z line and the edge of the H zone also remains constant at all stages during a normal contraction, indicating that the thin filaments likewise undergo no change in length. From such considerations, Huxley and other investigators have concluded that changes in muscle length must be due to sliding of the thick and thin filaments along each other, so that the degree of interpenetration or overlap of the thick filaments by the thin filaments varies (Figure 26-4). When muscle undergoes

Figure 26-4
Sliding filament model of muscle contraction.

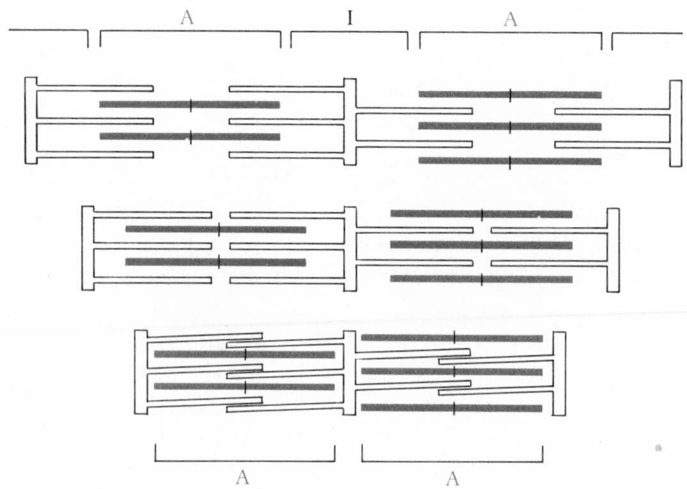

maximal shortening, the thin filaments may even slide past each other to form a new and more dense central zone, with an actual diminution of the normally constant distance from the Z line to the margin of the H zone.

These observations suggest that the crossbridges between the thick and thin filaments in the dense portions of the A band are rapidly formed and broken as the filaments slide along each other.

The Protein Components of Muscle Cells

The intracellular proteins of skeletal muscle cells consist of the water-soluble proteins of the sarcoplasm, which make up about 20 to 25 percent of the total muscle protein, and the water-insoluble filamentous proteins of the myofibrils. The soluble sarcoplasmic proteins are easily extracted from muscle with cold water; this fraction is often called *myogen*. The myogen fraction is rich in glycolytic enzymes, and from it the enzymes aldolase, glyceraldehyde 3-phosphate dehydrogenase, glycerol 3-phosphate dehydrogenase, and phosphorylase, among others, may be isolated in large yields.

The water-insoluble proteins of the myofilaments have proved to be much more difficult to separate and obtain in pure form. The modern era of biochemical research on the contractile elements of muscle began with the classic investigations of Edsall and von Muralt in the early 1930s on the muscle protein *myosin*. After first removing the soluble myogen fraction of minced rabbit skeletal muscle by extraction with cold water, they found that much of the protein of the remaining insoluble muscle residue can be removed in soluble form by prolonged extraction with cold 0.6 *M* KCl solutions. The protein so extracted can be precipitated by diluting or dialyzing the extract to reduce the KCl concentration; the precipitated protein can then be redissolved in 0.6 *M* KCl. This protein fraction, insoluble in water but soluble in 0.6 *M* KCl, was called "myosin"; today this fraction is more accurately called *actomyosin* or *myosin B*, as we shall see.

Two lines of evidence suggested that the fraction called "myosin" is a major component of the anisotropic bands of skeletal muscle. First, Edsall and von Muralt showed that solutions of myosin possess the property of *double refraction of flow*, also known as *flow birefringence*. This phenomenon is shown by solutions of long, thin, highly asymmetric molecules. When such solutions are static and unstirred, the solute molecules are randomly oriented; consequently, the refractive index of the solution is identical in all directions. However, when such a solution is forced to flow through a narrow capillary, the solute molecules orient themselves in the direction of flow, causing the solution to become optically anisotropic. A second line of evidence suggesting that myosin is the major component of the A bands came later from microscopic examination of the appearance of intact muscle fibers before and after myosin was extracted with 0.6 *M* KCl. After removal of myosin, the A bands became less dense and lost most of their anisotropic character.

In 1939, Engelhardt and Ljubimova in Moscow found that myosin prepared by the method of Edsall possesses enzymatic activity; in the presence of Ca^{2+} ions, myosin catalyzes hydrolysis of the terminal phosphate group of ATP to yield ADP and inorganic phosphate. Shortly thereafter, Engelhardt showed that if 0.6 *M* KCl solutions of myosin are squirted through a fine hypodermic needle into cold distilled water, the myosin is precipitated in the form of fragile threads. When ATP and Ca^{2+} ions are added to the medium bathing such artificial fibers of myosin, their length and extensibility undergoes marked alteration. Simultaneously, the ATP undergoes hydrolysis. These observations strongly supported the view that myosin is a major component of the A bands and that it is involved in the energy-dependent contractile process.

During World War II, Szent-Györgyi and his colleagues in Hungary made a number of new discoveries regarding the molecular components of the myofibrils which greatly clarified the relationship of myosin to the contractile process. In particular, they found that skeletal muscle contains another major protein component, which they called *actin*. Moreover, they found that the "myosin" isolated by Edsall and von Muralt consisted largely of a complex of myosin and actin, called actomyosin or myosin B.

Today it is recognized that there are three major protein components in the water-insoluble, filamentous elements of skeletal muscle, namely, *myosin*, *actin*, and *tropomyosin B*. Together they make up about 90 percent of the proteins of the contractile apparatus (Table 26-1). In addition, there are at least three minor protein components, which include *α-actinin*, *β-actinin*, and *troponin*. The three major proteins found in myofilaments may be selectively extracted from muscle after removal of the myogen fraction. Myosin may be removed from the myogen-free residue of muscle by a brief extraction with cold alkaline 0.6 *M* KCl. The actin may then be extracted from the acetone-dried muscle residue with cold, slightly alkaline water; it is obtained in a globular form called *G-actin*. Further extraction of the residue at higher temperatures yields tropomyosin B.

Table 26-1 Protein components of the myofilaments of rabbit skeletal muscle

	Total protein, %
Major	
Myosin	54
Actin	25
Tropomyosin B	11
Minor	
Troponin, α-Actinin, β-Actinin	10

Myosin

The protein known today as myosin is purified by cycles of solution in 0.6 *M* KCl and precipitation by dilution or dialysis. Since myosin has been subjected to intensive physical-chemical study by many investigators over the last 15 years, it may appear surprising that until recently there was still considerable ambiguity and disagreement about its size, subunit composition, and precise three-dimensional conformation. These difficulties arose in part from its highly asymmetrical nature, which causes it to show substantial deviations from ideal behavior in hydrodynamic measurements such as sedimentation and diffusion, and in part from the tendency of myosin and other myofilament proteins to associate tightly with each other, a property which can lead to the illusion of homogeneity.

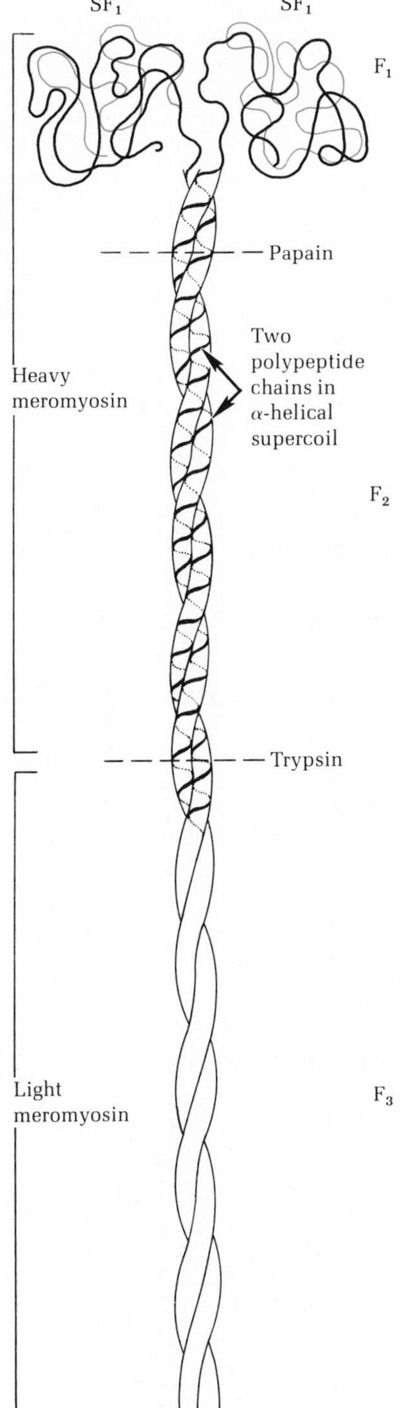

Figure 26-5
Schematic representation of the myosin molecule showing its globular head and long tail and the points of enzymatic fragmentation.

The most recent studies on highly purified myosin indicate rather conclusively that it has a molecular weight of about 470,000. It is a long (~1600 Å), asymmetric molecule containing a globular head, as is schematically represented in Figure 26-5. The bulk of the evidence now suggests that myosin contains two identical polypeptide chains of ~225,000 mol wt which can be separated on treating myosin with concentrated urea or guanidine solutions. These chains are quite remarkable, since they are the longest single polypeptide chains known, each having about 1,800 amino acid residues. It is believed that through most of the length of the myosin molecule, each chain exists in α-helical conformation and that the two chains are supercoiled, that is, wound around each other to form a double helical structure. At one end of the myosin molecule, both of the polypeptide chains are folded into globular structures. In addition, the head of the myosin molecule is believed to contain two smaller polypeptide chains.

Highly purified myosin preparations show the capacity to hydrolyze the terminal phosphate group from ATP; they also attack GTP, ITP, and CTP. The ATPase activity of myosin is distinctive in that (1) it is stimulated by Ca^{2+}, (2) it is profoundly influenced by KCl concentration, and (3) it has two pH optima, one at pH 6.0 and the other at pH 9.5. In addition, it is characteristically dependent on two different classes of sulfhydryl groups, which differ in their susceptibility to alkylation or to mercaptide formation. When the more susceptible —SH groups are blocked, the ATPase activity of the myosin molecule is increased, suggesting that this class of sulfhydryl groups is normally inhibitory to the enzyme. When the second class of sulfhydryl groups is then titrated, the ATPase activity is completely abolished, suggesting that the second class is required for the hydrolytic process.

Much important information regarding the structure of myosin and its ATPase activity has come from fragmentation studies. When myosin is briefly exposed to trypsin or chymotrypsin, specific peptide linkages near the center of the tail are cleaved to yield a heavy and a light fragment, called *heavy meromyosin* and *light meromyosin,* respectively (Figure 26-5). These fragments have been isolated in purified form. They are also designated as fragments (F_1 + F_2) and F_3 respectively. On the other hand, when myosin is treated with the enzyme papain, a different type of fragmentation results. It yields two fragments from the head, called *SF_1 fragments,* and a long fragment (F_2 + F_3), corresponding to the entire tail. If heavy meromyosin ($F_1 + F_2$) is treated further with trypsin, the F_1 portion is recovered in the form of two SF_1 fragments, identical to those obtained with papain. All these fragments have been recovered and purified; their characteristics are summarized in Table 26-2. Of particular interest is the finding that the ATPase activity of myosin survives these fragmentation procedures; it is located in the fragment $F_1 + F_2$ and also in SF_1. It has therefore been concluded that the ATPase activity of myosin resides entirely in its head, and that there are two catalytic sites per myosin molecule, one in each of the two SF_1 fragments. Each contains an inhibitory and a catalytic sulfhydryl group.

A second important conclusion has been drawn from the studies of myosin fragments; it pertains to the site on the myosin molecule to which actin binds. Purified intact myosin binds actin at two specific sites to form *actomyosin,* a phenomenon which represents a very crucial step in the contractile mechanism, as we shall see later. Much evidence suggests that the same sulfhydryl groups of myosin that are important in ATPase activity are also necessary in binding actin to myosin. For example, when actin is bound to myosin, an interesting and significant change in the ATPase activity occurs. Whereas the ATPase activity of pure myosin requires Ca^{2+} and is inhibited by Mg^{2+}, the ATPase activity of actomyosin is stimulated by Mg^{2+}. Moreover, it has been found that the entire actin-binding activity of myosin resides in the SF_1 fragments bearing the ATPase activity. From such experiments it has been concluded that the two catalytic ATPase sites on the head of the myosin molecule also participate in forming actomyosin.

Table 26-2 Fragments of myosin resulting from proteolytic cleavage (see Figure 26-5)

	Particle weight, daltons	*α-helix,* %	*Length,* Å
Myosin	470,000	60	1600
$F_1 + F_2$	350,000	44	750
$F_2 + F_3$	211,000	95	1100
F_2	61,000	80	400
F_3	150,000	99	700
SF_1	120,000	36	90

Actin

This protein occurs in two forms, *G-actin* (globular actin) and *F-actin* (fibrous actin), which is a polymer of G-actin. The monomeric G-actin is stable in distilled water, but, under certain conditions to be described, it polymerizes to form F-actin.

Rabbit muscle G-actin has been highly purified. It has a molecular weight of 46,000, is globular in shape, and consists of a single polypeptide chain, whose amino-terminal sequence has been identified as N-acetyl-Asp-Glu-Thr. A molecule of G-actin contains one residue of the unusual amino acid *ϵ-N-methyllysine* (margin); it also contains a large number of proline residues and seven cysteine residues.

ϵ-N-Methyllysine

$$\begin{array}{l} CH_3 \\ | \\ NH \\ | \\ CH_2 \\ | \\ CH_2 \\ | \\ CH_2 \\ | \\ CH_2 \\ | \\ CH—NH_2 \\ | \\ COOH \end{array}$$

Each molecule of G-actin binds one Ca^{2+} ion very tightly, a fact that may be related to the role of Ca^{2+} in initiation of contraction and in ATPase activity. It also binds one molecule of ATP or ADP with high affinity. Binding of ATP by G-actin is usually followed by its polymerization to form F-actin. For each molecule of G-actin added to the F-actin chain, one molecule of ATP is split to ADP and phosphate. The ADP so formed remains bound to the G-actin subunits of the F-actin chain. The polymerization is described by the equation

$$n(\text{G-actin-ATP}) \rightarrow \underset{\text{F-actin}}{(\text{G-actin-ADP})_n} + {}_nP_i$$

ATP is not a necessary requirement for polymerization of G-actin; neutral salts alone are capable of inducing polymerization of G-actin.

F-actin consists of two strands of G-actin monomers, in a supercoiled arrangement. One model favored by much evidence is shown in the margin. Such a two-stranded filament would have an average diameter of ~60 Å, in

The double helical structure of F-actin.

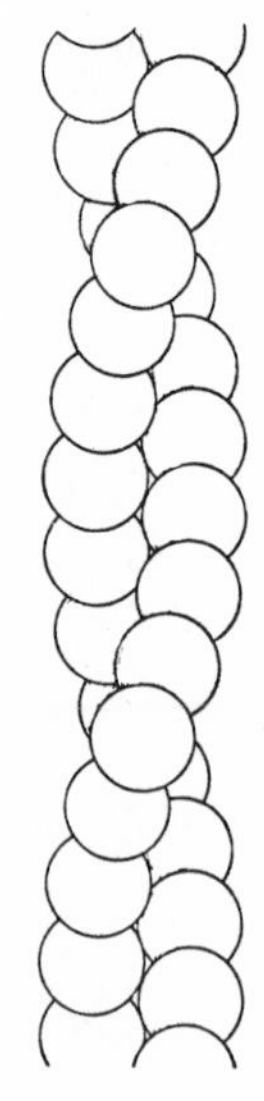

agreement with the diameter of the thin I filaments of muscle as observed in electron micrographs.

Actomyosin

When pure myosin and actin are mixed, a complex called *actomyosin* is formed. Its formation is accompanied by a large increase in viscosity and flow birefringence. The composition and particle weight of actomyosin depends heavily on the experimental conditions, such as the pH, the KCl and $MgCl_2$ concentration, and the protein concentration. Actomyosin complexes can also be extracted from muscle by prolonged exposure to 0.6 *M* KCl. The molar ratio of G-actin monomers to myosin in actomyosin complexes is approximately 1:1. Since an F-actin chain contains many G-actin monomers, each F-actin filament can bind many myosin molecules. Electron microscopy has not only confirmed this stoichiometry but also revealed that only the heads of myosin molecules bind to the actin filaments. A very significant property of actomyosin complexes is the fact that they undergo dissociation in the presence of ATP and Mg^{2+}; the dissociation is accompanied by a large and rapid decrease in the viscosity of the actomyosin solution (Figure 26-6). Simultaneous with the dissociation, ATP undergoes hydrolysis. When the hydrolysis of ATP is complete, the actin and myosin reaggregate, presumably through interactions of the essential sulfhydryl groups that appear to be common to the ATPase sites of myosin and to their actin-binding capacity. As seen below, the dissociation and reassociation of actin and myosin may be steps in the breaking and making of the cross-linkages between the thick and thin filaments of the myofibril.

Figure 26-6
Dissociation of actomyosin by ATP. The rapid drop of viscosity accompanies dissociation. As ATP is dephosphorylated the actin and myosin reassociate.

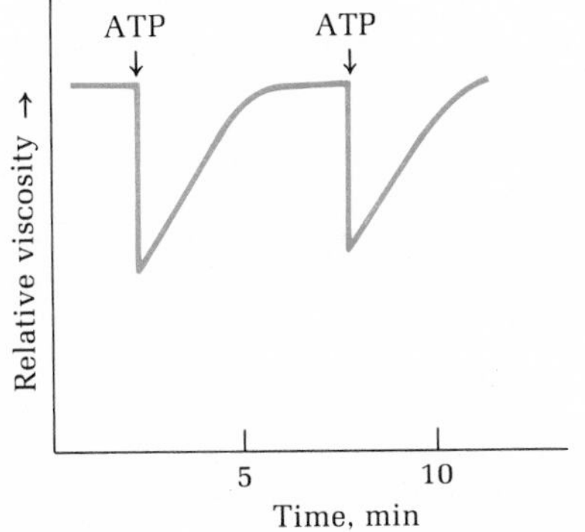

Tropomyosin A and B

Tropomyosin A and tropomyosin B are two other filamentous proteins associated with muscle. Both resemble in structure the long tails of the myosin molecule. Tropomyosin B (water-soluble tropomyosin) is found in all muscles, where it is an important component of the thin filaments of the I zone. Tropomyosin A, which is also called water-insoluble tropomyosin or *paramyosin*, is found in the "catch" muscles of mollusks (below).

Tropomyosin B is a rodlike molecule about 450 Å long and 20 Å thick. It has a molecular weight of about 130,000 and consists of two similar if not identical polypeptide chains of 70,000 mol wt. Both chains are almost entirely in α-helical configuration and are entwined around each other in a supercoiled arrangement, similar to that of the tail of myosin. Both chains contain free —SH groups.

Tropomyosin B forms a complex with F-actin when the two proteins are mixed. In this complex, the tropomyosin B molecule may occupy one groove of the helically coiled, two-stranded structure of the F-actin. By sensitive immunochemical methods applied to isolated myofibrils, it has been established that tropomyosin B is present in the thin filaments of the I zone.

Minor Protein Components

Recent research on the components of the I filaments has revealed that they contain another protein, troponin, which has been isolated and purified. It has a molecular weight of about 86,000. Troponin forms a complex with tropomyosin B; the troponin–tropomyosin B complex, which is also called "relaxing protein," can bind in turn with F-actin to form a troponin–tropomyosin B–actin complex.

The function of troponin has been identified by recent research. Troponin binds Ca^{2+} ions very tightly; presumably it serves as the Ca^{2+}-binding component in the troponin–tropomyosin B–actin–myosin complex. As we shall see later, muscular contraction is triggered or set off by free Ca^{2+} ions; troponin appears to confer Ca^{2+}-sensitivity to the cross-linked actin and myosin filaments.

The proteins α-actinin and β-actinin are also believed to be minor components of the actin filaments. It has been suggested that the former is a cross-linking protein, and the latter may be associated with troponin.

The Ultrastructure of Myofilaments

We may now assemble the foregoing information into a molecular description of the structure of the myofilaments. The thick filaments of the A bands of skeletal muscle, which are about 15,000 Å long and about 100 Å in thickness in rabbit muscle, consist of a bundle of myosin molecules arranged parallel to the long axis of the filament. The individual myosin molecules are so arranged that their heads are oriented away from the M line in the center of the A band; the heads project laterally out of the bundle in a regular, helical fashion. The cross section of the thick filament is occupied by eighteen myosin molecules. The projecting, barblike heads of the myosin molecules, which are about 90 Å long, are believed to form the cross-bridges that make contact with the six neighboring thin filaments in those portions of the A band that are interpenetrated by thin filaments. (Figure 26-7)

In vertebrate muscle, the thin filaments, which are ~60 Å in thickness and about 10,000 Å long, are arranged radially around the thick myosin filaments, so that each myosin filament is surrounded by six actin filaments, the axis of which is about 250 Å from the axis of the thick filaments. The projecting heads of the myosin molecules in the thick filaments are thus just long enough to reach the adjacent thin filaments. The thin filaments consist of double-stranded F-actin, in which the G-actin monomers appear to be not only structural but also functional units.

The gross physical mechanism of contraction appears to involve repetitive making and breaking of successive cross-linkages between the myosin heads of the thick filaments and the G-actin monomeric units of the thin filaments. (Figure 26-8) From the behavior of isolated actomyosin complexes, it has been postulated that the cross-bridges are stable in the *absence* of ATP but dissociate in the presence of ATP. As the cross-linkages are

Figure 26-7
Diagram showing arrangement of cross-bridges on myosin filaments in frog sartorius muscle deduced from low angle x-ray diagrams.

The 6/2 helical arrangement of cross-bridges on a bundle of myosin molecules.

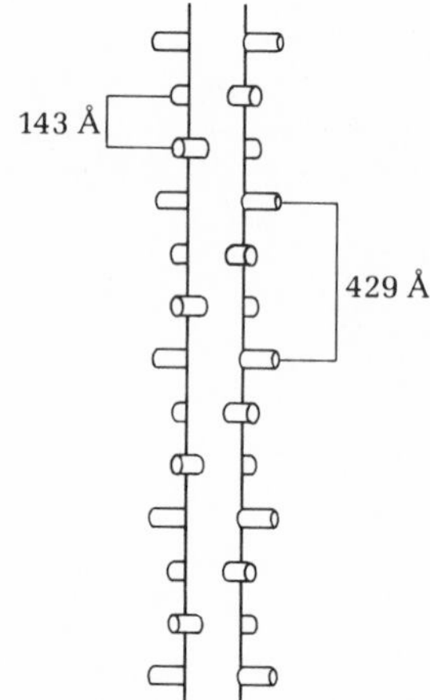

Cross section showing super-lattice of myosin and actin molecules and the arrangement of cross-bridges.

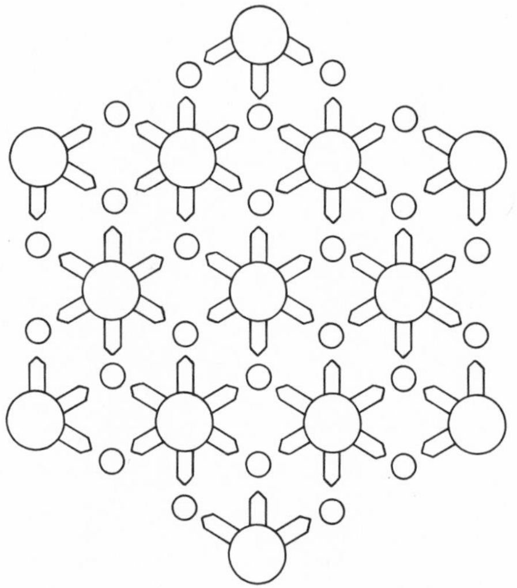

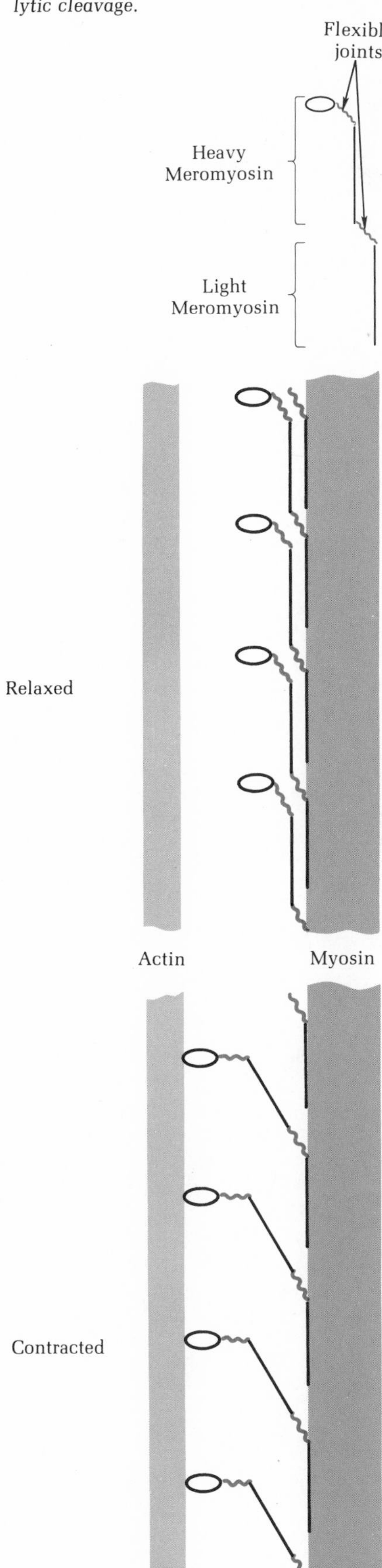

Figure 26-8
Formation of cross-bridges between actin and myosin filaments. The myosin molecule is postulated to have flexible joints at the points where it is susceptible to proteolytic cleavage.

made and broken, the filaments are caused to move past each other, presumably by a conformation change between the sites of cross-linkage in one of the two filaments, very likely the thick filament. The chemical trigger setting off a contraction, as we shall see, is the release of free Ca^{2+} into the sarcoplasm, which stimulates myosin ATPase and causes the breakdown of ATP and thus the formation of the cross-linkages. When the ADP so formed is rephosphorylated to ATP (see below), the cross-linkage is broken again. It has been estimated that one ATP molecule is required to break each cross-linkage as the filaments move a distance equal to the diameter of a G-actin monomer.

The Coupling of Excitation and Contraction

Two important questions remain to be answered regarding the molecular aspects of muscular contraction. How is the contraction process triggered or set off? How does the contracted sarcomere relax again? Clearly, the concentration of ATP in the sarcoplasm cannot be the triggering factor, since in resting muscle the ATP concentration in the sarcoplasm bathing the myofibril is very high.

The stimulus for contraction of muscle is an electrical impulse arriving from the motor nerve at the motor end plate or neuromuscular junction. This impulse is transmitted to the muscle cell and rapidly spreads over the entire sarcolemma. Normally there is a potential difference across the sarcolemma such that the outside is about 60 mv more positive than the inside. As the impulse spreads over the sarcolemma, this potential difference momentarily disappears, a phenomenon called *depolarization.* The depolarization is believed to be due to a sudden increase in permeability to certain cations such as K^+, Na^+, and Ca^{2+}, which flow in such a direction as to result in discharge of the transmembrane potential.

The mechanism by which the rapidly spreading impulse in the sarcolemma is instantly communicated to the interior of the muscle cell, some 50 μ deep, so that all filaments of the muscle fiber contract simultaneously, has only recently been recognized. Simple diffusion of a chemical messenger from the sarcolemma to the interior myofilaments had been ruled out as the means of communication, on the grounds that diffusion is much too slow to account for the great speed of the excitation process. The probable answer to this problem came from investigations with the electron microscope, which revealed that there are many repeating tubular invaginations of the surrounding sarcolemma, which run across the muscle cell at the Z line of the myofibrils in some muscles and near the A-I junctions in others, in such a manner that these tubules are in contact with nearly all the myofibrils in the cell. This complex system of transverse tubules is called the *T system* (Figure 26-9). When the sarcolemma is excited by an incoming impulse and undergoes depolarization, the entire T system also undergoes depolarization, thus communicating the electrical impulse nearly simultaneously to all the sarcomeres of the muscle fiber.

Figure 26-9
The sarcoplasmic reticulum (in color). The terminal cisternae are indicated by arrows.

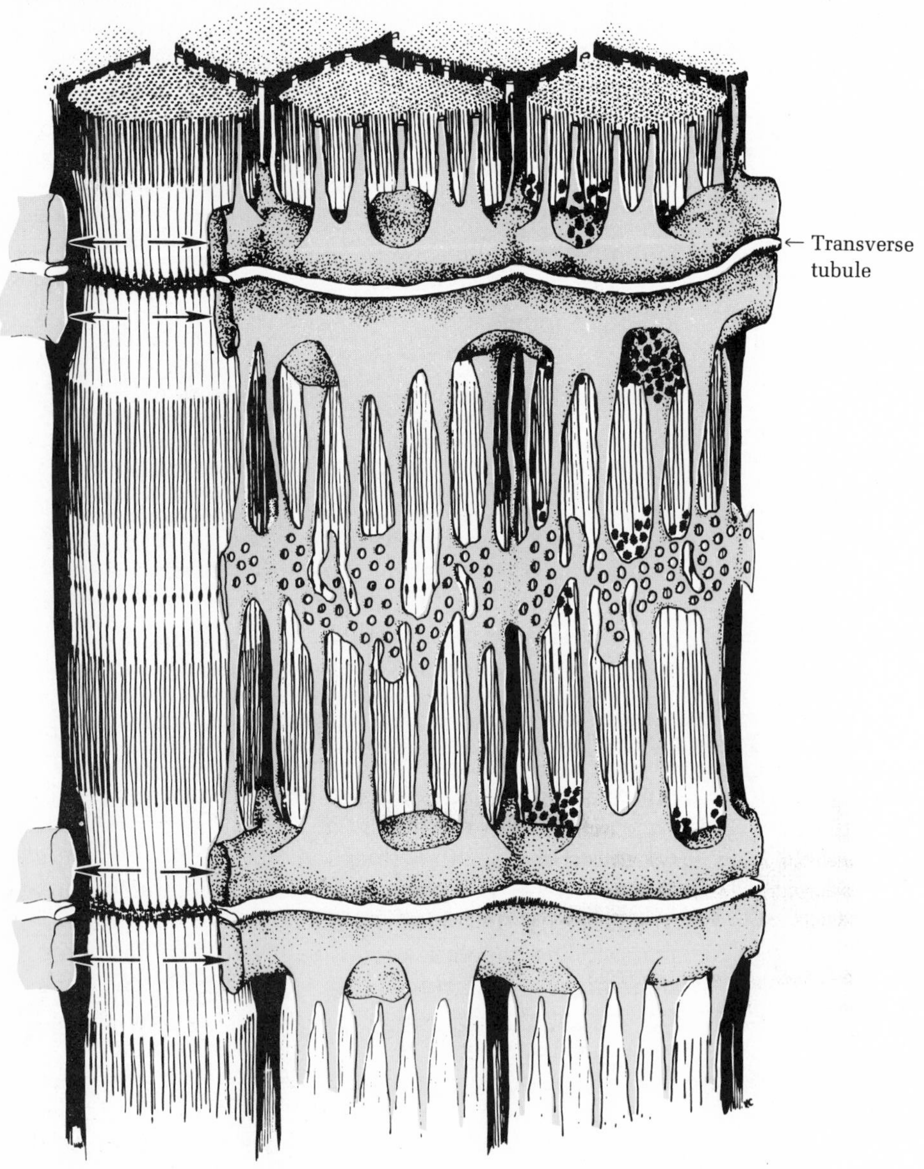

The mechanism of translation of the electrical change in the T system into chemical or molecular changes in the myofilaments has been revealed, partly by electron microscopy and partly by biochemical study. Surrounding each set of adjacent sarcomeres in a myofibril there is a flattened double-membrane vesicle with many perforations, resembling a lace cuff or sleeve; in the muscles of the frog and of mammals each vesicle extends from the A-I junction of one sarcomere to the A-I junction of the next (Figure 26-9). The entire sleevelike system of vesicles is called the *sarcoplasmic reticulum.* The internal compartment or cisterna of each vesicle is connected to all others in the same cross striation by transversely oriented connecting channels called *terminal cisternae.* Pairs of parallel terminal cisternae run across the myofibrils in close contact with the transverse tubules of the T system (Figure 26-9). When the sarcolemma is excited and the T system becomes depolarized, this change is transmitted to the membranes of the closely apposed sarcoplasmic reticulum, causing it to increase in permeability. As a result, Ca^{2+} ions escape from the cisternae of the reticulum, in which Ca^{2+} is normally segregated in resting muscle. The extremely rapid discharge of Ca^{2+} from the reticulum into the sarcoplasm is believed to trigger the interaction of ATP with the thick and thin myofilaments; it will be recalled that Ca^{2+} specifically stimulates the hydrolysis of ATP by myosin preparations. In the resting muscle cell, ATP cannot undergo hydrolysis by myosin, for lack of Ca^{2+}. It has been estimated that the Ca^{2+} concentration in the sarcoplasm of relaxed muscle is about 5×10^{-7} *M*; the Ca^{2+} concentration required to set off a contraction is estimated to be about 5×10^{-6} *M*.

Relaxation

After the exciting impulse has passed through the sarcoplasmic reticulum, causing it to release Ca^{2+} to the sarcoplasm, the sarcolemma and the sarcoplasmic reticulum return to their original polarized state, in which the outside of the cell membrane is some 60 mv more positive than the inside. Subsequently, the Ca^{2+} distribution across the membrane returns to its normal state in which the Ca^{2+} is segregated within the cisternae of the sarcoplasmic reticulum. The question arises as to how the Ca^{2+} that is released into the sarcoplasm by excitation is again sequestered inside the vesicles of the sarcoplasmic reticulum, to restore the muscle to its original resting state, ready to receive another impulse. This process has been directly studied by biochemical methods. When skeletal muscle is homogenized, the sarcoplasmic reticulum is fragmented into small closed vesicles. These vesicles can easily be isolated by differential centrifugation as the "microsome" fraction. Suspensions of such vesicles have been found to accumulate added Ca^{2+} ions very rapidly in the presence of excess ATP and some matching anion such as phosphate. It has therefore been concluded that the segregation of Ca^{2+} within the sarcoplasmic reticulum results from the action of an ATP-dependent Ca^{2+}-"pump" in the membrane, an enzymelike molecule which transfers Ca^{2+} across the membrane into the vesicle, even against a gradient of Ca^{2+} concentration, at the expense of the free energy of hydrolysis of ATP. For each molecule of ATP hydrolyzed to ADP and phosphate, one or more Ca^{2+} ions are accumulated. These vesicles are capable of removing Ca^{2+} from the surrounding medium down to a concentration of less than 10^{-7} *M*. The Ca^{2+} so segregated is discharged into the sarcoplasm again when the next impulse arrives. The Ca^{2+}-segregating activity of the sarcoplasmic reticulum is also referred to as the "relaxing factor."

Recent studies indicate that in some muscles rich in mitochondria (red muscles), segregation of Ca^{2+} during relaxation also takes place in the mitochondria. We have already seen that mitochondria have the capacity to accumulate Ca^{2+} at the expense of energy yielded by electron transport or ATP (Chapter 18).

The Source of Energy for Muscular Contraction

Isolated vertebrate muscles that are stimulated to contract repeatedly have been found to form large amounts of lactic acid; simultaneously, the level of glycogen in the muscle decreases. These observations indicate that glycolysis can provide the energy for muscular contraction. However, if a muscle is first treated with certain poisons of glycolysis, such as iodoacetate, which inhibits glyceraldehyde phosphate dehydrogenase, it will still contract when stimulated, indicating that glycolysis per se is not essential for contraction. Similarly, muscles may be poisoned with cyanide to inhibit respiration, without blocking their capacity to contract when stimulated. From such experiments it has been concluded that muscle contains energy-rich substances that can supply the energy for contraction, at least for short periods, in the absence of ATP-forming metabolic activity. At the time these observations were first made, ATP had just been discovered and its obvious relationship to cell energetics suggested that it was the immediate source of energy required for contraction when glycolysis or respiration were poisoned. However, for two reasons this explanation appeared to be inadequate. First, the amounts of ATP found in muscle are small in relation to the amount of chemical energy required to support contraction. Mammalian muscle would require hydrolysis of about 10^{-3} mole of ATP per gram muscle per minute during activity, but the amount of ATP actually present is about 5×10^{-6} mole gram^{-1}, an amount sufficient for only about 0.5 sec of activity. Secondly, careful analysis of the ATP content of muscles before and after single contractions showed essentially no decrease in ATP content nor an increase in ADP.

The answer to this dilemma is provided by the presence of *phosphagens* in muscle (Chapter 14). The skeletal muscle of vertebrates contains the high-energy compound phosphocreatine (Chapter 14), which is present in 4 to 5 times the concentration of ATP. Its high-energy phosphate group is rapidly transferred to ADP by the action of creatine phosphokinase. At the pH of the sarcoplasm, which is about 6.0, the creatine phosphokinase equilibrium

$$\text{Phosphocreatine} + \text{ADP} \rightleftharpoons \text{creatine} + \text{ATP}$$

is poised far to the right; i.e., ATP formation is favored at the expense of phosphocreatine. This fact explains why the ATP concentration of muscle does not decline during a single contraction: the terminal phosphate group lost from ATP during the contraction is instantly replenished at the expense of phosphocreatine. If the muscle is stimulated for longer periods in the absence of glycolysis or respiration, the phosphocreatine supply will eventually become depleted. Only then will the ATP concentration decline.

The importance of phosphocreatine as an energy reservoir during contraction is further shown by inhibitor studies. The creatine phosphokinase activity of intact muscle can be completely inhibited by treatment with

2,4-dinitrofluorobenzene, the Sanger reagent (Chapter 4). Presumably an essential functional group of the enzyme undergoes substitution by the 2,4-dinitrophenyl group to render the enzyme inactive. In muscles poisoned in this manner, the ATP quickly declines on stimulation, since ADP cannot be rephosphorylated at the expense of phosphocreatine.

The ultimate source of metabolic energy for rephosphorylation of ADP, and thus of phosphocreatine, is not identical in all muscles. Although all muscles of vertebrates possess both glycolytic and respiratory activity, the relative contribution of glycolysis and respiration to the regeneration of ATP from ADP may vary considerably. In highly active or red muscles, which owe their color to their high content of myoglobin and cytochromes, respiration serves as the chief source of energy for rephosphorylation of ADP via oxidative phosphorylation in the mitochondria. Such muscles include the flight muscles of birds and the leg muscles of active mammals. However, in relatively inactive or white skeletal muscles, which have little myoglobin or cytochromes, glycolysis is the chief source of energy for rephosphorylation of ADP, even though such muscles may be well supplied with oxygen. The relatively unused pectoral muscles of the domestic turkey are examples of white muscles. The fuel used for rephosphorylation of ADP in muscle also varies with its activity. Resting muscle in the mammal uses largely fatty acids and acetoacetate (from the liver) as fuel; very little glucose is removed from the blood under these conditions. However, during maximal activity glucose becomes the major fuel.

The rate of respiration, and thus of ATP production, is adjusted to the rate of ATP consumption in muscle by a series of feedback controls. In resting muscle the [ATP]/[ADP] ratio is quite high and the rate of electron transport is consequently low, since it is limited by the low concentration of phosphate acceptor. Under these conditions, the activities of phosphofructokinase, the pacemaker enzyme of glycolysis, and of isocitrate dehydrogenase, the rate-limiting enzyme of the tricarboxylic acid cycle, are also low, because of their inhibition by the negative modulator ATP. When the muscle is stimulated to maximal activity, the consumption of both glucose and oxygen is greatly increased; actually, the oxygen uptake of muscle may increase twentyfold or more in the transition from rest to full activity. This sudden increase is the result of the abrupt breakdown of ATP to ADP as the muscle contracts, making ADP available as a phosphate acceptor and thus stimulating both electron transport and isocitrate dehydrogenase, for which ADP is a positive modulator. Some of the ADP formed on contraction also undergoes conversion to AMP by the adenylate kinase reaction

$$2\text{ADP} \rightleftharpoons \text{ATP} + \text{AMP}$$

The AMP so formed, which is a positive modulator for phosphofructokinase, thus serves to stimulate glycolysis.

In maximal activity, the oxidation of glucose via the tricarboxylic acid cycle is supplemented by superimposed aerobic glycolysis with formation of extra lactic acid, which diffuses into the blood. After a bout of maximal exercise, such as a sprint, a mammal will continue to breathe in excess of the normal resting rate and consume considerable extra oxygen. The extra oxygen so consumed during the recovery period is called the *oxygen debt,* and it corresponds to the oxidation in the liver and heart of some of the excess lactic acid formed during maximal muscular activity. The remainder of the excess lactic acid accumulating in the blood during the sprint is converted to glycogen in the liver by pathways described in Chapter 22; the extra ATP required is derived from that portion of the lactic acid that is oxidized via the tricarboxylic acid cycle in the liver.

Specialized Muscles. Asynchronous and "Catch" Muscles

Two highly specialized types of muscles deserve special comment because of their distinctive biochemical specialization. Most muscles are classified as *synchronous* because they yield a single contraction per motor nerve impulse received. However, in those insects having a high frequency of wing beat, such as the housefly, bees, wasps, and mosquitoes, the flight muscles are termed *asynchronous,* since a single nerve impulse can set off a whole burst or train of contractions, the frequency of which may exceed 1,000 sec^{-1} in the midge. The asynchronous muscles of such insects are unique in several respects. First, they possess little or no sarcoplasmic reticulum, although they do contain a T system. This fact suggests that asynchronous flight muscles do not contract and relax by cyclic release and segregation of free Ca^{2+} from the sarcoplasmic reticulum, as occurs in vertebrate skeletal muscle. The second major difference is that asynchronous muscles consist of two sets of opposed fibers, which contract alternately, one set for the downbeat and the other for the upbeat of the wing. Recent research suggests that contraction of one set of fibers results in stretching of the other set, which is thereby stimulated to contract. Once the asynchronous muscle is set off by a single nerve impulse, its activity is self-sustaining over many contractions.

Asynchronous flight muscle fibers of insects are also remarkable in their intense respiratory activity; they are perhaps the most active eucaryotic cells known. In these muscles the mitochondria are very profuse and are regularly arranged along the myofibrils, so that there are either one or two mitochondria, depending on the species, per sarcomere (Figure 26-10). The inner membranes of these mitochondria possess an enormous surface area (Chapter 18).

The "catch" or adductor muscles of mollusks such as the clam or scallop are also of special interest, since such muscles can lock when contracted and remain so for long periods without any more consumption of metabolic

Figure 26-10
Longitudinal section of asynchronous flight muscle of wasp (Polistes), *showing regular arrangement of mitochondria along sarcomeres.*

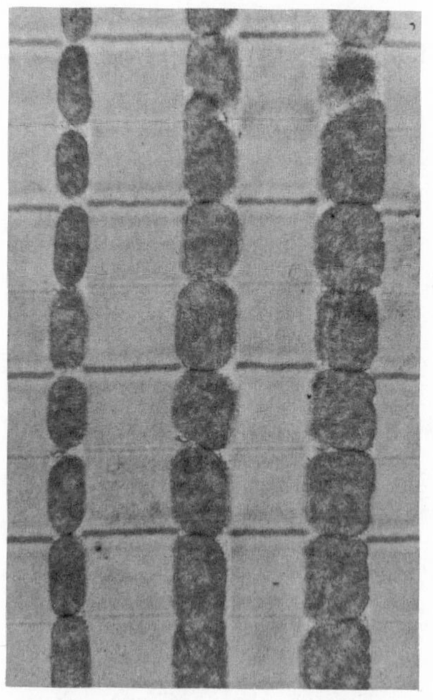

Figure 26-11
Electron micrograph of cross-sections of cilia of Halteria.

Longitudinal section

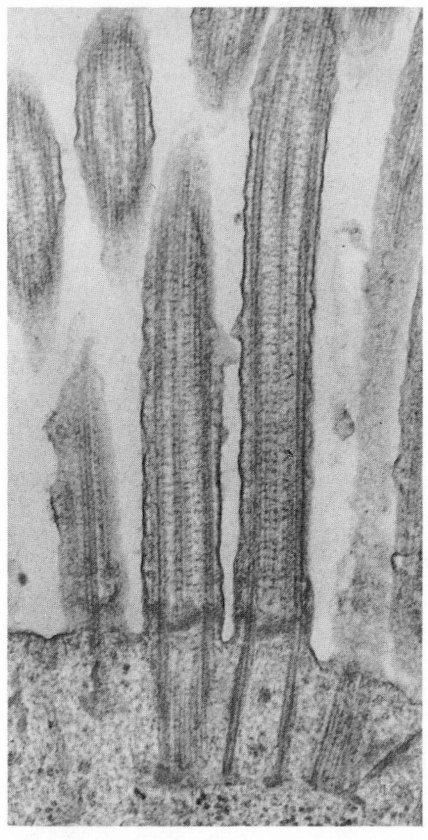

0.5 μ

Transverse section

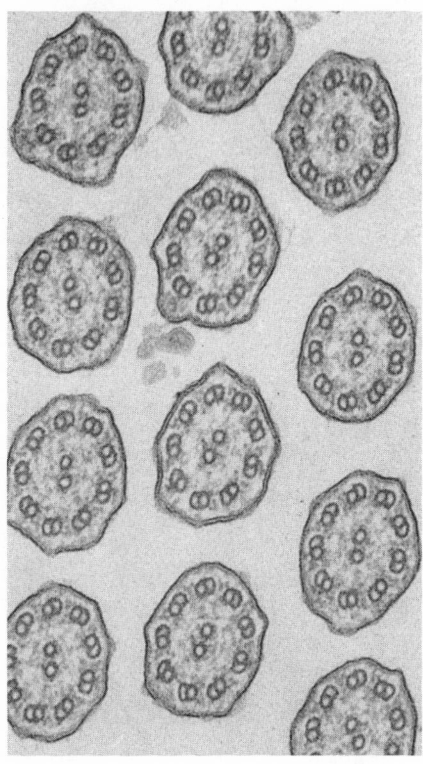

0.5 μ

energy than normal resting skeletal muscle. Catch muscles contain normal amounts of actin and myosin, and their filament structure as observed under the electron microscope is similar to that of normal muscle. However, they contain very large amounts of the water-insoluble tropomyosin A, or paramyosin, which is believed to function to lock the cross-bridges between the myosin and actin filaments in the contracted state, thus preventing relaxation until a release signal is received.

Cilia and Flagella of Eucaryotic Cells

Cilia and flagella occur in eucaryotic cells of both the animal and plant worlds, with the exception of crustaceans, angiosperms, and gymnosperms. They range in length from about 2 μ in some protozoa to several millimeters in certain sperm cells; their diameter is about 0.2 μ (Figure 26-11). Flagella occur singly or in pairs and move the cell through its environment, whereas cilia are very numerous and move extracellular materials along the cell surface. The tails of sperms cells are included among the flagella. Both types of appendage are remarkably similar in structural and molecular organization, although flagella are longer. The characteristic gyratory or sweeping motion of the cilia and flagella of eucaryotic cells is the result of ATP-dependent conformational changes taking place along the entire length of the appendage, whereas the motion of the flagella of bacteria, which will be considered later, is passive, since it is entirely imparted by their basal bodies within the cell.

Cilia and flagella of eucaryotic cells consist of a bundle of eleven microtubules, called an *axoneme,* embedded in a matrix and surrounded by a membrane, the *ciliary* or *flagellar membrane,* which is continuous with and appears to be identical to the cell membrane (Figure 26-11). The microtubules are characteristically arranged in a 9 + 2 pattern, that is, nine double tubules arranged in an outer ring surrounding two central fibers. At the base of the cilium or flagellum, and within the cytoplasm, is a cylindrical structure called a *basal body* or *kinetosome,* which is about 0.5 μ long and 0.15 μ in diameter. The wall of the kinetosome is made up of nine triple fibers, which have cross-bridges. The kinetosome serves to transfer ATP and possibly other materials to the shaft of the cilium or flagellum.

The 9 + 2 structure of the shaft of cilia and flagella has been subjected to very detailed study with the electron microscope (Figure 26-12). The two central fibers are circular in cross section and are about 240 Å in diameter; they appear to be tubular, with walls about 45 Å thick. The center-to-center distance between the two parallel central fibers is 360 Å. Both are surrounded by a central sheath. Each of the nine outer fibers consists of two subfibers, one of which is slightly thicker than the other. Both subfibers are tubular; the wall thickness is 45 Å. From the thinner subfiber A, short projections or arms arise. Each is about 50 Å thick and 150 Å long; all arms point in the same clockwise direction, viewed from the basal end. The outer and central fibers are connected in some instances by spokelike cross-linkages. The wall of each outer fiber consists of twelve or more parallel protofilaments about 45 to 50 Å in diameter; the protofilaments appear to consist of strings of globular subunits 45 Å in diameter (Figure 26-11).

Flagella and cilia may be readily detached from protozoa and other unicellular organisms and isolated by differential centrifugation. Addition of ATP and Mg^{2+} to suspensions of isolated cilia causes them to undergo localized, wavelike oscillations resembling those of cilia in the intact cell; simultaneously, the ATP is hydrolyzed to ADP and phosphate. By electron microscopic observations, it has recently been found that the ATP hydrolysis is localized to the nine outer fibers, and possibly to the arms on these fibers.

The proteins making up the outer fibers of the cilia of *Tetrahymena* and a few other organisms have been extracted in soluble form and fractionated. Three major fractions have been identified. Two consist of rather large proteins possessing ATPase activity in the presence of Mg^{2+}; they are called *dyneins*. Since they sediment at different rates, they are called 14*S* dynein (about 600,000 mol wt) and 30*S* dynein. The third component, which is much smaller (4*S*), has no ATPase activity. The 14*S* and 30*S* dyneins have been obtained in highly purified form. When 30*S* dynein in solution is mixed with a suspension of outer fibers from which the arms have been removed, it is bound to the fibers. Electron microscopy has revealed that this treatment restores the arms of the outer fibers. From such experiments it has been concluded that the arms consist of 30*S* dynein and that they possess ATPase activity. The 30*S* dynein may be a polymer of the 14*S* dynein, whereas the 4*S* component may be the structural monomer of the protofilaments of the outer fibers.

The mechanism by which ATP hydrolysis produces wavelike oscillations of the cilia or flagella is not known. Presumably the microtubules making up the paired outer fibers do not contract; rather they appear to participate in changing degrees of lateral association, as is the case in the contraction of myofibrils of skeletal muscle. One suggestion is that the matrix around the tubules undergoes a slight change in dimensions during enzymatic hydrolysis of ATP, thus leading to torsional changes in the cilium.

Figure 26-12
The 9 + 2 arrangement of outer and inner fibers of cilia and flagella.

Schematic drawing of ultrastructure.

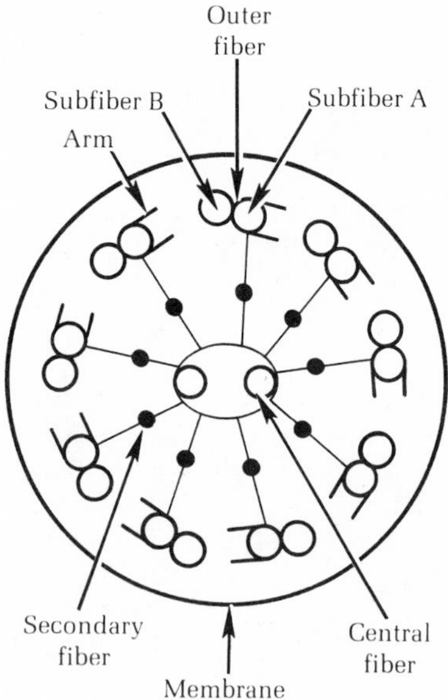

Models showing tubular structure of fibers and their protomer subunits.

Inner fiber

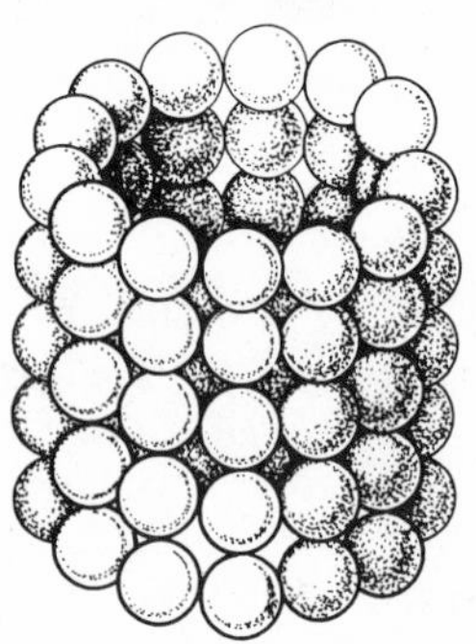

Outer fibers

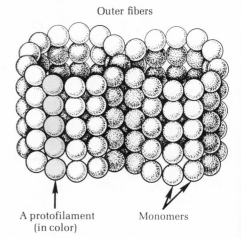

A protofilament (in color)

Monomers

Bacterial Flagella

In some bacteria there is but a single flagellum, others possess a tuft of flagella, and in still others the flagella are distributed over the entire cell surface. Bacterial flagella are between 100 and 350 Å in diameter and may sometimes exceed 10 to 15 μ in length, or many times the diameter of the cell. Most bacterial flagella possess a regular and uniform curl (Figure 26-13), with a wavelength of about 2.5 μ.

Bacterial flagella differ from the cilia and flagella of eucaryotes in that they are much thinner, they are not surrounded by a membrane, and they have no intrinsic

Figure 26-13
Electron micrographs of bacteria showing flagella.

Two cells of Pseudomonas aeruginosa, *each with a single polar flagellum (negative contrast).*

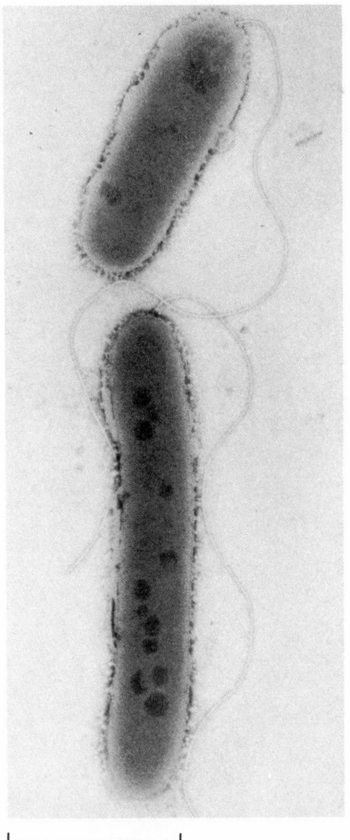

1.0 μ

Proteus mirabilis cell with profuse flagella. Note regular curl. The wavelength of the curl may be altered by mutation.

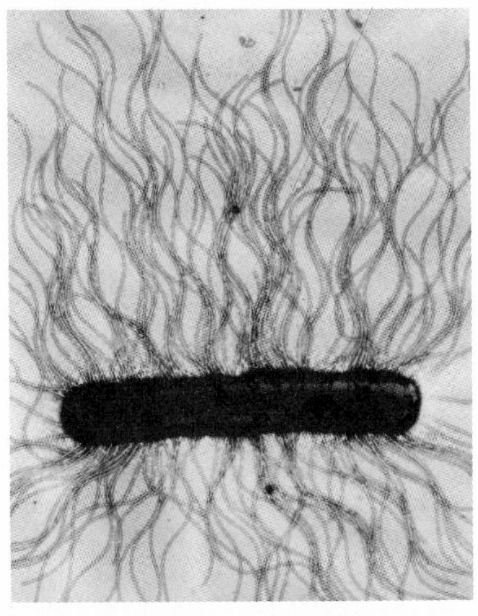

5.0 μ

mechanochemical activity. Their helical or gyratory motion is imparted to them at their base within the cell, by conversion of the chemical energy of ATP into mechanical energy in the *basal granules*, to which the flagella are attached. Flagellar motions may exceed 40 cps, and they may propel bacteria at velocities up to 50 μ sec^{-1}.

Bacterial flagella can be detached by agitation of the cells in a mechanical shaker and then isolated by differential centrifugation. Isolated flagella show no intrinsic motility nor does ATP cause them to undergo change in shape. When bacterial flagella are acidified to pH 3, they dissociate into identical subunit protein molecules, called *flagellin*, which have a molecular weight of 40,000 in most species. The flagellin of *Proteus vulgaris* has been crystallized. Flagellin shows no ATPase activity. X-ray evidence indicates that bacterial flagella consist of three intertwined strands of flagellin monomers.

The flagellin from *Salmonella typhimurium* and other bacteria contains many residues of ϵ-N-methyllysine, an amino acid that also occurs in muscle actin. It is remarkable that under appropriate conditions of pH and salt concentration, flagellin monomers will spontaneously reaggregate to form structures that appear to be identical with intact flagella, possessing regular curls of the same wavelength as the native flagella.

Summary

The myofibrils of skeletal muscle cells contain functional segments, sarcomeres, each of which consists of two types of interpenetrating parallel filaments. The dark or A band of the sarcomere contains a set of parallel thick filaments, and the light or I band a set of thin filaments. During contraction and relaxation, the thin filaments slide along the thick filaments, without change in the length of either. Cross-bridges between the thick and thin filaments are rapidly made and broken during muscle contraction.

The thick filaments consist of parallel bundles of myosin, long, rodlike molecules with projecting heads, each of which contains two identical long polypeptide chains. Myosin has Ca^{2+}-stimulated ATPase activity, which is kept in an inhibited state by one sulfhydryl group and requires a second sulfhydryl group for activity. Myosin may be cleaved by trypsin to yield two types of fragments, light meromyosin and heavy meromyosin. The latter, which contains the head of the myosin molecule, also contains the ATPase activity. Myosin also can bind actin, the major protein component of the thin filaments. Binding of actin involves the same —SH groups of the head that are involved in the ATPase activity.

F-actin is a polymer of the globular monomeric form, G-actin (46,000 mol wt). Polymerization of G-actin is promoted by ATP, which undergoes simultaneous dephosphorylation to ADP. Actin also binds Ca^{2+}. The thin filaments of the sarcomere consist of two supercoiled F-actin strands. Actin forms a complex with myosin, called actomyosin, which shows Mg^{2+}-stimulated ATPase activity and undergoes dissociation in the presence of ATP, a phenomenon which may be basic to the release of the cross-linkages between actin and myosin filaments in contraction.

An electrical impulse in the motor nerve of muscle rapidly spreads over the sarcolemma and a system of transverse tubules (T system) which connects with all the sarcomeres in the cell via the sarcoplasmic reticulum. It causes a sudden increase in permeability, which results in discharge or depolarization of the normal potential difference across the membrane. The subsequent release of Ca^{2+} from the sarcoplasmic reticulum into the sarcoplasm, is the trigger for contraction, since Ca^{2+} activates ATPase activity. During relaxation, the Ca^{2+} is transported from the sarcoplasm back into the cisternae of the sarcoplasmic reticulum in an ATP-dependent active transport process.

ATP is the immediate source of energy for contraction. Its level in the sarcoplasm is held constant at the expense of phosphocreatine by the action of creatine phosphokinase. ADP or AMP released during contraction activates not only electron transport but also isocitrate dehydrogenase, the pacemaker of the tricarboxylic acid cycle, and phosphofructokinase, the pacemaker of glycolysis.

Bacterial flagella consist of strings of flagellin molecules, which have no inherent mechanochemical activity. They have an inherent wave form which can be distorted from the base and to which they return. Cilia and flagella of eucaryotic cells are much larger, they are surrounded by a membrane, they contain nine pairs of peripheral and two inner tubular filaments, and they have intrinsic ATP-dependent motile activity. The outer pairs of tubules have arms or cross-bridges of dynein, a globular protein, which possesses ATPase activity and which may be responsible for the ATP-dependent torsional activity of the flagella.

References

Books

BENDALL, J. R.: "Muscles, Molecules, and Movement," Heinemann, Ltd., London (1969).

Articles

DAVIES, R. E.: "On the Mechanism of Muscular Contraction," in "Essays in Biochemistry," eds. P. N. Campbell and G. D. Greville, vol. I, Academic Press, New York (1965), pp. 29–56.

GIBBONS, I. R.: "The Biochemistry of Motility," *Ann. Rev. Biochem.*, **37**:521–546 (1968). A review stressing the comparative biological aspects of motility.

HOLWILL, M.: "Contractile Mechanisms in Cilia and Flagella," in D. R. Sanadi (ed.), *Current Topics in Bioenergetics*, vol. II, pp. 288–334, Academic Press, Inc., New York, 1967.

HUXLEY, H. E.: "The Mechanism of Muscular Contraction," *Science*, **164**:1356–1366 (1969). A model of cross-bridge function.

HUXLEY, H. E., and W. BROWN: "Low Angle X-ray Diagram of Vertebrate Striated Muscle and Its Behaviour during Contraction and Rigor," *J. Mol. Biol.*, **30**:383–434 (1967). Evidence for the geometrical arrangement of the cross-bridges.

PEACHEY, L. D.: "Sarcoplasmic Reticulum and Transverse Tubules of Frog Muscle," *J. Cell Biol.*, **25**:209–231 (1965). Excellent electron micrographs and drawings.

PERRY, S. V.: "The Role of Myosin in Muscular Contraction," in *Aspects of Cell Motility*, Cambridge University Press, London, England, 1968.

PORTER, K. R., and C. FRANZINI-ARMSTRONG: "The Sarcoplasmic Reticulum," *Sci. American*, **212**:72–80 (1965).

SACKTOR, B.: "Energetics and Respiratory Metabolism of Muscular Contraction," in *The Physiology of Insects*, vol. II, Academic Press, New York, 1965. A comprehensive review with many data on the performance of insect muscle.

SMITH, D. S.: "The Flight Muscles of Insects," *Sci. American*, **212**:76–90 (1965). A fascinating account of these highly specialized muscles.

SEIFTER, S., and P. M. GALLOP: "The Structure Proteins," in H. Neurath (ed.), *The Proteins*, vol. IV, pp. 372–430, 1966. Excellent review of the chemistry of the proteins of muscle, cilia, and flagella.

STRACHER, A., and P. DREIZEN: "Structure and Function of The Contractile Protein Myosin," in D. R. Sanadi (ed.), *Current Topics in Bioenergetics*, vol. I, pp. 154–202, Academic Press, Inc., New York, 1966. Review of the chemical aspects of myosin structure.

WEBER, A.: "Energized Ca^{++} Transport and Relaxing Factors," in D. R. Sanadi (ed.), *Current Topics in Bioenergetics*, vol. I, pp. 203–254, Academic Press, Inc., New York, 1966. A review of the role of the sarcoplasmic reticulum in accumulating Ca^{2+} during relaxation.

Problems

1. Skeletal muscle contains about 5×10^{-6} mole of ATP and 30×10^{-6} mole of phosphocreatine per gram wet weight. Calculate how much work (in calories) a 400-gram muscle can theoretically carry out at the expense of its high-energy phosphate compounds alone, assuming that both glycolysis and respiration are inhibited.

2. Calculate how long the supply of muscle glycogen (0.8 percent of wet weight of muscle) would last during full activity of skeletal muscle if it is the only fuel and if all of it is available. Recall (see text) that the normal content of ATP (5×10^{-6} mole gram^{-1}) is sufficient for only 0.5 sec of maximal activity. Assume that the muscle remains aerobic throughout.

3. During a 100-yard dash an athlete consumes about 1.2 liters of pure oxygen at STP, whereas during rest for an equal period he would consume only 40 ml. During the recovery period he consumes an additional 4.9 liters of extra oxygen above the resting level. Assuming that glucose was the sole fuel, calculate (*a*) the oxygen debt, (*b*) the amount of extra glucose oxidized during the 100-yard dash, (*c*) the amount of extra glucose oxidized during recovery, and (*d*) the amount of glucose converted into lactic acid during the sprint, above the basal resting level.

4. If the 100-yard dash in Problem 4 was completed in 10 sec, calculate the rate of total glucose consumption (moles glucose per gram muscle per minute) by the muscles of a 70-kg athlete. Assume that muscle constitutes 40 percent of the total body weight.

5. From data in Problems 3 and 4, calculate the rate of ATP utilization (moles per gram muscle per minute) in the muscles of the athlete during a 100-yard dash.

6. Now calculate the rate of ATP utilization in the flight muscle of the blowfly, which consumes about 1,000 mm^3 of oxygen per minute per gram body weight at 25°. A blowfly weighs 50 mg, of which about 10 mg is flight muscle.

7. Calculate the equilibrium constant for the phosphocreatine kinase reaction at 25°C and pH 7.0 from data in Table 14-4.

CHAPTER 27 ACTIVE TRANSPORT ACROSS MEMBRANES

We have seen that the cell membrane is intrinsically impermeable to most polar molecules. This property has a biological advantage, since it prevents the internal metabolites of the cell, most of which are polar, from diffusing out of the cell. However, living cells must obtain certain polar nutrients from the environment, such as glucose and amino acids. They have perfected specific transport or carrier systems to carry certain types of molecules across the membrane. Translocation of solutes across a membrane by means of such a carrier system is spoken of as *mediated* transport. Some membrane transport systems function merely as "gates" which allow solutes to cross the membrane in either direction, but always *down* a concentration gradient, that is, in the direction of *decreasing* concentration; this type of process is called *passive* mediated transport. However, the more important membrane transport systems bring about *active* transport, that is, transport *up* a gradient, in the direction of *increasing* concentration. Usually active transport systems are directional and can translocate a solute in but one direction, either into or out of the cell.

Active transport systems have several important functions. They allow cells to extract fuels and other essential nutrients from the environment, even when their concentration in the latter is extremely low. Actually, the concentration of a given nutrient in the environment is often much lower than the Michaelis constant of the intracellular enzyme acting on it. Active transport of a very dilute nutrient into the cell can raise its internal concentration sufficiently so that it can be utilized rapidly and efficiently. Active transport systems also participate in the regulation and maintenance of metabolic steady states, by their ability to adjust to wide fluctuations in the composition of the external environment of cells. They maintain constant and optimal internal concentrations of inorganic electrolytes, in particular K^+, which is essential for optimal function of several important intracellular activities. Active transport systems that extrude Na^+ from cells are important in maintaining the constancy of the osmotic pressure and of the volume of the intracellular fluid. Active transport is therefore a vital process in the economy of all cells, and it utilizes a significant fraction of the total flow of metabolic energy.

Until quite recently, little biochemical information was available concerning the molecular aspects of active transport. Most investigations were limited to studies of the rates and the specificity of active transport processes in intact cells and tissues. However, some interesting successes have recently been achieved in the isolation of transport proteins from membranes, which have for the first time opened this important energy-requiring cell function to direct biochemical study. Because of the directional nature of active transport processes, their molecular basis has become an especially great challenge to the biochemist.

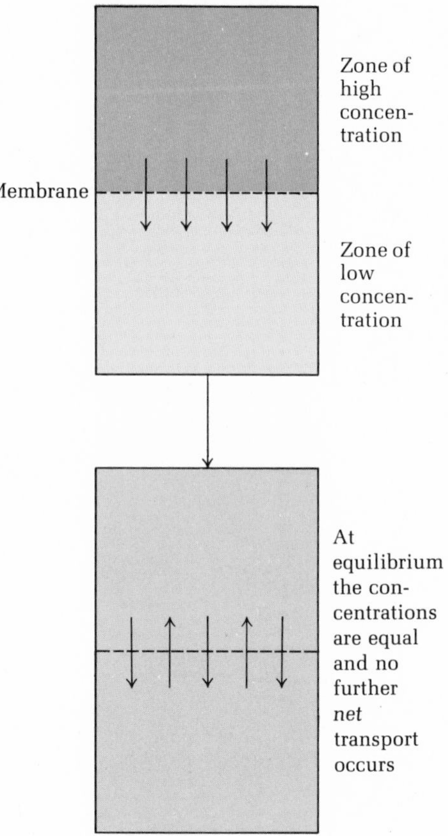
Passive transport down a concentration gradient
Zone of high concen-tration
Membrane
Zone of low concen-tration
At equilibrium the con-centrations are equal and no further *net* transport occurs
In passive transport the free energy of the system decreases

Figure 27-1
Schematic representation of active and passive transport energetics.

The Energetics of Active Transport against a Concentration Gradient

Before we examine the molecular components of active transport systems, it is necessary to analyze the thermodynamic aspects of transport processes, in particular, the amount of energy required to transport a solute against a gradient.

When a solution is diluted by addition of water, entropy increases, because the solute molecules are now farther apart and thus more randomly disposed. Conversely, when a dilute solution is concentrated, entropy decreases, because the solute molecules are brought closer together. It is therefore clear that work must be done to concentrate a solution, since such a process cannot occur spontaneously. In a similar way, the net movement of a solute from a compartment in which it is present in a low concentration into a compartment in which its concentration is higher, through a membrane permeable to the solute (Figure 27-1), cannot occur spontaneously because entropy would decrease and the system would show an increase in free energy. Active transport is thus rigorously defined as a transport process in which the system gains free energy, and passive transport is defined as one in which the system loses free energy.

The free-energy change occurring when 1.0 mole of an uncharged solute is concentrated from concentration C_1 to a higher concentration C_2, or when 1.0 mole of solute moves from a compartment in which it is present in a low concentration C_1 to a compartment in which it is present in a higher concentration C_2, as in Figure 27-1, is given by the equation

$$\Delta G = RT \ln \frac{C_2}{C_1} \qquad (1)$$

in which R and T have their usual meaning. This equation assumes that the transported solute exists in the same molecular species in both compartments; it also assumes that the solute is uncharged. From this equation we can calculate the free-energy change that occurs at 20° when 1.0 gram-molecular weight of a solute such as glucose is transported from a compartment in which its concentration is 0.01 M into a compartment in which its concentration is tenfold higher, namely, 0.1 M:

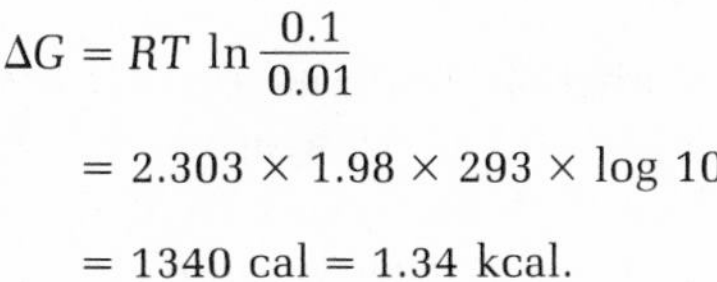

$$\Delta G = RT \ln \frac{0.1}{0.01}$$
$$= 2.303 \times 1.98 \times 293 \times \log 10$$
$$= 1340 \text{ cal} = 1.34 \text{ kcal.}$$

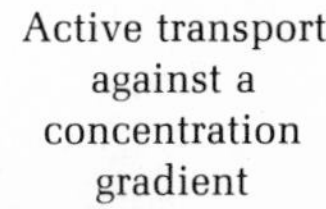

Active transport against a concentration gradient

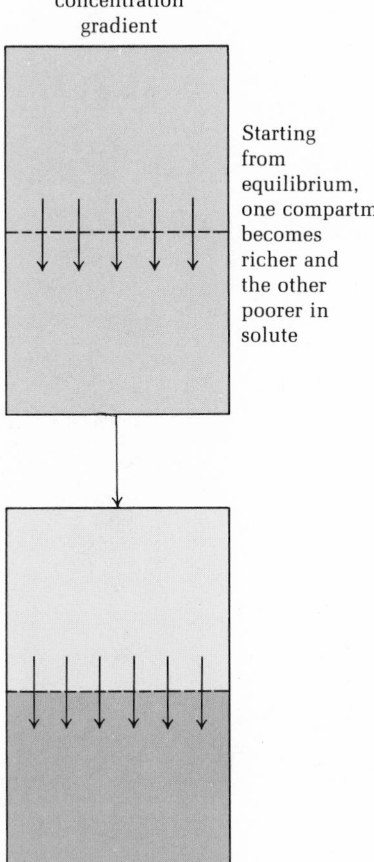

Starting from equilibrium, one compartment becomes richer and the other poorer in solute

In active transport the free energy of the system increases

Since the free-energy change is positive in sign, it is clear that transport of glucose against a 10:1 concentration gradient will not occur spontaneously. It can occur, however, if it is coupled to some other reaction proceeding with a decline in free energy, for example, the hydrolysis of ATP. Since the standard free energy of hydrolysis of ATP is −7.3 kcal, the hydrolysis of 1 mole of ATP could theoretically yield more than sufficient energy to transport 1.0 mole of glucose (or any other neutral solute) from one compartment to a second against a 10:1 gradient of concentration, provided that a mechanism exists for the transfer of free energy from the hydrolysis of ATP to the process by which glucose is moved across the membrane.

If the solute under consideration is electrically charged, then the equation for the free-energy change of a transport process between two compartments in which the concentration of the charged solute differs becomes somewhat more complex, since *two* gradients then exist: one a gradient of concentration and the other a gradient of electrical charge or potential. The total free-energy change occurring when an ion moves up or down a concentration gradient is thus the sum of (1) the free-energy change due to the concentration difference and (2) the free-energy change due to the difference in electrical potential. The sum of these two is known as the *electrochemical potential.* The overall expression for the free-energy change occurring during transport of an electrically charged ion is given by a modification of equation (1)

$$\Delta G = RT \ln \frac{C_2}{C_1} + Z\mathcal{F}\Delta\psi$$

in which the expression $Z\mathcal{F}\Delta\psi$ represents the free-energy contribution due to movement of electrical charges. In this expression Z is the number of charges on the solute molecule, $\mathcal{F}$ is the faraday [96,493 coul gram equiv^{-1}], and $\Delta\psi$ is the difference in electrical potential across the membrane in volts. It is assumed that the solvent is identical in both compartments. At a given temperature the electrical component of the free-energy change is a function of the presence of other ions and also of the properties of the membrane separating the two compartments. The electrical component is not always easily measured and is in most cases quite small, because of compensating movements of other ions. Nevertheless, the electrical potential component is of great importance in the analysis of the behavior of biological membranes, particularly those that are excitable. Although it is more rigorous to consider gradients of ions across membranes in terms of the electrochemical potential, we may, as a first approximation, neglect the electrical potential term and calculate standard-free-energy changes occurring during transport of ions by Equation (1).

Most active transport systems in cell membranes are capable of driving transport against gradients that are much higher than 10:1. Amino acids may be transported into some types of cells against a concentration gradient of over 300:1. One of the most impressive active transport gradients known occurs in the secretion of H^+ ions into the gastric juice of vertebrates (pH ~ 1) from the blood plasma (pH ~ 7.0). The H^+ ion gradient is thus $10^{-1}/10^{-7} = 10^6$, or 1,000,000:1. By use of Equation (1), the free-energy change occurring when 1.0 gram equivalent of H^+ ions is secreted from blood plasma into gastric juice is

$$\Delta G = RT \ln \frac{10^{-1}}{10^{-7}}$$

$$= 8040 \text{ cal} = 8.04 \text{ kcal}$$

In a similar way we may calculate the free-energy change involved in the transport of any solute from blood plasma into any body fluid if we know its concentration in the two fluids. (Figure 27-2 shows the solute composition of

Figure 27-2
The solute composition of some human body fluids. The values for sea water (color) are included for comparison; it is a much more concentrated fluid than blood plasma. From such data it is possible to calculate the amount of energy required to secrete body fluids from blood plasma.

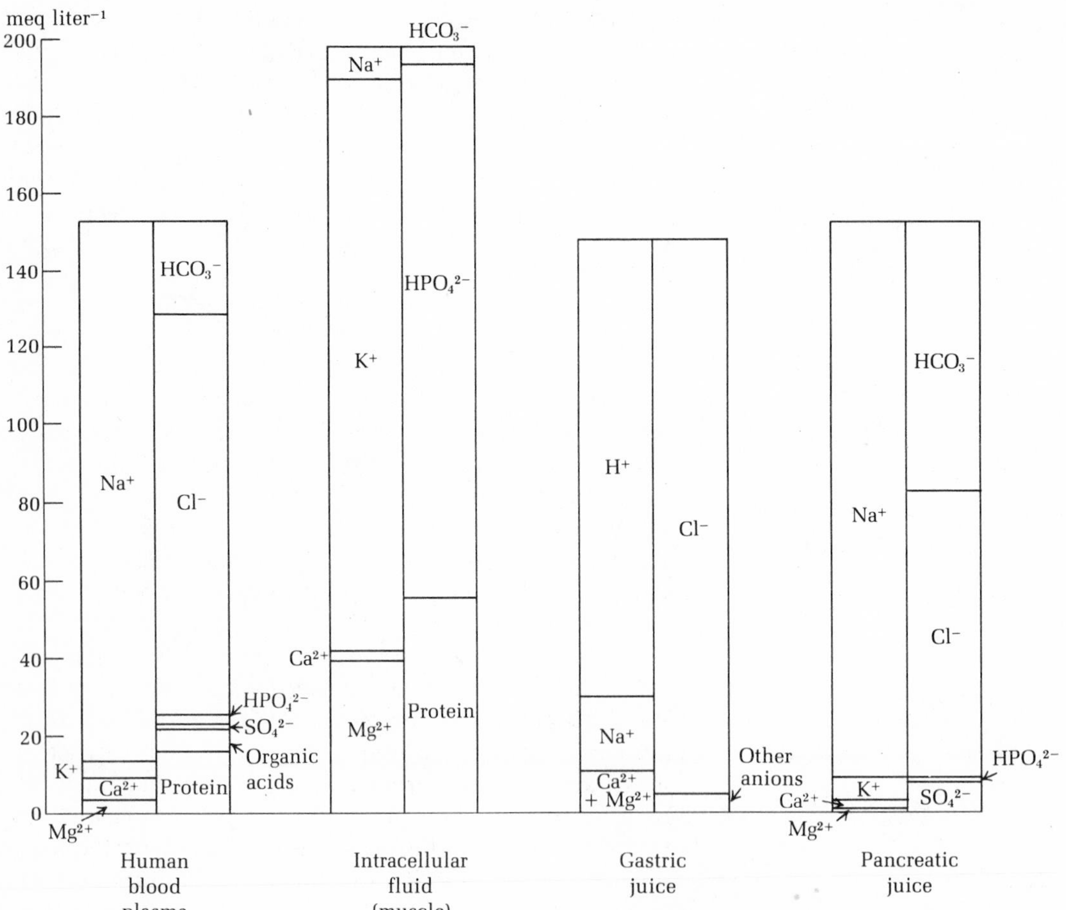

Figure 27-3
Saturation kinetics of a membrane transport system.

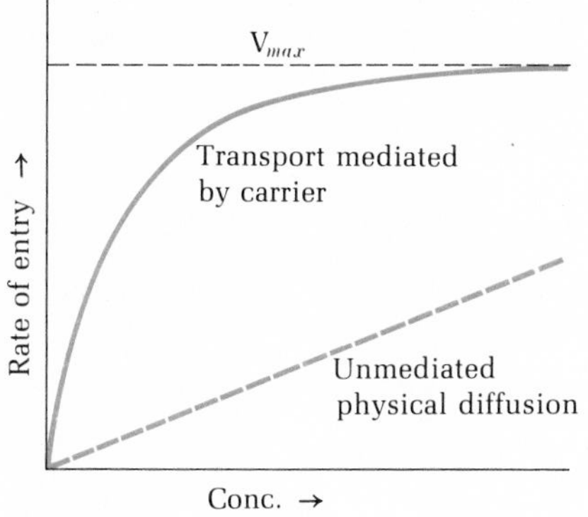

mediated similar to enzyme

some biological fluids.) Moreover, with Equation (1) we can calculate the total work required to form a given body fluid from blood plasma; it is the algebraic sum of the free energy changes for transport of each of the solutes in the two fluids.

The precise magnitude of the concentration gradient of a solute across the cell membrane is often difficult to estimate, since the analytical method used may not be able to distinguish between free and bound solute. Frequently a large fraction of a solute such as an amino acid or Mg^{++} may be strongly bound to intracellular proteins; the bound species does not contribute to the thermodynamic gradient. Moreover, cells are open systems and are not in thermodynamic equilibrium. A concentration gradient of any given solute across a cell membrane is a reflection of a steady-state, which is the resultant of two opposing forces, the pumping or active transport of the solute into (or out of) the cell and a passive back-leakage process. It has been calculated that some active transport mechanisms in the intact cell may have a *net* efficiency of only 10 to 20 percent; much of the energy loss is caused by back-leakage of the transported solute.

Identifying Characteristics of Mediated Transport across Membranes

Solutes may undergo a net movement or flux from one compartment or zone to another by either nonmediated or mediated processes. In nonmediated flux, the solute molecule remains in the initial molecular species throughout the transport process. The rate of the nonmediated process is at all times dependent on the concentration of the solute, and its temperature coefficient is usually that of physical diffusion, namely, about 1.4 per 10° rise in temperature. Nonmediated transport of a solute is entirely the result of simple physical diffusion of the solute in response to its concentration or electrochemical gradient.

Mediated transport, on the other hand, has a number of identifying characteristics which are often used as experimental criteria. These characteristics can be revealed by measurements of the kinetics of transport of various solutes across cell membranes. Such measurements may be made on suspensions of intact cells, such as erythrocytes or bacteria, or on intact tissues, such as gastric or intestinal mucosa.

The first identifying criterion of a mediated-transport process across a biological membrane is that it shows saturation kinetics; that is, the transport process may become saturated with the substance transported, just as enzymes may become saturated with their substrates. Plots of the initial rate of the transport process vs substrate concentration usually show a hyperbolic curve approaching a maximum, similar to the Michaelis-Menten curve of an enzyme (Figure 27-3). At a very low substrate concentration, the rate of entry of the substrate is usually proportional to its concentration and thus is first-order. However, as the substrate concentration is increased, the rate becomes zero-order with respect to

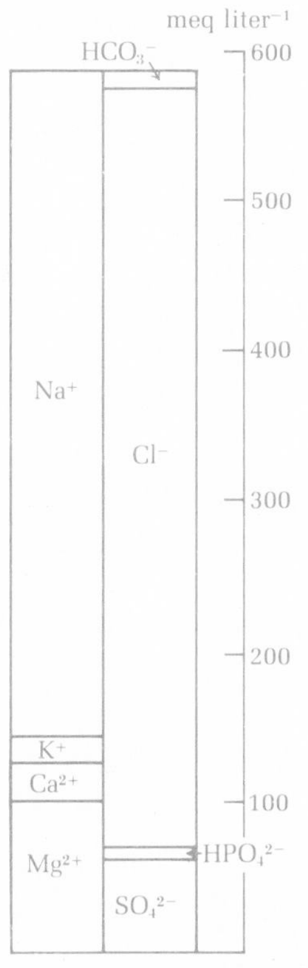

substrate. This behavior has suggested that mediated-transport systems or carriers contain specific sites to which the substance undergoes reversible binding. In contrast, the rate of simple, unmediated, physical diffusion of a solute is always exactly proportional to the concentration gradient of the solute, with no tendency to show saturation.

The second criterion of mediated transport is specificity for the substance transported. For example, the erythrocytes of some vertebrates have a membrane transport system which accelerates the influx of D-glucose and a number of structurally related monosaccharides, but it has little or no activity toward D-fructose or disaccharides such as lactose. Mediated transport also may show stereospecificity; thus, the amino acid transport systems of animal cell membranes are much more active with L-amino acids than the D-isomers. From such findings it has been postulated that mediated-transport systems in membranes contain a binding site complementary to the substance transported, resembling in its specificity the active site of enzyme molecules.

The third criterion of mediated transport is that it can frequently be inhibited quite specifically. Some biological transport systems are inhibited competitively by substances structurally related to the substrate, which compete with the substrate for its specific binding site. Transport systems may also be inhibited noncompetitively, by reagents capable of blocking or altering specific functional groups of proteins, such as N-ethylmaleimide, a sulfhydryl group blocking agent, or dinitrofluorobenzene, which blocks free amino groups.

Mediated transport is also called *facilitated diffusion,* in recognition of the fact that ultimately all transport processes are the result of diffusion. In the case of mediated transport it is the substrate-carrier complex that may undergo translational or rotational diffusion.

Figure 27-4
Models of membrane transport mechanisms.

A passive transport mechanism. The substance transported (S) combines with a specific transport protein (T) to form a TS complex, which carries S across the membrane. All processes are reversible and transport may occur in either direction depending on the concentration gradient.

An active transport mechanism. Application of energy makes possible transport against a concentration gradient. Active transport systems are unidirectional.

Characteristics of Active Mediated Transport

Although all mediated-transport processes across biological membranes share the three characteristic properties of substrate specificity, saturatability, and specific inhibition described above, they may be divided into two types, active and passive mediated transport, by application of other criteria.

The first is the question of whether the transport process is against or with a chemical or electrochemical gradient. This criterion requires precise knowledge of the concentration of the transported substance in the two compartments concerned, as well as assurance that the substance exists in the same molecular or ionic species in the two compartments. In the case of the secretion of gastric juice from blood plasma, pH measurements on both fluids with the glass electrode, which senses only *free* H^+ ions, give considerable assurance that a large gradient of H^+ ion exists. However, as mentioned above, it is not always possible to establish from analytical measurements alone whether or not a true thermodynamic gradient exists. Thus, the most fundamental criterion of an active-transport process is not always useful in actual practice.

The second criterion, however, does provide a practical but not necessarily infallible test of whether a given mediated transport process is active or passive. If the process under question is dependent upon a source of metabolic energy, then it may, tentatively at least, be considered to be an active-transport process. Some transport processes of cells are inhibited when glycolysis or respiration is blocked by such inhibitors as fluoride, iodoacetate, arsenate, or cyanide or when oxidative phosphorylation is uncoupled by agents such as 2,4-dinitrophenol. For example, the erythrocytes of some species normally maintain a high internal concentration of K^+ and extrude Na^+ ions. If fluoride, an inhibitor of glycolysis, is added, then the internal K^+ concentration declines and the Na^+ concentration increases, to approach the state in which their concentrations are equal on both sides of the membrane. Such systems, which are evidently dependent on a supply of metabolic energy such as ATP, are presumed to be doing work i.e. transporting the solute against a gradient. On the other hand, other mediated-transport processes, such as the movement of glucose into human erythrocytes, are not inhibited when metabolic energy sources are blocked; such systems may be concluded to be carrying out passive mediated transport.

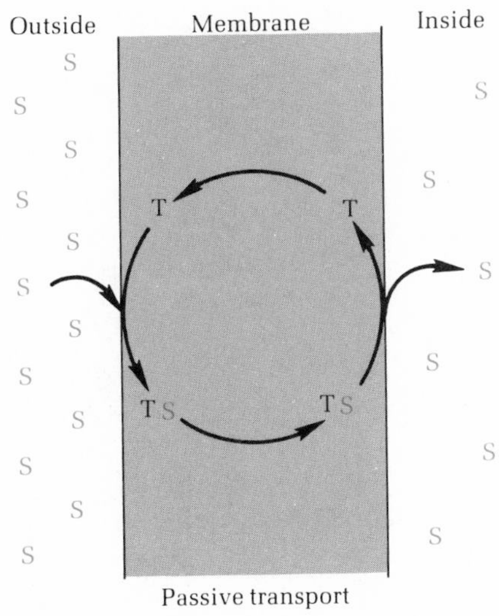

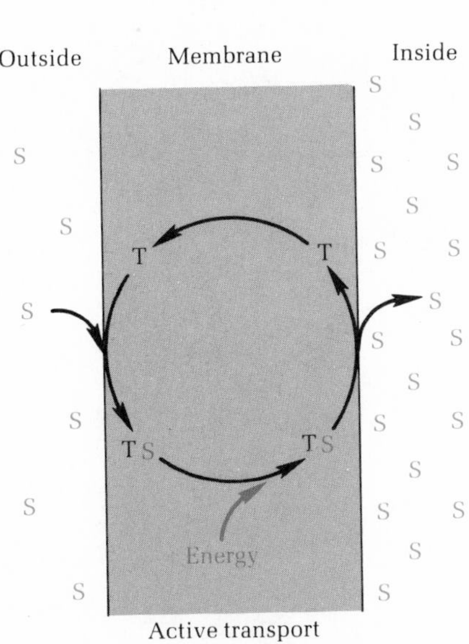

Another useful criterion is that active transport systems are *unidirectional* or *vectorial* in their normal energy-requiring function; that is, they will move the substrate across the membrane in only one direction. For example, erythrocytes contain an active transport system that moves Na^+ only in the outward direction and K^+ in the inward direction. This behavior is in sharp contrast to passive mediated transport, which may be in either direction, depending on the relative concentrations in the two compartments. However, it is very important to note that in the absence of an energy supply, some active transport systems of cells also facilitate passive transport of their substrates across the membrane, in either direction, depending on the relative concentration of the substrate in the two compartments.

Models of Mediated Transport

From the characteristic properties described above, generalized models of transport systems have been postulated (Figure 27-4). Such models postulate that a specific membrane component, presumably a protein or lipoprotein containing a binding site complementary to the substrate transported, serves as a carrier of the substrate. It binds a substrate molecule from one compartment, and then, by diffusing across the membrane or by a conformational change, it carries the substrate molecule across the membrane so that the binding site faces the other compartment, into which the bound substrate then dissociates. In passive mediated transport systems, the carrier is completely reversible, and the net movement of solute molecules may be in either direction, depending on the relative concentration of the substrate in the two compartments. In models of active transport systems, either the carrier molecule or its substrate may be "energized" in some manner to achieve unidirectional transport against a gradient. Since some active transport systems can function as passive transport systems if their energy supply is cut off, active transport systems have been postulated to contain two or more components. One functions to bind and carry the substrate reversibly, in either direction, whereas the other is required to couple the action of the carrier molecule to an energy source such as ATP, in such a way that the active process occurs in only one direction.

Genetic Evidence for Transport Systems

Membrane transport systems are genetically determined and genetic studies have yielded extremely important information on their function. To illustrate the nature of these approaches, some observations recorded in one of the early genetic studies of membrane transport may be recapitulated.

When certain bacteria are grown on glucose as the sole carbon source, they are unable to utilize external citrate added to the medium, although they oxidize internally formed citrate at high rates via the tricarboxylic acid cycle. However, if such cells are removed from the glucose medium and placed in a medium in which citrate is the sole carbon source, they quickly "adapt" and acquire the ability to utilize exogenous citrate as carbon source. This effect is not due to a generalized increase in permeability of the cell membrane, since the citrate-grown cells do not acquire the capacity to utilize exogenous nonpermeant substrates other than citrate. These findings led to the conclusion that these bacteria contain an inducible citrate transport system. When the bacteria have an ample supply of glucose from the medium, particularly if glucose is the sole carbon source, the citrate transport system is not needed and its synthesis is therefore repressed. However, when only citrate is available in the medium as a carbon source, the synthesis of the citrate transport system is derepressed. Mutants of such bacteria have been found in which the capacity to synthesize the citrate transport system in response to exogenous citrate has been lost. Since such mutants, which are generically termed *transport-negative*, are metabolically normal in all other respects, it is clear that the molecular components of the citrate transport system are genetically determined in the same manner as the protein components of a multienzyme sequence catalyzing a metabolic pathway.

Many similar genetic investigations have shown that bacteria contain specific transport systems for sugars, amino acids, inorganic sulfate, phosphate and phosphate esters, and for a number of important metabolites. In many cases, the capacity to synthesize a specific membrane transport system is latent or repressed and must be derepressed by exposure of the cells to a medium rich in its substrate (Chapters 13, 32).

Sometimes the biosynthesis of membrane transport systems is genetically linked to the synthesis of enzymes capable of degrading the substance transported or its precursors. A classic case is the transport system for β-galactosides in *E. coli* and other bacteria. Monod and his colleagues have shown that this transport system is genetically linked to the enzymes *β-galactoside transacetylase* and *β-galactosidase*. The latter hydrolyzes β-galactosides, including lactose, to yield free galactose. All three proteins are products of the same operon. The genetic implications of this association will be discussed in Chapter 32.

Figure 27-5
The C_1 chair conformation of the pyranose ring. The equatorial bonds are in color; the axial bonds in black. This conformation is preferred by the sugar carrier of the human erythrocyte; the hydroxyl groups must be on equatorial bonds for maximum activity.

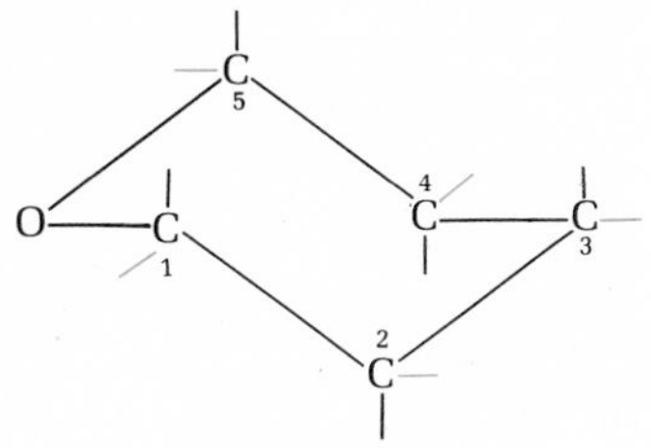

Passive-Transport Systems: The Glucose Carrier

Before considering the properties of the major active-transport systems of cells, it will be useful to consider representative passive-transport systems as prototypes.

One of the best known passive-transport systems is the glucose carrier of the human erythrocyte. The rate of entry of D-glucose into human erythrocytes increases with substrate concentration, but it approaches a maximum rate at which the system is saturated. However, the rate of entry of glucose into erythrocytes of certain other vertebrate species, such as the cow, does not show a saturation effect; apparently the glucose carrier is genetically lacking in the latter species. The glucose carrier in human erythrocytes has a rather broad specificity and is able to transport many sugars other than D-glucose, including D-mannose, D-galactose, D-xylose, L-arabinose, and D-ribose as well as the unnatural derivatives 2-deoxy-D-glucose and 3-O-methyl-D-glucose. For maximal activity, the transported sugar must be a pyranose in the C_1 chair form (Figure 27-5), with the hydroxy groups in equatorial positions. It has been postulated that the sugar carrier of the human erythrocytes binds the sugar by three equatorial hydroxyl groups.

needs chair → increase rate in direction of gradient

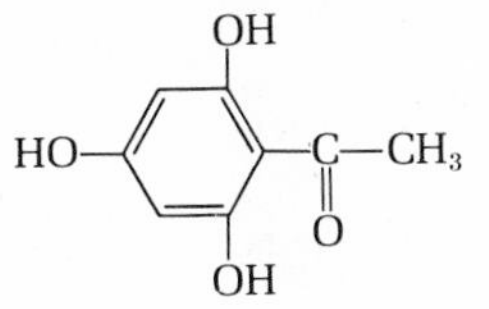

The erythrocyte sugar carrier has a characteristic affinity for each sugar. For D-glucose, K_M, defined as the concentration of D-glucose giving half-maximal rate of glucose transport, is 6.2 m*M*, and for D-mannose it is 18.5 m*M*. The glucose concentration in human blood is about 5.0 m*M*. Although D-fructose can be transported, the affinity of the carrier for fructose is so low ($K_M > 2000$ m*M*) that it probably does not function as a fructose carrier biologically.

Inhibitors of glucose transport

Phloretin

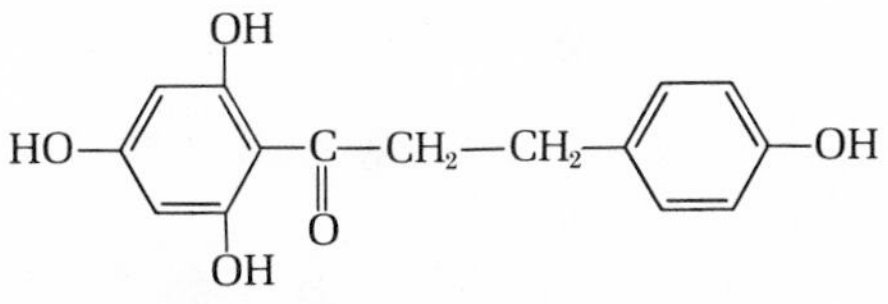

HO–C_6H_2(OH)(OH)–C(=O)–CH_2–CH_2–C_6H_4–OH

Trihydroxyacetophenone

HO–C_6H_2(OH)(OH)–C(=O)–CH_3

The compounds *phloretin* and *trihydroxyacetophenone* (margin) are competitive inhibitors of glucose transport in erythrocytes. Erythrocytes also contain passive-transport systems for neutral amino acids and for glycerol.

Passive-transport systems may be classified into two major types. The first type can promote or facilitate *net* movement of the substrate across a membrane *down* a gradient; net transport will continue only as long as the gradient exists. Since such transport systems can carry the substrate in either direction, the rate of net transport is equal to the inward rate minus the outward rate. When there is no concentration gradient, the rate of inward transport is exactly equal to the rate of the outward transport. The glucose carrier of erythrocytes is an example of such a system. As for the second type, certain passive-transport systems are not able to promote net transport of substrate across the membrane; they can only accelerate equimolar exchange of substrate molecules across the membrane, regardless of the concentration gradient across the membrane. Such a passive-transport process is often designated as an exchange diffusion. When passage of one substrate molecule to the inside of the cell is obligatorily linked to passage of another substrate molecule out of the cell, the transport mechanism is spoken of as being coupled. Such coupled exchange-diffusion processes must conform to another condition, namely, that there be equivalence in the transport of electrical charges.

Two examples of exchange diffusion may be cited. First, bacterial cells do not allow net passage of phosphate across the membrane but do promote a rapid exchange of external labeled phosphate with internal unlabeled phosphate. The second example is the ADP-ATP exchange-diffusion carrier which catalyzes equimolar exchange of ADP or ATP across the inner mitochondrial membrane. Presumably this carrier, which is inhibited by atractyloside (Chapter 18), normally functions to let one molecule of ATP out of the mitochondrion as the end product of oxidative phosphorylation, in exchange for an incoming molecule of external ADP, which then becomes phosphorylated in the inner compartment. However, the exchange of ADP for ATP would result in nonequivalence of charge transport. In the intact mitochondrion, the exchange of external ADP^{3-} for internal ATP^{4-} is accompanied by the entry of HPO_4^{2-} and probably some cation such as H^+ or K^+ so that electroneutrality is maintained.

Figure 27-6
Structure of nonactin and its K^+ complex. The structural formula of nonactin is shown at the top. Below are ball-and-stick models of the crystalline nonactin K^+ complex showing the fit of K^+ into the doughnut hole.

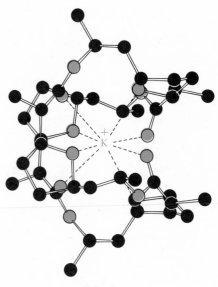

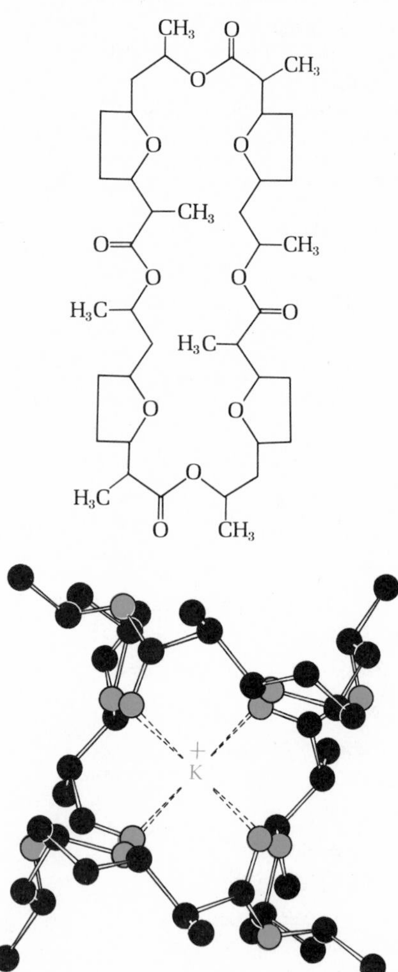

Side view

Ion-Transporting Antibiotics

Recent investigations on the action of certain antibiotics on mitochondria have revealed some clues about a possible molecular basis for passive mediated transport of certain ions across membranes. The inner membrane of mitochondria is normally impermeable to K^+. However, the antibiotics gramicidin and valinomycin, which inhibit oxidative phosphorylation (Chapter 18), cause external K^+ to enter mitochondria. Gramicidin promotes the entry of not only K^+ but also Na^+, Li^+, Rb^+, and Cs^+, whereas valinomycin promotes entry of K^+, Rb^+, or Cs^+ but not of Na^+, Li^+, or H^+. Many other antibiotics capable of inducing transport of ions in mitochondria and other membrane-surrounded structures have since been found.

A number of these antibiotics are annular, doughnut-shaped molecules with a central opening. It has been postulated that the transported ion is bound or complexed in the central opening, whose size may determine which of the alkali metal cations may be bound (Figure 27-6). This has been proved in the case of the cyclic antibiotic *nonactin,* which induces the penetration of K^+, but not Na^+, into mitochondria. This antibiotic has recently been crystallized in the form of its K^+ salt. X-ray diffraction patterns of these crystals indicate that the K^+ ion is bound within the "doughnut hole" (Figure 27-6); however, nonactin does not form a similar Na^+ salt. The outer border of the nonactin molecule is rather nonpolar; presumably the entire nonactin-K^+ complex can then pass through a nonpolar portion of the membrane. Valinomycin is also an annular molecule (Figure 18-7).

Although these permeability-inducing or "ionophorous" antibiotics are toxic substances not normally found in membranes, they may be illuminating models of passive-transport carriers. They evidently exert their toxic effects by inducing an ion-transport process in a membrane that normally does not possess such an activity, and in which this activity can be deleterious. Valinomycin and gramicidin are toxic to mitochondria because they cause them to expend the energy they normally use for oxidative phosphorylation in the inward pumping of K^+, accompanied by its rapid, passive efflux.

Active-Transport Systems

The Primary Sodium Pump

Ouabain (strophanthin G)

The last few years have seen the development of a unifying concept of the organization of active-transport systems in the cells of higher animals. In brief, this concept suggests that such systems have a basic economy and simplicity in that the active pumping of but a single substance out of the cell may furnish the driving force for the active transport of a variety of other substances into the cell. This concept has arisen from many observations that the active pumping of Na^+ ions out of the cell appears to be necessary for the active pumping of K^+, amino acids, and glucose into the cell; these are the solutes that are most actively pumped into animal cells. The active transport of Na^+ out of the cell by means of a Na^+ pump would leave the internal contents low in Na^+ concentration and the external fluid high in Na^+. This inward gradient of Na^+ ions is postulated to be the driving force for the *inward* active transport of K^+, glucose, and of amino acids. Also supporting this concept is the fact that the inhibition of Na^+ transport out of the cell by a very specific inhibitor, namely, the compound *ouabain* (margin), a member of the group of compounds known as cardiac glycosides, also causes inhibition of the transport of K^+, glucose, or amino acids into the cell. However, it is doubtful whether Na^+ transport is as fundamental to the economy of plant cells as it is in animal tissues. Many plant cells are unable to pump Na^+ and, indeed, do not seem to require Na^+ at all. In aerobic bacteria, H^+ is the cation which is pumped out of the cell.

The primary Na^+ pump of animal cells utilizes a significantly large fraction of the total ATP production of cells, particularly in certain epithelial cells, which are extremely active in absorption and secretion processes, such as those in the gastric mucosa, which secrete H^+ ions, the intestinal mucosa, which absorb glucose and amino acids from the lumen of the small intestine, and the renal tubules, which are active in reabsorbing glucose and Na^+ from the glomerular filtrate. When active transport of Na^+ in kidney preparations is completely inhibited by ouabain, the rate of respiration is depressed up to 80 percent. Since the rate of respiration in intact cells is geared to the rate of utilization of ATP, it is clear that most of the ATP production in kidney cells is used to transport Na^+.

The active pumping of Na^+ out of the cell appears to be carried out by two distinct types of Na^+ pumps. In one type, the inward transport of K^+ is linked to outward pumping of Na^+ in a compulsory manner, so that extrusion of Na^+ ions is always accompanied by inward transport of K^+. This type of Na^+ pump is called a *coupled neutral pump*, since K^+ is exchanged for Na^+ in a compulsory manner. In the second type of Na^+ pump, inward transport of K^+ is not obligatorily linked to Na^+ extrusion. Since outward pumping of Na^+, without compensating entry of K^+, would cause a gradient of electrochemical potential to be generated, such a pump is called an *electrogenic* pump. Presumably it is the electrogenic Na^+ pump that is primarily responsible for the generation of transmembrane potential differences which are conspicuous in muscle and nerve cells; such potentials may be as high as 100 mV. We shall now examine these two types of Na^+ pumps in more detail.

The K^+ and Na^+-Transporting ATPase System

Distribution and Some Properties

Most aerobic cells, whether animal, plant, or microbial, maintain intracellular K^+ at a relatively high and constant concentration, between 100 and 150 m*M*, depending on the species, even though the external concentrations of Na^+ and K^+ may vary widely. The constancy of the internal K^+ concentration is maintained by the transport of K^+ into the cell. Uptake of K^+ without compensating loss of some other cation would cause a net increase in the internal osmotic pressure. Cells would therefore swell and burst if the active accumulation of K^+ were not counterbalanced by the active extrusion of some other cation. The extruded cation is Na^+ in cells of higher animals but in many microorganisms it is H^+. In the following discussion we limit ourselves to the cells of higher animals.

Relatively high concentrations of internal K^+ are required for at least two processes that are vital in the internal economy of all cells. Perhaps the more critical is protein synthesis by ribosomes, which require a high concentration of K^+ for maximal activity (Chapter 30). The second is glycolysis, in which K^+ is required for maximal activity of pyruvate kinase. Moreover, gradients of Na^+ and K^+ across the cell membrane are primarily responsible for the transmembrane potential difference, which in nerve and muscle cells is the vehicle for transmission of the nerve impulse in the form of an action potential (Chapter 26). During the recovery phase following excitation of nerve and muscle, energy-linked extrusion of Na^+ and accumulation of K^+ take place to restore the original resting gradients of these ions.

In 1957 an important breakthrough opened the molecular basis of Na^+ extrusion and K^+ accumulation to direct biochemical study. Skou in Denmark discovered that a fraction of homogenized crab nerve known to contain cell membrane fragments exhibited Mg^{2+}-dependent ATPase activity that was greatly stimulated when both K^+ and Na^+ were added. Addition of either Na^+ or K^+ alone produced very little stimulation. This finding was unexpected, since most K^+-requiring enzymes are inhibited by Na^+. Most significant, however, was the observation that the stimulation of the ATPase activity of such cell membrane preparations by Na^+ and K^+ is inhibited by ouabain. Within a short time, these observations were confirmed and extended. The cell membrane fractions from many kinds of animal tissues were soon found to contain such a Na^+- and K^+-stimulated ATPase activity. Particularly rich in this activity are the membranes of excitable cells, such as brain, nerve, muscle, and the electric organ of *Electrophorus*, the electric eel. Also very rich in this enzyme are Na^+-transporting tissues such as the kidney cortex, the salivary gland, and the salt gland of the sea gull. It was also found that the concentrations of Na^+ and K^+ required for maximal stimulation of the ATPase activity of the cell membrane fractions were comparable to those which yield maximal rates of active transport of Na^+ and K^+ in intact tissues.

Sidedness of the Transport Process

It has been conclusively shown that the Na^+- and K^+-stimulated ATPase of erythrocyte membranes is in fact responsible for Na^+ and K^+ movements and that this enzyme is vectorial or directional in its action; i.e., it has "sidedness." When erythrocytes are exposed to distilled water under controlled conditions, they swell and their membranes increase in permeability. As a result, they lose their hemoglobin and other cytoplasmic proteins, as well as their internal electrolytes, which leak into the surrounding hypotonic medium. Such ghosts can now be "loaded" with a variety of different salts. For example, when isotonic NaCl solution is added to the ghosts, they shrink to normal size and their membranes return to their usual relatively impermeable state. Such preparations are called "reconstituted" or "resealed" erythrocytes. During the resealing process the ghosts entrap NaCl in a concentration equivalent to that in the suspending medium. However, if the reconstitution is carried out in an isotonic KCl solution, they will entrap KCl. In this manner, reconstituted erythrocytes can be prepared which are loaded with varying internal concentrations of KCl or NaCl, or, for that matter, other salts, such as LiCl. Moreover, such erythrocytes can also be loaded with MgATP, if the latter is added to the salt medium in which the ghosts are reconstituted.

Whittam and Ager prepared reconstituted erythrocytes containing internal MgATP and various concentrations of internal NaCl or KCl. They then examined the effect of various internal and external concentrations of Na^+ and K^+ on the rate of the enzymatic hydrolysis of the internal MgATP. When the external medium contained a high Na^+ concentration and the internal medium a high K^+ concentration, conditions resembling those existing in normal intact erythrocytes in the blood, the rate of hydrolysis of internal ATP was very low. Conversely, when the external medium contained a high concentration of K^+ and the internal medium a high concentration of Na^+, the rate of hydrolysis of internal ATP was very high. If the external medium contained no K^+, but only Na^+, then ATPase activity was not stimulated, regardless of the nature of the internal salt. From such experiments it was concluded that both internal Na^+ and external K^+ are required for maximal activity.

It was also found that movements of Na^+ and K^+ occurred in the anticipated directions during hydrolysis of internal ATP. If Na^+ was present in high concentration on the inside and the K^+ concentration was high on the outside, conditions which evoke maximal ATP hydrolysis, then Na^+ moved out of the cell and K^+ moved in as ATP was hydrolyzed. Thus, Na^+ and K^+ activate the ATPase *on the side of the membrane from which they are transported*. Moreover, it was found that the reconstituted erythrocyte ghosts can utilize only internal ATP; external ATP is not attacked. In similar studies, it has been found that external K^+ can be replaced by Rb^+ and NH_4^+ and other monovalent cations, but that internal Na^+ is an absolute requirement for the ATPase activity.

Stoichiometry and Mechanism

With such approaches, it was also found possible to measure the amount of K^+ or Na^+ transported per molecule of ATP hydrolyzed to ADP and phosphate. In erythrocytes, the molar ratio (Na^+ extruded): (ATP hydrolyzed) is about 3.0 and the ratio (K^+ accumulated): (ATP hydrolyzed) about 2.0. These ratios are relatively constant and independent of the existing concentration gradient. ATP and its hydrolysis products ADP and P_i remain inside the cell, as does the Mg^{2+}. Mg^{2+} appears to be required only because it is part of the true substrate, which is the Mg-ATP complex.

Cell membrane fragments bearing "NaK-ATPase" activity become labeled with ^{32}P when the substrate ATP is labeled in its terminal phosphate group. Such labeling requires that Na^+ be present but K^+ absent. When K^+ is added to the labeled membrane fragments, the label is discharged and appears as inorganic phosphate. From such findings the transport reaction was postulated to occur in two major steps. In the first, which requires the presence of Na^+ on the inside of the membrane, the terminal phosphate group is transferred from ATP to the enzyme molecule to form a covalent phosphoenzyme intermediate $E \sim P$. This reaction step is inhibited by Ca^{2+} but not by ouabain. In the second stage of the overall reaction the $E \sim P$ complex, to which the Na^+ ion from the inside is bound, is then hydrolyzed to form free enzyme and P_i. This reaction requires K^+ from the outside (or Rb^+ or NH_4^+), and causes delivery of the previously bound Na^+ to the outside. The K^+-dependent hydrolysis of $E \sim P$ is inhibited by ouabain, which competes with K^+. These two steps may be represented as follows:

$$Na^+_{In} + ATP + E \rightarrow [Na^+ \cdot E \sim P] + ADP$$

$$[Na^+ \cdot E \sim P] + K^+_{Out} \rightarrow Na^+_{Out} + K^+_{In} + P_i + E$$

Recent research suggests that the phosphorylated form of the enzyme contains an acyl phosphate group, probably the phosphoric acid anhydride of the γ-carboxyl group of a glutamic acid residue in the enzyme protein.

Many attempts have been made to obtain the NaK-ATPase, which is tightly bound to the cell membrane, in soluble, homogeneous form. This has not yet been achieved, although it is possible to obtain the enzyme in micellar form by treatment of cell membranes with detergents. Such preparations are often inactive but may be activated by certain lipids. Since the molecular weight of the enzyme has been deduced to be about 670,000, it is probable that the molecule is rather complex and contains several polypeptide chain components. Each erythrocyte has been estimated to contain about 5,000 molecules of the enzyme and each enzyme molecule catalyzes the extrusion of about 20 Na^+ ions per second.

The Role of Na^+ in Amino Acid Transport Systems

We shall now see how active Na^+ extrusion from cells, presumably by the action of an electrogenic Na^+ pump, can cause active transport of amino acids into cells.

The capacity to accumulate amino acids in an energy-dependent active-transport process has been found in most cell types examined, and is particularly pronounced in bacteria, in which the process is very conveniently studied. From the kinetics of transport of the various amino acids and from studies of competition between different amino acids for entry via the transport system, it has been deduced that there are five or more different amino acid transport systems, each of which can transport a group of closely related amino acids. These systems are specific for (1) small neutral amino acids, (2) large neutral amino acids, (3) basic amino acids, (4) acidic amino acids, and (5) imino acids. Each of these transport systems is characterized by an optimum pH and by specific K_M values for its substrates. At least two of them can be inhibited competitively by certain amino acid analogs.

An important clue to the mechanism of active transport of amino acids in cells of animals came with the recognition that external Na^+ ions are required in order to accumulate amino acids; this requirement appears to be absolute. Within limits, the higher the external Na^+ concentration, the greater the capacity of the amino acid transport system to transport amino acids into the cell. These observations led to the hypothesis that the energy inherent in a downward gradient of Na^+ into the cell is the driving force for inward transport of amino acids against a gradient; the downward gradient of Na^+ into the cell is in turn generated by active extrusion of Na^+ from cells.

Another significant observation is that interruption of the energy supply for an amino acid transport system causes the system to lose the capacity to accumulate amino acids against a gradient, as expected. However, under these conditions the system will still catalyze a rapid, facilitated diffusion of the amino acid across the membrane, which does not require a Na^+ gradient and which is passive in nature. These findings have led to the conclusion that amino acid transport systems may consist of at least two molecular components. One is a specific carrier protein that can recognize and bind the amino acid and facilitate its movement across the membrane. The other is a system that can supply energy to the amino acid carrier molecule so that it can move amino acids uphill against a concentration gradient. This energy may be applied in the form of a Na^+ gradient, which is in turn formed at the expense of ATP.

Recently a specific leucine-binding protein has been extracted from the membranes of *E. coli* cells, purified, and obtained in crystalline form. This protein, which has a molecular weight of about 36,000, has many of the attributes of the membrane-linked leucine-transporting carrier. It has about the same affinity for leucine as the leucine carrier in intact bacterial membranes, and contains one leucine binding site per molecule. Moreover, mutants of *E. coli* which are deficient in the capacity to transport leucine also were found to lack the leucine-binding protein.

The Role of Na^+ in the Active Transport of Sugars

Most cells possess the capacity to accumulate sugars from very dilute solutions. In vertebrates this capacity is especially well developed in the epithelial cell layers in the small intestine, where it functions in the absorption of ingested sugars, and in the kidney tubule, where it participates in the reabsorption of glucose from the glomerular filtrate. Many studies have been carried out on the specificity and kinetics of sugar absorption in tied-off loops of small intestine. Not only does sugar absorption by such preparations ultimately depend on a source of metabolic energy, but it has also been established that the inward transport of glucose against a concentration gradient requires the presence of external Na^+ in sufficiently high concentration so that there is a downward gradient of Na^+ into the cell, as in the case of amino acid transport. Ultimately, active transport of glucose into the cell is coupled to the extrusion of Na^+ out of the cell by

Figure 27-7
Function of an electrogenic Na^+ pump in transporting glucose into the cell. The ATP-dependent Na^+ pump keeps the internal concentration of Na^+ low and the external concentration high. The inward Na^+ gradient so generated "pulls" glucose into the cell by means of a passive carrier which requires both Na^+ and glucose to function.

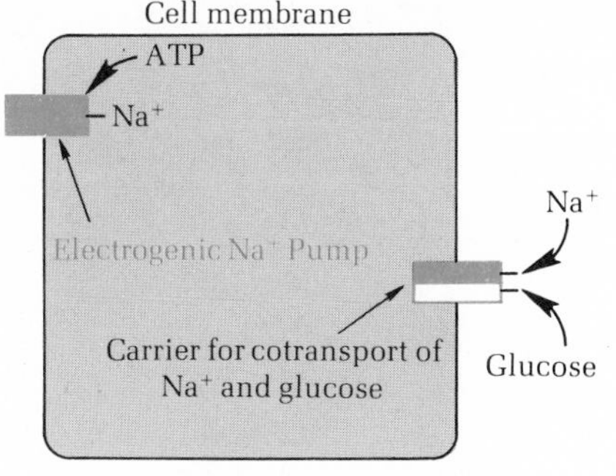

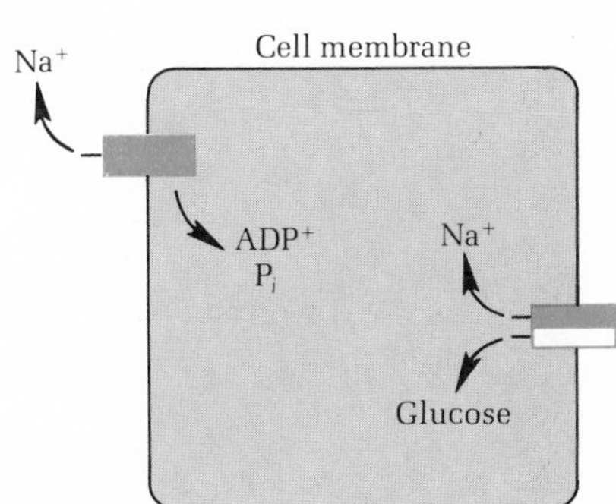

an electrogenic Na^+ pump. Moreover, it has been established that active-transport systems for sugars, like those for amino acids, may also function as passive carriers in the absence of a Na^+ gradient.

An interesting model for the mechanism of glucose transport in the epithelial cells of the small intestine has been postulated and put to some critical tests by Crane (Figure 27-7). He has suggested that glucose enters the cell by binding to a specific carrier molecule, which can also bind a Na^+ ion, probably at a second site. The carrier molecule can thus facilitate the simultaneous and compulsory cotransport of Na^+ and glucose into the cell in a passive process. The cotransport carrier is postulated to be located on the glucose-absorbing side of the epithelial cell barrier. On the other side of the cell is located an electrogenic Na^+ pump, which can pump Na^+ out of the cell, so that the external Na^+ concentration is always higher than the internal concentration. In the presence of an inward gradient of Na^+, Na^+ bound to the cotransport carrier will tend to move inward, down the Na^+ gradient. Since the carrier must also contain bound glucose in order to function, the inward transport of Na^+ drags glucose in with the Na^+. In this manner glucose may be accumulated against a glucose gradient, so long as the inward gradient of Na^+ generated by the Na^+ pump exceeds the outward gradient of glucose. We can now see how the ATP-requiring Na^+ pump can drive the inward transport of glucose via a carrier that is physically independent of the Na^+ pump; such a pump is termed *noncoupled*. Amino acids are believed to be transported into the cell in a similar manner.

Active Transport of Sugars into Bacterial Cells

Considerable progress has recently been made in the isolation of sugar carrier systems from bacteria, which differ from those in animal cells in that Na^+ transport appears not to play a role.

In one set of recent investigations, a component of the β-galactoside "permease" system of *E. coli* has been isolated by Kennedy and his colleagues. They found that galactoside transport in *E. coli* is inhibited by *N*-ethylmaleimide, an alkylating agent, which presumably blocks an essential —SH group of the galactoside carrier protein, which they called *M protein*. Under special experimental conditions, they were able to label the M protein of intact *E. coli* cells, previously induced for galactoside transport by exposure to a nonmetabolized galactoside, with ^{14}C-labeled *N*-ethylmaleimide. The isotopically labeled M protein was then extracted from the membrane and purified, and the progress of the purification was followed by radioactivity measurements.

The highly purified M protein was found to have a molecular weight of about 31,000. *E. coli* induced for galactoside transport was found to contain about 10^4 molecules of M protein per cell. Because the galactoside binding site of the isolated form of the M protein is irreversibly blocked with *N*-ethylmaleimide, it shows no capacity to bind β-galactosides. However, it appears most probable that M protein does in fact represent the β-galactoside carrier of *E. coli* cells since it is essentially absent in *E. coli* cells that have been grown on glucose alone; it is also absent in mutants of *E. coli* unable to transport β-galactosides.

Many bacteria contain a different type of sugar transport system, which functions by phosphorylating the sugar as it passes through the membrane. The sugar is actually accumulated as its phosphate ester; in this electrically charged form it cannot escape from the cell. This type of transport process does not conform to the thermodynamic criterion of active transport, since the molecular species accumulated within the cell is other than that extracted from the environment. Nevertheless, it is an energy-requiring process.

Kundig and Roseman, in a series of penetrating investigations, have found that active sugar transport by this system is brought about by a sugar-recognizing protein, called *enzyme II*, present in the membrane and two other proteins present in the cytoplasm, which participate in the phosphorylation of the sugar, namely, *enzyme I* and a protein designated *HPr*. The reactions taking place can be summarized by two equations. In the first, the cytoplasmic protein HPr is phosphorylated at the expense of phosphoenolpyruvate, a reaction which is catalyzed by enzyme I.

$$\text{Phosphoenolpyruvate} + \text{HPr} \xrightarrow[\text{Mg}^{2+}]{\text{E I}} \text{pyruvate} + \text{phospho-HPr}$$

This reaction is unusual in two respects. First, it employs phosphoenolpyruvate as the immediate phosphate donor, whereas most biological phosphorylations require a nucleoside triphosphate as phosphate donor. Secondly, the protein molecule becomes phosphorylated on nitrogen 1 of the imidazole ring of one of its two histidine residues (Figure 27-8). In only one other case has phosphorylation of a histidine residue of an enzyme been detected, namely, in succinyl thiokinase, in which phosphorylation takes place on nitrogen atom 3 (Chapter 16).

Figure 27-8
The 1-phosphohistidine residue of HPr protein.

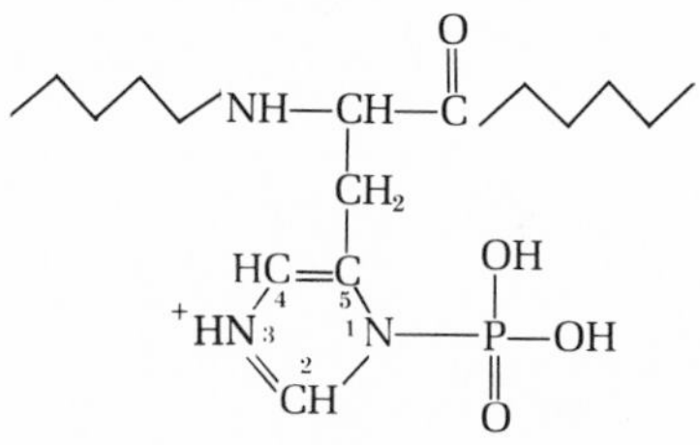

The HPr protein has been highly purified. It has a molecular weight of only 9,400. The highly purified HPr protein does not bind sugars itself, nor does its phosphorylated form. However, in a second enzymatic reaction, the phosphorylated HPr protein donates its phosphate group to the sugar that is to be transported, in a reaction catalyzed by enzyme II. When glucose is the sugar, the product of the reaction is glucose 6-phosphate:

$$\text{Phospho-HPr} + \text{glucose} \xrightarrow{\text{E II}} \text{HPr} + \text{glucose 6-phosphate}$$

This transphosphorylation reaction is also remarkable in that an adenine nucleotide is not involved. Enzyme II appears to carry the specificity for the sugar; in fact, there is some evidence that there is a different enzyme II for each sugar transported by this system. Many different sugars, including D-glucose and various glucosides,

Figure 27-9
Energy-linked transport of glucose across a bacterial membrane and accumulation of glucose 6-phosphate. (PEP = phosphoenolpyruvate).

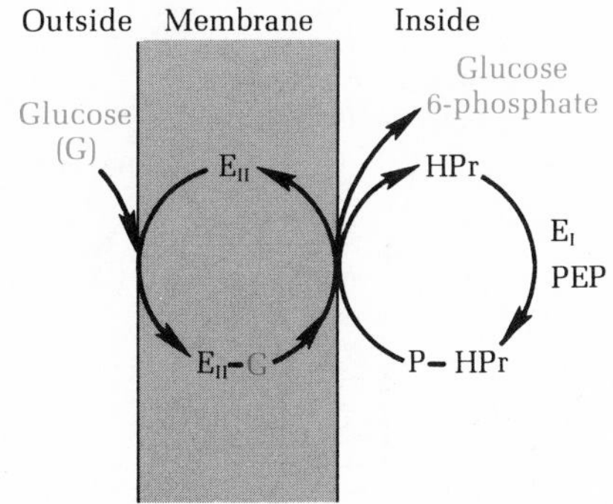

D-galactose and various galactosides, D-fructose, pentoses, pentitols, and hexitols, have been identified as phosphate acceptors in this system. The E II enzymes are tightly bound to the membrane of the *E. coli* cell, and it has been difficult to obtain them in soluble, active form.

Roseman and his colleagues have postulated the mechanism shown in Figure 27-9 for sugar transport by this system. Much genetic evidence supports this working hypothesis. Bacterial mutants which lack enzyme I or HPr were found to be unable to accumulate any of the transportable sugars. On the other hand, mutants defective in one or another species of enzyme II, each of which is specific for a given sugar, were defective in transporting only the corresponding sugar. Perhaps the most significant and convincing of the experiments carried out by Roseman and Kundig is their successful reconstitution of sugar transport in an in vitro system. They showed that membrane vesicles can be isolated from bacterial cells in such a manner that they lack HPr and enzyme I and are thus unable to accumulate sugars as their phosphates. When purified HPr and enzyme I were then added to such depleted membrane vesicles, they were bound to the vesicles, whose capacity to accumulate sugar phosphates was then restored.

The Sulfate Transport Protein

Pardee and his colleagues have succeeded in isolating from the bacterium *S. typhimurium* a protein which appears to be responsible for transporting sulfate from the medium into the cells. When this organism is grown in the presence of very low concentrations of sulfate, it develops an active sulfate transport system, through the process of derepression. When such transport-positive cells are subjected to osmotic shock, the cells lose about 5 percent of their protein, which is believed to come primarily from the membrane. Such osmotically shocked cells are no longer able to transport sulfate. From the protein fraction recovered after the shock treatment, a specific protein capable of binding sulfate was isolated and crystallized; it was in fact the first transport protein to have been obtained in crystalline form. This protein, which has a molecular weight of about 32,000, contains one sulfate binding site per molecule. Its affinity for sulfate is very high and approximately equal to the affinity of intact *S. typhimurium* cells for sulfate; it is half-saturated at about 3×10^{-5} *M* sulfate. That the isolated sulfate-binding protein is identical with the protein of the membrane that transports sulfate is strongly suggested by the finding that those agents that can inhibit sulfate transport or compete with sulfate in intact cells also can inhibit sulfate binding by the isolated protein.

Fundamental Processes in Active Transport

Ordinary chemical reactions occurring in a dilute aqueous solution, or in the gas phase, are nondirectional or *scalar* reactions, since they take place in an isotropic medium. A chemical reaction can be *vectorial* only if it takes place in one of two possible conditions. It must either occur in an *anisotropic* medium, one whose physical properties are not identical in all directions, or it must be coupled to another chemical reaction that is vectorial. We have seen an example of one vectorial transport process coupled to another, namely, the coupling of inward transport of amino acids to outward transport of Na^+. In the case of the Na^+ and K^+-stimulated ATPase, however, the energy-yielding reaction, the hydrolysis of ATP to ADP and phosphate, takes place inside the cell and is overall scalar, suggesting that either the Na^+-transporting molecule, or the membrane, or both must be anisotropic or asymmetric in their molecular organization. In fact, it is likely that both are asymmetric.

Although enzymes in dilute aqueous solution catalyze reactions that are scalar, many possess an inherent asymmetry which cells may have utilized during evolution of active-transport systems. We have already seen that the catalytic sites of many enzymes, such as aconitase, are asymmetric in their interaction with their substrates (Chapter 16). Within the microscopic domain of the asymmetric active site of an enzyme molecule, the substrate molecule must approach from one direction in a particular orientation, and after the bond-making or bond-breaking process is complete, the reaction products must also leave the catalytic site in a certain direction and orientation. This requirement is particularly true in enzymes catalyzing S_N2 or "backside" displacement reactions, in which the attacking group enters from one side of the transition complex and the leaving group departs from the other. When such an enzyme catalyzes a reaction in dilute aqueous solution, the overall reaction is scalar, because the active sites of all the enzyme molecules are randomly oriented at any given time. However, if a number of enzyme molecules were fastened to a very thin membrane so that their active sites were all identically oriented with respect to the plane of the membrane, one can then imagine how this set of oriented enzyme molecules might catalyze a vectorial reaction across the membrane (Figure 27-10). Moreover, if the membrane in which the carrier molecule is embedded is itself asymmetric, for example, if one side of the membrane were more hydrophilic than the other, the membrane asymmetry could also aid in the vectorial transport process.

The dimensions and viscous properties of the membrane across which transport takes place must also be considered. Membranes are between 60 and 100 Å thick. This distance is relatively large compared with the size of glucose or amino acid molecules (5 to 6 Å) or even small globular protein molecules (25 to 35 Å). The question is: how can the carrier molecules of transport systems translocate their substrates over such a large distance? Several possibilities are open. The carrier protein with its bound ligand may diffuse from one side of the membrane to the other, thus undergoing a physical translocation. Or, if it is a very large molecule whose diameter is about the same as the thickness of the mem-

Figure 27-10
Model showing how enzyme molecules possessing an asymmetric active site can be fixed in a membrane in such a manner as to carry out a vectorial reaction.

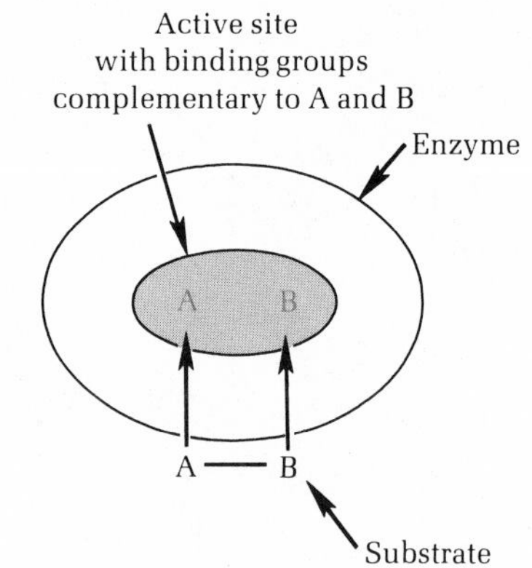

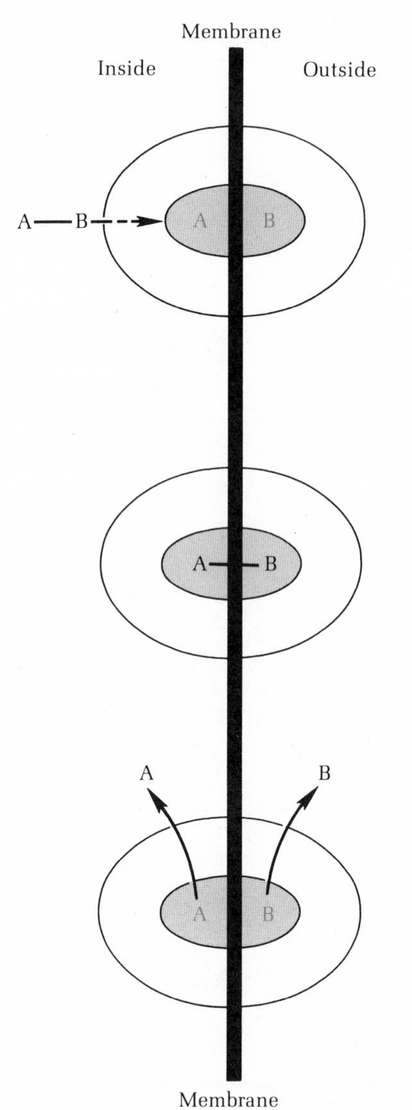

brane, it need only rotate in the membrane structure in order to carry its substrate across. However, neither type of diffusion through the membrane appears likely, since membranes have been found to be very viscous and nearly nonfluid. Such a medium would hardly permit large molecules to diffuse rapidly enough to account for the high rates at which transport systems translocate substrates across membranes. At present it appears more likely that the carrier molecule, which is presumably a protein, is relatively fixed in the membrane, but can undergo conformational changes of sufficiently great amplitude that it can carry the substrate across the membrane. Alternatively, the carrier molecule may be located in the center of a "thin spot" in the membrane. It is also possible that a carrier protein may undergo a conformational change resulting in the opening of a central "pore," through which the substrate may pass.

Summary

Cell membranes contain transport systems capable of promoting the passage of biologically important solutes. Such systems are substrate-specific, they show saturability with substrate, they may be inhibited either competitively or noncompetitively, and they are genetically determined. Presumably the substrate forms a complex with a specific carrier molecule in the membrane, analogous to an enzyme-substrate complex. Passive-transport systems facilitate the passage of specific solutes down a concentration gradient; they require no metabolic energy. An example is the glucose carrier of the human erythrocyte, which is competitively inhibited by phloretin and other analogs of glucose. Other membrane transport systems promote exchange diffusion, or equimolar exchange of solute molecules across the membrane. Active-transport systems promote passage of specific solutes against a concentration gradient; they depend on ATP or other forms of metabolic energy.

One of the most widely distributed active-transport systems in higher organisms is the NaK-ATPase, which extrudes Na^+ from cells and causes coupled accumulation of intracellular K^+. It consists of an ATPase system in the cell membrane which acts on internal MgATP; it is stimulated by Na^+ from the inside and by K^+ from the outside. In some erythrocytes three Na^+ ions are extruded and two K^+ ions accumulated per molecule of ATP hydrolyzed to ADP and phosphate. The transport reaction proceeds in two steps. The first requires Na^+ and is inhibited by Ca^{2+}; it leads to phosphorylation of the enzyme by ATP and binding of internal Na^+. In the second step, which is stimulated by K^+ and inhibited by ouabain, the phosphoenzyme is hydrolyzed and Na^+ is released to the outside. Most cells also contain another type of outwardly directed active Na^+ pump, which furnishes the driving force for active transport of amino acids and glucose into cells.

Active-transport systems for amino acids require an inward gradient of Na^+ ions as the energy source to transport amino acids into the cell. They consist of two components, an amino acid–carrying component, and an energy-furnishing component. A leucine-binding transport protein has been isolated from *E. coli* cells.

Most cells also contain transport systems for sugars. In animal tissues, glucose is believed to be transported into the cell by a carrier which also carries Na^+ into the cell. Since the outward Na^+ pump maintains an inward gradient of Na^+ ions, the inward flow of Na^+ in response to the gradient drags glucose into the cell against a gradient.

A protein component (M protein) of the β-galactoside permease system of galactoside-induced *E. coli* cells has been isolated in pure form; it is presumed to be the carrier for β-galactosides. Bacterial cells contain a second type of active-transport system for simple sugars. Three genetically distinct molecular components of this system have been identified, designated enzyme I, enzyme II, and a phosphate-transferring protein HPr. By their interaction, the transported sugar becomes phosphorylated and is accumulated in the cell in this form. From the isolated components, sugar transport can be reconstituted in depleted membrane vesicles.

References

Books

KLEINZELLER, A., and A. KOTYK, (eds.): *Membrane Transport and Metabolism*, Academic Press, Inc., New York, 1961. The proceedings of a comprehensive symposium, which contains important articles on the thermodynamics of active transport.

STEIN, W. D.: *Movement of Molecules across Cell Membranes*, Academic Press, Inc., New York, 1967. An excellent elementary account of the present knowledge of the theory and function of membrane transport systems.

Articles

ALBERS, R. S.: "Biochemical Aspects of Active Transport," *Ann. Rev. Biochem.*, **36:**727–756 (1967). Review of recent advances, particularly in the transport of Na^+ and K^+.

ANRAKU, Y.: "Transport of Sugars and Amino Acids in Bacteria" (3 papers), *J. Biol. Chem.*, **243:**3116–3135 (1968). Experimental papers.

CRANE, R. K.: "Na^+-dependent Transport in The Intestine and Other Animal Tissues," *Federation Proc.*, **24:**1000–1006 (1965). Excellent review of the coupling of glucose transport to Na^+ gradients.

FOX, C. F., and E. P. KENNEDY: "Specific Labelling and Partial Purification of The M Protein, A Component of The β-Galactoside Transport System of *E. coli*.," *Proc. Natl. Acad. Sci. (U.S.)*, **54:**891–899 (1965). An experimental paper.

KUNDIG, W., F. D. KUNDIG, B. ANDERSON, and S. ROSEMAN: "Restoration of Active Transport of Glycosides in *E. coli* by A Component of A Phosphotransferase System," *J. Biol. Chem.*, **241:**3243–3246 (1966). An important research paper.

MITCHELL, P.: "Translocations through Natural Membranes," *Advances in Enzymol.*, **29:**33–88 (1967). A penetrating review of fundamental processes and concepts of membrane transport.

PARDEE, A. B.: "Membrane Transport Proteins," *Science*, **162:** 632–637 (1968). A brief review article.

PIPERNO, J. R., and D. L. OXENDER: "Amino Acid Transport Systems in *E. coli* K_{12}," *J. Biol. Chem.*, **243:**5914–5920 (1968).

ROTHFIELD, L., and A. FINKELSTEIN: "Membrane Biochemistry," *Ann. Rev. Biochem.*, **37:**463–496, 1968. Review of recent research.

SIMONI, R. D., M. LEVINTHAL, F. D. KUNDIG, W. KUNDIG, B. ANDERSON, P. E. HARTMAN, and S. ROSEMAN: "Genetic Evidence for The Role of A Bacterial Phosphotransferase System in Sugar Transport," *Proc. Natl. Acad. Sci. (U.S.)*, **58**:1963–1970 (1967).

SKOU, J. C.: "Enzymatic Basis for Active Transport of Na^+ and K^+ across The Cell Membrane," *Physiol. Rev.*, **45**:596 (1965). Detailed review.

WHITTAM, R.: "The Molecular Mechanism of Active Transport," in G. C. Quarton, T. Melnechuk, and F. O. Schmitt, (eds.), *The Neurosciences*, Rockefeller Institute, New York, 1967, pp. 313–325. How the Na^+ and K^+ stimulated ATPase works.

Problems

1. Calculate the amount of free energy required to transport 1 gram-ion of K^+ from blood plasma to intracellular fluid of muscle at 37°, using data given in Figure 27-2.

2. Calculate the maximum gradient of Na^+ ion concentration that can theoretically be achieved by the hydrolysis of ATP to ADP and phosphate by a Na^+-transporting ATPase at equilibrium. Assume standard thermodynamic conditions.

3. (*a*) Calculate the maximum rate of K^+ uptake by an aerobic cell oxidizing glucose if its rate of respiration is 10.2 μg atoms of oxygen per milligram protein per hour at 37°. Assume that 80 percent of the respiratory energy is utilized for K^+ transport via the NaK-ATPase. Use data furnished in the text.
   (*b*) How many K^+ ions would be extruded from this cell per molecule of citric acid undergoing complete combustion to CO_2 and H_2O?

4. If 75 percent of the glycolytic energy of adult human erythrocytes, available as ATP, is devoted to extrusion of Na^+, how many Na^+ ions could be extruded by the NaK-ATPase per molecule of glucose undergoing glycolysis to lactic acid?

5. Calculate the net amount of energy required to concentrate the bicarbonate ion of pancreatic juice starting from blood plasma, using data in Figure 27-2.

6. If a single erythrocyte contains 5,000 molecules of the NaK-ATPase, what fraction of the cell membrane surface is occupied by the enzyme molecules? Assume that the erythrocyte is a disk 7 μ in diameter and 1 μ thick, and that the ATPase molecule is spherical and has a density of 1.2. Other necessary data are given in the text.

7. Calculate the minimum pH gradient across a membrane that could, theoretically at least, support the formation of one molecule of ATP at pH 7.0 under standard thermodynamic conditions in a process proceeding to an equilibrium. Now calculate the minimum pH gradient required to generate one molecule of ATP in a system in which the equilibrium concentrations are 3.0 m*M* ATP, 0.5 m*M* ADP, and 3.0 m*M* phosphate.

8. Calculate the free-energy change in the secretion of the components of 1 liter of urine from the solutes of blood plasma, starting from the data in Figure 27-2. The concentration of urea in the blood is 4.5 m*M* and in normal urine it may be assumed to be 320 m*M*. The NH_4^+ concentration in blood is 20 μM. Ignore solutes that contribute less than 2 percent of the total solute concentration of urine.

PART 4 REPLICATION, TRANSCRIPTION, AND TRANSLATION OF GENETIC INFORMATION

pCATCGATCGCGCGATAGCGCGATCGCGATCGCGATCGAGATCTCGAGCGATCGAGCGTAGCGCGATATAGCAGAGATC
ACGCTAGCGATCGAATCTCGAGAGCTAGCGATCGAATCGCCGCGATAGCGATCGAGACTTAGCGCGATAGCAGAGCTT
AGCTAGCTAGCGCGAGAGAGCTCTATAGAGCTATATCGAGAGCTATATCGCGATAGCTAGCTAGCGAGAGATCTAGAG
ATCGATCGAGATCTCGAGATCGAGATAGCGATATAGCGCGATATAGCGAGATCGAATATCGCATAGCGATAGCTAGCT
AGCGCGATAGCGCTATATAGCGCGAGATATAGACTAGCTAGCTAGATCTAGCTATTAGCCTAGACTAGATCTAGATCG
AGCTCTCGAGATCTTATATAGCGCGATAGCTATAGCGATATAGCTAGGCTAGCTAGCTAGCTAGAGATCGAGCTATAT
ACGAGATAGCGATATATGCGAGATATAGCGATAGCTATATATCGATAGCTAGCTAGCTAGCTCTAGACTCTCTAGATA
GACTCGATCGATCGATCTCTCGGAGACTCTAGCTATGCGATCGATCCGAGATCGCGATCGCATCGAAGCTAGCTAGCT
CTGACTAGCTAGCTATATCGCGATAGCGATCGAGATCGAAGCTAGCTAGCTAAAGCTCTAGAGCTAATAGAGACTAGT
GCGATAGCAGAGCTCGCGATCGAGATCTCTAGAGACTCTCGAGAGCTCGAGCTAGTCGGATCGAGCTAGAGATCGAGC
AACCGGTTAAAGGCCCTTAAGGCCCTTTAAGGCCTTAAGGCTCCTGGAACGCTAATGCAGGCTAGCGCTAGCCTTAGG
TTAGAGCTAGGACTCTAGACTCTCGACTCATAGAGCGCGCTATATAGCGCGAATATCGCGCGAATAAATTGGCCATTA
AAACTCGGAATCTCGAGGCCGAATTAAGGCGCGAGACTGACTGACTGACCGCGCTATATAGCGCGAGATCGCGATAGC
AGCTCTAGAGACTTCGAGACTCTAGCGCTAGCTCGATCGATCGGAAGGATATAGAGCTCTCTGAGCGCGATATAGCGA
TAGCTCGATCGATCGCGAGATATAGCGCGCGATATAGCGCGAGAATTTGAAGAGACTTTAAAGCCGAGATCGACTCGG
CGAGCTCGAGCGCTATAGCGCGATCGCGAGAGATCTCGCGCTCGCGATATAGCGCTATATAGCGCGATCGCGAGCGTC
AGCTAGCTAGCTAGCGCGATATAGCGCGAATATAGCGATAGCGAATTCGAGAGACCTAGCGAGAGCTACGAGACTAGA
TGCTAGCGCTAGCGCGATATAGCGCGAGATCTCTAGCGCATAGCGAGATCGAGCTATCTCTCAGAGAGCTATAGAGGT
AGCGCTATAGCGCTATAGCGCGATATATAGCGCGATATCTCTATATAGAGAGACACATATAGACAGATAGATATATAT
GCTATATAGAGACACACATATAGAGCGCGCTAGAGCTATAGCGCCGAATAAGAGACACATAGACTAGCTAGCGATAGA
CAGATCGCGATATCGAGAGCTCTAGAGCTCTCTATAGAGAGACACATAGAGCGCGATAGAGCGACGAGCAAGCGAGCT
TAGAGCGCGATATCGCGCGATATACACAAGAGACATATAGAGAGCGCGTGTGCTTAGAGATGATACAGAGATAGAGTC
GCAGATAGACACAGATACAGATACAGATACAGATAGATAGAGCGCTAGCGTGTGCGACATGAAGACTAGCGATGCTGA
AGAGCTCTAGAGCTAGCGCTCGCGATCTCGAGAGCGAGAGCTCTCGAGACATAGACAGCTCGATCGATCGAGGAACGA
TGGCGATATAGCGCGCGATATAGCGCGATATAGACACACAGATTATCGCGCTTAAGGCGGAATTGCCGTGCAGAAGTG
CTATATACTATATACACATATAGAGACACATAGAGAGCGCGGGGAATTAACCTTGGGAAACCTTGAAACCTTGTGCAC
ACTAGAGCCTAGCTAGCGCGATATAGCGCATAGAGCAGCGCGAGAGCGCGTGGCAGCTAGCTCGATCGGAGCGATGCA
GCGCGATATAGCCGCGATATAGCGCGGAGACACATAGAGCGCGATAGAGCGTGTGTACAGATACAGATAGACATGACT
CTCGCGGACAACCAGAATTAGGCGCTCGGACACATAGCCGGAGATACACATAGAGACAGATACAGATACAGATACAGC
TGCGCGATAGCGCGATATCGCGCTAGAGACAGATACAGATCGCGTAGCGCGATAGCGCGATATGCCGGATAGACATTG
GACACATAGACAGTAGACAGATATAGACACACAGATAGACACCAGGTTGTGCTCGAGAGACACAGAGATAGATGCGTG
AGACCATAGAACACAGATATGAGACACATAGAGAGCGCTCGCGAGACATGACCAGATAGAGCGTAGACAGATAGCAGT
TAGACACAGATATGCGCGCTAGAGACACAAGAGCTCTCGGACAGATACAGATAGAGACACAGATAGACAGGAGATTCG
CTCGGACACAGATAGAGCGCTAGAGCGCTCGCGCTAGACAGAGCTCGAGAGAGCTCTCGAGACACAGTAGGACAGATC
GCTGAGGACAACCAGGGATTTAGAGACACAAAGTTGGAACCGGATTAATGCCGGAACATAGCGATGACAGAATTGAGA
AGACCATAAGGAACCAGATATGGAACAGAGATAGACAGATAGACACGAGATAGAGACAGATAGACAGATACGCTGGAT
TTAGACCAGATAGAGACAAGAGAGACCCATTGGCCAAGGTCCGGAACTTAGGAACGAATTGGCCTGACAGATAGACGA
GCCTGGAACCAAGGCCTTGGAACCAGAAGACAATTAGACAGGAATTCCGTAGACGAATGGACAGGCTCGGACTAGACG
CCAGATATTCCGGAATTAGGCCGGAATTGCCGGCTTAGAGACACAAGGCCTGGAACGAATTCGGGAATGGGAACCAGT
AAGGCCTGGAAGCGCCTTGAAGGCCTGGAAGCCTCTAGAGCGCCTTAAGGCCGGAATTGGCCTTGGAACGGGAACTGA
GGCCTGGAACCAAGGCCTGGACCAATTAGAGAGAACCAGAGATTCCGGGAACCAATTAAGGCCTTGAACAGGCTGGAC
TTGGCCTTGGAATTCGGAACCAATTAGGGCCTGGAACCAAGGCCTTGAACGCCTTAGGACCTCGGTACAAGGCTGAGT
CATTGCGGATACCAGGCCTGGAACCTTCGGACAGGCCTGACAGGTCGGACATGCTGACAGGCTGACAGACAGTAGGCG
GGACCAATTGCCGGCTTAGACCAGGCCTGCCAGAGGACCTAGGCTTGAACGGTCCGGTGACAGGCTGACGTAGGCTGA
TGGCTTAGGACCATTGGCTCGCGCTTAGACAAGGCCTGACAGGCCTGGAACATAGGCCTGGAACCAGGCTGGACAGAT
TGCGGATAGAGACCAATGGACAGATTAGGACCAGGATTCGCGTAACCAGATTCGGACAATTCGGACTAGGACATGACG
AATTAGGAACCAAGGAATTCGCCCTTGGAACCAGGCTCCGGAACGGGTCCTGGAACAATGGAACGATAGACTGACAGT
GCTTAGGCCTTGACCAAGGCCTGGACAAGGCCTGACACAGATAGGCTTGGACCAGATTCGGACAATGCGGTAGACAGA
CCTGGAACCAGAATTCCGGAACCAATTGCCTGGACAGGGTCGGACCATTAAGGCCTGACCATAGGACATAGATTGTAT
AATTCGGACCAAGGTTAACCAGGAATTCCGGTAAGGCCTGGACAAGGCTTACGTGACGATTCGGACTAGACATGAGAC
CAGGATTCGGAATTAACCAGGGCCTTGGAACCAAGGCCTTGGAAGGTCGGAATTAGGACAGGATAGACATGAGCGTGA
TGCCTGGACCAGGATTCGCGCTTAGGAACCAGGCCTGGAACCAGAGGCCTGGACCAGGAACCATTGGAACTGACGACG
CTGGAACCAGAGGCCTGGACACAAGGCCTGGACAACAAGGCCTGACCAGGCCTGACAGGATGAGACGATGACGTCGAT
GCTTAGGAGCCTTGAGAGAGCTCTCGAGAGCTCTCGAGAGACACATAGCGCTCTCGAGACAGCTCGACAGGCTGAGCA
ACTTAGACCAAGGCCTGGACCCAAGGATTCCGGATTACCAAGGCTTGGACCAGGCTGGACAAGGTCGGATGACAGATG
CGGATTAGGCCTGGACCAGGCTGGACAGGCTGACAGGCTGACAGGCTTGAGGCTGACCAGGCTGGAACGATGATAGGT
TGGCCTGGAACCAATGCCGGATAGGCTGGACCAAGGCCTGGACAAGTTCGGACCAATGCGTAGGAACGATGAGACAGC
GCAATGCGGATGGAACCAGATTCGGACCAAGGCTTGGAACCAATGGCTTGAACCAGGCTTGAACCAGGCTGACAGGCA
AATTCGGAATTCGGAATTCCGGACCAATTCGGACCAATTCCGGAAATGGCTTAGAACGGAATGCTGAACATGACAGTG
GCTTAGGCTGGAACCAAGGATTCGGAATGGCCTGGAACCAGGCTGGACCAGGCTTGAACGAATTCGGACAGTGACAGT
CGGATTAGGCTGGAACCAAGGCCTGGACCAAGGCCTGGACAGGCTGACAGCTGACAGCTGACAGTTACAGTCGACGAG
AGCTGGACCAAGGCCTGGAACCAAGGCCTGGACAACAAGGCTATAAGGACCAAGGCCTGGACAGGCTGACAGATGCTC
TGGACCAGGCCTGGAACCAAGGCCTGGACCAAGGCCTGGAACCAGGCCTGGACAAGGCCTGGAACCAAGGCTGACAGT
GACCAATGCTGGACCAGGCCTTGGAACCAAGGCCTGGACAACCAAGGCTCCGGATACAAGGCCTGACAAGCTGACAGT
ATGAACCAAGGCCTGGACCCAAAGAGAGGCCTCTCGGGACACAGGCCTTGGAATTACCAAGGCCTGGACCAGGCTGAG
AAGGCCTGGAACCAAGGCCTGGACCAGGCCTGGAACCAAGGCCTGGAACCAAGGCCTGGGAACCAATGCGCTGACAGA
TTCCGGATTACCAAGGCCTGGACCAAGGCTGGAACCAGGCCTGGAACCAGGAATTCGGAATTCGGATACCAAGGCCTG
GGCCTGGAACCAGGCCTGGACCAATGGAACCAATGGCTGGACCAGGCCTGACAACCAATGGACAGGATACGATGCGGT
CCTGGAACCAAGGCCTGGACCAAGGCCTGGACCAGGCCTGGACCAGGCTGGACCAGGCTGACCAGGCTGACAGTGAGA
TGAGGCCTGGAACCAAGGCCTGGACCAAGGCCTGGACACAAGATACAGATAGGCTGACAGGCCTGACAGGCTGACGGT
AAGGCTGGAACCAAGGCCTGGACCAGGCCTGGACCAGGCTGGACAGGCTGACAGCTGACAAGCTGACAGTCGAGATGA
GCCTGGACCAAGGCCTGGACCAAGGCCTGGAAACGGTAGGACAAGGCTGACAAGGCCTGACAGGCCTGACAGTCGTGG
CCGGACCAATTGCCGGATTACCAAGGCCTGGACCAGGCTGGACCAGGCTGGACCAGGCTGACAGGCTGACAGCTGAGA—OH

An imaginary base sequence for the chromosome of bacteriophage ΦX174, one of the smallest bacteriophages known. About 2,000 of these pages would be needed to show the base sequence of the chromosome of a single E. coli cell, and about one million pages to show the base sequence of the DNA of a single human cell.

PART 4 REPLICATION, TRANSCRIPTION, AND TRANSLATION OF GENETIC INFORMATION

In the last part of this book we shall consider the biochemical basis of some of the most fundamental and central questions that are posed by the genetic continuity and the evolution of living organisms. What is the molecular nature of the genetic material and its functional units, the chromosomes, genes, coding symbols, and mutational units? How is genetic information replicated with such fidelity? How is it transcribed and used elsewhere in the cell? How is genetic information ultimately translated into the amino acid sequence of protein molecules, and thence into the characteristic three-dimensional structure of cells? How did living organisms develop the capacity for self-replication—indeed, how did life first arise?

The extraordinary advances made in our knowledge of the molecular basis of genetics in the last fifteen years have brought an intellectual revolution in biology that many consider comparable to that which commenced with Darwin's theory of the origin of species. All fields of biology have been profoundly influenced by these new developments. They have brought penetrating new insight into some of the most fundamental problems in cell structure and function and have led to a more comprehensive and a more widely applicable conceptual framework for the science of biochemistry. Today literally no biochemical problem can be studied in isolation from its genetic background. Moreover, these concepts have greatly increased the power of the molecular approach to biology and have encouraged biochemists to probe more confidently into such complex biological problems as cell differentiation, morphogenesis, immunity, and many others which, not too long ago, had been thought to be unapproachable by biochemistry except in a trivial way. Let us briefly examine the scientific and intellectual background which led to this new era in biochemistry.

Today's knowledge of the molecular basis of genetics arises from theoretical and experimental advances in three different fields of science: classical genetics, biochemistry, and molecular physics. In the field of genetics, experimental progress has been immensely accelerated by the use of x-rays and other mutagenic agents, which greatly increase the rate of spontaneous mutation, and by the use of organisms with a very short life cycle, such as molds, bacteria, and viruses. In addition, more efficient methods for the selection of rare mutants and genetic recombinants from huge populations have led to the construction of high-resolution genetic maps. Such maps have revealed the sequence of various genes in chromosomes and have shown that a gene has a large number of sites at which it may undergo mutation. But the most pervasive developments in the field of genetics, which initiated the confluence of genetics and biochemistry, were the enunciation of the "one gene-one enzyme" hypothesis by Beadle and Tatum and the discovery by Avery and his colleagues that DNA contains genetic information.

In the field of biochemistry important experimental advances were made possible by the refinement of chromatographic methods. They led to quantitative analysis of the amino acid composition and sequence of proteins and showed that the sequence varies with the function of the protein and its species of origin. New chromatographic methods were also instrumental in establishing the composition and covalent structure of nucleic acids. One of the most significant developments was the discovery of the molar equivalence of certain bases in DNA, which became an important element in deducing its three-dimensional structure. The isotope tracer technique also played a vital role, since it made possible direct experimental approaches to the enzymatic biosynthesis of nucleic acids and proteins.

In the field of molecular physics, the successful application of x-ray diffraction analysis to the conformation of fibrous protein molecules by Astbury and Pauling, and sometime later of globular proteins by Kendrew and Perutz, yielded the concept that each type of protein molecule has a specific conformation of precise dimensions, which determines its biological function. But the central event which triggered the development of molecular genetics was the application of the powerful x-ray method to the analysis of the three-dimensional structure of DNA. In 1953 Watson and Crick postulated a double-helical structure for DNA which not only accounted for its characteristic x-ray diffraction pattern, but also suggested a simple mechanism by which genetic information can be precisely transferred from parent to daughter cells. This hypothesis quickly resulted in a remarkable confluence of ideas and experimental approaches from genetics, biochemistry, and molecular physics.

The Watson-Crick hypothesis was soon built upon and extended to yield what Crick termed the *central dogma* of molecular genetics, which states that genetic information flows from DNA to RNA to proteins, a relationship often symbolized as "DNA → RNA → protein." The central dogma defined three major processes in the preservation and transmission of genetic information. The first is *replication*, the copying of DNA to form identical daughter molecules. The second is *transcription*, the process in which the genetic message in DNA is transcribed into the form of RNA, to be carried to the ribosomes. The third is *translation*, the process in which the genetic message is decoded and converted into the 20-letter alphabet of protein structure. The central dogma is supported not only by the discovery of messenger RNA, which carries genetic information from DNA to the ribosomes (the sites of protein synthesis), but also by the demonstration that the sequence of nucleotides in a gene bears a linear correspondence to the sequence of amino acids in the protein formed. Moreover, in one of the greatest achievements in contemporary science, the genetic "dictionary" of triplet codewords for the various amino acids has been deduced.

Now that the central dogma of molecular genetics has been firmly substantiated, it may appear that most of the important work has been done; as one distinguished investigator has put it, "that was the molecular biology that was." But we have had but a glimpse. As in many fields of science, the opening of one door only leads to another and there is an endless succession of doors. Let us now see where we stand today and what remains to be done.

Most of the illuminating research on the molecular basis of genetic information transfer over the last twenty years has been carried out on procaryotic organisms, particularly the bacterium *E. coli*, and on bacterial viruses. Procaryotes contain only one chromosome, a single molecule of double-stranded DNA, and they ordinarily reproduce by an asexual process of cell division, in which the daughter cells normally receive a genome identical to that of the parent cell. In the life cycle of procaryotes the cell is usually in the haploid state at all times. Therefore the genetics of bacteria can be studied without the complications of dominance and recessiveness which are characteristic of diploid eucaryotic organisms and with which the Mendelian principles are concerned. Moreover, the problems of genetic information transfer are even simpler in the single chromosomes of viruses, which contain only a few or at the most perhaps 200 genes, compared to several thousand genes in bacteria. Because of the relative simplicity of viruses and bacteria, and the speed and efficiency with which genetic experiments may be carried out on them, we are now in command of penetrating insight into the basic molecular processes in genetic information transfer, which we can with some confidence regard as biologically universal. But there is a vast gulf between bacteria and eucaryotic cells, in size, complexity, and in the capacity for differentiation and evolution.

Today molecular genetics stands on another threshold, one which opens to new problems of massive proportions, namely, the genetics of eucaryotic organisms and the variation of gene expression during differentiation and development, a field called *epigenetics*. Although much evidence now supports the view that the basic processes of genetic replication, transcription, and translation are essentially identical in procaryotic and eucaryotic organisms, in the latter a number of special complexities are superimposed. Eucaryotic organisms contain vastly more genetic information than procaryotes, and this is divided among several or many chromosomes. The somatic cells of eucaryotic organisms are usually diploid and contain twice the number of chromosomes found in the germ cells, which are haploid. Each gene in a eucaryote thus occurs in two forms or *alleles*, one of which is genetically dominant, the other recessive. Eucaryotic organisms usually reproduce by sexual conjugation, during which genes from both parents are exchanged and incorporated into the genome of the progeny by a process called *recombination*.

The molecular structure of the complex chromosomes of eucaryotic organisms, the manner in which various genes from different chromosomes interact together, the molecular mechanisms by which genes from the parents are recombined in specific ratios, and how gene expression is controlled in eucaryotes are major unsolved problems of great complexity. Moreover, it is now clear from recent research that many, if not all, eucaryotic organisms contain DNA not only in the nucleus, but also in the mitochondria and certain other organelles in the cytoplasm. The latter type of DNA appears to be involved in what is called *cytoplasmic inheritance*, a process expressed in a non-Mendelian and still little-understood manner. The biochemical aspects of the genetics and epigenetics of higher organisms thus constitute essentially a virgin field.

CHAPTER 28 DNA AND THE STRUCTURE OF CHROMOSOMES

In this chapter we shall try to answer three major questions. What is the evidence that DNA and DNA alone is the primary form in which genetic information is stored? What is the molecular basis for the capacity of DNA molecules to store information? What are the dimensions of some of the functional units of the genetic material, such as chromosomes, genes, and the units of mutation?

We have already considered the nature of the mononucleotide building blocks of DNA and the covalent structure of its backbone, matters that should first be reviewed (Chapter 12). In this chapter we shall consider DNA primarily as a molecule capable of storing information.

The Role of DNA in Bacterial Transformation

Although DNA was first discovered in cell nuclei as long ago as 1869, it was not directly identified as bearing genetic information until 1943, when Avery and his colleagues discovered that a non-virulent strain of the bacterium *Pneumococcus* can be transformed in a heritable manner into a virulent strain by simple addition of DNA extracted from virulent pneumococci. Virulent or pathogenic pneumococci had long been known to form smooth colonies (designated S) when cultured on agar, because of the presence of a distinctive polysaccharide capsule. Avirulent or nonpathogenic strains of pneumococci, on the other hand, form rough colonies (R). Griffith, a British investigator, had earlier found that addition of heat-killed virulent S cells to live, nonvirulent R cells caused some of the latter to become permanently transformed into virulent S cells, suggesting that the transformation was caused by a heat-stable compound present in S cells. Avery, MacLeod, and McCarty investigated this effect more closely. They found that DNA isolated in highly purified form from heat-killed S cells, when added to nonvirulent R cells, reproduces the effect of adding whole heat-killed S cells. However, DNA specimens from R cells, or from sources other than S cells, were found to be unable to produce transformation of R cells into S cells. Moreover, they found the DNA-induced transformation of R cells to be a permanent and heritable characteristic, since all progeny of the transformed cells, over many generations, were found to be virulent S cells. Avery and his colleagues therefore concluded that DNA can carry genetic information. However, this conclusion was not immediately accepted. Some investigators suggested that the DNA preparations contained a mutagen which could promote mutation to the S form. Others suggested that the transformation of R into S cells was actually caused by traces of some specific protein remaining in the DNA samples used. Eventually, however, these objections were removed by further experiments. Many other instances of bacterial transformation by DNA have since been observed, and today Avery's experiments are commonly regarded as an important historical landmark. It is now known that the transforming DNA is covalently incorporated into the DNA of the recipient cell and is thus replicated when the host chromosome is replicated.

No comparable evidence exists that new heritable traits can be permanently conferred on a given strain of bacteria by introduction of either RNA or proteins from another strain.

Biochemical Evidence for DNA as Genetic Material

Strong supporting evidence that DNA is the bearer of genetic information has come from other directions. For one thing, the amount of DNA in any given species of cell or organism is remarkably constant and cannot be altered by environmental circumstances or by changes in the nutrition or metabolism of the cell, a property to be expected of the genetic material.

Secondly, the amount of DNA per cell appears to be in proportion to the complexity of the cell and thus to the amount of genetic information it contains. Data in Table 28-1 show that the higher the organism in the evolutionary scale, the greater its content of DNA. Bacteria contain about 0.01×10^{-6} μg DNA per cell (about 1 percent of the total wet weight), whereas the tissues of higher animals contain about 6×10^{-6} μg DNA per cell. Moreover, the germ cells of higher animals, which are haploid and possess only one set of chromosomes, contain only one-half the amount of DNA found in somatic cells of the same species, which are diploid and have two sets of chromosomes (Table 28-2). In any given species of higher organism, the amount of DNA per diploid cell is approximately constant from one cell type to another. The amount of DNA present in DNA-containing animal and bacterial viruses, which have only a few genes and thus relatively little genetic information, is correspondingly very small.

Experiments on the replication of bacterial viruses also pointed to DNA as genetic material. Particularly significant are the isotopic experiments of Hershey and Chase. They labeled either the protein or the DNA portion of virus particles by incubating the host bacteria in media containing appropriate labeled precursors. With such labeled virus particles they showed conclusively that

Table 28-1 Approximate DNA content of some cells and viruses

Species	*DNA, picograms† per cell (or virion)*	*Number of nucleotide pairs millions*
Mammals	6	5500
Amphibia	7	6500
Fishes	2	2000
Reptiles	5	4500
Birds	2	2000
Crustaceans	3	2800
Mollusks	1.2	1100
Sponges	0.1	100
Higher plants	2.5	2300
Fungi	0.02–0.17	20
Bacteria	0.002–0.06	2
Bacteriophage T4 (per virion)	0.00024	0.22
Bacteriophage λ (per virion)	0.00008	0.07

† One picogram = 1.0 $\mu\mu$g = 10^{-12} grams.
The figures given for eucaryotic organisms are for somatic (diploid) cells.

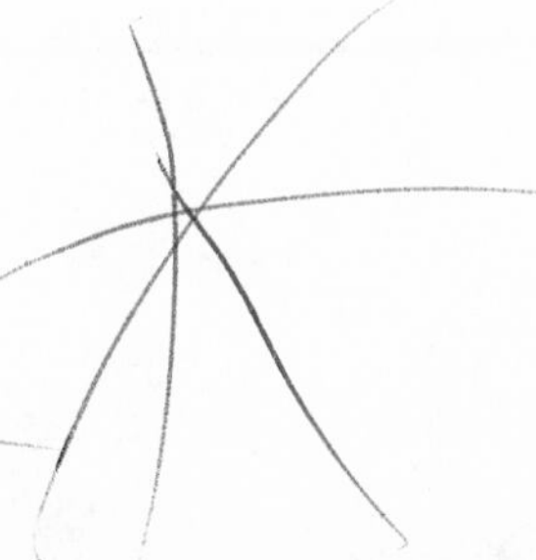

Table 28-2 DNA content of cells of the chicken

Tissue	DNA, picograms per cell
Heart	2.45
Kidney	2.20
Liver	2.66
Spleen	2.55
Pancreas	2.61
Erythrocyte	2.49
Sperm cells (haploid)	1.26

viral DNA rapidly enters the host cell whereas viral protein does not. These observations were later followed by the demonstration that the viral nucleic acid alone is infectious, in the absence of viral protein, and can lead to the formation of complete viral progeny in the host cell.

Base Equivalences in DNA

One of the most provocative pieces of evidence supporting the concept that DNA is the bearer of genetic information was the discovery that the base composition of DNA is related to the species of origin in a very specific manner. Before reliable chromatographic methods became available, it was thought that the four major bases found in DNA, adenine (A), guanine (G), cytosine (C), and thymine (T), occur in equimolar ratio in all DNA molecules. Then, in the period 1949 to 1953, Chargaff and his colleagues applied quantitative chromatographic methods to the separation and quantitative analysis of the four bases in hydrolyzates of DNA specimens isolated from different organisms. Some of the data collected by them and by others are shown in Table 28-3. From such data the following important conclusions were drawn:

1. DNA specimens isolated from different tissues of the same species have the same base composition.
2. The base composition of DNA varies from one species to another.
3. The base composition of DNA in a given species does not change with age, nutritional state, or changes in environment.
4. In nearly all DNAs examined, the number of adenine residues is equal to the number of thymine residues (i.e., A = T), and the number of guanine residues is

Table 28-3 Base equivalences in DNA

	Base composition, mole percent				Base ratios			Asymmetry ratio
	A	G	C	T	A/T	G/C	Pu/Py	$\frac{A+T}{G+C}$
Animals								
Man	30.9	19.9	19.8	29.4	1.05	1.00	1.04	1.52
Sheep	29.3	21.4	21.0	28.3	1.03	1.02	1.03	1.36
Hen	28.8	20.5	21.5	29.2	1.02	0.95	0.97	1.38
Turtle	29.7	22.0	21.3	27.9	1.05	1.03	1.00	1.31
Salmon	29.7	20.8	20.4	29.1	1.02	1.02	1.02	1.43
Sea urchin	32.8	17.7	17.3	32.1	1.02	1.02	1.02	1.58
Locust	29.3	20.5	20.7	29.3	1.00	1.00	1.00	1.41
Plants								
Wheat germ	27.3	22.7	22.8	27.1	1.01	1.00	1.00	1.19
Yeast	31.3	18.7	17.1	32.9	0.95	1.09	1.00	1.79
Aspergillus niger (mold)	25.0	25.1	25.0	24.9	1.00	1.00	1.00	1.00
Bacteria								
E. coli	24.7	26.0	25.7	23.6	1.04	1.01	1.03	0.93
Staphylococcus aureus	30.8	21.0	19.0	29.2	1.05	1.11	1.07	1.50
Clostridium perfringens	36.9	14.0	12.8	36.3	1.01	1.09	1.04	2.70
Brucella abortus	21.0	29.0	28.9	21.1	1.00	1.00	1.00	0.72
Sarcina lutea	13.4	37.1	37.1	12.4	1.08	1.00	1.04	0.35
Bacteriophages								
T7	26.0	24.0	24.0	26.0	1.00	1.00	1.00	1.08
λ	21.3	28.6	27.2	22.9	0.92	1.05	1.00	0.79
φX174, viral	24.6	24.1	18.5	32.7	0.75	1.30	0.95	1.34
φX174, replicative	26.3	22.3	22.3	26.4	1.00	1.00	1.00	1.18

always equal to the number of cytosine residues (G = C). As a corollary it is clear that the sum of the purine residues equals the sum of the pyrimidine residues; that is, A + G = C + T.

5. The DNAs of closely related species have similar base composition, whereas those of widely different species are likely to have widely different base composition. The base composition of the DNA can in fact be used to classify organisms taxonomically.

The Watson-Crick Model of DNA Structure

The base equivalences observed in DNA from different species raised the intriguing possibility that there is a level of structural organization of DNA molecules which is compatible with certain base equivalences and incompatible with others. It was in fact already suspected that DNA has a specific three-dimensional conformation. For example, solutions of native DNA are highly viscous, from which it was concluded that DNA molecules are long and rigid rather than compact and folded. Moreover, heating of freshly isolated DNA produces significant changes in its viscosity and other physical properties, without breaking the covalent bonds in the DNA backbone. Because of such observations, and the illuminating discovery of the α-helical arrangement of the polypeptide chains in some fibrous proteins, which had just been deduced by x-ray diffraction, it was inevitable that the powerful x-ray method was to be applied to the problem of DNA structure.

In fact, fibers of DNA had already been subjected to x-ray diffraction analysis. In 1938 Astbury first observed that fibrous DNA specimens show reflections corresponding to a regular spacing of 3.34 Å along the fiber axis, but the significance of this observation was not clear because the DNA was known to be impure. However, in the period 1950 to 1953 more refined x-ray data were obtained on fibers from highly purified DNA, particularly through the work of Franklin and of Wilkins. DNA can be obtained in two forms, A and B, which differ in degree of hydration; the B form is considered to be the biologically important form. The B form of DNA was found to possess two periodicities, a major one of 3.4 Å and a secondary one of 34 Å (Figure 28-1), reminiscent of the major and minor periodicities observed in α-keratins. About this time important x-ray data on the dimensions of the purine and pyrimidine bases and of nucleosides were also being collected in a number of laboratories. The stage was now set for the formulation of a 3-dimensional conformation of the DNA molecule which could account for the known dimensions of the bases, the observed periodicities in DNA structure, and the equivalence of certain bases. Interest in the problem was greatly heightened by the pervasive question of how the DNA molecule can undergo replication with such great fidelity. If the genetic information is encoded by a specific sequence of bases in DNA, as had been speculated, then how can this sequence be precisely replicated?

Figure 28-1
X-ray diffraction photograph of DNA in the B form taken by Rosalind Franklin late in 1952. The reflections crossing in the middle are indicative of helical structure; they are often called the "helical cross." The heavy dark regions at the top and bottom are due to the closely stacked bases perpendicular to the fiber axis (see Figure 28-2).

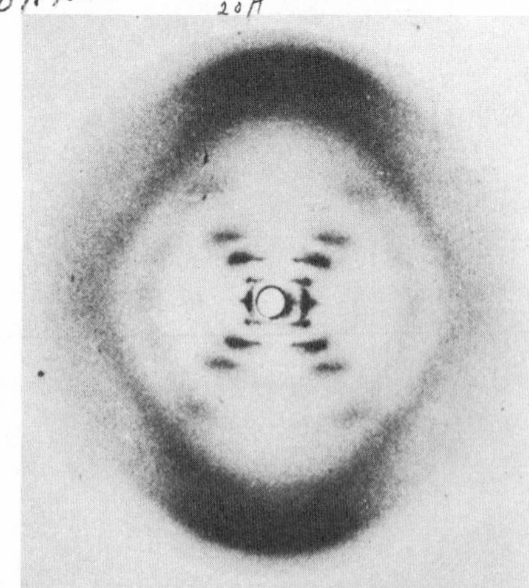

In 1953 Watson and Crick postulated a precise three-dimensional model of DNA structure which was based on the x-ray data of Franklin and Wilkins and the base equivalences observed by Chargaff. This model not only accounted for many of the observations on the chemical and physical properties of DNA, but also suggested a mechanism by which genetic information may be accurately replicated.

The Watson-Crick model of DNA structure is shown in Figure 28-2. It consists of two right-handed helical polynucleotide chains coiled around the same axis to form a double helix. The two chains or strands are antiparallel; that is, their 3′,5′-internucleotide phosphodiester bridges (see Chapter 12) run in opposite directions. The coiling of the two chains is such that they cannot be separated except by unwinding the coils; such coiling is termed *plectonemic*. The purine and pyrimidine bases of each strand are stacked on the inside of the double helix, with their planes parallel to each other and perpendicular to the long axis of the double helix. The bases of one strand are paired in the same planes with the bases of the other strand. The pairing of the bases contributed by the two strands is such that only certain base pairs fit inside this structure in such a manner that they can hydrogen-bond to each other. The allowed pairs are A-T and G-C, which are precisely the base pairs showing exact equivalence in

Figure 28-2
Structure of DNA.

Dreiding model of the backbone.

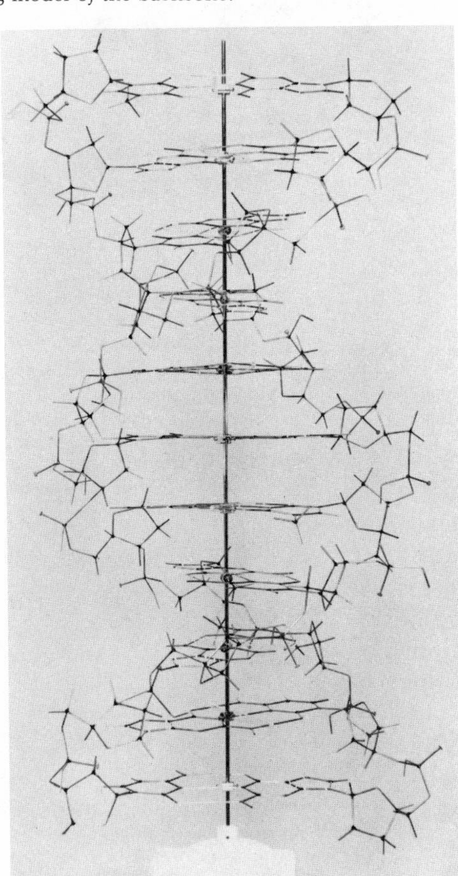

Space-filling model.

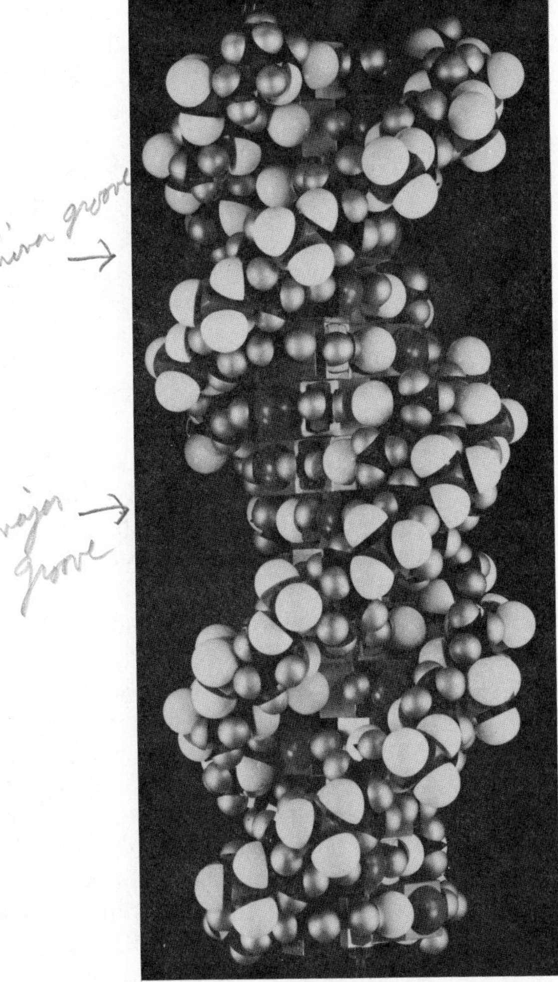

DNA. The manner in which they form hydrogen bonds is shown in Figure 28-3. The pair A-G would be too large to fit inside a helix having these dimensions, and C and T would be too far apart in such a helix to form stable hydrogen bonds with each other. Furthermore, hydrogen bonding in A-G and C-T pairs is in any case weaker than that in A-T and G-C pairs. Thus, the Watson-Crick double helix involves not only the maximum possible number of hydrogen-bonded base pairs but also those pairs giving maximum stability.

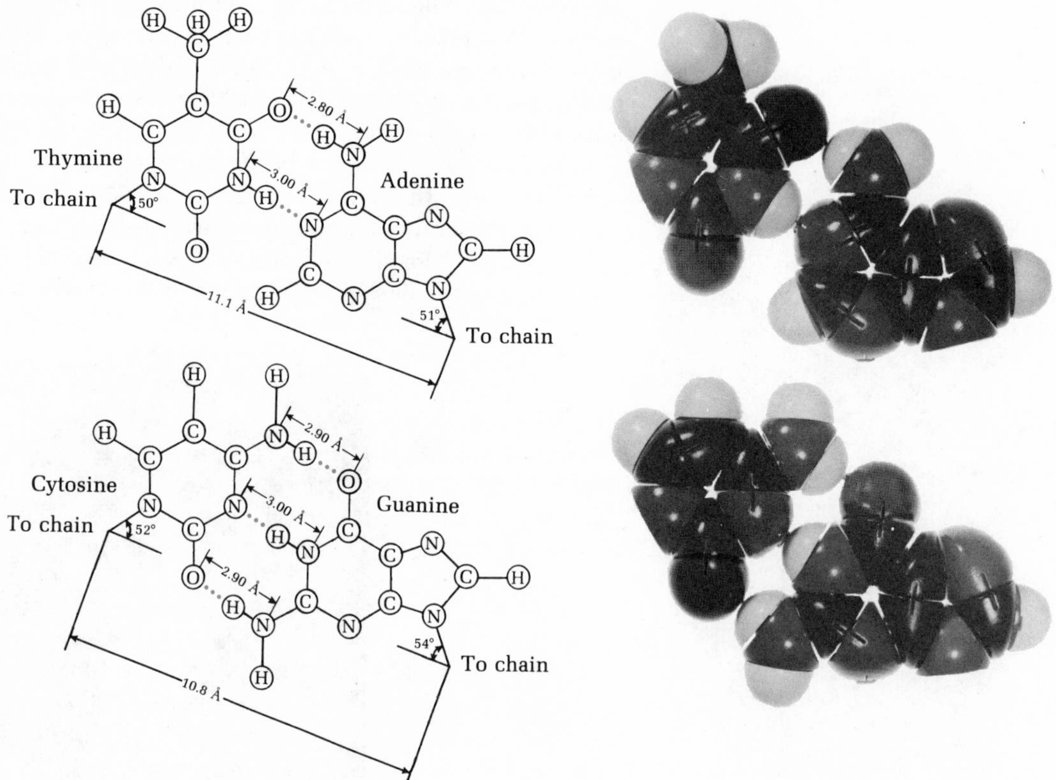

Figure 28-3
Scale drawings and space-filling models of the hydrogen-bonded base pairs adenine-thymine and cytosine-guanine. The former has two hydrogen bonds, the latter three. Cytosine-guanine pairs are slightly closer together, more compact, and thus slightly more dense than adenine-thymine pairs.

To account for the 3.4 Å periodicity observed by x-ray methods, Watson and Crick postulated that the bases are closely stacked perpendicular to the long axis at a center-to-center distance of 3.4 Å from each other. There are exactly 10 nucleotide residues in each complete turn of the double helix, to account for the secondary repeat distance of 34 Å. These repeat distances are possible only if the purines and pyrimidines are paired in the manner postulated. DNA can theoretically exist in other helical forms, but they would not have the 3.4-Å repeat distance along the long axis observed in native DNA. The Watson-Crick double helix has one shallow and one deep groove, and is about 20 Å in diameter. The hydrophobic, relatively insoluble bases are closely stacked within the double helix, shielded from water, and the hydrophilic sugar residues and electrically charged secondary phosphate groups are located on the periphery, exposed to water. The double

Complementary antiparallel strands of DNA

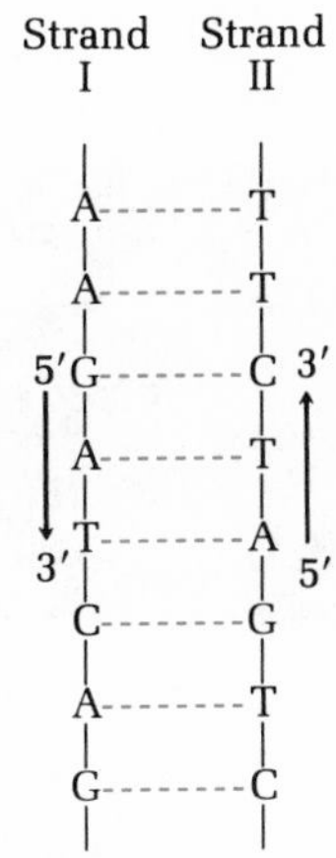

helix is thus stabilized not only by hydrogen-bonding within complementary base pairs but also by hydrophobic interactions between the stacked bases.

The two polynucleotide chains of double-helical DNA are not identical in either base sequence or composition. Instead, the two chains are complementary to each other: wherever adenine appears in one chain thymine is found in the other, and vice versa, and wherever guanine is found in one chain cytosine is found in the other, and vice versa. However, this complementarity exists *only* when the chains are oriented in opposite directions, as is demonstrated by a simple example of two complementary antiparallel DNA strands shown in the margin. The base composition of strand I is $A_4G_2C_1T_1$ and that of its complementary antiparallel strand II is $A_1G_1C_2T_4$.

The complementary double-helical structure of DNA leads to the second element of the Watson-Crick hypothesis, namely, a mechanism by which genetic information can be accurately replicated. Since the two strands of double-helical DNA are structurally complementary to each other and thus contain complementary information, the replication of DNA during cell division was postulated to occur by separation of the two strands, each becoming the template specifying the base sequence of a newly synthesized complementary strand. The end result of such a process is the formation of two daughter double-helical molecules of DNA, each identical to that of the parent DNA, and each containing one strand from the parent (Figure 28-4).

Figure 28-4
Replication of DNA as suggested by Watson and Crick. The complementary strands are separated and each forms the template for synthesis of a complementary daughter strand.

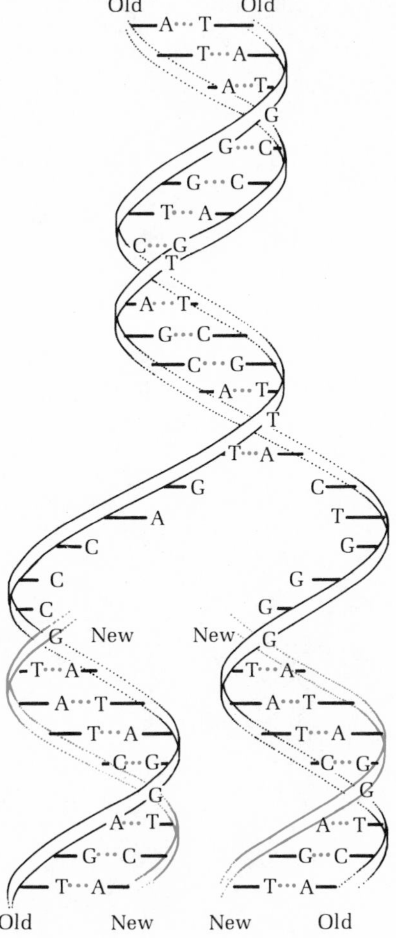

Although some years were to elapse before direct experimental proof emerged for the antiparallel polarity of the two strands of DNA and for the "semiconservative" nature of the replication process described above, the Watson-Crick hypothesis had an immediate impact and profoundly influenced the nature of the experimentation designed to unravel the molecular aspects of genetic information transfer. We shall see many instances in which this hypothesis has been substantiated and confirmed.

The double-helical or duplex structure for DNA is supported by many other kinds of evidence. For example, the length of single native DNA molecules of known molecular weight, such as the relatively small DNAs of certain bacterial viruses, can now be measured accurately and directly by electron microscopy (Figure 28-5). The observed contour lengths of single DNA molecules and the predicted lengths calculated from the double-helical model for a given molecular weight are in very good agreement for several different viral DNAs.

The Size of Native DNA Molecules

For some years it was thought that DNA molecules were linear and had molecular weights of the order of 7,000,000 to 20,000,000. These assumptions were based on physical observations made on DNA specimens extracted from bacterial cells or animal tissues with aqueous phenol or neutral NaCl solutions. However, it is now certain that intact native DNA molecules of bacterial cells are far larger than these early estimates. Moreover, there is increasing evidence that a native DNA molecule is not necessarily linear, but may have its ends covalently joined to form an endless or circular structure. In fact, native DNA molecules of bacteria and animal cells are so large that they are not readily isolated in intact form, since they are easily broken by shear forces during extraction and handling. Even simple stirring or pipetting of DNA solutions can cause fragmentation of DNA into pieces of about 5,000,000 to 10,000,000 molecular weight. Moreover, in cells of higher organisms there are probably several or many different types of DNA molecules, differing in base sequence. For these reasons little success has attended efforts to isolate and study homogeneous native DNA molecules from higher organisms.

On the other hand, the DNA molecules of some of the bacterial viruses can easily be obtained in native homogeneous form (Table 28-4), and they have served as valuable prototypes of the much larger DNA molecules of bacteria and higher cells. The DNAs of the small *E. coli* bacteriophages *lambda* (λ) and φX174 have received much attention. The former is a duplex DNA molecule with a molecular weight of 32 million, arrived at from sedimentation analysis. Its contour length, which can be measured from electron micrographs of specimens plated out on grids, is about 17.2 μ. The DNA of λ phage is exceptional in that it is linear as it is usually isolated, whereas the DNA of most known bacteriophages is circular. The DNA of φX174 virus, which is one of the smallest DNA viruses known, is circular and exists in both single-stranded (MW 1.7 million) and double-stranded (MW 3.4 million) forms (Figure 28-5). The contour length of the single-stranded form is only 1.77 μ. The φX174 virus and its DNA are of great experimental importance; they are discussed in much greater detail in Chapter 29. The DNA of the much larger bacteriophage T2 is shown in Figure 28-6. From the data in Table 28-4 it is seen that the contour lengths of duplex DNA molecules are related in a simple manner to their molecular weights; 1.0 μ in contour length is equivalent to about 2.0 million daltons.

Although the DNA molecules of *E. coli* and other bacteria are too large to study by standard hydrodynamic methods, they have been visualized in some cases by electron microscopy and also by radioautography (Figure 28-7). The chromosome of *E. coli* appears to consist of a

Figure 28-5
Electron micrographs of DNA of bacteriophages φX174 and λ.

φX174 DNA

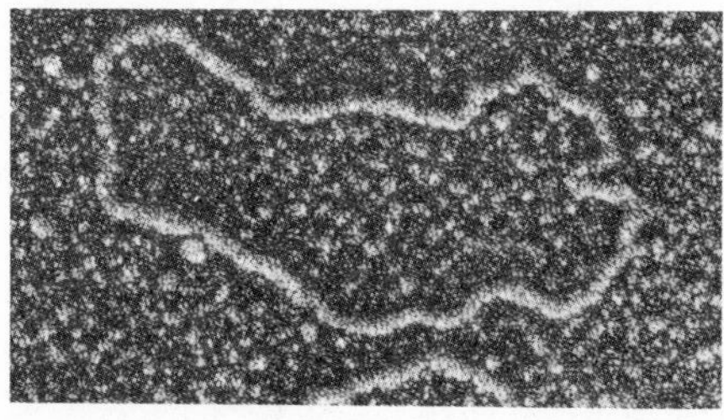

0.5 μ

λ DNA

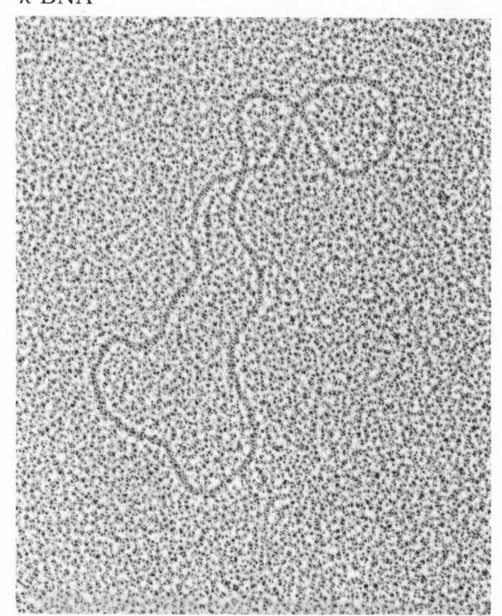

5.0 μ

Table 28-4 Dimensions of the DNAs of some viruses

	Contour length, μ	*Weight, daltons (millions)*	*Percent G + C*
E. coli bacteriophages			
φX174 (single-stranded)	1.77	1.7	42
φX174 (duplex)	1.64	3.4	42
λ	17.2	32	49
T2	56.0	130	35
T7	12.5	25	48
Animal viruses			
Herpes simplex	35.0	68	68
Polyoma	1.56	3.1	48

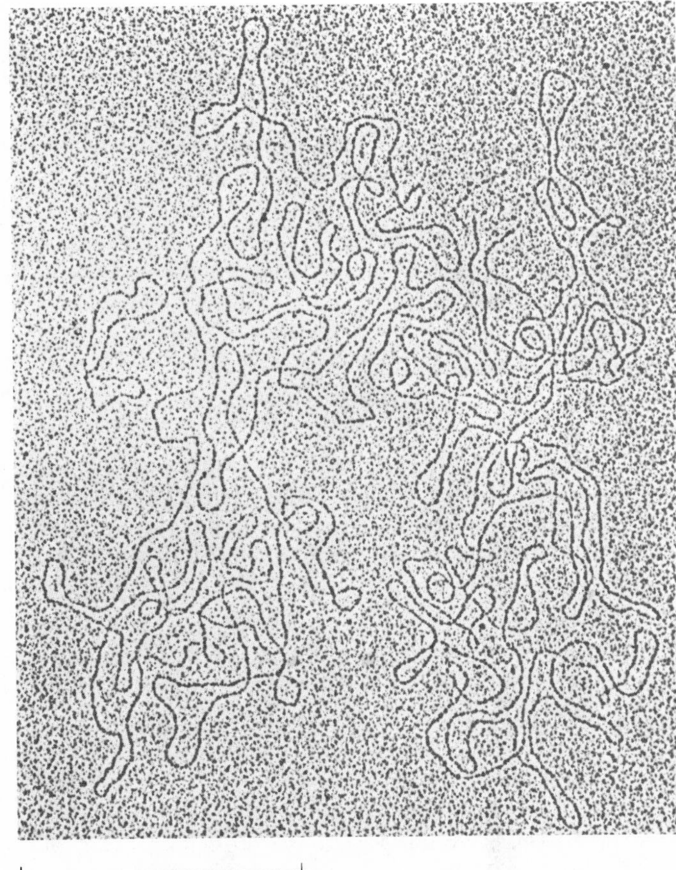

Figure 28-6
DNA of bacteriophage T_2 (linear form). Its contour length is 55.9 μ.

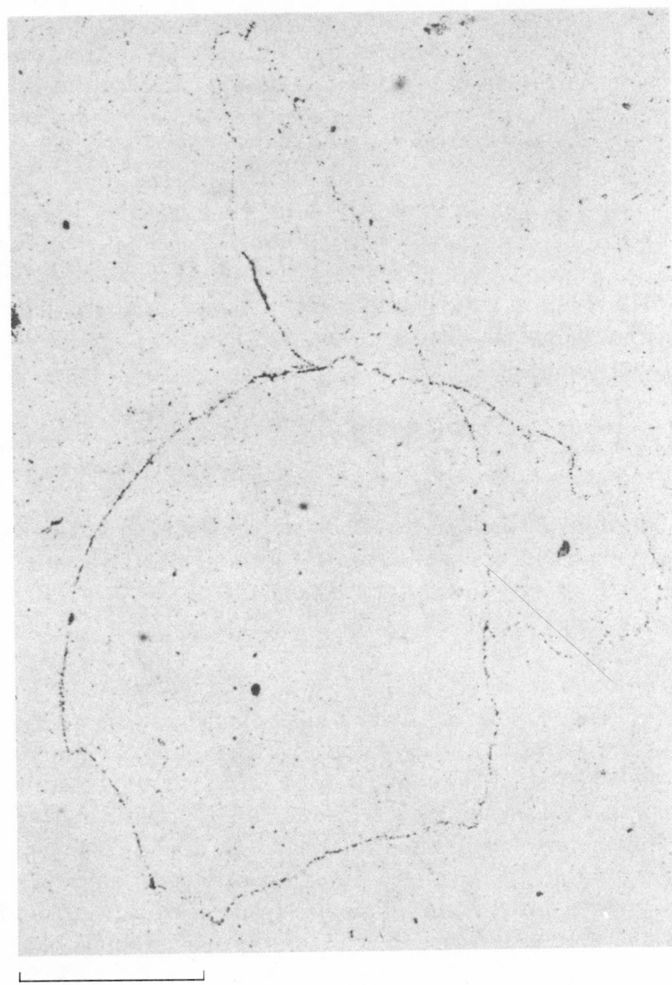

Figure 28-7
Radioautograph of a DNA molecule of E. coli. The DNA was extracted from E. coli cells grown on a medium containing thymidine labeled with the radioactive hydrogen isotope tritium. It was spread on a sensitive photographic plate and the radioactive "track" of the molecule detected microscopically. This DNA molecule is undergoing replication. From J. Cairns, Scientific American, January 1966.

single, enormous double-stranded DNA molecule with a molecular weight of about 2,800,000,000, a thickness of about 20 Å, and a contour length that exceeds 1200 μ, or 1.2 mm. *E. coli* DNA contains about 4.2 million base pairs (each base pair has an average molecular weight of 600). This enormous DNA molecule has no ends, in accordance with the fact that the genetic map of the single chromosome of *E. coli* is circular. What is most extraordinary is that this immensely long molecule, which is about 1,000 times as long as an *E. coli* cell, is packed into a relatively small volume in the nuclear zone.

Eucaryotic cells contain several or many nuclear chromosomes, depending on the species (Table 28-5), and each chromosome may contain one or more very large DNA molecules. Little or no information is available on the size of individual DNA molecules in higher cells, but they are believed to be much larger than those in bacteria. The total length of all the DNA present in a single mammalian cell has been calculated to be about 2 meters, on the assumption that it is double-helical. This is equivalent to about 5.5×10^9 base pairs. Figure 28-8 shows an electron micrograph of one of the 46 chromosomes of a human cell. The chromatin fibers of which this structure is composed consist of DNA molecules in association with specific proteins.

Mitochondria of eucaryotic cells contain a small amount of DNA which is quite different from that found in the nucleus. Mitochondrial DNA is double-stranded; it is usually circular and has in most cases a molecular weight of about 10 million or a small multiple of 10,000,000. It therefore resembles in size the DNA of the small bacteriophages. Usually mitochondrial DNA differs in base composition from nuclear DNA of the same cell. There are about 4 to 6 molecules of DNA per mitochondrion, but the total mitochondrial DNA is less than 1 percent of the total cellular DNA in somatic cells. Chloroplasts of higher plants also contain DNA.

It is curious that a small fraction of the mitochondrial DNA exists as pairs of interlocked circles called *catenated dimers;* the significance of such structures is not known (Figure 28-9).

Table 28-5 Normal chromosome number in different species

Procaryotic organisms (haploid)	
Bacteria	1
Eucaryotic organisms (diploid)	
Drosophila	8
Red clover	14
Garden peas	14
Honey bee	16
Corn	20
Frog	26
Hydra	30
Fox	34
Cat	38
Mouse	40
Rat	42
Rabbit	44
Man	46
Chicken	78

Figure 28-8
Electron micrograph of human chromosome 12. Human chromosomes contain about 15% DNA, 10% RNA and 75% protein. They consist of long chromatin fibers about 200–300 Å in diameter and about 700–800 μ long. Each chromatin fiber is believed to contain one DNA duplex about 4 cm long in supercoiled arrangement, around which the protein is wound (33,750 ×). From DNA and Chromosomes *by E. J. DuPraw. Copyright 1970 by Holt, Rinehart and Winston, Inc.*

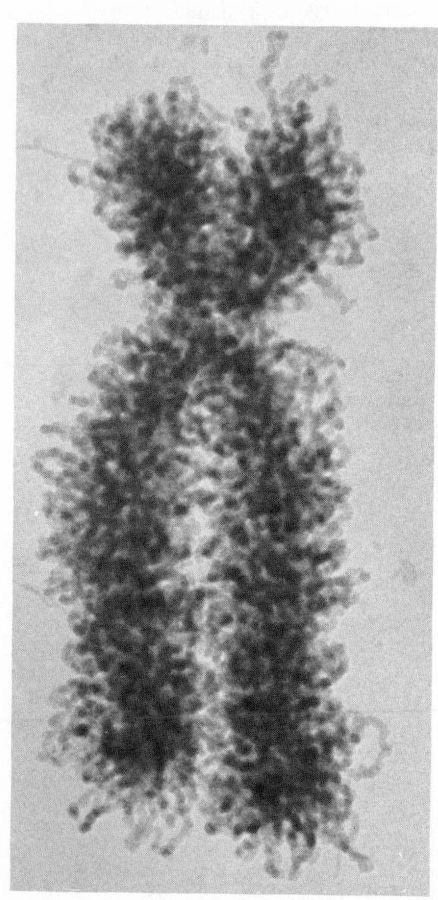

Properties of DNA Molecules in Solution

Solutions of small native DNA molecules, or of fragments of large DNA molecules, share a number of characteristic chemical and physical properties.

Acid-Base Properties

The highly polar secondary phosphate groups of DNA, which constitute the bridges between adjacent mononucleotides, have a rather low pK′. DNA is thus a strong polybasic acid which is fully ionized at any pH above 4. These phosphate groups are located on the outer periphery of the double helix, fully exposed to water. They strongly bind simple divalent cations such as Mg^{2+} and Ca^{2+}, as well as the polycationic amines spermine and

Figure 28-9
Forms of mitochondrial DNA.

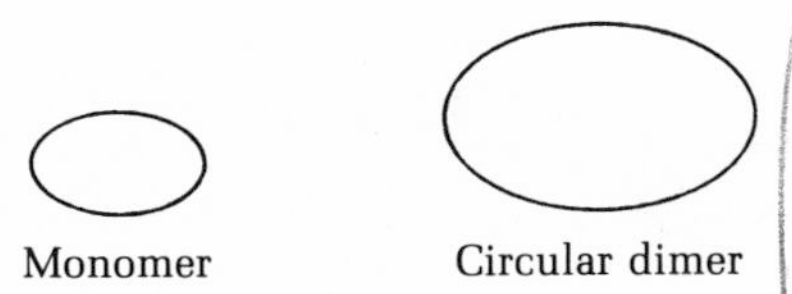

spermidine (margin), which are found associated with DNA in some viruses and bacteria. Binding of polyamines in the groove of double helical DNA neutralizes its negative charges and makes the molecule more flexible. DNA also binds strongly with *histones*, basic (i.e., positively charged) proteins found in the chromatin of eucaryotic cells. Histones have many regularly spaced lysine and arginine residues whose R groups are positively charged at pH 7.0; they can interact with the regularly spaced negatively charged groups on the periphery of the DNA double helix.

Since the hydrogen-bonding properties of the different bases depend on their ionic form, which in turn depends on pH (see Chapter 12), the stability of the hydrogen-bonded base pairs of double-helical DNA is a function of pH. The base pairs are maximally stable between pH 4.0 and pH 11.0. Outside these limits, double helical DNA becomes unstable and unwinds.

Viscosity

Because of the rigidity of the double helix and the immense length of DNA in relation to its small diameter, even very dilute DNA solutions are highly viscous. Viscosity measurements are often used to follow the course of unwinding or denaturation of DNA molecules.

There is another consequence of the rigidity and immense length of DNA molecules. When they diffuse, they sweep a relatively enormous volume of solution, more than 10,000-fold greater than their own volume. For this reason DNA shows ideal behavior as a solute only in extremely dilute solutions.

Spermine

$$^{+}NH_3-CH_2-CH_2-CH_2-{}^{+}NH_2-CH_2-CH_2-CH_2-CH_2-{}^{+}NH_2-CH_2-CH_2-CH_2-{}^{+}NH_3$$

Spermidine

$$^{+}NH_3-CH_2-CH_2-CH_2-{}^{+}NH_2-CH_2-CH_2-CH_2-CH_2-{}^{+}NH_3$$

Sedimentation Behavior

The sedimentation coefficient and the molecular weight of DNA specimens may be determined by the basic ultracentrifugal methods described earlier for the proteins (Chapter 7). However, because of the extremely elongated nature of DNA and the great viscosity of its solutions, it is necessary to carry out sedimentation measurements at a series of low concentrations of DNA and to extrapolate the observed values of the sedimentation coefficient to zero DNA concentration. The sedimenting boundary of DNA is usually detected by measuring the optical absorption at a wavelength of 260 nm, at which DNA shows an absorption peak (Chapter 12). Sedimentation coefficients of DNA molecules are often obtained by comparing their rate of sedimentation in a sucrose density gradient (Chapter 7) with the rate given by a DNA sample of known sedimentation coefficient.

Equilibrium sedimentation in cesium chloride gradients (Chapter 7) is very widely used to determine the *buoyant density* of DNA molecules. When a concentrated CsCl solution (7.7 *M*) is centrifuged to equilibrium in a high gravitational field, the CsCl becomes distributed in a linear gradient down the tube; at the top of a 1-cm column the density of the solution is about 1.65 grams ml^{-1} and at the bottom about 1.76 grams ml^{-1}. When DNA is present during formation of such a gradient, it concentrates into a stable band at that position in the tube at which its buoyant density is exactly equal to the density of the CsCl solution. The density of the DNA can be calculated directly, or by comparison with the density of a known standard DNA specimen centrifuged in the same gradient. Single-stranded DNA is more dense in such a CsCl gradient than double-stranded DNA, which in turn is more dense than proteins in general. Furthermore, it is possible to obtain valuable information on the molecular weight of a DNA specimen from its behavior in a CsCl gradient. Because large molecules diffuse more slowly than small ones, they tend to yield thinner and sharper bands.

Buoyant-density measurements are also capable of yielding information on the base composition of the DNA specimen because the G-C base pairs, which are joined by three hydrogen bonds, are more compact and dense than the A-T pairs, which are joined by only two hydrogen bonds. The buoyant density of any given DNA specimen measured in a CsCl gradient is a linear function of the ratio of G-C to A-T pairs (Figure 28-10). The base composition of even minute quantities of DNA can therefore be deduced from buoyant-density measurements. The CsCl gradient method has also revealed that the DNA of viruses, which gives very sharp bands, is homogeneous, whereas DNA fragments from cells of higher animals are not, since they give several broad bands over a wide density range.

Denaturation of DNA

The double-helical form of DNA undergoes unwinding into random, disordered structures, i.e., random coils

Figure 28-10
The relationship between buoyant density of double stranded DNA and base composition.

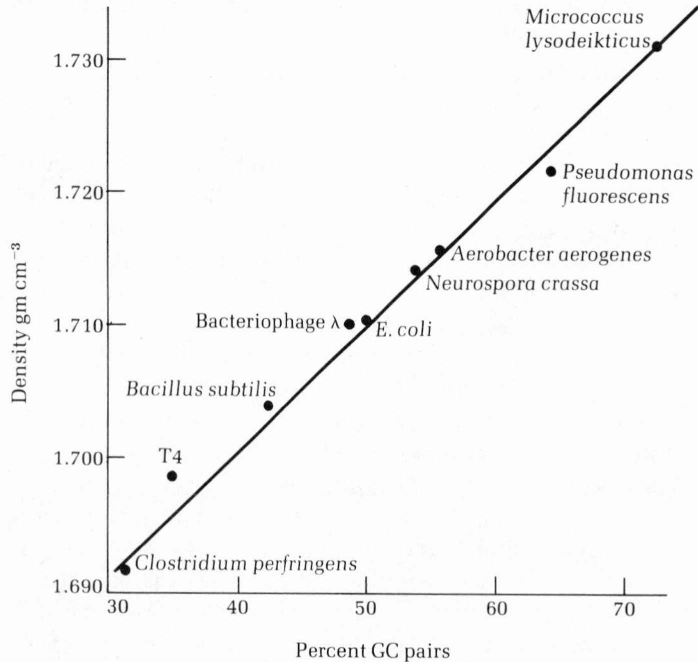

(Chapter 6), when subjected to (1) extremes of pH, (2) heat, (3) decrease in dielectric constant of the aqueous medium by alcohols, ketones, etc., and (4) exposure to urea, amides, and similar solutes. Since these agencies are identical to those producing denaturation or unfolding of globular proteins, it has been concluded that DNA undergoes a similar process. During denaturation of DNA no covalent bonds in the backbone are broken. Two sets of forces are responsible for maintaining the double-helical structure of DNA: (1) hydrogen bonding between base pairs and (2) hydrophobic interactions between successive stacked bases. When either or both sets of forces are interrupted, the native, double-helical structure undergoes transition into a random coil.

The Hyperchromic Effect

The denaturation of native DNA is accompanied by dramatic changes in its physical properties: (1) the viscosity decreases, (2) the light absorption at 260 nm increases, (3) the optical rotation becomes more negative, and (4) the buoyant density increases. The physical change that is simplest to use as a measure of denaturation of DNA is the increase in light absorption at 260 nm, which is termed the *hyperchromic effect*. As pointed out in Chapter 12, the purine and pyrimidine bases absorb ultraviolet light at 260 nm; the amount of light absorbed per residue is the same whether the bases are free or present as nucleosides or mononucleotides. However, native, double-stranded DNA absorbs much less light at 260 nm than would be predicted from the summation of the light absorbed by its constituent mononucleotides. This phenomenon is called *hypochromism*. However, if native double-stranded DNA is denatured by heating, there is a large increase in the light absorbed at 260 nm, anywhere from 20 to 60 percent, depending on the DNA specimen. The total absorption of fully denatured DNA is nearly equal to that of an equivalent number of the corresponding free mononucleotides. The percentage increase in light absorption at 260 nm produced by heating a native DNA sample is directly related to its content of A-T base pairs: the higher the proportion of A-T pairs, the greater the increase in light absorption. Thus the base composition of a DNA sample can be estimated by carrying out simple spectrophotometric measurements of the magnitude of the hyperchromic effect accompanying heating (Figure 28-11).

The hypochromism of double-stranded DNA molecules is due to electronic interactions between the stacked bases in the native double-helical structure, which have the effect of diminishing the amount of light each residue can absorb. When the double-helical structure is disordered, the bases "unstack" and in this less hindered form, they absorb as much light as they would were they present as free bases.

The Melting Point of DNA

Unlike many globular proteins, which denature gradually over a large temperature range, native DNA molecules

Figure 28-11
Maximum absolute increase in absorption at 260 nm given by some DNA specimens on heating. The largest hyperchromic effect is given by complementary poly dAT strands.

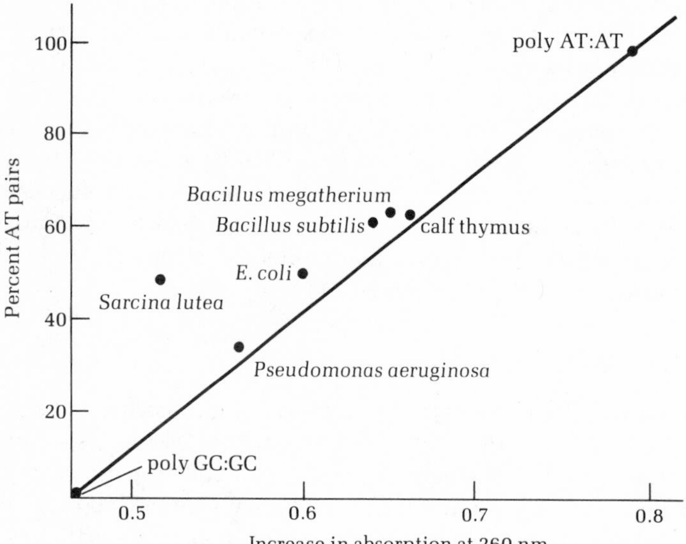

usually denature within a very small increment of temperature (Figure 28-12). This very sharp transition is similar to the melting point of a simple organic crystal. In fact, thermal denaturation of DNA is often designated as *melting*. DNA specimens from different cell types have characteristically different melting points, defined as the temperature at the midpoint of the melting curve (Figure 28-12). The melting point (designated T_m) increases in a linear fashion with the content of G-C base pairs. Again, the triply hydrogen-bonded G-C base pairs are more compact and stable than the A-T pairs. Therefore, the higher the content of G-C pairs, the more stable the structure and the more thermal energy required to disrupt it. Careful determination of the melting point of a DNA specimen, under fixed conditions of pH and ionic strength, can give a remarkably accurate estimate of its base composition. In general, the melting temperature of DNA is independent of its molecular weight.

Stages in Denaturation of DNA

There are two stages in the denaturation of duplex DNA molecules. In the first stage, the two strands are partially unwound but remain united by at least a short segment of double-helical structure, with complementary bases still in register. The unwound segment of each strand assumes a random, changing conformation. In the second phase, the two strands completely separate from each other. In this state, each free strand may double back on itself to form short intrachain double-helical segments (margin).

Denaturation of homogeneous DNA is easily reversible if the unwinding process has not gone past the first stage. As long as a double-helical segment of 12 or more residues unites the two strands, with base-pairing in register, the unfolded segments of the two strands will spontaneously rewind to reform a complete duplex when the

Stages in the denaturation of DNA

Double-helical DNA

Heat

Partially unwound DNA

Separated strands of DNA in random coils

Intrachain double helix

Figure 28-12
Melting points (Tm) of DNA and their relationship to content of GC pairs.

A plot of Tm for 40 different DNA specimens from plant, animal and viral sources against GC content. All samples were measured under identical conditions.

Characteristic melting curves for a viral DNA and a bacterial DNA. The former, being smaller and more homogeneous, shows a sharper melting transition. The two samples differ in GC content.

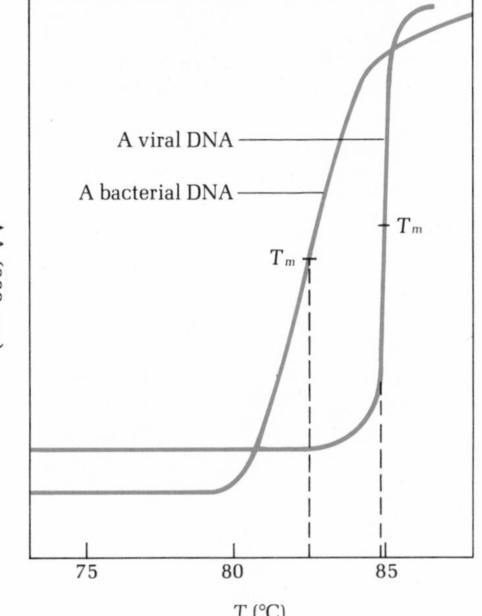

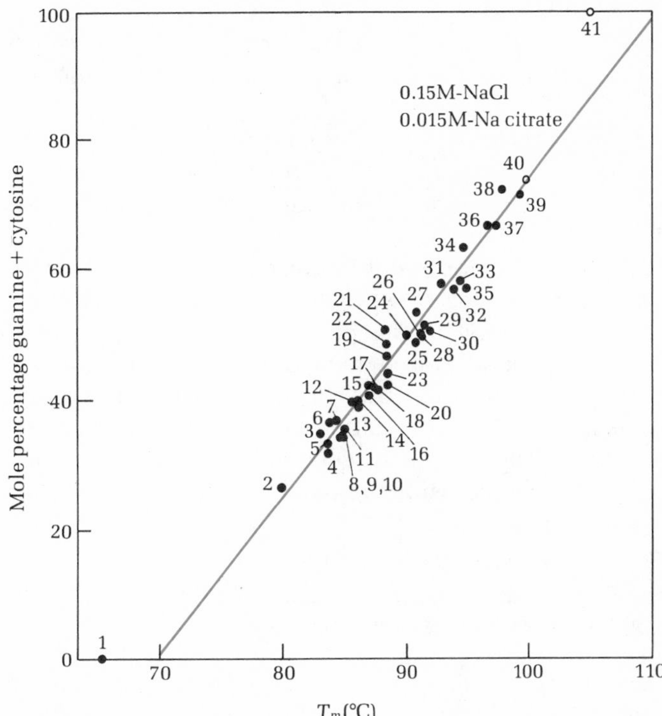

temperature is lowered. They literally "snap back" into their native conformation, which is the minimum-free-energy form. However, if the two strands have separated completely, renaturation is usually much slower, particularly if the DNA has a very high molecular weight.

The melting of homogeneous double-stranded DNA and its renaturation on cooling show very sharp temperature transitions because of the regularity of the double-helical structure, the large number of repetitive units that must come apart or come together, and the cooperative nature of the many successive interactions that occur, in which each interaction greatly increases the tendency of the next to take place. Thus the rate of rewinding and the stability of the rewound portion of two DNA strands increase with the length of the portion that has already rewound, at least up to certain limits. The rate of unwinding and rewinding of double-stranded DNA have received much study, since these processes may be rate-limiting during the replication of DNA in the intact cell (Chapter 29).

Major Functional Units in Chromosomes

Now that we have surveyed the dimensions and conformation of simple chromosomes we may correlate this information with the size and arrangement of their functional units. Of special interest are (1) the size of genes, (2) the sequential arrangement of genes along the chromosome, and (3) the size of the mutational unit in genes. Such information has been derived from both genetic and biochemical experimentation.

Mapping of Chromosome Structure: Sequence and Circularity

Genetic mapping of the relative positions of different genes in bacterial chromosomes is made possible by the fact that under special circumstances a segment of the chromosome of one type of cell, containing one or more genes, may become detached and transferred to the chromosome of a second type of cell, into which it becomes covalently incorporated. The identity of the recombined gene(s) can be deduced from changes in the phenotype of the acceptor cell and its progeny. Such recombination of genes is a common event in eucaryotic organisms, which usually reproduce by sexual conjugation, but it is relatively infrequent among procaryotes. By employing experimental conditions which favor such recombination processes in bacteria, powerful tools have been developed to map the relative positions of genes in chromosome structure. Three types of genetic recombination process have been employed for genetic mapping of bacterial and viral chromosomes: (1) sexual conjugation, (2) transformation, and (3) viral transduction.

Figure 28-13
Conjugation in E. coli.

Schematic representation of conjugation process, which begins by incorporation of the sex factor F into the chromosome to yield a (+) cell. Cells come together, and one strand of the chromosome of the (+) cell enters the (−) cell through the conjugation bridge. When the bridge is broken, the segment of (+) DNA that entered the (−) cell becomes incorporated into the (−) chromosome, with loss of a corresponding segment which is degraded by nuclease action. From new phenotypes introduced into the (−) cell after different time periods of conjugation, mapping of the chromosome is possible.

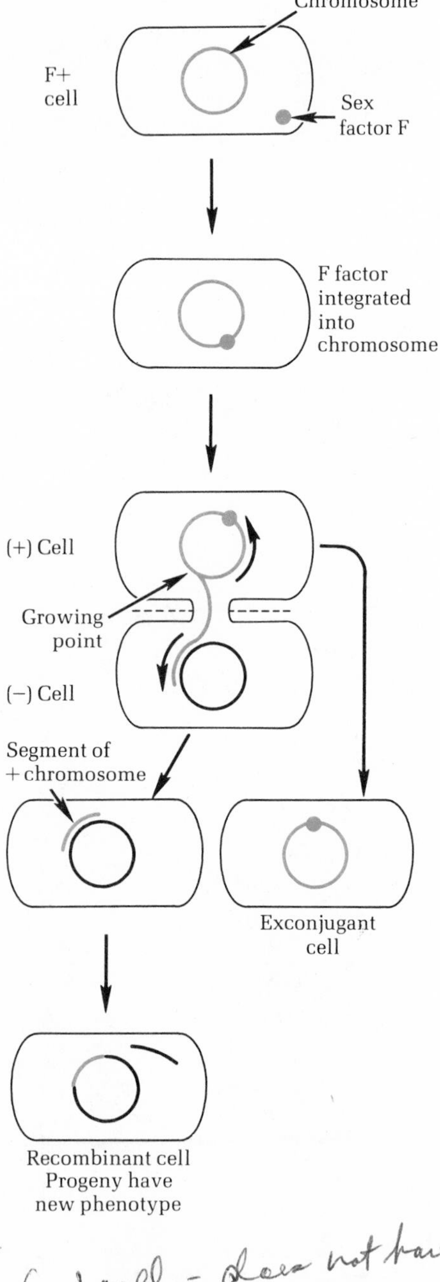

The first process, *sexual conjugation*, consists of the transfer of some or all of the chromosome of a "male" or (+) cell into a "female" or (−) cell through one of the pili or fimbriae (Chapters 1 and 11), which serves as a hollow connecting tube between the two cells (Figure 28-13). In *E. coli* the act of conjugation is relatively slow and requires about 90 min for complete transfer of the (+) chromosome. It is possible to interrupt the conjugation process at any time by agitating the cell suspension in a blender, which breaks the union between the cells and allows recovery of (−) cells carrying varying amounts of male chromosomal material, depending on the time of interruption. From the type and number of phenotypic traits specified by the acquired segments of the male chromosome in the asexual progeny of the (−) cells, as a function of the time of entry, the relative position of the genes specifying these traits in the inserted male chromosome can be deduced. Such direct mapping methods confirmed the sequences and distances between genes that had earlier been inferred by less direct genetic linkage tests.

One of the most significant conclusions arrived at from sexual conjugation experiments is that the chromosome of *E. coli* must consist of an endless, closed loop (Figure 28-14). The genetic map of bacterial chromosomes is therefore usually depicted in circular form. Although the corresponding chromosome is often spoken of as being circular, this term does not necessarily imply that the chromosome has the actual form of a Euclidean circle, but only that it is an endless, closed structure. In the cell the chromosome is, of course, tightly folded.

Another approach to mapping the sequence of genes in the chromosomes of bactera is afforded by the phenomenon of bacterial *transformation*. As we have seen above, a recipient bacterial cell may be genetically transformed by addition of exogenous DNA derived from another strain of bacteria, an effect due to the incorporation of one or

Figure 28-13 (continued)
Electron micrograph of conjugating E. coli cells.

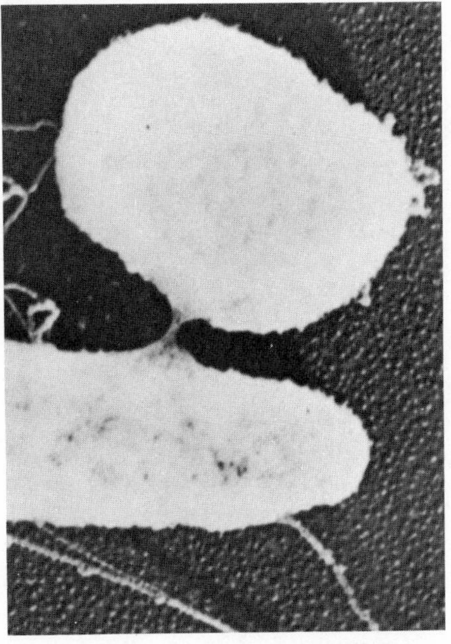

Figure 28-14
The circular genetic map of E. coli K 12 derived from sexual conjugation experiments. The scale is in terms of the time of entry of the male chromosome during conjugation; 89 minutes is required for the entire chromosome to enter. The positions of only a few genes are shown. The key indicates the effect of mutation of the gene.

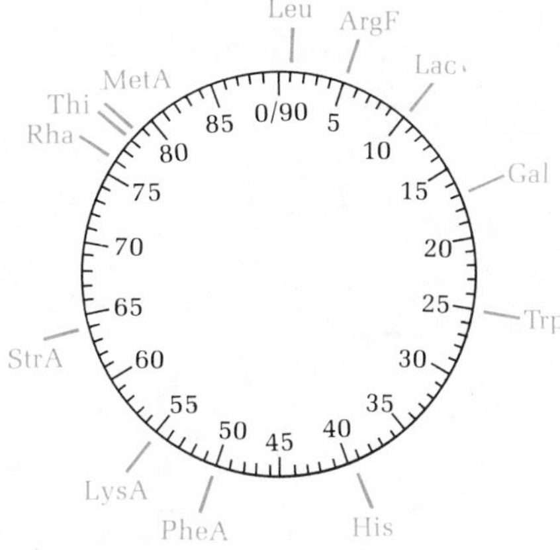

Key

Leu	requires leucine for growth
ArgF	requires arginine for growth
Lac	unable to use lactose
Gal	unable to use galactose
Trp	requires tryptophan for growth
His	requires histidine for growth
PheA	requires phenylalanine for growth
LysA	requires lysine for growth
StrA	resistant to streptomycin
Rha	unable to use rhamnose
Thi	requires thiamine
MetA	requires methionine

more genes from the donor DNA into the chromosome of the recipient cell. By determining the frequency with which two or more phenotypes from the donor cells appear together in the progeny of the recipient cells it is possible to deduce the relative positions of the two corresponding genes in the donor chromosome. Pairs of genes incorporated into the recipient cells with high frequency are closer together on the genetic map than those pairs that enter infrequently.

More useful for genetic mapping is the phenomenon of *transduction*, in which a small portion of the chromosome of a cell infected with a virus may become "packaged" within the sheath of a newly formed viral particle. When such a viral particle infects another cell, the genes derived from the original host cell may be incorporated into the chromosome of the second cell. In effect, the transducing viral particle is a carrier which transfers a portion of the chromosome of one bacterial cell to the chromosome of another (Figure 28-15). Transduction is of extremely great importance in fine-structure genetic mapping, because the transducing phage particle is relatively stable and the transduction process simpler to control than bacterial transformation. The transducing phage can carry only a very small portion of a bacterial chromosome, at most only 1 percent. Thus the gene linkages observed are suitable only for mapping very small segments of the chromosome, rather than its gross structure.

The preparation of detailed genetic maps has reached its pinnacle in the case of viral chromosomes. Bacterial viruses may themselves undergo spontaneous or induced mutations. When the chromosomes of two viral particles, one normal and the other a mutant, or two different mutants, enter the same host cell, they can fragment and then recombine in the course of viral replication to form hybrid viral chromosomes. Such hybrid chromosomes can then direct the formation of progeny containing genes derived from both parent viruses. which can be recognized by their phenotypic features. From such viral recombination experiments, it has been deduced that the chromosomes of T4 and other bacteriophages of *E. coli* are circular. They have also permitted some far-reaching conclusions concerning the size of genes.

The Size of Genes and Mutational Units

In a classic genetic study, Benzer examined a small region (rII) of the T4 chromosome. There is a class of mutants in this region which can be readily grown in one bacterial host strain (permissive) but not in others (nonpermissive). When nonpermissive cells were infected with two different mutants in the rII region, some recombinants between the two mutants were found which had regained the wild-type ability to grow on that host. That is, the "good" portions of the defective genes from two different T4 mutants came together to form a single "good" gene. Because many different pairs of T4 mutants were found to recombine to yield "good" rII genes, Benzer concluded that each gene (or cistron) must contain many mutable sites, which he was able to map in a linear sequence. This discovery was important because it had been thought for some years that the gene itself was the unit of mutation, i.e., that each gene contained only one mutable site. From the known length of the DNA molecule in the T4 viral particle and the known small fraction of the genetic map occupied by the rII region, the rII A gene of the T4 chromosome can be calculated to consist of about 2,500 nucleotides (Figure 28-16). Benzer found nearly 500 different mutants of the rII A region, a fact which suggested that the unit of mutation is no greater than about 5 nucleotides. Later, through other genetic tests, Benzer and other investigators came to the conclusion that mutation may involve a chemical change in only a single nucleotide. Such mutations are called *point mutations.* Their molecular nature is discussed below.

These conclusions, which derived from genetic experimentation, were later confirmed and much more precisely stated by the results of biochemical investigations. In particular, the later discovery that each amino acid is coded for by specific triplets of mononucleotide residues (Chapter 31), yielded precise information on the size of genes and on the size and nature of their mutational units. A cistron or gene specifying a single polypeptide chain of a protein may have anywhere from 300 to about 4,500 or more nucleotide pairs (molecular weights, 100,000 to 1,800,000), corresponding to polypeptide chains having from 100 to 1,800 amino acid residues, the extremes in polypeptide chain length in most proteins. Since a given protein or enzyme may have two or more polypeptide chains, each coded by a different gene, the "one gene–one enzyme" concept has now been modified into the "one gene–one polypeptide chain" hypothesis.

Some genes may be smaller than those specifying the polypeptide chains of proteins. Transfer RNA molecules have only 75 to 90 mononucleotide units (Chapters 12 and 30) and are in all probability formed enzymatically by complementary transcription from a segment of DNA (Chapter 30). The genes specifying some tRNAs are thus only about 75 nucleotides in length. Moreover, the genes specifying the sequence of amino acids in short polypeptide chains, such as those in proinsulin (84 residues) or ACTH (39 residues) are also relatively small.

Figure 28-15
Transfer of genes from donor to acceptor bacterial cells by transduction via defective carrier phage.

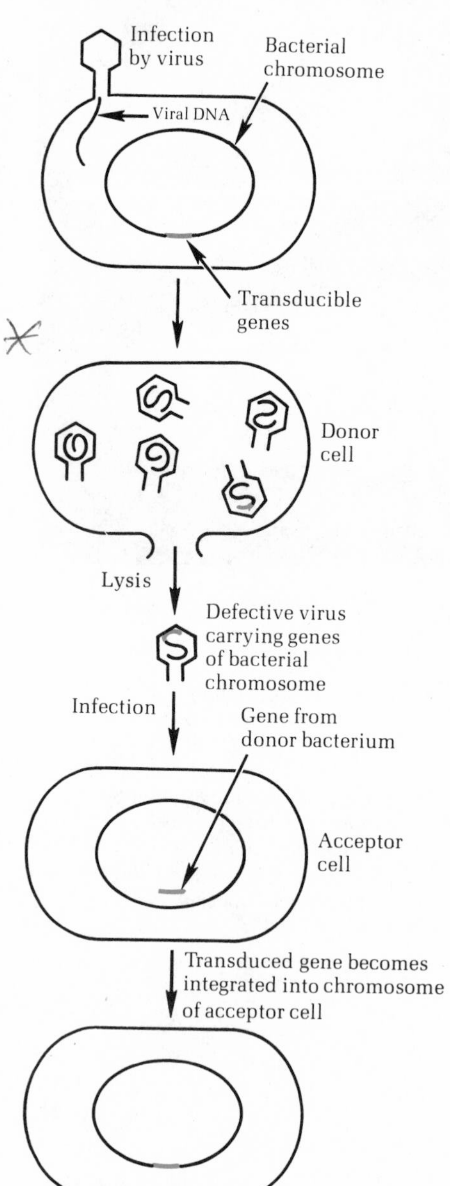

Molecular Nature of Mutation

Recent progress has made possible the identification of various types of chemical change in DNA that lead to mutant gene products. Single-point mutations can be divided into four major classes on the basis of the change produced in the DNA by the mutagenic agent (Figure 28-17). In *transitional* mutants, one purine-pyrimidine base pair is replaced by another, i.e., A—T for G—C or G—C for A—T, so that a purine in one chain is replaced by another purine, and a pyrimidine in the other chain by another pyrimidine. Transitional mutations occur spontaneously but may also be induced by base analogs, in particular *5-bromouracil* (BU) and *2-aminopurine* (AP). Since

Figure 28-16
The fine structure of the rII *region in the genetic map of bacteriophage* T4.

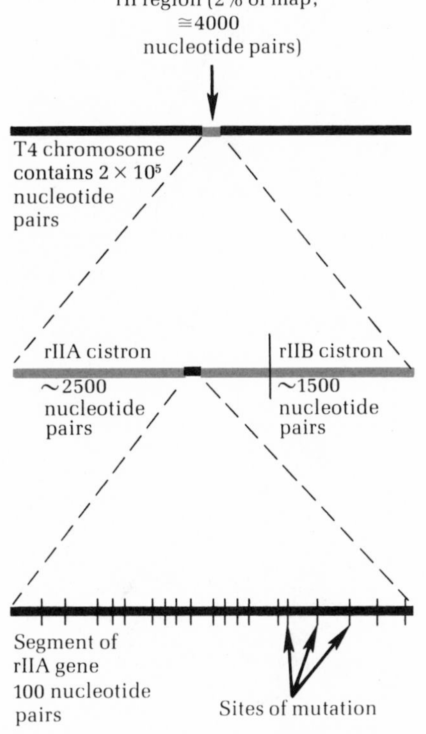

5-bromouracil has a close structural resemblance to thymine, during replication it is readily inserted into DNA in the form of 5-bromouridylic acid, in the positions normally occupied by thymine. However, the keto form of 5-bromouracil, which pairs readily with A, may undergo tautomerization to the enol form, which more readily pairs with G. In this way replacement of T by BU in one chain may lead to incorporation of G, rather than A, in the complementary chain. When the latter chain in turn is replicated, the G now specifies C in the new complementary chain. The analog 2-aminopurine acts similarly; it can be read either as A or G. Transitional mutations are also produced by nitrous acid, which deaminates adenine, whose normal partner is T, to form hypoxanthine (Chapter 12), which pairs with C.

In *transversional mutations,* a purine-pyrimidine pair is replaced by a pyrimidine-purine pair (Figure 28-17). The mechanism of transversion is not known, and no agents are known that selectively favor transversions. However, transversions are commonly observed in spontaneous mutations; in fact, about half of the mutations of the α and β chains of hemoglobin (Chapter 6) are transversions.

The third type of point mutation involves *insertion* of an extra nucleotide. The result is one type of *frame-shift mutation* (Figure 28-17), so called because the normal reading-frame relationship for readout of nucleotide triplets is put out of register by the mutation (Chapter 32). Insertions are readily induced by treating cells with acridine derivatives. *Acridine* (margin) is a planar heterocyclic molecule which can interact with double-helical

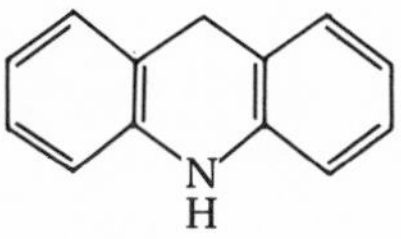

Figure 28-17
Types of point mutations.

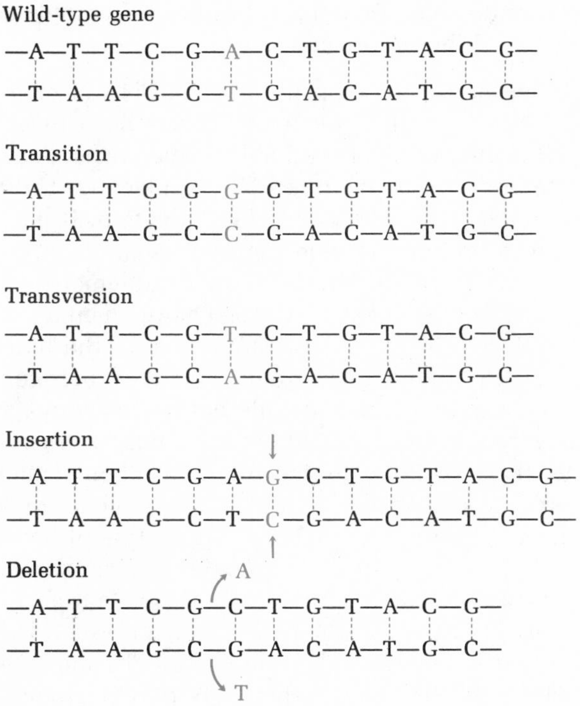

Wild-type gene
—A—T—T—C—G—A—C—T—G—T—A—C—G—
—T—A—A—G—C—T—G—A—C—A—T—G—C—

Transition
—A—T—T—C—G—G—C—T—G—T—A—C—G—
—T—A—A—G—C—C—G—A—C—A—T—G—C—

Transversion
—A—T—T—C—G—T—C—T—G—T—A—C—G—
—T—A—A—G—C—A—G—A—C—A—T—G—C—

Insertion
—A—T—T—C—G—A—G—C—T—G—T—A—C—G—
—T—A—A—G—C—T—C—G—A—C—A—T—G—C—

Deletion
A
—A—T—T—C—G—C—T—G—T—A—C—G—
—T—A—A—G—C—G—A—C—A—T—G—C—
T

Acridine

N
H

DNA by a process called *intercalation*. Because of its flat hydrophobic structure, acridine becomes inserted or intercalated between two successive bases in DNA, separating them physically. When the chain is replicated, an extra base is inserted into the complementary chain, opposite the intercalated acridine. When the latter chain is then replicated, the new chain will also contain an extra base.

The fourth type of mutation results from a deletion of a base from the DNA; it too is a frame-shift mutation (Figure 28-17). A deletion may result by hydrolytic loss of a purine base because of low pH or temperature, by action of a covalent cross-linking reagent, or by alkylating or deaminating agents which cause formation of bases that cannot pair.

Point mutations in DNA do not necessarily have lethal consequences. Transitions and transversions are relatively benign, because they result in replacement of only one amino acid in the peptide chain coded; very often the defective protein is still completely functional. Such a mutation is called a *silent mutation*. However, insertion or deletion point mutants cause all the DNA *beyond* the point of the mutation to be misread; they are usually lethal. Another class of mutants results from deletion of *segments* of DNA which may be many nucleotides long. If the number of deleted nucleotides is 3 or some multiple of 3, there is no frame-shift error beyond the site of mutation.

Mutations may be caused by many other chemical agents, among which is lysergic acid diethylamide (LSD). They may also be caused by radiant energy (ultraviolet light, γ-rays, and x-rays), which may be absorbed by the bases and cause a structural change in the molecule.

The Hybridization Technique: Sequence Homologies in DNA of Different Species

Although the base composition of the DNA of many different bacteria and higher animals has been measured, very little information is available on the precise sequence of nucleotides in native intact DNA molecules. However, by means of a method called *hybridization*, it has been possible to determine whether two given specimens of DNA have blocks or segments of complementary base sequences and how extensive the complementary blocks are. Such hybridization tests are based on the tendency of two DNA strands to pair and rewind at their complementary regions to form double helices. The greater the tendency for a given pair of DNA strands to rewind, the greater the extent of complementarity of their sequences. To carry out such tests, the two DNA specimens are mixed and heated beyond the melting temperature of both, and then "annealed" by slow cooling. If they possess complementary base sequences, they will associate to form partially duplex hybrids. The extent to which such hybrids form is easily determined if one of the DNA specimens is labeled with ^{32}P. After separation of the single- and double-stranded molecules from each other by filtration or by equilibrium centrifugation in CsCl gradients, determination of the amount of radioactivity in the double-stranded fraction is a measure of the extent of hybridization. From such experiments the important finding has been made that the tendency of the DNA from two given species to hybridize is a function of how close they stand in their taxonomic relationship. Thus, although the DNAs of various bacteria show very wide variations in base composition (Table 28-3), they may contain many zones of approximate complementarity of base sequence, possibly because the genes of many homologous enzymes are closely similar in some bacterial species. On the other hand, the DNA of bacteria does not tend to hybridize readily with the DNA from higher animals, or even with that of yeast cells. The tendency of DNA of various bacterial viruses to form hybrids has also been studied; DNA from various mutations of one virus tend to hybridize with each other much more readily than do DNAs from different types of viruses. The conclusion has been reached that the minimum stretch of perfectly complementary DNA sequences that can recognize each other and initiate the formation of stable hybrids is of the order of about 12 nucleotides. When a number of such short homologous stretches exist in two DNA molecules, a hybrid stable enough to be detected can be formed.

Figure 28-18
Hybridization tests with single stranded (denatured) reference DNA impregnated into an agar gel which is then finely subdivided into particles and packed in a column. Radioactive DNA from other species flows through the column. If it has nucleotide sequences complementary to the reference DNA, double stranded hybrids are formed, attached to the agar gel. The amount of labeled DNA retained by the column is a measure of the amount of complementarity.

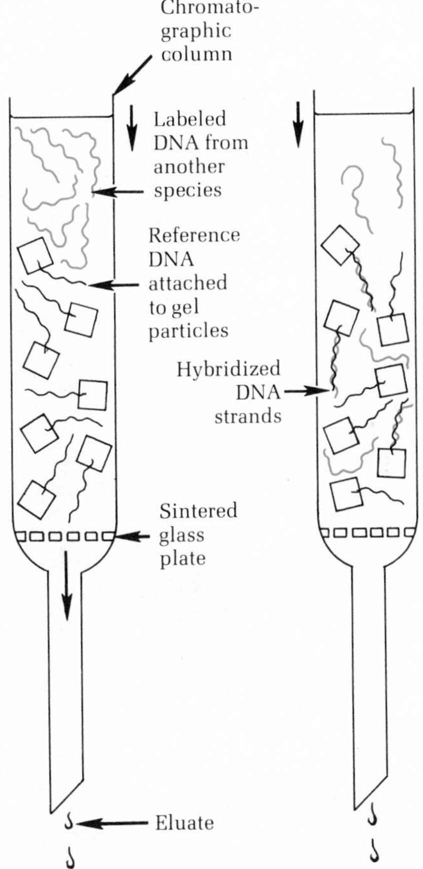

Hybridization between DNAs isolated from closely related higher animal species can be detected by means of a more sensitive technique. The denatured, single-stranded DNA of the reference species is incorporated into an inert support, such as finely divided agar gel particles, which are then packed into a chromatographic column. An isotopically labeled denatured DNA specimen from another species is then passed through the column; the extent of retention of the isotope by the column is an index of the tendency of the two DNAs to hybridize and thus of the extent of sequence homology (Figure 28-18).

DNA also will hybridize with RNA derived from the same species, again through complementary base pairing (the uracil residues of RNA pair with adenine residues of DNA). This finding strongly suggests, as has been confirmed more directly, that RNA is synthesized on a DNA template. Hybridization between DNA and RNA also can be used to show how much of the bacterial chromosome codes for a given type of RNA. For example, less than 2 percent of the bacterial chromosome codes for all the ribosomal RNA, which nevertheless represents over half the total RNA in the cell.

Repeated Sequences in DNA of Higher Animals

By means of column hybridization techniques such as those described above, Britten and his colleagues have discovered that the DNA of higher species, such as the mouse, calf, and salmon, may contain a great many repeated short nucleotide sequences. In fact, their observations suggest that a given nucleotide sequence may occur thousands of times in the DNA of a given species and that this phenomenon is of widespread and universal occurrence in DNA of higher organisms. They have estimated that more than half the entire DNA content of higher cells may consist of such extra or repeated copies. In any given species, there are many different sequences that exist in multiple copies. Some sequences occur in as many as 100,000 copies. In the DNA of viruses and bacteria, however, there appear to be no extra or repetitive copies of DNA.

The significance of multiple copies of DNA segments is not yet known. One possibility is that they make possible more rapid synthesis of certain proteins of higher animals that occur in very large numbers, such as collagen and keratin of connective tissue, the structure proteins of membranes, and the ribosomal proteins. It is significant that a few proteins, such as ferredoxin and the immune globulins, are known to contain repeating homologous amino acid sequences.

Summary

That DNA bears genetic information was first shown by experiments of Avery in which simple addition of DNA isolated from one type of bacterial cell transformed the phenotype of another strain in a heritable manner. Other evidence includes the fact that the amount of DNA per cell increases with the cell's position on the evolutionary scale. All somatic (diploid) cells of a given species of higher organism contain the same amount of DNA, which is not modified by diet or environmental circumstances. The base composition of DNA specimens varies characteristically from one species to another. Whatever the species, the number of adenine residues equals the number of thymine residues; similarly, the guanine residues equal the cytosine residues.

From x-ray analysis of DNA fibers and from the base equivalences of DNA, Watson and Crick postulated that native DNA consists of two antiparallel chains in a double-helical arrangement, with the complementary bases A-T and G-C paired by hydrogen bonding within the helix. The base pairs are closely stacked perpendicular to the long axis, 3.4 Å apart. The double helix is about 20 Å in diameter. This structure accounts for accurate replication of the two strands, since a duplex can form only from precisely complementary strands.

The molecular weight of native double-stranded DNA molecules, i.e., chromosomes, ranges from 1.0 million in the smallest DNA viruses to about 2.0 to 3.0 billion in bacteria. In many viruses and bacteria the chromosome is an endless, closed loop of DNA. Equilibrium centrifugation of DNA in cesium chloride gradients is a valuable analytical tool, since the buoyant density of DNA increases with its G-C base-pair content. DNA duplexes undergo unwinding or denaturation on heating, during which light absorption at 260 nm increases (hyperchromic effect). The magnitude of the hyperchromic effect increases with the A-T content, whereas the melting temperature (T_M) increases with the G-C content.

Functional subdivisions of chromosomes in procaryotic cells and in bacterial viruses have been deduced from genetic mapping, made possible by the fact that one or more genes may be transferred from one bacterial cell to another during sexual conjugation, transformation, or viral transduction. From the frequency with which specific pairs of genes are transferred together from one cell to another, the relative position and sequence of genes in some bacterial chromosomes have been identified. The genetic map of *E. coli* has been shown by such methods to be circular. From genetic recombination experiments with mutant *E. coli* viruses and from biochemical approaches, a gene has been found to have anywhere from about 75 to 4,500 or more nucleotide pairs. The smallest mutational unit is a single nucleotide pair. Mutations are produced by substitution of one purine for another, one pyrimidine for another, or a purine for a pyrimidine and *vice versa*. Mutations also result when one or more base pairs are deleted or additional bases are inserted.

From hybridization experiments, the DNA of eucaryotic organisms appears to contain many extra copies of certain genes, which may make up more than one-half the total DNA. The DNAs of closely related species hybridize more readily than those of phylogenetically distant species.

References

Books

CAIRNS, J., G. S. STENT, and J. D. WATSON, (eds.): "Phage and The Origins of Molecular Biology," *Cold Spring Laboratory of Quantitative Biology*, 1966. A collection of interesting articles written on the occasion of the 60th birthday of Max Delbrück, a pioneer in research on bacteriophages.

CANTONI, G. L., and D. DAVIES (eds.): *Procedures in Nucleic Acid Research*, Harper and Row, New York, 1966. A valuable compendium of research techniques.

DAVIS, B. D., F. DULBECCO, H. M. EISEN, H. S. GINSBERG, and W. B. WOOD, JR.: *Principles of Microbiology and Immunology*, Harper and Row, New York, 1968. Contains an excellent brief account of microbial and viral genetics and protein synthesis.

DAVIDSON, J. N.: *The Biochemistry of The Nucleic Acids*, Methuen, London, 6th edition, 1969. A popular and useful introduction (350 pages).

SRB, A., R. D. OWEN, and R. S. EDGAR: *General Genetics*, W. H. Freeman, San Francisco, 1965. A textbook with excellent treatment of both classical (Mendelian) and molecular genetics.

STENT, G. S.: *Molecular Biology of Bacterial Viruses*, W. H. Freeman, San Francisco, 1963. A detailed but very readable account of the role of phages in genetic research.

WATSON, J. D.: *Molecular Biology of The Gene*, W. A. Benjamin, New York, 1965. An excellent elementary account of the principles of molecular genetics.

———: *The Double Helix*, Atheneum, New York, 1968. A personal narrative of the origins of the Watson-Crick hypothesis.

ZUBAY, G.: *Papers in Molecular Genetics*, Holt, Rinehart, and Winston, New York, 1968. A collection of reprints of classical papers.

Articles

BRITTEN, R. J., and D. E. KOHNE: "Repeated Sequences in DNA," *Science,* **161**:529–540 (1968). Use of hybridization techniques to determine the frequency of occurrence of specific nucleotide sequences in DNA.

FELSENFELD, G., and H. T. MILES: "Physical and Chemical Properties of Nucleic Acids," *Ann. Rev. Biochem.,* **36**:407–448 (1967). A detailed review of recent research.

KLUG, A.: "Rosalind Franklin and The Discovery of The Structure of DNA," *Nature,* **219**:808 (1968).

THOMAS, C. A., JR., and L. A. MACHATTIE: "The Anatomy of Viral DNA Molecules," *Ann. Rev. Biochem.,* **36**:485 (1967). An important review of the molecular properties of viral DNAs.

Problems

1. From data on the contour length of the DNAs of bacteriophages λ, φX174, and T2, calculate the average weight in daltons of double-helical DNA (*a*) per angstrom and (*b*) per micron.
2. Calculate the average number of nucleotide pairs per micron of DNA double helix.
3. Calculate the average number of nucleotide pairs per 1,000,000 daltons of DNA double helix.
4. Bacteriophage T2 has a head about 95 Å long. Calculate the ratio of the length of its DNA to the length of the viral head.
5. Calculate the weight in grams of a double-helical DNA extending from the earth to the moon (200,000 miles).
6. Calculate the total weight in grams and the length in miles of all the DNA in the human neonate: use data in Table 28-1 and assume the human neonate contains 2×10^{12} cells. Compare with Problem 5.
7. Calculate the average length in Å and the average weight in daltons of the genes coding for (*a*) a tRNA (90 mononucleotide residues), (*b*) ribonuclease (104 amino acid residues), and (*c*) myosin (1,800 amino acid residues).
8. Calculate how many genes can be contained in the DNA of a single human cell, if each gene has 500 base pairs. Assume that all the DNA is used for coding and that there is no redundancy.
9. From data in this chapter, predict (i) the buoyant density (grams cm^{-3}), (ii) the melting temperature T_m, and (iii) the hyperchromic effect (in percent) of double-stranded DNA specimens having (*a*) 10 percent A-T pairs, (*b*) 50 percent A-T pairs, and (*c*) 90 percent A-T pairs.
10. Compare the contour length of a gene with the contour length of the protein it codes; assume the latter has 150 amino acid residues and is entirely in α-helical configuration (see Chapter 6).

CHAPTER 29 REPLICATION AND TRANSCRIPTION OF DNA

Now that we have surveyed the evidence that DNA is the genetic material of chromosomes and that its complementary double-helical structure furnishes a molecular basis for a template function, we shall proceed to examine the enzymatic mechanisms by which DNA is replicated to yield identical daughter molecules and transcribed to yield complementary RNA molecules.

The enzymes participating in replication of DNA are surely among the most remarkable enzymes known. A full molecular description of their action must account for not only the formation of the covalent 3′,5′-internucleotide linkage but also the transmission of information from the template to the new strand, in the form of a precisely complementary mononucleotide sequence. Moreover, it must also account for the complex geometrical, mechanical, and kinetic problems posed by the unwinding of the parental DNA and the proper rewinding of the new and old strands to yield the daughter duplexes, after completion of the covalent reaction. The polymerases responsible for the replication and transcription of DNA are thus very complex in their function, in contrast to enzymes acting on simple noninformational molecules.

It is altogether remarkable that by the action of a very small number of highly specialized enzymes, the genetic continuity of different species has been maintained in the form of the mononucleotide sequence of a very thin, fragile DNA duplex over hundreds of billions of generations.

The Mechanics of DNA Replication: The Meselson-Stahl Experiment

The most striking feature of the Watson-Crick hypothesis from the genetic point of view is its postulation that the two strands of double-helical DNA are complementary and that replication of each to form complementary daughter strands results in two daughter duplex DNA molecules, identical to the parent DNA, each of which contains one strand from the parental DNA. This process is called *semiconservative replication* (Figure 29-1).

However, there are two other mechanisms by which two complementary strands of the parental duplex DNA could yield daughter DNA duplexes chemically identical to those of the parent, *conservative* and *dispersive* replication. They are also illustrated in Figure 29-1.

Ingeniously contrived experiments carried out by Meselson and Stahl in 1957-1958 conclusively proved that in intact living *E. coli* cells DNA is replicated in the semiconservative manner postulated by Watson and Crick. They grew *E. coli* cells for several generations in a medium in which the sole nitrogen source was NH_4Cl, of which the nitrogen was nearly pure ^{15}N isotope instead of the normal ^{14}N. All nitrogenous components of these cells, including their DNA, thus contained ^{15}N instead of ^{14}N. The purified DNA of the ^{15}N-fed cells has a significantly greater buoyant density than normal ^{14}N DNA when subjected to equilibrium centrifugation in a cesium chloride gradient (Chapters 7 and 28), thus making it possible to separate and measure the heavy and light forms of DNA quantitatively.

To carry out their experiment on the mechanism of replication, they separated "heavy" *E. coli* cells from their ^{15}N medium and placed them in a "light" medium, which contained normal or $^{14}N—NH_4Cl$ as sole nitrogen source. The cells were then allowed to grow for several generations and samples were harvested at intervals. From these samples the DNA was extracted and its buoyant density determined by centrifugation in CsCl density

Figure 29-1
Possible mechanisms of replication of DNA. Newly replicated strands (or segments) are shown in color.

Conservative replication of heavy DNA. Each of the two "heavy" strands of parent DNA is replicated, without strand separation, to yield original heavy DNA and newly synthesized light DNA. F_2 generation yields one heavy DNA, no hybrids, and three light DNA's.

Semi-conservative replication of heavy DNA. In first daughters, each duplex contains one of parent "heavy" strands. F_2 generation yields two hybrid DNA's and two newly synthesized light DNA's.

Dispersive replication. During replication, parent chains break at intervals and replicated segments are combined into same strands with segments from parent.

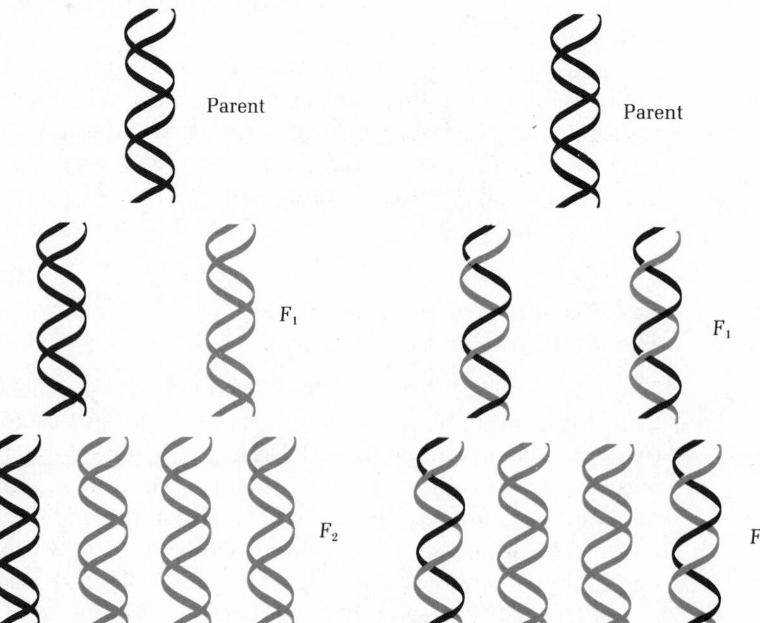

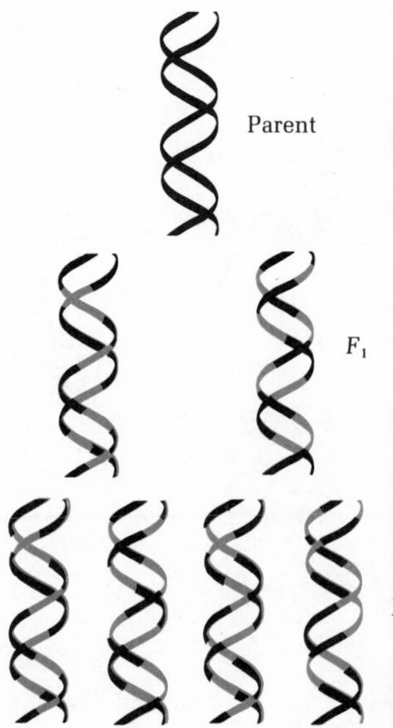

gradients. After exactly one generation time (doubling of the cell number), the DNA isolated showed but a single band in the density gradient, midway in density between the normal or light ^{14}N DNA and the heavy DNA of cells grown exclusively on ^{15}N; this result is what might be expected if the DNA contained one ^{15}N strand and one light, newly synthesized ^{14}N strand. After two generations on $^{14}N—NH_4Cl$, the DNA isolated exhibited two bands, one having a density equal to that of normal light DNA and the other equal to that of the hybrid DNA observed after one generation. These results, which are shown schematically in Figure 29-2, are exactly those expected from the hypothesis of semiconservative replication proposed by Watson and Crick; whereas they are not consistent with the alternative hypotheses of conservative or dispersive replication (Figure 29-1). Thus, the Meselson-Stahl experiment gave profound support to the Watson-Crick hypothesis and was particularly convincing because it was carried out on intact dividing cells without intervention of inhibitors or other injurious agents.

That semiconservative replication of chromosomal DNA also occurs during cell division in eucaryotic organisms was shown in conceptually similar experiments by Taylor and his colleagues on root cells of bean seedlings grown in tissue culture.

Figure 29-2
The Meselson-Stahl experiment. The tubes were centrifuged to equilibrium, yielding bands as shown.

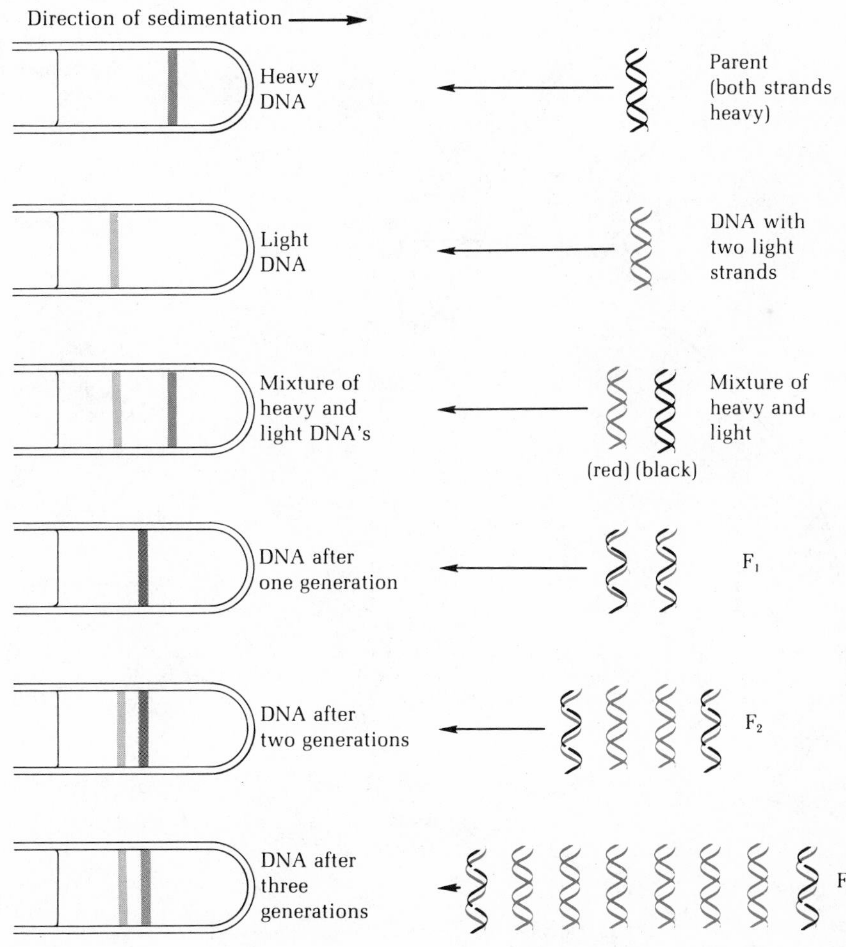

Radioautography of DNA Replication: The Single Growing Point

Another basic question concerning the mechanics of the replication process may now be asked. Is the DNA of the bacterial chromosome, which is a closed duplex, replicated at a single growing point, which moves around the circle, or does replication occur at several growing points simultaneously?

By rather intricate and ingenious genetic experiments which cannot be detailed here, Maalöe concluded that under normal conditions there is probably only *one* growing point per cell, which moves from one end of the bacterial chromosome to the other, replicating the parent strand of DNA as it goes. This picture at first seemed improbable, because such a large amount of biosynthesis must be accomplished in a relatively short period. Nevertheless, the concept was convincingly and directly verified by Cairns, who undertook the task of studying the geometrical arrangement of the two strands of the circular chromosome of growing *E. coli* cells at various stages during the replication process, using radioautography as a tool. *E. coli* cells were grown on a medium containing

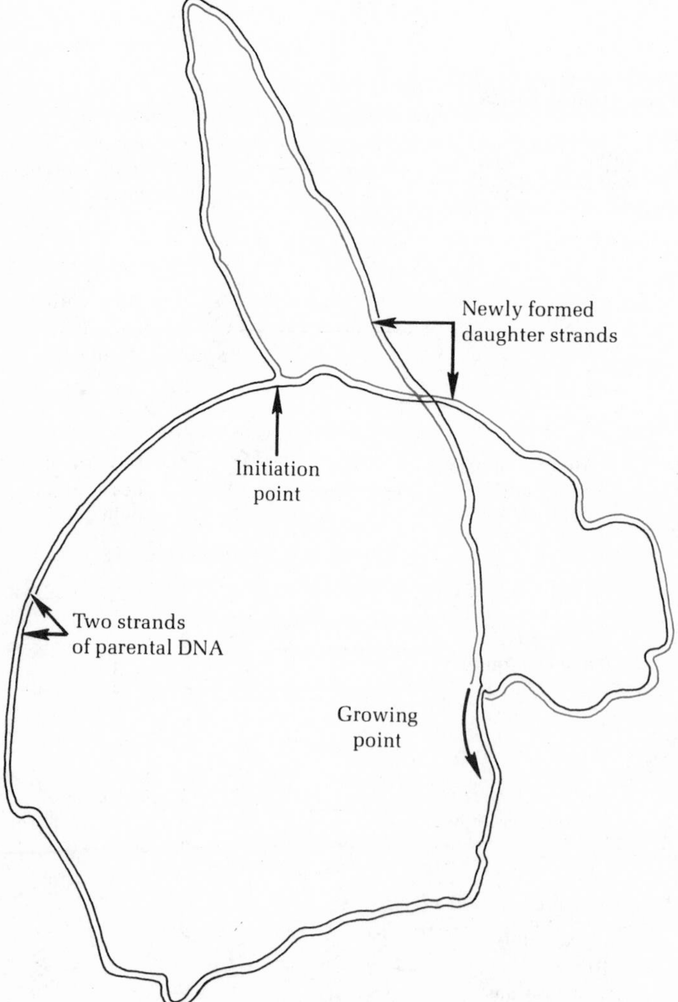

Figure 29-3
Chromosome of E. coli *undergoing replication. (See page 643.) Redrawn from "The Bacterial Chromosome" by J. Cairns. Copyright © January 1966 by Scientific American, Inc. All rights reserved.*

heavily tritiated thymine, which became incorporated into the DNA. At intervals the cells were harvested and the DNA was carefully extracted to avoid shear breakage (Chapter 28). The DNA molecules were spread on grids which were then covered with fine-grain photographic plates. The radioactivity due to the tritiated thymine caused reduction of AgCl in the sensitive emulsion to yield grains of metallic silver, which could be photographed under the microscope. Because only single chromosomes were examined, the photographic plates required exposure for many weeks to yield sufficient reduced silver grains to detect. The radioautographs showed that the chromosome was an endless closed structure, in conformity with its circular genetic map (Figure 29-3). Its contour length measured about 900 μ, or 0.9 mm. By comparing the images at different times of exposure to radioactive thymine, Cairns found that the newly synthesized DNA chain is formed at the rate of about 27 μ min^{-1}. This rate corresponds to the synthesis of about 9×10^4 internucleotide linkages per minute. The two strands of the bacterial DNA do not separate completely from each other before replication. Rather, they are gradually separated at a single Y-shaped locus which moves around the entire chromosome; the chromosome apparently remains circular at all times while it is being replicated (Figure 29-4). At the end of the process, the product is two circular duplex chromosomes, i.e., a total of four strands.

Figure 29-4
The course of replication of the E. coli chromosome. Redrawn from "The Bacterial Chromosome" by J. Cairns. Copyright © January 1966 by Scientific American, Inc. All rights reserved.

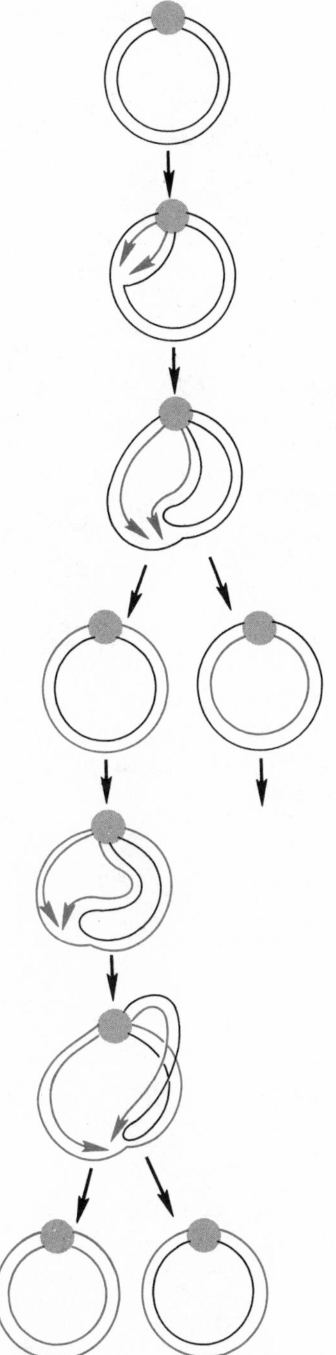

The observations of Cairns raised some fundamental questions about the mechanics and kinetics of unwinding and replication, since the two strands of the parent circular chromosome are intertwined and cannot be separated completely from each other without breaking one of them. He pointed out that separation of the two chains at the replicating fork must involve rotation of the parent molecule in relation to the two daughters. Such rotation must be extremely rapid, since if the entire DNA molecule of *E. coli* is to be replicated in a single division time of 30 min, over 300,000 turns of the double helix must be unwound, at a rate of at least 10,000 min^{-1}. More recent research has shown that when *E. coli* cells are forced to grow very fast, so that their division time is very short, there may be two or more growing points.

The observations of Cairns raised another question considered earlier by Kornberg and others. If the two strands of the parent DNA have opposite polarity, as the Watson-Crick hypothesis proposes, then one of the two new strands formed during replication must be synthesized in the $3' \rightarrow 5'$ direction and the other in the $5' \rightarrow 3'$ direction. As we shall see below, this consideration placed an important restriction on the enzymatic mechanism of DNA replication.

DNA Polymerase

The enzymatic mechanisms by which DNA is replicated was opened to direct biochemical investigation by the important research of Kornberg and his colleagues beginning in 1956. They incubated crude extracts of *E. coli* with mixtures of dATP, dGTP, dCTP, and dTTP, of which one was labeled with ^{32}P in the α-phosphate group, i.e., that esterified to the 5′-hydroxyl group of deoxyribose (margin). After incubation, the DNA present in the bacterial extract was isolated and found to contain a very small but significant amount of radioactivity, presumably in the phosphodiester bridges. There was no net formation of new DNA; in fact, the extracts possessed considerable deoxyribonuclease activity which caused net destruction of DNA. Nevertheless, the incorporated radioactive phosphate was proved to reside in a high-molecular-weight form of DNA, and to possess all the chemical characteristics of the phosphate groups of the internucleotide linkages.

α-^{32}P dNTP

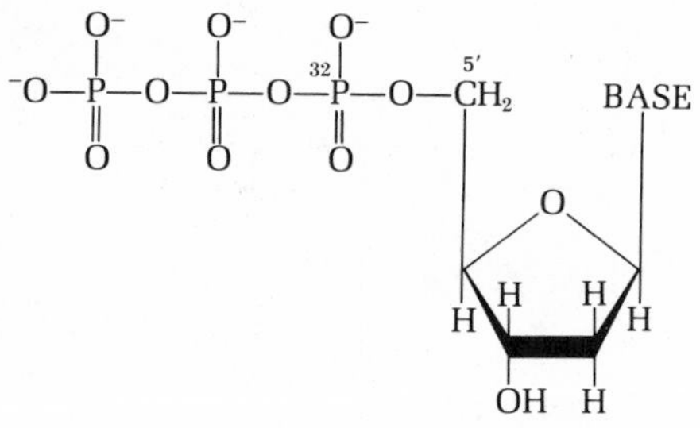

After painstaking purification procedures, Kornberg was ultimately able to obtain small quantities of a highly purified enzyme, called *DNA polymerase*, which catalyzes the synthesis of the internucleotide linkages of DNA starting from a mixture of dATP, dGTP, dCTP, and dTTP. The overall reaction was found to be

$$\begin{matrix} n_1\text{dATP} \\ n_2\text{dGTP} \\ n_3\text{dCTP} \\ n_4\text{dTTP} \end{matrix} \xrightarrow[\text{Mg}^{2+}]{\text{Preformed DNA}} \text{DNA}-\begin{bmatrix} \text{dAMP}_{n_1} \\ \text{dGMP}_{n_2} \\ \text{dCMP}_{n_3} \\ \text{dTMP}_{n_4} \end{bmatrix} + (n_1 + n_2 + n_3 + n_4)\text{PP}_i$$

This reaction occurs only in the presence of some preformed DNA, whose function is considered below. The enzyme specifically requires the 5′-triphosphates of the deoxyribonucleosides as precursors. The 5′-diphosphates and the 5′-monophosphates are inactive. Also inactive are the 5′-triphosphates of ribonucleosides. Moreover, the 5′-triphosphates of all four deoxyribonucleosides normally found in DNA must be present for the reaction to occur; when any single dNTP is omitted, no polymer is formed. Since the newly synthesized polymer can be hydrolyzed to mononucleotides by deoxyribonuclease and spleen phosphodiesterase, it contains 3′,5′-phosphodiester linkages (Chapter 12). The reaction requires Mg^{2+}.

DNA polymerase catalyzes the addition of mononucleotide units to the free 3′-hydroxyl end of a DNA chain; the direction of DNA synthesis is thus 5′ → 3′. Presumably the reaction occurs by a nucleophilic displacement in which the nucleophilic 3′-hydroxyl group of the terminal mononucleotide residue at the growing end of the chain attacks the α-phosphorus atom of the entering nucleoside 5′-triphosphate, causing displacement of its pyrophosphate group and formation of the internucleotide linkage (Figure 29-5).

Since pyrophosphate, the other reaction product, is rapidly hydrolyzed to orthophosphate by pyrophosphatase, the DNA polymerase reaction is normally strongly exergonic. But there is another potent force pulling the reaction to completion. The reaction product of the polymerase is a single strand of DNA, which we shall see combines with the complementary template strand to

Figure 29-5
Mechanism of chain extension by DNA polymerase.

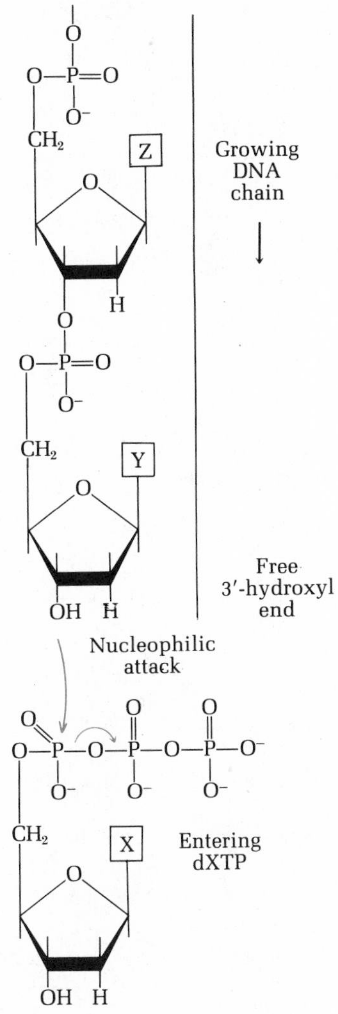

form the double helix. The large decrease in free energy associated with the formation of the double helix, which may be described as a 1-dimensional crystal, also assures that the polymerase reaction normally goes in the forward direction.

During the purification of DNA polymerase it was observed that fractions enriched in polymerase activity also contained considerable activity in hydrolyzing terminal nucleotide residues from DNA. At first this activity was thought to be due to a contaminating deoxyribonuclease, and much effort was devoted to its removal, since it seriously interfered with the measurement of the rate and amount of DNA formation. However, Kornberg and his colleagues ultimately discovered that highly purified DNA polymerase actually possesses, in addition to its primary polymerase activity, the capacity to function as an exonuclease. Thus pure DNA polymerase can catalyze the degradation of DNA by hydrolytic removal of successive mononucleotide residues from either end (5′ or 3′) of the chain to yield deoxyribonucleoside monophosphates. Actually, as we have seen, DNA polymerase can also degrade DNA by reversal of the polymerization, since in the presence of excess pyrophosphate it catalyzes pyrophosphorolysis of DNA with formation of deoxyribonucleoside 5′-triphosphates.

The most highly purified specimens of DNA polymerase of *E. coli* have a molecular weight of 109,000. It apparently possesses a single polypeptide chain having about 1,000 amino acid residues. The enzyme molecule appears to be roughly spherical and has a diameter of about 65 Å, in comparison with double-stranded DNA which has a diameter of about 20 Å. The enzyme possesses a single sulfhydryl group but this is not essential for activity; it also has a single disulfide bridge, presumably intrachain. It can add about 1,000 nucleotide residues per minute per molecule of enzyme and can form strands with molecular weights of several millions.

DNA polymerase activity has been detected in many animal, plant, and bacterial cells. In eucaryotic cells it is found primarily in the nucleus; small amounts are present in the mitochondria, where the enzyme presumably functions to replicate mitochondrial DNA. DNA polymerase activity in bacterial cells increases greatly during replication of certain viruses, such as the *E. coli* phages T2, T4, and T5. Presumably biosynthesis of the phage-induced polymerases is coded by the viral DNA.

The Role of Preformed DNA in The Action of DNA Polymerase

The most striking and characteristic property of DNA polymerase is that it requires the presence of some preexisting DNA. In the absence of the latter, the purified enzyme will make no polymer at all, except under very special conditions to be described. RNA will not substitute for DNA.

At least two alternative explanations were possible for the role of the preformed DNA. It could function as a primer by providing an end or growing point to which additional mononucleotide elements may be added, in much the same fashion that the end of a preformed glycogen chain is required as a primer to accept glucosyl residues in the action of glycogen synthetase (Chapter 22). Or it could serve as a *template* on which the enzyme could make a parallel strand of DNA, complementary to the preformed DNA in base composition and sequence. The preformed DNA could, of course, be required for both functions.

Kornberg and his colleagues examined the requirement for preformed DNA in two general approaches. The first was to investigate the structural features of DNA that are essential for it to function in the action of highly purified DNA polymerase. They found that native double-helical DNA is completely inactive in supporting DNA synthesis. However, melted or denatured DNAs, particularly those in which the two strands are largely separated, yield maximal activity. Heated DNAs from many different sources (animal, plant, bacterial, and viral) support the activity of *E. coli* DNA polymerase. Moreover, the single-stranded circular DNA of the ϕX174 virus of *E. coli* is also active in supporting DNA synthesis. Generally speaking, the longer the preformed DNA molecule, the greater the activity of the enzyme and the greater the amount of new DNA synthesized. In most such experiments the amount of newly synthesized DNA does not exceed the amount of preformed DNA added. These facts, considered in the light of the Watson-Crick hypothesis, strongly suggested that the polymerase requires a single strand of DNA primarily as a template for synthesis of a complementary chain.

That preformed DNA functions as a template was more conclusively supported by the results of measurements of the base composition of the newly synthesized DNA, in comparison with that of the preformed DNA added to the system (Table 29-1). When DNAs isolated from various species having widely different proportions of A-T and G-C pairs are heated to separate the strands and then added to promote DNA synthesis by the purified enzyme, the product always shows a base composition nearly identical to that of the added DNA, as would be expected

Table 29-1 Base composition of templates and products of *E. coli* DNA polymerase.

DNA	*A*	*T*	*G*	*C*
Mycobacterium phlei				
Template	0.65	0.66	1.35	1.34
Product	0.65	0.65	1.34	1.37
E. coli				
Template	1.00	0.97	0.98	1.05
Product	1.04	1.00	0.97	0.98
Calf thymus				
Template	1.14	1.05	0.90	0.85
Product	1.12	1.08	0.85	0.85
T_2 bacteriophage				
Template	1.31	1.32	0.67	0.70
Product	1.33	1.29	0.69	0.70
AT copolymer				
	1.99	1.93	<0.05	<0.05

if each of the two strands of the template DNA were replicated to form two complementary strands.

Nearest-Neighbor Base-Frequency Analysis

Figure 29-6
The 16 possible nearest-neighbor mononucleotide residues in DNA.

5′ → 3′

pApA
pGpA
pCpA
pTpA

pApG
pGpG
pCpG
pTpG

pApC
pGpC
pCpC
pTpC

pApT
pGpT
pCpT
pTpT

Kornberg and his colleagues developed a method called *nearest-neighbor base-frequency analysis* to determine with more certainty whether the new strand of DNA formed by the polymerase is complementary to the added DNA. This method, which has gained wide use, makes possible determination of the frequency with which any two mononucleotides occur as adjacent nearest neighbors in a given DNA chain. Figure 29-6 shows that the four bases of DNA can occur in 16 different nearest-neighbor pairs. Now, if two DNA chains are found to be identical in the frequency of occurrence of all possible nearest-neighbor pairs, the probability must be extremely high that they have identical base sequences. Moreover, it can be expected that the DNA of each species of organism will have a distinctive and characteristic set of nearest-neighbor base frequencies.

In order to carry out the nearest-neighbor analysis, the DNA polymerase reaction is allowed to take place with only one of the four deoxyribonucleoside 5′-triphosphates labeled in the α-phosphate group with ^{32}P, to form a polynucleotide in which the labeled 5′-phosphate groups contributed by the single labeled precursor dNTP are attached to the 3′-carbon of the adjacent mononucleotides (Figure 29-7). If such a ^{32}P-labeled DNA is now subjected to the action of micrococcal deoxyribonuclease and spleen phosphodiesterase (Chapter 12), all the internucleotide linkages of the DNA are hydrolyzed between the phosphorus atom and the 5′-carbon atom of the deoxyribose residues, to yield deoxyribonucleoside 3′-monophosphates as products. The ^{32}P originally introduced by the action of DNA polymerase on the 5′-carbon atom of the labeled mononucleotide precursor will therefore be recovered on the 3′ position of the preceding mononucleotide. For example, if the ^{32}P is introduced into the newly formed DNA as dGMP residues, after hydrolysis it is found in the neighboring nucleoside 3′-phosphates that precede the dGMP residues, reading in the direction 5′ → 3′. Since the labeled dGMP may have dAMP, dGMP, dCMP, or dTMP as preceding nearest neighbors, but in different frequencies, the relative amounts of radioactivity originally added in the form of dGMP that are recovered in the four labeled 3′-mononucleotides indicate the frequency with which the various possible neighboring pairs pApG, pGpG, pCpG, and pTpG occur in a given long stretch of newly formed DNA. If such a procedure of enzymatic synthesis of DNA and its enzymatic cleavage is carried out four times, each time with a different precursor dNTP labeled with ^{32}P, we will end up with four sets of ^{32}P-labeled deoxyribonucleoside 3′-monophosphates, which will give the frequency of occurrence of all 16 possible nearest-neighbor pairs. Kornberg and his colleagues found that each type of DNA used as template yielded a newly synthesized strand of labeled DNA having a distinctive and characteristic

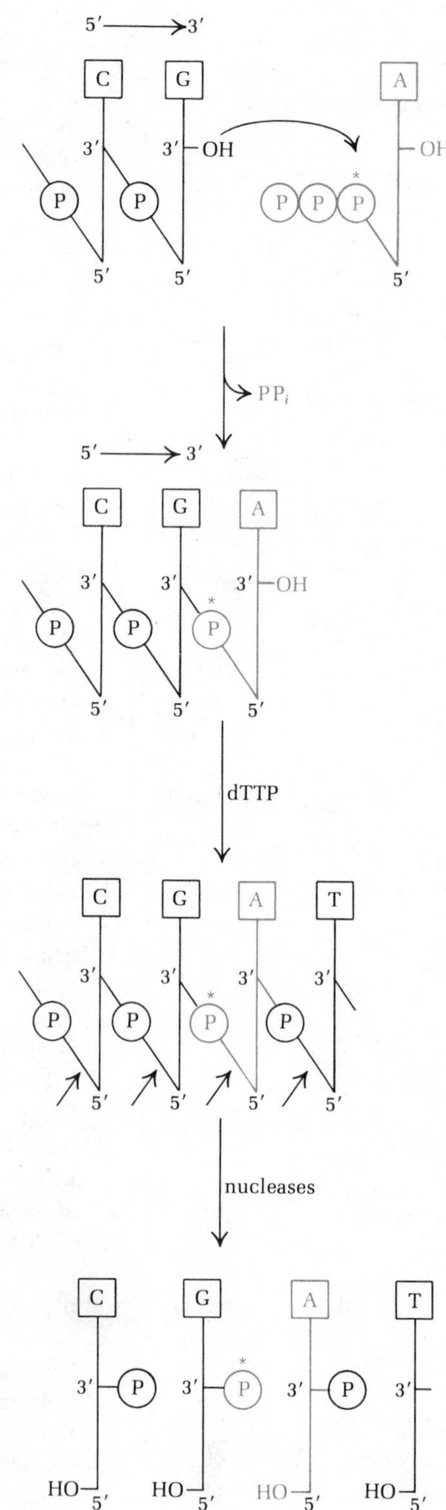

29-7
Nearest-neighbor base-frequency analysis, showing how the nearest-neighbor mononucleotide is labeled.

By the action of DNA polymerase dATP labeled with ^{32}P in the α-position (color) reacts with the 3′ end of DNA

The ^{32}P introduced as the 5′-phosphate group of the dAMP residue forms a bridge to the 3′ position of the preceding residue (dGMP)

Further action of the polymerase adds a dTMP residue, followed by subsequent residues, until chain is complete.

Specific nucleases cleave the phosphodiester bridges at the points shown by arrows. The newly formed DNA is hydrolyzed to yield 3′-mononucleotides. The ^{32}P originally introduced on the 5′ position of the dAMP residue now appears as the 3′-phosphate group of the preceding dGMP residue, thus labeling the nearest neighbor of dAMP.

nearest-neighbor base frequency. An example is shown in Table 29-2, which gives the nearest-neighbor base frequencies for DNA synthesized using double stranded DNA from *M. phlei* as template. All of the 16 possible nearest-neighbor pairs occur, but in widely varying

Table 29-2 Nearest-neighbor base frequencies in DNA synthesized from a double-stranded template DNA from *M. phlei.*

Dinucleotide	*Fraction of total* ^{32}P	*Frequency of occurrence*
	Precursor = dAT^{32}P	
pTpA	0.075	0.012
pApA	0.146	0.024
pCpA	0.378	0.063
pGpA	0.401	0.065
	Precursor = dTT^{32}P	
pTpT	0.157	0.026
pApT	0.194	0.031
pCpT	0.279	0.045
pGpT	0.370	0.060
	Precursor = dGT^{32}P	
pTpG	0.187	0.063
pApG	0.134	0.045
pCpG	0.414	0.139
pGpG	0.265	0.090
	Precursor = dCT^{32}P	
pTpC	0.182	0.061
pApC	0.189	0.064
pCpC	0.268	0.090
pGpC	0.361	0.122

The mole fractions of the bases in the template were T = 0.165, A = 0.162, C = 0.335, and G = 0.338. The frequency of occurrence of pCpA in the newly synthesized DNA is given by 0.378, the fraction of total A present as pCpA, times the fraction of total bases represented by A, or 0.378 × 0.162 = 0.063.

Table 29-3 Nearest-neighbor base frequencies of DNAs synthesized from templates of native and enzymatically formed calf thymus DNA

	Template	
Neighbors	*Native DNA*	*Enzymatically synthesized DNA*
pApA	0.089	0.088
pApG	0.072	0.074
pApC	0.052	0.051
pApT	0.073	0.075
pTpA	0.053	0.059
pTpG	0.076	0.076
pTpC	0.067	0.064
pTpT	0.087	0.083
pGpA	0.064	0.063
pGpG	0.050	0.057
pGpC	0.044	0.042
pGpT	0.056	0.056
pCpA	0.064	0.078
pCpG	0.016	0.011
pCpC	0.054	0.055
pCpT	0.067	0.068

non-random frequencies. Furthermore, the sum of all nearest-neighbor pairs in which A is the first member is equal to the sum of all nearest-neighbor pairs in which T is the first member. The observed equivalence of A and T thus proves the validity of the analytical method.

Kornberg and his colleagues then compared the nearest-neighbor base frequencies of the DNA products synthesized in response to (1) DNA isolated from calf thymus and to (2) DNA enzymatically synthesized in response to calf thymus DNA, to determine whether the frequencies are identical in the first-generation and second-generation strands, as should be the case if the DNA always serves as template. The results are shown in Table 29-3; they indicate that, within experimental error, first and second generation strands are essentially identical in nearest-neighbor base frequencies. This result has been observed with several different DNAs from widely varying sources and provides overwhelming statistical evidence that the DNA formed by action of DNA polymerase is complementary to the template DNA in the manner predicted by the Watson-Crick hypothesis; that is, A always pairs with T and G with C.

DNA polymerase has been found to incorporate certain analogs of the normal nucleotides into the newly formed strand, but only if the unnatural base can undergo hydrogen-bonding with the corresponding coding base in the template strand. Thus deoxyinosine triphosphate (dITP) can replace dGTP in response to a C residue in the template. Similarly, 5-bromodeoxyuridine triphosphate and 5-bromodeoxycytidine triphosphate are accepted by the polymerase in place of dTTP and dCTP respectively. As we shall see, this property provides a useful means of labeling a DNA strand.

All the evidence summarized above clearly demonstrates that preformed DNA strands serve as templates for the action of DNA polymerase. However, more recent investigation shows that preformed DNA may serve a second function, namely as a primer. DNA polymerase functions best when the preformed DNA furnishes not only a template strand but also a priming strand to which it can add mononucleotide residues in response to the template. The template strand and the priming strand are complementary to each other (margin page 670).

Binding of Substrates and Template by DNA Polymerase

Kornberg and his colleagues have carried out an analysis of the capacity of highly purified DNA polymerase to bind its substrates, products, and template. They found that the enzyme contains a single binding locus, presumably at the catalytic site, capable of binding any one of the four deoxyribonucleoside 5′-triphosphates, which may compete with each other. At a separate locus the polymerase also binds linear and circular single-stranded DNAs, which are known to serve as templates. It does not bind intact circular double-stranded DNAs, such as the replicative form of ϕX174 DNA, which cannot serve as template. However, if circular double-stranded DNA is denatured to separate the strands, then the strands are bound by the enzyme. Of particular significance is the observation that when closed circular double-stranded DNA is merely "nicked" at one point in one strand by the action of pancreatic deoxyribonuclease, to yield a free 3′-hydroxyl terminus and free 5′-phosphate terminus, it is strongly bound by the polymerase. The polymerase binds to such nicks very tightly, as well as to free ends of DNA chains.

Figure 29-8 shows a schematic representation of the active site on the DNA polymerase molecule, which depicts specific binding sites for the template strand, the primer strand, the primer-strand terminus, and the incoming deoxyribonucleoside triphosphate. Presumably this specific arrangement of binding sites guarantees the high fidelity with which the polymerase functions. Measurements of the rate of misincorporation indicate that the frequency of mistakes is much less than 1 in 10,000.

Template and priming strands of DNA.

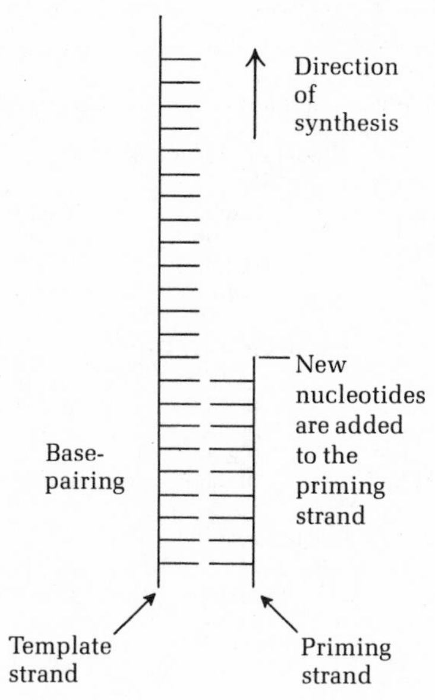

Figure 29-8
Specific binding sites in the active center of DNA polymerase.

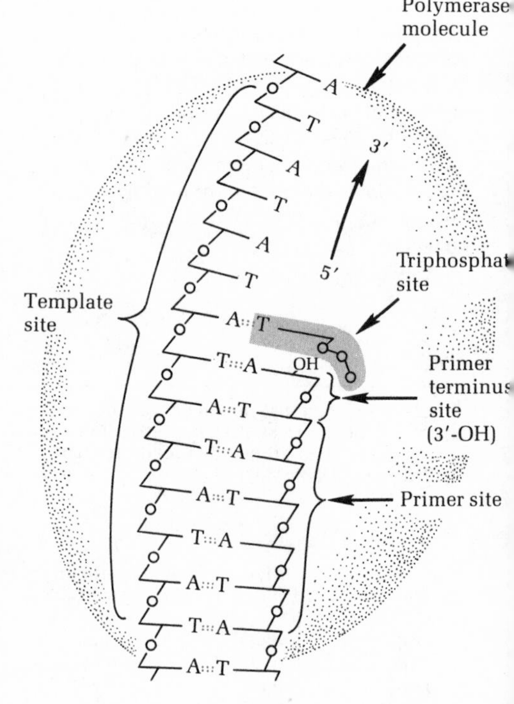

The Antiparallel Polarity of the DNA Strands

A second extremely important conclusion follows from the nearest-neighbor base-frequency analysis of template and product DNA, namely, that the newly synthesized DNA chain runs in the opposite direction from the template DNA chain, i.e., has opposite or antiparallel polarity. This is clearly evident from data in Figure 29-9, which shows the observed nearest-neighbor frequencies of three specific dinucleotides compared with the values expected on the basis (1) that the complementary strands have opposite polarity and (2) that they have similar polarity. The data are compatible only with the conclusion that the newly synthesized DNA chain is antiparallel to the template chain. For example, in chains of opposite polarity the frequency of occurrence of the nearest neighbors ApG is expected to be equal to that of the complementary CpT, whereas if the chains were parallel, the frequency of ApG would be expected to be identical to that of the complementary TpC.

From all available information it is now clear that DNA polymerase can make the internucleotide linkages of DNA in only the 5′ → 3′ direction. In intact cells, however, *both* chains of duplex circular DNA are replicated. If there is but a single growing point which moves around the circular chromosome in only one direction, a dilemma arises, since the Kornberg polymerase can make linkages only in the 5′ → 3′ direction. Is a second polymerase required to replicate the antiparallel chain? Or is some entirely different enzyme required, one that can replicate in both directions? Actually some investigators have questioned whether the Kornberg DNA polymerase is indeed the enzyme whose normal function is to replicate DNA during cell division in *E. coli*; one suggestion was that it is primarily a "repair enzyme," capable of repairing adventitious single-strand breaks by forming a new 5′ → 3′ linkage between the broken ends (see below). However, some of these doubts have been dispelled by (1) the discovery of the enzyme DNA ligase, (2) the demonstration that the Kornberg *E. coli* polymerase and DNA ligase can together synthesize a biologically active DNA molecule, and (3) the discovery of the role of an endodeoxyribonuclease, which enables DNA polymerase and DNA ligase to replicate *both* strands of an antiparallel duplex.

Figure 29-9
Comparison of matching nearest-neighbor frequencies in strands of opposite and similar polarity. The figures in parentheses are the observed data (Table 29-2) for the template M. phlei strand and the newly synthesized strands, which are seen to correspond when the strands have opposite polarity.

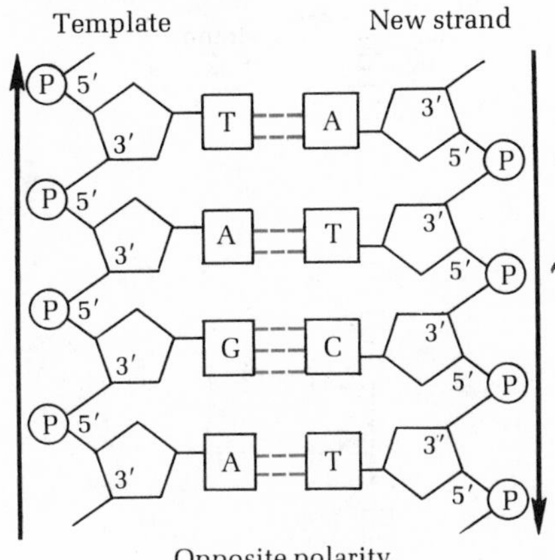

Opposite polarity (Watson–Crick model)

$T_pA(0.012) = T_pA(0.012)$

$A_pG(0.045) = C_pT(0.045)$

$G_pA(0.065 = T_pC(0.061)$

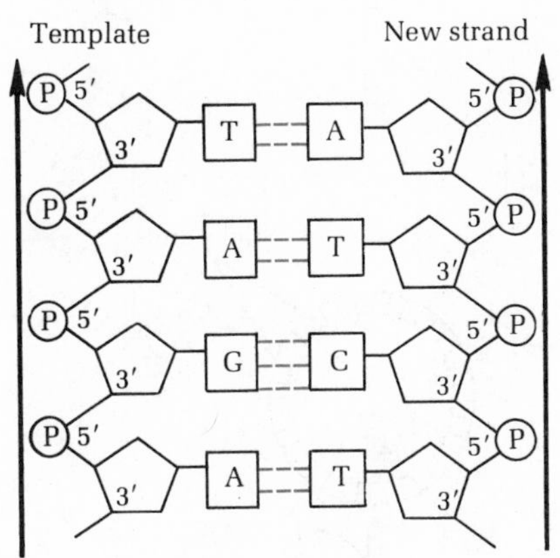

Similar polarity

$T_pA(0.012) = A_pT(0.031)$

$A_pG(0.045) = T_pC(0.061)$

$G_pA(0.065) = C_pT(0.045)$

DNA Ligase

Nearly simultaneously, several investigators reported the discovery in *E. coli* extracts of an enzyme, distinct from DNA polymerase, which can join the ends of two DNA chains or join the two ends of a single DNA chain to form a circular molecule; it cannot, however, replicate a whole chain. This enzyme is called *joining enzyme* or *DNA ligase*. The reaction mechanism differs from that of DNA polymerase and is rather unusual. The DNA ligase of *E. coli* requires the presence of NAD^+, normally a coenzyme for oxidation-reduction reactions (Chapter 15), but which functions here as a source of an adenylyl group. The DNA ligase reaction takes place in two steps. In the first, a covalent adenylylenzyme complex (E-AMP) is formed on reaction of the enzyme with NAD^+; nicotinamide mononucleotide (NMN) is the other product:

$$NAD^+ + E \rightleftharpoons E\text{-}AMP + NMN$$

In the second step, the 5′-terminal and 3′-terminal ends of two segments of DNA, both being in double-helical association with a complementary chain, are covalently joined. In this process the adenylyl group is transferred from the enzyme to the 5′-phosphate end of the DNA; the 3′-hydroxyl end then displaces the adenylyl group to form the phosphodiester linkage. The overall equation is thus

$$\text{E-AMP} + \text{5}'\text{-phosphate end} + \text{3}'\text{-hydroxyl end} \rightleftharpoons \text{5}' \rightarrow \text{3}'\text{phosphodiester bond} + \text{E} + \text{AMP}$$

In a similar way, the E-AMP complex can join the ends of a linear DNA duplex to form a circle (Figure 29-10). DNA ligase requires the presence of an intact complementary DNA strand to place the two ends in juxtaposition as the new phosphodiester linkage is formed. The formation of circular DNA duplexes by the enzyme is made possible by the occurrence of complementary "sticky ends" in the linear DNA precursor (Figure 29-10). In mammalian systems, as well as in *E. coli* infected with bacteriophage T4, the DNA ligase may employ ATP instead of NAD^+ as the donor of the adenylyl group.

DNA ligase is thought to have five biological functions: (1) to link the ends of linear DNA molecules to yield circular forms, (2) to catalyze the repair of breaks or nicks in one chain of double-stranded DNA, (3) to join segments of DNA to complete the process of genetic recombination during transformation, transduction, and lysogenization in bacteria, (4) to recombine genes during crossing-over in eucaryotic cells, and (5) to cooperate with DNA polymerase in the replication of both strands of antiparallel DNA, as we shall see below.

Enzymatic Synthesis of ϕX174 DNA

For years many attempts have been made to determine whether purified DNA polymerase can catalyze the synthesis of a biologically active form of DNA in the test tube. This objective was achieved in 1968 by Goulian, Kornberg, and Sinsheimer. They carried out the enzymatic synthesis of the circular, biologically active double-stranded or replicative form of the DNA of bacteriophage ϕX174 by the combined action of DNA polymerase and DNA ligase. The DNA of the small ϕX174 phage is a single-stranded circle, designated (+), which is copied by the host *E. coli* cell to make a complementary (−) strand, thus forming a duplex circular DNA molecule, the (+ −) or replicative form (Chapter 12). Both the (+) and (−) strands are known to be infective for *E. coli*.

In the first step of the sequence of enzymatic reactions (Figure 29-11), a circular (+) strand of ϕX174 DNA, labeled with tritium, was used as the template for the DNA polymerase reaction in the presence of a mixture of ^{32}P-labeled dATP, dCTP, dGTP, and dBUTP. The abbreviation dBUTP stands for 2′-deoxy-5-bromouridine 5′-triphosphate, an analog of dTTP which contains 5-bromouracil instead of thymine. This unnatural nucleotide residue is readily incorporated into DNA by DNA polymerase, instead of the normal thymidylic acid. This reaction thus resulted in the formation of a linear, complementary (−) strand of ϕX174 DNA, in which all the thymine residues were replaced by 5-bromouracil. The two ends of the latter strand were then joined by the action of DNA ligase, to produce double-stranded circular ϕX174 DNA, in which the (+) strand was labeled with tritium and the (−) strand with ^{32}P; the latter also contained BU instead of T.

The double-stranded ϕX174 DNA so formed was then lightly treated with deoxyribonuclease in order to cause single nicks in one chain of some of the duplexes, so that intact single-strand circles could be obtained from at least some of the double-strand circles. The mixture was then heated to unwind the duplexes; among the products were some intact (+) circles, some intact (−) circles, some intact (+) and (−) linear strands, as well as some smaller fragments. Since the newly synthesized circular (−) strands have a greater buoyant density, by virtue of their bromouracil content, than the circular (+) strands used as their template, they could be separated from the latter by centrifugation in CsCl density gradients. Completeness of separation was checked by appropriate radioactivity determinations on the two fractions.

The enzymatically formed circular (−) strand, which contained BU instead of T, was then used as a template with purified DNA polymerase to produce a complementary (+) strand from the four normal dNTP precursors. After the joining of its ends by DNA ligase to form a covalent circle, the enzymatically synthesized (+) strand was isolated and found to be fully infective and identical in its physical properties with the natural (+) strand. Figure 29-12 shows an electron micrograph of partially synthetic ϕX174 DNA.

Figure 29-10
Action of DNA ligase in repairing a single-strand nick (above) and in closing a circle (below). The ends to be joined must be held by complementary base pairing to a template strand.

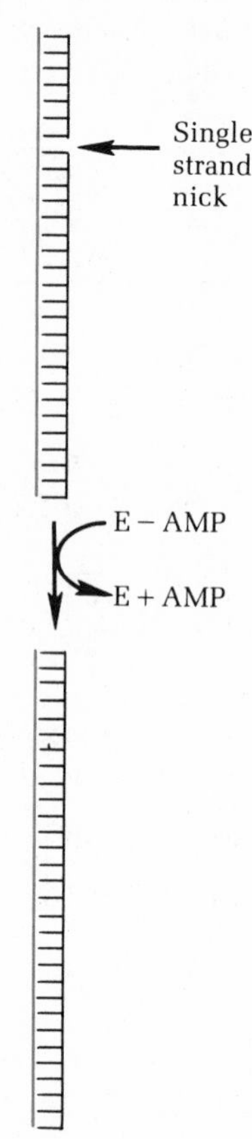

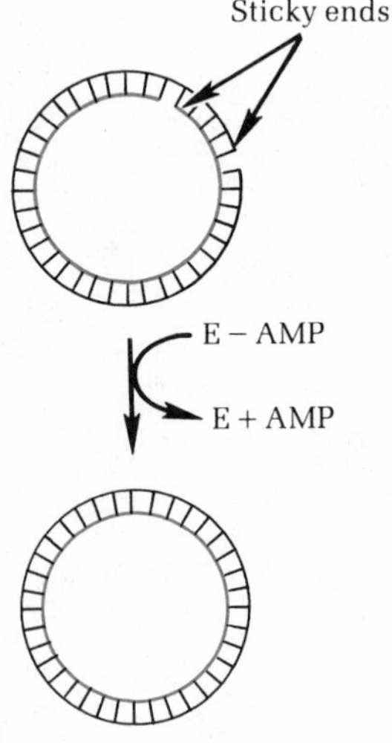

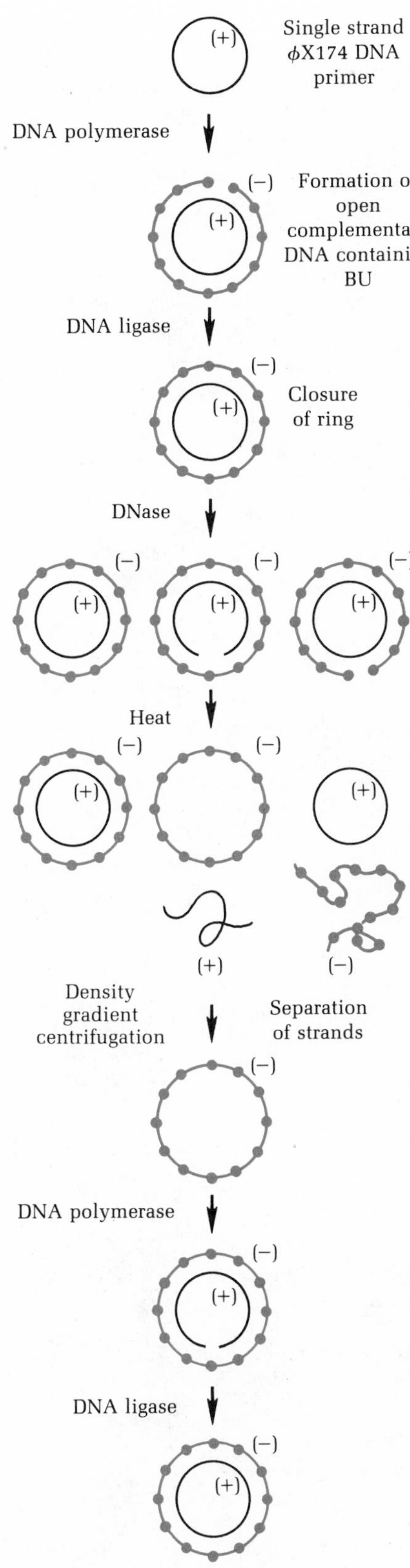

Figure 29-11
Enzymatic synthesis of both strands of circular ϕX174 DNA. A single strand (+) of ϕX174 (tritiated) was initially used as template to make complementary linear DNA containing ^{32}P and 5-bromouracil instead of thymine (the (−) strand). The ends were then closed by the ligase. Treatment with DNase followed by heat yielded some unchanged double circles, intact (+) circles, and intact (−) circles, which were separated by density gradient centrifugation. The enzymatically synthesized (−) circle was separated and used as template to synthesize a complementary (+) strand in open form. The ends were then closed to yield completely synthetic duplex circular ϕX174 DNA.

These elegant experiments established that DNA polymerase can synthesize a biologically active DNA molecule, the first ever created in the test tube by the action of highly purified enzymes acting on highly purified substrates with a pure template of known biological activity. This experiment also proved that DNA polymerase can make both the (+) and (−) strands of a viral DNA when the process is carried out in two steps.

The Replication of Double-Stranded DNA In Vivo

We are still confronted with a nagging question: How can *both* strands of antiparallel duplex DNA molecules be replicated *simultaneously*, as is known to occur in the intact cell, so that chains running in the $5' \rightarrow 3'$ and $3' \rightarrow 5'$ are made simultaneously? We have seen that DNA polymerase cannot replicate native double-stranded DNA by itself, and can build DNA linkages only in the $5' \rightarrow 3'$ direction. Recent experimental developments

Figure 29-12
Electron micrograph of two duplex circular ϕX174 DNA molecules, in which one strand is natural and the other synthetic.

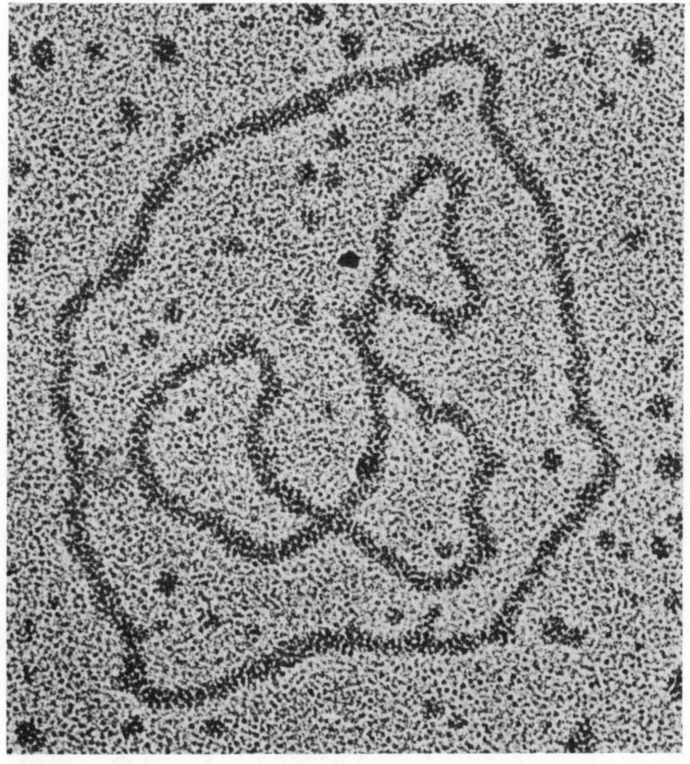

may provide the answer. Okazaki in Japan has found that rapidly growing cells of *E. coli* contain a number of small DNA fragments, even when extreme care is taken to avoid shear damage to the large circular DNA molecules of the bacterial chromosomes. Such fragments accumulate in large amounts in mutants of *E. coli* having defective DNA ligase molecules, suggesting that the DNA ligase normally "stitches" together a number of short DNA fragments to form a long strand. Since these fragments were shown to originate from near the growing region of the replicating fork, it has been suggested that they may be the means by which the 3′ → 5′ chain of antiparallel duplex DNA is synthesized during replication.

Kornberg and his colleagues, on the basis of these observations, as well as their finding that DNA polymerase binds duplex DNA only at nicks, have constructed an interesting hypothesis for the replication of DNA in the intact cell. Their mechanism (Figure 29-13), which accounts for the formation of the "Okazaki fragments," requires three enzymes: DNA polymerase, DNA ligase, and an endodeoxyribonuclease. They postulate that bacterial chromosomes, which are circular duplex structures, are inert as long as they have no nicks. Replication begins by introduction of a nick in one strand, possibly by action of an endonuclease. DNA polymerase then binds at this nick and begins to extend the 3′-hydroxyl end of the nicked strand by adding successive mononucleotide units complementary to the intact strand, while the 5′ end of the nicked strand undergoes displacement from the duplex structure, i.e., peels away. They suggest that the 5′ end may be held down by attachment to the cell membrane. The replication of one strand in the 5′ → 3′ direction proceeds for some distance as the 5′ end of the nicked strand is continuously peeled back. Then the DNA polymerase is postulated to switch or jump from the unbroken template strand to the nicked strand at the fork where the two strands are separated. It is then postulated to add mononucleotide units to the 3′ end of the growing chain in the 5′ → 3′ direction, now using the nicked strand as template. The enzyme continues until the entire loose end of the nicked strand is replicated and then leaves. An endonuclease then cleaves the newly formed strand at the fork, leaving a short fragment of complementary DNA duplexed with the 5′ end of the original nicked template strand.

The process is now repeated. The DNA polymerase begins to add residues again at the 3′-OH end of the previously synthesized strand, at the point where it was nicked, makes a short segment complementary to the original unbroken strand, switches over to the loose strand as template, and runs in the 5′ → 3′ direction from the fork until it reaches the first fragment. The two newly formed segments of DNA on the loose template strand are joined by DNA ligase, and the fork is again cleaved by an endonuclease. Another cycle then begins. In this manner, both strands of an antiparallel circular duplex can be replicated by the combined action of DNA polymerase, DNA ligase, and an endonuclease, the whole process proceeding by replication of short runs of the two strands,

Figure 29-13
Hypothesis of Kornberg for the replication of both strands of antiparallel duplex DNA by DNA polymerase.

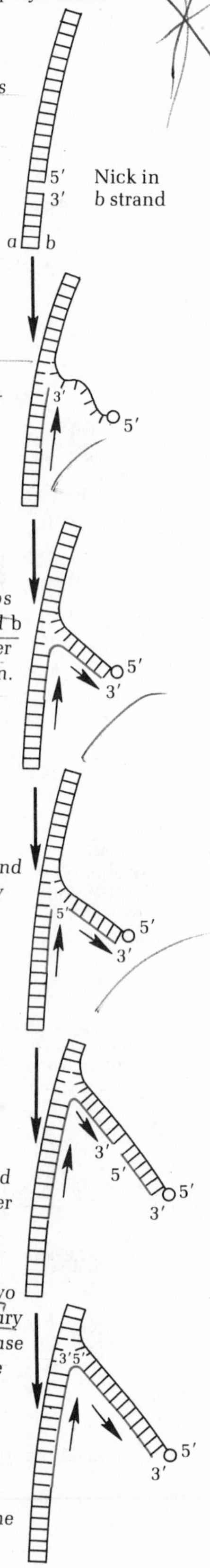

DNA polymerase binds to nick on strand b.

5′ 3′ Nick in b strand

a b

Strand a is replicated while nicked strand b is peeled back.

3′ 5′

DNA polymerase jumps from strand a to strand b and replicates the latter in the 5′ → 3′ direction.

5′ 3′

The newly formed strand is nicked at the fork by an endonuclease.

5′ 5′ 3′

DNA polymerase now returns and resumes replication of strand a at 3′ end. At the fork, it jumps to strand b and replicates it until earlier fragment is reached.

3′ 5′ 5′ 3′

DNA ligase joins the two fragments complementary to strand b. Endonuclease nicks new strand at the fork and a new cycle begins. In this fashion both strands are replicated in short lengths, with the polymerase replicating always in the 5′ → 3′ direction. The new strand which is complementary to strand b is formed by joining the fragments through the action of DNA ligase.

3′5′ 5′ 3′

Figure 29-14
Repair of ultraviolet-induced thymine dimer, which prevents replication.

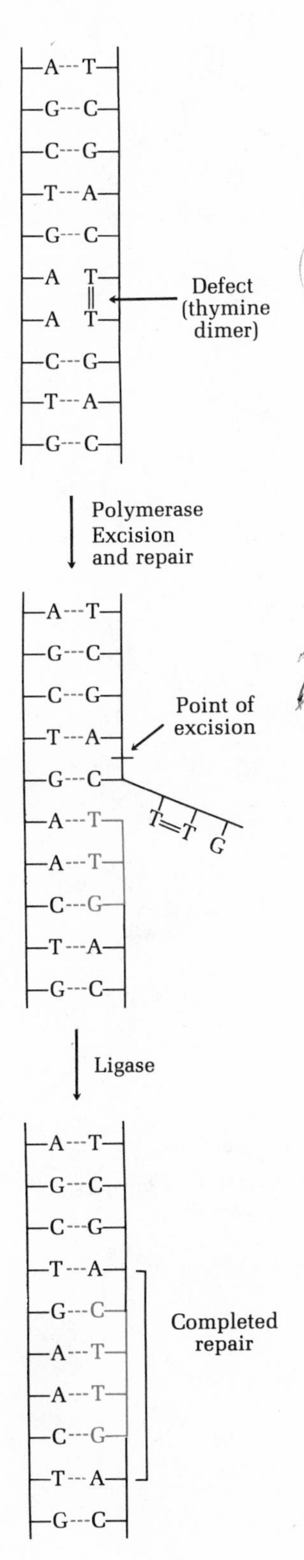

with DNA polymerase alternating between the two strands as templates, but always making bonds in the $5' \rightarrow 3'$ direction. If DNA ligase is genetically defective, the short fragments cannot be joined and accumulate in the cell. It is estimated that the short lengths of DNA that are formed in this process have about 1,000 nucleotides, or sufficient to code a reasonably large polypeptide chain.

Repair of DNA

There is growing evidence that cells contain enzymes capable of repairing breaks in DNA that are induced by adventitious causes. Single-strand nicks in duplex DNA may occur during thermal motion, or during the folding and bending of the DNA into tightly coiled structures in the nucleoid of bacterial cells. Such breaks are presumably repaired by DNA ligase.

Another type of damage that can be repaired is that due to ultraviolet irradiation, which causes adjacent pyrimidines in the DNA to undergo dimerization by formation of covalent bonds between them. Adjacent thymine residues are particularly susceptible to this reaction and form the *thymine dimer* (below). Formation of such a dimer blocks replication, just as though a zipper had become jammed. Such a defect can be enzymatically repaired by an enzyme system that can excise the defective thymine-thymine dinucleotide from the chain in which it occurs by hydrolysis of internucleotide linkages at both sides of the defect, one or two nucleotides away. The defect is then repatched by enzymatic insertion of nucleotides complementary to the good strand (see Figure 29-14). Evidently such defects or nicks occur relatively frequently in the intact cell, but as long as they occur in only one strand they can be readily repaired without loss in fidelity of transcription.

Thymine dimer. *This compound exists in four optically active forms. The meso form, shown here, is produced from* DNA *on irradiation.*

Open or planar form

Stacked form

Replication of Viral DNA

When DNA viruses infect susceptible host cells, the viral DNA is replicated in preference to the host-cell DNA. A portion of the viral DNA is also transcribed as complementary mRNA and then translated to form viral coat proteins on the ribosomes of the host cell. In some DNA viruses, the takeover of the host-cell machinery for replication of viral DNA is made easier by the fact that the viral DNA also codes for the formation of a deoxyribonuclease which is specific for destroying the host DNA by hydrolysis of its internucleotide linkages, but which does not hydrolyze the viral DNA.

Some small DNA viruses, such as ϕX174, possess a single-stranded DNA. When this DNA strand, the (+) strand, enters the host cell, it is replicated by the host DNA polymerase as a complementary (−) strand, to form the double-helical or replicative form within the host. However, the viral progeny formed contain only a single-stranded DNA of the (+) type. Clearly, the (+) strands of the viral progeny are made by replication of the complementary (−) strand of the double-helical or replicative form of the viral DNA. Evidently the virus-induced DNA polymerase specifically selects the (−) strand as the template. The mechanism by which such a choice is made is not known, but it appears to require that the DNA be in duplex form, since the isolated polymerase can replicate either the (+) or (−) chain when they are used separately as primers.

The methylated or glucosylated bases found in DNA are formed by enzymatic methylation and glucosylation *after* the chains have been built. Formation of such substituted bases in DNA may be a species-specific process to protect DNA against the action of endogenous deoxyribonuclease. There is some evidence that DNAs foreign to a cell are *restricted*, or prevented from replication, because they are readily degraded by endogenous nucleases.

Messenger RNA

In early investigations Caspersson, Brachet, and others had observed that the onset of protein synthesis in intact cells is sometimes accompanied by a simultaneous increase in the amount or rate of turnover of cytoplasmic RNA. Moreover, there is a very small fraction of RNA in bacteriophage-infected *E. coli* cells, only a few percent, which turns over very rapidly in comparison to the rest of the RNA. This RNA fraction has a base composition very similar to that of the phage DNA, but different from that of either bacterial DNA or the remainder of the bacterial RNA. The function of this RNA fraction of high turnover rate remained obscure for some time, but it later acquired special significance in connection with research on the rate of synthesis of inducible enzymes in *E. coli*, which is very high.

Inducible enzymes are those whose synthesis is stimulated when the host bacterial cell is placed in a medium rich in the substrate of the enzyme (Chapter 32). Such enzymes are formed very rapidly, in a matter of minutes. In fact, from various experiments Jacob and Monod calculated that the half-life of the intermediate templates used in enzyme synthesis in *E. coli* must be very short, about 2 min. On the basis of this and many other observations, they suggested that the RNA fraction showing a high rate of turnover may be functioning as templates for synthesis of enzymes. In 1961 they formulated the *messenger RNA hypothesis*. They proposed that the rapidly labeled RNA formed during or preceding protein synthesis is a species of RNA whose function is to serve as a messenger, carrying genetic information from the DNA of the chromosomes to the surface of the ribosomes. They postulated that messenger RNA is formed enzymatically in such a way that it has a base sequence complementary to that of one strand of DNA. The messenger RNA molecule was presumed to contain the complete message for specifying one or more polypeptide chains. It was postulated to bind to the ribosomes and to serve as the "working" template for protein synthesis. To account for the fact that the synthesis of some enzymes in bacterial cells can be turned on and off very quickly, with a lag of only 1 or 2 min, Jacob and Monod postulated that control over the rate of protein synthesis is exerted by the rate of messenger RNA synthesis and breakdown. They suggested that messenger RNA is used as a template to make but one or perhaps only a few copies of a given protein molecule and is then degraded to yield mononucleotides (Chapter 32).

Many experimental observations support the Jacob-Monod hypothesis, particularly the DNA-like base composition of the RNA fraction which has a high turnover rate. Moreover, actinomycin D, which inhibits formation of RNA by DNA-directed RNA polymerase (Chapter 29) causes induced enzyme synthesis to slow down and stop completely within a few minutes. When the rapidly synthesized RNA is pulse-labeled with ^{32}P, the addition of actinomycin D is followed by rapid loss of ^{32}P-labeled RNA, which is complete in a few minutes. Such experiments indicated that the messenger RNA fraction may have a half-life of only about 2 min in bacterial cells, in accord with the rate of synthesis of induced enzymes.

Messenger RNA is difficult to isolate, not only because of its short half-life, but also because it makes up only a few percent of the total cellular RNA. Moreover, if, as postulated, each protein or group of proteins requires its own specific messenger RNA molecule, isolation of one pure messenger RNA species from a small pool containing perhaps thousands of different mRNAs would appear to be an extremely difficult task. However, fractions rich in mRNA have been isolated from cells synthesizing only one or a few kinds of protein, such as reticulocytes, which synthesize largely hemoglobin, or bacterial cells infected with a DNA virus, which synthesize only viral proteins. Messenger RNA has also been isolated from polyribosomes. That such RNA preparations have a base sequence complementary to DNA has been shown in hybridization experiments; the messenger RNA hybridizes with DNA of the same cell but not of other cell types. Additional convincing evidence for the messenger concept has come from experiments on isolated ribosomes (Chapter 31).

We shall now examine the enzymatic mechanisms involved in the synthesis of messenger RNA, i.e., the process of transcription.

Transcription of DNA by DNA-Directed RNA Polymerase

The discovery of DNA polymerase and its dependence on a template began an active search for the enzymes that participate in the transcription of DNA, that is, the formation of RNA complementary to a strand of the chromosomal DNA. In 1959 three investigators, S. B. Weiss, Hurwitz, and Stevens, independently discovered a DNA-dependent enzyme capable of forming an RNA polymer from ribonucleoside 5′-triphosphates; the RNA formed is complementary to the DNA template. This enzyme, called *RNA polymerase,* is very similar in action to DNA polymerase. The reaction requires Mg^{2+} and it proceeds with elimination of pyrophosphate. RNA polymerase catalyzes the following reaction:

$$\begin{matrix} n_1\text{ATP} \\ n_2\text{UTP} \\ n_3\text{GTP} \\ n_4\text{CTP} \end{matrix} \xrightleftharpoons[\text{Mg}^{2+}]{\text{DNA template}} \text{RNA}\begin{bmatrix} \text{AMP}_{n_1} \\ \text{UMP}_{n_2} \\ \text{GMP}_{n_3} \\ \text{CMP}_{n_4} \end{bmatrix} + (n_1 + n_2 + n_3 + n_4)\text{PP}_i$$

All four ribonucleoside 5′-triphosphates are required simultaneously. The RNA polymer formed possesses 3′,5′-phosphodiester bridges and is hydrolyzed by ribonuclease and spleen phosphodiesterase. RNA polymerase adds mononucleotide units to the 3′-hydroxyl end of the RNA chain and thus builds RNA in the 5′ → 3′ direction. The RNA polymerase reaction can be reversed by increasing the pyrophosphate concentration to high levels. As in the case of DNA polymerase, enzymatic hydrolysis of pyrophosphate by pyrophosphatase helps ensure that the reaction goes in the direction of synthesis in the cell. RNA polymerase has been identified in many animal, plant, and bacterial cells. In higher organisms it appears to be located primarily in the nucleus, where it is usually found combined with high-molecular-weight DNA in an easily sedimentable form. The enzyme is also found in mitochondria, where it participates in transcription of mitochondrial DNA.

Initiation of the RNA polymerase reaction (sigma cycle)

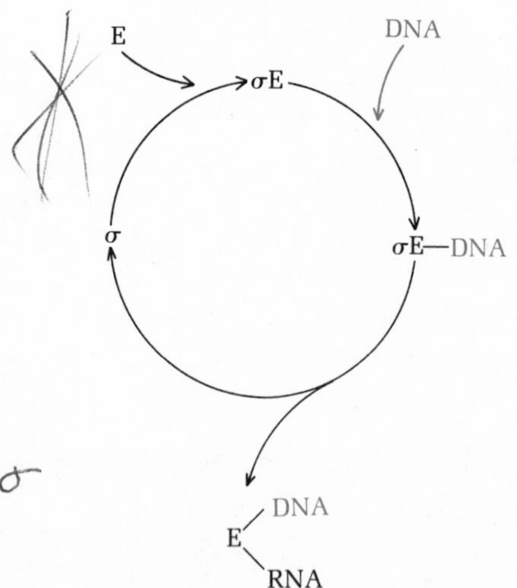

E = RNA polymerase
σ = sigma or initiation factor

RNA polymerase is purified only with some difficulty, and some of the properties of the enzyme appear to undergo change with purification. Two proteins are required for RNA formation, one of which, called *sigma,* is required only to initiate the RNA chain; the other forms the internucleotide linkages once the chain has been begun (margin). The sigma factor is presumably important in the regulation of the transcription process. The RNA polymerase system from *E. coli* has a high molecular weight, perhaps as high as 700,000, and it undergoes changes in its state of aggregation depending on substrate and enzyme concentration.

RNA polymerase will incorporate certain analogs of the normal bases into newly formed RNA, in replacement for specific normal bases. Thus UTP can be replaced by 5-fluoro-UTP or 5-bromo-UTP as mononucleotide precursors, in response to A residues in the template strand (see below). Similarly, GTP can be replaced by ITP and CTP by 5-bromo-CTP, in response to C and G residues, respectively.

The Template Requirement of RNA Polymerase

The requirement of a template for the RNA polymerase reaction appears to depend somewhat on the source of the enzyme and its state of purification. RNA polymerase is most active with a double-stranded DNA as primer and shows much less, though significant, activity with single-stranded or denatured DNA.

The RNA formed in response to various DNA templates has a base composition complementary to that of the template DNA; in the RNA so formed, uracil residues are complementary to adenine residues of the DNA template. The template DNA may derive from animal, plant, bacterial, or viral sources. Furthermore, when poly dAT copolymer formed synthetically by DNA polymerase is used as a template for RNA polymerase, the complementary polymer poly UA is formed by the enzyme, even when all four ribonucleoside 5′-triphosphates are present in the medium.

Nearest-neighbor base-frequency analysis shows that the base sequences of template and product are perfectly complementary to each other and that the newly formed RNA chain has the opposite polarity of the template DNA chain. No covalent linkages are formed between the template DNA and the RNA formed; thus, the template DNA can be recovered from the mixture in essentially unchanged form. That the template DNA and the newly formed RNA are complementary was also shown by the hybridization technique. When a single-strand DNA template and the RNA produced from it by RNA polymerase are separated by heating and the mixture is then slowly cooled, stable hybrid DNA-RNA complexes form spontaneously.

With crude preparations of RNA polymerase, the RNA formed on a single-stranded ϕX174 DNA template is perfectly complementary to the DNA. When double-stranded ϕX174 DNA is used as template, the RNA formed is complementary in base composition to both template strands, suggesting that both are transcribed to yield complementary RNA strands. However, this is not a general property. When highly purified RNA polymerase of *E. coli* is presented with completely intact duplex DNA templates, only one of the two strands is transcribed. The selection of one strand for transcription occurs by an unknown mechanism, which appears to depend on the integrity and circularity of the DNA template, the physical state of the RNA polymerase, and its degree of purity. There is considerable evidence that DNA contains specific initiation points where RNA transcription begins; presumably they are signaled by a specific sequence in DNA. The first or initiating ribonucleotide of the RNA is incorporated as the 5′-triphosphate.

Most available evidence suggests that in *E. coli* there is but a single DNA-directed RNA polymerase which can make mRNAs, tRNAs, and rRNAs. All 3 types of RNA hybridize with chromosomal DNA. Moreover, synthesis of all three types of RNA is blocked by the antibiotic rifamycin. The minor bases found in tRNAs are formed by enzymatic modification of the parent bases *after* the covalent backbone of the RNA has been formed. There are three types of ribosomal RNA (5S, 16S, and 23S in *E. coli*), some 60 types of tRNA, and a very large number of different mRNAs in any given cell. In intact *E. coli,* about one-half of the total RNA output is of mRNA.

In bacteria transcription and translation are closely synchronized, both temporally and geometrically (margin).

Functional complex of DNA duplex, mRNA, RNA polymerase, and ribosome in bacterial cell.

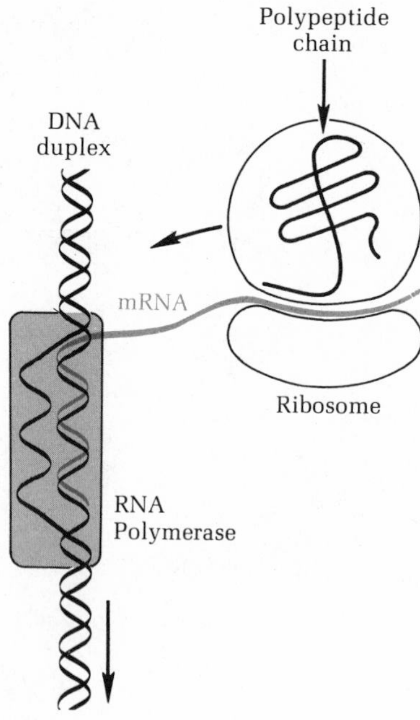

Inhibition of RNA Polymerase

The formation of RNA by DNA-directed RNA polymerase preparations is specifically inhibited by the antibiotic *actinomycin D* (Figure 29-15), which binds to DNA largely by hydrogen-bonding to guanine residues, perhaps blocking the minor groove of DNA. Actinomycin D also inhibits RNA synthesis in intact cells and has become a very important diagnostic tool for detection of processes dependent on transcription of DNA. Rifamycin also blocks RNA synthesis, but by binding to the polymerase rather than the template.

Figure 29-15
Structure of actinomycin D. Sarcosine is N-methylglycine. The linkages between sarcosine, L-proline, and D-valine are peptide bonds.

Visualization of the Transcription Process

In the egg cells of amphibia, the genes coding for the synthesis of ribosomal RNA are located in nucleoli. During early growth of the egg cell, ribosomal RNA is synthesized in large amounts. Electron microscopy of these cells, or of nucleolar material isolated from them, reveals that they contain long thin fibers about 100 to 200 Å in diameter which at periodic intervals are coated with a matrix of hairlike radial fibrils; the fibrils gradually increase in length (Figure 29-16). Analysis indicates that the core fiber extending continuously through these structures consists of a filament of DNA coated with protein. The long hairlike fibrils, of which about 100 occur

Figure 29-16
Electron micrograph of nucleolar genes of an amphibian egg cell. These genes, which code for ribosomal RNA, repeat along the DNA. They are identifiable because each is undergoing transcription into rRNA, about 100 strands of the latter being formed simultaneously as the RNA polymerase molecule moves along the gene. The segments between the active genes are probably genes that are inactive at this period.

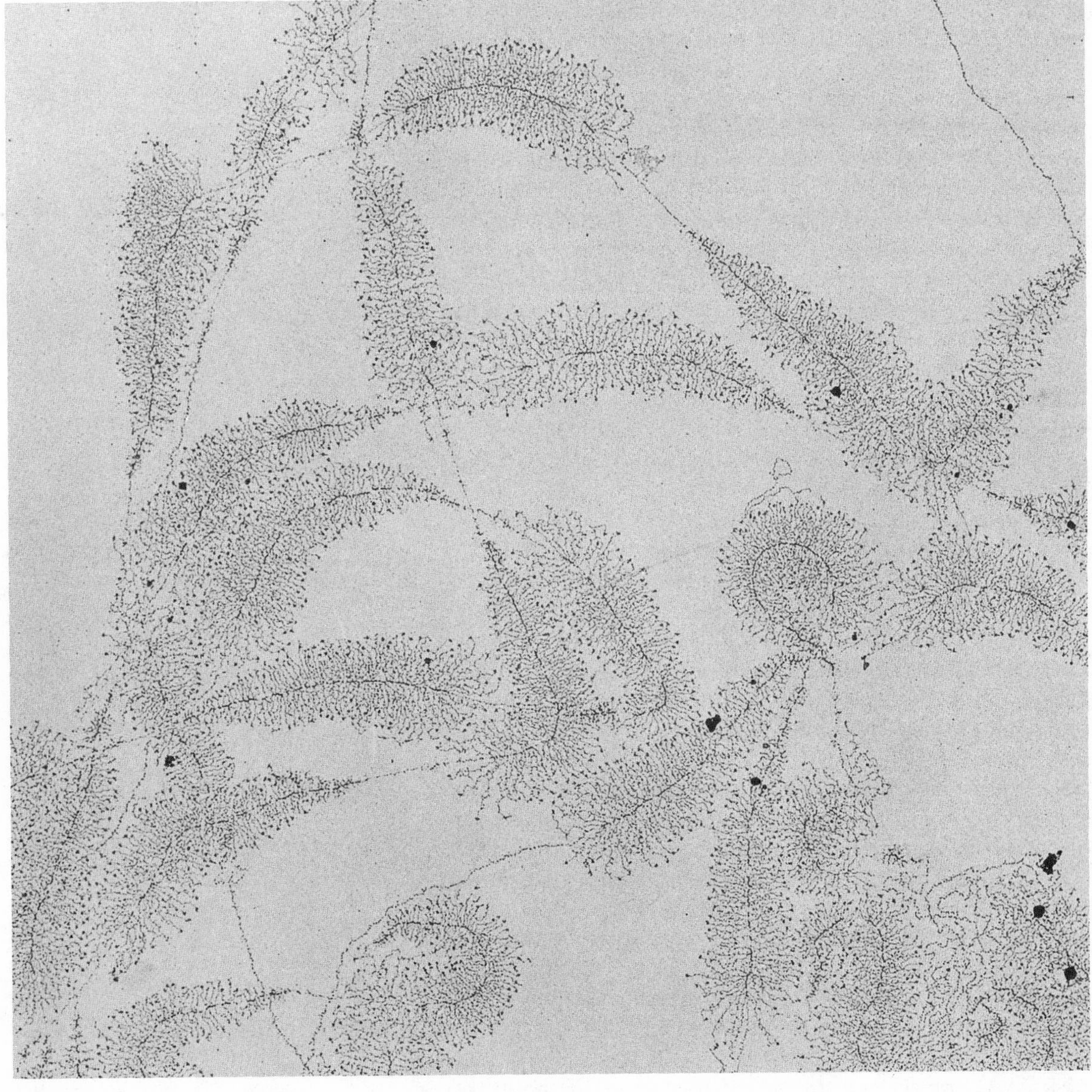

1.0 μ

in each segment, are strands of RNA coated with protein. Each DNA segment coated with the featherlike RNA fibrils appears to represent a gene for rRNA which is undergoing transcription. Up to 100 RNA chains are made on each gene simultaneously, each being formed by an RNA polymerase molecule which moves along the gene as the RNA chain grows. The length of the segment coated with RNA fibrils is about 2 to 3 μ, which is about the length of DNA required to code for 18S and 28S ribosomal RNA of eucaryotes. The segments of the DNA core fiber that are not coated with RNA fibrils, i.e., the intergene segments, are inactive, at least at the time of early egg-cell growth. This remarkable electron micrograph represents one of the first observations of the structure of individual eucaryotic genes of known function, together with their nascent transcription products.

RNA Replicases

Although many plant viruses contain RNA, no RNA-containing bacterial virus was discovered until 1961. Several are now known; they include the *E. coli* bacteriophages f2, MS2, and Qβ. The discovery of these RNA viruses has raised a fundamental question, how are they replicated? Can the viral RNA be replicated directly, or must the viral RNA be transcribed into the form of a complementary DNA first? This question is tantamount to asking whether the flow of information from DNA to RNA can be reversed. Convincing evidence came when Spiegelman and his associates discovered a new type of enzyme, RNA replicase, which can utilize viral RNA as template for formation of new RNA. RNA replicase is not normally present in the host cell, but is produced when the cell is infected with an RNA virus.

RNA replicase isolated from cells infected with the Qβ virus catalyzes the formation of RNA from the ribonucleoside 5′-triphosphates with elimination of pyrophosphate; the reaction is formally similar to that of DNA-directed RNA polymerase. The RNA replicase requires RNA as template and will not function with DNA if the enzyme has been highly purified. However, contrary to DNA and RNA polymerases, RNA replicase is template-specific. It can employ as template only the RNA of the Qβ virus; the RNAs of the host cell do not support replication. This finding obviously explains how RNA viruses are preferentially replicated in the host cell, which contains many other types of RNA. Presumably the viral RNA codes for formation of an RNA replicase which functions only with viral RNA as template and ignores all other RNA molecules. Further studies with the Qβ RNA replicase also show that it requires an intact viral RNA molecule and cannot utilize viral RNA fragments as templates. This property not only indicates that the Qβ RNA replicase has a highly developed template specificity but also suggests that the replicase is prevented from making incomplete or defective viral RNAs.

When the Qβ virus infects *E. coli*, its single (+) strand of RNA is transcribed and translated to yield the replicase, which replicates the infecting (+) strand to yield

Qβ (−) strands, and thus forms a (+ −) duplex. Free Qβ (−) strands are then generated from this duplex and form the template for synthesis of many Qβ (+) strands. Spiegelman and his colleagues have analyzed the various steps in this process utilizing highly purified RNA replicase preparations, which always replicate in the 5′ → 3′ direction. They have also shown that the newly synthesized RNA is complementary in base composition and identical in size to the viral RNA template. Moreover, they have succeeded in demonstrating the synthesis of new, biologically active Qβ RNA molecules by the enzyme. Starting with the Qβ RNA as template, they allowed the replicase to make large amounts of new RNA, whose infectiousness was equal to that of the template. The new RNA was recovered and used as template in another incubation, again yielding complementary Qβ RNA as product. This cycle was repeated some 15 times until the original natural template Qβ RNA was diluted to a negligible amount. At each stage the infectiousness of the RNA increased in exact proportion to the new RNA formed by the enzyme, demonstrating its biological activity. Actually, these experiments represented the first successful synthesis of a biologically active nucleic acid carried out with a highly purified enzyme.

Polynucleotide Phosphorylase

This enzyme, discovered by Grunberg-Manago and Ochoa in 1955, is apparently found only in bacteria. It catalyzes the reaction

$$\begin{matrix} n_1\text{ADP} \\ n_2\text{GDP} \\ n_3\text{CDP} \\ n_4\text{UDP} \end{matrix} \xrightleftharpoons[]{\text{RNA primer, Mg}^{2+}} \text{RNA}-\left[\begin{matrix} \text{AMP} \\ | \\ \text{GMP} \\ | \\ \text{CMP} \\ | \\ \text{UMP} \end{matrix}\right]_{n_1+n_2+n_3+n_4} + (n_1 + n_2 + n_3 + n_4)\text{P}_i$$

Polynucleotide phosphorylase requires the 5′-diphosphates of ribonucleosides, for it does not react on the homologous 5′-triphosphates or on deoxyribonucleoside 5′-diphosphates. Mg^{2+} is required for its action. The RNA-like polymer it forms contains 3′,5′-phosphodiester linkages, which can be attacked by ribonuclease. The reaction is reversible and can be pushed in the direction of breakdown of the polyribonucleotide by increasing the phosphate concentration.

The polynucleotide phosphorylase reaction does not utilize a template and therefore does not form a polymer having a specific base sequence. It does require a priming strand of RNA, which merely furnishes a free 3′-hydroxyl terminus to which additional residues may be added. The reaction proceeds as well with one species of monomer as with all four. In general, the base composition of the polymer reflects the relative concentrations of the 5′-diphosphate precursors in the medium.

It is thus extremely unlikely that polynucleotide phosphorylase normally functions to make RNA in the intact cell. Since at intracellular phosphate concentrations the reaction proceeds in the direction of breakdown of the polyribonucleotide, it appears that the probable biological function of the enzyme is to cause phosphorolytic breakdown of mRNA, which is known to have a short half-life in bacteria. Phosphorolysis can salvage the high-energy phosphate bonds of the internucleotide 3′,5′-phosphodiester linkages of mRNA as the high-energy phosphate bonds of ribonucleoside 5′-diphosphates, whereas hydrolysis by ribonuclease would cause complete loss of the high-energy bonds.

Although the synthetic activity of polynucleotide phosphorylase is probably not utilized in the cell, the enzyme has great historical significance. It was not only the first polynucleotide-synthesizing enzyme to be discovered, opening the way to the recognition of the DNA and RNA polymerase reactions, but it also made possible the synthesis of polymers of known base ratios, whose use as synthetic mRNAs played a very important role in the experimental identification of the nucleotide triplets coding for specific amino acids (see Chapter 31).

Laboratory Synthesis of Polydeoxyribonucleotides and Genes

Interesting attempts are now under way to deduce the base sequence of certain genes and to synthesize them by the techniques of organic chemistry. The direct analysis of base sequence in DNA presents some formidable difficulties, since only a relatively few small DNA molecules have been isolated in pure homogeneous form from viruses, and even the smaller among them, such as the DNA of phage ϕX174, have a very much larger number of repeating residues than those proteins whose amino acid sequence has been established. Only relatively short DNA fragments can be "sequenced" by use of chemical, enzymatic, and chromatographic procedures (Chapter 12).

On the other hand, it is now possible to deduce the base sequences in certain genes, particularly those specifying RNAs of known sequence, because the bases of the gene and those of the RNA it codes are complementary. The sequence of bases in the gene coding for yeast alanine tRNA, whose base sequence is known, has been proposed by Khorana and his colleagues. It is based on the assumption that the odd or minor bases present in tRNA are formed from the corresponding parent bases by enzymatic reactions occurring *after* the tRNA backbone is formed. Yeast alanine tRNA has 75 ribonucleotide residues; its gene therefore has the same number of dexoyribonucleotide residues.

Khorana and his colleagues are attempting to synthesize the gene for yeast alanine tRNA by a combination of chemical and enzymatic procedures. They have perfected chemical methods of synthesizing short stretches of oligodeoxyribonucleotides of known composition and sequence, starting from nucleosides or nucleotides. Basic to this approach is the use of protecting or blocking reagents for those functional groups in nucleosides and nucleotides that are sensitive to the condensing agents

Protection of the amino group of cytidylic acid by the benzoyl group, the 3′-hydroxyl group by an acetyl group, and the 5′-hydroxyl group by a trityl group. The protecting groups are in color.

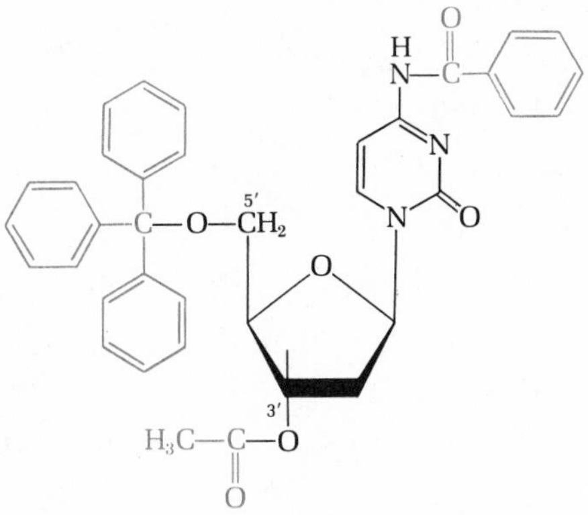

Dicyclohexyl-carbodiimide

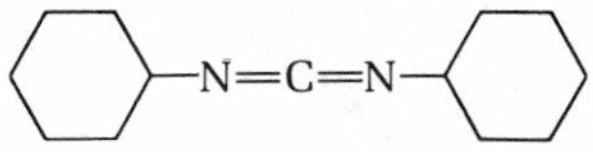

required to form phosphodiester bridges, such as the 3′- and 5′-hydroxyl groups of the deoxyribose moiety, the amino groups of the bases, and the phosphate group itself. The problem is thus very similar to that faced in chemical synthesis of polypeptide chains (Chapter 5). Some of the protecting groups developed by Khorana are shown in the margin. After the appropriate groups are blocked, the phosphodiester internucleotide linkage is formed by condensing the free 3′-hydroxyl group of one mononucleotide with the free 5′-phosphate group of the next. The condensing agent usually employed is a carbodiimide derivative, such as dicyclohexylcarbodiimide, which is also used in peptide-bond synthesis (margin). Usually short sequences of 4 or 5 residues are first built separately. They are then assembled to make longer chains. By such methods a polydeoxyribonucleotide chain having 20 bases in known sequence has been assembled from short blocks (Figure 29-17). This chain corresponds to residues 21 to 40 of the gene coding for yeast alanine tRNA. By joining several long chemically synthesized polydeoxyribonucleotide chains in the correct sequence by means of the DNA ligase reaction, Khorana and his colleagues hope to achieve the total synthesis of this gene.

Meanwhile, chemically synthesized oligodeoxyribonucleotides of known base sequence have been found to be exceedingly valuable as templates for the enzymatic preparation of messenger RNAs of known sequence, which have been used in deducing the nucleotide sequences of the genetic code-words (Chapter 31).

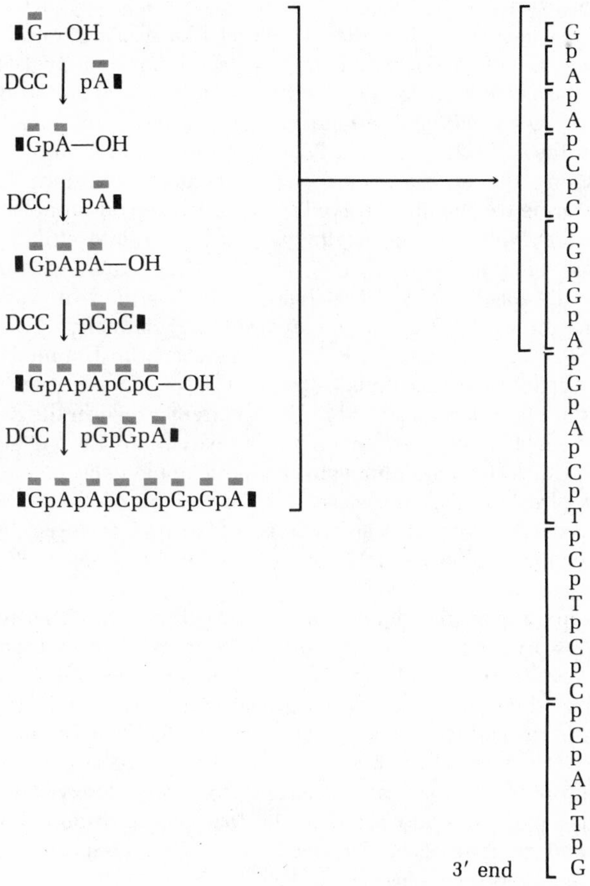

G—OH
DCC ↓ pA
GpA—OH
DCC ↓ pA
GpApA—OH
DCC ↓ pCpC
GpApApCpC—OH
DCC ↓ pGpGpA
GpApApCpCpGpGpA

G p A p A p C p C p G p G p A p G p A p C p T p C p T p C p C p C p A p T p G
3′ end

Figure 29-17
Chemical synthesis of an oligodeoxyribonucleotide chain of 20 residues, a segment of the gene coding for yeast alanine tRNA. The red bars are blocking groups for protection of bases; the black bars, for protection of 5′- or 3′-hydroxyl groups. Mononucleotide or oligonucleotide residues are added by the action of the condensing agent dicyclohexylcarbodiimide (DCC). At the right is shown the complete scheme for chemical synthesis of the 20-unit chain; the size of the added oligonucleotide blocks is shown by brackets. At the end of the synthesis the protecting groups are removed.

Summary

That double-stranded DNA undergoes semiconservative replication in intact procaryotic cells, as postulated by Watson and Crick, was proved by Meselson and Stahl by application of buoyant-density measurements of normal and ^{15}N-labeled DNA duplexes. Both strands of the parental DNA in ^{15}N-labeled *E. coli* cells were replicated to form two hybrid daughter DNA duplexes, in which one strand was labeled with ^{15}N. Bacterial DNA remains circular during replication. There is ordinarily but a single growing point during replication and both chains are replicated simultaneously.

DNA polymerase of *E. coli* catalyzes synthesis of DNA polymers from the four deoxyribonucleoside 5′-triphosphates in the presence of Mg^{2+}, with elimination of pyrophosphate. The reaction requires the presence of some preexisting single-strand DNA as template; the chain growth is in the 5′ → 3′ direction. Intact double-stranded DNA does not prime the reaction unless it has nicks. DNA polymerase has specific binding sites for the template, for the 3′ terminus of the growing chain, and for the incoming deoxyribonucleoside 5′-triphosphate. The enzyme replicates a strand of DNA complementary to the single-stranded template, as shown by analysis of base composition. Furthermore, nearest-neighbor base-frequency analysis proves not only that the newly synthesized strand is complementary in sequence but also that its polarity is opposite to that of the template strand.

Another enzyme, DNA ligase, can join the ends of two DNA chains, or join the ends of a single chain to make a circular DNA, providing their ends are duplexed to a complementary strand. Kornberg and his colleagues have achieved the total enzymatic synthesis of the biologically active circular DNA of the ϕX174 *E. coli* virus by the sequential action of the DNA polymerase and DNA ligase.

Short segments of DNA, discovered by Okazaki, are found in dividing *E. coli* cells. These fragments are formed by DNA polymerase acting on double-stranded DNA in which one strand is nicked. DNA polymerase replicates both strands, but operates only in the 5′ → 3′ direction. first along the intact strand, and then along the nicked strand in the reverse direction. The newly formed segment is cleaved at the fork by an endonuclease and the polymerase returns to the intact template strand to replicate another section. The resulting fragments are then "stitched" together by DNA ligase. Single-strand nicks or thymine dimers in DNA can be repaired enzymatically.

RNAs are synthesized by RNA polymerase from ribonucleoside 5′-triphosphates; double-stranded DNA is required as template, but only one strand of DNA is transcribed in the cell. The template choice mechanism is unknown. Many RNA chains may be transcribed simultaneously from a single gene.

RNA-directed RNA replicases are formed by cells infected by RNA viruses; the replicases will accept as primer only intact homologous viral RNA. DNA is not an intermediate in RNA replicase action.

Polynucleotide phosphorylase can reversibly form RNA-like polymers by elimination of phosphate from ribonucleoside 5′-diphosphates; it adds or removes mononucleotides at the 3′-hydroxyl end of the primer. It probably functions to degrade mRNA in the cell in such a manner as to salvage its high-energy bonds in the form of ribonucleoside 5′-diphosphates.

By appropriate chemical procedures, long oligodeoxyribonucleotides may be synthesized in the laboratory. Attempts are underway to synthesize the gene for a tRNA containing 75 mononucleotide residues.

References

See also references in Chapter 28

Books

Cold Spring Harbor Symposia in Quantitative Biology, Replication of DNA in Micro-organisms. Vol. 33, 1968. A collection of valuable articles on all aspects of DNA biosynthesis.

INGRAM, V. M.: *The Biosynthesis of Macromolecules,* W. A. Benjamin, New York, 1965. A primer.

KORNBERG, A.: *Enzymatic Synthesis of DNA,* John Wiley & Sons, New York, 1961. A personal account of earlier work.

ZUBAY, G. (ed.): *Papers in Biochemical Genetics,* Holt, Rinehart and Winston, Inc., New York, 1968.

Articles

CAIRNS, J.: "The Chromosome of *E. coli,*" *Cold Spring Harbor Symposia in Quant. Biol.,* **28:**43 (1963). Radioautographic studies on the rate and pattern of DNA replication.

GELLERT, M. B.: "Formation of Covalent Circles of Lambda DNA by *E. coli* Extracts," *Proc. Natl. Acad. Sci. (U.S.),* **57:**148–155 (1967). Evidence for the "joining" enzyme.

GOULIAN, M., A. KORNBERG, and R. L. SINSHEIMER: "Enzymatic Synthesis of DNA. XXIV. Synthesis of Infectious Phage ϕX174 DNA," *Proc. Natl. Acad. Sci. (U.S.),* **58:**2321 (1967). Total synthesis of infectious phage DNA with highly purified enzymes.

JOSSE, J., A. D. KAISER, and A. KORNBERG: "Enzymatic Synthesis of Deoxyribonucleic Acid. VIII. Frequencies of Nearest Neighbor Base Sequences in Deoxyribonucleic Acid," *J. Biol. Chem.,* **236:**864 (1961).

KORNBERG, A.: "Active Center of DNA Polymerase," *Science,* **163:**1410–1418 (1969). An important article describing the substrate and template binding specificity as well as the role of DNA ligase and endonuclease in replication of both strands of DNA.

MESELSON, M., and F. W. STAHL: "The Replication of DNA in *E. coli,*" *Proc. Natl. Acad. Sci. (U.S.),* **44:**671 (1958). A classical paper in molecular genetics, demonstrating the semiconservative replication of DNA *in vivo.*

MILLER, O. M., JR., and B. R. BEATTY: "Visualization of Nucleolar Genes," *Science,* **164:**955–957 (1969).

SPIEGELMAN, S., N. R. PACE, D. R. MILLS, R. LEVISOHN, T. S. EIKHOM, M. M. TAYLOR, R. L. PETERSON and D. H. L. BISHOP: "The Mechanism of RNA Replication," *Cold Spring Harbor Symposia in Quant. Biol.,* **33:**101–124 (1968).

THOMAS, C. A., JR.: "The Recombination of DNA Molecules," in G. C. Quarton, T. Melnechuk, and F. O. Schmitt (eds.), *The Neurosciences, A Study Program,* p. 162, Rockefeller University Press, 1967. Geometrical and conformational problems in recombination of DNA segments.

WEISS, B., and C. C. RICHARDSON: "Repair of Single Strand Breaks in DNA by an Enzyme System from *E. coli* Infected with T4 Bacteriophage," *Proc. Natl. Acad. Sci. (U.S.),* **57:**1021–1028 (1967).

WEISS, S. B.: "Enzymatic Incorporation of Ribonucleoside Triphosphates into The Internucleotide Linkages of RNA," *Proc. Natl. Acad. Sci. (U.S.),* **46:**1020 (1960).

Problems

1. Calculate how long it takes for the gene for ribonuclease (104 residues) to be synthesized during cell division in *E. coli*. Use data from the Cairns experiment.

2. If eucaryotic DNA is replicated by a single growing point at the same rate as DNA in *E. coli* cells, i.e., 27 μ min^{-1}, calculate the time required for the replication of all the DNA in a single human cell. Is it likely that DNA in eucaryotic cells is replicated by a single growing point? How many growing points would be required in a fast-growing human cell with a division time of 6 hr?

3. Pure *E. coli* DNA polymerase can catalyze the addition of 1,000 nucleotide residues per minute per molecule of enzyme *in vitro*. If there is but a single growing point in the replication of an *E. coli* chromosome, calculate the time required to replicate the entire chromosome by the purified polymerase and compare this with the time found by Cairns. Can you account for the discrepancy?

4. What is the base composition of a DNA strand synthesized by DNA polymerase on a template of single-stranded circular ϕX174 DNA, having the base composition G 24.1%, C 18.5%, A 24.6%, T 32.8%?

5. Indicate the base composition of DNA synthesized by DNA polymerase on templates provided by a mixture of (+) and (−) single-stranded circular ϕX174 DNAs.

6. A single (+) strand of DNA (base composition A 21%, G 29%, C 29%, T 21%) is replicated by DNA polymerase to yield a complementary (−) strand. The resulting duplex DNA is then used as a template by RNA polymerase, which transcribes the (−) strand. Indicate the base composition of the RNA formed.

7. If the *E. coli* chromosome is replicated at the rate of 27 μ min^{-1}, calculate the rate at which high-energy phosphate bonds of ATP are consumed in this process, if it begins with ATP and a mixture of 2-deoxyribonucleoside 5′-monophosphates.

8. How would you determine whether a short segment of double-helical DNA has parallel or antiparallel chains? The base sequence of one strand in the 5′ → 3′ direction is pApTpCpGpGpTpCpApApCpCpTpGpTpApGpG.

CHAPTER 30 RIBOSOMES AND PROTEIN SYNTHESIS

We come now to consider the third major question posed by the genetic continuity of living organisms. How is the genetic information contained in the nucleotide sequence of messenger RNA translated so that amino acids are assembled to form a polypeptide chain having a specific amino acid sequence?

In this chapter we shall deal with the enzymatic mechanisms by which the polypeptide chain is built and how ribosomes function to assure the proper transfer of information from messenger RNA. In the following chapters, we will consider other elements of the translation process, namely, the identification of the coding triplets for the amino acids, the regulation of protein synthesis, and the specification of three-dimensional structure from one-dimensional information.

The enzymatic mechanisms by which the peptide bonds of protein molecules are formed have long attracted the attention of biochemists. Before the modern era of research in this field began, in the early 1950's, little concrete information was available. One early view was that peptidases and proteolytic enzymes, which have considerable substrate specificity, may also participate in protein synthesis by simple reversal of their hydrolytic activity. However, as the central role of ATP in biosynthetic reactions emerged, as well as the concept that biosynthetic and catabolic reactions have different pathways, reversal of hydrolytic activity seemed an unlikely mechanism. Moreover, informative studies on model or prototype reactions, such as the enzymatic synthesis of the amide linkage of glutamine and the peptide linkages of glutathione, strongly suggested that ATP must play a role in peptide bond synthesis. In this early period, similarly, little information was available on the manner in which amino acids are assembled. For example, one early view suggested that short peptides are built first and then assembled to form polypeptide chains. It was not until the isotope tracer technique was applied that the first significant progress was made in the study of protein synthesis.

Early studies with this method, which were carried out largely on intact animals or intact cells, revealed that protein synthesis requires a source of metabolic energy, that amino acids and not simple peptides are the most immediate precursors of proteins, and that the liver of vertebrates is especially active in protein synthesis. It was also revealed that tissue proteins undergo metabolic turnover. Liver proteins were found to have a half-life of about 9 days and muscle proteins about 120 days.

The modern era of research on protein synthesis began with the important investigations of Zamecnik and his colleagues from 1950 onwards, which made it possible to study protein synthesis in cell-free systems and which led to the identification of the ribosomes as the site of protein synthesis, the discovery of tRNA, and the delineation of the major stages in protein synthesis.

Ribosomes as the Site of Protein Synthesis

Zamecnik and his colleagues injected radioactive amino acids into rats. At different time intervals after the injection the liver was removed, homogenized, and fractionated by differential centrifugation (Chapter 13). The various intracellular fractions so collected were examined for the presence of the labeled amino acid incorporated into peptide linkage. When long periods, i.e. hours or days, were allowed to elapse before removal and fractionation of the liver, then all the intracellular fractions contained labeled protein. However, if the liver was fractionated very shortly after the injection of labeled amino acid, only the microsome fraction contained labeled protein. It was therefore postulated that proteins are first synthesized in those intracellular structures from which the microsomes are derived and that newly synthesized proteins are then transferred from these structures to the other cell components. They soon found that incubation of freshly prepared cell-free homogenates of rat liver with labeled amino acids also resulted in incorporation of radioactivity into microsomal proteins, if the homogenates were supplemented with ATP and respiratory substrates. For the first time it was demonstrated that intact cell structure is not required for protein synthesis.

Liver homogenates were then fractionated into the nuclear, mitochondrial, microsomal, and soluble fractions; and various combinations of these were tested for their capacity to bring about incorporation of labeled amino acids into protein. A combination of two fractions is necessary for amino acid incorporation: the microsome and the soluble fractions. The microsome fraction serves as the recipient of the newly incorporated amino acids, whereas the soluble fraction appeared to furnish essential cofactors. Mitochondria are required in such reconstruction experiments only insofar as they supply energy in the form of ATP.

When the labeled microsome fraction was further subfractionated by centrifugal methods, the incorporated radioactivity was largely recovered in the form of small ribonucleoprotein particles. Such particles had earlier been found in the cytoplasm by Claude and observed on the surface of the endoplasmic reticulum by Palade, but their function was then unknown. They sediment with vesicular fragments of the endoplasmic reticulum to which they are attached. These ribonucleoprotein particles, which were later named *ribosomes* by Roberts (Chapter 12), can be detached from the endoplasmic reticulum by treatment with a neutral solution of a bile salt, such as sodium deoxycholate. The ribosomes can then be separated by differential centrifugation. Ribosomes purified in this manner incorporate amino acids into peptide linkage on incubation with the soluble fraction of rat liver, together with ATP and Mg^{2+}. Soon other workers found it possible to observe amino acid incorporation into ribosomes from many other cells, particularly from *reticulocytes,* immature red blood cells which are extremely active in synthesis of hemoglobin, and from *E. coli* cells. The latter have the great advantage of being far more active in amino acid incorporation than ribosomes from animal tissues.

Although a mixture of the 20 amino acids is added to ribosomal systems in such experiments, usually only one is labeled. Because the rate of protein synthesis in such reconstituted ribosomal systems is relatively low in comparison with the rate in intact cells, isotopically labeled amino acids are essential for measurement of protein synthesis, which is taken as the amount of radioactivity incorporated into the acid-insoluble protein of the incubation mixture.

Table 30-1 Components required in the four major stages in protein synthesis

Stage	*Components required*
1. Activation of the amino acids	Amino acids tRNAs Aminoacyl-tRNA synthetases ATP Mg^{2+}
2. Initiation of the polypeptide chain	The initiating amino acyl tRNA (fMet-tRNA in bacteria) mRNA GTP Mg^{2+} Initiation factors (F_1, F_2, F_3) 30S ribosomal subunit 50S subunit
3. Elongation	Aminoacyl-tRNAs specified by codons Mg^{2+} Factor T GTP Factor G
4. Termination	Termination codon in mRNA Polypeptide release factor (Factor R).

Essential Cofactors for Protein Synthesis: Stages in Protein Synthesis

Zamecnik and his colleagues found that the soluble fraction of liver furnishes at least two essential factors for protein synthesis, one of which is heat-labile and therefore presumably a protein, and the other heat-stable. The heat-labile soluble factor in liver cytoplasm catalyzes an ATP-dependent activation reaction by which free amino acids are esterified to some heat-stable component present in the soluble fraction. The heat-stable amino acid acceptor is a low-molecular-weight form of RNA, which at first was called "soluble RNA" or sRNA; more recently it has been given the name *transfer RNA* (abbreviated tRNA) to designate its function more accurately. The aminoacyl-tRNA ester so formed in the activation reaction is then bound to the ribosome and there serves as the donor of an aminoacyl residue in the ensuing reactions in which the peptide chain is elongated.

Subsequent research has revealed that the synthesis of polypeptide chains takes place in four major stages and that specific enzymes or cofactors are required to carry out each stage. These are summarized in Table 30-1, which provides some orientation for the more detailed discussion to follow. In the first stage of protein synthesis, which is called the activation step and which takes place in the soluble cytoplasm, amino acids are enzymatically esterified to their corresponding homologous tRNAs, at the expense of ATP energy. In the second stage, an *initiation complex* is formed by the binding of the messenger

RNA and the first or initiating aminoacyl-tRNA to a free 30S ribosomal subunit, to which is then attached the 50S ribosomal subunit. The initiating aminoacyl-tRNA enters as an N-acyl derivative, presumably to ensure that the polypeptide chain is started at the beginning of the genetic message.

In the third stage of protein synthesis, the peptide chain is elongated by sequential addition of new aminoacyl residues transferred from aminoacyl-tRNA esters, each of which is specified by a given codon in the mRNA. Following completion of each new peptide bond, both the mRNA and the peptidyl-tRNA chain are translocated or moved along the ribosome to bring the next codon into position, a process which requires energy provided in the form of GTP. In the last stage of protein synthesis, the polypeptide chain is terminated when appropriate termination signals in the mRNA are reached; the completed chain is then released from the ribosome (Figure 30-1).

We shall now proceed to examine the process of protein synthesis and the nature of the molecular components involved in more detail.

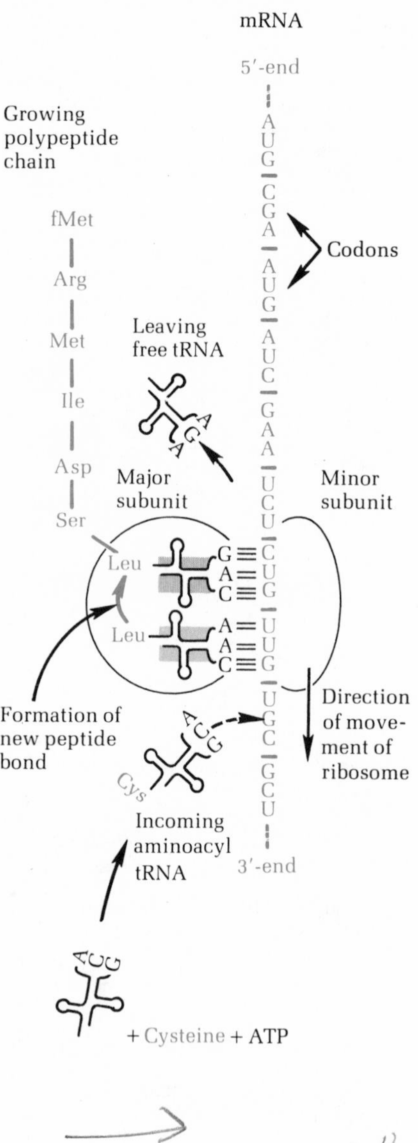

Figure 30-1
Major steps in protein synthesis.

NH₂ - - - — COOH
made in this direction

Direction and Rate of Chain Growth During Polypeptide Synthesis

Although it had long been assumed that the polypeptide chain was elongated during its synthesis by successive addition of single amino acid residues to one end, whether the chain was built starting from the amino-terminal or the carboxyl-terminal residue was an open question. The answer came from experiments of Dintzis and other investigators. Tritium-labeled leucine was added to suspensions of reticulocytes that were actively synthesizing the α and β chains of hemoglobin, which contain many leucine residues. They were incubated at a low temperature (15°) to slow down the rate of protein synthesis. Samples of the reticulocytes were then taken at different time intervals between 4 and 60 min; the labeled hemoglobin formed by them was isolated, and the α and β chains separated and cleaved into peptide fragments with trypsin. The specific radioactivity of the leucine-containing peptides, whose positions in the hemoglobin chains were by then known (Chapter 5), was determined and the results plotted as a function of their position in the chain (Figure 30-2). After 4 min incubation with ^{3}H-leucine, only the leucine-containing peptides from the COOH-terminal ends of the α and β chains were labeled. With longer exposure to ^{3}H-leucine, there was a gradual increase in the number of peptides labeled. This increase was graded; it started from the COOH-terminal end and proceeded toward the NH_2-terminal end with the passage of time. In samples recovered after 60 min incubation with the labeled leucine, all the tryptic peptides were labeled approximately equally. Obviously, the first hemoglobin chains to become labeled at the 4-min interval were nearly completed at the time isotopic leucine was added. Therefore only a few labeled leucine residues could have been added at the end of such chains before they were

Figure 30-2
Addition of labeled leucine residues to the COOH-terminal end of a polypeptide chain. The colored zones indicate the relative radioactivity of leucine residues along the α-chain of hemoglobin following exposure of reticulocytes to ^{3}H-leucine for the periods shown (15°). At 4 minutes only a few leucine residues at the COOH-terminal end were labeled.

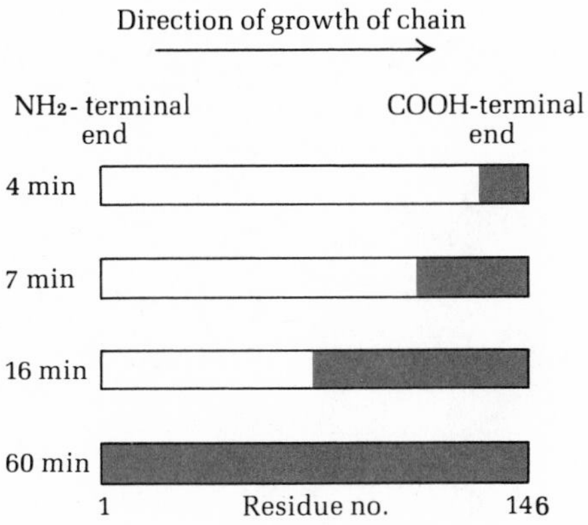

Direction of growth of chain →

NH₂-terminal end — COOH-terminal end

4 min
7 min
16 min
60 min

1 Residue no. 146

completed and discharged from the ribosome. In hemoglobin isolated after somewhat longer incubation, a larger number of leucine residues were labeled; these were also located near the COOH-terminal portion of the chain. In those peptide chains that had just been started when isotopic leucine was added, nearly all the leucine-containing peptides were labeled. Polypeptide chains are therefore constructed beginning with the NH_2-terminal amino acid, whose carboxyl group combines with the amino group of the incoming amino acid to form a peptide bond. Serial addition of new amino acid residues at the free COOH-terminal end of the growing peptide chain continues until the chain is complete. This conclusion has now been amply confirmed by other types of experiments.

A very interesting corollary of these experiments is that they give precise information on the time required to synthesize a complete polypeptide chain. At 37° the rabbit reticulocyte can complete an entire *α* chain of hemoglobin (approximately 150 residues) in about 3 min. In *E. coli* only about 15 to 20 sec is required to complete a chain of similar length, in consonance with the very high growth rate of these cells.

The Amino Acid Activation Reaction and Its Amino Acid Specificity

In the first stage of protein synthesis, the 20 different amino acids commonly found in proteins are activated, i.e., esterified to their corresponding tRNAs by the action of a class of enzymes known as the *aminoacyl-tRNA synthetases,* each of which is specific for one amino acid. This stage occurs in the soluble cytoplasm. The reaction catalyzed is

$$\text{Amino acid} + \text{tRNA} + \text{ATP} \xrightleftharpoons{Mg^{2+}} \text{aminoacyl-tRNA} + \text{AMP} + \text{PP}_i \quad (1)$$

Aminoacyl adenylic acid

$$\text{R—CH(NH}_2\text{)—C(=O)—O—P(=O)(OH)—O—CH}_2\text{—ribose(OH, OH)—Adenine}$$

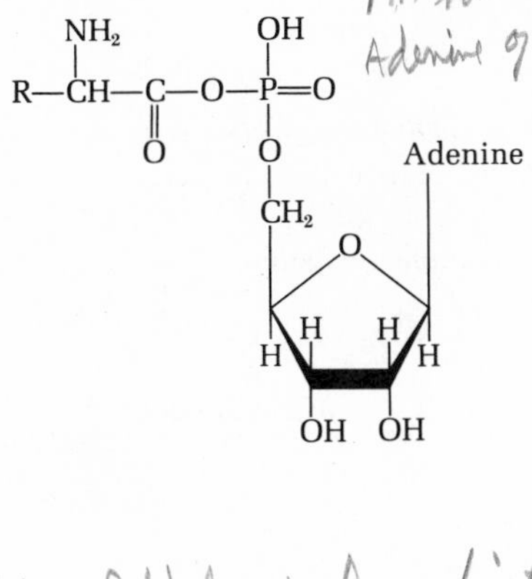

Nearly all of the activating enzymes for the different amino acids have been obtained in highly purified form, particularly from *E. coli* cells. All possess a molecular weight of about 100,000 except that for phenylalanine, which has a molecular weight of 180,000. All have an absolute requirement for Mg^{2+}, and all contain one or more sulfhydryl groups that are essential for activity. In bacterial cells there appears to be one aminoacyl synthetase for each amino acid (see below).

In the activation reaction, pyrophosphate cleavage of ATP takes place to yield AMP and pyrophosphate, as is true for the analogous activation reactions for acetate and fatty acids (Chapter 19). The activation reaction occurs in two separate steps on the enzyme catalytic site. In the first, an enzyme-bound intermediate, *aminoacyl adenylic acid,* is formed by reaction of ATP and the amino acid. The carboxyl group of the amino acid is bound in anhydride linkage with the 5′-phosphate group of the AMP (margin), with displacement of pyrophosphate:

ATP + amino acid ⇌
[aminoacyl adenylic acid] + pyrophosphate (2)

The second step consists of the transfer of the aminoacyl group from AMP to tRNA:

[Aminoacyl adenylic acid] + tRNA ⇌
aminoacyl-tRNA + adenylic acid (3)

The aminoacyl group is transferred to the free 2′- or 3′-hydroxyl group of the terminal AMP residue of that end of the tRNA molecule which bears the pCpCpA sequence (Chapter 12), as is shown in Figure 30-3.

The overall activation reaction has an equilibrium constant of about 1 and therefore proceeds with very little free-energy change. The ester linkage between the amino acid and the tRNA is obviously a high-energy bond, for which the $\Delta G^{\circ\prime}$ of hydrolysis is approximately −7.0 kcal. Since the inorganic pyrophosphate formed in the activation reaction is ultimately hydrolyzed to orthophosphate by pyrophosphatase, two high-energy phosphate bonds are ultimately split for each amino acid molecule activated. The overall reaction for amino acid activation in the cell would thus be essentially irreversible:

$$\text{Amino acid} + \text{tRNA} + \text{ATP} \xrightarrow{Mg^{2+}} \text{aminoacyl-tRNA} + \text{AMP} + 2P_i \qquad \Delta G^{\circ\prime} = -7.0 \text{ kcal}$$

The activation reaction is usually assayed by measuring the rate at which ^{32}P-labeled pyrophosphate is incorporated into added ATP in the first of the two reaction steps [i.e., Reaction (2)] catalyzed by the activating enzyme. This freely reversible exchange reaction requires the presence of the specific amino acid substrate.

The aminoacyl-tRNA synthetases are very highly specific for both the amino acid and the corresponding tRNA. This is a matter of the utmost importance, since once the aminoacyl-tRNA is formed, it is recognized only by the anticodon triplet in its tRNA moiety, and not by the amino acid moiety, as we shall see. Thus the aminoacyl-tRNA synthetases must possess two very specific binding sites, one for the amino acid substrate and the other for the corresponding tRNA; a third site for binding ATP must also exist. The aminoacyl-tRNA synthetases are so specific in discriminating among the naturally occurring amino acids that there is much less than 1 chance in 10,000 of an error under intracellular conditions. However, these enzymes can be fooled into accepting certain nonbiological amino acid analogs instead of their normal substrates. Among these are *p-fluorophenylalanine*, an analog of phenylalanine, and *ethionine* and *norleucine*, analogs of methionine (margin). When these analogs are fed to animals, they are actually incorporated into proteins in small amounts. Some aminoacyl-tRNA synthetases may be inhibited by analogs of their normal amino acid substrates; thus 5-methyltryptophan inhibits the activation of tryptophan by its specific aminoacyl-tRNA synthetase.

Amino acid analogs that are incorporated into peptide chains.

p-Fluorophenylalanine

F–C_6H_4–$CH_2CH(NH_2)COOH$

Ethionine

$CH_3CH_2SCH_2CH_2CH(NH_2)COOH$

Norleucine

$CH_3CH_2CH_2CH_2CH(NH_2)COOH$

Figure 30-3
Structure of tRNA.

The common features in the structure of tRNA's (in color). Some tRNA's, such as those for serine, have an extra arm of varying length. Maximal intrachain H-bonding yields the cloverleaf structure shown. X-ray evidence suggests, however, that the lateral arms are folded closely alongside the vertical arms. The anticodon is always demarcated by the neighboring bases shown. The symbols are ψ, pseudouridine; Py, pyrimidine; Pu, purine; Me, methyl; DiMe, dimethyl; DHU, dihydro-uridine.

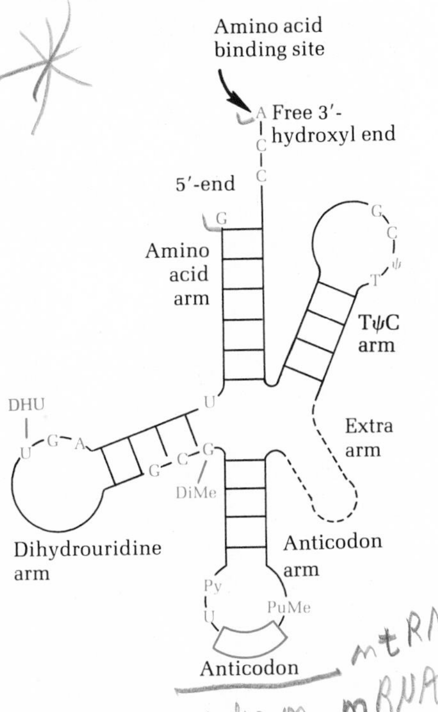

The 3-dimensional conformation of tRNA drawn from a model.

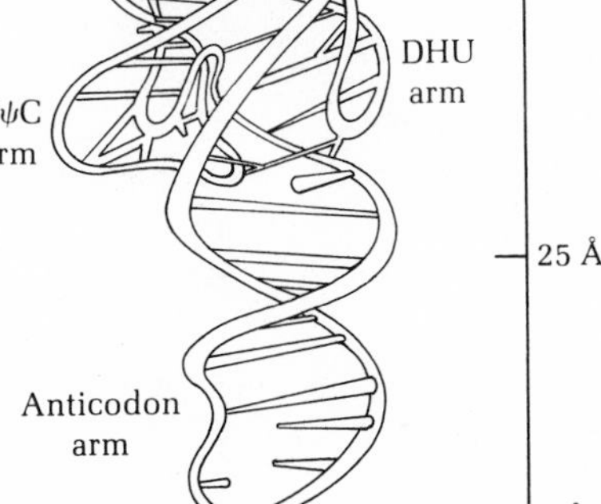

Structure of tRNAs and the Specificity of the Activating Enzymes

The specificity of the aminoacyl-tRNA synthetases for their corresponding tRNAs is a rather complex and interesting matter, which first requires review of the covalent structure and the mononucleotide components of tRNA molecules (see Chapter 12). Since the base sequences of a number of tRNA molecules are now known, important information is available on their conformation, their specificity, and the function of different parts of their structures.

There is now substantial evidence that tRNA molecules possess a specific 3-dimensional conformation. They show a substantial hyperchromic effect at 260 nm when heated, suggesting that many of their bases are paired, presumably by looping of the single-stranded tRNA chain. After tRNAs are melted by heating, they quickly resume their native configuration on cooling. Moreover, it has been demonstrated that the native conformation of tRNA molecules is essential for their biological activity; unfolded tRNA is not capable of acting as an amino acid acceptor. From the base sequences of tRNAs it has been possible to construct a number of spatial conformations which allow intrachain base pairing. The surprising finding has been made that, although the tRNAs for different amino acids have quite different base sequences, all tRNAs of known base sequence are potentially capable of existing in the same cloverleaf conformation (Chapter 12) if the chains are arranged in such a way as to yield maximal intrachain base-pairing (Figure 30-3). Some tRNAs, those with longer chains, are capable of forming a short fifth arm. Recently, several tRNAs have been obtained in crystalline form; it therefore appears probable that their precise 3-dimensional structures will very soon be deduced by x-ray diffraction methods.

From base-sequence data, some other biologically important structural features of tRNAs have been identified. All tRNA molecules have the same terminal sequence pCpCpA at one end. The last residue, adenylic acid, is the site to which the aminoacyl group is esterified at either the 2' or 3' position by action of the aminoacyl synthetases (Figure 30-3). Base-sequence studies have also revealed the presence of one base triplet in the polynucleotide chain that is different in all tRNAs examined; it is thought to represent the *anticodon* of the tRNA, namely, the specific nucleotide triplet complementary to the codon triplets in mRNA. Presumably the anticodon triplet of the aminoacyl-tRNA has the proper base sequence to form specific hydrogen bonds with the corresponding codon of the mRNA, in order to position the amino acid correctly for transfer to the growing polypeptide chain.

In addition to the anticodon site, tRNA molecules must contain at least one other specific binding site, the enzyme recognition site, at which it is bound to the corresponding activating enzyme. This site is not only highly specific for the "right" activating enzyme but also significantly specific for species; an aminoacyl synthetase for any given amino acid works best with the corresponding tRNA from the same species. Presumably there is a species variation in the base sequence of the tRNA molecule at the point (as yet unknown) at which it binds to the synthetase and a corresponding species variation in the amino acid sequence at the tRNA binding site of the enzyme.

A striking feature of the molecular structure of tRNA's is the presence of many minor bases (Chapter 12) in addition to the normal bases A, U, G, and C. Over 30 different minor bases have been discovered in tRNAs, most of which are methylated forms of the normal bases. An enzyme has been discovered which catalyzes the methylation of the bases in intact tRNA and other types of RNA; it requires S-adenosyl methionine (Chapter 25) as methyl donor. Sulfur-containing bases, such as *thiouridine*, have also been found in some tRNAs. It may be the function of some of these bases to prevent base-pairing by disallowing hydrogen-bonding, to yield specific three-dimensional configurations other than an intrachain double helix. The minor bases may also render tRNA less susceptible to the hydrolytic attack of nucleases.

A most curious discovery is that isopentenyl derivatives of purine are present in some plant tRNAs. One of these, 6-amino-3-(3-methyl-2-butenyl) purine, called *triacanthine* (margin) possesses biological activity as a *cytokinin*, a type of hormone that promotes the separation of daughter cells after mitotic division of a parent cell.

Triacanthine

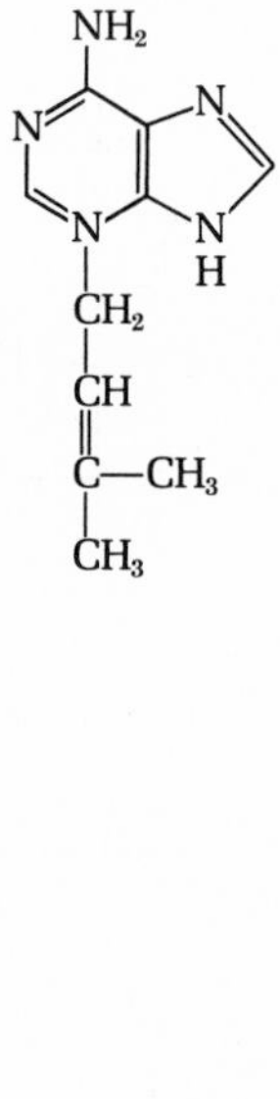

NH_2 / N / N / N / N H / CH_2 / CH / C—CH_3 / CH_3

The problem of tRNA specificity has been made more complicated by the discovery that there is more than one specific tRNA for each amino acid. Yeast cells contain 5 different tRNAs that react specifically with leucine and the leucine activating enzyme, five for serine, four for glycine, and four for lysine. However, a given aminoacyl-tRNA synthetase is not equally reactive with all of the homologous tRNAs. There appear to be two factors accounting for this multiplicity of homologous tRNAs. One is that the tRNAs for a given amino acid may differ in intracellular location. *Neurospora crassa* cells have been found to contain at least 2 species of tRNA for many amino acids. One species is present only in the mitochondria and the other(s) only in the cytoplasm, suggesting that cytoplasmic and mitochondrial protein synthesis occur by different types of tRNA. Furthermore, in *Neurospora* there are two different activating enzymes for some amino acids, one in the mitochondria and one in the cytoplasm. The mitochondrial enzyme is specific for the mitochondrial form of tRNA and the cytoplasmic enzyme is specific for the cytoplasmic tRNA. It has also been found that the leucine residues that are incorporated into different specific positions of hemoglobin chains are apparently carried by different species of leucine tRNA.

The Adapter Role of tRNA

Once an amino acid is esterified to its corresponding tRNA, it makes no contribution to the specificity of the aminoacyl-tRNA, since the aminoacyl group as such is not recognized by either the ribosome or the mRNA template. This was conclusively proved in clever experiments by von Ehrenstein and other investigators. Isotopically labeled cysteinyl-$tRNA_{Cys}$ was first formed by the action of the cysteine-activating enzyme from *E. coli*. It was then chemically converted to alanyl-$tRNA_{Cys}$ by reducing the cysteinyl moiety with hydrogen and a catalyst, a procedure which does not cause any chemical change in the tRNA molecule itself. This "hybrid" aminoacyl-tRNA, which contains the anticodon for cysteine but actually carries alanine, was then incubated with a ribosomal system from reticulocytes containing all the other tRNAs, amino acids, and activating enzymes. Protein synthesis was then allowed to take place. The newly synthesized polypeptide chains were then examined to determine whether the hybrid alanyl-$tRNA_{Cys}$ would transfer its anomalous alanine residue into those positions of the hemoglobin chain normally coded for cysteine. The answer was positive: labeled alanine was incorporated into the cysteine positions in significantly large amounts.

This experiment provided proof for the hypothesis, first postulated by Crick in 1958, that tRNA is a molecular "adapter," into which the amino acid is plugged so that it can be adapted to the nucleotide triplet language of the genetic code. This experiment also proved that the activating enzymes must have extremely high specificity for both their amino acids and tRNAs, because any errors arising during the activation reaction cannot be corrected during the formation of the polypeptide chain.

After completion of the amino acid activation reaction, the charged tRNA, symbolized as in the example Ala-$tRNA_{Ala}$, is ready for the next stage in protein synthesis on the surface of the ribosome.

Ribosomal Structure

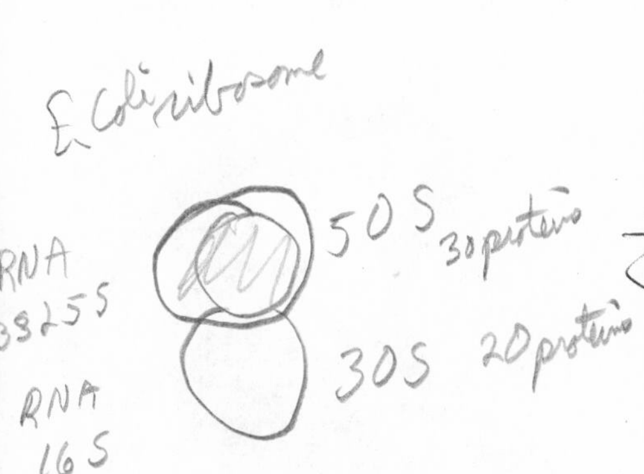

Before considering the details of the ribosomal stage of protein synthesis, the structure of ribosomes requires review (see Chapter 12), since the conformation and the surface arrangement of various specific binding sites on ribosomes must evidently be highly ordered. The 70S ribosomes found in bacteria have been most thoroughly studied. Under special conditions they dissociate into 50S and 30S subunits, each of which contains RNA and a number of proteins. The 50S subunit contains two RNA components, namely 23S and 5S RNA, as well as about 30 different proteins. The 30S subunit contains a molecule of 16S ribosomal RNA and 20 different proteins. The ribosomal proteins are insoluble in water at pH 7.0 under normal conditions, but can be extracted in soluble form with a solution of 8 *M* urea and 4 *M* LiCl; in this condition they are unfolded. The 20 different proteins of 30S subunits can be separated by polyacrylamide gel electrophoresis at pH 4.5. Mild extraction of the 30S subunit with concentrated CsCl solution yields a smaller number of dissolved proteins and a stable inner core, from which additional proteins can be extracted only by more drastic procedures; the core can be recovered as a 23S particle.

The ribosomes in the cytoplasm of eucaryotes are much larger than those of procaryotes; they have a sedimentation coefficient of 80S, a diameter of about 220 Å, and a molecular weight of about 4.0 million. Their subunits, which are not easily separated, have sedimentation coefficients of about 60S and 40S. However, the size of the subunits varies somewhat between plants and animals, as does the size of the ribosomal RNA. Plant ribosomes contain 25S and 16S or 18S rRNA and animal ribosomes 28S and 18S rRNA. The 28S rRNA of animal ribosomes varies somewhat in size in different species, depending on the time of evolutionary development, and ranges from molecular weight 1.4 million in sea urchins to 1.75 million in mammals.

Although some of the proteins of ribosomes must have a catalytic function, the function of ribosomal RNA is still not clear. It appears very likely that the rRNA and the different types of proteins clustered to form the 30S and 50S subunits of 70S ribosomes participate in conformational changes during protein synthesis, during which both the new polypeptide chain and the mRNA must be translocated along the ribosome. Ribosomes thus may be mechanochemical systems, to be considered in the same class of biostructures as the actomyosin of muscle and the microtubules of eucaryotic flagella. (Chapter 26).

The Initiating Amino Acid

For some time it has been thought that the codon for the first or NH_2-terminal amino acid residue of a polypeptide chain must have some distinctive characteristic enabling the ribosome to recognize it as the starting point for the growth of a polypeptide chain. It is now clear that in *E. coli* and other bacteria the synthesis of most, if not all, of their proteins begins with the amino acid methionine. The initiating methionine residue does not enter as methionyl tRNA but rather as *N*-formylmethionyl-tRNA (symbolized as fMet-tRNA) (margin), the product of an enzymatic transformylation in which a formyl group is transferred from N^{10}-formyltetrahydrofolate (Chapters 25 and 26) to methionyl-tRNA. There are two species of methionyl-$tRNA_{Met}$; that species capable of accepting the N-formyl group is designated methionyl-$tRNA_F$:

N-Formylmethionine

```
            H
            |
            C=O
            |
            NH
            |
CH3SCH2CH2CHCOOH
```

$$N^{10}\text{-formyltetrahydrofolate} + \text{Met-tRNA}_F \rightarrow \text{tetrahydrofolate} + \text{fMet-tRNA}_F$$

The enzyme catalyzing this reaction does not formylate free methionine or methionine attached to a second species of $tRNA_{Met}$ called $tRNA_M$. It now appears likely that fMet-$tRNA_F$ initiates peptide-chain synthesis not only in bacteria, but also in the mitochondria of eucaryotic cells (see below). Although the initiating residue in cytoplasmic protein synthesis in eucaryotic cells has not yet been identified, it does not appear to be fMet. Purified fMet-tRNA has been obtained in crystalline form (margin).

Crystals of N-formylmethionyl tRNA

The blocking of the amino group of methionine by the N-formyl group not only prevents the amino group from entering into a peptide linkage but also appears to allow fMet-tRNA$_F$ to be bound at the peptidyl site, which does not accept free Met-tRNA or any other free aminoacyl-tRNAs. The synthesis of all proteins of *E. coli* is believed to begin with the amino-terminal sequence *N*-formylmethionylalanylserine. The *N*-formyl group does not, however, appear in the finished protein; it is first removed by enzymatic cleavage. Moreover, one, two, or all three of the first three amino acids of *E. coli* proteins may be removed by successive cleavages, to yield the finished protein.

We have seen that some proteins are acetylated on the amino-terminal α-amino group, such as the coat protein of the tobacco mosaic virus. Since such acetyl groups are introduced *after* protein synthesis is complete, they are not directly related to chain initiation or elongation.

Figure 30-4
Formation of initiation complex and 70S ribosome, ready for chain elongation.

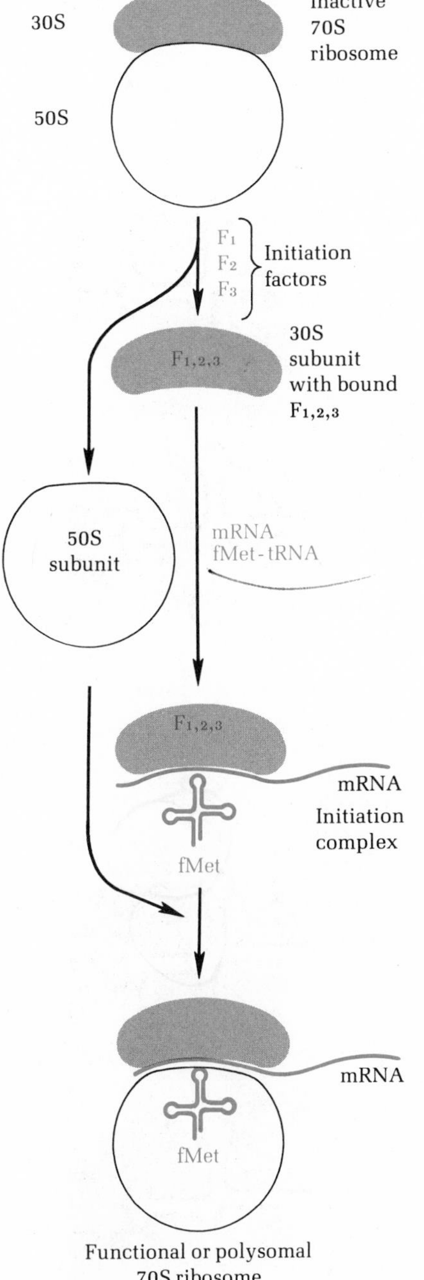

Initiation of Polypeptide Chains

Although it has long been appreciated that the ribosome must bind (1) the mRNA template, (2) the peptide chain being formed, and (3) the entering aminoacyl-tRNA molecules, only recently have the sequence and mechanism of these interactions been established, with the use of natural mRNAs and the natural initiating aminoacyl-tRNA.

Central to these developments is the discovery that during protein synthesis in *E. coli* cells there is continuous dissociation of 70S ribosomes into their 50S and 30S subunits and continuous reassociation of the subunits to form 70S ribosomes. This was shown in clever experiments by Kaempfer and associates, who grew *E. coli* cells for several generations in a medium in which the carbon, nitrogen and hydrogen sources were highly enriched with the heavy isotopes ^{13}C, ^{15}N, and ^{2}H. The ribosomes synthesized by these "heavy" cells have a greater density than ribosomes in cells grown on normal sources of carbon, hydrogen, and nitrogen. Such heavy ribosomes can be distinguished from normal or light ribosomes by density gradient centrifugation (Chapter 7). But when heavy *E. coli* cells were placed in a fresh medium containing normal or light sources of carbon, hydrogen, and nitrogen and then allowed to grow further, their ribosomes included two species of hybrids. One species contained a heavy 50S and a light 30S subunit, and the other a light 50S and a heavy 30S subunit. It was concluded that 70S ribosomes constantly undergo dissociation into subunits and that the subunits constantly reassociate, evidently at random. It was postulated that the 70S ribosomes normally dissociate into subunits after they have completed the synthesis of a polypeptide chain and that the subunits reassociate to form 70S ribosomes when they initiate a chain.

This hypothesis was given more direct support by Nomura and his colleagues. They have shown that the 70S ribosome must first dissociate into 50S and 30S subunits before either natural mRNA or the initiating aminoacyl-tRNA can be bound. They found that the 30S subunit binds both mRNA and fMet-tRNA to form an *initiation complex,* which then associates tightly with the 50S ribosome to form the functional 70S ribosome (Figure 30-4).

The initiation of the polypeptide chain with natural messengers involves three specific protein initiation factors, symbolized as F_1, F_2, and F_3 (or as A, C, and B, respectively). They can be extracted in soluble form from 30S ribosomal subunits with strong ammonium chloride solutions. The dissociation of 70S ribosomes into subunits, the binding of fMet-tRNA and mRNA to the 30S subunit, and the ensuing formation of the complete, functional 70S ribosome, require the presence of these factors, as well as GTP. Presumably this elaborate initiation process is required to ensure that ribosomes do not start making a polypeptide chain at the middle. The initiation factors are then released from the initiation complex: they are used over and over again to start new chains.

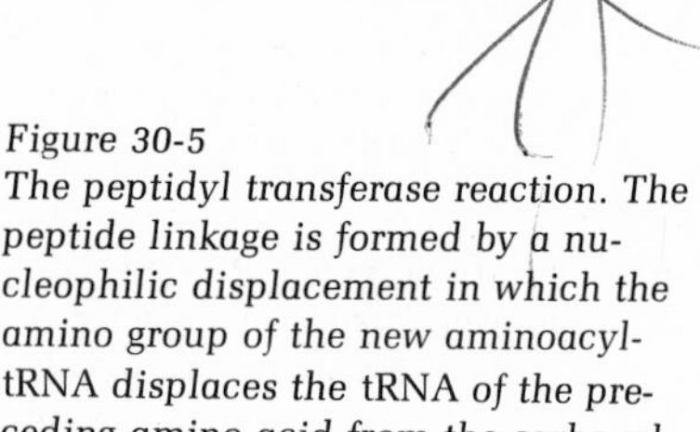

The Elongation Cycle

Step 1

Three major steps occur in chain elongation. In the first step, the incoming aminoacyl-tRNA binds to the aminoacyl site of the complete 70S ribosomal complex, positioned at the next codon of the mRNA. This binding process requires GTP and a specific cytoplasmic protein called T factor, which can be dissociated into two subunits, T_U and T_S. The T factor has been obtained in pure crystalline form.

Step 2

In the second step, the peptide bond is formed by reaction of the amino group of the newly bound aminoacyl-tRNA with the esterified carboxyl group of the COOH-terminal amino acid residue of the peptidyl-tRNA. This reaction presumably occurs by a nucleophilic displacement in which the departing group is the tRNA (Figure 30-5). The tRNA remaining, although no longer carrying its amino acid, remains bound to the peptidyl site; this tRNA is designated $tRNA_P$. As a result of this displacement, the elongated peptidyl-tRNA is now bound to the ribosome at the aminoacyl site. Neither ATP nor GTP is required for the formation of the new peptide bond, which is presumably made at the expense of the bond energy of the ester linkage between the amino acid and its tRNA. However, an enzyme called *peptidyl transferase,* which is part of the 50S subunit of the ribosome, is required to catalyze this reaction (Figure 30-6).

This picture is also supported by important experiments on the inhibition of protein synthesis by the antibiotic *puromycin* (below) which has a structure very similar to that of the terminal AMP residue of an aminoacyl-tRNA. However, instead of the ester linkage between the 2′- or 3′-hydroxyl group of the ribose moiety and the carboxyl group of the amino acid, puromycin possesses an amide linkage between its sugar component and the carboxyl group of *p*-methoxyphenylalanine, i.e.,

Figure 30-5
The peptidyl transferase reaction. The peptide linkage is formed by a nucleophilic displacement in which the amino group of the new aminoacyl-tRNA displaces the tRNA of the preceding amino acid from the carboxyl group to yield a lengthened peptidyl-tRNA.

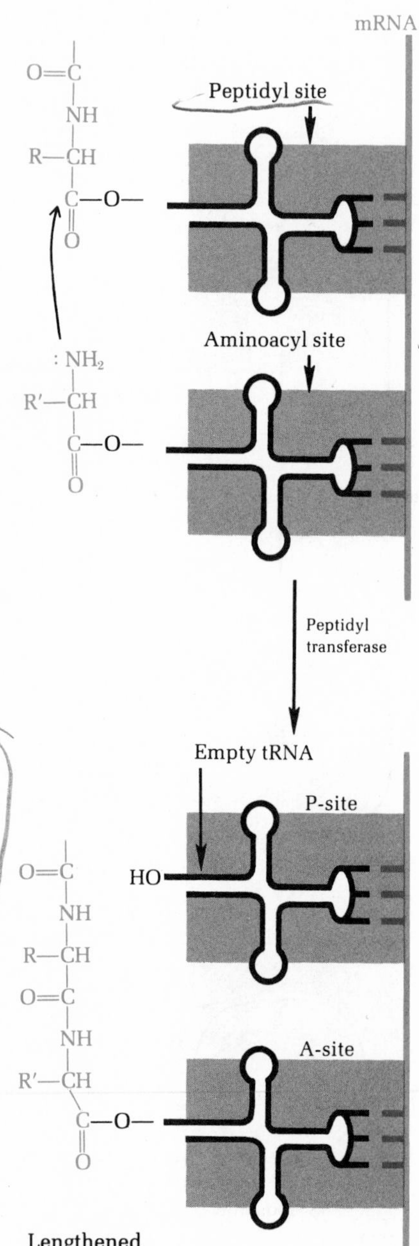

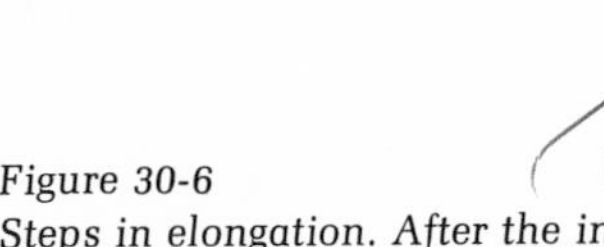

Figure 30-6
Steps in elongation. After the initiation complex is formed, the fMet-tRNA is on the peptidyl site. The next aminoacyl-tRNA is then bound to the aminoacyl site, a process that requires GTP and factor T. In the peptidyl transferase reaction the new peptide bond is formed; the lengthened peptidyl-tRNA is now on the aminoacyl or A site and the empty aminoacyl-tRNA on the peptidyl or P site. In the translocation reaction, which requires the G factor, GTP is hydrolyzed to furnish the energy required to translocate simultaneously the peptidyl-tRNA from the A site to the P site and the mRNA by one codon. The cycle then repeats with the next incoming aminoacyl-tRNA.

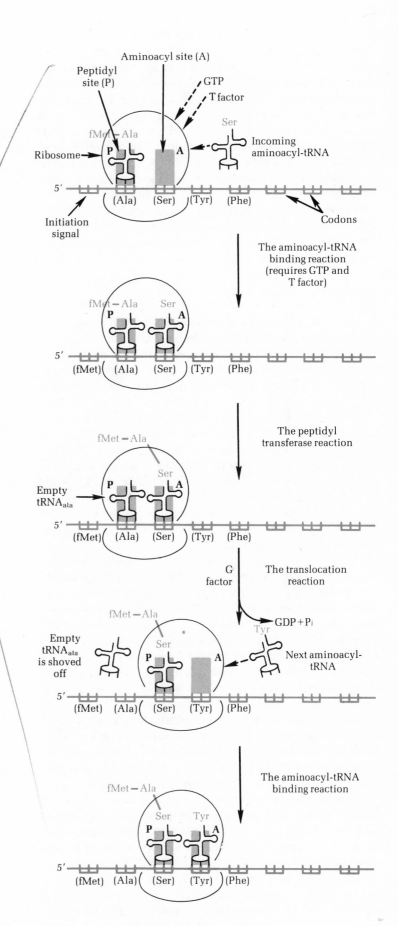

the methyl ether of tyrosine. Nathans and others have shown that puromycin interrupts peptide-chain elongation by virtue of its capacity to replace an entering aminoacyl-tRNA, with formation of a peptidyl-puromycin derivative (Figure 30-7). The peptidyl-puromycin so formed cannot be lengthened by a similar displacement reaction with the next aminoacyl-tRNA because its amide linkage is substituted and cannot be attacked. Moreover, the peptidyl-puromycin then detaches from the ribosome since the puromycin is a small molecule and contains no anticodon. These observations not only established the mode of action of this antibiotic but provided important confirmatory evidence that chain growth occurs by addition of aminoacyl-tRNAs at the COOH-terminal end of polypeptide chains through displacement reactions.

Step 3

After the peptide bond has been made, the peptidyl-tRNA which has just been elongated is bound to the aminoacyl site, positioned by the complementary codon in the mRNA. In the third step of the elongation cycle the peptidyl-tRNA is physically shifted from the aminoacyl site to the peptidyl site, displacing the "empty" $tRNA_P$ from the latter. This complex translocation reaction is believed to be the result of a conformational change in the ribosome, which occurs at the expense of the hydrolysis of GTP. A specific protein called G factor is required for this step; a fresh G-factor-GTP complex binds to the ribosome for each translocation step. Simultaneous with the translocation of the peptidyl-tRNA is a translocation of the mRNA, which moves along the ribosome by one codon (Figure 30-6).

These events require a highly specific topology of the two (or more) active sites for binding the peptidyl-tRNA, the aminoacyl-tRNA, and the mRNA, as well as the necessary enzymes on the 30S and 50S ribosomal subunits. Moreover, the ribosome probably undergoes complex, geometrically specific changes in shape during each bond-making cycle. The mRNA appears to "track" through a groove or tunnel formed by the ribosomal subunits, since in polyribosomes (see below) a substantial fraction of the mRNA chain is not susceptible to attack by ribonuclease. This fraction presumably consists of all the segments inside a ribosomal tunnel at any instant (about 25 nucleotides per ribosome). A comparable segment of the polypeptide chain being formed is also protected similarly from attack by proteolytic enzymes.

The 50S ribosomal subunits contain a small species of rRNA, called *5S RNA*, in addition to the major 23S rRNA component (Chapter 12). The complete base sequence of 5S RNA has been established. It is remarkable and very suggestive that 5S RNA is similar to tRNAs in size (the sedimentation coefficient of tRNA is about 4S) and possibly also in conformation, since 5S RNA also can exist in a clover-leaf conformation in which it is maximally base-paired. However, the role of 5S RNA in protein synthesis is still unknown.

Figure 30-7
Mode of inhibition by puromycin.

Peptidyl-puromycin

Puromycin resembles aminoacyl-tRNA and can react with peptidyl-RNA to yield peptidyl-puromycin. The chain cannot be elongated further and is discharged from the ribosome as a free peptidyl-puromycin. A number of peptidyl-puromycins varying in chain length have been isolated.

Peptidyl-tRNA

The amino group of an incoming aminoacyl-tRNA can displace the tRNA from the COOH-terminal amino acid and thus elongate the chain.

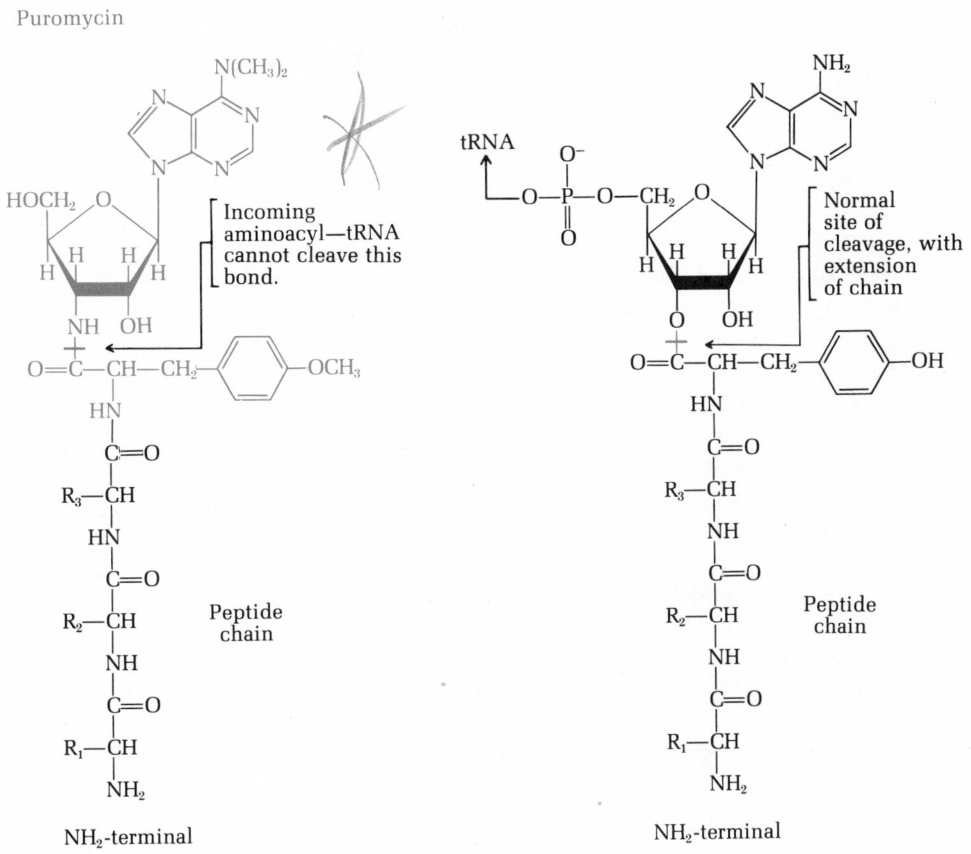

Puromycin

$N(CH_3)_2$

$HOCH_2$

NH OH

$O{=}C{-}CH{-}CH_2{-}C_6H_4{-}OCH_3$

Incoming aminoacyl—tRNA cannot cleave this bond.

Peptide chain

NH_2-terminal

tRNA

NH_2

Normal site of cleavage, with extension of chain

$O{=}C{-}CH{-}CH_2{-}C_6H_4{-}OH$

Peptide chain

NH_2-terminal

Termination of the Polypeptide Chain

The completion of a polypeptide chain and its detachment from the ribosome require special steps which are not yet fully understood. As we shall see in Chapter 31, the termination of polypeptide chains is signaled by three special termination codons in the mRNA. After the last or COOH-terminal amino acid residue has been added to a polypeptide chain on the ribosome, the polypeptide chain is still covalently attached to the tRNA, which is in turn noncovalently attached to the ribosome, through the codon-anticodon interaction with the mRNA. The release of the polypeptidyl-tRNA from the ribosome, when a termination codon is reached, is promoted by a specific *protein release factor*, which is bound to the ribosome and promotes the hydrolysis of the ester linkage between the polypeptide and the tRNA. The 70S ribosome then runs off the mRNA in free form. It may enter a new cycle when it undergoes dissociation into its 50S and 30S subunits, a reaction which appears to require one of the specific protein initiation factors (Figure 30-8).

Very little is known about the state in which a completed polypeptide chain leaves the ribosome, whether as a random coil or as a folded molecule in its native, functional conformation. The latter alternative appears more likely, however, because isolated ribosomes show a wide variety of enzymatic activities apart from those concerned in the mechanism of peptide-bond synthesis. These activities are believed to be due to tightly bound polypeptide chains of enzymes that are still undergoing synthesis, but are almost complete.

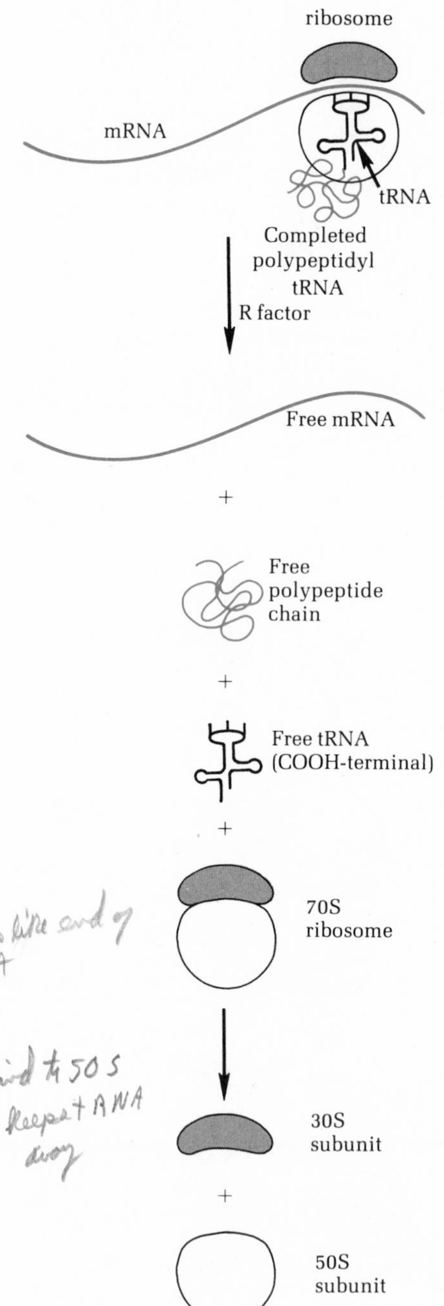

Figure 30-8
Termination steps and the release of the free polypeptide chain and the 30S and 50S ribosomal subunits.

Many proteins in their native state contain essential intrachain and/or interchain disulfide cross-linkages. These covalent cross-linkages are believed to be formed enzymatically after the covalent backbone of the polypeptide chain has been synthesized. Anfinsen and other investigators have found that microsomes can catalyze the oxidation of —SH groups of chemically reduced, inactive forms of ribonuclease, lysozyme, and other proteins, with formation of disulfide linkages. Because these oxidation products regain a large part of their enzymatic activity, it appears most likely that the reduced polypeptide chain folds itself spontaneously to approximately the native conformation, thus positioning the —SH groups properly to yield the correct cross-linkages when they are enzymatically oxidized. If the various —SH groups of a reduced polypeptide chain were randomly brought together into —S—S— cross-linkages, the probability would be high that many "wrong" cross-linkages would be formed. In the specific case of insulin, which has three —S—S— linkages, an enzyme called *glutathione-insulin transhydrogenase* catalyzes formation of the cross-linking —S—S— bonds of insulin, with oxidized glutathione (GSSG) serving as acceptor:

$$\text{Reduced insulin} + 3\text{GSSG} \rightleftharpoons \text{oxidized insulin} + 6\text{GSH}$$

The information necessary for establishing the correct cross-linkages of proteins is thus already inherent in the amino acid sequence of the polypeptide chain.

Other Inhibitors of Protein Synthesis

In addition to puromycin, whose action is described above, many other inhibitors of protein synthesis are known. The antibiotics *chloramphenicol* and *cycloheximide* (Figure 30-9) are of considerable interest since they appear to interfere with the peptide-forming steps. Chloramphenicol has been found to inhibit protein synthesis by the 70S ribosomes of procaryotic cells (and of the mitochondria of eucaryotes) but not by the 80S ribosomes of eucaryotic cells. It binds to 50S subunits. Cycloheximide (also called *actidione*) differs in that it inhibits

Figure 30-9
Other inhibitors of protein synthesis.

Cycloheximide (actidione)

Streptomycin

Chloramphenicol

Figure 30-10
Electron micrographs of polysomes of reticulocytes.

Shadowed preparation.

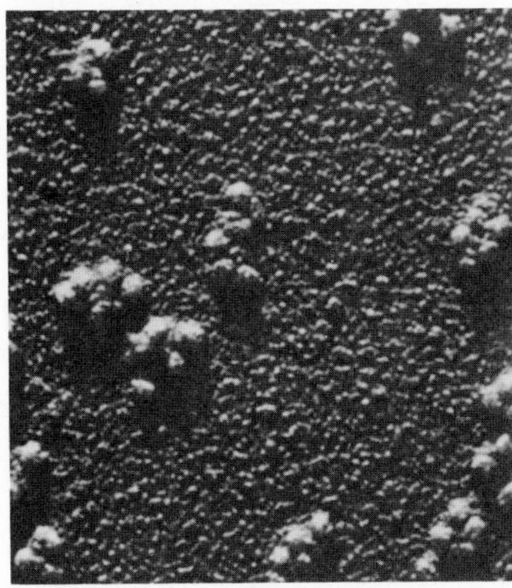

1.000 Å

Preparation stained with uranyl acetate to show the mRNA strand between the ribosomes.

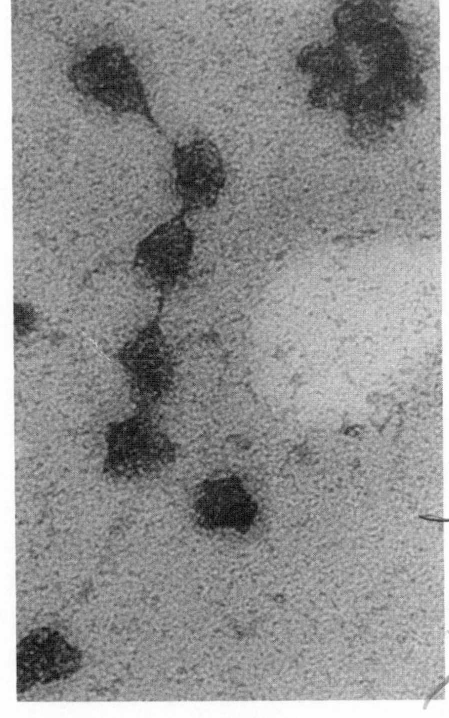

1.000 Å

protein synthesis in the 80S ribosomes of eucaryotic cells but not the 70S ribosomes of procaryotes.

Streptomycin and related antibiotics interfere in protein synthesis in another way. They bind to the 30S subunit of ribosomes, where they not only inhibit protein synthesis but also cause misreading of the genetic code. Presumably streptomycin alters the conformation of the ribosome so that the aminoacyl-tRNAs are less firmly bound to the codons of the mRNA and are thus less specific. These antibiotics are valuable tools for studying the ribosome. Mutant cells resistant to or dependent on streptomycin possess genetically altered 30S ribosomal subunits. *Actinomycin D* inhibits protein synthesis, but only indirectly. As shown in Chapter 29, it blocks formation of mRNA by the action of RNA polymerase. Since mRNA is required for protein synthesis and is also labile to hydrolysis by nucleases, actinomycin D inhibits protein synthesis after a short lag period, particularly in bacteria.

Polyribosomes

When ribosomes are carefully isolated under conditions in which ribonuclease activity and mechanical shear are avoided, they are obtained in clusters containing from as few as 3 or 4 to as many as 100 individual ribosomes. Such clusters, which are called *polyribosomes* (also *polysomes* or *ergosomes*) have been examined with the electron microscope (Figure 30-10) and studied chemically.

Since they can be fragmented into individual ribosomes by the action of ribonuclease, polyribosomes are apparently held together by a strand of RNA. A connecting fiber between adjacent ribosomes can actually be seen in electron micrographs. Because the number of ribosomes in a cluster is approximately proportional to the number of amino acid residues in the nascent polypeptide chains, it has been concluded that the RNA connecting strand is actually mRNA, which is being "read" by several ribosomes simultaneously, spaced some distance apart. Each individual ribosome of a polyribosome can make a complete polypeptide chain and does not require the presence of the other ribosomes. Such an arrangement therefore increases the efficiency of utilization of the mRNA template, since several polypeptide chains can be made from it simultaneously (Figure 30-11). The direction of translation is in the $5' \rightarrow 3'$ direction. The mRNA of bacteria is translated by ribosomes while its growing end is still attached to DNA via RNA polymerase.

The peptide chains of hemoglobin, which contain about 150 amino acid residues, are coded for by an mRNA molecule having about $3 \times 150 = 450$ mononucleotide units, which would be a chain about 1,500 Å long. Since each 80S reticulocyte ribosome is 220 Å in diameter, there is obviously ample room along the mRNA for several ribosomes to read off the mRNA simultaneously. Polyribosomes isolated from reticulocytes have been found to contain five or six ribosomes per cluster. If six is the maximum number, then the average distance between successive 220 Å ribosomes along the mRNA is about 30 Å. Evidently, individual ribosomes are able to work with relatively little "elbow room" along the mRNA chain, presumably with their rates of action synchronized. Among the largest polyribosome systems are those responsible for the biosynthesis of the major chains of myosin, which possess about 1800 amino acid residues. Such polysomes may contain 60 to 100 ribosomes.

High-resolution electron microscopy has shown that polyribosomes have a considerable degree of three-dimensional order. Polyribosomes having six or more ribosomes form regular, tight whorls, in which the small subunits face inward. When polyribosomes contain more than six ribosomes, they show a tightly coiled helical structure (Figure 30-12). The extraordinary finding has been made that when certain tissues of higher organisms, particularly those of the chick embryo, are chilled for some time at 0° prior to fixation and sectioning, the ribosomes are arranged in a very regular lattice within the cell and appear to organize into crystals (Figure 30-13). These observations suggest that in eucaryotic cells, ribosomes are not merely scattered about at random but function with considerable order and regularity (see below).

Figure 30-11
Mechanism of formation of a polyribosome. The ribosomes function independently of each other, each forming a polypeptide chain as it moves along the mRNA molecule.

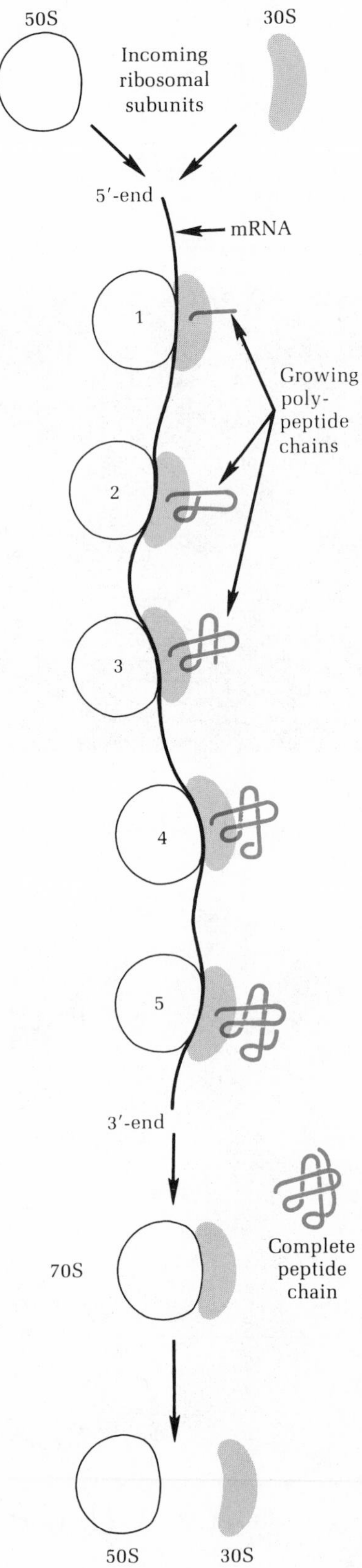

The Energy Requirement in Protein Synthesis

Two high-energy phosphate bonds are probably utilized in the formation of each molecule of aminoacyl-tRNA

Figure 30-12
Helical structure of polysomes in some animal cells.

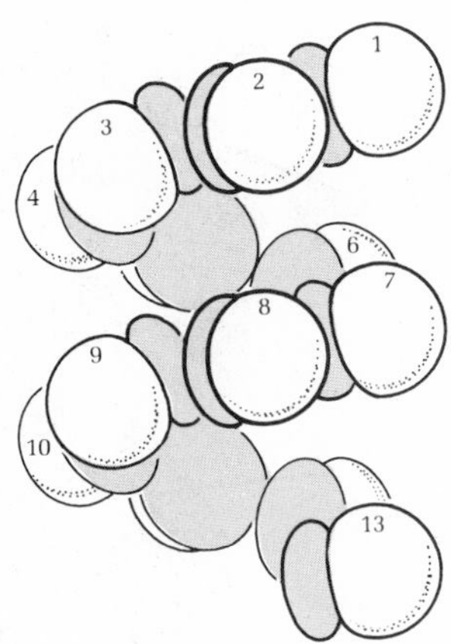

during the activation reaction (see above). In addition, at least one molecule of GTP is cleaved to GDP and phosphate during the formation of each peptide bond. Therefore a total of at least three high-energy bonds is ultimately required for the synthesis of each peptide bond of the completed protein. This represents an exceedingly large thermodynamic "pull" in the direction of synthesis, since a total of at least $7.3 \times 3 = 21.9$ kcal is invested to generate a peptide bond whose standard free energy of hydrolysis, although not known precisely, is probably about −5.0 kcal. The net $\Delta G^{\circ\prime}$ for peptide-bond synthesis is thus about −16.9 kcal, making peptide-bond synthesis at the expense of phosphate-bond energy overwhelmingly exergonic and essentially irreversible. Although this may appear to be exceedingly wasteful, very likely a large fraction of the energy loss is the price the cell must pay in order to guarantee nearly perfect fidelity in the translation of the genetic message of mRNA into the amino acid sequence of proteins.

Figure 30-13
Electron micrographs showing ribosomes in regular array in liver of chicken embryo held at 0° for some time prior to fixation.

Low magnification

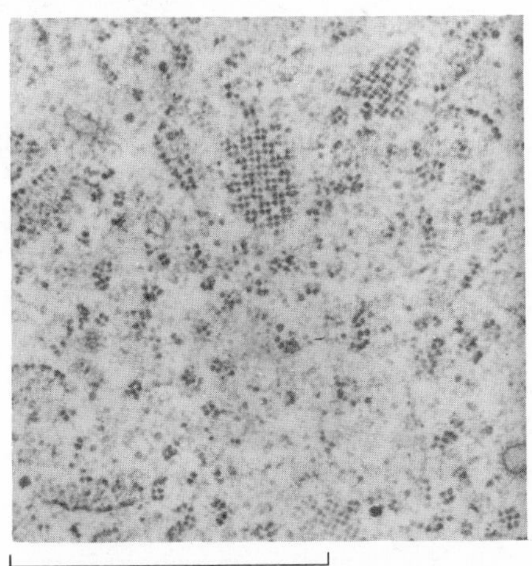

High magnification

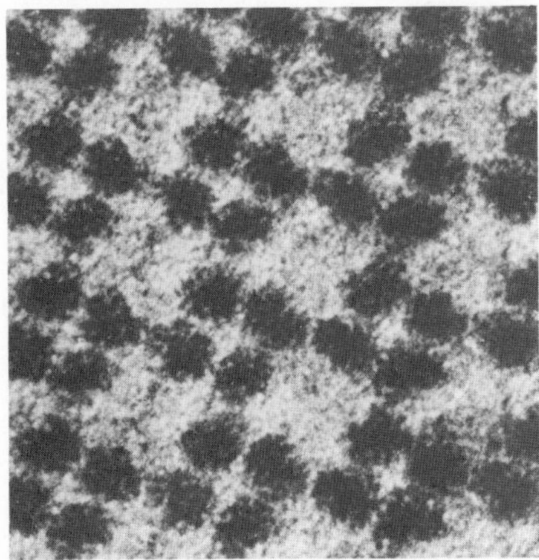

Protein Synthesis and Secretion in Eucaryotic Cells

In procaryotic cells the ribosomes are free in the cytoplasm, whereas, in eucaryotic cells, which possess an endoplasmic reticulum, the location of the ribosomes differs somewhat depending on the manner in which the protein is to be used. In those cells in which the protein is intended largely for internal use, as in reticulocytes, the ribosomes are free in the cytoplasm, largely as polyribosomes, and are not attached to endoplasmic reticulum. However, in those cells in which the protein is to be secreted outside the cell, most of the ribosomes are attached to the outer surface of the endoplasmic reticulum, on which they are often arranged in rows. This effect is particularly striking in pancreatic exocrine cells, which synthesize and secrete the digestive enzymes, and in liver cells, which form and secrete serum proteins.

The course of protein synthesis in pancreas exocrine cells has been studied in some detail by electron microscopic and biochemical means. The newly formed proteins, such as the zymogens trypsinogen and chymotrypsinogen, leave the ribosomes on the outer surface of the endoplasmic reticulum, pass through the membranes by a process that is not yet understood, and then enter the intracisternal space, which serves as a system of collecting channels. The contents of the intracisternal space are then concentrated and "packaged" by the Golgi apparatus into zymogen granules—large, dense, aggregates of zymogen molecules—which are surrounded by a single membrane. The zymogen molecules are stored in this form until they are secreted. They release their contents to the exterior of the cell after the membrane of the zymogen granule fuses with the plasma membrane and opens the lumen of the zymogen granule to the exterior (Figure 30-14).

Figure 30-14
Secretion of newly synthesized zymogen proteins in exocrine cell of pancreas.

Electron micrograph of a section of exocrine cell, showing electron dense zymogen granules.

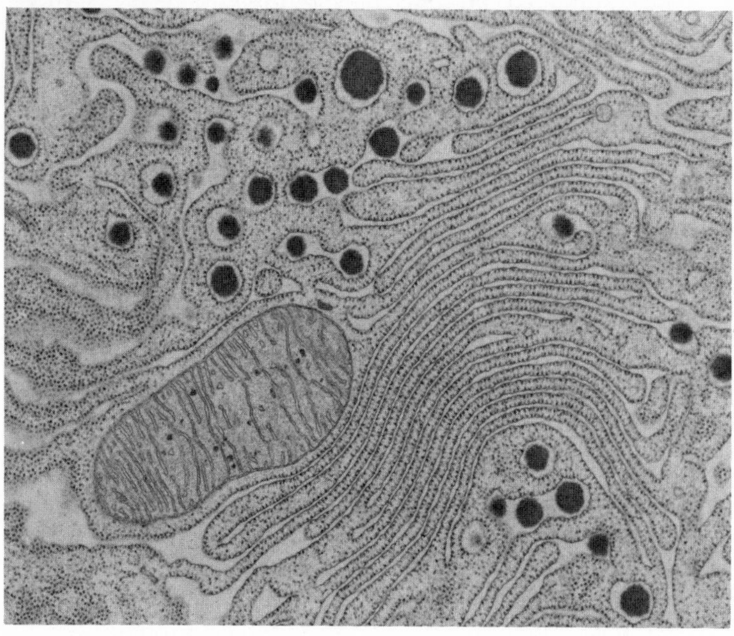

Schematic representation of a pancreatic cell to show the steps in protein secretion.

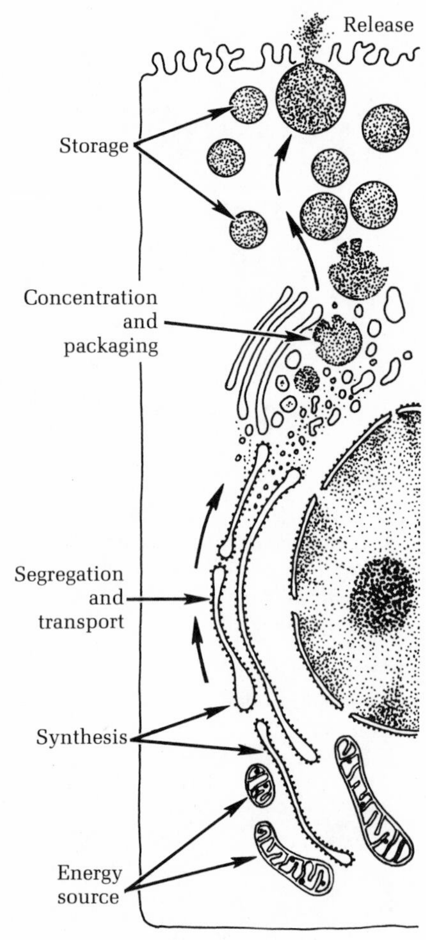

Protein Synthesis in Mitochondria

Isolated mitochondria from many types of eucaryotic cells have been found to incorporate labeled amino acids into mitochondrial protein. It has been possible to extract from mitochondria all the essential elements and components required for protein synthesis, including ribosomes and ribosomal RNA, amino acid activating enzymes, and tRNAs, all of which are distinctive and different from those required in extramitochondrial protein synthesis in eucaryotes. The ribosomes of mitochondria strongly resemble in behavior the 70S ribosomes found in bacteria. Recent investigations show that the major subunits of mitochondrial ribosomes are of the bacterial or 50S type.

The ribosomes are not ordinarily visible in electron micrographs of mitochondria in animal tissues, although ribosomal RNA can easily be extracted from isolated mitochondria. Perhaps most of the ribosomes of mitochondria are present in dissociated form as subunits and are therefore not easily visualized. If so, it may mean that most of the mitochondrial ribosomes are "resting."

As pointed out above, mitochondria of eucaryotic cells contain distinctive and specific tRNAs and aminoacyl-tRNA synthetases, which differ from those found in the extramitochondrial cytoplasm. It is highly significant that protein synthesis by the ribosomes of mitochondria is inhibited by chloramphenicol, whereas extramitochondrial protein synthesis in 80S ribosomes of eucaryotic cells is not. Moreover, mitochondrial protein synthesis employs fMet as initiating amino acid. Therefore the mitochondria may possess a characteristic protein synthetic apparatus rather similar to that in bacteria. These observations strongly support the hypothesis that mitochondria originated from parasitizing aerobic bacteria during the evolution of eucaryotic cells.

Mitochondria also contain, in addition to a specific circular mitochondrial DNA (Chapters 12 and 28), a DNA-dependent RNA polymerase that is inhibited by actinomycin D. Mitochondria thus are able to generate mRNA from their DNA. That mitochondrial protein synthesis requires mRNA generated in the mitochondria is shown by the finding that actinomycin D inhibits protein synthesis in isolated mitochondria completely if it is added under conditions in which it can pass through the mitochondrial membrane.

A point of major interest is the identity of the proteins synthesized by the mitochondria. Genetic evidence indicates very strongly that cytochrome *c* and probably most other mitochondrial enzymes are specified by nuclear chromosomes and are synthesized in extramitochondrial ribosomes. It appears likely that mitochondrial DNA may code only for a few mitochondrial proteins, which are apparently located in the membranes. Chloroplasts also contain DNA and have the capacity to incorporate amino acids into membrane proteins. This process also has similarities to protein synthesis in bacteria.

Summary

The synthesis of proteins from activated amino acids takes place on the surface of ribosomes. Amino acids are activated in the cytoplasm by aminoacyl-tRNA synthetases, which catalyze the formation of the aminoacyl esters of homologous tRNAs; simultaneously, ATP is cleaved to AMP and pyrophosphate. The activating enzymes are highly specific for both the amino acid and its corresponding tRNA. There is more than one type of tRNA for each amino acid. In eucaryotic cells, the mitochondria contain tRNAs and aminoacyl-tRNA synthetases which are different from those in the nonmitochondrial cytoplasm. The aminoacyl-tRNA synthetases also have considerable species-specificity. The amino acid moiety of aminoacyl-tRNA makes no contribution to the specificity of interaction of the aminoacyl-tRNA with its complementary codon of the mRNA; the tRNA thus is an "adapter."

The growth of peptide chains begins with the NH_2-terminal residue. New residues are added to the COOH-terminal carboxyl group of the peptidyl-tRNA by nucleophilic displacement of tRNA from peptidyl-tRNA by the amino group of the entering aminoacyl tRNA. Puromycin inhibits peptide-chain synthesis by interacting with peptidyl-tRNA on the ribosome to form peptidylpuromycin, which is discharged from the ribosome. In *E. coli*, the first or NH_2-terminal amino acid laid down is metnionine, which enters as N-formylmethionyl-tRNA (fMet-tRNA). Polypeptide synthesis begins by the binding of fMet-tRNA and of mRNA to the free 30S subunits of ribosomes to form the "initiation complex," which then binds to the 50S subunit to form a complete 70S ribosome. Three specific proteins (F_1, F_2, and F_3), which are not permanent components of ribosomes, are required to promote formation of the initiation complex. In the subsequent chain elongation a cytoplasmic factor, T and GTP are required for proper binding of the incoming aminoacyl-tRNA. The peptidyl transfer reaction is then catalyzed by an enzyme contained in the 50S subunit. The cytoplasmic factor G plus GTP are required for translocation of the peptidyl-tRNA from the aminoacyl site to the peptidyl site. During this cycle at least 1 GTP is hydrolyzed to GDP + Pi.

Polyribosomes consist of mRNA molecules to which are attached several or many ribosomes, each independently reading the mRNA and forming protein. At least three high-energy phosphate bonds are required to generate each peptide bond. In eucaryotic cells, protein synthesis usually occurs in ribosomes attached to the endoplasmic reticulum, whose cisternae form channels for transport and secretion of the newly synthesized protein. Protein synthesis also takes place in the mitochondria, which possess a specific circular DNA, a DNA-directed RNA polymerase, specific mitochondrial forms of tRNA and activating enzymes, and ribosomes similar to those of bacteria.

References

Books

Cold Spring Harbor Symposia in Quantitative Biology, vol. XXXIV, *The Mechanism of Protein Synthesis*, 1969. In press. The proceedings of an important symposium.

Reviews and Articles

CAMPBELL, P. N.: "Biosynthesis of Proteins," *Progress in Biophys. and Mol. Biol.*, **15**:1–38 (1965). An excellent review of earlier work.

CRICK, F. H. C.: "On Protein Synthesis," in "The Biological Replication of Macromolecules," *Symposia of the Society for Experimental Biology*, **12**:138 (1958). An absorbing analysis of the problem of protein synthesis as it appeared to a central figure before present knowledge developed.

ELSON, D.: "Ribosomal Enzymes," in D. B. Roodyn (ed.), *Enzyme Cytology*, Academic Press, New York, 1967, pp. 407–472.

GUTHRIE, C., and M. NOMURA: "Initiation of Protein Synthesis: A Critical Test of the 30S Subunit Model," *Nature*, **219**:232 (1968). Reconstruction of the initiation complex from purified components.

KAEMPFER, R. O. R., M. MESELSON, and H. J. RASKAS: "Cyclic Dissociation into Stable Subunits and Reformation of Ribosomes during Bacterial Growth," *J. Mol. Biol.*, **31**:277–289 (1968).

LENGYEL, P., and D. SÖLL: "Protein Synthesis in Bacteria," *Bacteriological Reviews*, 1969. In Press. An excellent summarizing account.

LIPMANN, F.: "Polypeptide Chain Elongation in Protein Biosynthesis," *Science*, **164**:1024–1031 (1969). A helpful short review of recent progress on the elongation steps.

MOLDAVE, K: "Nucleic Acids and Protein Synthesis," *Ann. Rev. Biochem.*, **34**:419–443 (1965).

NOVELLI, G. D.: "Amino Acid Activation for Protein Synthesis," *Ann. Rev. Biochem.*, **36**:449–484 (1967). Activating enzymes and their specificity.

ZAMECNIK, P. C.: "Protein Synthesis," *Harvey Lectures,* **54:**256 (1960). A personal account of the early research which led to the identification of ribosomes, transfer RNA, and the activation reaction.

CHAPTER 31 THE GENETIC CODE

We have just seen how the ribosome functions in synthesizing the peptide bonds of proteins and how it makes possible alignment of amino acids in the correct sequence specified by messenger RNA. We shall now consider the questions: How is the 4-letter language of nucleic acids translated into the 20-letter language of proteins? What is the formal correspondence between nucleotide sequence and amino acid sequence? What are the genetic code words for the amino acids?

The experimental and conceptual advances described in this chapter were literally undreamed of only a few years ago. Although it had appeared certain for some time that each amino acid is ultimately coded for by a small number of successive nucleotides in DNA, the complete identification of the sequence of nucleotides specifying each of the amino acids appeared to be a hopelessly difficult task. But a sudden breakthrough came with the important experiments of Nirenberg and his colleagues, which made possible a simple and direct approach to the problem. As a result, the genetic dictionary of code words for the amino acids is now well known and is fully confirmed by independent genetic experiments. Its elucidation has inevitably evoked a host of new and interesting problems.

The Size of the Coding Units

From mathematical considerations alone, it had appeared very likely that each amino acid residue is coded for by only a small number of consecutive nucleotides in the DNA chain. Obviously, more than one nucleotide is required since there are only four bases in DNA and 20 amino acids in proteins. Furthermore, since the four code letters of DNA (A, G, C, and T) arranged in groups of two can yield only $4^2 = 16$ different combinations, the code words for amino acids must contain more than two letters. The four bases in combinations of three can theoretically specify for $4^3 = 64$ different amino acids. A triplet code is therefore feasible for coding amino acids.

That each amino acid residue is coded for by a relatively short nucleotide sequence also was evident from

 uuu codon needs AAA anticodon

structural studies on viruses. For example, the tobacco necrosis satellite virus contains an RNA molecule having 1,200 nucleotides, which codes for the synthesis of its coat protein subunits. Since each of the subunits has 400 amino acid residues, it appeared likely that each amino acid requires at least 1,200/400 = 3 nucleotides for coding, providing the code requires no punctuation, i.e. is commaless. However, more compelling evidence for a triplet code came from important genetic studies of Crick and his colleagues employing "frame-shift" mutations of bacteriophage T4 of *E. coli* (Chapter 28). In such mutations, a single nucleotide is either deleted or inserted into the DNA coding for the viral protein, causing synthesis of defective viral coat proteins, the result of a shift of one nucleotide in the reading frame (Figure 31-1). If two such frame-shift mutations occur simultaneously in the same gene, so that one mutation causes the addition and the other the deletion of a nucleotide, then the correct reading frame relationship is reestablished in that portion of the DNA read after the second of the two mutations (Figure 31-1). Such double mutations of opposite sign within a single gene are called *intragenic suppressor mutations.* When three mutations of the same sign (either all deletions or all additions) occurred within the same gene, the correct reading-frame relationship was restored *beyond* the site of the third mutation, a result that could happen only if the code is composed of nucleotide triplets without punctuation (Figure 31-2). These observations were of the greatest assistance in the first direct biochemical experiments on the genetic code.

Figure 31-1
Correction of frame-shift mutation by intragenic suppressor mutation. When a deletion or insertion of a single nucleotide occurs, all the subsequent triplets will read missense (color). *When a deletion and an insertion occur in the same gene the effect of the first mutation is suppressed, since all triplets after the second mutation read sense again. The missense codons are bracketed in color.*

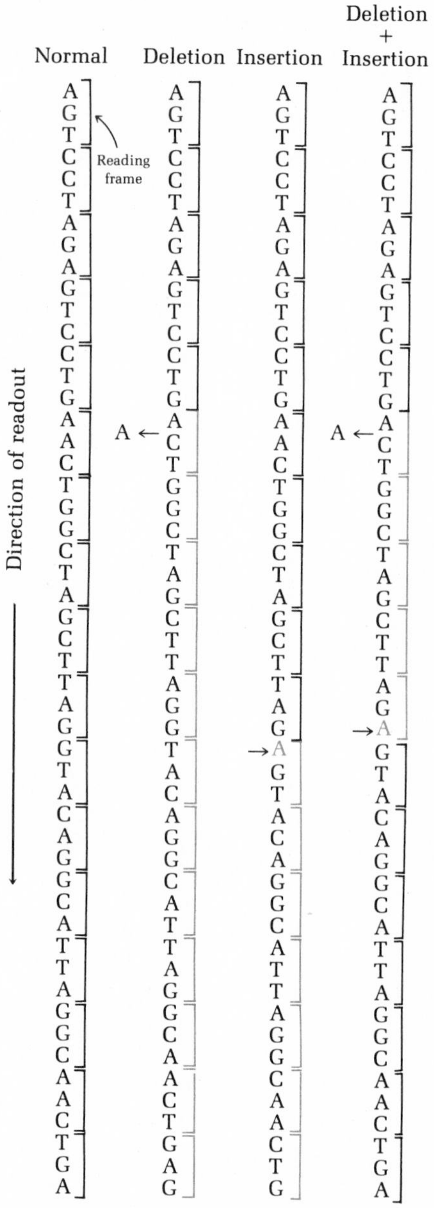

Normal: A G T C C T A G A G T C C T G A A C T G G C T A G C T T A G G T A C A G G C A T T A G G C A A C T G A

Deletion: A G T C C T A G A G T C C T G (A ←) A C T G G C T A G C T T A G G T A C A G G C A T T A G G C A A C T G A G

Insertion: A G T C C T A G A G T C C T G A A C T G G C T A G C T T A G (→ A) G T A C A G G C A T T A G G C A A C T G

Deletion + Insertion: A G T C C T A G A G T C C T G (A ←) A C T G G C T A G C T T A G (→ A) G T A C A G G C A T T A G G C A A C T G A

Reading frame

Direction of readout

poly uuu yields phenylalanine protein
poly CCC proline protein
poly AAA lysine protein

Messenger Dependence of Isolated Ribosomal Systems

In early studies on the incorporation of labeled amino acids into protein by isolated ribosomes supplemented with ATP, GTP, Mg^{2+}, amino acids, and appropriate fractions containing tRNAs and the activating enzymes, it was observed that amino acid incorporation often ceases after short periods of incubation, particularly in ribosomes from bacteria such as *E. coli*. Furthermore, short pretreatment of the isolated ribosomes with ribonuclease also causes loss of their activity in amino acid incorporation. These findings suggested that freshly isolated ribosomes already contain some mRNA, but that it is rapidly destroyed by action of endogenous ribonuclease. When RNA previously isolated from *E. coli* cells is added to such messenger-depleted ribosomes, their capacity for amino acid incorporation is restored. Moreover, isolated ribosomes from *E. coli* respond to the RNA of RNA viruses such as the f2 virus.

In similar experiments, reticulocyte ribosomes depleted of adhering mRNA could be induced to synthesize the polypeptide chains of hemoglobin again, provided that they were supplemented with RNA extracted from reticulocytes. Such experiments established that isolated ribosomes depleted of their endogenous mRNA respond to the addition of RNA by synthesizing polypeptide

Figure 31-2
Genetic evidence that the code words are triplets. When three deletions or three insertions occur in a single gene, all triplets following the third mutation will read sense again. The missense triplets are bracketed in color.

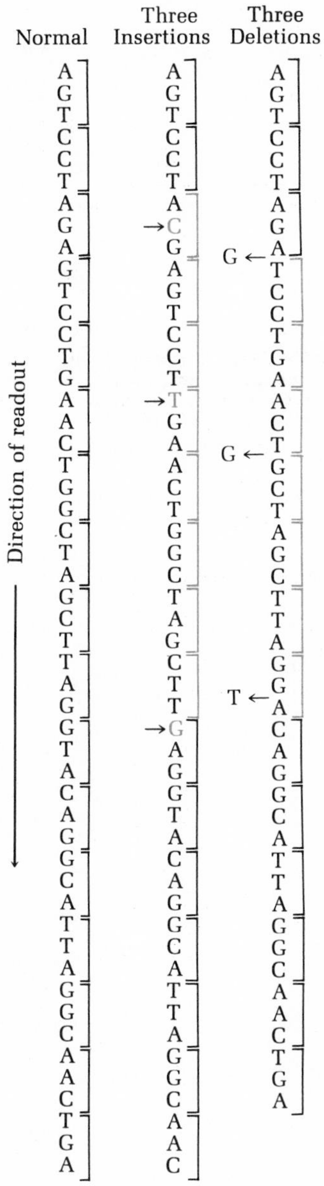

Normal	Three Insertions	Three Deletions
AGTCCTAGAGTCCTGAACTGGCTAGCTTAGGTACAGGCATTAGGCAACTGA	AGTCCTA→CGAGTCCT→TGAACTGGCTAGCTT→GAGGTACAGGCATTAGCAAC	AGTCCTAGA(G←)TCCTGAACT(G←)GCTAGCTTAGGA(T←)CAGGCATTAGGCAACTGA

Direction of readout

chains. The stage was thus set for important experiments in which synthetically prepared polyribonucleotides of known base composition were added to isolated ribosomes in order to determine the relationship between base sequence in mRNA and amino acid sequence of the protein formed.

Synthetic Messengers: Composition of Code-Word Triplets

In 1961 Nirenberg and Matthaei reported their first dramatic experiments with synthetic polyribonucleotides as messengers in isolated ribosomal systems from *E. coli.* They incubated the RNA-like polymer polyuridylic acid (poly U), prepared by the action of polynucleotide phosphorylase on uridine 5′-diphosphate (Chapter 29), in a series of tubes containing messenger-depleted *E. coli* ribosomes, supplemented with the usual ingredients required to support protein synthesis, including all the amino acids. A different amino acid was labeled in each tube. Analysis of the acid-insoluble polypeptide fraction recovered from the tubes at the end of the incubation showed that with only one labeled amino acid out of the 18 tested, namely, phenylalanine, was radioactivity found incorporated into the protein fraction. Further analysis showed that the newly formed polypeptide chain contains only phenylalanine residues. They therefore suggested that the triplet UUU is the code word for phenylalanine. Very soon they found in similar experiments that poly C codes for polyproline and others showed that poly A codes for polylysine.

Subsequently, Nirenberg and Ochoa and their colleagues carried out intensive and detailed studies with various ribonucleotide copolymers prepared by the action of polynucleotide phosphorylase on appropriate nucleoside 5′-diphosphate substrates (Chapter 29). By varying the ratio of two NDPs used as substrates, for example, UDP and GDP, copolymers were prepared in which the ratio of U and G varied correspondingly. In such a UG copolymer the sequence of U and G residues is unknown. However, if the ratio of bases in the copolymer is known, the relative abundance of various possible triplets of U and G in poly UG, i.e., UUU, UUG, UGU, GUU, UGG, GUG, GGU, and GGG, can be calculated from simple statistical considerations (Table 31-1). By comparison of these figures with the identity and amount of the radioactive amino acids incorporated into ribosomal proteins in the presence of a poly UG messenger, some conclusions could be drawn on the probable base composition of the code words specifying certain amino acids. By such experiments, these two groups of workers succeeded, in a very short period of time, in identifying the composition of some 50 code words for the various amino acids, with exceptionally good agreement. These extremely important experiments not only opened the door to establishing how each amino acid code word is "spelled," but also proved directly that the amino acid code is *degenerate,* since more than one triplet was found to code for some of the amino acids (Table 31-2).

Sequence of Bases in The Code Words

Although the experimental approach described above quickly yielded information on the nucleotide composition of the code words, it yielded very little information on the sequence of nucleotides in the triplets, i.e., their spelling. In 1964 Nirenberg and Leder described a new and more direct method for studying the composition and sequence of nucleotides in the code words. They found that isolated *E. coli* ribosomes incubated in 0.02 *M* $MgCl_2$ in the absence of GTP bind synthetic messenger RNA preparations, such as poly U. Simultaneously, they also bind a molecule of that specific aminoacyl-tRNA which is specified by the messenger. For example, ribosomes incubated with poly U simultaneously bind phenylalanyl-$tRNA_{Phe}$, but no other aminoacyl-tRNA. No polypeptide of phenylalanine is formed in such a system because GTP is absent.

With this binding assay it was found that the shortest U oligonucleotide which supports specific binding of phenylalanyl-$tRNA_{Phe}$ is the trinucleotide UUU or U_3 (Figure 31-3). Increase of the chain length from U_3 to U_{12} does not further enhance binding of phenylalanyl-$tRNA_{Phe}$. The most effective trinucleotides for specifying binding of an aminoacyl-tRNA are those in which one end possesses a free 3′-hydroxyl group and the other end a phosphate group at the 5′ position; trinucleotides with the 3′-hydroxyl group phosphorylated are inactive (Figure 31-4). Thus the most active codon for phenylalanine is pUpUpU-OH (3′). Furthermore, the reading of

Figure 31-3
Binding of labeled Phe-$tRNA_{Phe}$ *to a ribosome bearing bound* pUpUpU. *Binding is detected by radioactivity measurements on ribosomes recovered by filtration.*

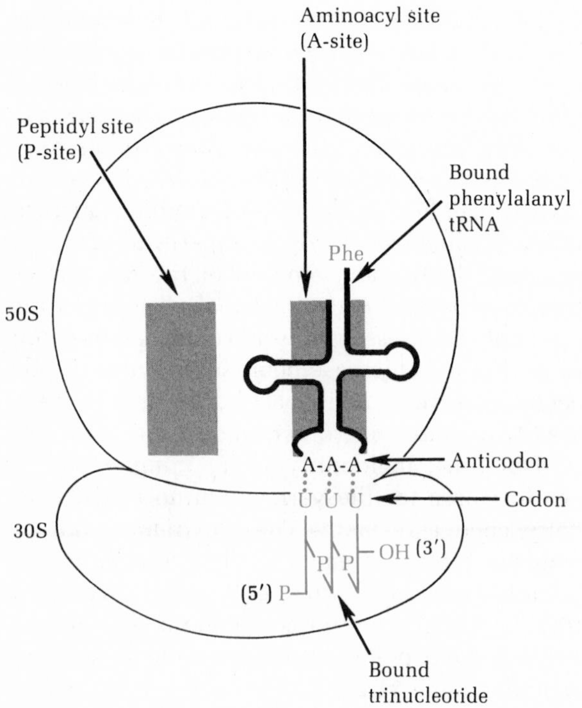

Table 31-1 Amino acids coded for by the random copolymer poly UG (U:G ratio 5:1)

Possible triplets	*Calculated frequency of occurrence*†	*Relative amounts of amino acid incorporation observed*
UUU	100	Phe (100)
UUG, UGU, GUU	20	Cys (20), Val (20)
UGG, GUG, GGU	4	Gly (4), Trp (5)
GGG	0.8	—

† Assumes frequency of UUU = 100.

Table 31-2 Degeneracy of codons for leucine. Templates having the following compositions all code for leucine incorporation

U_2A	C_2U
U_2G	A, U, G
U_2C	C, U, G

Figure 31-4
Relative activities of trinucleotides. in promoting binding of phenylalanyl-tRNA$_{phe}$ (above) and lysyl-tRNA$_{lys}$ (below) to ribosomes.
Although pUpUpU, UpUpU, and UpUpUp all code for phenylalanine, they differ in activity, indicating that the coding activity of UUU depends on whether it is a 5′ terminal, 3′ terminal, or internal codon. Trinucleotides linked in 2′,5′ fashion are inactive, as are deoxyribonucleotide triplets.

Trinucleotide structure

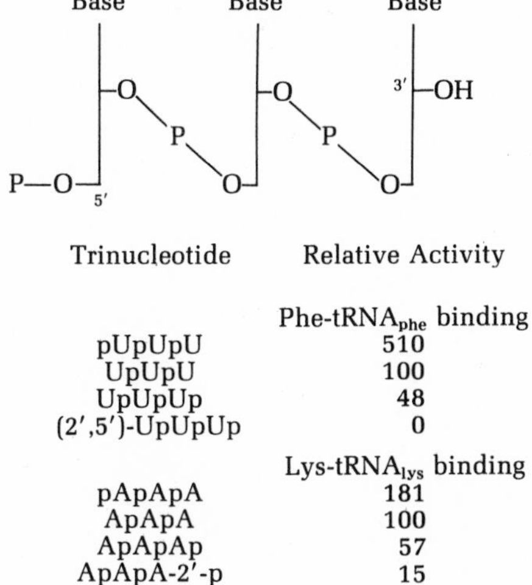

Trinucleotide	Relative Activity
	Phe-tRNA$_{phe}$ binding
pUpUpU	510
UpUpU	100
UpUpUp	48
(2′,5′)-UpUpUp	0
	Lys-tRNA$_{lys}$ binding
pApApA	181
ApApA	100
ApApAp	57
ApApA-2′-p	15
oligodeoxy A	0

the trinucleotide code words has a specific polarity or direction: GpUpU promotes binding of valyl tRNA$_{Val}$ whereas UpUpG does not. The latter actually promotes binding of leucyl tRNA$_{Leu}$. Readout or decoding of the codons in mRNA thus occurs in a specific direction, a matter to be discussed further below. These important findings thus revealed that simple trinucleotides suffice as synthetic messengers to specify the binding of specific aminoacyl-tRNAs to ribosomes in the absence of GTP. Since many trinucleotides of known base sequence are available or can be made, either enzymatically or by synthetic methods, this binding assay opened the way to determination of the sequence of bases in the coding triplets for the various amino acids.

Another technique which proved to be valuable is the use of synthetic polyribonucleotide messengers having repeating dinucleotides or trinucleotides, employed by Khorana and his colleagues. Those with repeating dinucleotides, such as UGUGUGUGUGUG . . . , contain two triplets, UGU and GUG, in alternation and should code for two amino acids in alternating sequence. Repeating trinucleotides, such as AGCAGCAGCAGCAGC . . . , contain three repeating triplets, AGC, GCA, and CAG, which should yield three different homopolypeptides, depending on where the readout begins.

By use of these methods, Nirenberg, Khorana, Ochoa, and other investigators quickly succeeded in determining the base sequence of the code-word triplets for all the amino acids. The results of these studies, confirmed by parallel but less direct studies on the effect of point mutations on amino acid replacements in coat proteins of mutant viruses, are summarized by the amino acid code-word dictionary in Figure 31-5.

General Features of the Code-Word Dictionary

It is now firmly established that the amino acid code is *degenerate*; i.e., there is more than one code word for most of the amino acids. In fact, all of the amino acids except tryptophan and methionine have more than one code word. The term degenerate should not, however, be taken to mean imperfect, for there is no code word that specifies more than one amino acid. Actually, the degeneracy of the amino acid code possesses some regularity. Furthermore, it appears to have some biological advantages, as will be developed later.

It is striking that the degeneracy is not uniform. Thus, the code for serine and leucine has sixfold degeneracy (i.e., there are six code words for leucine and for serine), whereas the code for other amino acids, such as glutamic acid, tyrosine, histidine, and several others, has only twofold degeneracy.

In many cases the degeneracy involves only the third base in the codon (Figure 31-5). For example, alanine is coded for by the triplets GCU, GCC, GCA, and GCG; that is, the first two bases GC are common to all Ala codons. Furthermore, when two different amino acids have code words in which the first two bases are identical, the third position of each may be filled by only purines or by

Figure 31-5
The genetic code-word dictionary. The third nucleotide of each codon (in color) is less specific than the first two. The codons read in the 5′ → 3′ direction. For example, $\overrightarrow{\text{pUpUpA}}$ = leucine. The three nonsense codons are in color.

	U		C		A		G	
U	UUU	Phe	UCU	Ser	UAU	Tyr	UGU	Cys
	UUC	Phe	UCC	Ser	UAC	Tyr	UGC	Cys
	UUA	Leu	UCA	Ser	UAA	Ochre	UGA	(Umber)
	UUG	Leu	UCG	Ser	UAG	Amber	UGG	Trp
C	CUU	Leu	CCU	Pro	CAU	His	CGU	Arg
	CUC	Leu	CCC	Pro	CAC	His	CGC	Arg
	CUA	Leu	CCA	Pro	CAA	Gln	CGA	Arg
	CUG	Leu	CCG	Pro	CAG	Gln	CGG	Arg
A	AUU	Ile	ACU	Thr	AAU	Asn	AGU	Ser
	AUC	Ile	ACC	Thr	AAC	Asn	AGC	Ser
	AUA	Ile	ACA	Thr	AAA	Lys	AGA	Arg
	AUG	Met	ACG	Thr	AAG	Lys	AGG	Arg
G	GUU	Val	GCU	Ala	GAU	Asp	GGU	Gly
	GUC	Val	GCC	Ala	GAC	Asp	GGC	Gly
	GUA	Val	GCA	Ala	GAA	Glu	GGA	Gly
	GUG	Val	GCG	Ala	GAG	Glu	GGG	Gly

only pyrimidines. For example, for His (CAU, CAC), the third symbols are the pyrimidines U and C, and for Gln (CAA, CAG), the third positions are the purines A and G. Nearly all of the amino acid codons therefore consist of the triplets XY^{A}_{G} or XY^{U}_{C}. Evidently the first two letters of each codon are the primary determinants of its specificity. The third position (i.e., the nucleotide at the 3′-OH end of the codon) is of less importance; to use Crick's phrase, it is loose and tends to "wobble." Since the third position may often be filled with either of the two purines or either of the two pyrimidines, it has been suggested that the amino acid code has 2½ letters rather than three.

Another conspicuous feature of the genetic code is that no punctuation or signal is required to indicate the end of one codon and the beginning of the next. The reading frame must therefore be correctly "set" at the beginning of the readout of an mRNA molecule and then moved sequentially from one triplet to the next, or all codons will be out of register and lead to formation of a missense protein, with a garbled amino acid sequence.

A third conspicuous feature of the code is that 3 of the 64 triplets do not code for any known amino acids: UAG, UAA, and UGA. As will be seen below, these nonsense triplets have a different function: they are signals for the termination of polypeptide chains.

In Vivo Evidence for the Amino Acid Code

Although the code words for the various amino acids were largely deduced from *in vitro* experiments with ribosomes, as described above, their identities were confirmed and checked in extremely important *in vivo* experiments on the effect of genetic mutations on the amino acid sequence of proteins. Such evidence came not only from study of induced bacterial mutations but also from spontaneous mutations in humans.

Table 31-3 shows a number of amino acid replacements that have been observed in several abnormal human hemoglobins (α chain), together with their code words. The great majority of spontaneous mutations are single-point mutations, involving the alteration of but one nucleotide (Chapter 28). If we examine the mutations in human hemoglobin, we find that all those listed can be explained on the basis that only a single nucleotide in a coding triplet is altered. The result is to convert the codon into a triplet coding for another amino acid. Analysis of a very large number of such mutations, not only in human hemoglobins but also in bacterial and viral systems, reveals complete consistency between the code words established from *in vitro* tests and the nature of the amino acid replacements observed, assuming that each mutation is the result of a change in a single base. Such point mutations leading to a replacement of one amino acid by another are called *missense mutations.* The great majority of them are the result of the conversion of one purine to the other or one pyrimidine to the other, such as A → G and G → A, or C → U and U → C. However, U → A and A → U changes are also common.

Table 31-3 Some amino acid replacements in α chain of abnormal human hemoglobins. Bases undergoing mutation are in color.

Normal		*Abnormal*	*Base replacement*
Lys (AAA)	→	Glu (GAA)	A → G
Glu (GAA)	→	Gln (CAA)	G → C
Gly (GGU)	→	Asp (GAU)	G → A
His (CAU)	→	Tyr (UAU)	C → U
Asn (AAU)	→	Lys (AAA)	U → A
Glu (GAA)	→	Lys (AAA)	G → A
Glu (GAA)	→	Gly (GGA)	A → G

A second set of mutations that proved to be of great importance in checking out the code-word dictionary are the nitrous acid mutants of the tobacco mosaic virus. Treatment of pure TMV particles with nitrous acid causes chemical deamination of the amino group of one or more purine or pyrimidine bases of the viral RNA; such treatment may result in conversion of an adenine residue to hypoxanthine, and thus the conversion of adenylic acid (A) to inosinic acid (I), or the conversion of cytosine to uracil. When A, which normally base pairs with U, undergoes mutation to I, which base pairs with C, the net effect is that I mimics the action of G, since the normal base partner of G is also C. Therefore, in nitrous acid mutations of RNA, A is read as G. Similarly, C is read as U, since cytosine is directly converted to uracil by deamination. The nitrous acid–treated TMV particles are caused to replicate themselves in leaves of the host plant, the progeny viral particles are isolated, and the amino acid replacements in their coat proteins studied by means of peptide maps. Some results of such experiments are shown in Table 31-4. In every case, the amino acid replacement can be explained by the chemical conversion of A → I (which mimics G) and of C → U in a single nucleotide of the coding triplet.

Table 31-4 Some amino acid replacements in coat protein of tobacco mosaic virus mutants induced by nitrous acid. Bases undergoing change are in color

Wild-type		*Mutant*	*Base replacement*
Pro (CCC)	→	Ser (UCC)	C → U
Pro (CCC)	→	Leu (CUC)	C → U
Ile (AUU)	→	Val (GUU)	A → G
Glu (GAA)	→	Gly (GGA)	A → G
Thr (ACA)	→	Ile (AUA)	C → U
Ser (UCU)	→	Phe (UUU)	C → U

nitrous acid causes C → U or A → G

Very similar experiments have also been carried out on mutants of *E. coli* showing amino acid replacements in the protein *tryptophan synthetase.* Such replacements are completely consistent with results from the hemoglobin and the nitrous acid mutations, and thus fully confirm the code-word dictionary derived from *in vitro* studies on *E. coli* ribosomes. These findings also strongly indicate that the code is universal, since the same code words are used in man, the tobacco plant, and *E. coli* cells.

The Direction of Readout of Messenger RNA

We have already seen that the enzymatic synthesis of RNA proceeds in the direction 5′ → 3′ (Chapter 30), since the RNA polymerase adds mononucleotide units to the free 3′-hydroxyl end of the growing RNA chain. Much evidence also indicates that translation or readout of mRNA also occurs in the 5′ → 3′ direction. As we have seen, the triplet GpUpU codes for valine whereas UpUpG does not, indicating that the triplets have directional polarity. When the oligonucleotide pApApApUpUpU was tested it was found to code for Lys·Phe but not for Phe·Lys. Readout therefore begins at the phosphorylated 5′ end (which codes the NH_2-terminal residue of the amino acid) and proceeds to the 3′-OH end (which codes the COOH-terminal residue). The 5′ → 3′ readout polarity is also supported by more complex experiments involving two frame-shift mutations in a single gene.

Universality of the Code

As mentioned above, the amino acid code words appear to be identical in man, the tobacco plant, and *E. coli*. Very recently, Nirenberg and his colleagues have carried out another series of critical tests which greatly extend and confirm the general conclusion that the code is universal. They compared the ability of 50 different aminoacyl-tRNAs of two widely different species, namely, the guinea pig and the South African clawed toad, *Xenopus laevis*, to be recognized by the amino acid codons already established for *E. coli*. They isolated tRNAs from the livers of both animals and charged them with labeled amino acids, using aminoacyl-tRNA synthetase preparations obtained from the liver of each species. Such aminoacyl-tRNAs were then tested for binding to *E. coli* ribosomes, using the synthetic messengers previously employed by Nirenberg and Leder to establish the code words in *E. coli* (see above). They found that in all cases the aminoacyl-tRNAs from both the mammal and the amphibian respond correctly to the *E. coli* codons bound to *E. coli* ribosomes (Table 31-5). Furthermore, they found that no differences exist between the aminoacyl-tRNAs of liver and muscle from a single species. On the other hand, *E. coli* ribosomes bind the argininyl-tRNAs of *E. coli* corresponding to the codons AGG and CGG only weakly, but they bind their amphibian and mammalian counterparts rather strongly. Perhaps the AGG and CGG codons are not used frequently by *E. coli*, but are more important in amphibia and mammals because the latter organisms contain protein types not present in *E. coli*. Taken together, these findings suggest that the genetic language is identical in all species but that it may be modulated

Table 31-5 Species-dependent differences in binding of aminoacyl-tRNAs to trinucleotide codons. The + signs indicate the relative strength of binding.

		Source of tRNA		
AA	*Codon*	*E. coli*	*Xenopus liver*	*Guinea pig liver*
Arg	AGG	±	++++	++
	CGG	±	++++	++++
Ala	GCG	++++	±	++
Ile	AUA	±	++	++
Lys	AAG	±	++++	++++
Ser	UCG	++++	±	++
	AGU	±	+++	+++
	AGC	±	+++	+++

differently in different species, possibly as a function of evolutionary development and differentiation. For example, the homologous tRNAs of the mitochondria and cytoplasm are not identical in some eucaryotic cells (Chapter 31), a finding that supports the view that the multiple forms of tRNA for a given amino acid may reflect the degree of differentiation or evolution of the cell. The role of the degeneracy of the code in biological differentiation deserves much further study.

Evolution of the Amino Acid Code

A number of interesting hypotheses of the origin and evolution of the genetic code have been proposed. First of all, the universality of the code suggests that it arose but once in the course of biological evolution. Since fossil evidence suggests that bacteria existed as early as 3000 million years ago, it appears probable that the genetic code must have been functional at that time. The finding that the first two letters of the code words bear most of the specificity has been interpreted to mean that the amino acid code may once have been a doublet code coding for a group of 15 "primordial" amino acids (Table 31-6). Possibly in its primitive form the doublet code employed a third nucleotide as a comma. Later, a group of "new" amino acids may have arisen, namely, asparagine, glutamine, methionine, tyrosine, and tryptophan, which then required triplets for their coding; the third nucleotide for such triplets may have arisen from the symbols used for commas in the original doublet code.

Table 31-6 Proposed primordial doublet code

Doublet	*Primordial amino acid*	*Additions*	*"New" amino acid*
AA	Lys	C or U	Asn
AC	Thr		
AG	Ser, Arg		
AU	Ile	G	Met
CA	His	A or G	Gln
CC	Pro		
CG	Arg		
CU	Leu		
GA	Asp, Glu		
GC	Ala		
GG	Gly		
GU	Val		
UA	End	C or U	Tyr
UC	Ser		
UG	Cys	G	Trp
UU	Phe		

The degeneracy of the genetic code is a feature that gives it survival value. If there were only one code word for each amino acid, only 20 of the possible 64 codons would be used, and most point mutations of coding triplets would result in nonsense triplets, not coding for any amino acid. On the other hand, in the existing code, a mutation in most cases simply yields a missense triplet, and thus a replacement of one amino acid by another, or a syonym triplet (i.e., a "silent" mutation), which results in an unchanged gene product. With the degenerate code, protein resulting from the mutation is often still functional and, indeed, may even be a better protein than the wild-type. The degenerate code thus allows for gradual improvement of the genome and its gene products, because it permits a variety of different amino acid replacements to occur by mutation, from which that replacement with the best survival value can be selected.

Since the most frequent mutations involve transitions, especially A → G or C → T changes, which usually have no effect on the amino acid coded if they occur in the third position, the degeneracy of the code may be considered to have protective value in stabilizing the genome against mutation.

Finally, another interesting and very significant feature is the relationship between the code words of amino acids having similar R groups. For example, all codons having U as the second letter belong to amino acids having nonpolar or hydrophobic side chains (Phe, Leu, Ile, Val). The very similar amino acids alanine and glycine contain only C and G as first or second letters. Similarly, the negatively charged amino acids aspartic and glutamic acid both have GA as their first two letters. Similar but less specific relationships may be observed between the similar amino acids serine, threonine, and cysteine. In all probability, the specific code words for the various amino acids arose because of some relationship to the chemical structures and physical properties of the amino acids, whose specific nature is not yet apparent.

Despite the universality of the genetic code, the proportion of the four bases in DNA varies widely with the species (Chapter 28). Thus, the DNA in various bacteria contains anywhere from 30 to 70 percent G + C. Those bacteria having a high G + C content may therefore use more frequently those codons in which the third position is either G or C, compared with the bacteria having a low G + C content. The reason for the evolution of these striking variations is not clear.

Code Words for Initiation and Termination of Chains

Although no punctuation is required between separate amino acid code words, punctuation is used for the initiation and termination of a polypeptide chain. Actually, considerable evidence suggests that a special termination signal is always required before a completed polypeptide chain can be released in free form. When protein synthesis is coded for by a natural messenger, the polypeptide chain is released in free form, presumably after hydrolytic removal from its COOH-terminal tRNA. However, when polypeptide synthesis is coded for by synthetic messengers, such as poly U, the newly formed chain remains attached to the ribosomes as polyphenylalanyl-$tRNA_{Phe}$, presumably because poly U contains no termination signal. Presumably the chain-termination signal promotes the binding of a specific protein release factor which promotes hydrolysis of peptidyl-tRNA. Similarly, an initiating signal may be necessary to ensure that the ribosome will begin readout of a given mRNA at its 5′-phosphate end, and not at some indefinite point in the middle of the chain.

After many negative efforts to ascertain which amino acids are coded for by the unassigned or nonsense triplets UAG, UAA, and UGA, it was ultimately concluded that they are not used for amino acid coding. Many genetic experiments were then carried out to determine the consequence of mutation to or from these triplets. The two nonsense triplets UAG and UAA, which are called *amber* and *ochre*, respectively, were ultimately identified as signals for chain termination, from the observation that a mutation of a codon normally specifying an amino acid to form an *amber* or *ochre* codon leads to synthesis of a polypeptide chain which is terminated at the amino acid residue prior to that specified by the mutated codon. Among the amino acid codons that are mutational precursors of the *amber* codon UAG are serine (UCG), glutamine (CAG), and tyrosine (UAU or UAC).

Figure 31-6
Identification of the amber codon from mutations to amber and reversions from amber. The bases undergoing mutation or reversion are in color.

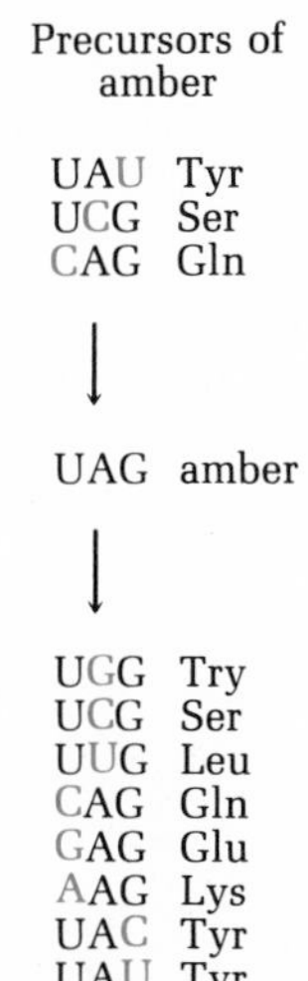

Each of these codons can be converted to UAG by a single base change (Figure 31-6). An example of an *amber* mutant is the *sus* 13 mutant of the f2 RNA bacteriophage of *E. coli*. The wild-type f2 coat protein begins with the NH_2-terminal sequence fMet-Ala-Ser-Asn-Phe-Thr-Gln. In the *sus* 13 *amber* mutant, only the hexapeptide fMet-Ala-Ser-Asn-Phe-Thr is synthesized and then released in free form. Since CAG, the codon for the next amino acid (glutamine) can undergo mutation to the *amber* codon UAG, it was concluded that *amber* signals the termination of the chain and its release in free form. Normally, in the absence of the mutation, the next amino acid glutamine would be introduced and the resulting heptapeptide would remain attached as heptapeptidyl-$tRNA_{Gln}$.

Other genetic experiments have shown that *amber* mutants, which make incomplete, prematurely discharged proteins, may revert on further mutation to forms which can now make a complete protein but in which one amino acid is not necessarily identical with the corresponding amino acid in the wild-type protein. In such cases, the amber codon UAG has reverted in a single point mutation to a sense codon that specifies an amino acid, but it may not be the same amino acid present in the wild-type protein, as is seen in Figure 31-6. Such mutations to and from the chain-terminating codon identified UAG as *amber*. Similar genetic experiments have also identified the *ochre* codon UAA and the codon UGA (also called *umber*) as termination codons. The three termination codons are probably not used with equal frequency; indeed, recent research suggests that the *ochre* codon UAA is the normal termination signal.

The tRNAs and the code words for the initiating fMet residue have been given much attention. It now appears that there are actually two tRNAs specific for methionine, $tRNA_F$ and $tRNA_M$. The former may be used for transfer of *N*-formylmethione into the initiating position, and the latter only for transfer of methionine into interior positions of a polypeptide chain. The identity of the signal for fMet vs. interior Met residues is not clear, since there is only one code word for methionine, namely, AUG, which is known to be employed for coding all interior methionine residues.

Formation of Uncoded Amino Acids in Proteins

Some proteins contain amino acids in peptide linkage that do not possess genetic code words. Thus, collagen contains hydroxyproline and hydroxylysine, and elastin contains desmosine and isodesmosine. In all cases in which uncoded amino acids have been proved to be present in proteins, they are derivatives of amino acids that do possess code words. Hydroxyproline is derived from proline, and hydroxylysine and desmosine are derived from lysine. These rare amino acids are formed enzymatically from the parent amino acids *after* the latter have been inserted into peptide linkage in response to coding by their specific triplets.

Colinearity of the Gene and the Polypeptide Chain

It has long been assumed, as part of the central dogma of molecular genetics, that there is a linear correspondence between the sequence of codons in the gene and the sequence of amino acids in the polypeptide chain it codes. This assumption became quite explicit with the experiments of Crick and his colleagues on intragenic suppressor mutations, particularly those in which three mutations of the same sign (deletions or insertions) yield the correct reading-frame relationship and often also yield functional proteins. However, a more direct type of proof of colinearity of the gene and the polypeptide chain was required. One of the most elegant studies is that of Yanofsky and his colleagues, who have painstakingly analyzed a number of mutant forms of the polypeptide chain of an enzyme to determine the position of the amino acid changes and then related these positions to a high-resolution genetic map of the structural gene for the enzyme.

They studied mutational changes in the A chain of *tryptophan synthetase,* which catalyzes the last step in the synthesis of tryptophan in *E. coli*. This enzyme consists of two identical A chains, each of 267 residues, and two identical B chains. The complete amino acid sequence of the A chain of the normal wild-type enzyme has been established. Yanofsky isolated many *E. coli* mutants which possessed an amino acid replacement somewhere in the A protein. Each of these mutants was grown in large quantities and the defective A protein isolated from each. By means of the peptide-mapping technique the residues that underwent replacement were located at specific points along the 267-residue chain of the A protein.

By means of genetic mapping techniques, the relative sequence of the mutations on the linear map of the A gene and the sequence of the amino acid replacements in the A protein could be compared. For 12 different mutations of the A gene, the relative positions of the mutated sites in the gene map were identical with the relative positions of the amino acid replacements in the polypeptide chain (Figure 31-7). These important experiments, which have more recently been extended to a total of over 20 mutants, have clearly established that the gene and its homologous polypeptide chain are colinear.

This conclusion has also been reached by Brenner and his colleagues, who studied nonsense mutations in the T4 bacteriophage gene coding for the head protein of the virus. In these mutations the polypeptide chain was prematurely terminated in different positions. The relative length of the polypeptide chains formed agreed with the relative positions of the amino acids whose codons were mutated into nonsense codons. These findings, together with evidence that the triplet amino acid code is commaless, that codons are read in one specific direction, and, as we shall see in Chapter 33, that an entire sequence of genes is read in one direction, provide compelling proof for the colinearity of the gene and its polypeptide products.

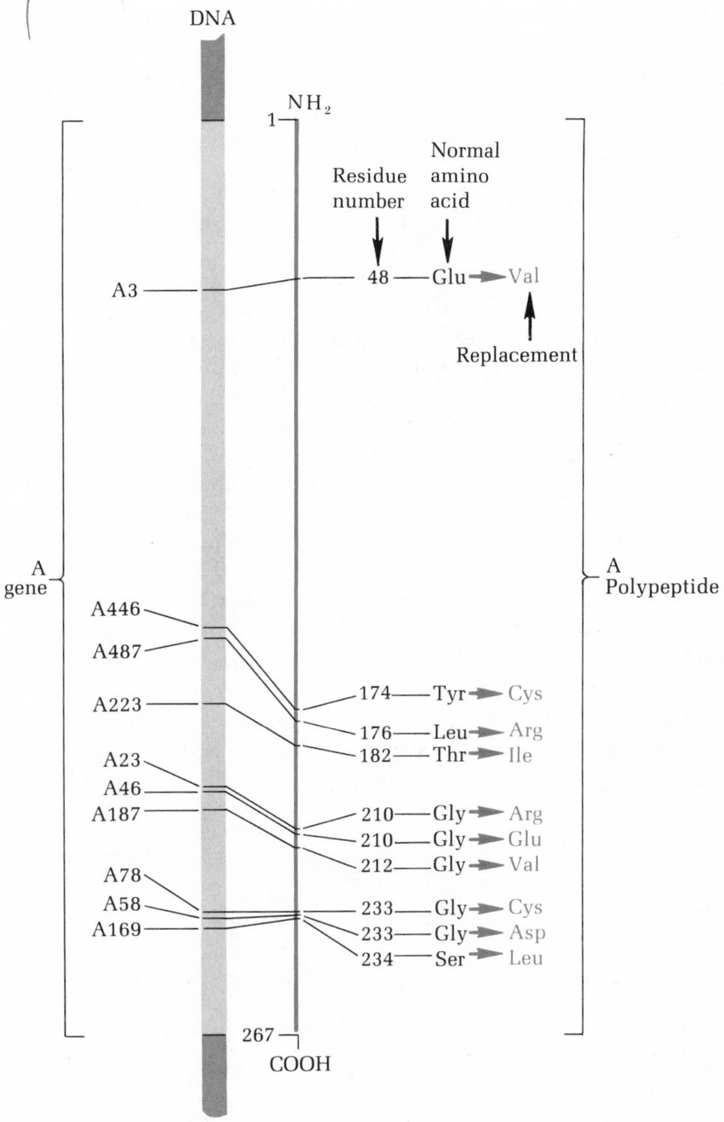

Figure 31-7
Colinearity of the A gene and A polypeptide of tryptophan synthetase in E. coli. The mutants in the genetic map are numbered arbitrarily. Redrawn from "Gene Structure and Protein Structure" by C. Yanofsky. Copyright © May, 1967 by Scientific American, Inc. All rights reserved.

Summary

From structural studies on viruses and from genetic studies utilizing intragenic suppressor mutations, the amino acid code words are deduced to consist of triplets of successive nucleotides in DNA and the messenger RNA transcribed from it. The most important evidence for a commaless triplet code comes from the finding that three mutations of the same sign (all deletions or all insertions) within a single gene cause complete suppression of missense in that part of the peptide chain coded after the point of the third mutation.

The nucleotide composition of the coding triplets for amino acids was deduced by incubating *E. coli* ribosomes, previously depleted of their normal messenger RNA, with synthetic messengers, i.e., polyribonucleotides of known base composition and ratio, together with mixtures of amino acids of which only one was labeled at a time. Observation of the specific amino acids incorporated in the presence of a given synthetic messenger led to identification of the nucleotide composition of coding triplets for the various amino acids.

The sequence of bases in each triplet was deduced from experiments on the effect of nucleotide triplets of known base sequence on the binding of various labeled aminoacyl-tRNAs to ribosomes, in the absence of ATP and GTP. A given aminoacyl-tRNA is bound to ribosomes only in the presence of its specific coding triplet. The codons so identified are consistent with observed amino acid replacements in abnormal human hemoglobins and nitrous acid mutants of tobacco mosaic virus protein, on the assumption that each mutation is a point mutation. Codons are read in the $5' \rightarrow 3'$ direction, i.e., from the 5′-phosphate end.

The amino acid code is degenerate: it has multiple code words for all amino acids except tryptophan and methionine. The third position in each codon is much less specific than the first and second; the degeneracy is usually in the third position. Since the genetic code is identical in *E. coli*, tobacco mosaic virus, the amphibian *Xenopus*, and mammals, it is probably universal. The "nonsense" triplets UAA (ochre), UAG (amber), and UGA code for no amino acids but are signals for chain termination. UAA (ochre) is probably the normal chain terminator. Chain initiation begins with *N*-formylmethionine, which is probably coded by AUG.

The colinearity of coding triplets in DNA with the amino acid sequence of the polypeptide product, which was implicit in earlier studies on the genetic code, is explicitly proved by the work of Yanofsky, who showed that the sequence of sites of mutation in the linear map of the A gene of tryptophan synthetase corresponds to the sequence of amino acid replacements in the corresponding A polypeptide.

References

Books

JUKES, T. H.: *Molecules and Evolution*, Columbia University Press, New York, 1966. A theory of the evolution of the genetic code.

The Genetic Code, Cold Spring Harbor Symposia in Quant. Biol., vol. 31, 1966. A collection of reviews and articles on the experimental basis of the amino acid code words.

WOESE, C. R.: *The Genetic Code*, Harper and Row, New York, 1967. The origin and evolution of the code.

ZUBAY, G. (ed.): *Papers in Biochemical Genetics*, Holt, Rinehart and Winston, Inc., New York, 1968.

Articles

BRENNER, S., L. BARNETT, E. R. KATZ, and F. H. C. CRICK: "UGA: A Third Nonsense Triplet in the Genetic Code," *Nature*, **413:**449–450 (1967).

CRICK, F. H. C.: "The Origin of the Genetic Code," *J. Mol. Biol.*, **38:**367–379 (1968). The biological evolution and logic of the code.

———: "Codon-Anticodon Pairing: The Wobble Hypothesis," *J. Mol. Biol*, **19:** 584 (1966). The structural explanation of the play or "wobble" in the fit of the third nucleotide of a codon.

GAREN, A.: "Sense and Nonsense in the Genetic Code," *Science*, **160:**149–159 (1968). A short review of the significance of the nonsense code words.

GHOSH, H. P., D. SOLL, and H. G. KHORANA: "Studies on Polynucleotides, LXVII. Initiation of Protein Synthesis in vitro as Studied by Using Ribopolynucleotides with Repeating Nucleotide Sequences as Messengers," *J. Mol. Biol.*, **25**:275 (1967). Use of repeating or block polymers of ribonucleotides as synthetic messengers.

HELINSKI, D., and C. YANOFSKY: "Genetic Control of Protein Structure," in H. Neurath (ed.), *The Proteins*, vol. 4, pp. 1–93, 1966.

MARSHALL, R. E., C. T. CASKEY, and M. NIRENBERG: "Fine Structure of RNA Codewords Recognized by Bacterial, Amphibian, and Mammalian Transfer RNA," *Science*, **155**:820–826 (1967). An important survey of species differences in use of the codons.

NIRENBERG, M. W., and J. H. MATTHAEI: "The Dependence of Cell-free Protein Synthesis in *E. coli* upon Naturally Occurring or Synthetic Polyribonucleotides," *Proc. Natl. Acad. Sci. (U.S.)*, **47**:1588–1602 (1961). Classic paper showing dependence of ribosomes on RNA messengers and coding of polyphenylalanine by poly U.

NIRENBERG, M. W., and P. LEDER: "RNA Codewords and Protein Synthesis," *Science*, **145**:1399–1407 (1964). The binding assay: the sequence of bases in amino acid codons.

SINGER, M. F., and P. LEDER: "Messenger RNA: An Evaluation," *Ann. Rev. Biochem*, **35**:195 (1966). A review of the evidence for the messenger hypothesis and of the response of ribosomes to various RNA messengers and codons.

Problems

1. Write the amino acid sequences of polypeptides corresponding to the DNA sequences in Figure 31-1. Indicate the missense sequences resulting from the frame-shift and suppressor mutations shown.
2. *E. coli* ribosomes depleted of their endogenous messenger RNA were incubated with the random polymer poly AG, in which the molar ratio A:G was 5:1. Predict which amino acids were incorporated by such a polymer and the relative frequency of their incorporation.
3. In an experiment similar to that in problem 2 the synthetic messenger was poly UG in which the molar ratio U:G was 1:1. Predict which amino acids would be most frequently incorporated.
4. Predict the amino acid sequences of peptides formed by ribosomes in response to the following messengers, assuming each chain begins with the triplet on the left.
   (a) GGUCAGUCGCUCCUGAUU
   (b) UUGGAUGCGCCAUAAUUUGCU
   (c) CACGACGCUUGUUGCUAU
   (d) AUGGACGAA
5. Which of the following amino acid replacements in mutant proteins are consistent with the genetic code? If any are inconsistent, state why. (a) Phe → Leu (b) Ile → Leu (c) Ala → Thr (d) Pro → Ser (e) Lys → Ala (f) His → Glu (g) Phe → Lys
6. One strand of DNA contains the following sequence, reading from 5′ → 3′. Write (a) the sequence of bases in the other strand of the DNA (b) the sequence of bases in the mRNA

transcribed from the first strand of DNA and (c) the actual amino acid sequence coded. A-T-C-G-T-C-G-A-C-G-A-T-G-A-T-C-A-T-C-G-G-C-T-A-C-T-C-G-A

7. Using the information of Tables 5-6 and 31-5 on the abnormal α chains of hemoglobin, state whether each mutation is a transition or transversion. Assume that all mutations are single-point.

CHAPTER 32 REGULATION OF PROTEIN SYNTHESIS: CELL DIFFERENTIATION

Living cells must possess accurately programmed mechanisms for regulating the relative amounts of different types of proteins that are synthesized. For example, the number of molecules of those enzymes catalyzing a mainstream metabolic pathway is in all probability much greater than the number of molecules of the enzymes catalyzing the biosynthesis of the coenzymes, which are needed in only trace amounts. Furthermore, certain enzymes in bacterial cells change in concentration in response to changes in the availability of nutrients from the environment. Regulation of the rate of synthesis of various enzymes makes possible economy in the synthesis of both RNA and of protein, just as allosteric control of biosynthetic reactions results in economical use of carbon and nitrogen sources in the synthesis of small biomolecules. Regulation of enzyme synthesis may be thought of as affording coarse control over metabolism, whereas allosteric regulation yields fine control.

Regulation of protein synthesis has another fundamental role: in the differentiation of cells. Different cell types in higher organisms possess characteristically different sets of enzymatic activities, superimposed on the common enzymes all cells possess for catalysis of central metabolic pathways. Moreover, different types of noncatalytic proteins, specialized to serve in one or another function, are known to be formed as cells and tissues differentiate. The synthesis of different proteins during cell differentiation must obviously be accurately programmed, with respect not only to the relative numbers of each protein but also to the time and sequence of their appearance.

Most of our present knowledge of the regulation of protein synthesis has come from genetic studies on bacteria, which have yielded important theoretical concepts and hypotheses regarding the nature of the regulatory processes. However, biochemical approaches have recently yielded some major advances.

Enzyme Induction

The amount of certain enzymes in bacterial cells responds dramatically to the nature of the nutrients in the culture medium. Study of these changes has led to our present knowledge of the molecular mechanism of the regulation of protein synthesis. Two types of response have been recognized, *enzyme induction* (formerly called enzyme adaptation) and *enzyme repression*.

An *adaptive* or *inducible enzyme* is normally present only in traces in bacterial cells, but its concentration increases greatly when its substrate is added to the culture medium. Enzyme induction is most conspicuous when the inducing substrate is the only carbon or nitrogen source of the cell; the enzyme in question is therefore required to transform the substrate into a metabolite that can be directly utilized by the cell. The classic example of an inducible enzyme is *β-galactosidase*. Wild-type *E. coli* cells do not utilize lactose (glucose-4-β-D-galactoside) if glucose is available to them. However, if wild-type *E. coli* cells are placed in a culture medium containing lactose as sole carbon source, they are at first unable to utilize lactose but very quickly respond by synthesizing β-galactosidase in large amounts. Since this enzyme can hydrolyze lactose to D-galactose and D-glucose, the induced enzyme makes it possible for the cell to use lactose as sole carbon source. If the induced cells are now transferred to a medium containing glucose and no lactose, further synthesis of the enzyme ceases immediately and the already induced galactosidase activity is diluted by further growth of the cell population until it reaches its usually low level. Most known inducible enzymes catalyze reactions important in catabolism.

Some bacteria show exceptional capacity to form inducible enzymes in response to a great number of different substrates, many of which appear to be "unphysiological." *Pseudomonads*, for example, have been found to form enzymes in response to hundreds of different organic compounds. For this reason, early investigators suggested that the presence of the substrate molecule helped to "adapt" or "mold" the active site of the induced enzyme and that all induced enzymes may be molded from a single protein.

Early studies also led to the concept that induced enzymes are fundamentally different from another class of enzymes, the *constitutive* enzymes, which appeared to be formed at constant rates and in constant amounts, regardless of the presence of their substrates. Constitutive enzymes were held to be part of the permanent and basic enzymatic machinery of the cell, such as the enzymes of the glycolytic sequence.

Enzyme Repression

When *E. coli* cells grow on a medium containing an ammonium salt as sole nitrogen source, they must make all their nitrogenous components from the NH_4^+ ion and a carbon source. Such cells contain all the requisite enzymes for synthesis of the 20 different amino acids required in protein synthesis. However, if one of these amino acids, such as histidine, is added to the culture medium, the enzymes required for making histidine quickly disappear from the cells. This effect is called *enzyme repression.* Repression is clearly a reflection of the principle of cellular economy: when the enzymes required for histidine synthesis are no longer required, they are no longer made. Repression of the synthesis of a group of enzymes catalyzing a sequence of consecutive metabolic reactions, which is called *coordinate repression,* has suggested that the genes coding these enzymes are grouped together in the chromosome. Coordinate repression is ordinarily evoked by the end product of the series of biosynthetic reactions catalyzed by the repressed enzymes; for this reason it is also called *end-product repression.* Most cases of enzyme repression involve enzymes participating in biosynthetic reactions.

There is another type of enzyme repression that has raised some fundamental questions regarding the relationships between enzyme induction and repression. It is a general observation that glucose and other "main-line" fuel sources can suppress the formation of many inducible enzymes. For example, the presence of glucose in the culture medium represses the formation of β-galactosidase even in the presence of lactose. Glucose also represses some enzymes which had earlier been thought to be constitutive, for example, certain of the enzymes of respiration and electron transport, possibly because the presence of a readily fermentable fuel supply makes it unnecessary for a facultative bacterial cell to use respiration pathways. Since the signal for this kind of repression is presumably given by the elevation of the intracellular level of some catabolic product of the main-line fuel, such enzyme repression is often called *catabolite repression.*

Regulator Genes and Repressors

The molecular and genetic relationships between enzyme induction and enzyme repression, which at first were thought to be wholly different processes, became much clearer in the 1950s from extended studies by Monod and Jacob and their colleagues on the induction of β-galactosidase in *E. coli* cells. They made the important discovery that the formation of this enzyme can be stimulated not only by those β-D-galactosides that are hydrolyzed by the enzyme, such as lactose or methyl β-D-galactoside, but also by some β-galactosides that are not, such as methyl β-D-thiogalactoside, the sulfur analog of methyl β-D-galactoside. In fact, methyl β-D-thiogalactoside was found to induce formation of β-galactosidase even more effectively than its normal substrates. This effect, called *gratuitous induction,* made it possible to separate the induction phenomenon from the metabolic consequences of the hydrolysis of the inducing molecule.

For some years it had appeared questionable that cells would contain many different genes for making many different enzymes to act on substrates which are unphysiological and which the cell would not ordinarily encounter outside the laboratory. However, there is today no doubt that all inducible enzymes are specified by genes. Actually, mutants of *E. coli* cells unable to form β-galactosidase in response to its inducer have long been known; moreover, similar mutants have since been found for many other inducible enzymes in a number of organisms. It is important to note that such mutations are specific; that is, a mutant defective in the capacity to form β-galactosidase can still form other inducible enzymes. No evidence whatsoever supports the older view that many different induced enzymes could be molded from one gene product.

There is, however, another class of mutants of *E. coli* which became extremely important in analyzing the regulation of β-galactosidase synthesis. These mutants contain large amounts of β-galactosidase, even though the cells have never been exposed to an inducing agent. Such mutants are called *constitutive mutants,* because they behave as though β-galactosidase is a constitutive rather than an inducible enzyme. Further study showed that there are three different loci in the genetic map of *E. coli* that influence formation of β-galactosidase; these are designated z, R, and O. One of these loci, z, determines the amino acid sequence of the β-galactosidase molecule; mutations in this locus lead to synthesis of a defective or inactive enzyme molecule possessing amino acid replacements. This type of gene is called a *structural gene,* and it is defined as a gene that carries the message coding for the amino acid sequence of a specific protein, in this case the β-galactosidase. The second or R locus was postulated to have no influence on the structure of β-galactosidase, but rather to function as a "switching" gene; it controls whether the structural gene for β-galactosidase is transcribed. Such a gene is called a *regulatory* or *R gene,* and it was postulated to inhibit the transcription of the structural gene. When the R gene undergoes mutation and becomes defective, it can no longer inhibit the transcription of the structural gene, and β-galactosidase is then synthesized whether or not the inducer is present. The R gene thus explains the origin of constitutive mutants.

An important clue to the nature of the R gene product came from experiments of Pardee, Jacob, and Monod. They found that when an intact R gene is introduced into a mutant cell with a defective R gene (designated as an R^- cell), in the form of a segment of DNA from an R^+ donor cell, it can repress the transcription of not only the corresponding structural gene in the DNA segment from the donor cell but also the structural gene in the acceptor cell, which is thus transformed from a constitutive mutant into an R^+ cell. This observation means that the R gene forms a product that is diffusible; it can reach its corresponding structural gene wherever it is located in the cell.

Jacob and Monod then formulated a general hypothesis relating the function of structural genes and R genes; it provides a unifying explanation of both enzyme induction and enzyme repression. In their hypothesis enzyme repression is the basic process; enzyme induction is simply the release of repression. The structural gene codes for the amino acid sequence of a given enzyme; synthesis of this enzyme will normally occur unless it is repressed by the action of a specific regulatory gene R. The R gene may

Figure 32-1
Steps in induction of β-galactosidase activity in E. coli.

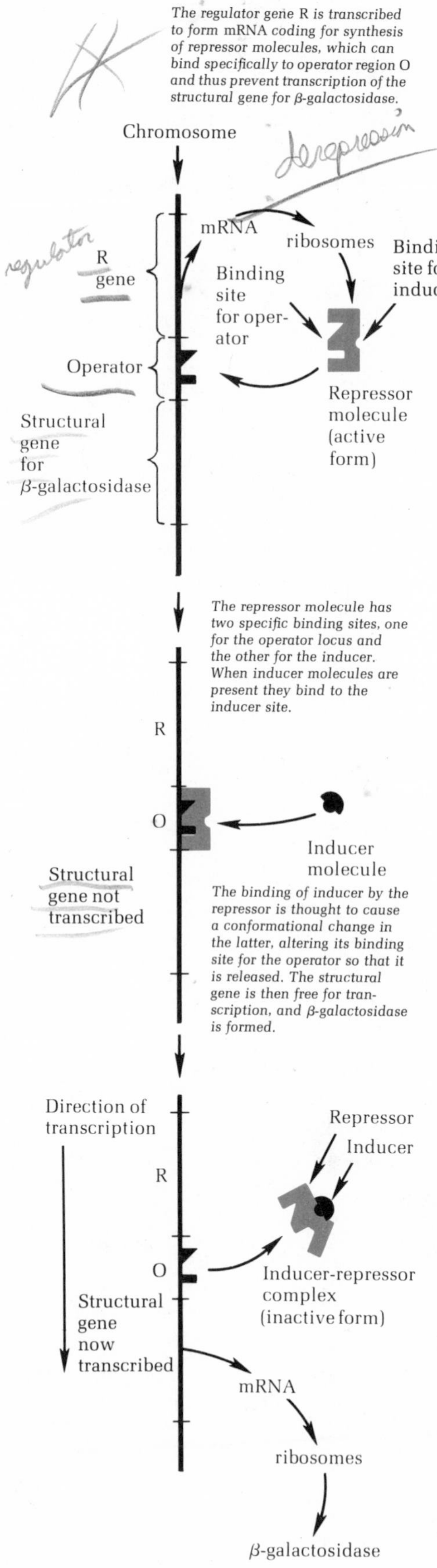
The regulator gene R is transcribed to form mRNA coding for synthesis of repressor molecules, which can bind specifically to operator region O and thus prevent transcription of the structural gene for β-galactosidase.
Chromosome
mRNA
ribosomes
Binding site for inducer
R gene
Binding site for operator
Operator
Repressor molecule (active form)
Structural gene for β-galactosidase
The repressor molecule has two specific binding sites, one for the operator locus and the other for the inducer. When inducer molecules are present they bind to the inducer site.
R
O
Inducer molecule
Structural gene not transcribed
The binding of inducer by the repressor is thought to cause a conformational change in the latter, altering its binding site for the operator so that it is released. The structural gene is then free for transcription, and β-galactosidase is formed.
Direction of transcription
Repressor
Inducer
R
O
Inducer-repressor complex (inactive form)
Structural gene now transcribed
mRNA
ribosomes
β-galactosidase

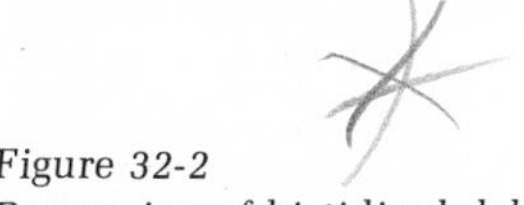

Figure 32-2
Repression of histidinol dehydrogenase.

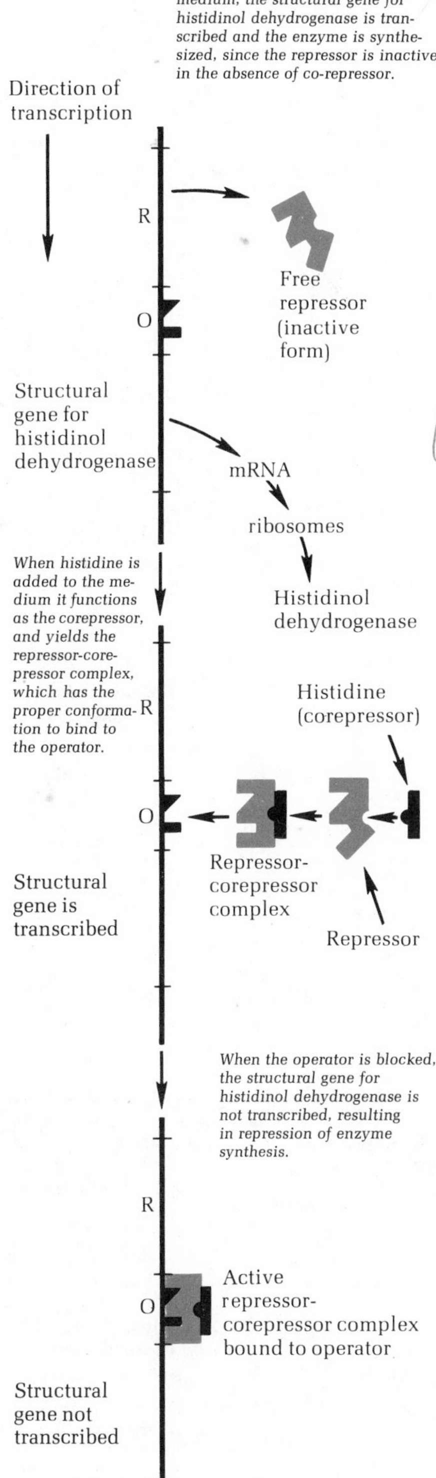
When no histidine is present in the medium, the structural gene for histidinol dehydrogenase is transcribed and the enzyme is synthesized, since the repressor is inactive in the absence of co-repressor.
Direction of transcription
R
Free repressor (inactive form)
O
Structural gene for histidinol dehydrogenase
mRNA
ribosomes
Histidinol dehydrogenase
When histidine is added to the medium it functions as the corepressor, and yields the repressor-corepressor complex, which has the proper conformation to bind to the operator.
R
Histidine (corepressor)
O
Repressor-corepressor complex
Repressor
Structural gene is transcribed
When the operator is blocked, the structural gene for histidinol dehydrogenase is not transcribed, resulting in repression of enzyme synthesis.
R
O
Active repressor-corepressor complex bound to operator
Structural gene not transcribed

inhibit the synthesis of but one specific enzyme, or a series of functionally related enzymes.

How can the regulatory gene function in both repression and induction of enzyme activity? To account for repression, it was postulated that the R gene codes for the amino acid sequence of a specific protein called the *repressor*. The repressor molecule was postulated to diffuse from the ribosomes, where it is formed, and to become physically bound to the segment of DNA containing the structural gene of the enzyme whose synthesis it controls. When the repressor is bound, it prevents the transcription of the structural gene to form the corresponding mRNA. The repressor molecule was postulated to possess a binding site specific for a segment of DNA near the gene that normally codes for the synthesis of the enzyme; the precise location of the binding site of the repressor, namely, the *operator*, or *O locus*, will be considered below.

How can this hypothesis explain the phenomenon of enzyme induction? In the absence of inducer, Jacob and Monod postulated that the repressor molecule occurs in its free or active state, in which it combines with the segment of DNA bearing the structural gene, thus preventing its transcription (Figure 32-1). But when inducer is present, it combines with the repressor protein at a specific complementary binding site on the latter to form an inactive *repressor-inducer complex*; the complex is not able to bind to the segment of DNA containing the structural gene. The structural gene thus becomes free for transcription and the enzyme is then synthesized. The interaction between the inducing agent and the repressor molecule was postulated to be reversible, to account for the fact that when the inducing agent is removed from the culture medium or is used up by enzymatic action, enzyme synthesis is repressed again rapidly. The repressor molecule was thus conceived to be a protein having two specific binding sites, one for the inducer and one for the operator locus. When the inducer site is filled, the operator binding site is no longer functional.

The hypothesis of Jacob and Monod also accounts for repression of an enzyme or enzyme system by a biosynthetic end product. For example, the presence of histidine in the culture medium of *E. coli* represses the formation of the enzyme (i.e., histidinol dehydrogenase) required to form histidine from its immediate precursor histidinol. Constitutive mutants of *E. coli* have been found, however, which make this enzyme in maximal amounts whether or not histidine is present in the medium. The enzyme is therefore specified by a structural gene that can be repressed by its end product. To account for end-product repression, it was postulated that the repressor molecule in such cases is inactive by itself, but when it binds the repressing metabolite, which is called the *corepressor*, to form a *repressor-corepressor complex*, the complex combines with the operator locus for the structural gene and thus prevents transcription of the latter (Figure 32-2). Therefore, there are two classes of repressor molecules, one operative in the control of inducible enzymes and the other in end-product repression. Both types contain two binding sites, one being specific for the operator locus.

The Operon and the Operator

Jacob and Monod extended their hypothesis for the regulation of protein synthesis to provide mechanisms for *coordinate repression*, in which a group of enzymes may be repressed by a single repressor, and *coordinate induction*, in which a group of enzymes can be induced by a single inducer. For example, when the presence of histidine in the medium represses histidine synthesis, it represses not only the formation of the last enzyme in the sequence forming histidine but several preceding enzymes as well. Similarly, when the gratuitous inducing agent methyl β-thiogalactoside is added to *E. coli* cells, it induces the formation of not only β-galactosidase, but also two functionally related enzymes, *β-galactoside permease* and *β-thiogalactoside-transacetylase*. The former is a protein in the membrane of the *E. coli* cell which can promote the passage of β-galactosides into the cell against a concentration gradient; the function of the latter is not entirely clear, but presumably it is used in some step in the utilization of thiogalactosides in the cell. These three enzymes are coded for by three structural genes, designated z, y, and a, respectively (Figure 32-3). Together they constitute an *operon*, defined as a group of related genes mapping close to each other in the chromosome, which can be coordinately turned on or off by a single inducing or a single repressing agent, respectively. The group of three genes coding for the formation of the three proteins involved in β-galactoside hydrolysis and transport is known as the *lac operon* (Figure 32-3). The histidine or *his* operon mentioned above has a total of 15 genes coding a total of 10 enzymes (Figure 32-4). A number of other operons are now well known, including one for galactose metabolism (*gal*) and operons for leucine, isoleucine, and valine biosynthesis (Table 32-1). Not all enzyme systems are specified by genes that lie close to each other on the metabolic map. Some, such as the system catalyzing arginine biosynthesis, are coded for by genes that are scattered throughout the chromosome. Regulation of the latter type of system is only roughly coordinated, and the genetic and biochemical principles underlying their control are not fully understood.

The question now arises: How can an entire operon be repressed by a single repressor, in an all-or-none manner? Two types of constitutive mutants of *E. coli* have been found in which all the enzymes of the *lac* operon are fully active whether or not inducer or corepressor is present. One type affects the regulatory gene for the operon and leads to formation of a defective repressor molecule, as we have already discussed. The other type of constitutive mutant affects neither the regulatory gene nor the structural genes coding for the proteins of the lac operon. It has been concluded that such mutants fail to respond to the repressor substance because the specific site on the chromosome to which the repressor

Figure 32-3
The lac operon, *showing the sequence of the three genes.*

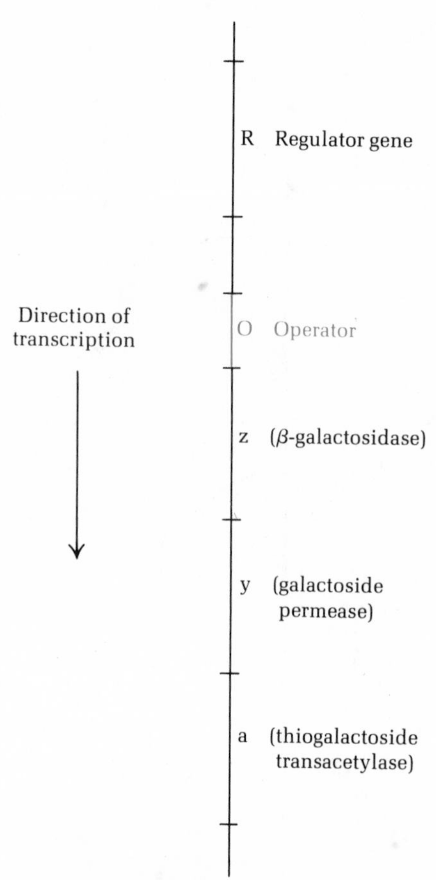

Table 32-1 Some operons in bacteria. (The operons listed have been most thoroughly studied in *E. coli*, except the *his* operon, which has been examined in detail in *Salmonella typhimurium*.)

Operon	*Number of Enzymes*	*Function*
lac	3	Hydrolysis and transport of β-galactosides
his	10	Synthesis of histidine
gal	3	Galactose transport and conversion to glucose 1-phosphate
leu	4	Conversion of α-ketoisovalerate to leucine
trp	4	Conversion of anthranilic acid to tryptophan
ara	4	Transport and utilization of arabinose
ile	5	Synthesis of isoleucine from threonine

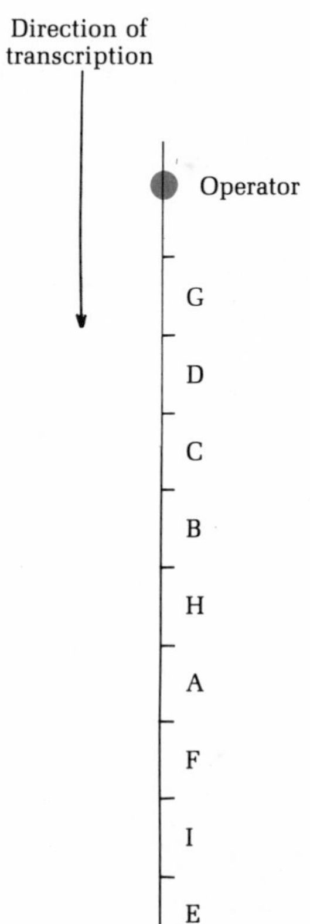

Figure 32-4
Map of the genes (A–I) of the his operon.

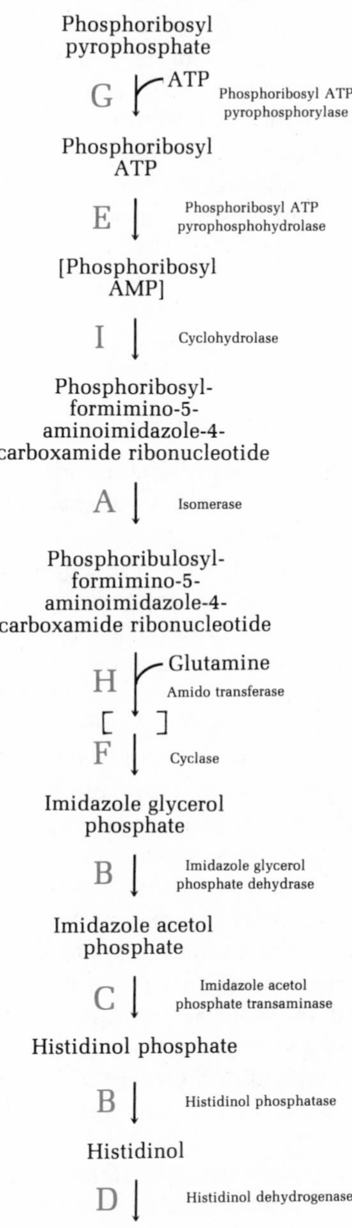

Steps in the enzymatic synthesis of histidine (Chapter 24). The enzymes are lettered to correspond with the genetic map.

molecule normally binds is defective. The existence of these mutants also suggested that the locus in the DNA molecule which is the receptor or binding site for the repressor is not part of the structural gene for any one of the constituent enzymes of the operon, nor of the regulatory gene, since they can be shown to have normal activity. This locus was called the <u>operator</u> by Jacob and

Monod. The independent existence of the operator, separate from the structural genes and regulatory genes, was more firmly established by crucial genetic experiments. When the repressor molecule is bound to the operator locus, none of the enzymes of the operon are formed. When the repressor is removed, all of the enzymes are formed. When the operator locus itself undergoes mutation to form an *operator-constitutive mutant*, all the enzymes of the operon are synthesized whether or not inducers are present. Presumably the operator is located on the chromosome in such a way that it can control the transcription of a whole segment of the chromosome.

The Isolation and Chemical Nature of Repressors

Although the hypothesis of Jacob and Monod brilliantly succeeded in explaining many aspects of the behavior of inducible and repressible enzymes and has withstood many stringent genetic tests, for a long time no direct chemical evidence for the existence of the hypothetical repressor molecules could be adduced. In fact, it appeared unlikely that direct chemical identification of such repressors would ever be feasible. For one thing, genetic calculations indicated that a single *E. coli* cell contains only about 10 hypothetical repressor molecules for the *lac* operon. Since the *E. coli* cell contains altogether millions of protein molecules, it would appear to be a most formidable task to isolate the *lac* repressor substance in pure form. However, since the Jacob-Monod concept of repression is fundamental to so much genetic theory and experimentation, the task of isolating repressor molecules has been a major goal. Recent research by Gilbert and by Ptashne has led to the isolation and identification of two different repressor molecules and to experimental verification of a central feature of the Jacob-Monod hypothesis: direct and specific binding of the repressor to DNA.

The repressor isolated by Gilbert and his colleague Müller-Hill is that responsible for repressing β-galactosidase activity. We shall describe it in some detail in the light of the preceding discussion on the *lac* operon. Because of the very small number of *lac* repressor molecules normally present in unadapted *E. coli* cells, Gilbert and Müller-Hill began their work by isolating mutant *E. coli* cells containing abnormally large amounts of *lac* repressor, some 10 times as great as the amount present in normal *E. coli* cells. They made extracts of such cells and then searched for the presence of a specific protein that could bind a gratuitous inducer of β-galactosidase activity, namely, *isopropyl thiogalactoside* (margin), abbreviated as IPTG. Analysis of such activity was carried out by allowing the cell extract, placed within a dialysis bag, to come to equilibrium with an external solution of radioactive IPTG, a small molecule which freely passes through the membrane. The cell extract can bind significant amounts of IPTG, as shown by the fact that the

Isopropyl β-D-thiogalactoside

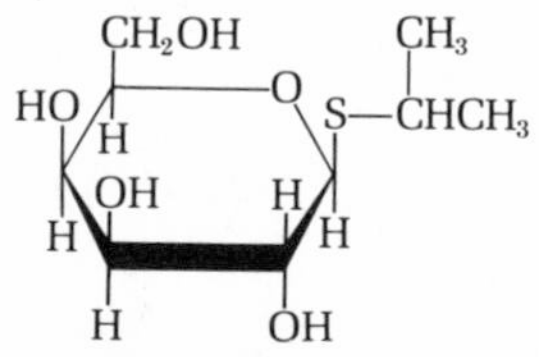

equilibrium concentration of the IPTG within the bag was higher than that in the external bathing medium. With this technique, called *equilibrium dialysis*, various nondiffusible fractions of the cell extract could be assayed. Ultimately the IPTG-binding material was purified some 100-fold. The IPTG binding substance is a heat-labile protein. In order to prove that the IPTG-binding protein is specific for binding the inducer, similar experiments were carried out with cell extracts of constitutive mutants of *E. coli* having no repressor activity. Such extracts contain no IPTG-binding protein.

Gilbert and Müller-Hill then grew *E. coli* cells on a medium containing radioactive sulfate and isolated the IPTG-binding repressor protein, which was labeled with ^{35}S in the sulfur atoms of its methionine and cysteine residues. The labeled protein was then mixed with a fraction of DNA derived from *E. coli* which was known to contain the gene loci controlling the synthesis of β-galactoside. The mixture was then subjected to density-gradient centrifugation. The DNA, which has a much higher sedimentation coefficient than the protein, sedimented first. It contained a significant amount of the bound ^{35}S-labeled repressor protein. However, when the inducer molecule IPTG was added, the DNA then bound no labeled repressor protein. This finding is fully consistent with the Jacob-Monod hypothesis that the repressor and inducer combine to yield an inactive complex unable to bind to the operator on the chromosome. The specificity of the isolated *lac* repressor protein was confirmed by other tests using DNA isolated from *E. coli* mutants defective in the operator region; as predicted from the Jacob-Monod hypothesis, no binding of the *lac* repressor to the DNA of such mutants was observed. It was also shown that the repressor molecule fails to bind to heat-denatured DNA from *E. coli*, whether it is obtained from cells possessing an intact or a defective structural gene for β-galactosidase. Moreover, Gilbert and Müller-Hill showed that the repressor molecule contains no RNA, since its binding activity is not influenced by treatment with ribonuclease.

More recent studies by Riggs and his colleagues have resulted in much further purification of the *lac* repressor. Its molecular weight is about 150,000 and it probably contains four subunits, each capable of binding a molecule of IPTG. The isolated repressor molecule has an extraordinarily high affinity for its specific locus in *E. coli* DNA; half-maximal binding of repressor to operator occurs at a repressor concentration of only 2×10^{-10} *M*.

These experiments, as well as those of Ptashne on the repressor of *E. coli* that prevents the lysogenic *lambda* phage from replicating, have provided convincing support for the Jacob-Monod theory of gene regulation and open the way for more penetrating investigation of the molecular aspects of repression and derepression. Other recent work has revealed that the corepressor of some operons leading to biosynthesis of amino acids is not the end-product amino acid itself, but rather its aminoacyl-tRNA derivative. Thus, histidine-$tRNA_{his}$, rather than free histidine, is the corepressor for the *his* operon.

Translation of Polycistronic Messengers

It is now clear that a single polycistronic mRNA transcribed from an operon codes for all of the individual enzymes specified by the operon. Moreover, with many operons, such as the *his* operon in *S. typhimurium*, the polypeptide gene products are synthesized in equal numbers under normal conditions. However, the number of times each cistron is translated may possibly vary under certain conditions. For example, when the *lac* operon is translated, *E. coli* cells may produce 25 times as many β-galactosidase molecules as β-thiogalactoside transacetylase molecules. Furthermore, it is possible to change experimentally the molar ratio in which two or more proteins coded by one operon are synthesized, for example, by altering the temperature at which translation takes place.

The mechanism by which the translation rate of individual cistrons is modulated is not known. Actually, since enzymes differ greatly in their absolute catalytic activity or turnover number, it would not be surprising if the enzymes of a given operon are synthesized in other than equimolar ratios.

Closely related to this question is the matter of messenger stability. Once an mRNA molecule specifying an enzyme is synthesized, it might well be translated many times. In order to provide an explanation for the fast "turnoff" of enzyme activity during repression, Jacob and Monod suggested that the mRNA for a given inducible or repressible enzyme may be translated only once or a very few times before it is destroyed. Later work proved that the half-life of the mRNA for β-galactosidase is about 2 min at 37°; this is about the time required for *E. coli* cells to stop making β-galactosidase after removal of the inducing agent.

Homeostatic Regulation of Enzyme Synthesis in Higher Organisms

There is now growing evidence that some enzymes and enzyme systems may undergo reversible repression or induction in higher organisms, but the observations are relatively scattered and little information on the genetic aspects is available. Studies on yeasts and *Neurospora* indicate that the response of these eucaryotic cells to the presence of inducing or repressing metabolites is relatively slow and less dramatic than that of bacteria. For example, the β-galactosidase activity of *E. coli* cells can change about 1000-fold in a matter of minutes, whereas comparable induced enzymes in yeast or *Neurospora* change only over limited ranges of activity, in some cases only 10-fold.

Reversible enzyme induction and repression in response to the levels of amino acids and sugars in the diet has also been observed in tissues of higher animals, particularly in the liver. Some examples of inducible liver enzymes are given in Table 32-2. One of the best studied is *threonine dehydrase,* which increases in activity some 300-fold in rat liver as a response to the feeding of

Table 32-2 Some inducible enzymes in the liver

Enzyme	*Inducing agent*	*Repressing agent*
Glycerol phosphate dehydrogenase (mitochondrial)	Thyroxine	
Malic enzyme		Fasting
Phosphoenolpyruvate carboxykinase	Cortisone Fasting	
Pyruvate carboxylase	Cortisone Fasting	
Serine deaminase	Glucagon, hydrocortisone, some amino acids	Glucose Serine
Serine dehydratase	Some amino acids	Glucose
Serine phosphate phosphatase		Serine
Threonine dehydrase	Some amino acids	
Tryptophan pyrrolase	Cortisone Tryptophan α-Methyltryptophan	
Tyrosine transaminase	Cortisone, insulin, glucagon	Growth hormone

certain amino acids. However, the full response of the liver to these agents may require many hours or even days to develop. Return of the concentration of the enzyme to the normal or repressed level also may require some days after removal of the inducer from the diet. Another enzyme that has received much study is *tryptophan pyrrolase,* which increases greatly in activity not only when tryptophan is present in large amounts in the diet but also when certain hormones are administered to the animal. That induction of these enzymes in the liver is indeed due to net synthesis of new enzymes has been proved by the use of actinomycin D, which inhibits their formation, presumably through inhibition of the transcription of DNA.

Enzyme induction and repression in vertebrates occur for the most part only in the liver, and not in muscle, brain, and other tissues. This fact is in keeping with the metabolic organization of vertebrates, in which most tissues are provided with a constant environment and supply of nutrients via the blood and interstitial fluid, and thus have little need of quickly-responding repression-derepression systems. The liver, however, is the first organ exposed to the incoming nutrient mix from the intestine and also serves as the major nutrient-distributing center for the whole organism; hence the liver may require induction and repression mechanisms to adjust to changes in the nutritional intake of the animal.

Certain hormones of vertebrates appear to function by increasing the transcription rate and thus the amount of mRNA specifying the synthesis of one or another enzyme. For example, administration of adrenal cortical steroid hormones to rats causes a large increase in tryptophan pyrrolase activity in the liver. Since this increase is inhibited by actinomycin D, the steroid hormone molecule may act as a specific inducer molecule, combining with the repressor and thus releasing the structural gene for transcription. Administration of the estrogenic hormones estrone and estradiol causes a large increase in protein synthesis in the uterus of ovariectomized rats in a few hours, which is completely blocked by administration of actinomycin D. Some recent experiments support the possibility that the hormone first combines with some receptor in the cell, probably a protein, and that the resulting protein-hormone complex may directly or indirectly release a repressed state of an operon or a set of operons, resulting in rapid synthesis of specific proteins.

In eucaryotic cells the genes specifying a given multienzyme system are frequently scattered among several chromosomes. Indeed, two polypeptide chains of a single protein in a higher animal may be coded for by unlinked genes in different chromosomes. The classical case is hemoglobin, whose α and β chains are coded for by genes that show no tendency to link. The genetic "ground rules" and mechanisms of coordinate induction and repression of multienzyme systems in higher animals are thus rather different from those in procaryotes and are still largely unknown.

Differentiation of Cells as a Process of Repression and Derepression of Protein Synthesis

The differentiation of the cells of the embryo into specialized forms, such as muscle cells and nerve cells, was at one time thought to occur by selective, permanent loss of various genes from the genome of the embryo. However, it now seems far more likely that all cells of a higher organism contain all the genes of that organism, but that in any given cell type most of them are turned off or repressed. For example, all cells of a vertebrate probably contain the genes for making myosin, but these genes are turned on only in muscle cells. In fact, the genetic totipotence of somatic cells can be demonstrated in some plants; under certain conditions an entire tomato plant may be grown from single differentiated cells of this organism. The concept that all diploid cells of a higher organism contain all its genes is also supported by the fact that they contain precisely the same amount of DNA.

Jacob and Monod have extended the operon–regulator gene hypothesis to include the regulation of gene product synthesis during cell development and differentiation in higher organisms, an area of study called *epigenetics*. However, the operon hypothesis must be modified somewhat. For one thing, an extremely large number of different kinds of repressor molecules would be required in higher organisms, since most of the total cell genome might well be repressed in most cells. Repressor mechanisms such as those which function in bacteria might therefore be uneconomical. Secondly, the process of cellular differentiation appears to be less easily reversible than enzyme induction and repression. For example, nerve cells cultured *in vitro* continue to behave like nerve cells, and no reproducible way, such as by mutation, has been found to make them revert to primitive cells with genetic totipotency, or to undergo transformation to other specialized forms, such as kidney cells. Thus, if differentiation is the result of repression of certain groups of operons, the repressors must be more or less permanent, at least in higher animals.

One of the striking characteristics of cellular differentiation is that different genes must be activated at different times during development of multicellular organisms. These events must therefore be programmed in some way in the genome so that the many different cell types in a higher organism develop on schedule by selective and precisely timed derepression of different operons. The turning on of various genes during this process is very likely carried out in stages, first through some form of reversible regulator gene action, such as that in bacterial cells. But as differentiation consolidates and proceeds further, repressor molecules specified by regulator genes may be replaced by a more permanent type of repression mechanism, which may prevent a long stretch of DNA from being transcribed. The development of the embryo of the sea urchin and other species is accompanied by characteristically timed increases in the synthesis of ribosomal RNA and tRNA, consistent with the concept that the availability of DNA for transcription is programmed.

The molecular identity of such hypothetical permanent gene inhibitors is a matter of much speculation. One possibility is that the *histones,* a class of basic proteins present in the nuclei of diploid eucaryotic cells, may serve this function. Histones have molecular weights in the range 8,000 to 26,000; 10 to 20 percent of their amino acid residues are lysine. Each cell type contains a complex mixture of histones, some of which can be separated. Because of their regularly spaced positive charges contributed by their lysine and arginine residues, histones combine readily with the negatively charged DNA to form complexes. In the nucleus of higher organisms, much of the DNA apparently exists in the form of deoxyribonucleohistone complexes. The fact that such basic proteins are not present in procaryotic cells, which undergo no true differentiation, but are conspicuously present in the nuclei of eucaryotes, suggests that they play some important role in the differentiation process.

Another possible molecular mechanism for a more permanent repression of DNA is enzymatic methylation of certain bases. Actually, enzymes have been found which methylate DNA according to the equation

$$\text{DNA} + \text{S-adenosylmethionine} \rightarrow \text{methyl DNA} + \text{S-adenosylhomocysteine}$$

Experimental Systems for Biochemical Study of Differentiation

One of the problems faced in biochemical study of differentiation is the choice of suitably simple organisms, in which the developmental changes may be subjected to reasonably direct experimentation. Perhaps the most primitive type of differentiation model is the sporulation of bacteria, a process in which the cells become dormant and show no metabolic activity. The germination of such spores results in a return of the bacterium to the normal metabolizing state. The various biochemical changes taking place during the life cycle of *Neurospora* are also being studied with great profit. Among lower multicellular organisms that are being studied is the water mold, *Blastocladiella emersonii,* which undergoes a transition from a unicellular to a multicellular form. Similar changes are observed in the cellular slime mold *Dictyostelium discoideum,* which consists of separate amoeboid cells in one stage of its life cycle. After a feeding period the amoebae aggregate to form a multicellular migrating slug. Characteristic biochemical changes accompany this transformation.

Among the vertebrates, the metamorphosis of the tadpole into the adult frog is accompanied by a transition from the aquatic to the terrestrial mode of life. This transition is triggered by external environmental changes, such as temperature, acting through the hypothalamus, which stimulates secretion of anterior pituitary hormones, which in turn cause thyroid hormone to be produced. Thyroxine administration can also initiate and accelerate metamorphosis. The atrophy of the tadpole tail involves characteristic changes in the pattern of protein synthesis and degradation. Metamorphosis is also accompanied by a spectacular increase in serum albumin, whose synthesis begins when the animal undergoes a large change in the osmotic relationships between blood and environment. Moreover, there is a dramatic transition in the mechanism of excretion of nitrogen as the tadpole changes from an aquatic life, in which it is ammonotelic, to a terrestrial life, in which it is ureotelic (Chapter 20). This transition is accompanied by the appearance in the liver of the four enzymes required to generate urea from ammonia by the Krebs urea cycle. These findings strongly suggest that these enzymes are coordinately derepressed during metamorphosis of the tadpole.

The Immune Response as an Example of Cell Differentiation

One experimental model of cell differentiation, namely, the immune response and antibody synthesis, is currently being attacked at the biochemical and genetic level with great success. The results of these investigations may have far-reaching consequences and implications.

The basic elements of the immune response and the antigen-antibody reaction have been described in Chapter 3. An antibody or immune globulin is produced by plasma cells of the lymphoid system of vertebrates in response to the presence of an antigen, usually a protein or some other macromolecule foreign to that species. Such an antibody is recognized by its capacity to form a specific complex with the antigen that evoked its formation. A remarkable feature of the immune response is that animals may be made immune to an extraordinarily large number of different macromolecules, including various synthetically prepared derivatives of proteins which animals would normally never encounter in their natural habitat. Moreover, a single animal may be made immune to many different antigens simultaneously. The ability of vertebrates to form many specific antibodies in response to many different antigens is reminiscent of the ability of bacteria to form many different enzymes in response to many different inducing molecules. As in the case of enzyme induction, at one time it was thought that all antibody molecules are identical in amino acid composition but may be folded in the presence of different antigens to form complementary antibodies. However, this view had to be abandoned with the more recent discovery that antibodies to different antigens do in fact differ in amino acid composition and sequence.

Because of the enormously great number of different antigens to which vertebrates can respond by synthesis of a specific antibody, the question has been raised whether the plasma cells that produce antibody molecules possess a sufficient number of genes to code for so many different antibodies. Moreover, the question arises about the mechanism by which a given type of antibody molecule is synthesized in response to a given antigen. Clues to these questions have come from analysis of the amino acid sequence of the polypeptide chains of immune globulins.

The Structure of Antibodies

There are four major classes of immune globulins in human blood plasma, of which the IgG globulins are by far the most abundant and the best understood. They have a molecular weight of about 150,000 and possess four peptide chains: two identical "heavy" (H) chains (MW 50,000) and two identical "light" (L) chains (MW 25,000), linked together by disulfide bonds into the structure schematized in Figure 32-5, which has 2 binding sites for the antigen. Each heavy chain contains a covalently bound oligosaccharide component.

The blood serum of a normal human individual contains a mixture of many different immunoglobulins, most of which are constructed in the fashion just described. Each individual type of immunoglobulin is specific for combining with one specific antigen. From such a mixture it is impossible to obtain a single molecular species of an immunoglobulin for analysis. However, in the disease *multiple myeloma*, a cancer of the antibody-forming cells, one single type of plasma cell begins to multiply and produces excessive amounts of a single type of immunoglobulin, which appears in the blood. In such patients, the urine contains large amounts of another protein, called a *Bence-Jones protein*, which has been found to consist solely of free light or L chains, which are evidently made in excess of the H chains and then excreted. In any given patient only a single type of Bence-Jones protein is synthesized; however, no two patients have identical Bence-Jones proteins. Amino acid–

Figure 32-5
Structure of the IgG (γG) immunoglobulin. The segments of the polypeptide chains having variable amino acid sequence are in color; the segments having a constant sequence are in black. The oligosaccharide groups are designated CHO*. The molecule has two binding sites for antigens (see Chapter 3).*

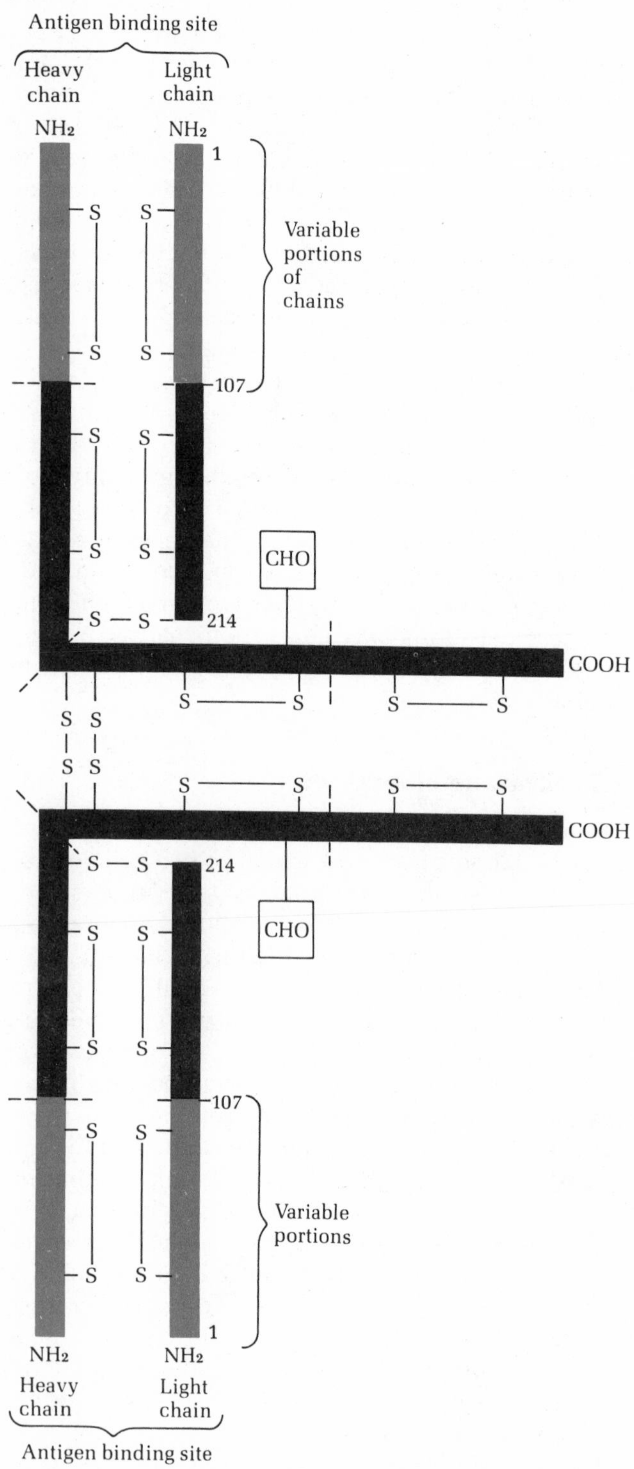

sequence determinations made on Bence-Jones proteins from the urine and the immune globulin from the blood of different individual multiple myeloma patients have revealed some extraordinary relationships (Figure 32-6). The carboxyl-terminal half (107 residues) of the Bence-Jones proteins or L chains has the same amino acid

Figure 32-6
A single human light chain showing the positions in the variable portion of the chain in which amino acid replacements have been observed (in color).

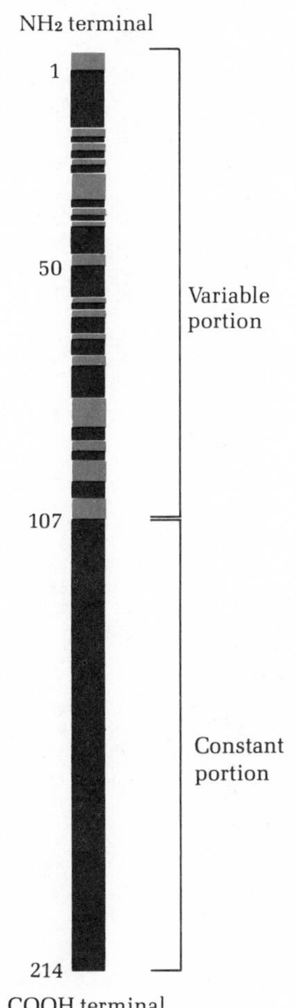

sequence in all patients, whereas the amino-terminal half of about 107 residues differs in sequence from one patient to another, although there is some sequence homology. Moreover, there are some sequence homologies between the two halves of the L chains. Similarly, in the H chains from such patients, which contain over 400 residues, the amino-terminal segment of about 107 residues varies in sequence from one individual to another, whereas the other 300 residues are constant in sequence.

These findings have three major implications. One is that the variable-sequence portions of each L and H chain represent the binding site for the specific antigen. Secondly, the immune globulin chain appears to be coded for by successive duplication or repetition of primordial precursor genes, because there are sequence homologies between the variable and constant halves of L chains and among the four segments of the H chains, each about 107 residues in length. However, there are no homologies between the variable regions of L chains and of H chains. Thirdly, the sequence studies give at least some indication of how many different IgG antibody molecules can theoretically be formed.

Of the 107 residues in the variable-sequence segment of the light chains, 40 have been found to differ from one multiple myeloma patient to another, the remainder being invariant. In a chain of 107 residues of which 40 can be occupied by two different amino acids, it may be calculated that 2^{40} or more than 10 billion different sequences are possible. If each of the 40 variable sites may be occupied by any one of the 20 amino acids, the number of different possible sequences is enormous. Since each antibody molecule also has a heavy chain, in which many residues may also vary, it is immediately evident that a fantastically large number of antibodies may be made by a human individual, through replacement of the variable amino acid residues (Figure 32-6).

These considerations now bring us to the question: how can such an immensely large number of different antibody molecules be genetically specified? Does each individual human being possess all the genes necessary to specify the many billions of different antibodies which can theoretically be formed?

Cellular Mechanism of Antibody Formation

The old view that the antigen helped to shape or mold the antibody from a single plastic type of antibody molecule, which was called the "instruction" hypothesis, has been abandoned in favor of the *clonal selection* hypothesis. It postulates that all antibody-forming cells are genetically identical but that they occur in many different types, called *clones,* each of which possesses the capacity to make only a single type of antibody with a characteristic amino acid sequence. In each clone, then, the capacity to synthesize all other antibodies is permanently repressed. This conception can most aptly be described as the "one cell–one antibody" hypothesis. In the absence of the antigen, each clone exists only in small numbers and makes only vanishingly small amounts of its particular antibody. When a specific antigen is introduced, it stimulates one specific clone to proliferate and increase in number; simultaneously there is a large increase in the amount of specific antibody formed by that type of clone. Presumably the capacity of the antigen to "select" and stimulate a single clone lies in its capacity to attach to the cell surface and to combine with the antibody it produces. This would account for the fact that an animal can be immunized against many antigens simultaneously, each stimulating a specific cell type to proliferate and make a specific antigen. The clonal selection theory is in fact supported by studies on single plasma cells, with the aid of extremely sensitive immunochemical methods. We now see why the immune response is such a useful model for the study of cell differentiation. The different clones of plasma cells differ from each other in a heritable manner in the formation of but one protein. This single difference is much easier to study than the enormous variety of biochemical differences that exist between other cell types, such as liver cells and muscle cells.

Several possible explanations may be offered for the immense diversity of different antibodies that can be made by an individual vertebrate organism. One is that the DNA of each antibody-producing cell contains an immensely large number of genes capable of specifying many different L and H chains, nearly all of which must be permanently repressed or silent. The cell is thus committed in a heritable manner to make only one specific antibody before it "sees" the antigen, according to this theory. Only two sets of all the antibody genes are active, one set coding for a specific heavy chain and the other set for a light chain. According to this hypothesis, then, all other genes for antibodies must stay repressed after one pair is released for transcription.

This hypothesis requires that a sizable fraction of the genome of all vertebrate cells must be used to code for antibodies alone. A mammalian cell contains about 1×10^{-11} gram DNA, which can code for about 10^7 polypeptides of MW 50,000. If each light chain (MW 25,000) and each heavy chain (MW 50,000) required a separate gene, and if a total of 10^6 different genes were required to make all the possible antibodies from combinations of two light and two heavy chains, the genes for antibody formation might make up more than 15 percent of the total mammalian genome. This may seem very high, but we have already seen that the DNA of higher animals contains many repetitive copies of some genes (Chapter 28). Moreover, since the immune response has great survival value to higher animals, allowing them to resist bacterial infection, use of a rather large fraction of their genome to code for antibodies would not be surprising.

A second possible mechanism is that a much smaller number of genes can provide the requisite genetic capacity for making many antibodies, perhaps only a few C genes for the constant portions and a few V genes for the variable portions of the two sets of chains. In response to specific antigens, these few genes may rapidly undergo fragmentation and "resplicing," to yield many new combinations. Once formed, such a new combination of DNA fragments would be a permanent part of the chromosome of the clone, which is now permanently committed to produce only one type of immunoglobulin.

Another possible explanation is that antigens are specific mutagenic agents, each of which is capable of greatly increasing the rate of a certain type of mutation in the genes for the variable segments of the L and H chains (Chapter 29). Such a mechanism can also result in formation of a large number of possible antibody structures from a relatively few genes. Whatever the explanation, the solution of the problem of antibody synthesis not only should bring much clarification to the genetic basis of the differentiation of cells but may also lead to ways and means of altering immune reactions of the host which may be medically useful.

Summary

Some bacterial enzymes increase in concentration when the cells are exposed to their substrates; this response is called enzyme adaptation or induction. Some decrease in concentration in cells exposed to the end product of their activity; this response is called enzyme repression. Enzyme induction and enzyme repression are related: induction is the release from repression. Inducible and repressible enzymes are determined by three types of genes: a structural gene, which codes for the amino acid sequence of the enzyme, a regulatory or R gene, which codes for a protein called a repressor, and an operator or O gene or locus, to which the repressor must bind. In the case of inducible enzymes the repressor molecule is normally bound to the operator locus in the chromosome in such a way that the structural gene for the enzyme is prevented from being transcribed. When an inducing agent is added, it combines with the repressor molecule and converts it into a form that no longer has high affinity for the operator, thus making the structural gene available for transcription. In the case of enzymes repressed by an end product of biosynthesis, the repressor molecule formed by the regulator gene is not capable of preventing transcription of the structural gene of the enzyme by itself, but gains this capacity when it combines with the corepressor, the end product of the biosynthetic pathway.

A group of functionally related genes is called an operon. It may be induced as a group (coordinate induction) or repressed as a group (coordinate repression). Each operon has an operator. The repressor of the *lac* operon has been isolated and is a protein of MW 150,000, containing a number of subunits, each of which can bind the inducer. The *lac* repressor binds *in vitro* with very high affinity to those segments of *E. coli* DNA which determine the *lac* operon.

Extension of the operon-regulator gene theory may account for some aspects of cellular differentiation. It is believed that all cells of higher organisms contain the entire genome of the organism, but much of it is repressed. Differentiation is thought to be the result of the programmed derepression of different operons. This area of genetics is called epigenetics.

The molecular and genetic mechanisms of the differentiation of antibody-producing plasma cells may yield important clues to differentiation processes. The immune globulins, which are specific for their antigens, consist of four polypeptide chains, two identical light and two identical heavy chains. Each type of chain has a constant and a variable segment; in the latter there are amino acid replacements depending on the antigen for which the immune globulin is specific. One hypothesis holds that all plasma cells possess all the enormous number of genes for making all possible immunoglobulins, but that each type or clone of plasma cells can make but one immunoglobulin, because the genes for all others are permanently repressed. Other hypotheses suggest that only a relatively few genes are required to specify different antibodies, through breakage and recombination to produce new combinations, or by mutations induced by the antigen.

References

Books

Antibodies, Cold Spring Harbor Symposia Quant. Biol., vol. 32, 1967. A series of review articles and research papers.

DAVIS, B. D., R. DULBECCO, H. N. EISEN, H. S. GINSBERG, and W. B. WOOD, JR.: *Principles of Microbiology and Immunology*, Harper and Row, New York, 1968. A textbook. Chapters 9 (regulatory mechanisms) and 13 to 15 (the formation of antibodies and the antigen-antibody reaction) are especially germane.

MAALOE, O., and N. O. KJELDGAARD: *Control of Macromolecular Biosynthesis*, W. A. Benjamin, New York, 1965. A review of genetic and biochemical approaches.

Morphogenesis, Differentiation, and Development, Comprehensive Biochemistry, vol. 28, M. Florkin and E. H. Stotz (eds.), Elsevier, Amsterdam, New York, 1967.

Reviews and articles

BRETSCHER, M. S.: "How Repressor Molecules Function," *Nature*, **217**:509–511 (1968). A short overview.

BRITTEN, R. J. and E. H. DAVIDSON: "Gene Regulation for Higher Cells: A Theory," *Science* **165**:349–357 (1969). A model for regulation of protein synthesis in eucaryotic cells.

EDELMAN, G. M., B. A. CUNNINGHAM, W. E. GALL, P. D. GOTTLIEB, U. RUTTISHAUSER and M. J. WAXDAL: "The Covalent Structure of an Entire γG Immunoglobulin Molecule." *Proc. Natl. Acad. Sci. (U.S.)* **63**:78–85 (1969).

GILBERT, W., and B. MÜLLER-HILL: "The *lac* Operator is DNA." *Proc. Natl. Acad. Sci. (U.S.)*, **58**:2415 (1967). The specific binding of the isolated *lac* repressor to the operator site of DNA.

HILL, R. L., R. DELANEY, R. E. FELLOWS, and H. E. LEBOVITZ: "The Evolutionary Origins of the Immunoglobulins," *Proc. Natl. Acad. Sci. (U.S.)*, **56**:1762 (1966).

JACOB, F., and J. MONOD: "Genetic Regulatory Mechanisms in the Synthesis of Proteins," *J. Mol. Biol.*, **3**:318 (1961). Classic paper postulating the function of repressors, operators, and structural genes, as well as the messenger concept.

——— and ———: "Genetic Repression, Allosteric Inhibition, and Cell Differentiation," in M. Locke (ed.), *Cytodifferentiation and macromolecular synthesis, The 21st Growth Symposium*, Academic Press, 1963. General paper relating the operon concept to differentiation.

MARTIN, R. G., and B. N. AMES: "Biochemical Aspects of Genetics: The Operon," *Ann. Rev. Biochem.*, **33**:235 (1964). An important statement of the evidence supporting the operon concept.

PTASHNE, M.: "Isolation of the λ Phage Repressor," *Proc. Natl. Acad. Sci. (U.S.)*, **57**:306 (1967).

PUTNAM, F. W.: "Immunoglobulin Structure: Variability and Homology" *Science*, **163**:633–644 (1969).

RIGGS, A. D. and S. BOURGEOIS: "On the Assay, Isolation and Characterization of the *lac* Repressor." *J. Mol. Biol.*, **34**:361–364, (1968).

STENT G.: "Induction and Repression of Enzyme Synthesis," in *The Neurosciences, a Study Program*, Rockefeller University Press, New York, 1967, pp. 152–161.

CHAPTER 33 THE MOLECULAR BASIS OF MORPHOGENESIS

In the last few years it has come to be recognized that many macromolecular and supramolecular systems of the cell are self-organizing and self-assembling. The behavior of such systems provides a molecular approach to the processes known collectively as *morphogenesis,* by which the characteristic structures of organelles, cells, tissues, organs, and indeed whole organisms grow and develop in space and time, as a result of genetic programming.

The central question in the molecular basis of morphogenesis can be stated in simple terms. How is the genetic information in DNA, which is encoded in one-dimensional form as a linear sequence of mononucleotides, translated into the three-dimensional form characteristic of such biological structures as enzyme complexes, viruses, ribosomes, membranes, organelles, cells, and multicellular organisms? One important key lies in the properties of polypeptide chains, which have the ability to convert one-dimensional into three-dimensional information. The polypeptide chain spontaneously folds into a characteristic three-dimensional conformation which is determined by its specific amino acid sequence. The three-dimensional conformation of a native polypeptide chain is not imposed on it by external forces; rather it is the inevitable and automatic outcome of its tendency to seek its most stable form, in which its free energy is least.

Recent research has shown that the spontaneous formation of biologically active three-dimensional structures occurs not only at the level of single polypeptide chains, but also in oligomeric proteins, in multienzyme complexes, in lipoproteins and membranes, and in ribosomes and viruses. Although it seems paradoxical that such intricate, information-rich structures can assemble themselves spontaneously from their components, we shall see that there is no violation of thermodynamic principles. Living organisms simply have learned to capitalize on the properties of water to ensure the formation and stability of their characteristic three-dimensional structures. The study of the molecular basis of morphogenesis is now an exciting and promising field.

Translation of Linear into Three-Dimensional Information

In Chapters 31 and 32 the biochemical and genetic proof for the colinearity of the gene and its polypeptide chain product was outlined. The primary emphasis developed in those experiments was that the sequence of coding triplets in a gene determines the sequence of amino acids in the polypeptide chains it codes, in a precisely corresponding manner. Although both kinds of chains can be represented as linear molecules, we must recall that in their native state all DNA molecules, regardless of the genetic information they carry, have the same double-helical conformation, in which base pairs are arranged in a linear sequence, whereas the polypeptide chains they specify possess different three-dimensional conformations, of which no two are alike.

Such conformations may be extended, essentially linear structures, as in β-keratins; coiled structures, as in the α helix of keratins and myosin; or asymmetrical folded arrays, as in globular enzyme molecules. That the native or biologically active conformation of a polypeptide chain is assumed quite spontaneously in an aqueous environment, without the input of external work, has been amply proved by many direct observations. For example, some enzymes having only a single polypeptide chain, such as ribonuclease, may be denatured by heating, acidification, or exposure to high concentrations of urea or neutral salts, with loss of biological activity. The loss of biological activity is accompanied by an alteration of the specific three-dimensional conformation to form a randomly coiled structure. When such a denatured enzyme is gradually brought back to the normal conditions in which it is active, by cooling, by readjustment of pH, or by removal of urea, respectively, its catalytic activity often returns, as does its characteristic native three-dimensional structure, provided that the system is given a long enough period of time and the proper conditions so that the polypeptide chain can "find" its minimum-free-energy conformation. A given protein may possibly have more than one active conformation, and the active conformation of any given protein is not necessarily that having the least free energy. However, we may simplify a rather complex matter by referring to the native conformation as the minimum-free-energy form in most cases.

The specific three-dimensional conformation of a polypeptide chain in its natural environment is determined by two sets of properties: the intrinsic properties of the polypeptide chain itself and the properties of the aqueous medium. Those features of the polypeptide chain that are important in determining its conformation are the rigidity of the peptide bond; its planar *trans* structure; and the space-filling properties, polarity, and electrical charges of the R-groups of the amino acid residues (Chapter 6). The properties of the surrounding aqueous medium that are important determinants are the pH, the ionic strength, the nature of other solutes, and the tendency of water molecules to hydrogen bond with each other. Since equilibrium is defined thermodynamically as the con-

Figure 33-1
The energetics of the self-folding of a polypeptide chain.

The unfolded polypeptide chain (the "system") is randomly coiled in the aqueous medium (the "surroundings"). The chain contains both charged R groups and hydrophobic R groups (in color). The latter tend to keep adjacent water molecules immobilized.

Because of the tendency of water molecules to hydrogen-bond with each other maximally, the polypeptide chain spontaneously assumes a configuration in which most of its charged groups are exposed on the surface and the hydrophobic groups are hidden in the anhydrous interior. Thus, the polypeptide chain (the "system") has acquired specific orderliness and has decreased in entropy, while the aqueous medium (the "surroundings") has increased in entropy sufficiently to more than counterbalance the decrease in entropy of the polypeptide chain.

dition in which the system (i.e., the polypeptide chain) plus its surroundings (i.e., the aqueous environment), which together constitute the thermodynanic "universe," have attained the state of maximum entropy, it is clear that the three-dimensional conformation of the peptide chain is determined by the intrinsic tendency of two domains of matter, the polypeptide chain and the surrounding aqueous medium, to seek their most stable configuration.

Entropy and the Native Conformation of Proteins: An Apparent Paradox

The general conclusion that the native, biologically active conformation of a polypeptide chain is probably its most stable form may at first seem paradoxical and not consistent with thermodynamic principles as we see them operate in nonliving systems. Systems having a high degree of order are relatively nonrandom and thus have relatively little entropy. It therefore may appear paradoxical that, at pH 7.0, an unfolded, randomly coiled polypeptide chain having no biological activity, i.e., a system having much entropy, will spontaneously form a more ordered structure with specific biological activity, i.e., a system with less entropy. However, this paradox is only apparent and does not violate thermodynamic laws. We can resolve it simply by recalling that the Second law states that processes proceed to an equilibrium state in which the entropy of the system (the polypeptide chain) plus the entropy of the surroundings (the aqueous environment) are maximum. It is, however, perfectly possible for the entropy of the system alone (the polypeptide chain) to *decrease*, providing the entropy of the surroundings (the aqueous environment) increases by a compensating amount, so that the entropy of the system *plus* its surroundings stays constant or increases (Chapter 14). Under conditions of constant temperature and pressure, when the entropy of system plus surroundings is a maximum, the free energy of the system alone will be minimum. Therefore, in its native state, the polypeptide chain is in its minimum-free-energy form.

From these considerations it is clear that the tendency of the aqueous environment surrounding the polypeptide chain to seek its own state of maximum entropy is an important factor in endowing native protein molecules with their three-dimensional structure and thus their biological specificity. Put into molecular terms, the real driving force for the formation of the stable native conformation of polypeptide chains is the tendency of water molecules to assume the condition in which they are maximally hydrogen bonded to each other (Figure 33-1). In the unfolded, randomly coiled state of a polypeptide chain, the nonpolar R groups tend to immobilize a layer of water molecules and thus hinder them from achieving the state of maximal hydrogen bonding. Because the polypeptide chain has some degrees of freedom, its rearrangement in space will proceed spontaneously to such a conformation, in which the contact of water mole-

The initial state (unfolded)

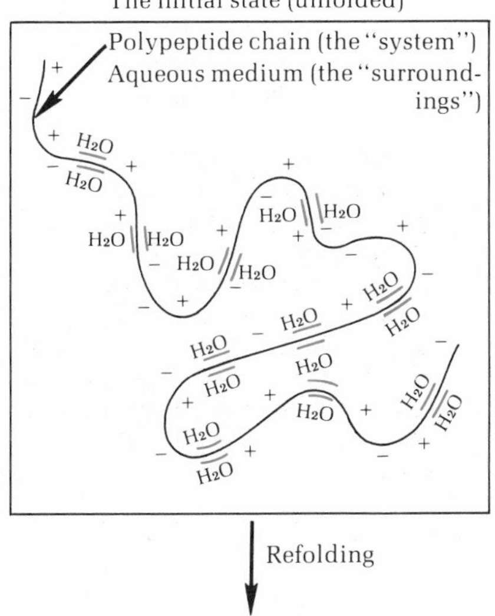

Refolding

The final state (native)

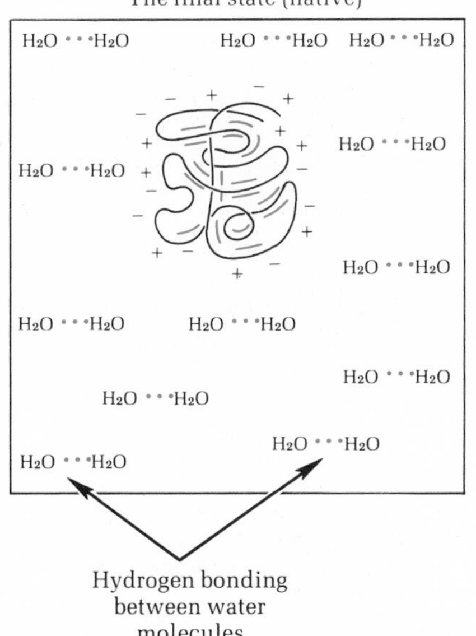

cules with the hydrophobic R groups is minimized, thus allowing the water molecules to hydrogen-bond with each other maximally. As a result, a conformation of the peptide chain arises in which hydrophobic residues are largely in the interior of the structure, hidden from water, and the charged groups are on the surface, exposed to water.

It is generally assumed that during synthesis of polypeptide chains on ribosomes, the growing chain spontaneously folds as it is being made, starting from the NH_2-terminal end, so that as each amino acid residue is added, it quickly finds its minimum-free-energy conformation. In contrast, when a completely unfolded polypeptide chain refolds in the test tube, all parts of the chain are simultaneously seeking their minimum-free-energy conformation, causing obvious geometrical and kinetic hindrances to the refolding process.

Association of Peptide Chains into Oligomeric Structures

In some oligomeric proteins the polypeptide chains are linked by covalent disulfide bonds. However, in others the polypeptide chains are held together only by noncovalent forces. Yet they have surprisingly great stability and specificity in their interactions. Hemoglobin and aldolase, which contain no covalent linkages between their subunits, retain their molecular identity when mixed and show no tendency to exchange subunits. The fit of the subunits of hemoglobin molecules to each other is so specific and stable that when native hemoglobins from two different mammalian species are mixed in the test tube, they will not exchange subunits to form hybrids, even though they are nearly identical in conformation and have many homologies in their amino acid sequences.

Oligomeric proteins such as hemoglobin and aldolase do however dissociate into subunits (Chapter 6) under conditions similar to those leading to unfolding of single polypeptide chains, namely, high temperatures, extremes of pH, or high concentrations of salts or urea. Two stages in this process can be detected, and they may overlap. In the first stage the subunits dissociate from each other; in the second, each subunit unfolds. If no covalent damage has occurred, the dissociated subunits will spontaneously reassemble into the native oligomeric structure if the conditions are such as to give the components ample time and opportunity to allow natural thermodynamic forces to operate. For example, when aldolase is acidified, it dissociates into inactive subunits, which then unfold into random coils. When the solution is gradually brought back to pH 7.0, the subunits will refold themselves into their native conformation and then assemble into their original oligomeric arrangement, with full restoration of enzymatic activity. Such self-assembly of subunits also proceeds according to the same thermodynamic principles that govern the refolding of a single polypeptide chain into the conformation having minimum free energy. The subunits associate spontaneously to form the oligo-

Figure 33-2
A model for the noncovalent association of two polypeptide subunits.

The subunits of oligomeric proteins have contact surfaces which are complementary in their distribution of opposite charges and which also possess matching hydrophobic or non-polar areas sometimes called "greasy spots." When the subunits are dissociated, the non-polar areas immobilize water molecules and keep them from hydrogen bonding with each other.

The tendency of water molecules to seek the state of maximum entropy by hydrogen-bonding to each other forces the two subunits to arrange themselves in such a way as to minimize the exposure of their hydrophobic areas to water. The association of the subunits is made geometrically specific by the complementary interaction of charged groups on the contact surfaces.

meric protein because the surrounding water sufficiently increases in entropy to more than counterbalance the decrease in entropy occurring as the subunits assemble. It has been calculated that in a 5 percent solution of hemoglobin, less than one molecule in 10,000 is in dissociated form, so that the equation for the association of the fractional subunits, each possessing an α and β chain,

$$\alpha\beta + \alpha\beta \rightleftharpoons \alpha\beta\alpha\beta$$

has an extremely high equilibrium constant and thus a very negative standard-free-energy change.

In oligomeric proteins the amino acid sequence of the individual polypeptide chains evidently carries two levels of information. At one level the sequence specifies the three-dimensional conformation of the single polypeptide chain itself. But superimposed on this level is another level of information, since each subunit contains one or more specific binding sites at which it binds to adjacent subunits. The amino acid residues at these binding sites must be coded in such a manner that noncovalent interactions between the binding sites of two adjacent subunits allow not only specificity and precision of fit but also great stability (Figure 33-2). The amino acid residues contributing to these binding sites are not necessarily confined to a given segment of the chain, but may be contributed from several regions, because of the folding of the chain in the subunit. As a generalization, specificity of fit between subunits is provided by hydrogen-bonding and other ionic interactions, whereas stability is conferred by hydrophobic interactions (Chapters 2 and 6).

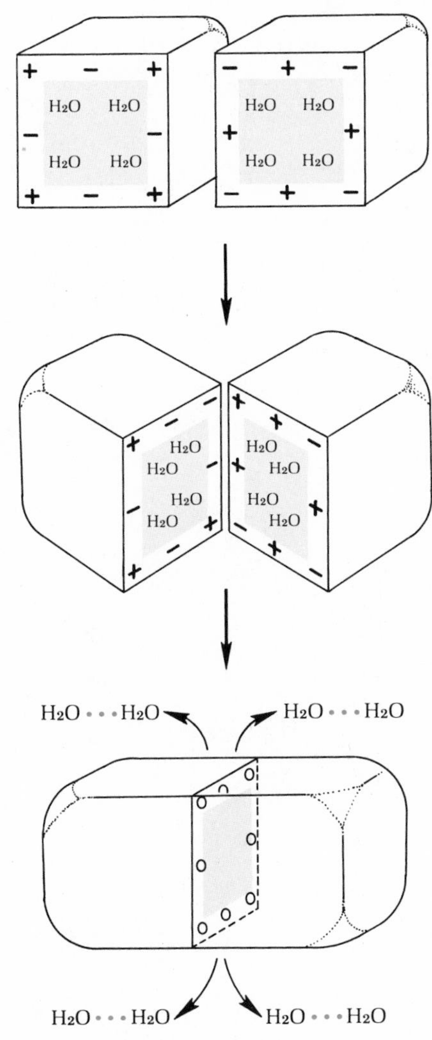

Self-Assembling Systems of a Higher Order: Multienzyme Complexes

We shall now examine the self-assembling properties of some supramolecular protein-containing systems. From oligomeric proteins such as hemoglobin we now turn to assemblies of protein molecules in which each protein may in turn contain subunits. One of the best studied examples is the fatty acid synthetase system of yeast described in Chapters 9 and 24, which consists of seven different enzymes associated in a complex. Each of these enzymes contains three apparently identical subunit polypeptide chains, making a total of 21 chains in the complex. The amino acid sequence of each of the 21 chains of this assembly specifies three levels of information. The first level is that which determines the three-dimensional conformation of each subunit. The second is that required to specify the fit between the three subunits in each enzyme molecule. Superimposed on these two levels of coding is another level that specifies how the seven individual enzyme molecules fit together to form the assembly.

The yeast fatty acid synthetase complex also illustrates another important aspect of self-assembling systems, namely, that the whole is more than the sum of the parts.

Lynen has found that the seven individual enzyme molecules of this complex are inactive when tested in isolation from the others. However, when they are all mixed together and assemble themselves into the intact complex, then enzymatic activity is restored. Presumably the separated subunits are inactive because they are not in the correct conformation. When the complete enzyme complex forms from the component enzymes, the conformation of each of the seven enzyme molecules presumably undergoes a transition into the enzymatically active form. Therefore, the association of subunits is important not only in the morphogenesis of a supramolecular system but also in endowing it with biological activity.

Other self-assembling enzyme complexes include the α-keto acid dehydrogenase complexes (Chapter 16) and tryptophan synthetase (Chapter 32).

Self-Assembly of Membrane Structure

Many lines of evidence strongly indicate that the lipid and protein components of biological membranes are held together by noncovalent forces and that membranes may also spontaneously assemble themselves from their components. Most if not all of the different types of lipid molecules in membranes can be extracted from the protein portion by procedures which break no covalent bonds. Furthermore, the individual proteins of membranes, which are normally very insoluble in aqueous systems at pH 7.0, may be dissociated into separate soluble polypeptide chains by treatment with acids, bases, or media with low dielectric properties.

We have seen (Chapter 10) that the polar phosphoglycerides, in the absence of proteins, spontaneously form micelles, monolayers, bilayers, or vesicles in aqueous systems, depending on the circumstances. Of greatest interest is the fact that mixtures of phosphoglycerides and cholesterol spontaneously form lipid bilayers between two aqueous compartments. The driving force for this assembly process is again the tendency of the surrounding aqueous medium to seek the state of maximum entropy, in which the lipid molecules are so arranged as to minimize the exposure of their hydrocarbon chains to water. Since such bilayers are about 70 Å in thickness and possess many of the properties of natural membranes, such as high electrical resistance and capacitance, high water permeability, and low permeability to electrolytes, they have been postulated to serve as the "core" of natural membranes. Various proteins have been found to attach themselves to such artificial lipid bilayers. Recently Rudin and Mueller have shown that such a phospholipid bilayer, when supplemented with certain specific proteins or polypeptides, will mimic the electrical behavior of the membranes of nerve cells, if a gradient of K^+ ion concentration is imposed across it. Electrical stimulation of the membrane yields a transient action potential resembling that accompanying the conduction of the nerve impulse along the axon. Synthetically formed phospholipid bilayers also mimic natural membranes with respect to their response to antibiotics known to increase or alter the permeability of natural membranes (Chapters 18 and 27).

The self-assembling characteristics of natural membranes are also evident from other observations. For example, when mitochondria are extracted with acetone, over 90 percent of the lipid is removed from the membrane, and electron transport by the respiratory chain electron carriers in the membrane becomes inactivated. When the extracted lipid is added back to the membrane, the lipid is bound to the membrane again and, simultaneously, much of the capacity for electron transport is restored.

Most natural membranes can be disrupted and fragmented to yield small vesicles, in which the membrane is completely continuous. For example, when the membranes of the endoplasmic reticulum are fragmented during homogenization of a tissue, the membrane fragments are recovered in the form of small, completely enclosed vesicles called *microsomes.* Such observations show that membranes have self-sealing properties. Membrane sheets with free edges are never observed in cells nor are they usually found in preparations of disrupted membranes; the broken edges reseal by a self-assembly process. In fact, the inner mitochondrial membrane can be fragmented in such a way that the outer surface of the resulting vesicle may correspond to either the outer or inner surface of the original intact membrane, depending on the conditions under which the fragmentation takes place.

Very recently it has been found that large areas of what appear to be intact native membrane form spontaneously from components derived from a natural membrane. The membrane of the small bacterium *Mycoplasma laidlawii* may be dispersed by detergents and separated into lipid and protein components. On mixing and subsequent removal of the detergent, the lipids and proteins reassociate to form a flat sheet of membrane, which appears to be identical in composition and structure with the natural membrane. The chemical composition and the ultrastructure of such membranes appear to be nearly identical with those of the native membrane.

Enzyme complexes that are normally attached to a natural membrane can in some cases be detached and separated. For example, the F_1 or ATP-synthesizing protein required in oxidative phosphorylation (Chapter 17) has been detached from the mitochondrial membrane and purified by Racker. When the purified F_1 enzyme is mixed with mitochondrial membrane vesicles previously stripped of their F_1 particles, it recombines with the membrane in a specific manner so that oxidative phosphorylation is restored.

Assembly of Ribosomal Structure

Recent research has revealed that ribosomes are also self-assembling structures. The 70S ribosomes of *E. coli* contain two major subunits, 30S and 50S. Each of these contains a single long RNA molecule, a 16S RNA chain in the

30S subunit and a 23S RNA chain in the 50S subunit. The 30S ribosomal subunit of *E. coli* contains 20 different polypeptide chains subunits and the 50S subunit at least 30.

Nomura and his colleagues have succeeded in reconstituting biologically active 30S ribosomal subunits from purified 16S RNA and the separated ribosomal proteins. The 16S RNA was first extracted from detergent-treated ribosomes with phenol and then purified. The polypeptides were extracted from 30S subunits with a mixture of 8 *M* urea and 4 *M* LiCl and freed of RNA. When the RNA and the mixture of polypeptides were mixed and incubated 10 min at 40° under appropriate conditions, complete, intact 30S subunits formed and were separated by centrifugal methods. That these reconstituted particles possess biological activity was demonstrated by mixing them with native 50S subunits; in the presence of poly U as messenger RNA, the reconstituted ribosomes were found to be capable of synthesizing labeled polyphenylalanine. The reconstituted 30S subunits also were found to contain the same proteins as native 30S subunits (Figure 33-3).

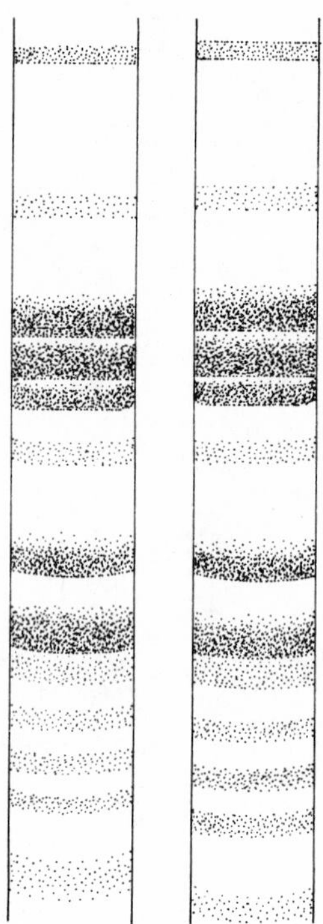

Figure 33-3
(Left) Gel electrophoresis of proteins of native 30S subunits. (Right) Gel electrophoresis of proteins of reconstituted 30S ribosomes.

Nomura and his colleagues have also found that the 30S ribosomal proteins isolated from *E. coli* ribosomes may be mixed with the 16S rRNA isolated from the distantly related bacteria *Azotobacter vinelandii, Micrococcus lysodeikticus,* and *Bacillus stearothermophilus* to reconstitute hybrid 30S ribosomes which were also found to possess activity in protein synthesis. Conversely, the 16S RNA of *E. coli* can be mixed with the 30S ribosomal proteins of two other bacterial species to yield biologically active hybrids. On the other hand, there is no evidence that there is exchange of parts when intact 30S ribosomes of these species are mixed, an observation which suggests that there may be a specific order or sequence in which the parts must reassemble to yield the native, active structure.

Self-Assembly of Tobacco Mosaic Virus

One of the most significant advances in the study of self-assembling systems was the work of Fraenkel-Conrat and his colleagues on the reconstitution of tobacco mosaic virus from its protein subunits and its RNA, to yield biologically active, i.e., infectious, viral particles. The TMV particle (MW 40,000,000; length 3,000 Å) is composed of about 2,200 identical polypeptide chains, each having 158 amino acid residues, and a single RNA chain (MW 2.1 million), which makes up about 5 percent of the total weight. The viral particle is a long rod (Chapter 12) in which a chain of globular protein subunits is arranged around a core furnished by the helically coiled RNA chain. The TMV particle can be dissociated into polypeptide chains and RNA by detergents or by exposure to weakly alkaline solutions. The polypeptide chains alone are noninfectious. The RNA is infectious alone, but very weakly so; only one molecule of many applied succeeds in entering the host cells in the tobacco leaf. Fraenkel-Conrat found that when the protein subunits of TMV are solubilized by weak alkali and then mixed with the isolated RNA, the mixture becomes distinctly turbid, resembling the opalescence of a suspension of intact TMV virus particles. Application of this mixture to the surface of the tobacco leaves results in typical viral lesions, whereas none appears on application of the protein fraction alone and very little with RNA alone. With further refinement of such reconstitution experiments very large yields of active viral particles were obtained, up to 50 percent.

The successive stages in the spontaneous reconstitution of TMV particles have been examined by electron microscopic and physical-chemical methods (Figure 33-4). The process is initiated by the formation of a dimer

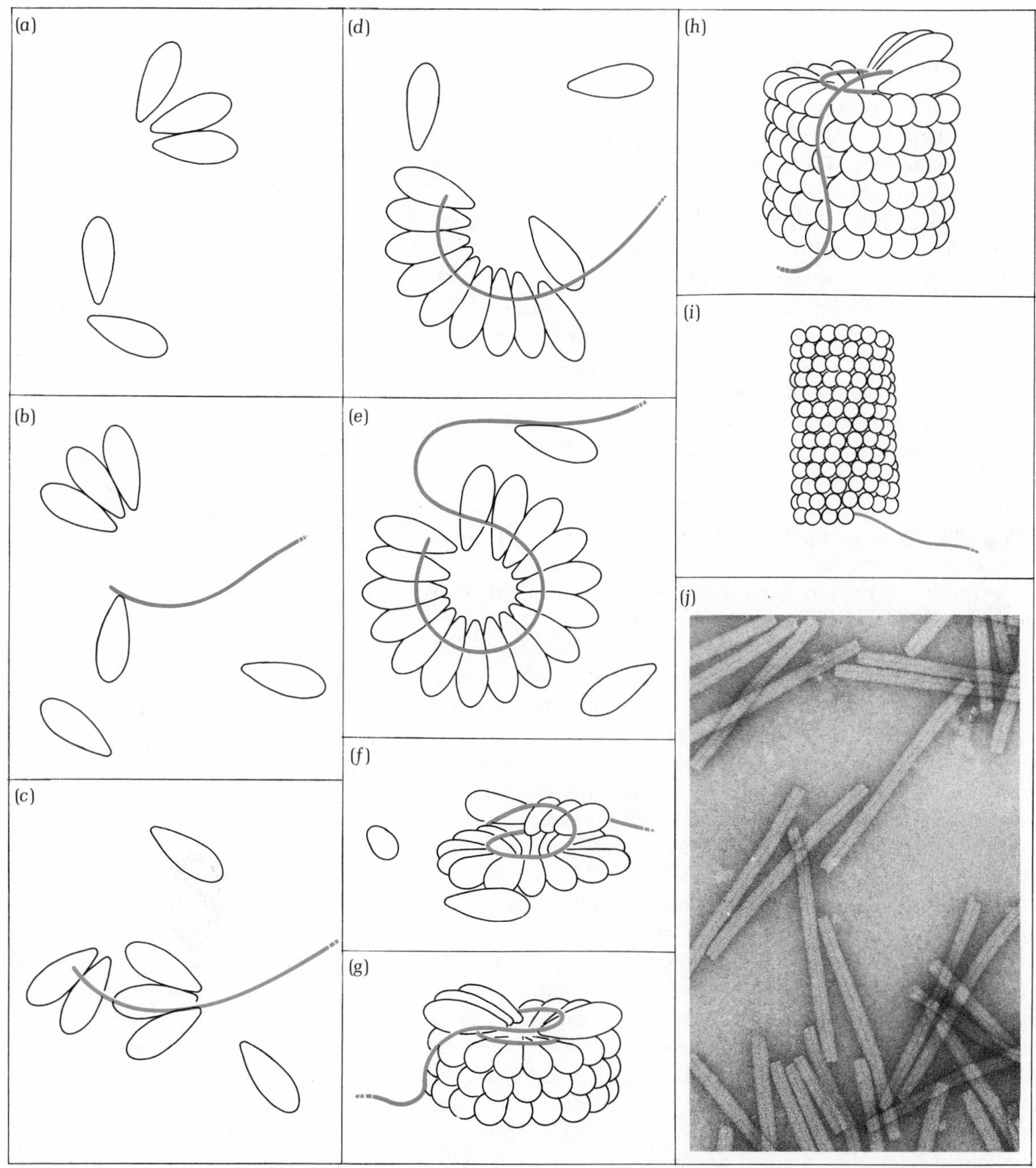

Figure 33-4
Steps in the self-assembly of tobacco mosaic virus from its RNA and protein subunits. Each subunit is a single polypeptide chain of 158 residues; there are 2200 subunits. The RNA chain has 6500 mononucleotide residues. The completed viral particle (j) has a length of 3000 Å, and a total of 130 helical turns.

from two monomeric subunits. The dimer then combines with another subunit to make a trimer, which then aggregates with one end of the RNA. The RNA serves as the anchoring structure to which successive protein units are bound. Since each protein subunit is bound by noncovalent forces to six nearest-neighbor subunits, the system stabilizes itself as more subunits are added. The assembly process is therefore cooperative in nature, so that the stability of the assembled portion increases with its size. Moreover, the rate of assembly also increases as the already assembled portion increases in size. The entire process ceases abruptly when the rod reaches a length of 3,000 Å since it is limited by the length of the RNA molecule, which, before it associates with protein, has a contour length of about 30,000 Å (Figure 33-4). The protein subunits assemble themselves into hollow tubes spontaneously in the absence of RNA, but these tubes are of indefinite length and are not infectious.

Morphogenesis of the *E. coli* T4 Bacteriophage

The pinnacle of recent research on the molecular and genetic basis of morphogenesis is represented by the important work of Edgar and Wood on the genetic determination and assembly of the structural components of the T4 virus of *E. coli*. This virus is far more complex than TMV, both structurally and genetically. It has a hollow polyhedral head, consisting of a number of different types of protein subunits, into which is folded the DNA molecule (Figure 33-5). The tail resembles a spring-loaded hypodermic syringe; it has a contractile sheath surrounding a central passage through which the DNA is injected into the host cell. The tail is connected to the end plate, to which are attached six long, thin tail fibers and six short spikelike structures which fasten to the cell wall. T4 is also genetically complex, since it contains well over 100 genes, compared with only a very few in TMV. These genes code for all the proteins of the virus, as well as a number of enzymes required to synthesize viral DNA and to cause lysis of the host cell wall.

Many mutations of the T4 bacteriophage have been observed. Some of them result in synthesis of viral structural proteins that are defective owing to single amino acid replacements. Others result in defective auxiliary proteins that aid in the replication process, such as the viral deoxyribonuclease, which destroys the DNA of the host cell, or the viral lysozyme, which makes possible the rupture of the host-cell wall and release of the newly formed viral particles. When mutations occur in which the protein components of the viral structure are defective, the assembly of the progeny virus particles usually stops at the point at which the defective protein molecule is inserted. Such mutations are usually lethal, either because the mutant virus is unable to replicate or is unable to enter the host cell. However, some mutants of T4 defective in one or another structural component are <u>*conditional lethal mutants*</u>; that is, the mutant protein may appear in either a functional or a defective form, depending on the conditions of culture and growth,

Figure 33-5
Structure of bacteriophage T4. The head is 30-sided. The tail is hollow and surrounded by a contractile sheath. The six tail fibers are attached to the end plate, which has six short spikes. From "Building a Bacterial Virus" by W. B. Wood and R. S. Edgar. Copyright © July, 1967 by Scientific American, Inc. All rights reserved.

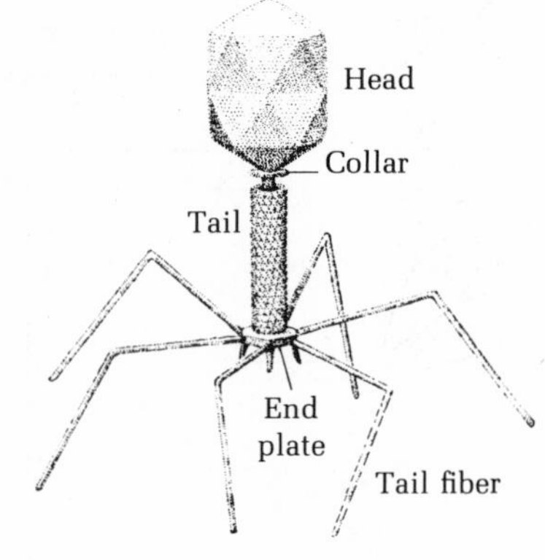

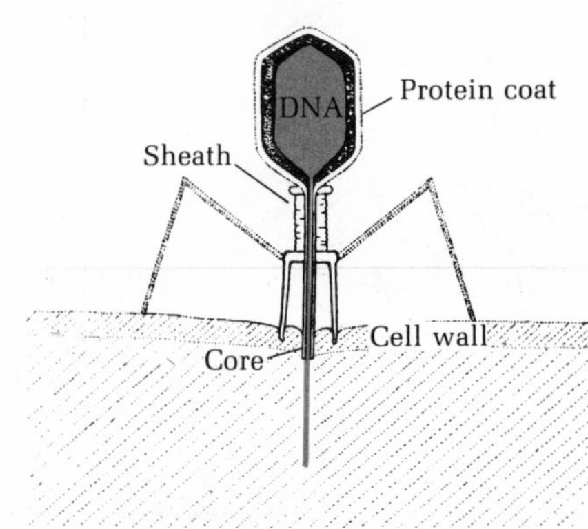

particularly the temperature. Under what are called *permissive conditions*, i.e., a temperature of 25°, intact functional viral particles are formed, whereas under what are called *restrictive conditions*, i.e., a temperature of 40°, viral infection leads to formation of defective viral proteins. The permissive conditions allow growth and replication of the virus and study of its genetic constitution, whereas the restrictive conditions lead to formation of defective virus particles, which may be observed in the host cell with the electron microscope and also may be isolated from host-cell extracts.

From such experiments, Edgar has mapped the various genes of the T4 virus that specify the synthesis of the various component parts of the T4 particle. Figure 33-6 shows a genetic map of T4 (see also Chapter 29). More than 40 of its genes participate in the formation of the complete virus particle, each specifying a distinct type of protein subunit. In mutants in which one or another of these genes are defective, the usually orderly process of viral morphogenesis is interrupted and leads to the accumulation within the host cell of incomplete parts, such as heads, tails, or tail fibers, depending on the site of mutation. These parts can be visualized inside the mutant cells by electron microscopy. The identity of the parts accumulating in various mutations of T4 are shown in the boxes (Figure 33-6). Such incomplete viral parts can be recovered from extracts of the mutant cells by differential centrifugation.

Wood and Edgar prepared extracts of *E. coli* cells infected with 40 different mutants of T4 leading to incomplete viral particles. In no case were the extracts infectious. By mixing pairs of these extracts in many combinations they found that some pairs produced active viral particles and others did not. For example, incomplete viral particles in extracts of mutants of genes 34, 35, 37, or 38, which lack tail fibers, combine with the tail fibers in extracts of mutants of gene 23, which cannot form heads. The combination occurs on simple mixing of the extracts and incubation at 30°. The mixture now contains infectious T4 particles, the number of which increases with time of incubation. Electron microscopy of the incubated mixture confirmed the net formation of new, complete T4 viral particles (Figure 33-7). Such a recombination process also occurs if the heads and tails are first separated from the extracts and then incubated together. In such experiments, the combination of the heads and tails to form viral particles requires no enzymes and is thus a self-assembly process. Such experiments, in which the gene products of one mutant complement gene products of another, are called *complementation tests*.

From many such complementation tests, the various T4 mutants could be classified into 13 groups. A mutant from any given group is unable to complement with another of the same group, but it can complement with mutants of any of the other groups. On further analysis of the mutants in these groups, the sequence of the assembly reactions and the assignment of various genes to various critical steps could be carried out. Figure 33-8 shows the

Figure 33-6
The genetic map of bacteriophage T4, showing the position of the genes specifying its structure and assembly (black segments). The boxes show the nature of the parts formed by the host cell in response to mutations at the site shown. When genes 11 or 12 undergo mutation, a complete viral particle is formed but is abnormally fragile.

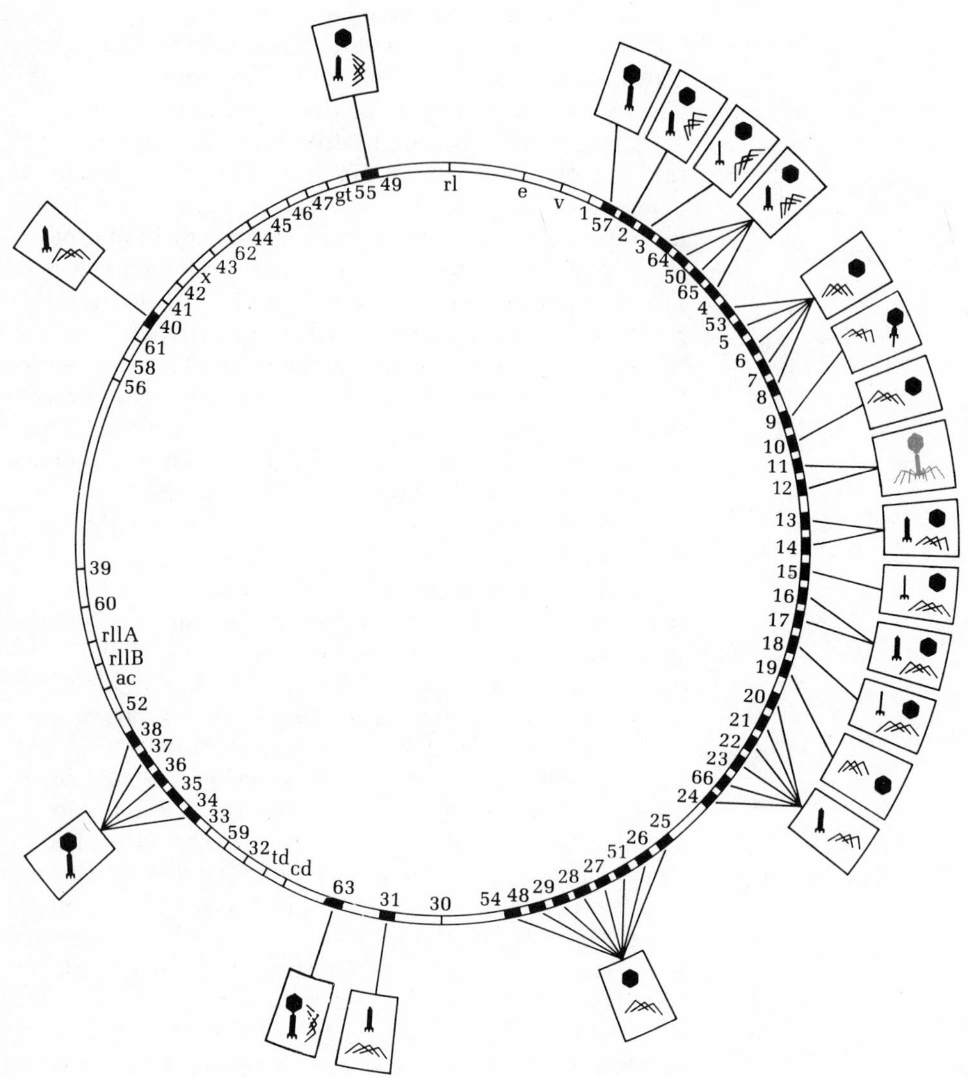

results. First, it may be concluded that the intact infectious T4 particle results from combination of intact heads, intact tails, and intact tail fibers, each previously formed in a separate "assembly line." There is a specific sequence in the assembly process, since the viral particle cannot be built starting from the top of the head and finishing with the ends of the tail fibers.

For the formation of complete heads at least 16 genes are required, each presumably coding for synthesis of a specific type of structural protein. The assembly of the tail begins with the formation of the end plate, which requires participation of at least 15 genes. Four or more

Figure 33-7
In vitro reconstitution of bacteriophage T4 by mixing mutant viral particles lacking tail fibers with an extract from cells infected with a virus defective in head structure. From "Building a Bacterial Virus" by W. B. Wood and R. S. Edgar. Copyright © July, 1967 by Scientific American, Inc. All rights reserved.

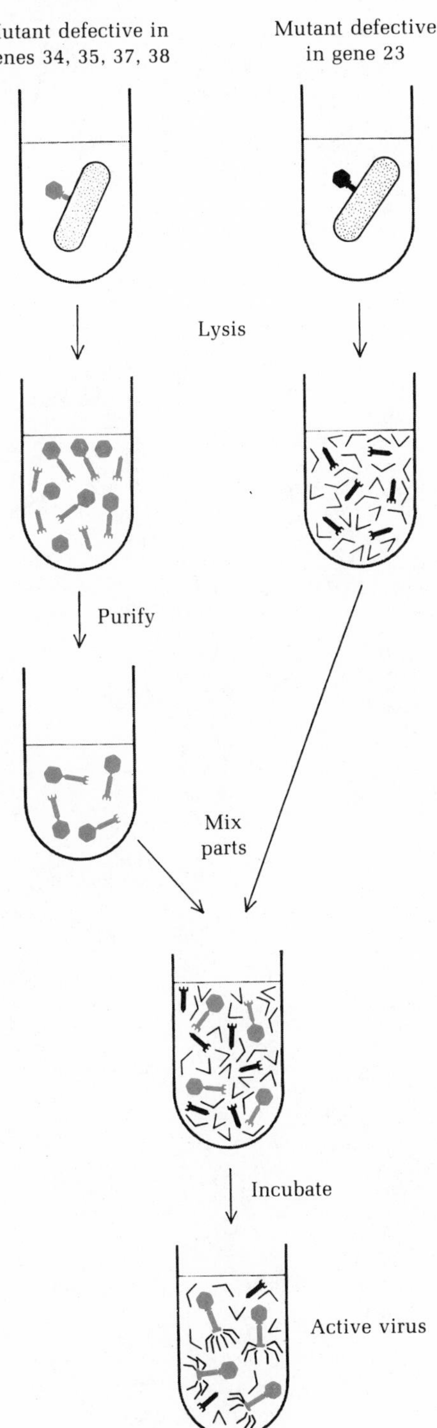

Figure 33-8
Three separate assembly processes lead to heads, tails and tail fibers, which are then combined in the sequence shown to form the complete particle.

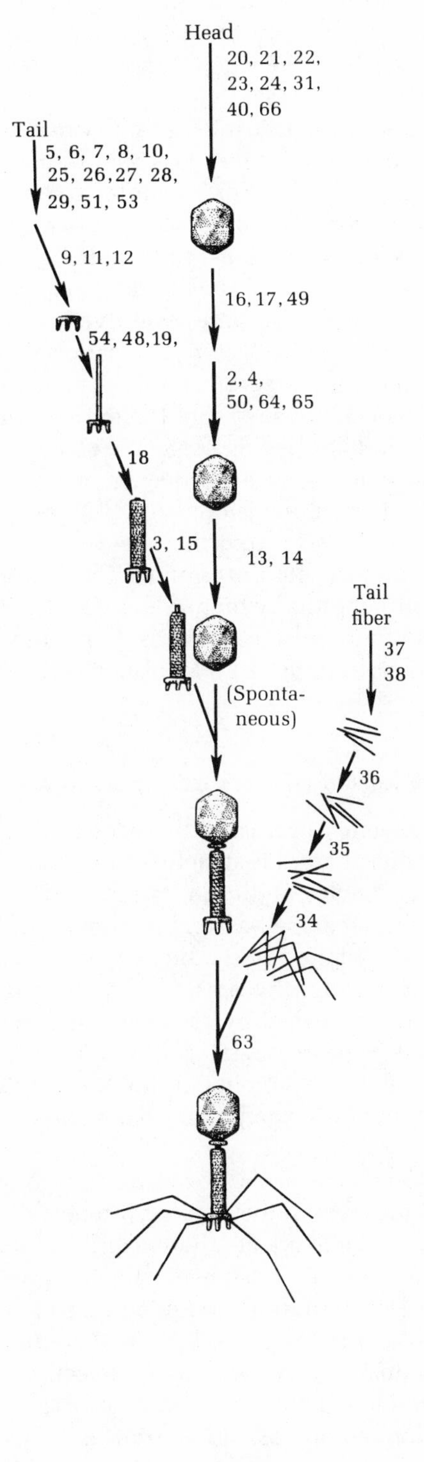

additional gene products are required to build the complete tail on the end plate. The heads and the complete tails then combine with each other spontaneously; no enzyme-catalyzed reaction is required. Once they have combined, another gene product, that of gene 9, is required before the tail fibers can attach. The tail fibers require a total of five gene products to be assembled. However, the entire tail fiber must be built before it can be attached to the end plate. The latter step is of particular interest, since it takes place in what appears to be an enzyme-catalyzed reaction, the only step in the entire process of assembly of the T4 particle that may require such a step; all other steps appear to be spontaneous nonenzymatic processes.

Another very significant finding is that in each of the three assembly lines there is a requirement for a given sequence of assembly. For example, assembly of the tail cannot begin from the middle. The obligatory sequence of assembly suggests that as each subunit is added and bound to the preceding one, it undergoes a conformational change which makes it more receptive to binding the next subunit, and so on. Each step then can promote the occurrence of the next step in a series of consecutive, cooperative interactions, so that the entire structure can be made only in one specific sequence of steps.

In these remarkable experiments, we begin to see not only how a three-dimensional structure of a high order of complexity can arise from the one-dimensional information programmed into the amino acid sequence of each of the protein subunits, which codes for the conformation of each subunit, but also how each subunit fits the next and how the assembly can take place in only one sequence of steps.

Morphogenesis of Higher-Order Structures

Can self-assembly processes also account for the morphogenesis of more complex structures, such as the contractile systems of muscles and cilia, mitochondria, and chloroplasts? Indeed, can self-assembly operate in the morphogenesis of the whole eucaryotic cell? In principle, there is no *a priori* reason why most of the ordered structure of cells cannot be formed by self-assembly processes, since much of it appears to be composed of noncovalently bonded subunits of proteins, lipids, and nuclei acids, and at least some of the component parts show self-assembly characteristics.

The molecular aspects of the morphogenesis of mitochondria are just now coming under close scrutiny. Because yeast cells are facultative and can readily live by fermentation alone if oxygen is lacking, the assembly of certain mitochondrial components can be studied in mutations of the yeast cell in which one or another specific mitochondrial protein is defective. Such mutations are not lethal since the cell can survive on alcoholic fermentation alone. Mitochondrial mutants have been isolated in which cytochrome *c* is defective and electron transport fails. Simple mixing of cytochrome *c* with mitochondria from a mutant defective in this protein results in complete restoration of electron transport and oxidative phosphorylation, and the binding of cytochrome *c* to the genetically empty sites in the mitochondria.

Another approach to the morphogenesis of mitochondria in yeast is afforded by catabolite repression (Chapter 32) of the formation of the electron carriers and of mitochondrial structure. When yeast cells are supplied with a high concentration of glucose, they ferment glucose to yield ethanol, CO_2, and energy, even though ample oxygen is present. Under these conditions the formation of mitochondria is repressed. However, once the glucose concentration in the medium declines to low values, intact mitochondria quickly appear from precursors in the cytoplasm. Some of these precursors have been isolated by density-gradient centrifugation of extracts of yeast cells repressed by glucose or by anaerobic circumstances. A precursor structure containing an oligomycin-inhibited ATPase activity has been separated from such cells. Important experiments on the molecular basis of the morphogenesis of chloroplasts are also under way.

There is some evidence that large supramolecular structures may not be completely self-assembling and can perpetuate themselves only by a process of accretion of specific building blocks to some kind of preformed structure. For example, the gullet of certain *Paramecia* is built from small molecular parts furnished by the cytoplasm. However, assembly at the gullet occurs only if some preformed gullet structure is present. If a portion of an extra gullet is implanted into a *Paramecium*, which normally has only one gullet, it will grow to form a second complete gullet. All progeny of such a *Paramecium* will then be found to have two gullets regardless of their genotype. *Paramecium* therefore has the genetic competence to make the building blocks for gullet morphogenesis, but ordinarily makes only one, evidently from some preformed growing point. If some preformed gullet structure is introduced into the cell, it becomes a template for accretion of subunits, which can be passed on to the progeny.

Finally, we must not forget the important influence of various factors in the environment on the ultimate external form of living organisms, such factors as pressure, temperature, tonicity, chemical factors, and the physical geometry of the surroundings. As organisms evolve, there is a continuous interplay between the genome and the environment in which mutation and selection are the mediating processes.

The molecular and genetic basis of the morphogenesis of eucaryotic cells, and of the formation of specific tissues and organs such as muscle, kidney, and the brain of animals and of the leaf and flower shapes of plants, offer many absorbing problems for the biochemistry and genetics of the future.

Summary

The one-dimensional genetic code is translated into three-dimensional biostructures through the tendency of a polypeptide chain spontaneously to assume a specific three-dimensional conformation which is determined by its amino acid sequence. Because various sequences of R groups interact with each other and with the solvent in characteristic ways, through their bulk, polarity, and charge, the freedom of the single bonds in the backbone of the peptide chain is severely hindred, and only one or a very few stable conformations exist under the conditions in which the molecule is native and biologically active. The transition from a randomly coiled peptide chain to its specific native conformation, which represents an intrinsic increase in information and thus a decrease in entropy of the chain, proceeds spontaneously only because water molecules of the medium tend to seek the state of maximum entropy. This tendency is the driving force which stabilizes the native, minimum-free-energy conformation of the polypeptide chains.

The amino acid sequence of the polypeptide chain subunits of oligomeric proteins codes not only for the conformation of each chain but also for their precise interaction with each other to form stable associated forms, like hemoglobin. Again, the main driving force is the tendency of the surrounding water to seek the position of maximum entropy.

Specific protein molecules may also associate with each other spontaneously to form supramolecular structures such as multienzyme complexes. Often the isolated free enzymes from such complexes are catalytically inactive when tested alone but acquire activity on self-assembly into the complex. The lipids and proteins of membranes can in some cases be separated and will reassociate spontaneously to reform membranes in the form of vesicles or sheets. Specific membrane-bound enzymes also can spontaneously and specifically reattach to membrane surfaces.

The 30S subunits of ribosomes, which contain a single 16S RNA molecule and 20 more protein subunits, can reassemble themselves quickly from their components. The 30S subunits so formed can react with native 50S subunits to yield 70S ribosomes capable of synthesizing protein. By mixing together the protein subunits and the RNA of tobacco mosaic virus, intact virus particles spontaneously form; these particles are infective. By complementation tests using temperature-sensitive conditional lethal mutants of bacteriophage T4 of *E. coli*, the sequential steps in the morphogenesis of infectious T4 particles by self-assembly of some 40 or more gene products have been established.

References

Books

FRAENKEL-CONRAT, H.: *Design and Function at The Threshold of Life: The Viruses*, Academic Press, New York, 1962. The self-assembly of tobacco mosaic virus.

SLATER, E. C., J. M. TAGER, S. PAPA, and E. QUAGLIARIELLO (eds.): *Biochemical Aspects of the Biogenesis of Mitochondria*, Adriatica Editrice, Bari, 1968.

THOMPSON, D'ARCY: *On Growth and Form*, abridged edition, J. T. Bonner (ed.), Cambridge University Press, London, 1961. A classic analysis of biological form at the macroscopic level.

WOLSTENHOLME, G. E. W. (ed.): *Principles of Biomolecular Organization*, Ciba Foundation Symposium, Little, Brown, Boston, 1966. An extremely rewarding analysis of the molecular design of biostructures.

Articles

EPSTEIN, C. J., R. F. GOLDBERGER, and C. B. ANFINSEN: "The Genetic Control of Tertiary Protein Structure: Studies with

Model Systems," *Cold Spring Harbor Symposia Quant. Biol.*, **28**:439–449 (1963).

LEHNINGER, A. L.: "Supramolecular Organization of Enzymes and Enzyme Systems," *Naturwissenschaften*, **53**:57–63 (1966) (in English). The organization of membrane-linked multienzyme systems.

LYNEN, F.: "Coordination of Metabolic Processes by Multienzyme Complexes," in M. Sela (ed.), *New perspectives in Biology*, Elsevier, Amsterdam, 1964, pp. 132–146.

MUELLER, P. and D. O. RUDIN: "Translocators in Biomolecular Lipid Membranes," in D. R. Sanadi, ed., *Current Topics in Bioenergetics*, Vol. 3, Academic Press, New York, 1969, pp. 157–242.

NOMURA, M., P. TRAUB, and H. BECHMANN: "Hybrid 30S Ribosomal Particles Reconstituted from Components of Different Bacterial Origins," *Nature*, **219**:793 (1968).

REED, L., and D. J. COX: "Macromolecular Organization of Enzyme Systems," *Ann. Rev. Biochem.*, **35**:57–84 (1966). Self-assembly and properties of multienzyme complexes.

SONNEBORN, T. M.: "Does Preformed Cell Structure Play A Role in Cell Heredity?," in J. M. Allen (ed.), *The Nature of Biological Diversity*, pp. 165–221, McGraw-Hill Book Company, New York, 1963.

THOMPSON, T. E.: "Experimental Phospholipid Model Membranes," in E. Racker (ed.), *Structure and Function of Membranes in Mitochondria and Chloroplasts*, Reinhold, New York, 1969.

TRAUB, P., and M. NOMURA, "Structure and Function of *E. coli* Ribosomes. V. Reconstitution of Functionally Active 30S Ribosomal Particles from RNA and Proteins," *Proc. Natl. Acad. Sci. (U.S.)*, **59**:777 (1968).

WEISS, P.: "$1 + 1 \neq 2$ (One Plus One Does Not Equal Two)," *The Neurosciences, A Study Program*, p. 801, Rockefeller University Press, New York, 1967. An absorbing and penetrating essay on biological form and its molecular basis.

WOOD, W. B., R. S. EDGAR, J. KING, I. LIELAUSIS and M. HENNINGER: "Bacteriophage Assembly," *Federation Proc.*, **27**:1160–1166 (1968). An account of the experiments on self-assembly of bacteriophage T4.

CHAPTER 34 THE ORIGIN OF LIFE

In our study of biochemistry we have had many glimpses into the group of organizing principles which we have called the molecular logic of living matter. Cells may be regarded from the viewpoint of the physical scientist as collections of organic molecules which are self-organizing and self-replicating, which are capable of exchanging energy and matter with their environment by means of consecutive enzyme-catalyzed organic reactions, and which appear to function on the basis of maximum economy of parts and processes. We have identified many of the molecular components of cells, how they obtain and use energy, and how they replicate themselves. It is now in order to return to such fundamental questions as: How did biomolecules arise? How did they "learn" to interact with each other? How did the first cells arise from organic molecules? Why does organic and biological matter tend to organize itself?

Not too long ago, inquiry into the origin of life was considered to be a matter of pure armchair speculation, with little hope of yielding conclusive information. But many scientific advances made in the last decade have given encouragement to the view that valid answers to some of these questions may be deduced and that at least some of the steps in the origin of biomolecules and of living cells may be simulated in the laboratory. In this final chapter we shall survey some of the experimentation and the shades of thought in this increasingly active field. Although much progress has been made with new techniques, such as isotope dating methods, there is still considerable uncertainty and even disagreement regarding the chemical composition of the atmosphere and sea of the primitive earth and the nature of the energy sources then available. For this reason there have been widely varying views as to the mechanism of origin of organic compounds and of the first cells.

The Time Scale of Chemical and Biological Evolution

Shown in Figure 34-1 is an orienting outline of the geological and biological history of the earth. The earth is believed to have been formed no later than about 4,600

Figure 34-1
The time scale of chemical and biological evolution. Although the evolution of higher forms of life can be fairly accurately dated, the times of origin of lower species indicated are only approximations.

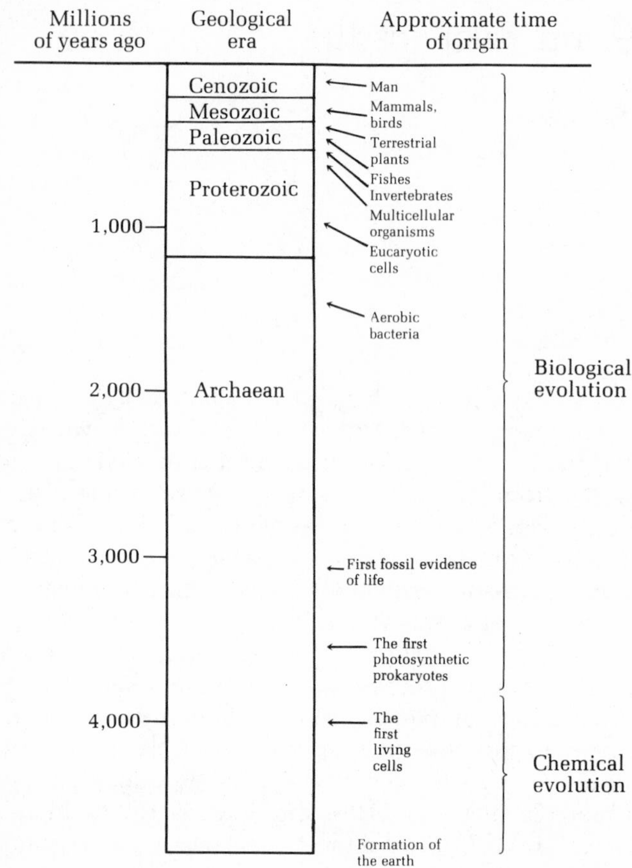

million (4.6×10^9) years ago. Its earliest atmosphere probably contained water, ammonia, methane, hydrogen sulfide, hydrogen, nitrogen, and carbon dioxide. With the passage of time, hydrogen, ammonia, and methane were lost, so that the atmosphere became less reducing.

Much evidence now suggests that, early in the history of the earth, organic compounds first arose from various inorganic components of the atmosphere, under the influence of energy in the form of ultraviolet light, electrical discharges, or heat. These organic compounds became dissolved in the sea, which then covered most of the earth. This early period, which has been called the period of chemical evolution, may have lasted almost 1,000 million years, or nearly one-fifth of the earth's history. In this period amino acids and other simple precursors are believed to have undergone abiotic condensation to form primitive polypeptides, polynucleotides, polysaccharides, and lipids. From this broth of organic molecules and polymers the first living organisms arose.

The oldest known organic material has been found in the Fig Tree shale deposits in South Africa, which contain many hydrocarbons, some of isoprenoid nature, as well as porphyrins, purines, and pyrimidines. Isotope dating methods indicate that these shales were deposited about 3,100 million years ago. Recent investigations on the structure of the Fig Tree isoprenoid compounds show that some of them are related to those found in modern cells. If they had a biological origin, then life may have originated substantially earlier than 3,100 million years ago. This view has in fact been given independent support by the discovery of cell-like structures, about 0.6 μ long, by electron microscopy of the Fig Tree sediments.

It is generally believed that the first living cells were anaerobic heterotrophs, which used organic compounds from the sea as building blocks and as a fuel source. With the growth and multiplication of these early cells, the primitive sea gradually became depleted of organic compounds. Only those cells could survive that were able to use simpler carbon compounds, particularly carbon dioxide, as their carbon source and sunlight as energy source. It is believed that the first photosynthetic cells arose somewhat later. They probably did not evolve oxygen, but may have utilized hydrogen sulfide instead of water as hydrogen donor, as do present-day purple sulfur bacteria.

The first oxygen-producing photosynthetic cells were the blue-green algae, fossils of which have been found in Fig Tree shales (~3.100 million years old). Until their appearance there was little or no free oxygen in the atmosphere. The first oxygen-utilizing aerobic heterotrophs arose much later. However, the build-up of the atmospheric oxygen level as a result of photosynthesis was very slow; the concentration of oxygen in the atmosphere did not reach a level of 1 percent until about 600 to 1,000 million years ago and a level of 10 percent until about 400 million years ago. Thus, over 1,000 million years were required for the development of aerobic vertebrates and of vascular higher plants, following the first appearance of oxygen in the atmosphere. The appearance of *Homo sapiens* is a matter of only the last 2 million years, which in the history of the earth is comparable to the last 30 seconds of a 24-hour day.

Some Working Assumptions

It is a mathematical and philosophical necessity to assume that the first living cells did not arise by a single, chance physical encounter among a large number of simple building-block molecules to yield, in one miraculous happening, a full-blown cell. Far more likely, the first "cells" were much simpler than present-day bacteria and arose as the result of a long chain of single events, so that each stage in their evolution developed from the preceding one by only a very small change. Moreover, a corollary assumption is that each single step in the evolution of the first cells must have had a reasonably high probability of happening, in terms of the laws of physics and chemistry. These assumptions constitute what has been called the *principle of evolutionary continuity*.

The principle of evolutionary continuity has two significant consequences. First, at least some of the most vital molecular components of present-day cells must have emerged very early in evolution and did not undergo much further change. Among these may be the amino acids and the purine and pyrimidine bases. The second consequence is that the sequential steps in prebiotic evolution may be sufficiently probable in terms of the laws of chemistry and physics that they will be observable in the laboratory within a reasonable period of time. If so, at least some of the early events leading to the origin of life can be validly studied by experimental methods.

A second set of working assumptions may be made. In the process of chemical evolution toward life, three stages may be postulated. In the first, certain types of organic molecules may have predominated in the primordial sea because they were easily formed and possessed superior stability. In the second stage, some of the more complex or polymeric organic molecules may have acquired a "function", such as a catalytic activity or the capacity to modify their environment or to resist changes in it. But perhaps the most crucial stage in chemical evolution may be that point at which self-organization of organic matter first appeared, so that a specific set or cluster of different types of organic molecules was better able to survive as a group than singly. It is this last stage that is most difficult for us to comprehend and study, since there are very few familiar molecular prototypes of self-organizing systems.

Finally, it appears necessary to accept the possibility that cells may conceivably have arisen from non-living matter several or even many times, at different places or times, and possibly from different building blocks. However, it appears certain that only one line of cells survived, from which all present-day organisms derived. From studies on the evolution of species, it has been estimated that possibly 99 per cent of all species of organisms that ever existed are now extinct and have no present-day descendants. From such considerations it appears possible that there may have been many false starts in the origin of the first stable line of living organisms.

A possible pathway from HCN to adenine

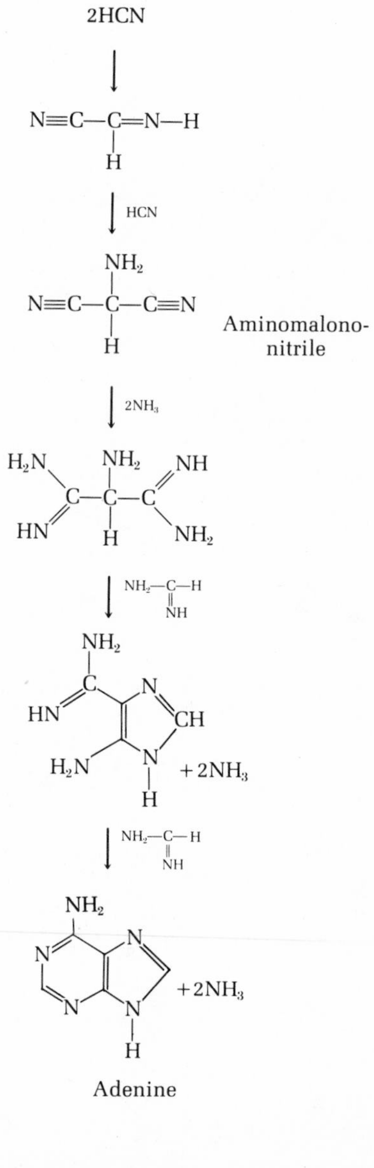

2HCN

↓

N≡C—C(H)=N—H

↓ HCN

N≡C—C(H)(NH₂)—C≡N   Aminomalononitrile

↓ $2NH_3$

H_2N(HN=)C—C(H)(NH₂)—C(=NH)NH_2

↓ NH_2—C(=NH)—H

(aminoimidazole intermediate: NH_2, HN, H_2N, N, CH, N—H) + $2NH_3$

↓ NH_2—C(=NH)—H

Adenine (NH_2, N, N, N, N—H) + $2NH_3$

Adenine

Conditions Leading to the Abiotic Origin of Organic Compounds

We have seen (Chapter 1) how laboratory experiments under simulated primitive-earth conditions have yielded organic molecules from inorganic precursors likely to have been present in the primitive environment, under the influence of various forms of radiant energy. Most of the earlier experiments were carried out in a reducing gas mixture, rich in ammònia, hydrogen, and methane. However, as has been amply demonstrated, amino acids, purines, pyrimidines, and sugars may also arise by irradiation of more oxidizing mixtures, in which carbon monoxide and carbon dioxide are major components.

Central to most of the reaction pathways leading to formation of simple organic compounds is hydrogen cyanide, which is readily formed by reactions such as

$$CH_4 + NH_3 \rightarrow HCN + 3H_2$$

$$CO + NH_3 \rightarrow HCN + H_2O$$

HCN readily reacts with unsaturated hydrocarbons, such as ethylene, to yield nitriles, which are precursors of amino acids (Chapter 1). More recent studies have shown that HCN is also an important precursor of pyrimidines and purines (margin). As we shall see, HCN also yields potent agents capable of bringing about dehydrating condensations, such as the formation of peptides from amino acids and polyphosphates from orthophosphates (Figure 34-2).

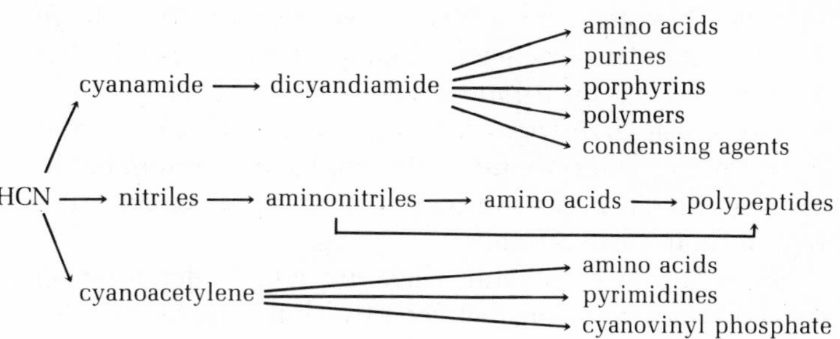

Figure 34-2
Chemical evolution of biomolecules from HCN. From three known immediate products of HCN (cyanamide, nitriles, and cyanoacetylene) over 50 different organic derivatives are formed under simulated primitive earth conditions.

The energy sources on the primitive earth which were responsible for activating the components of the primitive atmosphere have been under some debate. Ionizing radiations can have represented only a very small fraction of the energy available on the primitive earth (Table 34-1). Since visible light is not very effective in promoting abiotic formation of organic compounds, ultraviolet light and electrical discharges are more likely to have served as energy sources. Heat is extremely effective in promoting abiotic formation of simple organic compounds, and high enough temperatures may have existed near sites of volcanic action on the primitive earth.

Table 34-1 Sources of energy, averaged over the surface of the earth

Source	*Calories per cm² per year*
Total solar radiation	260,000
Ultraviolet light	660
Electric discharges	4
Radioactivity	0.8
Volcanic action	0.13
Cosmic radiation	0.0015

The fact that most of the common building-block biomolecules, such as amino acids, purines, pyrimidines, and fatty acids, have been repeatedly found in simulated primitive-earth experiments, in ancient rocks and sediments, and in meteorites, clearly suggests that they may be ubiquitous and perhaps even dominant products of energy-activated chemical evolution, partly because of energetically favorable reaction pathways leading to their formation and partly because they are more stable than other possible synthetic products. Thus the basic biomolecules we know today may be the inevitable products of chemical evolution, not only on the earth but wherever appropriate conditions exist for abiotic formation of organic compounds. However, these conditions do not necessarily exist on all extra-terrestrial bodies. Although spectroscopic analysis suggests that simple hydrocarbons occur in the atmosphere of Mars, Jupiter, and Venus, the first samples of dust and rock recovered from the moon have shown no sign of organic matter, nor any indication that the moon once had an aqueous surface.

Linkage of Primordial Building-Block Molecules by Condensation Reactions

Once the primordial building-block molecules were formed by abiotic synthesis, the next step in their chemical evolution toward biomolecular systems must have been the formation of covalent bonds linking them into chainlike oligomers and polymers. But here we come to a paradox. The covalent linkages between the building blocks of proteins, nucleic acids, polysaccharides, and lipids are the result of the removal of the elements of water from successive monomeric units. However, peptide bonds, glycosidic bonds, and ester linkages are thermodynamically unstable in dilute aqueous systems; that is, they tend to undergo hydrolysis with a large negative standard-free-energy change (Chapter 14), so that at equilibrium in dilute aqueous systems only small amounts of such linkages can exist. In order for primordial polypeptides and polynucleotides to have accumulated in the sea, the rate of their formation must have exceeded the rate of their degradation.

There are two general ways in which dehydrating condensation reactions between two building-block molecules, as in the reaction

$$\text{Amino acid}_1 + \text{amino acid}_2 \rightarrow \text{dipeptide} + H_2O$$

can take place with large yields. One way is to carry out the reaction under anhydrous conditions, for example, at temperatures above the boiling point of water. The second way is by the action of chemical condensing agents, compounds capable of combining preferentially with the elements of water removed from the molecules undergoing condensation, rather than with free water. Both types of process may have been possible under primitive-earth conditions.

Thermal formation of polymers of amino acids has been demonstrated by Fox and his colleagues, who have shown that both short-chain and long-chain peptides may be formed simply by heating mixtures of amino acids at temperatures above 100°. The conditions necessary to achieve thermal polymerization of amino acids are not far removed from those favorable for the abiotic formation of amino acids. Hot gases of active volcanoes may have contained NH_3, CH_4, and steam. Amino acids formed from the latter could then be expected to undergo dehydrating polymerization into polypeptides in hot lava or volcanic ash. The polymers so formed could be extracted from the ash by rainfall and thus find their way into the surface waters of the earth; the thermal polymerization of amino acids to yield "proteinoids" will be described in more detail below.

Because the living cells of today use a chemical condensing agent, that is, the pyrophosphate group of ATP, to effect the synthesis of such water-unstable linkages as glycosidic, ester, amide, and peptide bonds, we must also give close attention to the possibility that polyphosphates or other abiotic condensing agents participated in the abiotic formation of the first primordial macromolecules. As an example, we will recall (Chapter 5) that the compound dicyclohexyl carbodiimide can bring about the condensation of two amino acids by extraction of the elements of water from them, to yield a dipeptide and a

Formation of dicyandiamide (top) and its action as a condensing agent (bottom).

2HCN
↓
$NH_2—C≡N$ Cyanamide
↓
N≡C—NH—C(=NH)—NH_2 Dicyandiamide
↓ H^+
HN=C=N—C(=$\overset{+}{N}H_2$)—NH_2 Amidinium carbodiimide

Condensation reaction

NH_2—C(H)(R_1)—COOH Amino acid$_1$
+
NH_2—C(H)(R_2)—COOH Amino acid$_2$
+
HN=C=N—C(=$\overset{+}{N}H_2$)—NH_2 Carbodiimide form of dicyandiamide
↓
NH_2—C(H)(R_1)—C(=O)—NH—C(H)(R_2)—COOH Dipeptide
+
NH_2—C(=O)—NH—C(=NH)—NH_2 Guanidourea

Other condensing and phosphorylating agents formed under primitive-earth conditions.

Hydrogen cyanate

$$H—C{\equiv}N{=}O$$

Cyanogen

$$N{\equiv}C—C{\equiv}N$$

Cyanovinyl phosphate

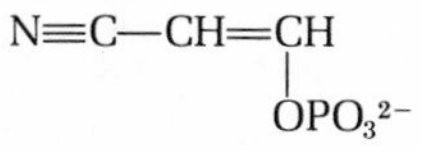

$$N{\equiv}C—CH{=}CH—OPO_3^{2-}$$

Polymetaphosphate

$$^{-}O—\overset{O^-}{\underset{O}{P}}—\left[O—\overset{O^-}{\underset{O}{P}}\right]_n—O—\overset{O^-}{\underset{O}{P}}—O^-$$

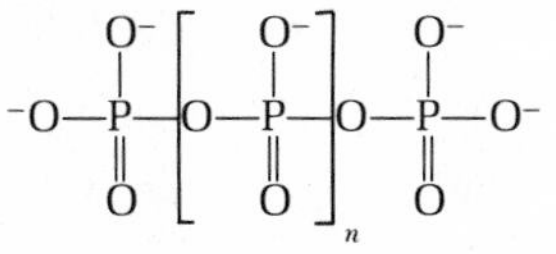

Polyphosphate ethyl ester

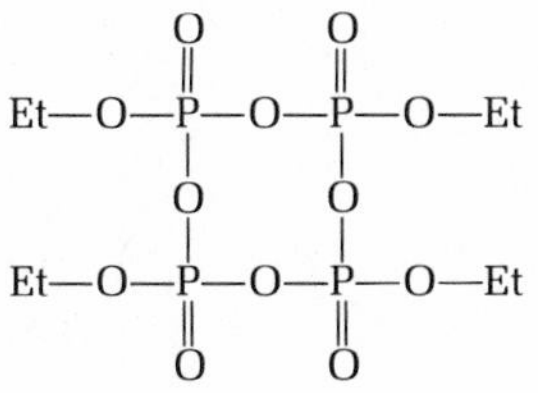

$$\begin{array}{c} Et—O—\overset{O}{P}—O—\overset{O}{P}—O—Et \\ \quad\; | \qquad\quad | \\ \quad\; O \qquad\quad O \\ \quad\; | \qquad\quad | \\ Et—O—\underset{O}{P}—O—\underset{O}{P}—O—Et \end{array}$$

Cyanoacetylene

$$N{\equiv}C—C{\equiv}CH$$

hydrated product, a derivative of urea. Carbodiimides are capable of promoting many other types of dehydrating condensation reactions.

Calvin and his colleagues have pointed out that HCN is the precursor of very potent condensing agents which are derivatives of carbodiimide. They have found that *cyanamide*, which was earlier shown to be formed from HCN in the presence of radiant energy, dimerizes under primitive-earth conditions to yield *dicyandiamide* or *cyanoguanidine*, which is readily converted into a carbodiimide derivative. This condensing reagent promotes formation of simple peptides from amino acids, as shown in the margin p. 774. It also promotes formation of phosphate and acetate esters from alcohols, of pyrophosphate from orthophosphate, and of ADP from AMP and phosphate. *Cyanate* and *cyanogen* (margin) are also effective condensing agents.

Of most interest are derivatives of polyphosphoric acid, which may be forerunners of ATP. Linear polyphosphates (also called polymetaphosphates) as well as cyclic polymers (margin) could easily have arisen in the prebiotic era in local high-temperature zones, near the sites of volcanic action. They may also have arisen from the action of nitrogenous condensing agents, such as cyanoguanidine, on orthophosphates. Another possible pathway of formation of polyphosphates, as well as other phosphorylated compounds, is through the action of organic phosphorylating agents. Among those postulated is *cyanovinyl phosphate*, the phosphate ester of cyanovinyl alcohol, which is formed by the action of phosphate on *cyanoacetylene* (margin), one of the major products resulting from the action of electrical discharges on mixtures of methane and nitrogen. When cyanovinyl phosphate is mixed with inorganic orthophosphate in dilute aqueous solution, pyrophosphate is formed; similarly, cyanovinyl phosphate brings about the phosphorylation of uridine to yield uridylic acid in water.

Polyphosphates or their esters have been found to bring about formation of peptides from amino acids when the system is irradiated with ultraviolet light or gently heated. Polyphosphate esters also promote formation of AMP, ADP, and ATP from adenine, ribose, and phosphate, of polynucleotides from mononucleotides, and of glucose polymers from glucose, as shown by Schramm, Ponnamperuma, and other investigators. Polyphosphates possess very desirable advantages from the biological point of view, for they react only very slowly with water (that is, they are kinetically stable) but at the same time possess a large negative value for $\Delta G^{\circ\prime}$ of hydrolysis (that is, they are thermodynamically unstable). Very likely the polyphosphate group of ATP was selected as a biological condensing agent because of these chemical advantages. The adenosine moiety confers on ATP an easily recognized molecular "handle" by which it is bound to the active site of phosphate-transferring enzymes. An important evolutionary role of simple polyphosphates is also supported by the fact that many present-day bacteria contain polyphosphate polymers (Chapter 14), which function as a storage form of phosphate bond energy.

The Abiotic Formation of Polypeptides

Several investigators have observed the formation of polymers resembling polypeptides when amino acids are heated, subjected to electrical discharges, or treated with condensing agents such as polyphosphoric esters under primitive-earth conditions. Fox, in particular, has described the formation of what he has called *proteinoids*, by heating amino acid mixtures at about 170° for a few hours, or by warming them with polyphosphates at 50-60° for longer periods. These procedures result in the formation of a mixture of polymers, in which a few types predominate and may be separated by chromatographic procedures. Acidic polymers are formed from mixtures rich in aspartic and glutamic acids, and basic polymers from lysine-rich mixtures. Neutral proteinoids have also been prepared. Proteinoids have relatively high particle weights, which may exceed 10,000 daltons, and they may contain as many as 18 different amino acids. Fox has found that proteinoids form more readily from mixtures of amino acids than from single amino acids. Proteinoids are not totally random polymers, although their amino acid composition is determined by the composition of the starting amino acid mixtures. With any given starting mixture the proteinoids produced are surprisingly constant in amino acid composition, which may resemble that of mixtures of natural proteins (Table 34-2). On hydrolysis with acids, proteinoids yield free amino acids, as well as some non-amino acid components evidently formed as by-products in the thermal polymerization. Proteinoids are attacked by some proteolytic enzymes. Moreover, they show other properties characteristic of proteins: they may be salted-in or salted-out and they undergo isoelectric precipitation.

One of the most significant properties of the thermally formed proteinoid mixtures is that they have been found to enhance the rate of certain chemical reactions. One proteinoid fraction, for example, catalyzes the hydrolysis of *p*-nitrophenyl acetate, and thus resembles an esterase. Although such catalytic activity is rather weak compared to that of true esterases, it is very much greater than that given by comparable mixtures of free amino acids. Moreover, certain proteinoids have been found to have weak but definite hormonal activity resembling that of the polypeptide melanocyte-stimulating hormone (MSH). These observations, as well as amino acid sequence analysis of purified proteinoid fractions, clearly indicate that polypeptide chains having non-random amino acid sequences will form spontaneously under relatively simple conditions.

Krampitz and Fox have shown that incubation of a mixture of the aminoacyl adenylates of the common amino acids at pH 9.0 causes spontaneous formation of proteinoids of high molecular weight at mild temperatures. Since aminoacyl adenylates readily form from free adenylic acid and free amino acids in the presence of condensing agents such as dicyclohexyl carbodiimide, it appears possible that proteinoids may even be formed non-enzymatically, and at low temperatures in dilute

Table 34-2 Amino acid composition of a neutral soluble proteinoid prepared from an equimolar mixture of amino acids

	Mole per cent
Lys	8.4
His	3.3
Arg	3.9
Asp	4.6
Glu	10.1
Thr	0.4
Ser	0.2
Pro	2.7
Gly	8.4
Ala	12.1
Val	9.6
Met	6.8
Ile	4.7
Leu	6.0
Cys	5.2
Tyr	5.1
Phe	4.5

Figure 34-3
The Akabori hypothesis for the origin of proteins.

3HCN
↓
$N{\equiv}C{-}CH(NH_2){-}C{\equiv}N$ Aminomalononitrile
↓
$HOOC{-}CH(NH_2){-}C{\equiv}N$
↓ Polymerization
$NH_2{-}CH_2{-}C({=}NH){-}(NH{-}CH_2{-}C({=}NH))_n{-}NH{-}CH_2{-}COOH$ Polyglycinimide
↓ H_2O
$NH_2{-}CH_2{-}C({=}O){-}(NH{-}CH_2{-}C({=}O))_n{-}NH{-}CH_2{-}COOH$ Polyglycine
↓ HCHO
$NH_2{-}CH(CH_2OH){-}C({=}O){-}(NH{-}CH(CH_2OH){-}C({=}O))_n{-}NH{-}CH(CH_2OH){-}COOH$ Polyserine

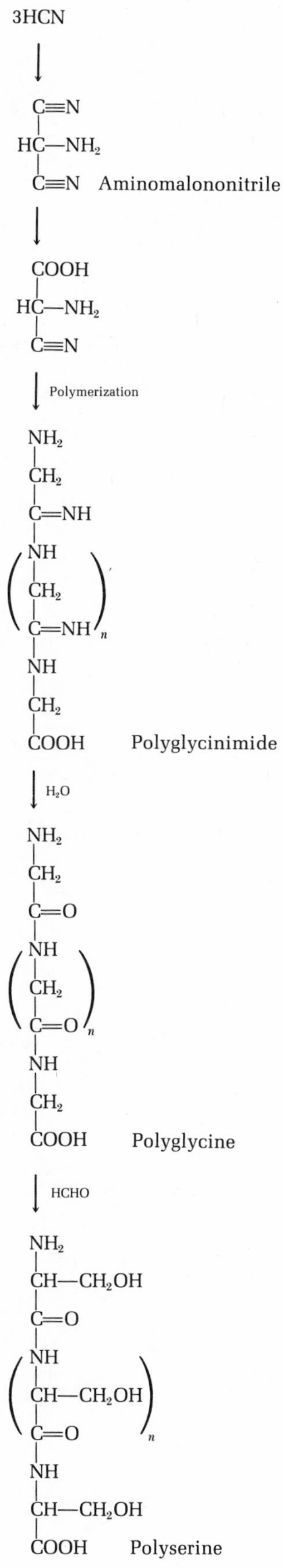

solutions, through a reaction pathway resembling that taken by aminoacyl tRNA's in present-day protein synthesis.

There are other hypotheses for the origin of proteins. The first proteinlike polymers may have arisen by polymerization of monomeric units other than amino acids, for example, aminoacetonitrile, which is readily formed from ammonia, formaldehyde, and hydrogen cyanide (Chapter 1). Polymerization of this monomer, followed by hydrolytic loss of ammonia, could have yielded polyglycine (Figure 34-3). Akabori has postulated that polyglycine formed in this manner could serve as the precursor of true proteins if α-hydrogen atoms of the glycine residues are substituted by appropriate R groups through secondary reactions. Although the Akabori hypothesis is chemically feasible, it implies that the first proteins arose independently of amino acid building blocks; indeed, it suggests that free amino acids may have arisen by hydrolysis of such polypeptides. Although it is difficult to choose between these hypotheses, it seems more probable, in the light of present-day biochemistry, that amino acids arose first and from them arose the first proteins.

Since peptide bonds in aqueous solutions are thermodynamically unstable, it is only reasonable to expect that once a primitive proteinoid had formed abiotically, it would be highly susceptible to hydrolytic breakdown in the warm primeval broth. No single proteinoid molecule could thus be expected to have a long life. This consideration brings us face-to-face with the most fundamental problem posed by the evolution of informational macromolecules, such as proteins and nucleic acids, from simple monomers of different types. It is difficult to see how any given proteinoid could have undergone residue-by-residue "improvement" to a sequence better able to survive if each proteinoid molecule had but a short life and if there were no means of recording or replicating the amino acid sequence of the "better" proteinoids. In all of the known species today there are only about 10^{12} different types of proteins, whereas over 10^{300} different types of proteins could conceivably have been formed from 20 different amino acids.

The Abiotic Origin of Organic Catalysts

The water molecules of the early sea yielded the most primitive catalysts known, namely, H^+ and OH^- ions, which promote specific-acid or specific-base catalysis. Later, when the first organic acids and bases were formed abiotically, they yielded the first general-acid and general-base catalysts, for example, compounds containing substituted ammonium or carboxylate groups, respectively. Moreover, minerals in the bed of the primitive sea, or at the sites of volcanic action, yielded the possibility of heterogeneous catalysis by insoluble metal salts, such as phosphates or silicates.

In the evolution of enzymes from simple precursors, it seems highly probable that catalytic capacity appeared first and that substrate specificity followed as a later evolutionary development. For example, general acids and general bases acting as catalysts have no substrate specificity; they enhance the rate of many different organic reactions involving the uptake or loss of protons. It is very likely also that the first precursors of present-day enzymes yielded only very small rate enhancements, perhaps only several-fold, compared with present-day enzymes, which are capable of rate enhancements of 10^8 to 10^{12}-fold.

The first primitive catalysts may well have been simple peptides containing, for example, an especially reactive α-ammonium or a carboxylate group functioning as a general-acid or general-base catalyst. The evolution of such a peptide into a more potent and a more specific catalyst may have involved, in one way or another, the selection of those modifications of the peptide structure which were better able to survive because they were better catalysts and thus were better able to modify their environment. Alternatively, high-molecular weight proteinoids, such as those described above, may have been the precursors of enzymes. Fox and others have been able to detect a large number of rate-enhancing activities in various proteinoids, including hydrolyses, decarboxylations of α-keto acids, and aminations. In two cases they have been proved to be truly catalytic effects, with regeneration of the catalyst. One of these is the esterase activity of certain proteinoids toward *p*-nitrophenyl acetate, which has been found to have an optimum pH, to exhibit saturation by substrate, i.e. Michaelis-Menten kinetics, to be destroyed by heat, and to depend on the presence of histidine residues; histidine-less proteinoids showed no catalytic activity. Zinc-containing proteinoids have been found to have ATPase activity. Figure 34-4 shows the catalysis of a decarboxylation by a proteinoid.

Figure 34-4
Decarboxylation of pyruvic acid catalyzed by a proteinoid.

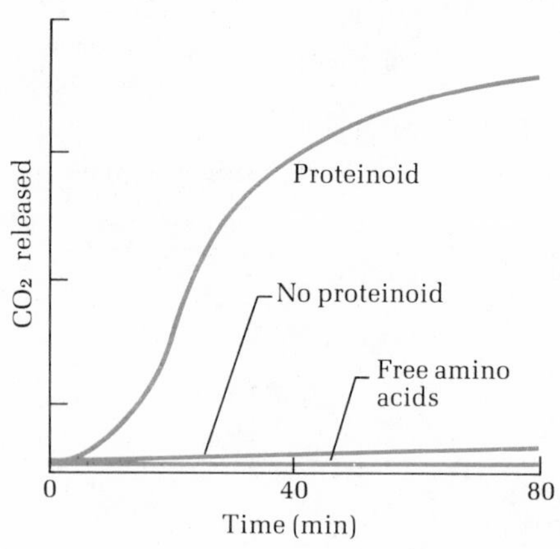

Again, not much progress could have been made toward the evolution of enzymes until very long polypeptide chains arose which were capable of assuming specific three-dimensional folded conformations. We know today that the tertiary structure of an enzyme is required to bind substrate specifically to yield the ES complex, to position the substrate and the catalytic group favorably, to provide the appropriate dielectric environment at the catalytic site, and to enable the enzyme to release its reaction products through a cycle of conformational changes. The gradual residue-by-residue improvement of primitive peptide catalysts to the enzyme molecules of today simply could not have taken place without some form of template capable of replicating amino acid sequences.

The Abiotic Origin of Nucleotides and Nucleic Acids

That the organic building blocks of mononucleotides, namely, the nitrogenous bases and ribose (or 2-deoxyribose), may have arisen under primitive-earth conditions also appears highly probable. From the appropriate bases and pentoses, abiotic formation of nucleosides such as adenosine and deoxyadenosine has been detected in simulated primitive-earth experiments, particularly in the presence of abiotic condensing agents such as polyphosphoric esters. Moreover, mononucleotides arise when nucleosides and polyphosphoric esters are heated or irradiated with ultraviolet light. The mononucleotides so formed represent mixtures in which the phosphate group may be present on the 2′, 3′, 4′, or 5′ carbon atoms of the ribose moiety. The culmination of such primitive-earth simulation experiments is the demonstration by Ponnamperuma and other investigators that not only 5′-adenylic acid (AMP) but also ADP and ATP may be generated by heating or irradiating adenine and ribose, or AMP, with an abiotic phosphorylating agent.

The next step in the chemical evolution of nucleic acids is the formation of internucleotide linkages between successive mononucleotides. This also has been achieved in simulated primitive-earth experiments in which mononucleotides have been heated at 50 to 65° in the presence of polyphosphoric acid as condensing agent. To date, the internucleotide linkage in abiotically formed oligonucleotides is in most cases the 2′,5′ linkage; the 3′,5′ linkage does not appear to form readily. But this need not concern us greatly. The primordial nucleic acids might well have had 2′,5′ linkages. The 3′,5′ linkage, which probably possesses significant advantages over the other possible types, may have arisen later, after the development of specific enzymes capable of enhancing synthesis of 3′,5′ linkages in preference to others.

Abiotic Formation of Template Systems

We have seen in the preceding discussion of the origin of proteins and nucleic acids that polypeptide and polynucleotide chains could well have been formed in the primitive broth. The question however is: How can a specific sequence of monomers in such a chain be recorded or replicated during the molecular evolution of polypeptides and nucleic acids? From the vantage point of today's knowledge of template function in molecular genetics, we know that nucleic acids function as templates but that proteins do not. It is therefore only natural that nearly all model experiments on primitive template systems have been based on nucleic acids rather than proteins.

The most revealing model experiments are those which employ the base-pairing principle inherent in the DNA double helix. One of the most significant observations is the discovery that when solutions of simple derivatives of adenine and of uracil, not containing ribose and phosphoric acid, are mixed, adenine-uracil complexes spontaneously form in solution, stabilized by hydrogen bonding. Such complexes are detectable by physical-chemical methods; in fact, they can be crystallized from solution under some conditions. Similarly, cytosine and guanine derivatives will also form mixed complexes in solution, but the pairs cytosine-adenine or uracil-guanine are far less stable. Similar physical-chemical tests of all possible pairs of bases dissolved in anhydrous solvents show that adenine tends preferentially to complex with uracil and guanine with cytosine. Thus neither the sugar moiety or the phosphodiester backbone of nucleic acids is required for specific pairing of bases, although the stability of such free A–U or G–C pairs is much lower than the stability of the analogous base pairs in duplex nucleic acids.

Such experiments have been extended with most interesting results. Miles and Ts'o and their colleagues have shown that free mononucleotides will tend to associate in a preferential manner with specific mononucleotide residues of a single-stranded polynucleotide in dilute solution. For example, when free adenosine 5′-phosphate is mixed with polyuridylic acid, free AMP molecules associate with successive uridylic acid residues of poly U through hydrogen bonding between the complementary bases, to yield, quite spontaneously, a helical structure having but one covalent backbone (Figure 34-5). Similarly, polycytidylic acid forms a stable complementary helix when mixed with free GMP. Thus a polynucleotide chain can act as a template to bind free mononucleotides in a complementary fashion. Is it possible, then, by the action of abiotic condensing agents, to form internucleotide linkages between the template-bound mononucleotides, thus yielding a complementary polynucleotide?

Orgel and his colleagues have provided such a demonstration. They added a water-soluble carbodiimide condensing agent to a solution containing a single-stranded poly-U template molecule to which free AMP was added. Not only was polyadenylic acid formed, but it was formed at a much higher rate than in the absence of the template (Figure 34-5). These and other similar experiments have therefore shown that polynucleotides can serve as templates for nonenzymatic synthesis of complementary polynucleotides under abiotic primitive-earth conditions. The complementary polynucleotides formed under these conditions possess 2′,5′-internucleotide linkages.

Little or no evidence supports the possibility that a polypeptide chain may have served as a template for making other polypeptide chains, either in the prebiotic era or in terms of the biochemistry of contemporary organisms. To be sure, a primitive complementarity might exist between positively charged and negatively charged amino acid R groups, such as those of lysine and glutamic acid, but there appears to be no comprehensive system of structural complementary that can include all the known amino acids.

However, recent research has shown that α-helical polyamino acids may bind certain mononucleotides with some selectivity. For example, synthetic poly-L-arginine and poly-L-lysine bind guanylic and adenylic acids strongly, whereas cytidylic acid is only weakly bound. From molecular models it has been suggested that an α-helical polyamino acid, such as poly-L-lysine, can bind free adenylic acid molecules to form a helix-like structure, in which 3 mononucleotides correspond to one amino acid residue. In such a structure the R-group of the amino acid residue intercalates between two stacked AMP molecules, which may be visualized as the first two units of a codon. If internucleotide linkages are then formed it is possible to see how the amino acid sequence of an abiotically formed polypeptide may be recorded as a sequence of nucleotide triplets. This is one of several models which

Figure 34-5
Template function in an abiotic system. Polyuridylic acid binds free AMP molecules through hydrogen bonds, positioning them in such a way as to facilitate the formation of polyadenylic acid by the action of a carbodiimide condensing agent (right). *The rate of formation of poly A is greatly increased by the presence of the poly U template* (below).

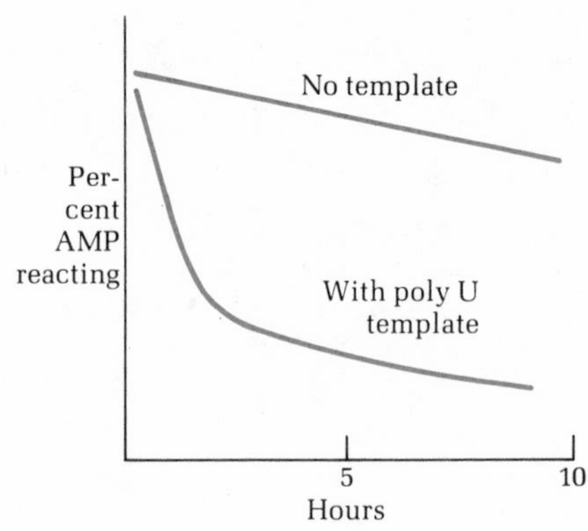

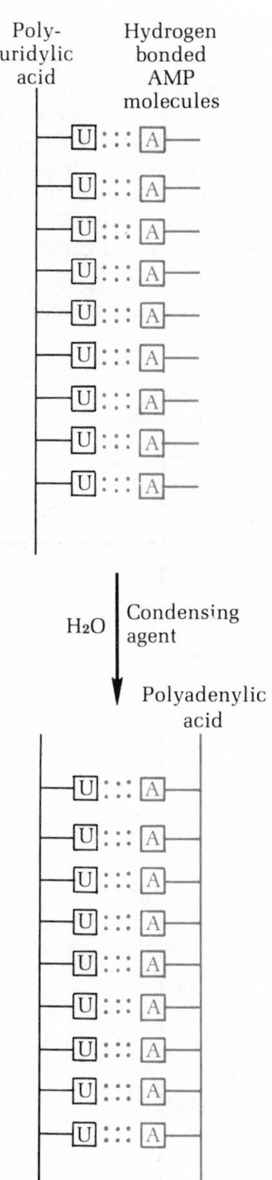

have been proposed for the origin of the genetic code. Such a hypothesis requires that information must flow from a polypeptide to a polynucleotide, which is not known to happen in the present-day genetic system.

The Origin of Asymmetric Biomolecules

One of the distinguishing characteristics of living matter is that essentially all of its organic compounds which possess one or more asymmetric carbon atoms occur in only one stereochemical configuration and thus possess optical activity, whereas optical activity is not seen in inanimate matter except under laboratory conditions designed to produce it.

Because amino acids were in all likelihood first formed from inorganic precursors in nonbiological reactions, they most probably occurred in the primeval broth as racemic mixtures. How then can we account for the fact that natural proteins contain only L-amino acids?

As we have seen (Chapter 6), an α-helix will form from polypeptide chains containing either all L- or all D-amino acids. Since the L- and D-stereoisomers of any given amino acid are identical in structure and reactivity, and differ only in the fact that they are non-superimposable mirror images of each other, biologicallly active proteins could theoretically be made from either series. However, a stable α-helix will not form from a polypeptide containing a random mixture of L- and D-stereoisomers. Therefore there may be a selective biological advantage in having the amino acids either all L or all D, since they would more readily organize into specific two- and three-dimensional structures than would optically mixed polypeptides. From these considerations it has been suggested that L-amino acids were selected as the building blocks of proteins merely by chance, not because they had any intrinsic advantage over D-amino acids. This line of thought also suggests that all living organisms are derived from one cell or a closely related population of cells, since the proteins of all living forms today possess L-amino acids.

Ultimately it is the structure of the active site of enzymes that has preserved biological stereospecificity. Several investigators have shown that certain catalysts, particularly those effective in the solid state, may possess asymmetry in the manner in which they bind the substrate acted on and thus favor formation of one stereoisomer over another. Stereospecific catalysis of some polymerization reactions has also been observed in situations in which the catalyst itself is an optical enantiomer.

The importance of optical specificity in the replication of nucleic acids has been shown in interesting recent experiments by Orgel and his colleagues. When polyuridylic acid, in which all the ribose units are of the D-form, is used as a template to promote the nonenzymatic condensation of hydrogen-bonded AMP molecules to form polyadenylic acid, the condensation of the D-stereoisomer of adenylic acid is favored over that of the L-stereoisomer. It therefore appears that once a polynucleotide template having optically homogenous monomer units is formed, it will preferentially direct the synthesis of another polynucleotide chain of the same optical type, even if the mononucleotide pool from which the new chain is formed is a mixture of D and L forms.

The Origin of "Life" versus the Origin of Cells

We now come to that critical moment in evolution in which the first semblance of "life" appeared, through the chance association of a number of abiotically formed macromolecular components, to yield a unique system of greatly enhanced survival value.

However, the first structure possessing "life" was not necessarily a modern cell, complete with membranes, nucleus, a metabolism, and the property of self-replication. Rather, the minimum requirement is that it could potentially lead to a complete cell. It may of course be argued whether the term "life" can be accurately enough defined so as to be able to determine at what point "life" began in the chain of events leading from preformed macromolecular components to a complete cell. Although it is generally agreed that an informational macromolecule is a minimum requirement for life, the question is: Which had primacy in the origin of life, nucleic acids or proteins? One view suggests that proteins were the first informational molecules and that the first primitive cells functioned in the absence of nucleic acids and a genetic system. The other hypothesis suggests that nucleic acids arose first and that they provided the information for the evolution of proteins. We shall now examine these hypotheses in detail.

Life without Nucleic Acids: Coacervate Droplets and Microspheres

Oparin in the Soviet Union has suggested that the first cells, which he called *protobionts*, arose when a boundary or membrane formed around one or more macromolecules possessing catalytic activity, presumably proteins. A corollary of his hypothesis is that the genetic apparatus which yielded precise self-replication of cell catalysts may have been a later event in biological evolution. He proposed that a cell phase could have arisen from the concentrated primeval broth by the process of *coacervation*, a well-known phenomenon which often takes place in aqueous solutions of highly hydrated polymers. It is defined as the spontaneous separation of a continuous one-phase aqueous solution of such a polymer into two aqueous phases, one having a relatively high polymer concentration and the other a relatively low concentration. The tendency to undergo coacervation is primarily a function of the molecular size of the polymer and the extent to which its interstices may be penetrated by water. Such a coacervation process occurring in the primordial organic broth may have yielded microscopic droplets consisting of that phase in which the polymer concentration is high.

Oparin postulated further that some of these droplets may have entrapped certain small molecules, such as

Figure 34-6
Primitive metabolism in synthetic coacervate droplets containing enzymes. (Top) A droplet capable of synthesizing maltose from glucose 1-phosphate. (Middle) A droplet exhibiting electron transport. (Bottom) A coacervate droplet capable of transferring electrons from ascorbic acid to a dye on illumination. $\overset{*}{\text{Chl}}$ *represents chlorophyll in its excited state.*

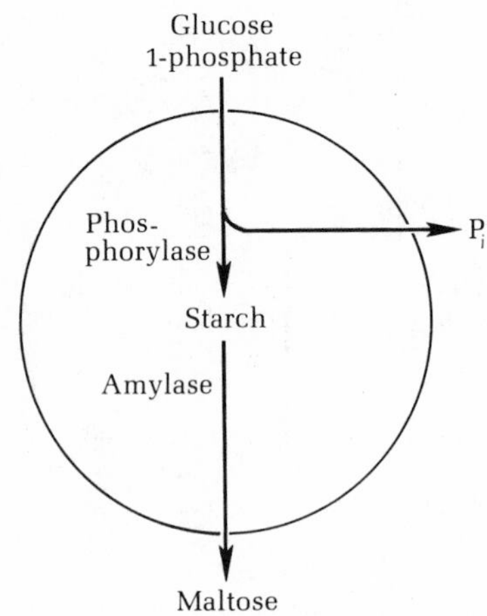

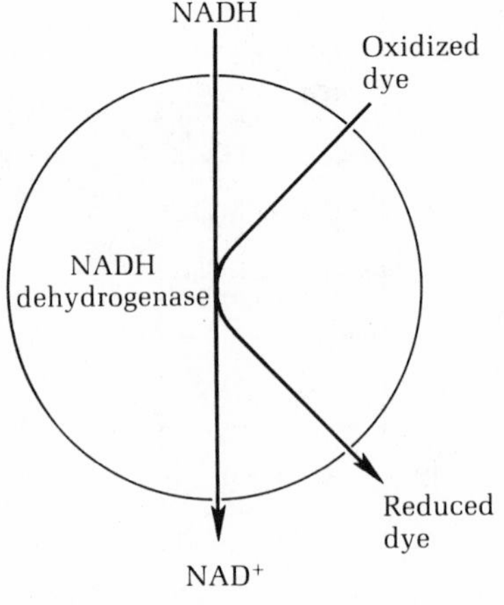

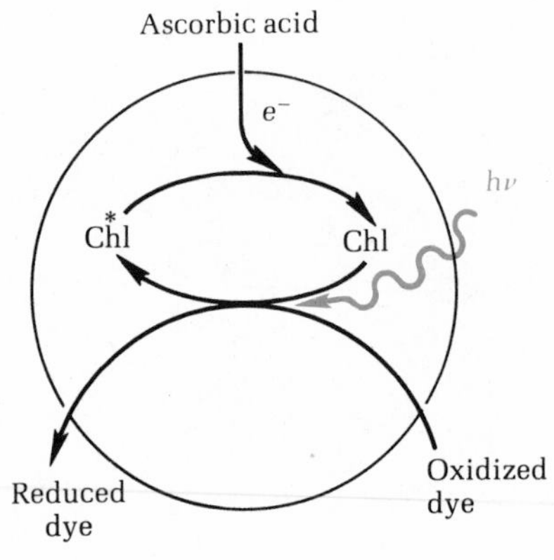

glucose or amino acids, as well as a primitive catalyst, so that they possessed both substrate and catalyst. Such droplets would thus possess a simple, one-reaction "metabolism." He further postulated that such a metabolizing droplet interacted further with the surrounding aqueous environment, to acquire other compounds that it could incorporate into its own structure, causing the droplet to grow. As it reached a size limited by physical considerations, the droplet would break up into smaller droplets as a result of external forces, such as wind or waves, just as a coarse emulsion of oil in water disperses into a finer emulsion when shaken. Some of the progeny droplets so formed might retain catalyst molecules derived from the parent droplet and thus could "grow" another generation of droplets.

Figure 34-7
Photomicrograph of proteinoid microspheres. Their average diameter is 1.9 μ.

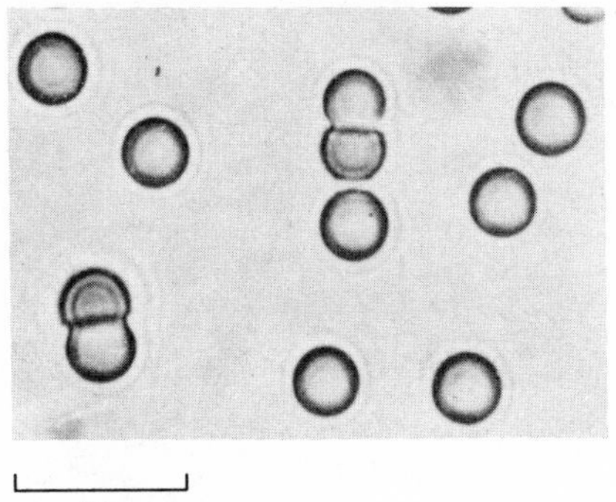

Oparin and his colleagues carried out a number of interesting model experiments with coacervating systems to illustrate the feasibility of his hypothesis. Under certain conditions concentrated aqueous solutions of polypeptides, polysaccharides, or RNA were found to form coacervate droplets having a volume of from 10^{-8} to 10^{-6} cm^3 and polymer concentration of from 5 to 50 percent. Such droplets possess a surrounding boundary, which could be visualized in the microscope. When coacervate droplets containing the enzyme glycogen phosphorylase were placed in a solution of glucose 1-phosphate, a starch-like polymer was formed in the droplets. If the droplets also contained β-amylase, which breaks down starch to maltose, then they were found to convert glucose 1-phosphate, obtained from the medium, into maltose, which then returned to the medium. Synthetic coacervate droplets could also be prepared containing the flavoprotein NADH dehydrogenase and a reducible dye. Such droplets could accept reducing equivalents from external NADH and transfer them to the dye molecule, which was liberated into the medium in reduced form (Figure 34-6).

Other self-forming, cell-like structures, called *microspheres,* have been described in great detail by Fox and his colleagues. These remarkable bodies arise spontaneously when hot concentrated solutions of thermally-formed proteinoids are allowed to cool slowly over a period of one or two weeks, under appropriate conditions of pH and salt concentration. Microspheres are rather uniform spherical droplets about 2.0 μ in diameter (Figure 34-7). When the pH is properly adjusted, their outer boundary shows a double-layer structure resembling that of natural membranes; however, microspheres contain no lipid. Microspheres appear to be rather stable at pH 3-7. When placed in salt solutions hypertonic or hypotonic in relation to the solution in which they were formed, microspheres will either shrink or swell, suggesting they have a semipermeable membrane surrounding an inner compartment containing entrapped salts and soluble proteinoid. Microspheres also possess the capacity for enhancement of the rate of certain reactions, if they are formed from proteinoids having this capacity.

It is remarkable that microspheres can be induced to undergo cleavage or division when exposed to $MgCl_2$ or by suitable changes in pH. Moreover, if suspensions of microspheres are allowed to stand for one or two weeks they undergo a budding process, akin to the budding of yeasts. Such buds may detach from the mother microsphere and form a second generation of microspheres (Figure 34-8). Presumably the buds are formed by accretion and accumulation of proteinoid from the surrounding medium into the microsphere. Although the microspheres are devoid of nucleic acid and have no metabolism, they are self-organizing systems which may be of much value as models of the first primitive cell-like structures, since they form spontaneously from components which are themselves generated from primitive earth gases at elevated temperatures.

Still another possibility suggests itself for the origin of a cell boundary. It is possible that droplets rich in organic matter may have become surrounded by phospholipid bilayers resembling the lipid systems present in some natural membranes. We have seen that polar lipids will spontaneously form monolayers on air-water interfaces (Chapter 10). By the action of wind on such a surface, a spray of lipid-coated droplets could be formed which on return to the surface, might acquire another lipid layer, to yield a droplet surrounded by a lipid bilayer (Figure 34-9).

Although such models of primitive cells are very plausible, they could not evolve very far without a genetic system. Moreover, such models require that information must have passed from primitive proteins to primitive nucleic acids until a stable genome could develop, a process which has no present-day counterpart.

Figure 34-8
Budding and replication of microspheres.

Buds on parent microspheres

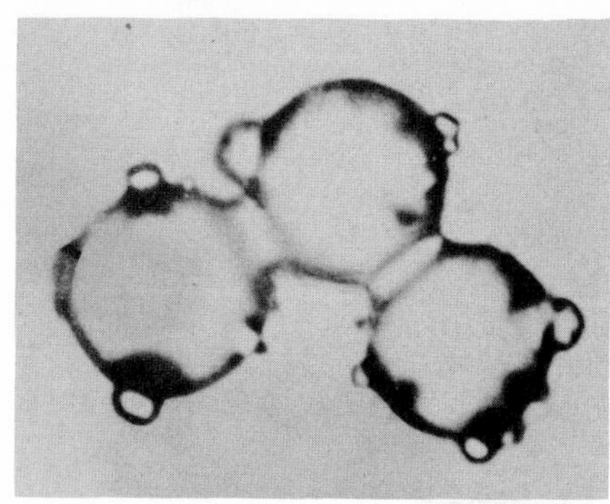

Liberated buds

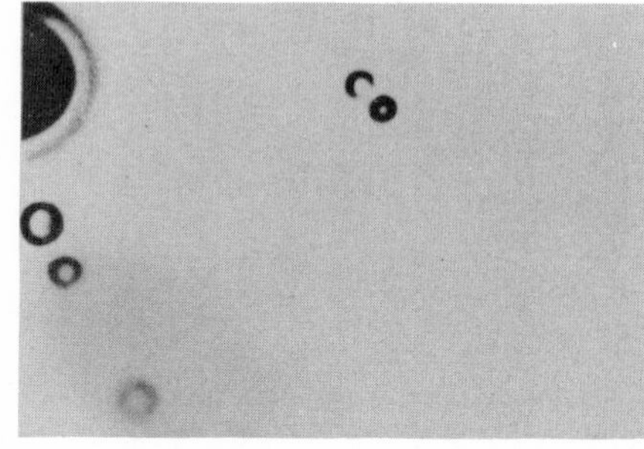

Microspheres grown from a central darkly-stained bud

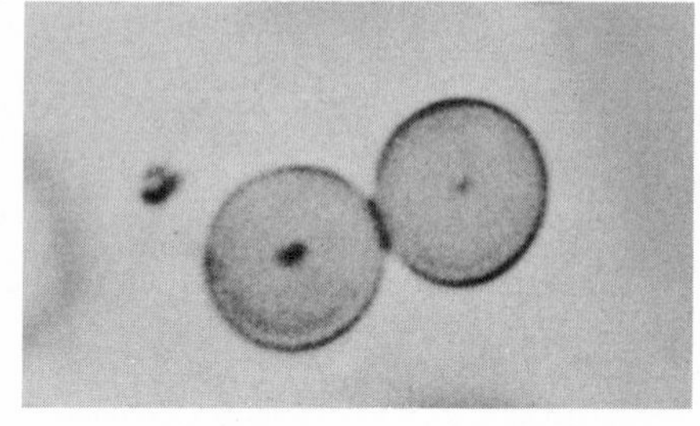

Mature second-generation microsphere with bud

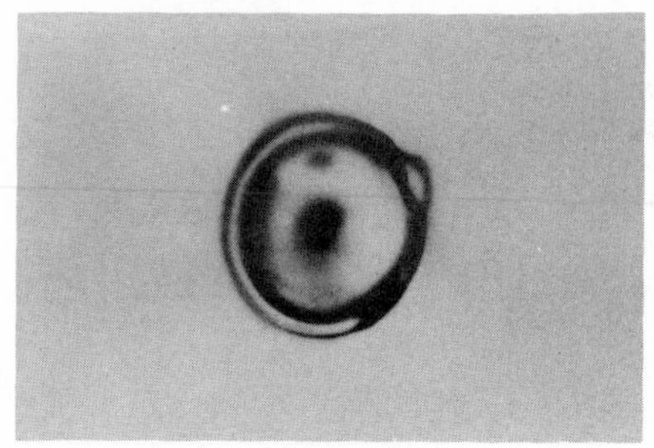

The Gene Hypothesis: Life without Proteins

The alternative hypothesis for the origin of life is based on the primacy of nucleic acids. This hypothesis was stated by the geneticist Muller in 1929, who proposed that life first began with the abiotic formation of one or more genes. The gene hypothesis remained incompletely developed for some years, but with the advent of our new knowledge of molecular genetics, it has been elaborated by Pirie, Horowitz, Crick, Orgel, and others. Muller argued that the minimum properties of a living system (that is, the capacity to carry out metabolism and the capacity for self-replication) are already *potentially* present in genes, which, when placed in the proper molecular environment within a cell, can code for the formation of daughter cells. When Muller first postulated this idea, the chemical nature of genes was still unknown. Stated in modern terms, this hypothesis postulates that a nucleic acid molecule may possess the potential capacity to "live" by virtue of its ability to code for proteins, to undergo self-replication, and to undergo mutation. The acquisition of a boundary membrane and the development of catalysts are thus regarded as later evolutionary events.

Let us examine the three major lines of thought and evidence supporting the nucleic acid hypothesis. One arises from modern knowledge of the molecular structure and self-replicability of viruses. Another arises from the role of noninformational RNA in protein synthesis. The

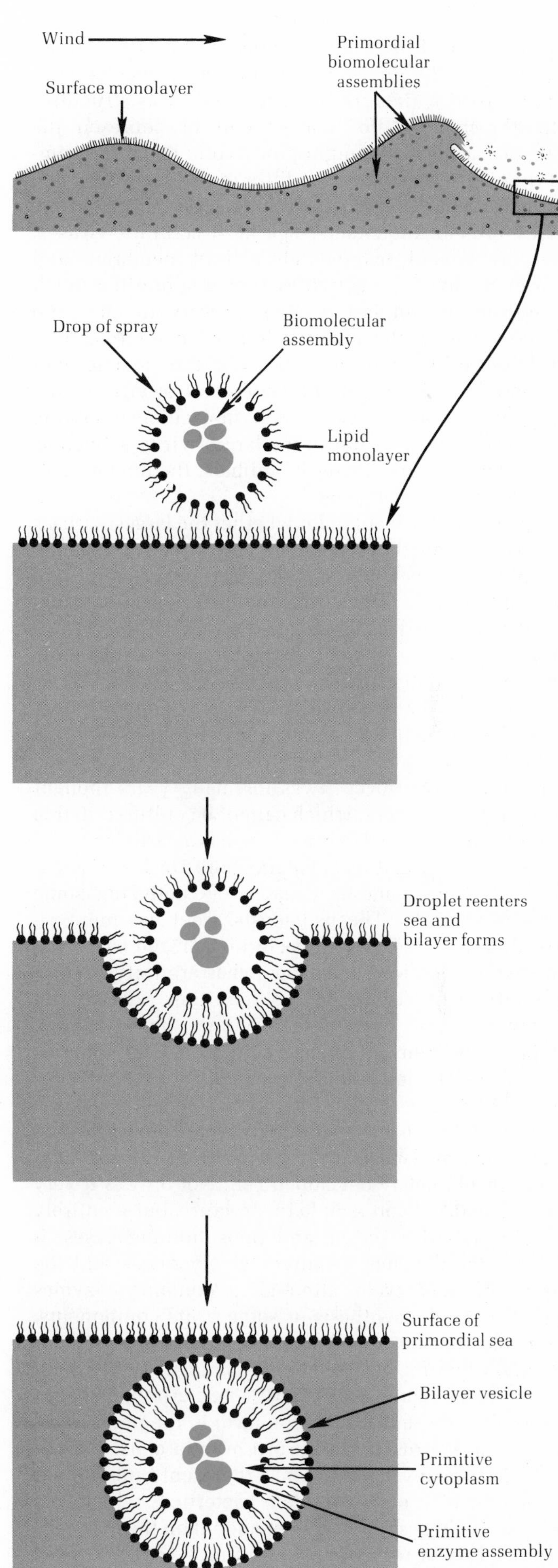

Figure 34-9
Formation of lipid bilayer membranes.

third line arises from the wide range of biological functions possessed by nucleotides in present-day cells.

The viruses, which are often referred to as structures "at the threshold of life," may conceivably represent the precursors of the first simple procaryotic cells. The simplest, like tobacco mosaic, are little more than a complex of a single nucleic acid molecule and a sheath of recurring, identical protein monomers. The most complex viruses, on the other hand, may contain a lipid membrane and one or more enzymatic activities; they do not differ much in size from the simplest, smallest procaryotic cells. We now know that it is the nucleic acid portion of viruses that carries its genetic information, since the nucleic acid alone may be infective. In the very smallest viruses, the nucleic acid is a relatively small molecule containing only a very few genes, but in the largest viruses, such as the vaccinia and pox viruses of animals, the nucleic acid possesses hundreds of genes.

It has long been a moot point whether the largest viruses are viruses or small cells. The largest viruses are somewhat similar in size and infectious behavior to a group of very small bacteria which can live only within specific host cells as parasites. These small parasitic procaryotes include the *chlamydia,* among which are the infectious agents of the human diseases *psittacosis* and *lymphogranuloma,* and the *rickettsia,* which are somewhat larger organisms causing tick fever and Rocky Mountain spotted fever. As an example, the causative agent of the disease psittacosis ("parrot fever") was for many years thought to be a virus. This agent, which cannot be cultured in free form independent of a host organism, has a particle weight of about 6 billion daltons, contains both DNA and RNA, as well as lipids, and is capable of catalyzing some metabolic reactions. The psittacosis agent has more recently been reclassified as a bacterium on the basis of a more rigorous (and perhaps somewhat arbitrary) definition of viruses. According to this definition, a virus is an intracellular agent with an infectious phase, which (1) reproduces from its nucleic acid alone, (2) contains only one type of nucleic acid, either RNA or DNA, (3) contains no ATP–ADP system for the transfer of metabolic energy, and (4) is unable to grow or undergo binary fission. However, the psittacosis agent is an extremely rudimentary and incompletely developed cell. Not only is it very small (0.2 to 0.5μ) and simple in structure, but it entirely lacks an ATP–ADP system and phosphotransferases. It also lacks the enzymes required for glycolysis and the tricarboxylic acid cycle, although it contains enzymes required in the biosynthesis of some of its components. Presumably this organism depends on the host cell for ATP energy and for its precursor biomolecules. Although the psittacosis agent is officially a bacterium, it could conceivably represent a transition form in the progressive evolution of a virus into true procaryotic cells. On the other hand, as many believe, it may represent a mutational degeneration of a once complete bacterium, which lost genes irreversibly as it became dependent on the host cell.

Another line of reasoning supporting a central role of nucleic acids in the origin of life is suggested by the striking versatility of function of nucleotides in present-day organisms. Mononucleotides serve as the monomeric units in the structure of DNA and of the three major types of RNA. Specific nucleotides or nucleotide derivatives also serve as energy carriers (ATP, ADP), as hydrogen or electron carriers (NAD, NADP, FMN, FAD), as sugar carriers (UDP), as carriers of lipid components (CDP), as acyl carriers (CoA), and as methionine carriers (S-adenosyl methionine). Thus nucleotides are important functional elements in all aspects of metabolism and energy transfer, as well as in the genetic apparatus. From nucleic acids may also be descended the characteristic phosphodiester linkages which join successive glycerol or ribitol residues to form the backbone of the teichoic acids (Chapter 11), and the phosphodiester linkages which join glycerol and other alcohols to form the backbones of the phosphoglycerides (Chapter 10). These metabolic and structural relationships suggest very strongly that much of the important metabolic and genetic machinery of the cell could have evolved or developed from nucleotides.

Perhaps we can now begin to see how a primitive form of life based on nucleotide chemistry may have arisen. The most primitive nucleic acids could have replicated themselves in the absence of enzymes, by the action of abiotically formed condensing agents, as we have seen above. Similarly, the most primitive form of the present-day ATP–ADP system for energy transfer could have functioned without enzymes such as phosphotransferases, possibly through the action of primitive mineral or organic catalysts. The earliest forms of the pyridine-linked dehydrogenases may possibly have consisted of oligonucleotides of which one mononucleotide unit contained the reducible nicotinamide ring as a base, rather than one of the standard bases. It is thus quite plausible that a primitive nucleotide-based life could have existed in the absence of proteins. But it is quite clear that not much evolutionary progress could have been made without proteins, especially enzymes. How, then, did the first proteins arise, if genes arose first?

This issue has recently been discussed in the light of modern developments in molecular genetics, particularly by Crick and by Orgel. They suggest that the real answers to the origin of life may lie in the origin of ribosomes, of transfer RNA, and of the genetic code. They have pointed out that protein synthesis by ribosomes involves two types of nucleic acid which are noninformational, that is, do not serve a template function, namely, transfer RNA and ribosomal RNA. Transfer RNA does possess an anticodon triplet, but it makes up but a very small fraction of its total structure. Both tRNA and rRNA resemble globular proteins in that they possess complex folded three-dimensional structures, made possible by short segments of intrachain base pairing. These two forms of RNA are suggested to be the vital parts of a primordial system which "learned" how to make true informational proteins, not merely random polymers of amino acids.

The provocative suggestion has been made that the first primitive ribosomes consisted entirely of RNA. (Parenthetically, we may note that the ribosomes of procaryotic cells contain significantly more RNA than those of eucaryotic cells, which evolved later). Such a primitive proteinless ribosome may have been able to make the first ordered peptides with the participation of tRNA, a smaller molecule which can bind to the primordial ribosomal RNA, presumably by base pairing. Such a primitive tRNA may have had the capacity to bind a given amino acid noncovalently, perhaps at or near the anticodon site, which might conceivably form a cagelike amino acid binding site. Indeed, much thought is now being given to the possible molecular or conformational relationships between specific base sequences of tRNA's and their corresponding amino acids. For example, why should UUU specifically code for phenylalanine and not for some other amino acid? Why do the codons for all amino acids having hydrophobic R groups have U as the second letter? If primitive tRNA's could bind the R group of amino acids noncovalently in a cavity of specific dimensions and if such a "loaded" tRNA molecule could bind to ribosomal RNA by base pairing, it is possible to imagine how a sequence of "loaded" tRNA molecules might have become aligned on the surface of a ribosomal RNA molecule, in such a way as to juxtapose the carboxyl group of one amino acid with the amino group of the next. If a prebiotic condensing agent, such as a polyphosphate, then extracted the elements of water from the properly aligned carboxyl and amino groups, a peptide bond could then arise. Thus the primitive peptide-forming machinery possibly consisted only of two different types of specifically folded RNA. At this stage in evolution, before the appearance of specific amino acid activating enzymes, the association of the amino acid to the tRNA may have been noncovalent. Thus many coding mistakes could have occurred. Nevertheless, the primitive forms of transfer RNA and ribosomal RNA may have performed one of the important functions of an enzyme molecule, namely, the provision of specific binding sites to position the loosely bound amino acid "substrates" in such a way as to allow them to interact in the presence of a nonenzymatic condensing agent.

The next step may have been the development of the first template for specifying the sequence of tRNA's and thus of the amino acids they carry. This may have been provided by a loop of the primordial ribosomal RNA, or by another RNA strand which could bind not only to the primitive tRNA's but also to the primitive ribosome, to constitute the first messenger RNA. Perhaps one of the many different abiotically formed polyribonucleotides in the primeval broth coded for the sequence of some polypeptide that endowed the ribosomal apparatus with enhanced stability or activity, which became the precursor of present-day ribosomal proteins. Perhaps others coded for the synthesis of a polypeptide that stabilized and provided a sheath for the first messenger RNA, and thus became the forerunner of a viral coat protein.

Later the primitive ribosomes may have "learned" to synthesize an enzyme capable of catalyzing the formation of peptide bonds, which enzyme became the forerunner of the present-day peptidyl transferase. Still later, they may have learned to synthesize activating enzymes which may have greatly enhanced the precision of translation, through formation of a covalent bond between the amino acid and its transfer RNA. Possibly DNA arose later than RNA to provide a more permanent engram, one capable of self-replication. In support of this idea we may recall that the direct precursors of the 2′-deoxyribonucleotide building blocks of DNA are corresponding ribonucleotides, by the action of a reductase system (Chapter 25).

Ultimately, the most compelling and probably overriding feature of the nucleic acid hypothesis, whatever its details, is that nucleic acids do have the capacity to serve as templates in the absence of enzymes or proteins, in such a way that a complementary nucleic acid can be formed by an abiotic catalyst or condensing agent. Moreover, through the tendency of nucleic acids to undergo mutation, the capacity of a nucleic acid–based life to undergo rather refined and subtle evolutionary modulations became greatly enhanced.

Later Steps in Biochemical Evolution

Once a template system, a set of catalysts, and a surrounding membrane evolved, in whatever sequence, the process of cellular evolution becomes much easier to comprehend. Presumably in the early stages of biological evolution, chemical evolution continued for some time, so that the first cells continued to select those organic molecules from the environment which enhanced their survival. As the primeval broth became depleted of organic compounds by the first anaerobic heterotrophs, which utilized them as sources of energy and carbon, the first autotrophic cells, capable of using carbon dioxide, and the first photosynthetic cells arose. Depletion of organic nitrogen compounds in the primeval broth may also have led to the elaboration of the capacity to fix atmospheric nitrogen. In the photosynthetic, nitrogen-fixing blue-green algae we see the culmination of a metabolic adaption to a primitive sea which may have become completely devoid of organic carbon and nitrogen compounds. After oxygen appeared in the atmosphere the first oxygen-consuming aerobic cells presumably arose, which possessed a selective advantage because they could extract more energy per molecule of exogenous glucose than anaerobic fermenting organisms. The evolution of aerobic respiration and oxidative phosphorylation thus completed the development of the basic repertoire of energy-yielding metabolic processes which survive in the living organisms of today. Although most evidence and current thought supports this sequence of events in the metabolic evolution of cells, we cannot exclude the possibility that some other sequence occurred. In fact, some investigators have proposed that autotrophic cells may have arisen first.

Only after these developments had taken place, which may have involved some 2500 million years, or about one-half the earth's history, do we have our second great jump in cell evolution, the appearance of eucaryotic cells, which has rightfully been called one of the most significant events in biological evolution. Without it, the higher multicellular organisms might not have developed. One hypothesis, which is given major support from recent investigations, holds that eucaryotic cells originated as the result of metabolic symbiosis. Presumably eucaryotes evolved from large anaerobic procaryotic cells, whose fermentation capacity may no longer have been able to keep up with their energy demands. Such anaerobes may have engulfed small photosynthetic or aerobic procaryotes, which became metabolic endosymbionts, the host cell furnishing glycolytic fermentation capacity and the parasite either photosynthetic or respiratory capacity. Such endosymbionts thus may have been the forerunners of modern chloroplasts and mitochondria, respectively, whose ability to extract energy from sunlight or organic fuels may have endowed the host anaerobic cell with greatly enhanced survival value. Eucaryotes are much larger and more versatile cells, far better equipped to act on, and thus modify, their environment.

Throughout the course of biological evolution the formation of non-lethal mutants, as the result of chemically or physically induced changes in the base sequence of the genome, made possible selection of those organisms best able to survive their contemporary conditions of life.

But the most striking of all the interlinked events which have led to the incredibly complex biological organisms we know today still remains on the other side of the curtain that separates chemical from biological evolution. Why do organic compounds tend to undergo molecular evolution and become self-organizing systems? The laws of chemistry and physics we know today do not forbid the process of self-organization; they simply provide no explanation for it. Our biggest task is to divine the molecular logic of self-organizing systems of organic compounds. Living organisms may thus be an inevitable outcome of the evolution of self-organizing systems of organic molecules. Indeed, they may be but stages in the further evolution of matter toward levels of organization that are still incomprehensible to us.

These questions need not remain philosophical speculations. They may well be experimentally approachable, since, with the advantage of modern knowledge of the properties of organic molecules and of biochemistry, molecular science may be able to accelerate greatly the chemical processes leading to, or involved in, the tendency of organic molecules to undergo self-organization. We may onè day be able to study the properties of simple molecular automata in the laboratory and to simulate the successive stages in their evolution to cells.

Summary

Available evidence indicates that the earth was formed about 4,600 million years ago and that the first living organisms arose about 3,100 million years ago. The appearance of life was probably preceded by a period of chemical evolution. It is believed that in this phase, which can be studied under simulated primitive-earth conditions, components of the primitive atmosphere were converted into simple organic compounds, among which were amino acids, purines, pyrimidines, hydrocarbons, and sugars, by the action of ultraviolet irradiation, electrical discharges, or heat. Hydrogen cyanide is a probable intermediate in the formation of the nitrogenous products. Condensing agents capable of removing the elements of water from simple monomeric building-block molecules, thus linking them into chains, may have arisen by further reactions of HCN, to form carbodiimide derivatives, such as dicyandiamide, which can condense phosphoric acid to polyphosphate derivatives, possible precursors of ATP. By the action of such condensing agents, or by the action of heat alone, peptides, nucleosides, nucleotides, and sugar polymers may be formed. Protein-like amino acid polymers, called proteinoids, form readily on heating amino acids above 100°. However, further chemical evolution of polypeptides and polynucleotides could not have taken place without a template system to record the monomer sequence of "good" polymers and to enable them to undergo evolutionary improvement. In simulated primitive-earth experiments it has been found that polynucleotides can act as complementary templates in the absence of enzymes, through base pairing.

There are two major hypotheses for the origin of the first cells. One, first postulated by Oparin, stresses the development of enzymes and a cell boundary as the first important events; it postulates that a genetic system developed later. Boundaries or membranes may be formed by coacervation of a polymer solution, or by formation of lipid bilayers. Cell-like behavior, including a primitive metabolism and division process, is exhibited by coacervate droplets containing enzymes, and also by microspheres, which are formed from thermally polymerized proteinoids. However, it is not likely that such a primitive cell could have progressed further without nucleic acids and a genetic system.

The other hypothesis suggests that a nucleic acid or "naked" gene was the first form of life or potential life. This hypothesis is supported by modern knowledge of the structure and self-replication of viruses and the fact that their nucleic acid molecules bear all the essential information for their replication. It is also supported by the wide range of cell activities in which specialized nucleotides are involved. It has also been suggested that non-informational nucleic acids, the precursors of tRNA and rRNA, may have played an enzyme-like role in primitive protein synthesis, prior to the advent of enzymes. Primitive transfer RNA may later have evolved into the amino acid activating and transfer systems, and primitive ribosomal RNA into ribosomes.

The capacity for self-organization may be the ultimate and inevitable outcome of the evolution of organic matter. Life may therefore arise under any physical conditions in which organic compounds may undergo the full range of their potential evolution.

References

Books

CALVIN, M.: *Chemical Evolution: Molecular Evolution towards the Origin of Living Systems on the Earth and Elsewhere,* Oxford University Press, London, 1969, 288 pp. Reconstruction of chemical evolution from molecular paleontology and from simulated primitive-earth experiments.

CLARK, F., and R. L. M. SYNGE (eds.): *The Origin of Life on the Earth,* Pergamon Press, New York, 1959. A collection of important articles and essays; the beginnings of recent progress.

KEOSIAN, J.: *The Origin of Life,* 2nd ed., Reinhold, New York, 1968, 120 pp. A brief paperback review of some old ideas and new experiments, particularly those based on simulated primitive-earth conditions. Extensive bibliography.

WOESE, C. R.: *The Genetic Code,* Harper and Row, New York, 1967. The origin of the genetic code and of living organisms are discussed.

WOOLDRIDGE, D. E.: *The Machinery of Life,* McGraw-Hill, New York, 1966. Unification of the naked gene and protobiont hypotheses.

Articles

BERNAL, J. D.: "Molecular Structure, Biochemical Function, and Evolution," in T. H. Waterman and H. J. Morawitz (eds.), *Theoretical and Mathematical Biology,* Blaisdell, New York, 1965, pp. 96–135. A short unifying essay on the molecular basis of biology.

CRICK, F. H. C.: "The Origin of the Genetic Code," *J. Mol. Biol.,* **38**:367–379 (1968). A provocative article emphasizing the origin of amino acid–transfer RNA specificity.

EGLINTON, G., and M. CALVIN: "Chemical Fossils," *Sci. American,* **216**:32–43 (1967). The development of organic geochemistry.

FERRIS, J. P.: "Cyanovinyl Phosphate: A Prebiological Phosphorylating Agent?," *Science,* **161**:53–54 (1968). The formation, stability, and efficiency of a possible prebiotic phosphorylating agent.

FOX, S. W.: "Self-ordered Polymers and Propagative Cell-like Systems," Naturwissenschaften, **56**:1–9 (1969). An interesting short review (in English) of the properties of proteinoids and microspheres.

LACEY, J. C., and K. M. PRUITT: "Origin of the Genetic Code," Nature, **223**:799–804 (1969). An attempt to provide a model for the interaction between mononucleotides and polypeptides.

LOHRMANN, R., and L. E. ORGEL: "Prebiotic Synthesis: Phosphorylation in Aqueous Solution," *Science,* **161**:64–66 (1968). An experimental survey of prebiotic condensing agents.

OPARIN, A. I.: "The Origin of Life and the Origin of Enzymes," *Adv. Enzymology,* **27**:347–380 (1965). The most recent statement of the protobiont hypothesis.

ORGEL, L. E.: "Evolution of the Genetic Apparatus," *J. Mol. Biol.,* **38**:381–393 (1968). A penetrating comparison of life without nucleic acids vs life without proteins.

WALD, G.: "The Origins of Life," *Proc. Natl. Acad. Sci.,* **52**:595–611 (1964). An eloquent statement of the continuity of matter in the universe.

APPENDIXES

APPENDIX A

A Chronology of Biochemistry

Biochemistry had its earliest origins in speculations on the role of air in the utilization of food and on the nature of fermentation. Leonardo da Vinci (1452–1510) was among the first to compare animal nutrition to the burning of a candle, a line of reasoning that was further developed by Van Helmont (1648). However, the real history of biochemistry did not begin until the late 18th century, when the science of chemistry began to take form.

1770–1774	Priestley discovered oxygen, showed it was consumed by animals and produced by plants.
1770–1786	Scheele isolated glycerol, as well as citric, malic, lactic, and uric acids, from natural sources.
1773	Rouelle isolated urea from urine.
1779–1796	Ingen-Housz showed that light is required for oxygen production by green plants. He also proved that plants use carbon dioxide.
1780–1789	Lavoisier demonstrated that animals require oxygen, recognized that respiration is oxidation, and first measured oxygen consumption by a human subject.
1783	Spallanzani deduced that protein digestion in the stomach is a chemical rather than mechanical process.
1804	Dalton enunciated the atomic theory.
1804	deSaussure carried out the first balance sheet for the stoichiometry of gas exchanges in photosynthesis.
1806	Vauquelin and Robiquet first isolated an amino acid, asparagine.
1810	Gay-Lussac deduced the equation for alcoholic fermentation.
1815	Biot discovered optical activity.
1828	Wohler synthesized the first organic compound from inorganic components: urea from lead cyanate and ammonia.
1830–1840	Liebig developed techniques of quantitative analysis and applied them to biological systems.
1833	Payen and Persoz purified diastase (amylase) of wheat, showed it to be heat-labile, and postulated the central importance of enzymes in biology.
1837	Berzelius postulated the catalytic nature of fermentation.
1838	Schleiden and Schwann enunciated the cell theory.
1838	Mulder carried out the first systematic studies of proteins.
1842	Mayer enunciated the First Law of thermodynamics and its applicability to living organisms.
1850–1855	Bernard isolated glycogen from the liver and showed it is converted into blood glucose.
1854–1864	Pasteur proved that fermentation is caused by microorganisms and demolished the spontaneous generation hypothesis.
1857	Kölliker discovered mitochondria ("sarcosomes") in muscle.
1859	Darwin published *Origin of Species*.
1862	Sachs proved that starch is a product of photosynthesis.
1864	F. Hoppe-Seyler first crystallized a protein: hemoglobin.
1866	Mendel published his experiments leading to the principles of independent segregation and assortment of genes.
1869	Miescher discovered DNA.
1872	Pfluger proved oxygen is consumed by all the tissues of animals rather than by the blood or lungs alone.

1877	Kühne proposed the term enzyme and distinguished enzymes from bacteria.
1886	MacMunn discovered histohematins, later renamed cytochromes.
1890	Altmann described procedures for staining mitochondria, studied their distribution, and postulated them to have metabolic and genetic autonomy.
1893	Ostwald proved enzymes are catalysts.
1894	Emil Fischer demonstrated the specificity of enzymes and the lock-and-key relationship between enzyme and substrate.
1897	Bertrand coined the term coenzyme.
1897	Edward Buchner discovered that alcoholic fermentation may occur in cell-free yeast extracts.
1897–1906	Eijkman proved that beriberi is a dietary deficiency disease, and that a water-soluble component of rice polishings can cure it.
1901–1904	Takamine and Aldrich, and also Abel, first isolated a hormone, epinephrine, and Stoltz achieved its synthesis.
1902	Emil Fischer and Hofmeister demonstrated that proteins are polypeptides.
1903	Neuberg first used the term biochemistry.
1905	Harden and Young showed the requirement of phosphate in alcoholic fermentation and isolated the first coenzyme, cozymase, later shown to be NAD.
1905	Knoop deduced the β-oxidation of fatty acids.
1907	Fletcher and Hopkins showed that lactic acid is formed during anaerobic muscle contraction.
1909	Sørensen showed the effect of pH on enzyme action.
1911	Funk isolated crystals with Vitamin B activity and coined the name vitamin.
1912	Neuberg proposed a chemical pathway for fermentation.
1912	Batelli and Stern discovered dehydrogenases.
1912	Warburg postulated a respiratory enzyme for the activation of oxygen, discovered its inhibition by cyanide, and showed the requirement of iron in respiration.
1912–1922	Wieland showed the activation of hydrogen in dehydrogenation reactions.
1913	Michaelis and Menten developed a kinetic theory of enzyme action.
1913	Wilstätter and Stoll isolated and studied chlorophyll.
1914	Kendall isolated thyroxine.
1917	McCollum showed that xerophthalmia in rats is due to lack of Vitamin A.
1922	Ruzicka recognized isoprene as the building block of many natural products.
1922	McCollum showed that lack of Vitamin D causes rickets.
1922	Warburg and Negelein carried out the first measurements of the quantum efficiency of photosynthesis.
1923	Keilin rediscovered histohematins (cytochromes) and demonstrated changes in their oxidation state during respiratory activity.
1925	Briggs and Haldane made important refinements in the theory of enzyme kinetics.
1925–1930	Levene elucidated the structure of mononucleotides and showed they are building blocks of nucleic acids.
1925–1930	Svedberg invented the ultracentrifuge for determination of sedimentation rates of proteins.
1926	Sumner first crystallized an enzyme, urease, and proved it to be a protein.
1926	Jansen and Donath isolated Vitamin B_1 (thiamine) from rice polishings.

1927	Muller, and also Stadler, demonstrated artificial transmutation of genes by x rays.
1927	Windaus showed ergosterol is a precursor of Vitamin D.
1928	Eggleton discovered phosphagen in muscle.
1928	Euler isolated carotene and showed it to have Vitamin A activity.
1928–1932	Szent-Györgyi, and later Waugh and King, isolated ascorbic acid (Vitamin C).
1928–1933	Warburg deduced the iron-porphyrin nature of the respiratory enzyme.
1929	Fiske and Subbarow isolated ATP and phosphocreatine from muscle extracts.
1930	Lundsgaard proved that muscles may contract in the absence of lactic acid formation.
1930–1933	Northrop isolated crystalline pepsin and trypsin and proved their protein nature.
1930–1935	Edsall and von Muralt isolated myosin from muscle.
1931	Engelhardt discovered that phosphorylation is coupled to respiration.
1932	Lohmann discovered the ATP-phosphocreatine reaction.
1932	Warburg and Christian discovered the "yellow enzyme," a flavoprotein.
1933	Keilin isolated cytochrome *c* and reconstituted electron transport in particulate heart preparations.
1933	Krebs and Henseleit discovered the urea cycle.
1933	Embden and also Meyerhof demonstrated crucial intermediates in the chemical pathway of glycolysis and fermentation.
1935	Williams and his colleagues deduced the structure of Vitamin B_1.
1935	Rose discovered threonine, the last essential amino acid to have been recognized.
1935	Kuhn discovered that riboflavin (Vitamin B_2) is a component of the "yellow enzyme."
1935	Schoenheimer and Rittenberg first used isotopes as tracers in the study of intermediary metabolism of carbohydrates and lipids.
1935	Stanley first crystallized a virus, tobacco mosaic.
1935	Szent-Györgyi showed the catalytic effect of dicarboxylic acids on respiration.
1935–1936	Warburg and Euler isolated and determined the structure and action of pyridine nucleotides.
1937	Krebs postulated the citric acid cycle.
1937	Lohmann and Schuster showed that thiamine is a component of the prosthetic group of pyruvate carboxylase.
1937–1938	Warburg showed how formation of ATP is coupled to the dehydrogenation of glyceraldehyde 3-phosphate.
1937–1941	Kalckar and Belitser independently carried out the first quantitative studies of oxidative phosphorylation.
1937	Cori and Cori began their incisive studies of glycogen phosphorylase.
1938	Hill found that cell-free suspensions of chloroplasts yield oxygen when illuminated in the presence of an electron acceptor.
1938	Braunstein and Kritzmann discovered transamination reactions.
1939–1941	Lipmann postulated the central role of ATP in the energy transfer cycle.
1939–1942	Engelhardt and Ljubimova discovered the ATPase activity of myosin.
1939–1946	Szent-Györgyi discovered actin and actomyosin.
1940	Beadle and Tatum proposed the one gene–one enzyme hypothesis.
1940–1943	Claude isolated and studied a mitochondrial fraction from liver.
1942	Bloch and Rittenberg discovered that acetate is the precursor of cholesterol.

1943	Chance first applied sensitive spectrophotometric methods to enzyme-substrate interactions.
1943–1947	Leloir and Munoz demonstrated fatty acid oxidation in cell-free systems; Lehninger showed the requirement of ATP and the stoichiometry of fatty acid oxidation.
1944	Avery, MacLeod, and McCarty demonstrated that bacterial transformation is caused by DNA.
1947–1950	Lipmann and Kaplan isolated and characterized coenzyme A.
1948	Leloir discovered the role of uridine nucleotides in carbohydrate biosynthesis.
1948	Hogeboom, Schneider, and Palade refined the differential centrifugation method for cell fractionation.
1948	Calvin and Benson discovered that phosphoglyceric acid is an early intermediate in photosynthetic carbon dioxide fixation.
1948–1950	Kennedy and Lehninger discovered that the tricarboxylic acid cycle, fatty acid oxidation, and oxidative phosphorylation take place in mitochondria.
1948–1950	Loomis and Lipmann deduced the action of uncoupling agents.
1950–1953	Chargaff discovered the base equivalences in DNA.
1951	Lehninger demonstrated that oxidative phosphorylation is coupled to electron transport in the respiratory chain.
1951	Lynen postulated the role of Coenzyme A. Shortly later the laboratories of Lynen, Green, and Ochoa isolated the enzymes of fatty acid oxidation.
1951	Pauling and Corey proposed the α helix.
1952–1953	Palade, Porter, and Sjostrand perfected thin sectioning and fixation methods for electron microscopy of intracellular structures.
1952–1954	Zamecnik and his colleagues discovered that ribonucleoprotein particles, later named ribosomes, are the site of protein synthesis.
1953	DuVigneaud carried out the first laboratory synthesis of the peptide hormones oxytocin and vasopressin.
1953	Work of Horecker, Dickens and Racker elucidated the 6-phosphogluconate pathway of glucose catabolism.
1953	Sanger deduced the amino acid sequence of insulin.
1953	Watson and Crick postulated the double-helical model of DNA structure.
1954	Arnon and his colleagues discovered photosynthetic phosphorylation.

The Research Literature of Biochemistry

Annual review publications:

Advances in Carbohydrate Chemistry
Advances in Comparative Physiology and Biochemistry
Advances in Enzyme Regulation
Advances in Enzymology and Related Areas of Molecular Biology
Advances in Immunology
Advances in Lipid Research
Advances in Protein Chemistry
Annual Review of Biochemistry
Annual Review of Microbiology
Annual Review of Physiology
Annual Review of Plant Physiology
Bacteriological Reviews
Biochemical Society Symposia
Biological Reviews
Chemical Reviews
Cold Spring Harbor Symposia in Quantitative Biology
Essays in Biochemistry
Harvey Lectures
Physiological Reviews
Progress in Biophysics and Biophysical Chemistry
Progress in the Chemistry of Fats and Other Lipids
Progress in Nucleic Acid Research and Molecular Biology
Vitamins and Hormones

Research journals in biochemistry and related fields:

Analytical Biochemistry
Angewandte Chemie (International Edition in English)
Archives of Biochemistry and Biophysics
Biochemical and Biophysical Research Communications
Biochemical Journal
Biochemistry
Biokhimiya (Russian; also translated into English)
Biochimica et Biophysica Acta
Biopolymers
Bulletin de la Société Chimie Biologique
Canadian Journal of Biochemistry
Canadian Journal of Microbiology
Cell and Tissue Kinetics
Chemistry and Physics of Lipids
Comparative Biochemistry and Physiology
Comptes Rendus de l'Academie des Sciences (Paris) Parts C and D
Comptes Rendus des Séances de la Société de Biologie
European Journal of Biochemistry (formerly Biochemische Zeitschrift)
Experimental Cell Research
Federation Proceedings
Letters of the Federation of European Biochemical Societies (FEBS Letters)
General Cytochemical Methods
Hoppe-Seyler's Zeitschrift für Physiologische Chemie
Immunology
Indian Journal of Biochemistry
Journal of the American Chemical Society
Journal of the American Oil Chemists' Society
Journal of Bacteriology
Journal of Biochemistry (Tokyo)
Journal of Biological Chemistry
Journal of Cell Biology
Journal of Cellular Physiology
Journal of Chemical Education
Journal of Chromatography
Journal of Colloid and Interface Science
Journal of Electron Microscopy
Journal of Experimental Biology
Journal of General Microbiology
Journal of General Virology
Journal of Histochemistry of Cytochemistry
Journal of Immunology
Journal of Lipid Research
Journal of Membrane Biology
Journal of Molecular Biology
Journal of Neurochemistry
Journal of Pharmacology and Experimental Therapeutics
Journal of Theoretical Biology
Journal of Ultrastructure Research
Journal of Virology
Lipids
Macromolecules
Metabolism—Clinical and Experimental
Molecular Pharmacology
Methods of Biochemical Analysis
Nature
Naturwissenschaften
Physiological Chemistry and Physics
Plant Physiology
Proceedings of the National Academy of Sciences (U.S.)
Proceedings of the Royal Society (London) (Part B)
Proceedings of the Society for Experimental Biology and Medicine
Protoplasma
Science
Steroids
Tetrahedron Letters
Zeitschrift für Naturforschung

Survey works:

Comparative Biochemistry, M. Florkin and H. S. Mason, eds., Academic Press, New York, 7 volumes (1960ff).

Comprehensive Biochemistry, M. Florkin and E. H. Stotz, eds., Elsevier Publishing Co., New York, 16 volumes (1967ff).

Collections of biochemical data and constants:

Handbook of Biochemistry and Selected Data for Molecular Biology, H. A. Sober (ed.), The Chemical Rubber Co., 1968.

Data for Biochemical Research, R. M. C. Dawson, D. C. Elliott, W. H. Elliott, and K. M. Jones (eds.), Oxford University Press, 1959.

Biochemist's Handbook, C. Long (ed.), D. Van Nostrand Company, Inc., Princeton, N.J., 1968.

Atlas of Protein Sequence and Structure, M. O. Dayhoff and R. V. Eck, National Biomedical Research Foundation, Silver Spring, Maryland, 1969.

Frequently used abbreviations in biochemical research literature

ACTH	Adrenocorticotrophic hormone
ADH	Alcohol dehydrogenase
AMP, ADP, ATP	Adenosine 5′-mono, di- and triphosphate
dAMP, dGMP, dADP, etc.	2′-Deoxyadenosine 5′-monophosphate, 2′-deoxyguanosine 5′-monophosphate, 2′-deoxyadenosine 5′-diphosphate, etc.
ATPase	Adenosine triphosphatase
CMP, CDP, CTP	Cytidine nucleotides
CM-cellulose	Carboxymethyl cellulose
CoASH, acyl-CoA, acyl-S-CoA	Coenzyme A and its acyl derivatives
CoQ	Coenzyme Q; ubiquinone
DEAE-cellulose	Diethylaminoethyl cellulose
DFP	Diisopropyl phosphofluoridate
DNA	Deoxyribonucleic acid
DNase	Deoxyribonuclease
DNP	2,4-Dinitrophenol
Dopa	Dihydroxyphenylalanine
E.C. (followed by numbers)	Enzyme Commission, followed by numbers indicating classification of the enzyme
EDTA	Ethylenediaminetetraacetic acid
ESR	Electron spin resonance
ETP	Electron transfer particle (of mitochondrial membrane)
Fd	Ferredoxin
FA	Fatty acid
FAD, $FADH_2$	Flavin adenine dinucleotide and its reduced form
FCCP	Carbonylcyanide *p*-trifluoromethoxyphenyl-hydrazone
FDNB (DNFB)	Fluorodinitrobezene
FDP	Fructose 1,6-diphosphate
FH_2, FH_4	Dihydro- and tetrahydrofolic acid
FMN, $FMNH_2$	Flavin mononucleotide and its reduced form
FP	Flavoprotein
GDH	Glutamate dehydrogenase
GH	Growth hormone
GMP, GDP, GTP	Guanosine nucleotides
G3P	Glyceraldehyde 3-phosphate
G6P	Glucose 6-phosphate

GSH, GSSG	Glutathione and its oxidized form
Hb, HbO_2, HbCO	Hemoglobin, oxyhemoglobin, carbon monoxide hemoglobin
IMP, IDP, ITP	Inosine nucleotides
LDH	Lactate dehydrogenase
MDH	Malate dehydrogenase
Mb, MbO_2	Myoglobin; oxymyoglobin
MSH	Melanocyte-stimulating hormone
NAD^+, NADH, DPN^+, DPNH	Nicotinamide adenine dinucleotide (diphosphopyridine nucleotide) and its reduced form
$NADP^+$, NADPH TPN^+, TPNH	Nicotinamide adenine dinucleotide phosphate (triphosphopyridine nucleotide) and its reduced form
NANA	N-Acetylneuraminic acid
NEFA	Non-esterified fatty acid
NMN^+, NMNH	Nicotinamide mononucleotide and its reduced form
NMR	Nuclear magnetic resonance
OAA	Oxaloacetic acid
OD	Optical density
P_i	Inorganic orthophosphate
PAB or PABA	*p*-Aminobenzoic acid
PEP	Phosphoenolpyruvate
3PG	3-Phosphoglycerate
PGA	Pteroylglutamic acid (folic acid)
PMS	Phenazine methosulphate
PP_i	Inorganic pyrophosphate
PRPP	5-phosphoribosyl 1-pyrophosphate
RNA	Ribonucleic acid
mRNA	Messenger RNA
rRNA	Ribosomal RNA
tRNA	Transfer RNA
RNase	Ribonuclease
RQ	Respiratory quotient
TMP, TDP, TTP	Thymidine nucleotides
TMV	Tobacco mosaic virus
TPP	Thiamine pyrophosphate
Tris	Tris (hydroxymethyl) aminomethane
UDP-gal	Uridine diphosphate galactose
UDP-glucose	Uridine diphosphate glucose
UMP, UDP, UTP	Uridine nucleotides
UV	Ultraviolet

Some physical constants

Avogadro's number	N	6.023×10^{23}
Curie	C_i	3.7×10^{10} dps
Faraday	$\mathscr{F}$	96,494 coul gram equiv^{-1}
Gas constant	R	8.314 joule deg^{-1} mole^{-1} or 1.98 cal deg^{-1} mole^{-1}
Planck's constant	h	6.62×10^{-27} erg sec^{-1} or 1.58×10^{-34} cal sec^{-1}
Velocity of light	c	2.997×10^{10} cm sec^{-1} or 186,000 miles sec^{-1}

International Atomic Weights

	Symbol	Atomic Number	Atomic Weight		Symbol	Atomic Number	Atomic Weight
Aluminum	Al	13	26.97	Neodymium	Nd	60	144.27
Antimony	Sb	51	121.76	Neon	Ne	10	20.183
Argon	A	18	39.944	Nickel	Ni	28	58.69
Arsenic	As	33	74.91	Niobium	Nb	41	92.91
Barium	Ba	56	137.36	Nitrogen	N	7	14.008
Beryllium	Be	4	9.02	Osmium	Os	76	190.2
Bismuth	Bi	83	209.00	Oxygen	O	8	16.000
Boron	B	5	10.82	Palladium	Pd	46	106.7
Bromine	Br	35	79.916	Phosphorus	P	15	30.98
Cadmium	Cd	48	112.41	Platinum	Pt	78	195.23
Calcium	Ca	20	40.08	Potassium	K	19	39.096
Carbon	C	6	12.01	Praseodymium	Pr	59	140.92
Cerium	Ce	58	140.13	Protactinium	Pa	91	231
Cesium	Cs	55	132.91	Radium	Ra	88	226.05
Chlorine	Cl	17	35.457	Radon	Rn	86	222
Chromium	Cr	24	52.01	Rhenium	Re	75	186.31
Cobalt	Co	27	58.94	Rhodium	Rh	45	102.91
Copper	Cu	29	63.57	Rubidium	Rb	37	85.48
Dysprosium	Dy	66	162.46	Ruthenium	Ru	44	101.7
Erbium	Er	68	167.2	Samarium	Sm	62	150.43
Europium	Eu	63	152.0	Scandium	Sc	21	45.10
Fluorine	F	9	19.00	Selenium	Se	34	78.96
Gadolinium	Gd	64	156.9	Silicon	Si	14	28.06
Gallium	Ga	31	69.72	Silver	Ag	47	107.880
Germanium	Ge	32	72.60	Sodium	Na	11	22.997
Gold	Au	79	197.2	Strontium	Sr	38	87.63
Hafnium	Hf	72	178.6	Sulfur	S	16	32.06
Helium	He	2	4.003	Tantalum	Ta	73	180.88
Holmium	Ho	67	164.94	Tellurium	Te	52	127.61
Hydrogen	H	1	1.0081	Terbium	Tb	65	159.2
Indium	In	49	114.76	Thallium	Tl	81	204.39
Iodine	I	53	126.92	Thorium	Th	90	232.12
Iridium	Ir	77	193.1	Thulium	Tm	69	169.4
Iron	Fe	26	55.84	Tin	Sn	50	118.70
Krypton	Kr	36	83.7	Titanium	Ti	22	47.90
Lanthanum	La	57	138.92	Tungsten	W	74	183.92
Lead	Pb	82	207.21	Uranium	U	92	238.07
Lithium	Li	3	6.940	Vanadium	V	23	50.95
Lutecium	Lu	71	175.00	Xenon	Xe	54	131.3
Magnesium	Mg	12	24.32	Ytterbium	Yb	70	173.04
Manganese	Mn	25	54.93	Yttrium	Y	39	88.92
Mercury	Hg	80	200.61	Zinc	Zn	30	65.38
Molybdenum	Mo	42	95.95	Zirconium	Zr	40	91.22

Logarithms

N	0	1	2	3	4	5	6	7	8	9
10	0000	0043	0086	0128	0170	0212	0253	0294	0334	0374
11	0414	0453	0492	0531	0569	0607	0645	0682	0719	0755
12	0792	0828	0864	0899	0934	0969	1004	1038	1072	1106
13	1139	1173	1206	1239	1271	1303	1335	1367	1399	1430
14	1461	1492	1523	1553	1584	1614	1644	1673	1703	1732
15	1761	1790	1818	1847	1875	1903	1931	1959	1987	2014
16	2041	2068	2095	2122	2148	2175	2201	2227	2253	2279
17	2304	2330	2355	2380	2405	2430	2455	2480	2504	2529
18	2533	2577	2601	2625	2648	2672	2695	2718	2742	2765
19	2788	2810	2833	2856	2878	2900	2923	2945	2967	2989
20	3010	3032	3054	3075	3096	3118	3139	3160	3181	3201
21	3222	3243	3263	3284	3304	3324	3345	3365	3385	3404
22	3424	3444	3464	3483	3502	3522	3541	3560	3579	3598
23	3617	3636	3655	3674	3692	3711	3729	3747	3766	3784
24	3802	3820	3838	3856	3874	3892	3909	3927	3945	3962
25	3979	3997	4014	4031	4048	4065	4082	4099	4116	4133
26	4150	4166	4183	4200	4216	4232	4249	4265	4281	4298
27	4314	4330	4346	4362	4378	4393	4409	4425	4440	4456
28	4472	4487	4502	4518	4533	4548	4564	4579	4594	4609
29	4624	4639	4654	4669	4683	4698	4713	4728	4742	4757
30	4771	4786	4800	4814	4829	4843	4857	4871	4886	4900
31	4914	4928	4942	4955	4969	4983	4997	5011	5024	5038
32	5051	5065	5079	5092	5105	5119	5132	5145	5159	5172
33	5185	5198	5211	5224	5237	5250	5263	5276	5289	5302
34	5315	5328	5340	5353	5366	5378	5391	5403	5416	5428
35	5441	5453	5465	5478	5490	5502	5514	5527	5539	5551
36	5563	5575	5587	5599	5611	5623	5635	5647	5658	5670
37	5682	5694	5705	5717	5729	5740	5752	5763	5775	5786
38	5798	5809	5821	5832	5843	5855	5866	5877	5888	5899
39	5911	5922	5933	5944	5955	5966	5977	5988	5999	6010
40	6021	6031	6042	6053	6064	6075	6085	6096	6107	6117
41	6128	6138	6149	6160	6170	6180	6191	6201	6212	6222
42	6232	6243	6253	6263	6274	6284	6294	6304	6314	6325
43	6335	6345	6355	6365	6375	6385	6395	6405	6415	6425
44	6435	6444	6454	6464	6474	6484	6493	6503	6513	6522
45	6532	6542	6551	6561	6571	6580	6590	6599	6609	6618
46	6628	6637	6646	6656	6665	6675	6684	6693	6702	6712
47	6721	6730	6739	6749	6758	6767	6776	6785	6794	6803
48	6812	6821	6830	6839	6848	6857	6866	6875	6884	6893
49	6902	6911	6920	6928	6937	6946	6955	6964	6972	6981
50	6990	6998	7007	7016	7024	7033	7042	7050	7059	7067
51	7076	7084	7093	7101	7110	7118	7126	7135	7143	7152
52	7160	7168	7177	7185	7193	7202	7210	7218	7226	7235
53	7243	7251	7259	7267	7275	7284	7292	7300	7308	7316
54	7324	7332	7340	7348	7356	7364	7372	7380	7388	7396
N	0	1	2	3	4	5	6	7	8	9

N	0	1	2	3	4	5	6	7	8	9
55	7404	7412	7419	7427	7435	7443	7451	7459	7466	7474
56	7482	7490	7497	7505	7513	7520	7528	7536	7543	7551
57	7559	7566	7574	7582	7589	7597	7604	7612	7619	7627
58	7634	7642	7649	7657	7664	7672	7679	7686	7694	7701
59	7709	7716	7723	7731	7738	7745	7752	7760	7767	7774
60	7782	7789	7796	7803	7810	7818	7825	7832	7839	7846
61	7853	7860	7868	7875	7882	7889	7896	7903	7910	7917
62	7924	7931	7938	7945	7952	7959	7966	7973	7980	7987
63	7993	8000	8007	8014	8021	8028	8035	8041	8048	8055
64	8062	8069	8075	8082	8089	8096	8102	8109	8116	8122
65	8129	8136	8142	8149	8156	8162	8169	8176	8182	8189
66	8195	8202	8209	8215	8222	8228	8235	8241	8248	8254
67	8261	8267	8274	8280	8287	8293	8299	8306	8312	8319
68	8325	8331	8338	8344	8351	8357	8363	8370	8376	8382
69	8388	8395	8401	8407	8414	8420	8426	8432	8439	8445
70	8451	8457	8463	8470	8476	8482	8488	8494	8500	8506
71	8513	8519	8525	8531	8537	8543	8549	8555	8561	8567
72	8573	8579	8585	8591	8597	8603	8609	8615	8621	8627
73	8633	8639	8645	8651	8657	8663	8669	8675	8681	8686
74	8692	8698	8704	8710	8716	8722	8727	8733	8739	8745
75	8751	8756	8762	8768	8774	8779	8785	8791	8797	8802
76	8808	8814	8820	8825	8831	8837	8842	8848	8854	8859
77	8865	8871	8876	8882	8887	8893	8899	8904	8910	8915
78	8921	8927	8932	8938	8943	8949	8954	8960	8965	8971
79	8976	8982	8987	8993	8998	9004	9009	9015	9020	9025
80	9031	9036	9042	9047	9053	9058	9063	9069	9074	9079
81	9085	9090	9096	9101	9106	9112	9117	9122	9128	9133
82	9138	9143	9149	9154	9159	9165	9170	9175	9180	9186
83	9191	9196	9201	9206	9212	9217	9222	9227	9232	9238
84	9243	9248	9253	9258	9263	9269	9274	9279	9284	9289
85	9294	9299	9304	9309	9315	9320	9325	9330	9335	9340
86	9345	9350	9355	9360	9365	9370	9375	9380	9385	9390
87	9395	9400	9405	9410	9415	9420	9425	9430	9435	9440
88	9445	9450	9455	9460	9465	9469	9474	9479	9484	9489
89	9494	9499	9504	9509	9513	9518	9523	9528	9533	9538
90	9542	9547	9552	9557	9562	9566	9571	9576	9581	9586
91	9590	9595	9600	9605	9609	9614	9619	9624	9628	9633
92	9638	9643	9647	9652	9657	9661	9666	9671	9675	9680
93	9685	9689	9694	9699	9703	9708	9713	9717	9722	9727
94	9731	9736	9741	9745	9750	9754	9759	9763	9768	9773
95	9777	9782	9786	9791	9795	9800	9805	9809	9814	9818
96	9823	9827	9832	9836	9841	9845	9850	9854	9859	9863
97	9868	9872	9877	9881	9886	9890	9894	9899	9903	9908
98	9912	9917	9921	9926	9930	9934	9939	9943	9948	9952
99	9956	9961	9965	9969	9974	9978	9983	9987	9991	9996
N	0	1	2	3	4	5	6	7	8	9

APPENDIX F

Solutions to Problems (to 3 significant figures)

Chapter 1

1 3.44×10^7 molecules
2 (*a*) 1.91×10^{-6} *M* (*b*) 5.74×10^{-3} *M* (*c*) 172 g $liter^{-1}$
3 15.1×10^2 μ, 750 times the length of the cell
4 0.157%
5 4.86%
6 (*a*) 5100:1 (*b*) 306:1 (*c*) 0.3 μ^{-1}, 5.0 μ^{-1}
7 0.27%
8 31.4×10^3 μ^2, 13 times the area of the cell membrane

Chapter 2

1 (*a*) pH 3.0 (*b*) pH 9.0 (*c*) pH 13.1 (*d*) pH 10.8 (*e*) pH 10.9
2 (*a*) 3.98×10^{-8} *M* (*b*) 7.94×10^{-7} *M* (*c*) 3.98×10^{-2} *M* (*d*) 5×10^{-5} *M* (*e*) 6.31×10^{-4} *M* (*f*) 3.16×10^{-6} *M*
3 302 H^+ ions
4 4.2×10^{20}
5 1.13×10^8 K^+ ions
6 2%
7 $K' = 1.35 \times 10^{-5}$, $pK' = 4.87$
8 $H_2PO_4^-/HPO_4^{2-} = 6.3$
9 0.813 volumes of NaOH plus 1 volume of acetic acid
10 1.28 ml, 10^{-5} *M*

Chapter 4

1 pH_I 5.97, pH_I 6.01, pH_I 5.68, pH_I 6.53, pH_I 3.22
2 (*a*) ++++ (*b*) +O++ (*c*) O−++ (*d*) −−O−
3 (*a*) Glu (*b*) Lys, Arg (*c*) Ala, Gly, Ser.
4 0.382 g
5 pH 2.71, pH 9.23
6 0.44°
7 (*a*) Tube 1, Tube 2 (*b*) 51.2 mg Gly plus 24 mg Phe, 38.4 mg Gly plus 36 mg Phe
8 4.45 g

Chapter 5

1 (*a*) Lys-Asp-Gly-Ala-Ala-Glu-Ser-Gly (*b*) Ala-Ala-His-Arg, Glu-Lys, Phe-Ile (*c*) Tyr-Cys-Lys, Ala-Arg, Arg, Gly (*d*) Phe-Ala-Glu-Ser-Ala-Gly (*a*) DNP-Lys, (*b*) DNP-Ala, DNP-Glu, DNP-Phe (*c*) DNP-Tyr, DNP-Ala, DNP-Arg, DNP-Gly (*d*) DNP-Phe
2 Val-Ala-Lys-Glu-Glu-Phe, Val-Met-Tyr, Cys-Glu-Trp-Met-Gly-Gly-Phe; Val-Ala-Lys-Glu-Glu-Phe, Val-Homoserine lactone, Tyr, Cys-Glu-Trp-Homoserine lactone, Gly-Gly-Phe
3 Val-Ala-Lys, Glu-Glu-Phe-Val-Homoserine lactone, Tyr-Cys-Glu-Trp-Homoserine lactone, Gly-Gly-Phe
4 NH_2 and COOH terminal analysis, trypsin digestion, chymotrypsin digestion
5 Val-Arg/Lys-Pro/Hypro-Gly
6 (*a*) CCCC (*b*) CCOA (*c*) CCAA (*d*) COAA (*e*) CCCO
7 *d*, *c*, *b*, $a \simeq e$
8 Gly-Ileu-Val-Glu-Glu-Cys-Cys-Ala-Ser-Val-Cys-Ser-Leu-Tyr-Glu-Leu-Glu-Asp-Tyr-Cys-Asp
9 Asn-Ala-Tyr-Glu-Lys-His-Gln-Pro-Val
10 Changes in anionic mobility: decrease, increase, decrease, increase, decrease.

Chapter 6

1 (*a*) 1.75×10^2 Å (*b*) 3.78×10^2 Å
2 4.95 cm
3 (*a*) Residues 1 to 6, 8 to 15, 20 to 28 (*b*) Residues 7, 16 to 19 (*c*) Residues 13 to 24
4 3850 per 1,000,000; 1.8 per 1,000,000
5 51%
6 Enzyme has 4 noncovalently associated subunits, 2 of molecular weight 50,000, and 2 catalytic subunits of M. Wt. 100,000. Each of the latter consists of two inactive polypeptides (M. Wt. 50,000) joined by disulfide crosslinkage(s).
7 17,500 times
8 1.39 g cm^{-3}

Chapter 7

1 13,200 daltons
2 13,800 daltons
3 50,300 daltons
4 (*a*) pH 4.85 (*b*) 25% (*c*) Raise NaCl concentration above 10 m*M*.
5 13,000 daltons
6 494,000 daltons
7 (*a*) A (*b*) C, A (*c*) C, O, A
8 (*a*) pH 5.85 (*b*) pH 8.25 (*c*) pH 4.90

Chapter 8

1 0.089 m*M*
2 [A]/[B] = 1.5
3 2.31 sec^{-1}
4 See the text
5 1.54×10^{-6} *M*
6 Noncompetitive, 2.41×10^{-3} *M*, 2.4×10^{-2} *M*
7 Competitive, 5×10^{-3} *M*, 6.65×10^{-3} *M*, 0.49 μg $hour^{-1}$
8 2,920,000 daltons

Chapter 10

1 6 isomers
2 PPP, PPO, POO, POP, OPO, PPS, PSS, PSP, SPS, OOO, OOS, OSS, OSO, SOS, SSS, POS, PSO, SPO
3 (*a*) 1.09 g cm^{-3} (*b*) Sediment
4 Phosphatidic acid
5 (*a*) A (*b*) A (*c*) O (*d*) A
6 (*a*) Glycerol, sodium stearate, sodium palmitate (*b*) Glycerol phosphate, sodium stearate, sodium elaidate, inositol (*c*) Glycerol phosphate, sodium palmitate, sodium oleate, choline
7 (*a*) Stearic acid, oleic acid, serine, glycerol, phosphoric acid (*b*) 1-Palmitoyl-2-linoleyl phosphatidic acid, choline
8 (*a*) 6 (*b*) 6 (*c*) 3 isoprene units
9 Lipids/Proteins = 4.17

Chapter 11

1 (*a*) 93.3° (*b*) 52.7° (*c*) 124.7°, 124.7°
2 (*a*) Penta-acetyl-α-D-galactose (*b*) 2,3,4,6-Tetra-

O-methyl-α-D-glucose; 2,3,4,6-Tetra-O-methyl-β-D-glucose.

3 (a) D-Galactitol (b) L-Mannaric acid (c) 1,3,4,6-Tetra-O-methyl-N-dimethyl D-galactosamine
4 (a) 2,3,4,6-Tetra-O-methyl-D-galactose; 2,3,6-Tri-O-methyl-D-glucose (b) 2,3,4,6-Tetra-O-methyl-D-glucose; 1,3,4,6-Tetra-O-methyl-D-fructose
5 4-O-D-Glucosyl-6-O-D-galactosyl-D-glucose, or 6-O-D-glucosyl-4-O-D-glucosyl-D-galactose
6 Unbranched polymer of (6-O-D-glucosyl-4-O-D-glucosyl-) units
7 (a) 9.72% (b) 10.3 glucose residues (c) 55.8 mmoles (d) 12,300 glucose residues
8 247 glucose residues
9 820 glucose residues

Chapter 12

1 (a) $A = 0.429$ (b) $A = 0.264$ (c) $A = 0.049$
2 (a) 4.51×10^{-5} *M* (b) 1.22×10^{-5} *M*
3 $A = 0.906$
4 GMP, 0.306 m*M*; AMP, 1.92×10^{-2} m*M*
5 (a) A, pU, pA, pA, pC, pU (b) ApUp, ApApCp, U (c) No effect (d) dCpCp (e) No effect
6 pGpCpCpApUpCpGpApC
7 ApUpCpApGpCpCpGpUpCpGpG

Chapter 14

1 (a) 5.94% (b) 24%
2 -56.5 kcal mole^{-1}
3 (a) $K' = 263$ (b) $K' = 302$
4 (a) -1.13 kcal mole^{-1} (b) 19.4 kcal mole^{-1} (c) 11.1 kcal mole^{-1} (d) 16.5 kcal mole^{-1}
5 (a) -7.3 kcal mole^{-1} (b) -8.66 kcal mole^{-1} (c) -10.0 kcal mole^{-1} (d) -11.4 kcal mole^{-1}
6 -11.0 kcal mole^{-1}
7 0.044°C
8 3.56×10^{-3} *M*
9 -1.30 kcal mole^{-1}
10 Phosphoenolpyruvate and ADP, 0.018 m*M*; pyruvate and ATP, 9.98 m*M*. Phosphoenolpyruvate and ADP, 0.015 m*M*; ATP 5.98 m*M*, pyruvate 11.98 m*M*.
11 0.74 m*M*

Chapter 15

1 -23.14 kcal, free energy change rises to -18.98 kcal.
2 D-Fructose + 2ADP + 2P_i ⟶ 2 lactic acid + 2ATP + $2H_2O$
3 (a) Glycerol + NAD^+ + ADP + P_i ⟶ lactic acid + NADH + H^+ + ATP + $2H_2O$ (b) L-Glycerol 3-phosphate + NAD^+ + 2ADP + P_i ⟶ ethanol + CO_2 + NADH + H^+ + 2ATP + H_2O (c) D-Mannose + 2NAD^+ + 2P_i ⟶ 2 phosphoenolpyruvate + 2NADH + $2H^+$ (d) Glucose 1,6-diphosphate + 4ADP + 2P_i ⟶ 2 ethanol + $2CO_2$ + 4ATP + H_2O
4 Becomes less negative
5 Fructose 1,6-diphosphate, dihydroxyacetone phosphate, D-glyceraldehyde 3-phosphate, D-glyceraldehyde, fructose 1-phosphate, acetaldehyde, 5-deoxyketopentose 1-phosphate
6 (a) 0.79% (b) 2.49% (c) 7.6% (d) 22.5% (e) 48%
7 Fructose 1,6-diphosphate + 2NAD^+ ⟶ 2 phosphoenolpyruvate + 2NADH + $2H^+$
8 190 mmoles glucose, 20 mmoles ethanol; add at least 380 mmoles pnosphate

Chapter 16

1 Carbon atom 2 of citrate, carbon atom 4 of malate, carbon atom 4 of α-ketoglutarate, carboxyl carbon atom of succinate.
2 (a) Citrate + 2NAD^+ + GDP + P_i ⟶ succinate + $2CO_2$ + 2NADH + $2H^+$ + GTP + H_2O (b) 2 Pyruvate + 3NAD^+ + ATP + GDP + $2H_2O$ ⟶ succinate + $2CO_2$ + 3NADH + $3H^+$ + GTP + ADP (c) Fumarate + acetyl CoA + 3NAD^+ + GDP + P_i + $2H_2O$ ⟶ succinate + CoA + $2CO_2$ + 3NADH + $3H^+$ + GTP
3 $K' = 6.6 \times 10^{-2}$, 1.61 kcal mole^{-1}
4 $K' = 2.85$, -0.62 kcal mole^{-1}
5 Fructose 6-phosphate + $6O_2$ + 39ADP + 38P_i ⟶ $6CO_2$ + $44H_2O$ + 39ATP
6 (a) 2 Acetic acid + NAD^+ + 2ATP + $2H_2O$ ⟶ succinate + NADH + H^+ + 2AMP + 2PP_i (b) Acetic acid + oxaloacetate + 2NAD^+ + ATP + GDP + P_i + H_2O ⟶ succinate + $2CO_2$ + 2NADH + $2H^+$ + AMP + PP_i (a) Both carboxyl carbon atoms (b) One carboxyl carbon atom
7 Glucose + 2$NADP^+$ + ATP + H_2O ⟶ ribose 5-phosphate + CO_2 + 2NADPH + $2H^+$ + ADP. Carbon atom 2.
8 6 Ribose 5-phosphate + H_2O ⟶ 5 glucose 6-phosphate + P_i. Carbon atoms 1 and 3 or carbon atom 1 only.
9 Glucose + 6$NADP^+$ + NAD^+ + ADP + P_i + $2H_2O$ ⟶ pyruvate + $3CO_2$ + 6NADPH + NADH + $7H^+$ + ATP

Chapter 17

1 0.81 v
2 (a) -3.23 kcal per pair of electron equivalents (b) 1.38 kcal (c) 6.92 kcal (d) -26.8 kcal
3 Malate and NAD^+, 39.87 m*M*; oxaloacetate and NADH, 0.13 m*M*
4 (a) Rise (b) Supply 20 m equivalents
5 Malate 19.93 m*M*, oxaloacetate 7.0×10^{-2} m*M*
6 40%
7 (a) NAD and NADH dehydrogenase reduced; cytochromes *b*, *c*, *a* oxidized, (b) NAD, NADH dehydrogenase and cytochrome *b* reduced; cytochromes *c*, *a* oxidized (c) All reduced
8 (a) 16 molecules (b) 12 molecules (c) 20 molecules (d) 21 molecules
9 Isocitrate + O_2 + 7ADP + 7P_i ⟶ succinate + $2CO_2$ + 7ATP + $8H_2O$
10 Isocitrate + O_2 ⟶ succinate + $2CO_2$ + H_2O

Chapter 18

1 8.75×10^7 molecules min^{-1}, 1.75×10^4 molecules min^{-1}
2 Inner mitochondrial membrane area 22.4 times greater than cell membrane area.
3 (a) 850 H^+ ions (b) 85.0 H^+ ions (c) 0.85 H^+ ions.
4 NADH + H^+ + $\frac{1}{2}O_2$ + 2ADP + 2P_i ⟶ NAD^+ + $3H_2O$ + 2ATP
5 NADH + H^+ + $\frac{1}{2}O_2$ + 3ADP + 3P_i ⟶ NAD^+ + $4H_2O$ + 3ATP
6 Energy charge = 0.64, 0.90

Chapter 19

1 (a) Myristic acid + 7CoASH + $12O_2$ + 30ADP + 28P_i ⟶ 7 Acetyl CoA + 29ATP + AMP + $37H_2O$ (b) Arachidonic acid + $28O_2$ + 157ADP +

$155P_i \longrightarrow 20CO_2 + 173H_2O + 156ATP + AMP$ (c) Butyric acid + 2 oxaloacetate + $2O_2$ + 19ADP + $17P_i \longrightarrow$ 2 succinate + $4CO_2$ + 18ATP + AMP + $20H_2O$ (d) Palmitic acid + $7O_2$ + 35ADP + $33P_i \longrightarrow$ 4 acetoacetic acid + AMP + 34ATP + $38H_2O$ (e) Mono-oleyl-palmitylglycerol + $75O_2$ + 430ADP + $424P_i \longrightarrow$ $53CO_2$ + 427ATP + 3AMP + $477H_2O$ (f) (f) D-β-Hydroxybutyric acid + $4\frac{1}{2}O_2$ + 27ADP + $25P_i \longrightarrow 4CO_2$ + 26ATP + AMP + $30H_2O$ (g) Propionic acid + $3\frac{1}{2}O_2$ + 29ADP + $27P_i \longrightarrow$ $3CO_2$ + AMP + 28ATP + $31H_2O$ (h) Nonanoic acid + $12\frac{1}{2}O_2$ + 77ADP + $75P_i \longrightarrow 9CO_2$ + 76ATP + AMP + $85H_2O$

2 (a) Carbon atom 1 (b) 1 or 4 (c) 1

3 Carbon atoms 1, 3, 5.

Chapter 20

1 (a) Phenylalanine + $10O_2$ + 51ADP + $51P_i \longrightarrow$ $9CO_2$ + NH_3 + 50ATP + AMP + PP_i + $54H_2O$ (b) 2 Phenylalanine + $20O_2$ + 100ADP + $100P_i \longrightarrow 17CO_2$ + urea + 97ATP + 3AMP + $3PP_i$ + $105H_2O$

2 (a) 45 molecules (b) 26.5 molecules

3 (1) γ-Carboxyl carbon atom (2) β-Carbon atom (3) α-Carbon atom (4) No labeling (5) No labeling (6) Amino nitrogen

4 2 Alanine + $4NAD^+$ + 3ATP + $5H_2O \longrightarrow$ acetoacetate + urea + CO_2 + 4NADH + $4H^+$ + 2ADP + AMP + PP_i + $2P_i$

5 (a) γ-Carboxyl carbon atom (b) γ-Carboxyl carbon atom (c) Carbon atom 2 or 3

6 22.4%

Chapter 21

1 9, 7, 5 molecules

2 −7.76 kcal per pair of electron equivalents; −5.18 kcal

3 6.88%, 15.8%

4 1 phosphorylation

Chapter 22

1 2 Citric acid + $4NAD^+$ + 2FAD + 2ATP + $6H_2O \longrightarrow$ glucose + $6CO_2$ + 4NADH + $4H^+$ + $2FADH_2$ + 2ADP + $2P_i$

2 2 Phenylalanine + $7O_2$ + 2NADPH + 2NADH + $4H^+$ + 2FAD + 2GTP + 2ATP + $6H_2O \longrightarrow$ glucose + 2 acetoacetate + $4CO_2$ + $2NH_3$ + $2NADP^+$ + $2NAD^+$ + $2FADH_2$ + 2GDP + 2ADP + $4P_i$

3 Palmitic acid + $11NAD^+$ + 11FAD + 5ATP + 4GTP + $27H_2O \longrightarrow$ 2 glucose + $4CO_2$ + 11NADH + $11H^+$ + $11FADH_2$ + 4ADP + AMP + 4GDP + PP_i + $8P_i$

4 4 Leucine + $18NAD^+$ + 6FAD + 10ATP + 6GTP + $38H_2O \longrightarrow$ 3 glucose + $4NH_3$ + $6CO_2$ + 18NADH + $18H^+$ + $6FADH_2$ + 6ADP + 6GDP + 4AMP + $4PP_i$ + $12P_i$

5 Carbon atoms 1 and 6; carbon atoms, 2, 4, 6, 8, 10, 12, 14 and 16.

6 2 Pyruvic acid + 2NADH + $2H^+$ + 4ATP + 2GTP + UTP + $6H_2O \longrightarrow$ glucose + $2NAD^+$ + 4ADP + 2GDP + UDP + $7P_i$, 8 high energy phosphate bonds.

7 2 Pyruvic acid + NADPH + H^+ + NAD^+ + 4ATP + 2GTP + UTP $\longrightarrow$ ascorbic acid + $NADP^+$ + NADH + H^+ + 4ADP + 2GDP + UDP + $7P_i$

8 (1) Carbon atoms 3 and 4 (2) Carbon atoms 3, 4 and 5 (3) Carbon atoms 1, 2, and 3

9 D-Glucose + $NAD^+ \longrightarrow$ D-glucuronic acid + NADH + H^+; D-Glucuronic acid + NAD(P)H + $H^+ \longrightarrow$ gulonic acid + $NAD(P)^+$; Gulonic acid + NAD(P)H + $H^+ \longrightarrow$ L-xylulose + $NAD(P)^+$; L-Xylulose + NAD(P)H + $H^+ \longrightarrow$ xylitol + $NAD(P)^+$; Xylitol + $NAD^+ \longrightarrow$ D-xylulose + NADH + H^+; D-Xylulose $\rightleftharpoons$ D-xylose.

Chapter 23

1 9 Acetyl-S-CoA + 16NADPH + $16H^+$ + 8ATP + $H_2O \longrightarrow$ stearic acid + $16NADP^+$ + 9CoASH + 8ADP + $8P_i$

2 8 Acetyl-S-CoA + 12NADPH + $12H^+$ + 7ATP + $H_2O \longrightarrow$ palmitoleic acid + $12NADP^+$ + 8CoASH + 7ADP + $7P_i$

3 Lauric acid + 3 Acetyl-S-CoA + 6NADPH + $6H^+$ + 4ATP + $H_2O \longrightarrow$ stearic acid + $6NADP^+$ + 3CoASH + 4ADP + $4P_i$

4 $12\frac{1}{2}$ Glucose + 42NADPH + $42H^+$ + $48NAD^+$ + $FADH_2$ + 2ADP + $2P_i \longrightarrow$ tripalmitin + $24CO_2$ + $42NADP^+$ + 48NADH + $48H^+$ + FAD + 2ATP + $23H_2O$

5 6 high energy phosphate bonds

6 12 high energy phosphate bonds

7 18 Acetic acid + $4O_2$ + 12NADPH + $12H^+$ + 36ATP + $9H_2O \longrightarrow$ cholesterol + $9CO_2$ + $12NADP^+$ + 18ADP + 18AMP + $18PP_i$ + $18P_i$; 36 high energy phosphate bonds

8 0.5 per carbon atom of glucose; 0.062 high energy bonds are produced per carbon atom stored as palmitate

Chapter 24

1 Succinate + FH_4 + $2NAD^+$ + NAD(P)H + H^+ + FAD + NH_3 + GTP + $H_2O \longrightarrow$ glycine + CO_2 + N^5N^{10} methylene FH_4 + 2NADH + $2H^+$ + $NAD(P)^+$ + $FADH_2$ + GDP + P_i

2 Isocitrate + NAD^+ + NAD(P)H + H^+ + FAD + NH_3 + 2ATP + GDP + $H_2O \longrightarrow$ threonine + $2CO_2$ + $NADH_2$ + $NAD(P)^+$ + $FADH_2$ + 2ADP + P_i + GTP

3 Glycine + arginine $\longrightarrow NH_2{-}\underset{\underset{NH}{\|}}{C}{-}NHCH_2COOH$ + $NH_2(CH_2)_3CHNH_2COOH$

$NH_2{-}\underset{\underset{NH}{\|}}{C}{-}NHCH_2COOH$ + methionine $\longrightarrow$ creatine + homocysteine

4 5 high energy phosphate bonds

5 Serine $\longrightarrow$ ethanolamine + CO_2; Ethanolamine + 3 S-adenosyl methionine $\longrightarrow$ choline + 3 homocysteine + 3 methionine

6 Carbon 4 of the histidine moiety.

7 $10CO_2$ + 2 nitrate + 31 NADPH + $31H^+$ + $4NAD^+$ + 34ATP + $16H_2O \longrightarrow$ 2 glutamate + $31NADP^+$ + 4NADH + $4H^+$ + 34ADP + $34P_i$

8 α-Ketoglutarate + NH_3 + 3NAD(P)H + $3H^+ \longrightarrow$ proline + $3NAD(P)^+$ + $3H_2O$; α-carbon atom

9 α-Ketoisovalerate + $[CH_2]$ $\xrightarrow{\text{p-aminobenzoic acid}}$ α-ketopantoate; α-Ketopantoate + NAD(P)H + $H^+ \longrightarrow$ pantoate + $NADP^+$; Aspartate $\longrightarrow$ β-alanine + CO_2; Pantoate + β-alanine $\longrightarrow$ pantothenate

10 2 high energy phosphate bonds (a) None (b) Carbon atom 2

Chapter 25

1 (*a*) Carbon atom 4 of purine ring (*b*) Carbon atom 4 of purine ring and carbon atom 2 of ribose moiety (*c*) Carbon atom 5 of purine ring (*d*) Nitrogen atom 1 of purine ring and amino nitrogen atom (*e*) Nitrogen atoms 3 and 9 of purine ring
2 (*a*) Carbon atom 6 of pyrimidine ring (*b*) Nitrogen atoms 1 and 3 and amino nitrogen (*c*) Nitrogen atoms 1 and 3 and amino nitrogen
3 6 high energy phosphate bonds
4 Oxaloacetate + ribose 5-phosphate + $3NH_3$ + NAD^+ + NAD(P)H + H^+ + 5ATP $\longrightarrow$ CTP + NADH + H^+ + $NAD(P)^+$ + 4ADP + AMP + $4P_i + H_2O$ 0.13 molecules.
5 Nicotinic acid + ribose 5-phosphate + NH_3 + 3ATP + $H_2O \longrightarrow$ $NADP^+$ + AMP + ADP + $2PP_i$
6 (1) Nitrogen atom 3 of uric acid (2) Carbon atom 5 of uric acid (3) Nitrogen atoms of urea (1) Nitrogen atoms of urea (2) Carboxyl carbon of glyoxylate (3) Nitrogen atom of ammonia

Chapter 26

1 139.0 cal
2 188 sec
3 (*a*) 4.9 liters (*b*) 8.67 mmoles (*c*) none (*d*) 36.3 mmoles
4 1.9×10^{-6} moles (g muscle)$^{-1}$ min^{-1}
5 7.22×10^{-5} moles (g muscle)$^{-1}$ min^{-1}
6 1.41×10^{-3} moles (g muscle)$^{-1}$ min^{-1}
7 $K' = 1.66 \times 10^2$

Chapter 27

1 2.21 kcal (g-ion)$^{-1}$
2 $2.24 \times 10^5/1$
3 (*a*) 51.6 μ equivalents hr^{-1} mg^{-1} (*b*) 57 K^+ ions
4 $9Na^+$ ions
5 610 cal (g-ion)$^{-1}$
6 0.5%
7 pH gradient 5.35, 8.65
8 NH_4^+, 408 cal; Na^+, 16.4 cal; K^+, 198 cal; Cl^-, 85.2 cal, HPO_4^{2-}, 43.3 cal; SO_4^{2-}, 100 cal; urea, 762 cal

Chapter 28

1 (*a*) 2.03×10^2 daltons Å^{-1} (*b*) 2.03×10^6 daltons μ^{-1}
2 3.4×10^3 nucleotide pairs μ^{-1}
3 1.67×10^3 nucleotide pairs
4 590/1
5 1.1×10^{-3} g
6 12 g, 2.02×10^9 miles
7 (*a*) 264 Å, 5.36×10^4 daltons (*b*) 918 Å, 1.86×10^5 daltons (*c*) 1.59×10^4 Å, 3.23×10^6 daltons
8 11×10^6 genes
9 (i) (*a*) 1.748 g cm^{-3} (*b*) 1.710 g cm^{-3} (*c*) 1.672 g cm^{-3}
(ii) (*a*) 107°C (*b*) 90.5°C (*c*) 74.5°C
(iii) (*a*) 50% (*b*) 63% (*c*) 77%
10 1320 Å

Chapter 29

1 0.203 sec
2 6.0×10^4 min, No, 167 growing points
3 3,000 min cf. 30 min
4 G, 18.5%; C, 24.1%; A, 32.8%; T, 24.6%
5 G, 21.3%; C, 21.3%; A, 28.7%; T, 28.7%
6 A, 21%; G, 29%; C, 29%; U, 21%
7 2.76×10^5 min^{-1}
8 Nearest neighbor base frequency analysis. For parallel chains, TpC = ApG, TpG = ApC, CpT = GpA etc. For antiparallel chains, TpC = GpA, TpG = CpA, CpT = ApG, etc.

Chapter 31

1 Ser-Gly-Ser-Gln-Asp-Leu-Thr-Asp-Arg-Ile-His-Val-Arg-Asn-Pro-Leu-Thr·
Ser-Gly-Ser-Gln-Asp [Pro-Ile-Asp-Ser-Met-Ser-Val-Ile-Arg]
Ser-Gly-Ser-Gln-Asp-Leu-Thr-Asp-Arg-Ile-[Ser-Cys-Pro Ser-Val-Asp]
Ser-Gly-Ser-Gln-Asp [Pro-Ile-Asp-Ser]-His-Val-Arg-Asn-Pro-Leu-Thr.
Missense sequences are shown in brackets.
2 Lys 150, Arg 30, Asp 25, Gly 6, Glu 5
3 Valine, Glycine
4 (*a*) Gly-Glu-Ser-Leu-Leu-Ile (*b*) Leu-Asp-Ala-Pro, Phe-Ala (*c*) His-Asp-Ala-Cys-Cys-Tyr (*d*) Met-Asp-Asp
5 (*a*), (*b*), (*c*), (*d*), consistent; (*e*), (*f*), (*g*), inconsistent
6 (*a*) 5′ TCGAGTAGCCGATGATCATCGTCGA-CGAT3′ (*b*) 5′ UCGAGUAGCCGAUGAUCA-UCGUCGACGAU3′ (*c*) Ser-Ser-Ser-Arg, Ser-Ser-Ser-Thr
7 HbI, transition; $HbG_{(Honolulu)}$, transversion; $Hb_{(Norfolk)}$, transition; $HbM_{(Boston)}$, transition; $HbG_{(Phil.)}$, transversion; $HbO_{(Indonesia)}$, transition.

ACKNOWLEDGMENTS

Page 16, M. Kunitz.

Page 30, Figure 1–7, *E. coli* (showing pili), A. Ryter; *E. coli* (dividing), G. Decker; *E. coli* (showing ribosomes), L. D. Simon.

Page 32, Figure 1–8, G. Decker.

Page 34, Figure 1–9, M. C. Ledbetter.

Page 40, Figure 2–2 (right), J. D. Watson, *The Molecular Biology of the Gene,* W. A. Benjamin, New York, 1965, p. 120.

Page 55, (margin) E. Margoliash.

Page 57, Table 3–2, data from I. Klotz, *Science,* **155:**697 (1967); H. Sund and K. Weber, *Angew. Chem.* (Eng.), **5:**234 (1966).

Page 64, Table 3–4, data from W. O. Weigle, *J. Immunol.,* **88:**9 (1962).

Page 84, Figure 4–12, redrawn from D. H. Spackman, W. H. Stein and S. Moore, *Analyt. Chem.,* **30:**1190 (1958).

Page 101, Figure 5–9, from E. Margoliash in B. Chance and R. Estabrook (eds.), *Hemes and Hemoproteins,* Academic Press, New York, 1966, p. 373.

Page 102, Figure 5–10, redrawn from C. Baglioni, *Biochem. Biophys. Acta.,* **48:**392 (1961).

Page 102, Photomicrograph, Walter Dawn, from National Audubon Society.

Page 110, Figure 6–2, redrawn from T. P. Bennett, *Graphic Biochemistry,* vol. 1, The Macmillan Co., New York, 1968.

Page 111, Figure 6–3, redrawn from E. Blout in G. C. Quarton, T. Melnechuk and F. O. Schmitt (eds.), *The Neurosciences,* Rockefeller University Press, New York, 1967, pp. 57–66.

Page 112, Figure 6–4, Dimensions of α-helix from L. Pauling and R. B. Corey, *Proc. Intern. Wool Textile Research Conf.,* **B:**249 (1955); Models of α-helix from G. H. Haggis, D. Michie, A. R. Muir, K. B. Roberts and P. M. B. Walker, *Introduction to Molecular Biology,* John Wiley & Sons, New York, 1964.

Page 113, Figure 6–5 redrawn from P. Doty in J. L. Oncley (ed.), *Biophysical Science,* John Wiley & Sons, New York, 1959, p. 108.

Page 115, Figure 6–6 (left) redrawn from T. P. Bennett, *Graphic Biochemistry,* vol. 1, The Macmillan Co., New York, 1968. (Right) redrawn from H. D. Springall, *The Structural Chemistry of Proteins,* Academic Press, New York, 1954, p. 64.

Page 116, Figure 6–7, K. R. Porter.

Page 118, Figure 6–8, 6 A conformation redrawn from J. C. Kendrew, *Nature,* **181:**622, 1958; 2 A conformation redrawn from R. E. Dickerson in H. Neurath (ed.) *The Proteins,* **II,** Academic Press, 1964, p. 634.

Page 123, Figure 6–10 (top), A. F. Cullis, H. Muirhead, A. C. T. North, M. F. Perutz, and M. G. Rossmann, *Proc. Roy. Soc. London A,* **265:**161 (1962).

Page 131, Figure 7–2 (bottom) redrawn from R. Alberty, *J. Chem. Educ.,* **25:**619, 1948.

Page 132, Figure 7–3 redrawn from K. Linderstrom-Lang and S. O. Nielson in M. Bier (ed.), *Electrophoresis,* Academic Press, New York, 1967, p. 139.

Page 139, Figure 7–9 redrawn from Spinco Div. Beckman Instruments, Inc.

Page 147, M. Kunitz.

Page 172, Table 9–1 adapted from T. C. Bruice and S. J. Benkovic, *Bioorganic Mechanisms,* vol. 1, p. 178, W. A. Benjamin, New York (1966).

Page 176, Figure 9–5 redrawn from B. W. Matthews, P. B. Sigler, R. Henderson and D. M. Blow, *Nature,* **214:**652, 1967.

Page 178, Figure 9–6 (upper right) from the *Atlas of Protein Sequence and Structure 1967–68,* Margaret O. Dayhoff and Richard V. Eck, National Biomedical Research Foundation, Silver Spring, Maryland, 1968. The drawing was made by Irving Geis based on his perspective painting of the molecule which appeared in *Scientific American,* November, 1966. The painting was made from an actual three-dimensional model assembled at the Royal Institution, London, by D. C. Phillips and his colleagues, based on their x-ray crystallography results.

Page 185, Figure 9–12 redrawn from I. H. Fine, N. O. Kaplan, and P. Kuftinec, *Biochemistry,* **2:**116 (1963).

Page 211, Figure 10–13, J. D. Robertson.

Page 228, D. Fawcett.

Page 231, Figure 11–5, D. M. Jones, *Advances in Carbohydrate Chemistry,* **19:**219 (1965).

Page 234, Figure 11–7 redrawn from J. L. Strominger and J. M. Ghuysen, *Science,* **156:**213–221, (1967).

Page 236, (top) D. Fawcett; (bottom) S. Ito, *Federation Proceedings,* **28:**12 (1969).

Page 257, Figure 12–8, R. Holley, *Scientific American,* **214:**30 (1966).

Page 258, Figure 12–9, redrawn from R. W. Holley, J. Apgar, G. A. Everett, J. T. Madison, M. Marguisee, S. H. Merrill, J. R. Penswick, and A. Zamir, *Science,* **147:**1462 (1965).

Page 260, Figure 12–11, (left) L. D. Simon; (right) T. Anderson.

Page 261, Figure 12–11, C. Breedis, L. Berwick and T. F. Anderson.

Page 266, M. C. Ledbetter.

Page 346, L. Reed.

Page 347, Figure 16–9 and p. 348, Figure 16–10 redrawn from J. P. Glusker, *J. Mol. Biol.,* **38:**149 (1968).

Page 396, Figure 18–1, (top) K. R. Porter; (bottom) Peter Raven and Helena Curtis, *Biology of Plants,* Worth Publishers, New York, 1970.

Page 398, Figure 18–3, (top and middle) H. Fernández-Morán, T. Oda, P. V. Blair and D. E. Green, *J. Cell Biol.,* **22,** no. 1. p. 63 (1964); (bottom) A. Claude and V. D. Menghelli.

Page 399, Figure 18–4, J. Greenawalt.

Page 401, (bottom) J. Greenawalt.

Page 402, Figure 18–7 redrawn from B. C. Pressman in E. Racker (ed.), *Membranes of Mitochondria and*

Chloroplasts, Van Nostrand Reinhold Co., New York, 1970.

Page 404, Figure 18–9, C. Hackenbrock.

Page 440, (top) G. Decker.

Page 459, Figure 21–1, M. Jost.

Page 460, Figure 21–2, M. C. Ledbetter.

Page 463, Figure 21–5, F. T. Haxo and L. R. Blinks, *J. Gen. Physiol.*, **33**:408, 1950.

Page 475, Figure 21–11, D. Branton.

Page 482, J. L. Strominger, K. Izaki, M. Matsuhashi, and D. J. Tipper, *Fed. Proc.*, **26**:9 (1967).

Page 516, Figure 23–1, M. D. Lane.

Page 557, Figure 24–20, late Dr. Robin Valintine, donated by E. Stadtman.

Page 584, Figure 26–2 (left) C. Franzini-Armstrong; (right) D. Smith.

Page 585, Figure 26–3 redrawn from Sylvia Colard Keene in W. Bloom and D. W. Fawcett, *Textbook of Histology*, W. B. Saunders Co., Philadelphia, 1968.

Page 592, Figure 26–7, H. E. Huxley and W. Brown, *J. Mol. Biol.*, **30**:383 (1967).

Page 594, Figure 26–9, L. D. Peachey, *J. Cell Biol.*, **25**, no. 3, part II, p. 222.

Page 598, Figure 26–10, D. S. Smith.

Page 599, Figure 26–11, R. Allen.

Page 600, Figure 26–12, I. R. Gibbons.

Page 601, Figure 26–13 (top) J. F. M. Hoeniger and H. D. Tauschel; (bottom) J. F. M. Hoeniger, *J. Gen. Microbiol.*, **40**:29, 1965.

Page 614, Figure 27–6, B. T. Kilbourn, *J. Mol. Biol.*, **30**:559, (1967).

Page 630, adapted from a slide of F. J. Bollum reproduced by F. Lipmann in P. N. Campbell and G. D. Greville (eds.), *Essays in Biochemistry*, Academic Press, London, 1968.

Page 638, Figure 28–1, James D. Watson, *The Double Helix*, Copyright © 1968 by James D. Watson.

Page 639, Figure 28–2 (left) W. Büchi; (right) M. H. F. Wilkins, Medical Research Council, Biophysics Unit, King's College, London.

Page 640, Figure 28–3 redrawn from L. Pauling and R. B. Corey, *Arch. Biochem. Biophys.*, **65**:164 (1956), Academic Press Inc., New York.

Page 641, Figure 28–4 redrawn from James D. Watson, *The Molecular Biology of the Gene*, W. A. Benjamin Inc., New York, 1965, p. 267.

Page 642, Figure 28–5 (top) T. R. Broker and A. Kornberg; (bottom) A. Kornberg.

Page 643, Figure 28–6, L. MacHattie and C. A. Thomas, Jr.

Page 643, Figure 28–7, John Cairns, *Scientific American*, January 1966, p. 36.

Page 644, Figure 28–8, E. J. DuPraw.

Page 646, Figure 28–10 data from C. L. Schildkraut, J. Marmur and P. Doty, *J. Mol. Biol.*, **4**:430 (1962).

Page 648, Figure 28–11 data from H. R. Mahler, B. Kline, and B. D. Mehrotra, *J. Mol. Biol.*, **9**:801 (1964).

Page 649, Figure 28–12 redrawn from P. Doty in D. J. Bell and J. K. Grant (eds.), "The structure and biosynthesis of macromolecules," *Biochem. Soc. Symposia*, **21**:8 (1962), Cambridge Press.

Page 651, Figure 28–13, T. F. Anderson, F. Jacob and E. Wollman.

Page 651, Figure 28–14 redrawn from A. L. Taylor and C. D. Trotter, *Bact. Rev.*, **31**:332 (1967).

Page 653, Figure 28–16 redrawn from J. D. Watson, *The Molecular Biology of the Gene*, W. A. Benjamin Inc., New York, 1965.

Page 670, Figure 29–8 redrawn from A. Kornberg, *Science*, **163**:1410 (1969).

Page 671, Figure 29–9 redrawn from J. Josse, A. D. Kaiser, and A. Kornberg, *J. Biol. Chem.*, **236**:864 (1961).

Page 673, Figure 29–11 redrawn from M. Goulian, A. Kornberg, and R. L. Sinsheimer, *Proc. Nat. Acad. Sci.*, **58**:2321 (1967).

Page 673, Figure 29–12, A. Kornberg.

Page 681, Figure 29–16, O. L. Miller, Jr. and Barbara R. Beatty, Biology Division, Oak Ridge National Laboratory.

Page 695, Figure 30–3, (top) redrawn from W. Fuller and A. Hodgson, *Nature*, **215**:817 (1967); (bottom) redrawn from M. Levitt, *Nature*, **224**:759 (1969).

Page 698, (Margin) A. Rich.

Page 705, Figure 30–10, A. Rich.

Page 707, Figure 30–12 redrawn from E. Shelton and E. L. Kuff, *J. Mol. Biol.*, **22**:23 (1966).

Page 707, Figure 30–13, B. Byers.

Page 708, Figure 30–14 (left) K. R. Porter; (right) redrawn from D. Fawcett, "Structural and Functional Variations in the Membranes of the Cytoplasm," in S. Seno and E. V. Cowdry (eds.), *Intracellular Membrane Structures*, Japanese Society for Cell Biology, Okayama, Japan, 1963.

Page 744, Figure 32–5 redrawn from G. M. Edelman, B. A. Cunningham, W. E. Gall, P. D. Gottlieb, U. Ruttishauser and M. J. Waxdal: "The Covalent Structure of an Entire γG Immunoglobulin Molecule." *Proc. Natl. Acad. Sci. (U.S.)*, **63**:78–85 (1969).

Page 758, Figure 33–3 redrawn from P. Traub and M. Nomura, *Proc. Nat. Acad. Sci.*, **59**:780 (1968).

Page 759, Figure 33–4 redrawn from H. Fraenkel-Conrat, *Design and Function at the Threshold of Life*, Academic Press, New York, 1962. Electron micrograph from L. D. Simon.

Page 762, Figure 33–6 redrawn from W. B. Wood, R. S. Edgar, J. King, I. Lielausis and M. Henninger, *Fed. Proc.*, **27**, 1968, p. 1160.

Page 763, Figure 33–8 redrawn from W. B. Wood, R. S. Edgar, J. King, I. Lielausis and M. Henninger, *Fed. Proc.*, **27**, 1968, p. 1160.

Page 783, Figure 34–7 and Figure 34–8 from S. W. Fox.

INDEX

Page numbers in boldface indicate (1) where the structure of the compound is given, or (2) when several page references are given, the main discussion.